FEATURES AND BENEFITS
Core-Plus Mathematics, Course 3 TEACHER'S GUIDE PART B ©2009

Content and Organization — See page(s):

- Alignment to the NCTM Grades 9–12 Content Standards. — x
- Introduction and Organization of Course 3. — xi–xvii
- Access, Equity, and Differentiation. — xvi–xvii
- Implementing the Curriculum. — xvii–xxviii

Student and Teacher Friendly

- Engaging student-centered applications invite students to read and do more mathematics on their own. Read *Custom Thrills* and *Concert Profit Prospects Reprise*. — 320, 368
- Lesson development organizes problems for students into easy-to-understand instructions. See *The Quadratic Formula and Complex Numbers,* Investigation 2. — 353–356
- Full color **Student Edition** page alongside **Teacher Guide** page for easy reference. — 319–T319
- Effective **Teacher Guide** design provides point-of-use support to make it easier for you to focus on managing students' progress in completing investigations. — 319–T326

Extensive and Varied Practice

- **Applications** tasks help students use and apply ideas from each lesson. — 357–358
- **Connections** tasks connect each lesson's topics with other mathematics students know. — 359–360
- **Reflections** tasks help students avoid developing misconceptions and help them rethink key ideas that were developed in the lesson. — 360–361
- **Extensions** tasks provide opportunities to explore further or more deeply important ideas developed in the lesson. — 361–362
- **Review** tasks help students maintain important skills. — 362–363

Test Preparation and Assessment

- **Think About This Situation** assesses students' prior knowledge before the start of the lesson. — 321
- **Summarizing the Mathematics** assesses students' ability to correctly articulate the mathematics developed after each investigation in the lesson. — 326
- **Check Your Understanding** assesses students' ability to solve problems based upon the mathematics developed in each investigation in the lesson. — 326–327
- **Looking Back** lessons help students review and practice key ideas that were developed in the unit. — 390–394

Technology

- ***CPMP-Tools™*** expands student use of technology by including software tools for algebra, geometry, statistics, and discrete mathematics and time-saving access to selected lesson data sets. **www.wmich.edu/cpmp/CPMP-Tools/** — xi
- ***StudentWorks™* CD-ROM** includes the Student Edition and more on CD.
- ***ExamView® Assessment Suite* CD-ROM** is a powerful state-of-the art test generator that combines ease of use with enormous flexibility in creating customized assessments.
- ***TeacherWorks™ Plus* CD-ROM** is the latest in all-in-one planners and teaching resource center including the ability to edit many of your print resources.
- ***Core-Plus Mathematics* Web site** resources at **www.glencoe.com**.

Teacher's Guide
Part B

Course 3

Core-Plus Mathematics

Contemporary Mathematics in Context

2nd Edition

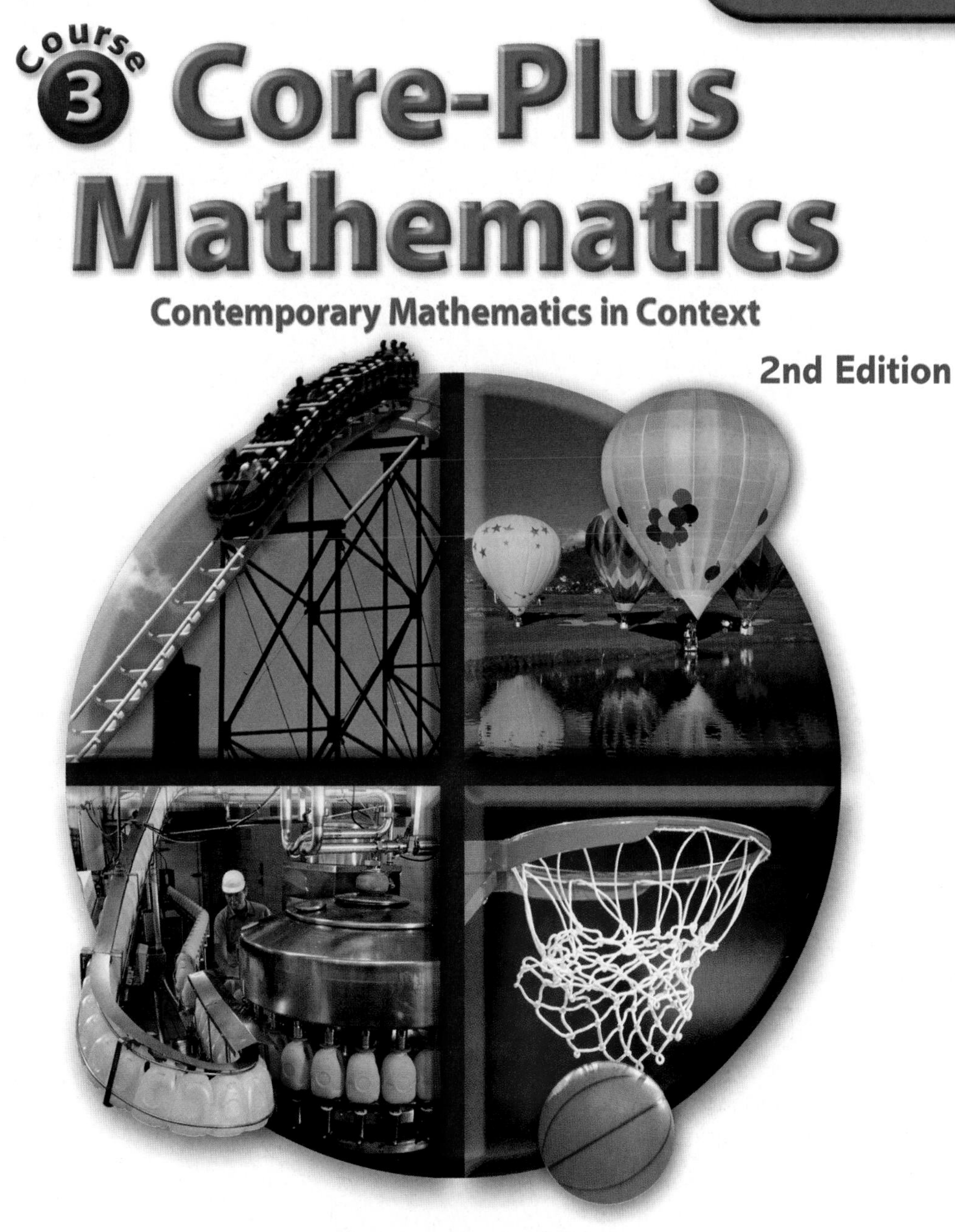

James T. Fey • Christian R. Hirsch • Eric W. Hart
Harold L. Schoen • Ann E. Watkins
with
Beth E. Ritsema • Rebecca K. Walker • Sabrina Keller
Robin Marcus • Arthur F. Coxford • Gail Burrill

Glencoe

New York, New York Columbus, Ohio Chicago, Illinois Woodland Hills, California

The McGraw·Hill Companies

This material is based upon work supported, in part, by the National Science Foundation under grant no. ESI 0137718. Opinions expressed are those of the authors and not necessarily those of the Foundation.

Send all inquiries to:
Glencoe/McGraw-Hill
8787 Orion Place
Columbus, OH 43240-4027

ISBN: 978-0-07-877262-7
MHID: 0-07-877262-1

Core-Plus Mathematics
Contemporary Mathematics in Context
Course 3 Teacher Edition, Part A

ISBN: 978-0-07-877263-4
MHID: 0-07-877263-X

Core-Plus Mathematics
Contemporary Mathematics in Context
Course 3 Teacher Edition, Part B

Printed in the United States of America.

1 2 3 4 5 6 7 8 9 10 071/055 17 16 15 14 13 12 11 10 09 08

Core-Plus Mathematics 2 Development Team

Senior Curriculum Developers
James T. Fey
University of Maryland

Christian R. Hirsch (Director)
Western Michigan University

Eric W. Hart
Maharishi University of Management

Harold L. Schoen
University of Iowa

Ann E. Watkins
California State University, Northridge

Contributing Curriculum Developers
Beth E. Ritsema
Western Michigan University

Rebecca K. Walker
Grand Valley State University

Sabrina Keller
Michigan State University

Robin Marcus
University of Maryland

Arthur F. Coxford (deceased)
University of Michigan

Gail Burrill
Michigan State University
(First edition only)

Principal Evaluator
Steven W. Ziebarth
Western Michigan University

Advisory Board
Diane Briars
Pittsburgh Public Schools

Jeremy Kilpatrick
University of Georgia

Robert E. Megginson
University of Michigan

Kenneth Ruthven
University of Cambridge

David A. Smith
Duke University

Mathematical Consultants
Deborah Hughes-Hallett
University of Arizona / Harvard University

Stephen B. Maurer
Swarthmore College

William McCallum
University of Arizona

Doris Schattschneider
Moravian College

Richard Scheaffer
University of Florida

Evaluation Consultant
Norman L. Webb
University of Wisconsin-Madison

Technical Coordinator
James Laser
Western Michigan University

Collaborating Teachers
Mary Jo Messenger
Howard County Public Schools, Maryland

Jacqueline Stewart
Okemos, Michigan

Graduate Assistants
Allison BrckaLorenz
Christopher Hlas
University of Iowa

Madeline Ahearn
Geoffrey Birky
Kyle Cochran
Michael Conklin
Brandon Cunningham
Tim Fukawa-Connelly
University of Maryland

Dana Cox
Dana Grosser
Anna Kruizenga
Nicole Lanie
Diane Moore
Western Michigan University

Undergraduate Assistants
Cassie Durgin
University of Maryland

Rachael Kaluzny
Jessica Tucker
Western Michigan University

Core-Plus Mathematics 2 Field-Test Sites

Core-Plus Mathematics 2 builds on the strengths of the 1st edition, which was shaped by multi-year field tests in 36 high schools in Alaska, California, Colorado, Georgia, Idaho, Iowa, Kentucky, Michigan, Ohio, South Carolina, and Texas. Each revised text is the product of a three-year cycle of research and development, pilot testing and refinement, and field testing and further refinement. Special thanks are extended to the following teachers and their students who participated in the testing and evaluation of 2nd Edition Course 3.

Hickman High School
Columbia, Missouri
Sandra Baker
Lindsay Carlson
Melissa Hundley
Stephanie Krawczyk
Tiffany McCracken
Dana Meyer
Ryan Pingrey

Holland Christian High School
Holland, Michigan
Brian Lemmen
Mike Verkaik

Malcolm Price Lab School
Cedar Falls, Iowa
Megan Balong
James Maltas

Riverside University High School
Milwaukee, Wisconsin
Cheryl Brenner
Scott Hanson
Alice Lanphier

Rock Bridge High School
Columbia, Missouri
Cynthia Francisco
Donna Lillard
Linda Shumate

Sauk Prairie High School
Prairie du Sac, Wisconsin
Joan Quenan
Mary Walz

Washington High School
Milwaukee, Wisconsin
Anthony Amoroso

Overview of Course 3

UNIT 1 Reasoning and Proof

Reasoning and Proof develops student understanding of formal reasoning in geometric, algebraic, and statistical contexts and of basic principles that underlie those reasoning strategies.

Topics include inductive and deductive reasoning strategies; principles of logical reasoning—Affirming the Hypothesis and Chaining Implications; relation among angles formed by two intersecting lines or by two parallel lines and a transversal; rules for transforming algebraic expressions and equations; design of experiments including the role of randomization, control groups, and blinding; sampling distribution, randomization test, and statistical significance.

UNIT 2 Inequalities and Linear Programming

Inequalities and Linear Programming develops student ability to reason both algebraically and graphically to solve inequalities in one and two variables, introduces systems of inequalities in two variables, and develops a strategy for optimizing a linear function in two variables within a system of linear constraints on those variables.

Topics include inequalities in one and two variables, number line graphs, interval notation, systems of linear inequalities, and linear programming.

UNIT 3 Similarity and Congruence

Similarity and Congruence extends student understanding of similarity and congruence and their ability to use those relations to solve problems and to prove geometric assertions with and without the use of coordinates.

Topics include connections between Law of Cosines, Law of Sines, and sufficient conditions for similarity and congruence of triangles, centers of triangles, applications of similarity and congruence in real-world contexts, necessary and sufficient conditions for parallelograms, sufficient conditions for congruence of parallelograms, and midpoint connector theorems.

Overview of Course 3

UNIT 4 SAMPLES AND VARIATION

Samples and Variation extends student understanding of the measurement of variability, develops student ability to use the normal distribution as a model of variation, introduces students to the binomial distribution and its use in decision making, and introduces students to the probability and statistical inference involved in control charts used in industry for statistical process control.

Topics include normal distribution, standardized scores, binomial distributions (shape, expected value, standard deviation), normal approximation to a binomial distribution, odds, statistical process control, control charts, and the Central Limit Theorem.

UNIT 5 POLYNOMIAL AND RATIONAL FUNCTIONS

Polynomial and Rational Functions extends student ability to represent and draw inferences about polynomial and rational functions using symbolic expressions and manipulations.

Topics include definition and properties of polynomials, operations on polynomials; completing the square, proof of the quadratic formula, solving quadratic equations (including complex number solutions), vertex form of quadratic functions; definition and properties of rational functions, operations on rational expressions.

UNIT 6 CIRCLES AND CIRCULAR FUNCTIONS

Circles and Circular Functions develops student understanding of relationships among special lines, segments, and angles in circles and the ability to use properties of circles to solve problems; develops student understanding of circular functions and the ability to use these functions to model periodic change; and extends student ability to reason deductively in geometric settings.

Topics include properties of chords, tangent lines, and central and inscribed angles of circles; linear and angular velocity; radian measure of angles; and circular functions as models of periodic change.

Overview of Course 3

UNIT 7 Recursion and Iteration

Recursion and Iteration extends student ability to represent, analyze, and solve problems in situations involving sequential and recursive change.

Topics include iteration and recursion as tools to model and analyze sequential change in real-world contexts, including compound interest and population growth; arithmetic, geometric, and other sequences; arithmetic and geometric series; finite differences; linear and nonlinear recurrence relations; and function iteration, including graphical iteration and fixed points.

Lesson 1 Modeling Sequential Change Using Recursion and Iteration

Lesson 2 A Recursive View of Functions

Lesson 3 Iterating Functions

Lesson 4 Looking Back

UNIT 8 Inverse Functions

Inverse Functions develops student understanding of inverses of functions with a focus on logarithmic functions and their use in modeling and analyzing problem situations and data patterns.

Topics include inverses of functions; logarithmic functions and their relation to exponential functions, properties of logarithms, equation solving with logarithms; and inverse trigonometric functions and their applications to solving trigonometric equations.

Lesson 1 What Is An Inverse Function?

Lesson 2 Common Logarithms and Their Properties

Lesson 3 Inverse Trigonometric Functions

Lesson 4 Looking Back

Contents

Contents

NCTM Standards

Core-Plus Mathematics and the instructional and assessment practices it promotes address the focal points of the National Council of Teachers of Mathematics' *Principles and Standards for School Mathematics*. By design, the **process standards** on Problem Solving, Reasoning and Proof, Communication, Connections, and Representation are an integral part of each lesson of every unit in the curriculum. The chart below correlates Course 3 units with the **content standards** for grades 9–12 in terms of focus (Ⓕ) and connections (Ⓒ).

Correlation of Course 3 to NCTM Standards

NCTM Grades 9–12 Content Standards	Unit 1 *Reasoning and Proof*	Unit 2 *Inequalities and Linear Programming*	Unit 3 *Similarity and Congruence*	Unit 4 *Samples and Variation*	Unit 5 *Polynomial and Rational Functions*	Unit 6 *Circles and Circular Functions*	Unit 7 *Recursion and Iteration*	Unit 8 *Inverse Functions*
Number and Operations								
Understand numbers, ways of representing numbers, relationships among numbers, and number systems	Ⓒ	Ⓒ						
Understand meanings of operations and how they relate to one another	Ⓒ	Ⓒ						Ⓒ
Compute fluently and make reasonable estimates	Ⓒ	Ⓒ						
Algebra								
Understand patterns, relations, and functions	Ⓒ	Ⓕ			Ⓕ	Ⓕ	Ⓕ	Ⓕ
Represent and analyze mathematical situations and structures using algebraic symbols	Ⓒ	Ⓕ			Ⓕ	Ⓕ	Ⓕ	Ⓕ
Use mathematical models to represent and understand quantitative relationships	Ⓒ	Ⓕ			Ⓕ	Ⓕ	Ⓕ	Ⓕ
Analyze change in various contexts	Ⓒ	Ⓕ			Ⓕ	Ⓕ	Ⓕ	Ⓕ
Geometry								
Analyze characteristics and properties of two- and three-dimensional geometric shapes and develop mathematical arguments about geometric relationships	Ⓕ		Ⓕ			Ⓕ		
Specify locations and describe spatial relationships using coordinate geometry and other representational systems			Ⓒ			Ⓒ		
Apply transformations and use symmetry to analyze mathematical situations			Ⓕ			Ⓒ		Ⓒ
Use visualization, spatial reasoning, and geometric modeling to solve problems	Ⓒ		Ⓕ			Ⓕ	Ⓒ	
Measurement								
Understand measurable attributes of objects and the units, systems, and processes of measurement	Ⓒ					Ⓒ		
Apply appropriate techniques, tools, and formulas to determine measurements	Ⓒ					Ⓒ		
Data Analysis and Probability								
Formulate questions that can be addressed with data and collect, organize, and display relevant data to answer them	Ⓕ			Ⓕ				
Select and use appropriate statistical methods to analyze data	Ⓕ			Ⓕ				
Develop and evaluate inferences and predictions that are based on data	Ⓕ			Ⓕ				
Understand and apply basic concepts of probability	Ⓒ			Ⓒ				

Overview

Introduction

The first three courses in *Core-Plus Mathematics* provide a significant common core of broadly useful mathematics for all students. They were developed to prepare students for success in college, in careers, and in daily life in contemporary society. Course 4 continues the preparation of students for success in college mathematics and statistics courses. The program builds upon the theme of mathematics as sense-making. Through investigations of real-life contexts, students develop a rich understanding of important mathematics that makes sense to them and which, in turn, enables them to make sense out of new situations and problems.

Each course in *Core-Plus Mathematics* shares the following mathematical and instructional features.

• Integrated Content

Each year, the curriculum advances students' understanding of mathematics along interwoven strands of algebra and functions, statistics and probability, geometry and trigonometry, and discrete mathematics. These strands are unified by fundamental themes, by common topics, and by mathematical habits of mind or ways of thinking. Developing mathematics each year along multiple strands helps students develop diverse mathematical insights and nurtures their differing strengths and talents.

• Mathematical Modeling

The curriculum emphasizes mathematical modeling including the processes of data collection, representation, interpretation, prediction, and simulation. The modeling perspective permits students to experience mathematics as a means of making sense of data and problems that arise in diverse contexts within and across cultures.

• Access and Challenge

The curriculum is designed to make mathematics accessible to more students, while at the same time challenging the most able students. Differences in student performance and interest can be accommodated by the depth and level of abstraction to which core topics are pursued, by the nature and degree of difficulty of applications, and by providing opportunities for student choice of homework tasks and projects.

• Technology

Numeric, graphic, and symbolic manipulation capabilities such as those found on many graphing calculators are assumed and appropriately used throughout the curriculum. The curriculum materials also include a suite of computer software called *CPMP-Tools* that provide powerful aids to learning mathematics and solving mathematical problems. (See pages xviii–xix for further details.) This use of technology permits the curriculum and instruction to emphasize multiple representations (verbal, numerical, graphical, and symbolic) and to focus on goals in which mathematical thinking and problem solving are central.

- **Active Learning**

  Instructional materials promote active learning and teaching centered around collaborative investigations of problem situations followed by teacher-led whole-class summarizing activities that lead to analysis, abstraction, and further application of underlying mathematical ideas and principles. Students are actively engaged in exploring, conjecturing, verifying, generalizing, applying, proving, evaluating, and communicating mathematical ideas.

- **Multi-dimensional Assessment**

  Comprehensive assessment of student understanding and progress through both curriculum-embedded assessment opportunities and supplementary assessment tasks supports instruction and enables monitoring and evaluation of each student's performance in terms of mathematical processes, content, and dispositions.

Core-Plus Mathematics is designed to make mathematics accessible and more meaningful to more students. Developing mathematics along multiple strands nurtures the differing strengths and talents of students and simultaneously helps them to develop diverse mathematical insights. Developing mathematics from a modeling perspective permits students to experience mathematics as a means of making sense of data and problems that arise in diverse contexts within and across cultures. Engaging students in collaborating on tasks in small groups develops their ability to both deal with, and find commonality in, diversity of ideas. Using technology as a means for learning and doing mathematics enables students to develop versatile ways of dealing with realistic situations and reduces the manipulative skill filter which has prevented large numbers of students from continuing their study of significant mathematics. In addition, technology-produced graphics offer powerful new ways of visualizing mathematics across each of the strands.

Integrated Mathematics

Core-Plus Mathematics replaces the traditional Algebra-Geometry-Advanced Algebra/Trigonometry-Precalculus sequence of high school mathematics courses with a sequence of courses that features concurrent and connected development of important mathematics drawn from four strands.

Algebra and Functions

The Algebra and Functions strand develops student ability to recognize, represent, and solve problems involving relations among quantitative variables. Central to the development is the use of functions as mathematical models. The key algebraic models in the curriculum are linear, exponential, power, polynomial, logarithmic, rational, and trigonometric functions. Modeling with systems of equations, both linear and nonlinear, is developed. Attention is also given to symbolic reasoning and manipulation.

Geometry and Trigonometry

The primary goal of the Geometry and Trigonometry strand is to develop visual thinking and ability to construct, reason with, interpret, and apply mathematical models of patterns in visual and physical contexts. The focus is on describing patterns in shape, size, and location; representing patterns with drawings, coordinates, or vectors; predicting changes and invariants in shapes under transformations; and organizing geometric facts and relationships through deductive reasoning.

Statistics and Probability

The primary role of the Statistics and Probability strand is to develop student ability to analyze data intelligently, to recognize and measure variation, and to understand the patterns that underlie probabilistic situations. The ultimate goal is for students to understand how inferences can be made about a population by looking at a sample from that population. Graphical methods of data analysis, simulations, sampling, and experience with the collection and interpretation of real data are featured.

Discrete Mathematics

The Discrete Mathematics strand develops student ability to solve problems using vertex-edge graphs, recursion, matrices, systematic counting methods (combinatorics), and voting methods. Key themes are discrete mathematical modeling, optimization, and algorithmic problem-solving.

Connected Strands

Each of these strands of mathematics is developed within focused units connected by fundamental ideas such as symmetry, matrices, functions, data analysis, and curve-fitting. The strands also are connected across units by mathematical habits of mind such as visual thinking, recursive thinking, searching for and explaining patterns, making and checking conjectures, reasoning with multiple representations, inventing mathematics, and providing convincing arguments and proofs.

The strands are unified further by the fundamental themes of data, representation, shape, and change. Important mathematical ideas are frequently revisited through this attention to connections within and across strands, enabling students to develop a robust and connected understanding of mathematics.

Organization of Course 3

Course 3 consists of eight units. Each of the units is comprised of two to four multi-day lessons in which major ideas are developed through investigation of rich applied problems. Units vary in length from approximately two to six weeks.

Unit 1 *Reasoning and Proof*
Unit 2 *Inequalities and Linear Programming*
Unit 3 *Similarity and Congruence*
Unit 4 *Samples and Variation*
Unit 5 *Polynomial and Rational Functions*
Unit 6 *Circles and Circular Functions*
Unit 7 *Recursion and Iteration*
Unit 8 *Inverse Functions*

The 2nd Edition of Course 3 builds on the strengths of the 1st Edition. It includes mathematical content which the developers believed is the most important mathematics all students should have the opportunity to learn. In particular, the content of the last units in the text are not viewed as optional as is often the case with traditional textbooks. Depending on the mathematics standards and content expectations for your state, you may wish to have students complete all Course 2 units before they embark on Course 3 of the *Core-Plus Mathematics* series.

Instructional Model

The manner in which students encounter mathematical ideas can contribute significantly to the quality of their learning and the depth of their understanding. *Core-Plus Mathematics* units are designed around multi-day lessons centered on big ideas. Each lesson includes 2–4 focused mathematical investigations that engage students in a four-phase cycle of classroom activities, described in the following paragraphs—*Launch, Explore, Share and Summarize,* and *Apply.* This cycle is designed to engage students in investigating and making sense of problem situations, in constructing important mathematical concepts and methods, in generalizing and proving mathematical relationships, and in communicating, both orally and in writing, their thinking and the results of their efforts. Most classroom activities are designed to be completed by students working collaboratively in groups of two to four students.

LAUNCH class discussion

Think About This Situation

The lesson launch promotes a teacher-led discussion of a problem situation and of related questions to think about. This discussion sets the context for the student work to follow and helps to generate student interest. It also provides an opportunity for the teacher to assess student knowledge and to clarify directions for the investigation to follow.

EXPLORE group investigation

Investigation

Classroom activity then shifts to investigating focused problems and questions related to the launching situation by gathering data, looking for and explaining patterns, constructing models and meanings, and making and verifying conjectures. As students collaborate in pairs or small groups, the teacher circulates among students providing guidance and support, clarifying or asking questions, giving hints, providing encouragement, and drawing group members into the discussion to help groups collaborate more effectively. The investigations and related questions posed by students and teachers drive the learning.

SHARE AND SUMMARIZE class discussion

Summarize the Mathematics

This investigative work is followed by a teacher-led class discussion (referred to as Summarize the Mathematics) in which students summarize mathematical ideas developed in their groups, providing an opportunity to construct a shared understanding of important concepts, methods, and approaches. This discussion leads to a class summary of important ideas or to further exploration of a topic if competing perspectives remain. Varying points of view and differing conclusions that can be justified should be encouraged.

APPLY individual tasks

Check Your Understanding

Students are given a task to complete on their own to check and reinforce their initial understanding of concepts and methods.

Homework

In addition to the classroom investigations, *Core-Plus Mathematics* provides sets of On Your Own tasks, which are designed to engage students in applying, connecting, reflecting on, extending, and reviewing their evolving mathematical knowledge. On Your Own tasks are provided for each lesson in the materials and are central to the learning goals of each lesson. These tasks are intended primarily for individual work outside of class. Selection of homework tasks should be based on student performance and the availability of time and technology. Also, students should exercise some choice of tasks to pursue, and, at times should be given the opportunity to pose their own problems and questions to investigate. The chart below describes the types of tasks in a typical On Your Own set.

On Your Own: Homework Tasks	
Applications	These tasks provide opportunities for students to use and strengthen their understanding of the ideas they have learned in the lesson.
Connections	These tasks help students to build links between mathematical topics they have studied in the lesson and to connect those topics with other mathematics that they know.
Reflections	These tasks provide opportunities for students to re-examine their thinking about ideas in the lesson.
Extensions	These tasks provide opportunities for students to explore further or more deeply the mathematics they are learning.
Review	These tasks provide opportunities for just-in-time review and distributed practice of mathematical skills to maintain procedural fluency.

Additional Summarizing Activities

In *Core-Plus Mathematics*, students learn mathematics by doing mathematics. However, it is important that students prepare and maintain summaries of important concepts and methods that are developed. Students should create a Math Toolkit that organizes important class-generated ideas and selected Summarize the Mathematics responses as they complete investigations. Math Toolkit Prompts are provided in this *Teacher's Guide* to assist in identifying and summarizing key concepts and methods as they are developed by students.

In addition, the final lesson in each unit is a Looking Back lesson that helps students review and synthesize the key mathematical concepts and techniques developed in the unit. The Summarize the Mathematics questions in this lesson are focused on key ideas of the unit. The Check Your Understanding asks students to prepare a summary of the important concepts and skills developed in the unit. Templates to guide preparation of these unit summaries can be found in the *Unit Resource Masters.* Completed Unit Summaries should become part of students' Math Toolkits.

Students should retain their Math Toolkits as they continue on to Course 4. In some districts, teachers collect these resources at the end of the school year and return them to students in the fall.

Multiple Approaches to Assessment

Assessing what students know and are able to do is an integral part of *Core-Plus Mathematics.* There are opportunities for assessment in each phase of the instructional cycle. Initially, as students pursue the investigations that comprise the curriculum, the teacher is able to informally assess student understanding of mathematical processes and content and their disposition toward mathematics. At the end of each investigation, a class discussion to Summarize the Mathematics provides an opportunity for the teacher to assess levels of understanding that various groups of students have reached as they share and explain their findings. Finally, the Check Your Understanding tasks and the tasks in the On Your Own sets provide further opportunities to assess the level of understanding of each individual student. Quizzes, in-class tests, take-home assessment tasks, and extended projects are included in the teacher resource materials.

A more detailed description of the complete assessment program is given on pages xxi–xv of this text and in *Implementing Core-Plus Mathematics*.

Practicing for Standardized Tests

Opportunities for additional review and practice are provided in eight Preparing for Standardized Tests practice sets included in the *Unit Resource Masters*. Each Practicing for Standardized Tests master presents 10 questions and a test-taking tip. The questions are presented in the form of test items similar to how they often appear in standardized tests such as state assessments tests, the Scholastic Aptitude Test (SAT), or the ACT test. By using these practice sets, students can become familiar with the formats of standardized tests and develop effective test-taking strategies for performing well on such tests.

Access, Equity, and Differentiation

Several research studies have provided evidence that introducing activities through class discussion, teaching students to explain and justify, and making real-world contexts accessible to students promote greater access and equity in mathematics classrooms. (Boaler, J. "Learning from Teaching: Exploring the Relationship Between Reform Curriculum and Equity," *Journal for Research in Mathematics Education,* 2002, Vol. 33, No. 4, 239–258, and Brown, C.A., Stein, M.K., and Forman, E. A. "Assisting teachers and students to reform their mathematics classroom," *Education Studies in Mathematics,* 1996, 31–93). These practices that help promote equity are briefly discussed below.

Introducing Activities Through Class Discussions Group and class discussions of the aim of activities, the meaning of contexts, the challenging points within problems, and possible problem access points to which students might turn make tasks more evenly accessible to all students.

Teaching Students to Explain and Justify their Thinking Giving explicit attention to explaining thinking and evaluating what makes a good piece of work helps students improve their work.

Making Real-world Contexts Accessible Considering the constraints that real situations involve and connecting these situations with issues and topics in their own lives helps students view mathematics as something that will help them interpret their world.

Other Practices that Promote Equity Mixed-ability classes, a focus on problems solving, high expectations for all students, attention to a broad array of mathematical topics, and allowing students to restate problems in their own words also appear to help students from different racial, ethnic, and linguistic groups be more successful in mathematics.

Core-Plus Mathematics offers many opportunities for teachers to incorporate these practices into daily routines. One such built-in opportunity is the Think About This Situations (TATS) used to introduce lessons through discussions. Although no TATS questions are in the student text for individual investigations there are often suggestions in the *Teacher's Guide* for class launches of investigations. Since much of the mathematical content is based on real contexts, it is important that all students understand the contexts and draw on their own or a classmates background knowledge. Opportunities for students to explain and justify their thinking are built into all curriculum features. Look for opportunities to encourage the habit of mind of justifying one's thinking as students work individually and participate in small-group or class discussions.

The *Teacher's Guide* periodically includes notes that provide specific ideas for differentiation at point of use. Look for the margin notes.

Implementing the Curriculum

Considering mathematics topics and knowledge presented at each grade level and how that knowledge is built upon in succeeding grades is key to improving student learning. To support building the teacher expertise to effectively implement *Core-Plus Mathematics* the developers recommend that districts begin adoption with Course 1 and add a course level each year. Encourage teachers to progress from Course 1 to Course 4 in stages, so they can develop an understanding of the growth of mathematical ideas in the curriculum. Realize that teachers will need time and support to improve instruction for their students.

Additional advice related to successful implementation is on the Core-Plus Mathematics Project (CPMP) Web site at www.wmich.edu/cpmp under Implementation.

Planning for Instruction

The *Core-Plus Mathematics* curriculum is not only changing what mathematics all students have the opportunity to learn, but also changing how that learning occurs and is assessed. Active learning is most effective when accompanied with active teaching. Just as the student text is designed to actively engage students in doing mathematics, the teacher's resource materials are designed to support teachers in planning for instruction; in observing, listening, questioning, and facilitating student work, and orchestrating classroom discussion; and in managing the classroom.

The *Teacher's Guide* provides suggestions, based on the experiences of field-test teachers, for implementing this exciting new curriculum in your classroom. You probably will find new ideas that can at first be overwhelming. The developers highly recommend that teachers who are teaching *Core-Plus Mathematics* for the first time do so at least in pairs who share a common planning period.

Each of the items listed below is included in the *Teacher's Guide* for each unit.

- Unit overview and lesson overviews
- Objectives, suggested timeline and assignments, and materials needed
- Instructional notes and suggestions
- Solutions for investigations and homework tasks
- Promoting Mathematical Discourse scenarios

Each *Unit Resource Masters* includes reproducible masters for teaching, student activities, technology tips, a unit summary, and practicing for standardized tests. Also included in each *Unit Resource Masters* is the assessment package for the unit as outlined on pages xxi–xxiv.

A first step toward planning the teaching of a unit is to review the scope and sequence of the unit. This review provides an overall feel for the goals and coherence of the unit. The *Scope and Sequence* guide (www.glencoe.com) shows where specific mathematical topics fit in the complete four-year curriculum. Working through the student investigations, if possible with a colleague, provides help in thinking about possible student responses and understanding mathematical ideas that may be unfamiliar.

In the *Teacher's Guide*, at the beginning of each unit, you will find a Planning Guide to assist in overall planning. This resource gives a quick overview of lessons, suggested assignments, materials needed, and pacing suggestions.

You will also find teaching notes for each lesson, including instructional suggestions and sample student responses to investigations and homework sets. Thinking about the range of possible responses and solutions to problems proves to be very helpful in facilitating student work.

Some teachers choose to post the homework assignment at the beginning of a lesson along with the due date—usually a day or two following planned completion of the lesson. Other teachers prefer to assign particular tasks at appropriate points during the course of the multiday investigation, and then assign the remaining tasks toward the end of the lesson. Review tasks can be assigned before the completion of the investigation. Note that all recommended assignments include provision for student choice of some tasks. This is but one of many ways in which this curriculum is designed to accommodate and support differences in students' interests and performance levels.

It is strongly recommended that student solutions to Connections tasks be discussed in class. These tasks help students organize and formalize the mathematics developed in context and connect it to other mathematics they have studied. Structuring the underlying mathematics and building connections are best accomplished by comparing and discussing student work and synthesizing key ideas within the classroom.

Some recommended assignments include Just-in-Time Review tasks. It is important that these tasks be assigned as indicated in the Planning Guide to help ensure understanding of ideas or procedures needed in the next investigation.

Technology in Course 3

In the 21st century, anyone who faces the challenge of learning mathematics or using mathematics to solve problems can draw on the resources of powerful information technology tools. Calculators and computers can help with calculations, drawing, and data analysis in mathematical explorations and solving mathematical problems. (See the NCTM position paper on technology at: www.nctm.org/about/content.aspx?id=14233)

Graphing Calculators: Graphing calculators with iteration capabilities are assumed for class work and homework. Computer algebra system (CAS) capabilities are desirable.

Overview

Computers: Periodically, it would be valuable to have one classroom computer for whole class discussions, 4–6 classroom computers for groups to use as stations during investigations, portable classroom sets of computers, or computer lab access. For some homework tasks, school or home computer availability is also desirable.

Computer software: The use of spreadsheet, interactive geometry, data analysis, simulation, and function iteration software and computer algebra systems (CAS) is incorporated into Course 3 units. The curriculum materials include computer software called *CPMP-Tools* specifically designed to support student learning and problem solving.

The software toolkit includes four families of programs:

Algebra The software for work on algebra problems includes an electronic spreadsheet and a computer algebra system (CAS) that produces tables and graphs of functions, manipulates algebraic expressions, and solves equations and inequalities.

Geometry The software for work on geometry problems includes an interactive drawing program for constructing, measuring, and manipulating geometric figures and a set of custom tools for exploring properties of figures and geometric models of physical mechanisms.

Statistics The software for work on data analysis and probability problems provides tools for graphic display and analysis of data, simulation of probabilistic situations, and mathematical modeling of quantitative relationships.

Discrete Mathematics The software for work on graph theory problems provides tools for constructing, manipulating, and analyzing vertex-edge graphs.

In addition to the general purpose tools provided for work on tasks in each strand of the curriculum, *CPMP-Tools* includes files of most data sets essential for work on problems in *Core-Plus Mathematics* Course 3. When students see an opportunity to use computer tools for work on a particular investigation, they can select the *CPMP-Tools* menu corresponding to the content involved in the problem. For problems involving built-in or student-provided data sets, they can select the submenu items corresponding to the required mathematical operations and data sets. Each unit overview in the *Teacher's Guide* provides general information related to *CPMP-Tools* use in the unit. Technology notes at point of use alert teachers to applicable software and specific data sets included in the software.

Materials Needed for Course 3

The following is a complete list of items used in the eight units of Course 3. Each unit Planning Guide indicates the items used in that unit.

Necessary

Compass, straightedge, protractor
Pennies (100 per group)
Quarters (1 per pair)
Rulers with metric and English markings
Linkage strips (Glencoe order number 39494)
Pipe cleaners, dental floss, or string

Electronic Resources

The *Core-Plus Mathematics* student text, *Teacher's Guide,* and *Unit Resource Masters* are included for viewing and printing from the *Core-Plus Mathematics TeacherWorks Plus* CD-ROM. Custom tailoring of assessment items can be accomplished by using the *ExamView* Assessment Suites. *CPMP-Tools* is available on both the *StudentWorks* and *TeacherWorks Plus* CD-ROMs.

Orchestrating Lessons

Core-Plus Mathematics is designed to engage students in a four-phase cycle of classroom activities. The activities in Course 3 often require both students and teachers to assume roles quite different than those in more traditional mathematics classrooms. Students successfully completing Courses 1 and 2 should have become accustomed to these new roles. Although realistic problem solving and investigative work by students are the heart of the curriculum, how teachers orchestrate the launching of an investigation and the sharing and summarizing of results is critical to successful implementation.

Students enter the classroom with differing strengths, experience, and knowledge. These differences can be viewed as assets. Engaging the class in a free-flowing give-and-take discussion of how students think about the launch situations serves to connect lessons with the informal understandings of data, shape, change, and chance that students bring to the classroom. Try to maximize the participation of students in these discussions by emphasizing that their ideas and possible approaches are valued and important and that definitive answers are not necessarily expected at this time.

Once launched, an investigation may involve students working together collaboratively in small groups for a period of days punctuated occasionally by brief class discussion of questions students have raised. In this setting, the investigation becomes driven primarily by the instructional materials themselves. Rather than orchestrating class discussion, the teacher shifts to circulating among the groups and observing, listening, and interacting with students by asking guiding or probing questions. These small-group investigations lead to (re)invention of important mathematics that make sense to students. Sharing, and agreeing as a class, on the mathematical ideas that groups are developing is the purpose of the Summarizing the Mathematics (STM) in the instructional materials.

Class discussions at STMs are orchestrated somewhat differently than during the launch of a lesson. At this stage, mathematical ideas and methods still may be under development and may vary for individual groups. So class discussion should involve groups comparing their methods and results, analyzing their work, and arriving at conclusions agreed upon by the class.

Periodically, you will find samples of class discussions centered around Think About This Situation or Summarize the Mathematics questions at point of use. These sample discussions, called Promoting Mathematical Discourse, may provide some ideas for your class discussions. These sample discussions are indicated by PROMOTING MATHEMATICAL DISCOURSE.

Assessment

Throughout the *Core-Plus Mathematics* curriculum, the term "assessment" is meant to include all instances of gathering information about students' levels of understanding and their disposition toward mathematics for purposes of making decisions about instruction. You may want to consult the extended section on assessment in *Implementing Core-Plus Mathematics*.

The dimensions of student performance that are assessed in this curriculum (see chart below) are consistent with the assessment recommendations of the National Council of Teachers of Mathematics in the *Assessment Standards for School Mathematics* (NCTM, 1995). They are more comprehensive than those of a typical testing program.

Assessment Dimensions		
Process	**Content**	**Disposition**
Problem Solving	Concepts	Beliefs
Reasoning	Applications	Perseverance
Communication	Mathematical Representation	Confidence
Connections	Procedures	Enthusiasm

Sources of Assessment Information

Several kinds of assessment are available to teachers using *Core-Plus Mathematics*. Some of these sources reside within the student text itself, some of them are student-generated, and some are materials designed specifically for assessment. Understanding the nature of these sources is a prerequisite for selecting assessment tools, establishing guidelines on how to score assessments, making judgments about what students know and are able to do, and assigning grades.

Curriculum Sources

Two features of the curriculum, questioning and observation by the teacher, provide fundamental and particularly useful ways of gathering formative assessment information. The student text uses questions to facilitate student understanding of new concepts, of how these concepts fit with earlier ideas and with one another, and of how they can be applied in problem situations. Whether students are working individually or in groups, the teacher is given a window to watch how the students think about and apply mathematics as they attempt to answer the questions posed in the curriculum materials. In fact, by observing how students respond to the curriculum-embedded questions, the teacher can assess student performance across all process, content, and attitude dimensions described in the chart on page xxi.

Specific features in the student material that focus on different ways students respond to questions are the Summarize the Mathematics, Check Your Understanding, and the On Your Own homework sets. Summarize the Mathematics features are intended to bring students together, usually after they have been working in small groups, so they may share and discuss the progress each group has made during a sequence of related activities. The questions in the Summarize the Mathematics are focused on the mathematical concepts and procedures developed in the investigation. They should help the teacher and the students identify and formalize the key ideas of the investigation. Each Summarize the Mathematics is intended to be treated as a whole-class discussion, so it should provide an opportunity for teachers to assess, informally, the levels of understanding that the various groups of students have reached.

Following each Summarize the Mathematics, the Check Your Understanding tasks are meant to be completed by students working individually. Student responses to these tasks provide an opportunity for teachers to assess the level of understanding of each student.

The tasks in the On Your Own homework sets serve many purposes, including post-investigation assessment. Each type of task in the On Your Own homework sets has a different instructional purpose. Applications tasks provide opportunities for students to demonstrate how well they understand and can use the ideas they learned in the investigations of the lesson. Work on Connections tasks demonstrates how well the students understand links between mathematical topics they studied in the lesson and their ability to connect those topics with other mathematics that they know. Reflections tasks provide insight into students' mathematical thinking and strategic competence. Extensions tasks reveal how well students are able to extend the present content beyond the level addressed in the investigations. The Review tasks allow for pre-assessment of students' understanding of ideas or procedures needed in the upcoming lessons and also provide information on how well students are retaining previously learned mathematics. The performance of students or groups of students on each of these types of tasks provides the teacher with further information to help assess each student's evolving ability to use, connect, and extend the mathematics of the lesson.

Finally, an opportunity for group self-assessment is provided in the last element of each unit, the Looking Back lesson. These tasks help students pull together and demonstrate what they have learned in the unit and at the same time provide helpful review and confidence-building for students.

Student-Generated Sources

Mathematics Toolkits Students should create a Math Toolkit that organizes important class-generated ideas and selected Summarize the Mathematics responses as they complete investigations. Constructing a Math Toolkit prompts are provided in the *Teacher's Guide* to assist in identifying key concepts and methods as they are developed by students.

Unit Summaries A summary template intended to help students organize and record the main ideas learned in the unit is provided in each *Unit Resource Masters*. The synthesis of ideas that occurs during completion of the "Looking Back" lesson and the final unit Summarize the Mathematics discussion should provide the background for student completion of the unit summary.

Assessment Resources

Each *Unit Resource Masters* includes lesson quizzes and unit assessments in the form of tests, take-home tasks, and projects. There are also banks of questions and projects from which you can form end of semester exams following the Unit 4 and Unit 8 assessment masters. Calculators are assumed in most cases and are intended to be available to students. Teacher discretion should be used regarding student access to their textbook and Math Toolkit for assessments. In general, if the goals to be assessed are problem solving and reasoning, while memory of facts and procedural skill are of less interest, resources may be allowed. However, if automaticity of procedures or unaided recall are being assessed, it is appropriate to prohibit resource materials.

The *ExamView* software can be used to modify the curriculum provided assessment items or to create formal assessments using a combination of curriculum supplied items and ones by the teacher.

Lesson Quizzes Two forms of a quiz covering the main ideas of each lesson are provided. These quizzes are comprised of problems meant to determine if students have developed understanding of the important concepts and procedures of each lesson. The two forms of each quiz are not necessarily equivalent, although they assess essentially the same mathematical ideas. Since many rich opportunities for assessing students are embedded in the curriculum itself, you may choose not to use a quiz at the end of every lesson.

Unit Tests Two forms of tests are provided for each unit and are intended to be completed in a 50-minute class period. The two forms of each test are not necessarily equivalent, although they assess essentially the same mathematical ideas. Teachers should preview the two versions carefully to be sure that the unit assessment aligns with the learning goals emphasized.

Take-Home Assessments Take-home assessment tasks are included for each unit. The students or the teacher should choose one or, at most, two of these tasks. These assessments, some of which are best done by students working in pairs or small groups, provide students with the opportunity to organize the information from the completed unit, to work with another student or group of students, to engage in in-depth problem solving, to grapple with new and more complex situations related to the mathematics of the unit, and to avoid the time pressure often generated by in-class exams. These problems may also require more extensive use of technology than is often available in the regular classroom during testing situations. You may wish to use these more in-depth problems as a replacement for a portion of an in-class end-of-unit exam.

Projects Assessment traditionally has been based on evaluating work that students have completed in a very short time period and under restricted conditions. Some assessment, however, should involve work done over a longer time period and with the aid of resources. Thus, assessment projects are included in unit assessments. These projects, which are intended to be completed by small groups of students, provide an opportunity for students to conduct an investigation that extends and applies the main ideas from the unit and to write a summary of their findings. Many of these might also allow for students to present their work in a variety of ways. You may have students who would rather prepare and present their work orally or visually using computers and/or video equipment. In this way, the projects can provide an opportunity for students to use their creativity while demonstrating their understanding of mathematics.

Midterm and Final Assessments A bank of assessment tasks, from which to construct midterm and final exams that fit your particular class needs and emphases, are provided in the Unit 4 and Unit 8 *Unit Resource Masters*. In addition to problems similar in form to those on the quizzes and tests, these assessment banks include several multiple-choice problems for each unit.

Extended assessment projects are also included with the end-of-year assessments. These projects are investigations that make use of many of the main ideas encountered in the curriculum. They require use of material from more than one unit. The projects are intended to be completed by small groups of students working over a period of time. You may wish to have different groups work on different projects and then give presentations or create posters of their work.

Portfolios The *Core-Plus Mathematics* assessment program provides many tasks that can be placed in students' portfolios, including reports of individual and group projects, Math Toolkits, teacher-completed observation checklists, unit assessments (especially the take-home tasks), and projects. See *Implementing Core-Plus Mathematics* for additional portfolio information.

Scoring Assessments

High expectations of the quality of students' written work will encourage students to reach their potential. Assigning scores to open-ended assessments and to observations of students' performance requires more subjective judgment by the teacher than does grading short-answer or multiple-choice tests. It is therefore not possible to provide a complete set of explicit guidelines for scoring open-ended assessment items and written or oral reports. However, some general guidelines may be helpful. When scoring student work on open-ended assessment tasks, the goal is to reward, in a fair and consistent way, the kinds of thinking and understanding that the task is meant to measure. To score open-ended assessment tasks, teachers should have a general rubric, or scoring scheme, with several response levels in mind; a specific rubric and anchor items. (See *Implementing Core-Plus Mathematics* for more details.) The general rubric is the foundation for scoring across a wide range of types of open-ended tasks. The following general rubric can be used for most assessment tasks provided with *Core-Plus Mathematics*.

General Scoring Rubric	
4 points	Contains complete response with clear, coherent, and unambiguous explanation; includes clear and simple diagram, if appropriate; communicates effectively to identified audience; shows understanding of question's mathematical ideas and processes; identifies all important elements of question; includes examples and counterexamples; gives strong supporting arguments
3 points	Contains good solid response with some, but not all, of the characteristics above; explains less completely; may include minor error of execution but not of understanding
2 points	Contains complete response, but explanation is muddled; presents incomplete arguments; includes diagrams that are inappropriate or unclear, or fails to provide a diagram when it would be appropriate; indicates some understanding of mathematical ideas, but in an unclear way; shows clear evidence of understanding some important ideas while also making one or more fundamental, specific errors
1 point	Omits parts of question and response; has major errors; uses inappropriate strategies
0 points	No response; frivolous or irrelevant response

Assigning Grades

Since the *Core-Plus Mathematics* approach and materials provide a wide variety of assessment information, the teacher will be in a good position to assign appropriate grades. With such a wide choice for assessment, a word of caution is appropriate. *It is easy to overassess students.* The developers believe it is best to vary assessment methods from lesson to lesson, and from unit to unit. If information on what students understand and are able to do is available from their homework and in-class work, it may not be necessary to take the time for a formal quiz after each lesson. Similarly, information from take-home assessments or project work may replace all or portions of an in-class test.

Deciding exactly how to weigh the various kinds of assessment information is a decision that the teacher will need to make and communicate clearly to students.

Managing Classroom Activities

Active Learning and Collaborative Work

The *Core-Plus Mathematics* curriculum materials are designed to promote active, collaborative learning and group work for two important reasons. First, a collaborative environment fosters students' ability to make sense of mathematics and develop deep mathematical understandings. Collaborative learning is an effective method for engaging all the students in the learning process, particularly students who have been under represented in mathematics classes. Second, practice in collaborative learning in the classroom is practice for real life: students develop and exercise the same skills in the classroom that they need in their lives at home, in the community, and in the workplace.

Value of Individuals

Perhaps the most fundamental belief underlying the use of collaborative learning is that every student is viewed as a valuable resource and contributor. In other words, every student participates in group work and is given the opportunity and time to voice ideas and opinions. Implementing this concept is not easy nor does it happen automatically. In order to set a tone that will promote respect for individuals and their contributions, classroom norms should be established. Teachers should initiate a discussion and together write all the student formulated classroom rules for both individual and group behavior. The positively stated rules of behavior should be posted in the classroom and every member of the learning community should be held responsible for adhering to them.

Importance of Social Connections

Even in classrooms in which the rules for showing respect have been clearly established, experience has shown that students still cannot talk with one another about mathematics (or social studies, or literature, or any other subject) if they do not first have positive social connections.

One way to develop this kind of common base is through team-building activities. These short activities may be used at the beginning of the year to help students get acquainted with the whole class, and may be used during the year whenever new groups are formed to help groupmates know one another better. Team-building activities help students learn new and positive things about classmates with whom they may have attended classes for years, but have not known in depth. The time taken for these quick team builders pays off later in helping students feel comfortable enough to work with the members of their group.

Need for Teaching Social Skills

Experience also has shown that social skills are critical to the successful functioning of any small group. Because there is no guarantee that students of any particular age will have the social skills necessary for effective group work, it often is necessary to teach these skills to build a collaborative learning environment.

These social skills are specific skills, not general goals. Examples of specific social skills that the teacher can teach in the classroom include responding to ideas respectfully, keeping track of time, disagreeing in an agreeable way, involving everyone, and following directions. Though goals such as cooperating and listening are important, they are too general to teach.

One of the premises of collaborative learning is that by developing the appropriate skills through practice, anyone in the class can learn to work in a group with anyone else. Learning to work in groups is a continuous process, however, and the process can be helped by decisions that the teacher makes.

One method of teaching social skills is to begin by selecting a specific skill and then having the class brainstorm to develop a script for practicing that skill. Next, the students practice that skill during their group work. Finally, in what is called the processing, the students discuss within their groups how well they performed the assigned social skill. Effective teaching of social skills requires practicing and processing; merely describing a specific social skill is not enough. The *Teacher's Guide* includes specific collaborative skills to practice and processing prompts for student self-assessment.

The culture and teaching-learning norms created within the classroom are crucial to the success of this curriculum. It is important to inculcate in students a sense of inquiry and responsibility for their own learning. Without this commitment, active, collaborative learning by students cannot be effective. Some students seem satisfied with the rationale that collaboration is important in workplace. Others may need to understand that the struggle of verbalizing their thinking, listening to others' thinking, questioning themselves and other group members, and coming to an agreement increases their understanding and retention of the mathematics while contributing to the formation of important thinking skills or habits of mind.

Issues of helping students to work collaboratively will become less pressing as both you and your students experience this type of learning. *Implementing Core-Plus Mathematics* provides additional information related to the challenge of facilitating collaborative work including support to help teachers make decisions about group size, composition, method of selection, the duration of groups and dealing with student absences. This resource also offers a number of practical suggestions from *Core-Plus Mathematics* teachers on effectively pacing instruction in a student-centered classroom.

Additional Resources

Implementing Core-Plus Mathematics contains expanded information on:

- the scope and sequence of Courses 1–4,
- managing classroom activities,
- differentiation built into the program,
- the assessment program,
- communication with parents, and
- mathematics program evaluation.

You will find it useful to have the implementation guide available for reference throughout the school year. This booklet can found on the *TeacherWorks* CD.

Scope and Sequence contains information on:

- the scope and sequence of Courses 1–4
- units in which key mathematical ideas are developed

You can download this booklet at: glencoe.com and www.wmich.edu/cpmp/pdfs/scopeandsequence.pdf

Math Link articles related to *Core-Plus Mathematics* written by developers and teachers are available on the *Core-Plus Mathematics* Project Web site at www.wmich.edu/cpmp under Publications. These articles were written based on first edition experiences, but in many cases are still applicable to the second edition materials.

Topics include:

- selecting and implementing *Core-Plus Mathematics*,
- effectively using collaborative groups,
- the four-year mathematics program,
- options for acceleration paths to AP Calculus or AP Statistics,
- meeting the needs of ELL and LEP students,
- college placement,
- the International Baccalaureate Program, and
- achievement in Science.

Annotated Bibliography Available on the CPMP Web site under Publications are references to articles, book chapters, dissertations, papers presented at conferences, and field-test reports based on the program. Some of these resources can be downloaded.

Professional Development Opportunities A variety of professional development opportunities are provided by Glencoe and the Core-Plus Mathematics Project. Workshops are listed on the CPMP Web site www.wmich.edu/cpmp under Implementation. Experienced *Core-Plus Mathematics* teacher-consultants can be contracted to provide onsite inservice. Contact your Glencoe sales representative or the CPMP office (cpmp@wmich.edu) for provider names.

Parent Resource Information and resources for parents including helping with homework, research supporting *Core-Plus Mathematics*, evidence of success, and frequently asked questions is available at www.wmich.edu/cpmp/parentresource/index.html.

Unit 5

Polynomial and Rational Functions

In prior units of *Core-Plus Mathematics*, you developed understanding and skill in the use of linear, quadratic, and inverse variation functions. Those functions are members of two larger families of versatile and useful algebraic tools, the polynomial and rational functions.

In this unit, you will learn how to use polynomial and rational expressions and functions to represent and analyze a variety of quantitative patterns and relationships. The key ideas will be developed through work on problems in three lessons.

Lessons

1 Polynomial Expressions and Functions

Use linear, quadratic, cubic, and quartic polynomial functions to represent quantitative relationships, data patterns, and graphs. Analyze the connections between symbolic expressions and graphs of polynomial functions. Combine polynomials by addition, subtraction, and multiplication.

2 Quadratic Polynomials

Extend skills in expanding and factoring quadratic expressions. Use a completing-the-square strategy to write quadratic expressions in equivalent forms and to prove the quadratic formula for solving quadratic equations.

3 Rational Expressions and Functions

Use quotients of polynomial functions to represent and analyze quantitative relationships. Analyze the connections between symbolic expressions and graphs of rational functions. Combine rational expressions by addition, subtraction, multiplication, and division.

POLYNOMIAL AND RATIONAL FUNCTIONS

Unit Overview

In units of the algebra and functions strand in Courses 1 and 2, students built a repertoire of function families that model linear, quadratic, exponential, and power variation (direct and inverse) relationships. They developed skill in using algebraic expressions to represent those patterns of change, in manipulating the expressions to solve equations and inequalities and to gain insight into relationships, and in solving a wide variety of authentic quantitative problems.

The lessons of this unit extend students' knowledge and skill in work with algebraic functions and expressions in three ways. First, they learn how to use polynomials that go beyond linear and quadratic functions and expressions to model data and graph patterns that are more complex than the familiar straight lines and parabolas. They discover ways of predicting the shape of polynomial function graphs, especially the number of local maximum and local minimum points and the number of zeroes, and ways of combining polynomials by addition, subtraction, and multiplication.

Second, they revisit quadratic functions and expressions to learn about completing the square to produce vertex forms for their rules. They learn how to use vertex form to locate maximum or minimum points on the graphs of quadratic functions and to solve equations by algebraic reasoning. They also study proof of the quadratic formula for solving equations.

Finally, they explore properties and applications of rational functions and expressions. They learn how to identify undefined points of algebraic fractions and vertical and horizontal asymptotes of their graphs. They explore simplification of algebraic fractions and the ways that cautious use of such algebraic work can provide insights into rational functions and the problems they model. Then they learn how to combine rational functions and expressions by addition, subtraction, multiplication, and division.

This is an introduction to polynomial and rational functions and expressions that should be accessible to most students (with judicious use of computer algebra system software for more complex calculations). Further work toward developing proficiency with symbol manipulation occurs in subsequent Review tasks and in Course 4.

Unit 5

Unit Objectives

- Recognize patterns in problem conditions and in data plots that can be described by polynomial and rational functions
- Write polynomial and rational function rules to describe patterns in graphs, numerical data, and problem conditions
- Use table, graph, or symbolic representations of polynomial and rational functions to answer questions about the situations they represent: (1) calculate y for a given x (i.e., evaluate functions); (2) find x for a given y (i.e., solve equations and inequalities); and (3) identify local max/min points and asymptotes
- Rewrite polynomial and rational expressions in equivalent forms by expanding or factoring, by combining like terms, and by removing common factors in numerator and denominator of rational expressions
- Add, subtract, and multiply polynomial and rational expressions and functions
- Extend understanding and skill in work with quadratic functions to include completing the square, interpreting vertex form, and proving the quadratic formula
- Recognize and calculate complex number solutions of quadratic equations

CPMP-Tools

In this unit, *CPMP-Tools* CAS software can be used to investigate parameter changes in polynomial and rational functions. The CAS software can be used to solve equations as well as perform arithmetic operations on these functions. Other features include factoring and expanding expressions. The screens below show some features of the software. Notes on page T325 provide additional technology information.

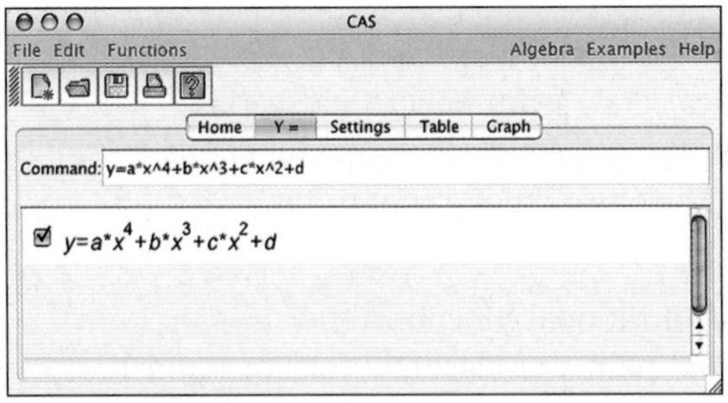

CAS
File Edit Functions Algebra Examples Help
Home Y= Settings Table Graph
Command: y=a*x^4+b*x^3+c*x^2+d
$y=a*x^4+b*x^3+c*x^2+d$

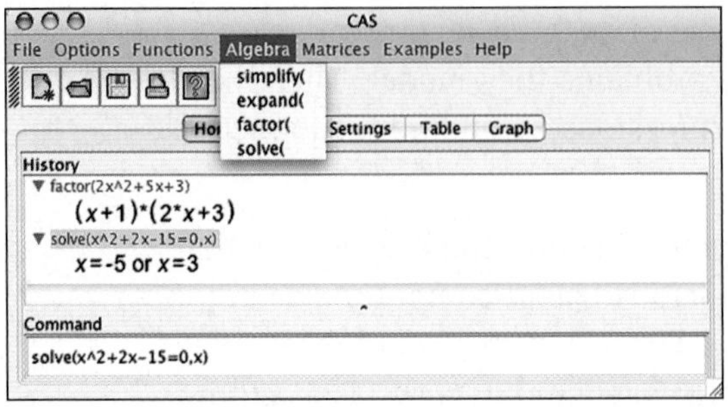

CAS
File Options Functions Algebra Matrices Examples Help
simplify(expand(factor(solve(
Settings Table Graph
History
factor(2x^2+5x+3)
$(x+1)*(2*x+3)$
solve(x^2+2x-15=0,x)
$x=-5$ or $x=3$
Command
solve(x^2+2x-15=0,x)

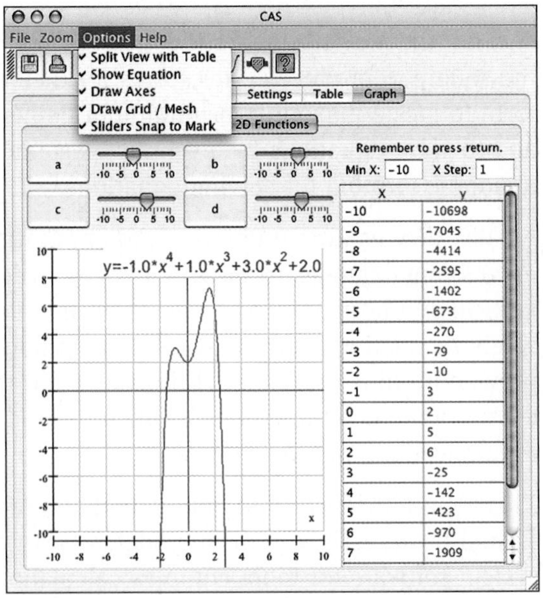

CAS
File Zoom Options Help
Split View with Table
Show Equation
Draw Axes
Draw Grid / Mesh
Sliders Snap to Mark
Settings Table Graph
2D Functions
a b c d
Remember to press return.
Min X: -10 X Step: 1
$y=-1.0*x^4+1.0*x^3+3.0*x^2+2.0$

X	Y
-10	-10698
-9	-7045
-8	-4414
-7	-2595
-6	-1402
-5	-673
-4	-270
-3	-79
-2	-10
-1	3
0	2
1	5
2	6
3	-25
4	-142
5	-423
6	-970
7	-1909

Unit 5 Planning Guide

Lesson Objectives	On Your Own Assignments*	Suggested Pacing	Materials
Lesson 1 ***Polynomial Expressions and Functions*** • Model problem situations using polynomial functions • Identify patterns relating rules and graphs of polynomial functions—connecting polynomial degree to local maximum and local minimum values and zeroes • Add, subtract, and multiply polynomials—connecting degrees of component polynomials to degrees of sums, differences, and products • Find zeroes of polynomial functions and create polynomial functions with prescribed zeroes	**After Investigation 1:** A1, A2, C9, E17, E18, Rv21, Rv22 **After Investigation 2:** A3, C10, R14, Rv23–Rv27 **After Investigation 3:** A4, A5, A6 and A7 *or* A7 and A8, C11 or C12, C13, R15, R16, E19, E20, Rv28, Rv29	8 days (including assessment)	• *CPMP-Tools* CAS software or other CAS software capable of polynomial parameter investigation • Unit Resources
Lesson 2 ***Quadratic Polynomials*** • Express quadratic function rules in vertex form • Use vertex form of quadratic expressions to solve quadratic equations and locate the vertex of parabolic graphs • Use completing the square to prove the quadratic formula • Use the quadratic formula to analyze solution possibilities for quadratic equations and indicate the rationale for extending the number system to include complex numbers	**After Investigation 1:** A1–A5, C10, C11, choose two of R15–R17, E20–E22, Rv26–Rv28 **After Investigation 2:** A6–A8, C12–C14, R18 or R19, choose one of E23–E25, Rv29–Rv31	5 days (including assessment)	• *CPMP-Tools* CAS software or other CAS software • Unit Resources
Lesson 3 ***Rational Expressions and Functions*** • Create rational functions to model problem situations • Analyze graphs of rational functions and their asymptotes • Simplify rational expressions • Add, subtract, multiply, and divide rational expressions	**After Investigation 1:** A1, A2, A4, A6, C12–C14, C15, R21, Rv31–Rv33 **After Investigation 2:** A3, A5, A7, C16, choose one of C17–C19, R22, E24, Rv34–Rv36 **After Investigation 3:** A8, C20, E25 or E26, Rv37–Rv39 **After Investigation 4:** A9–A11, R23, choose one of E27–E30, Rv40, Rv41	9 days (including assessment)	• *CPMP-Tools* CAS software or other CAS software • Unit Resources
Lesson 4 ***Looking Back*** • Review and synthesize the major objectives of the unit		3 days (including assessment)	• *CPMP-Tools* CAS software or other CAS software • Unit Resources

** When choice is indicated, it is important to leave the choice to the student.*

Note: *It is best if Connections tasks are discussed as a whole class after they have been assigned as homework.*

LESSON 1

Polynomial Expressions and Functions

Working for a company that designs, builds, and tests rides for amusement parks can be both fun and financially rewarding. Suppose that in such a position, your team is in charge of designing a long roller coaster. One morning, your team is handed sketches that show ideas for two sections of a new roller coaster.

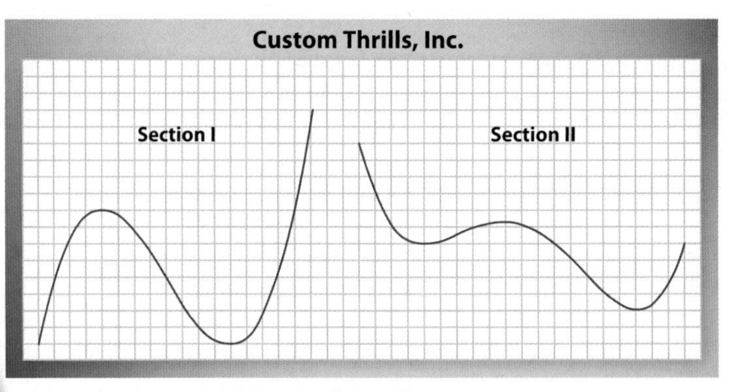

As team leader, your task is to find algebraic functions with graphs that match the two sketches. The functions will be useful in checking safety features of the design, like estimated speed and height at various points of the track. They will also be essential in planning manufacture of the coaster track and support frame.

320 UNIT 5 • Polynomial and Rational Functions

Polynomial Expressions and Functions

Unit 5

The purpose of this lesson is to extend students' repertoire of useful function models to the family of polynomials and to analyze the new possibilities for table and graph patterns, equations, inequalities, and algebraic operations that arise from consideration of polynomials of degree greater than two.

The lesson is organized into three investigations. The first introduces students to cubic and quartic polynomial functions through work on problems modeling the shape of proposed roller coaster designs. Then the general concept of polynomial functions is introduced, along with the standard notation for polynomial expressions. Then students explore graph possibilities for polynomial functions of various degrees, focusing on local maximum and minimum points of those graphs.

The second investigation develops a rationale and procedures for adding and subtracting polynomial functions and expressions through work on problems related to analysis of business prospects for a concert promotion. Then students explore possibilities for zeroes of polynomial functions—connecting the number of zeroes to degree of the polynomial.

Finally, the third investigation develops procedures for multiplying polynomial functions and expressions, again connecting degree and zeroes of factors to degree and zeroes of products.

Lesson Objectives

- Model problem situations using polynomial functions
- Identify patterns relating rules and graphs of polynomial functions—connecting polynomial degree to local maximum and local minimum values and zeroes
- Add, subtract, and multiply polynomials—connecting degrees of component polynomials to degrees of sums, differences, and products
- Find zeroes of polynomial functions and create polynomial functions with prescribed zeroes

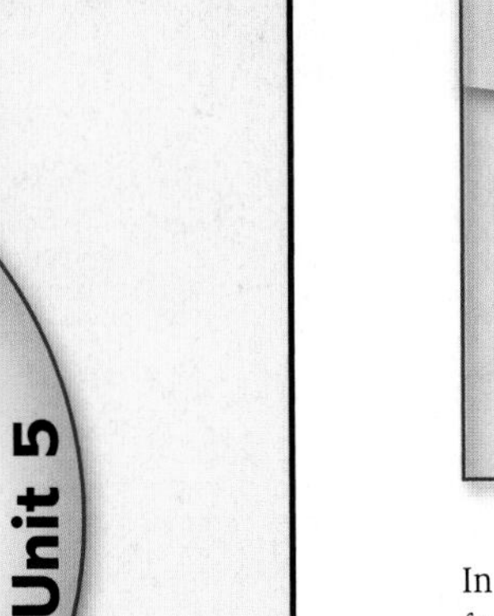

Think About This Situation

Study the sketches of Section I and Section II of the proposed coaster design.

a) What familiar functions have graphs that match all or parts of the design sketches?

b) What strategies could you use to find functions with graphs that model the sketches?

c) What do you think are the key points on each sketch that should be used in finding a function model for the graph pattern?

In this lesson, you will begin study of an important class of algebraic functions called *polynomial functions*. You will learn how to use polynomial functions to model complex graphical patterns, like the roller coaster design proposals, and how to use operations on polynomials to solve problems in business situations.

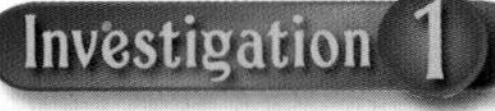

Modeling with Polynomial Functions

The roller coaster design sketches are not modeled well by graphs of linear, exponential, or quadratic functions. But there are other kinds of algebraic functions that do have such graphs, and there are techniques for using sample graph points to find rules for those functions. In this investigation, you should look for answers to these questions:

What are polynomial functions and what kinds of graphs do those functions have?

How are rules for polynomial functions related to patterns in their graphs?

Lesson Launch

The given sketches have been designed to have elements that look familiar (mostly parts that look like parabolas), but taken as wholes they are not like graphs of any functions that students will have encountered in *Core-Plus Mathematics* thus far. When discussing strategies to find functions in Part b, you may wish to introduce the language "curve-fitting" as it is used in Problems 1 and 2.

It would also be helpful to have students consider how many points they needed to write an exact equation of a line and that in most cases of curve-fitting, the data set has many points. At this point, do not suggest that they, for example, use only 4 points for cubic regression, but plant the seed that choosing too few points may not give a good model.

Think About This Situation

a Both sketches have pieces that look somewhat like parabolas, so one could expect that quadratic functions might be pieced together to provide useful models. It seems unlikely that students will even suggest exponential, linear, or inverse power models. But you might ask why they did not believe that those familiar functions would be appropriate. This question provides an excellent opportunity to check students' prior knowledge and to review important things about functions.

b A set of axes could be drawn on the sketches and a scale could be set. Then several points on each could be identified with coordinates and a calculator or spreadsheet regression tool could be used to find the function to model the sketch. A more informal modeling strategy would involve trying an example from the repertoire of possibilities already known and adjusting parameters in that first guess to see if it is possible to get something reasonably close to the shape of even part of one of the given graphs.

c The points on each graph where the graph changes direction (local maximum or local minimum points) and several points in between are more critical than those on the far left or far right of each sketch.

Investigation 1 Modeling with Polynomial Functions

In this investigation, students will learn how to model complex graphical patterns with polynomial functions of degree 3 and 4. Then they will explore a variety of polynomials to discover the type of graph possibilities. They should begin to see the relationship between the degree of a polynomial function and other important features of its graph, especially the number of local maximum and local minimum points.

PROMOTING MATHEMATICAL DISCOURSE

Unit 5

Teaching Resources

Transparency Master 1.

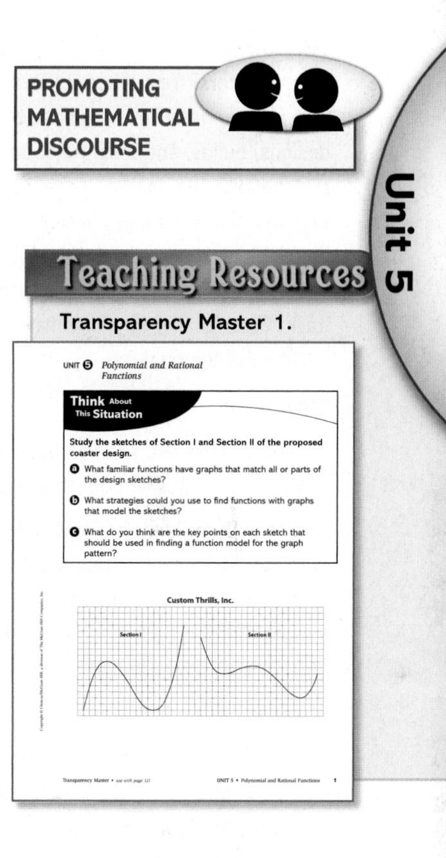

UNIT 5 *Polynomial and Rational Functions*

Think About This Situation

Study the sketches of Section I and Section II of the proposed coaster design.

a What familiar functions have graphs that match all or parts of the design sketches?

b What strategies could you use to find functions with graphs that model the sketches?

c What do you think are the key points on each sketch that should be used in finding a function model for the graph pattern?

Transparency Master • UNIT 5 • Polynomial and Rational Functions 1

COLLABORATION SKILL
Ask thought-provoking questions during the investigation to make sure we are developing deep understanding of an idea.

Promoting Mathematical Discourse

Think About This Situation, *page 321*

Teacher: Have some of you been to amusement parks and ridden roller coasters? Yes. Where? *(Students offer some specific parks and ride names.)* Let's suppose that you work for a company that designs, builds, and tests roller coasters and you are handed sketches like the ones on page 320 that show ideas for two sections of a new roller coaster. Your job is to find algebraic functions for these curves that will help in checking safety features of the design and also could be used to manufacture the coaster track. What familiar functions have graphs that match part or all of Section I of the track?

Viho: None

Marcie: It looks like two parabolas pieced together to me—one upside-down and one right-side-up.

Teacher: Other ideas? *(The teacher is wondering if someone will think of the sine or cosine function briefly studied in Course 2, Unit 6. Since no one mentions it, she moves on.)* How about Section II of the track? Does that sketch look like one of the functions we have studied?

Elise: Not really

Teacher: These sketches do look quite different from what we have studied before. In this lesson, we will learn about these polynomial functions, their rules and their graphs that are similar to these two sections of track. What strategies could you use to find functions with graphs that model these sketches? Kawan?

Kawan: Maybe we could pick some points and use technology to find a function.

Steve: Yeah, my calculator shows lots of other options—like **CubicReg**, **QuartReg**, and **LnReg**. I wonder if **LnReg** is another line.

Teacher: If we did that, what do you think would be the key points on each sketch that should be used to find the function model for the graph pattern to Section I? Takoda?

Takoda: I'd pick the top and bottom points on the curves.

Susanna: I would also add the first point, the last point, and some points on the way up and down the curves. More points might be better.

Teacher: Why might more points be better, Susanna?

Susanna: Well, it might make it easier for the technology to match the graph.

Teacher: What do others think?

Layla: Well, when we found equations of lines for data sets, it didn't seem to matter to the calculator whether we had a small number of points or a large number of points, so I'm not sure it matters how many we pick.

Josh: But we did need at least two points to write an equation of a line.

Layla: Of course, I didn't mean only picking one point. But it seems like we need more than two points to describe these curves.

Teacher: Good thinking. Which key points would you select for the second section of the coaster design? Darim which points would you use?

Darim: Let's see, can I point to them on the display? *(The teacher indicates that he can. Darim selects beginning and ending points, local maximum and minimum points, and a couple others.)*

Teacher: Good discussion. In this lesson, we will learn more about the class of functions called polynomial functions. Let's read the focus questions on page 321 together before you begin your work on Investigation 1.

Teacher Notes

Unit 5

To the *n*th degree The following diagram shows the graph of a function that could represent a roller coaster design based on the Section I sketch.

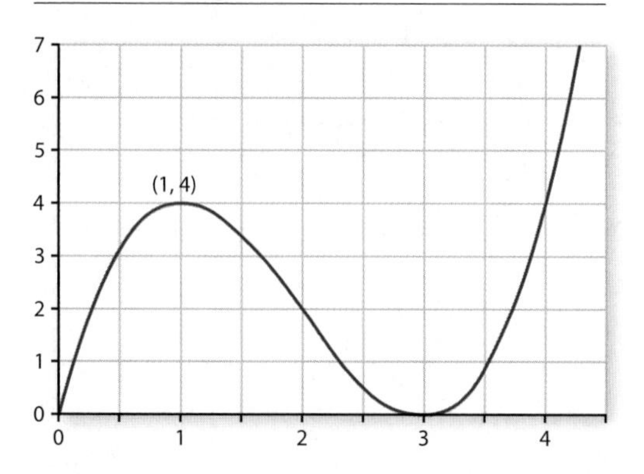

1. When you used curve-fitting tools in earlier work, all you had to do was supply coordinates of points that capture key features of the graph or data pattern and then select a function type for the model. Why would neither linear, quadratic, exponential, nor inverse variation functions provide good models for the graph pattern representing the Section I Design?

2. You might have noticed that most curve-fitting tools offer other modeling options. The one listed right after the quadratic option is usually *cubic*.
   - **a.** What key points on the graph, beside (1, 4), do you think would be helpful in finding a cubic function that models the proposed Section I Design?
   - **b.** Using the points you selected in Part a, apply a cubic curve-fitting routine to find a function model for the graph pattern.
   - **c.** Compare the graph of the resulting cubic function to the shape of the Section I Design. Describe ways that the cubic function is or is not a good model of that pattern.

3. Compare results of your work toward a function model for the Section I Design with those of others in your class.
   - **a.** Did everyone use the same points from the given graph?
   - **b.** For those who used different points or even different numbers of points, were the resulting function models still the same?
   - **c.** What do you think might be the minimum number of points needed to find a cubic model for a data or graph pattern?

322 UNIT 5 • Polynomial and Rational Functions

1. A linear function would not capture the curvature of the roller coaster. The graph of a quadratic function would not make two changes in direction like the roller coaster design for Section I. The graph of exponential and inverse power functions would not have "hills" and "valleys" like the sketch.

2. **a.** Student answers will vary but they may suggest (0, 0), (2, 2), (3, 0), or (4, 4) since these points seem to have integer values.

   b. Using these points, the cubic function model is $y = x^3 - 6x^2 + 9x$. (Eliminating (2, 2) results in the same function.)

   c. This function above seems to be a very good model for the roller coaster design. They both have the same general shape and critical points as described in Part a.

TECHNOLOGY NOTE The *CPMP-Tools* software for Course 3 offers another curve-fitting option. If you choose Data Analysis from the Statistics menu, you can enter some sample (*x*, *y*) data pairs in the data sheet that appears. Then you can make a scatterplot of those pairs, choose a function type from the Models menu, and select the Draw Moveable Line or Model icon. The model that appears is a linear function. But by clicking on and dragging any of the control points on that line, you can reshape the graph to better fit the data points that have been entered. If, for example, you had chosen the cubic model, when you drag the control points, you will see the corresponding cubic equation and graph on the screen. These will change as the control points are dragged.

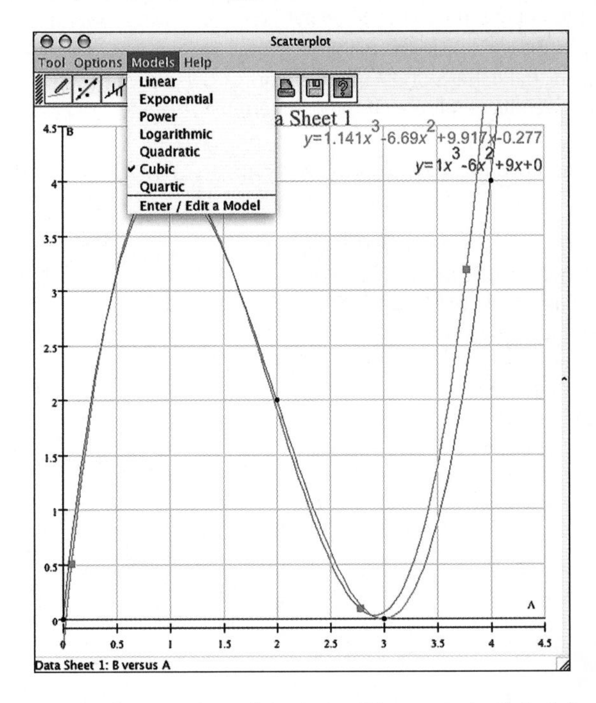

3. **a.** Students may choose 4 or 5 points. The points listed in Problem 2 Part a will probably be popular points.

   b. The resulting function models will probably not be exactly alike for students who use two different sets of points. However, they should be similar.

   c. The minimum number is 4, but answers could vary. Students might reason by generalization from the case of linear and quadratic functions that they know well, two points for linear and three points for quadratic. They might also find that their technology tool will produce an error message for a cubic regression with only 3 points.

INSTRUCTIONAL NOTE
Problem 3 provides an opportunity for a whole class sharing of models and conjectures of the minimum number of points. The fact that $n + 1$ data points are needed to find a polynomial function of degree n can be revealed at STM Part d on page T326.

Unit 5

4 As you may have noted, there are some significant differences between the design ideas for Sections I and II of the proposed roller coaster. The next diagram shows a graph of a function that could represent a roller coaster design based on the Section II sketch.

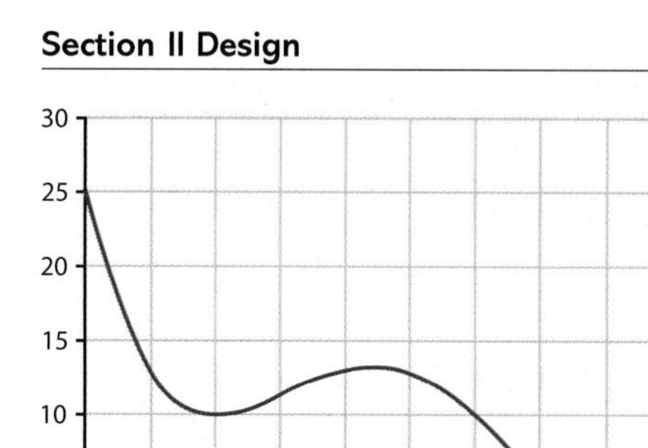

a. Find coordinates of key points outlining the shape of this graph. Then find the cubic function model for the pattern in those points and compare its graph to the shape of the proposed Section II Design.

b. You may have noticed there are other curve-fitting options on your calculator or computer software list. One such option is *quartic*. What do you think might be the minimum number of points needed to find a quartic model for a data or graph pattern?

c. Find a quartic function model for the pattern of data points you identified in Part a. Check how well its graph matches the pattern in the Section II Design.

d. Compare your result with those of others in your class. See if you can explain any differences.

Though you may not have been aware of it at the time, in earlier *Core-Plus Mathematics* units involving linear and quadratic functions, you were learning about functions from a larger class called polynomial functions. Cubic and quartic functions, like those that you explored in a search for models of the roller coaster designs, are also polynomial functions. A **polynomial function** is any function with a rule that can be written in the form $f(x) = a_nx^n + a_{n-1}x^{n-1} + \cdots + a_1x + a_0$, where n is a whole number and the coefficients $a_n, a_{n-1}, a_{n-2}, \ldots, a_1, a_0$ are numbers.

4 **a.** Some plausible points here include (0, 25), (1, 10), (3, 10), and (5, 10). An estimated point could be (3.5, 5). If the first 4 points are used, a cubic function to model the data pattern would be $y = -x^3 + 9x^2 - 23x + 25$. This function will have a graph that seems to catch the first part of the desired shape but not the last valley. Using the 5 points above, the cubic regression equation is $y = -0.594x^3 + 6.231x^2 - 19.301x + 24.631$. This function also does not capture the last valley.

b. The minimum number is 5, but answers may vary as in Problem 3 Part c.

c. A quartic model that uses all 5 points identified in Part a is $y = 1.048x^4 - 10.429x^3 + 33.095x^2 - 38.714x + 25$. It does a fairly good job of matching the desired pattern, although it drops below the x-axis. If you add the point (4.25, 0), the quartic regression model (rounded to integer coefficients) $y = x^4 - 10x^3 + 32x^2 - 38x + 25$ picks up the feature that the graph is close to the x-axis near $x = 4.25$.

d. Students should reconcile any differences.

INSTRUCTIONAL NOTE You will probably want to have a mini-summary discussion of Problem 4 when most students have completed that work. Then you can launch them into the next phase of the investigation by introducing the general notion of a polynomial and the standard notation as described before Problem 5. You might want to draw their attention to the interesting hill and valley features of cubic and quartic function graphs they have just met. Then observe that it is useful to have some general ideas about what can happen with different sorts of polynomial rules (in the way that they know how to use rules for linear and quadratic functions to predict shapes of those graphs) and that the next several questions guide exploration of that question.

TECHNOLOGY NOTE It is possible but a bit tedious to use standard graphing calculators to explore effects of parameters in function rules on shapes and locations of graphs for cubic and quartic polynomial functions. It is much more efficient to use a computer tool with sliders set up for parameters, like *The Geometer's Sketchpad* or *CPMP-Tools*, to do this kind of exploration. Alternatively, the Transformation Graphing application for TI-83 and TI-84 calculators allows you to enter a general equation for a function, such as **Y1=Ax^3+Bx^2+Cx+D**, then change the parameters to see how these changes are reflected in the graph of the function. A Technology Tip for this feature is included in the *Unit 5 Resource Masters*. A summary of the features of this application, including links to download, can be found at the Texas Instruments Web site: education.ti.com/educationportal/sites/US/productDetail/us_transg83_84.html

Teaching Resources

Student Master 2.

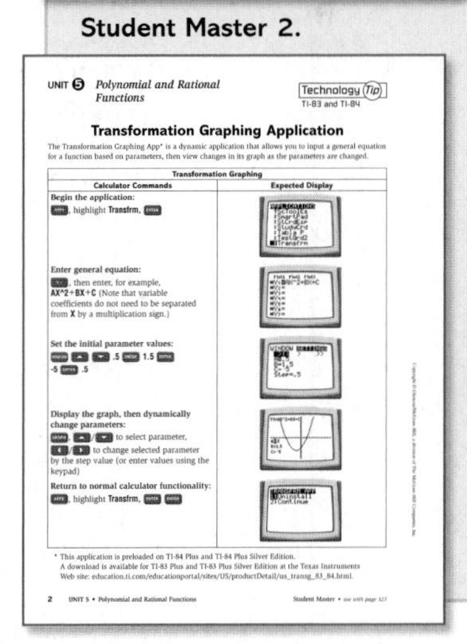

UNIT 5 *Polynomial and Rational Functions*

Technology Tip
TI-83 and TI-84

Transformation Graphing Application

The Transformation Graphing App* is a dynamic application that allows you to input a general equation for a function based on parameters, then view changes in its graph as the parameters are changed.

Transformation Graphing	
Calculator Commands	**Expected Display**
Begin the application: , highlight **Transfrm**,	
Enter general equation: , then enter, for example, **AX^2+BX+C** (Note that variable coefficients do not need to be separated from **X** by a multiplication sign.)	
Set the initial parameter values: .5 1.5 -5 .5	
Display the graph, then dynamically change parameters: , / to select parameter, / to change selected parameter by the step value (or enter values using the keypad)	
Return to normal calculator functionality: , highlight **Transfrm**,	

* This application is preloaded on TI-84 Plus and TI-84 Plus Silver Edition. A download is available for TI-83 Plus and TI-83 Plus Silver Edition at the Texas Instruments Web site: education.ti.com/educationportal/sites/US/productDetail/us_transg_83_84.html.

2 UNIT 5 • Polynomial and Rational Functions   Student Master • use with page 323

The functions described by information on these calculator screens are cubic and quartic polynomials.

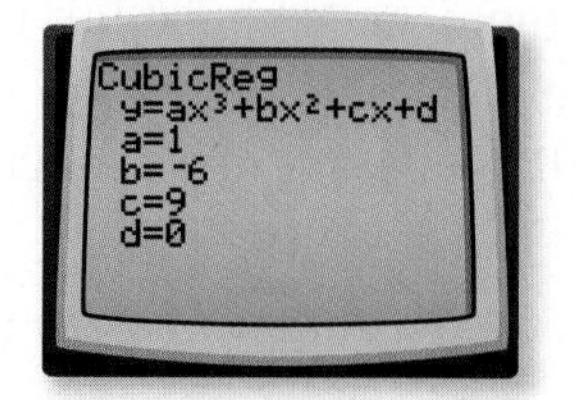

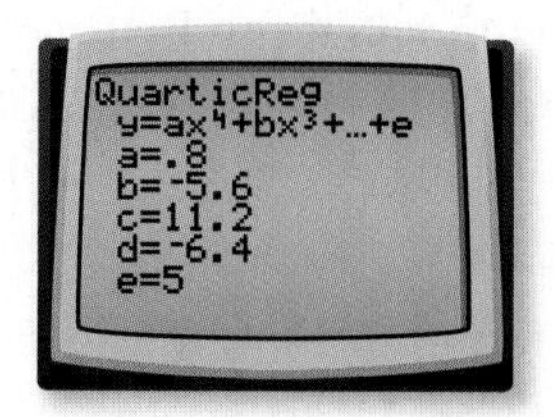

Any algebraic expression in the form $a_nx^n + a_{n-1}x^{n-1} + \cdots + a_1x + a_0$ is called a **polynomial expression**. One of the most important characteristics of any polynomial function or expression is its degree. The **degree of a polynomial** is the greatest exponent of the variable that occurs in the expression. For example, a quadratic polynomial has degree 2, a cubic polynomial has degree 3, and a quartic polynomial has degree 4. A nonzero constant is a polynomial of degree 0.

Connecting Polynomial Expressions and Graphs From earlier work with linear, quadratic, exponential, and power functions, you know that it is often helpful to inspect a function rule and estimate the shape of its graph. In the other direction, it is helpful if you can inspect a graph and predict the kind of function rule that will model its pattern.

5 As you have seen in exploring polynomial models for roller coaster designs, one of the most interesting and important characteristics of polynomial functions is the number and location of *peaks* or *valleys* in their graphs. A peak indicates a *local maximum* value for the function, and a valley indicates a *local minimum* value for the function.

a. Graph and then estimate coordinates of local maximum and local minimum points for each polynomial function.

i. $g(x) = -x^3 + 6x^2 - 9x$

ii. $h(x) = -x^4 + 2x^3 + 7x^2 - 8x - 12$

b. How do the examples in Part a help to explain why the adjective "local" is used in describing function values at peaks and valleys of polynomial functions?

c. Why are the points (0, 0) and (4.25, 7) *not* considered local minimum or local maximum points for the cubic function you found in Problem 2 to model the Section I Design for the roller coaster?

d. Why are the points (0, 25) and (5, 10) *not* considered local maximum or local minimum points for the quartic function you found in Problem 4 to model the Section II Design?

6 Consider the relationship between the degree of a polynomial function and the number of local maximum and/or local minimum points on the graph of that function.

a. Give an example of a polynomial function with no local maximum or local minimum point.

b. How many local maximum and/or local minimum points can there be on the graph of a quadratic polynomial?

324 UNIT 5 • Polynomial and Rational Functions

5 **a.** **i.** Local maximum point: (3, 0)
Local minimum point: (1, −4)

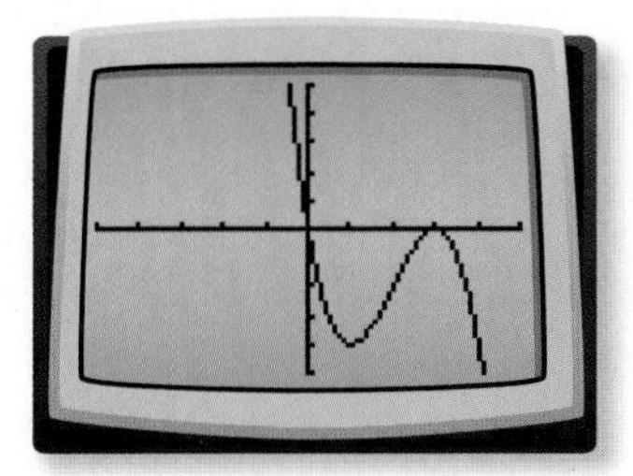

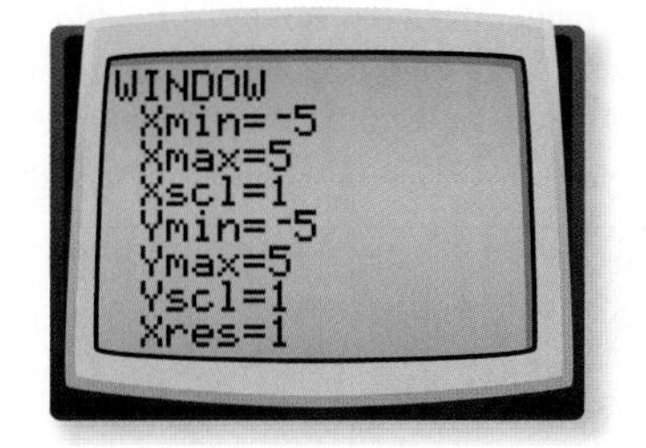

ii. Local maximum points: (−1.56, 4) and (2.56, 4)
Local minimum point: (0.5, −14.06)

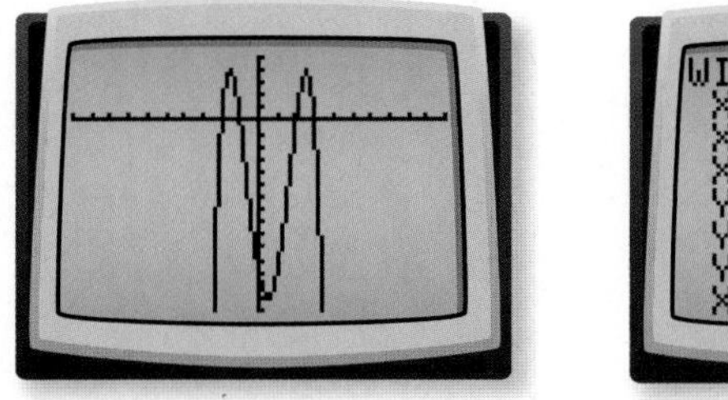

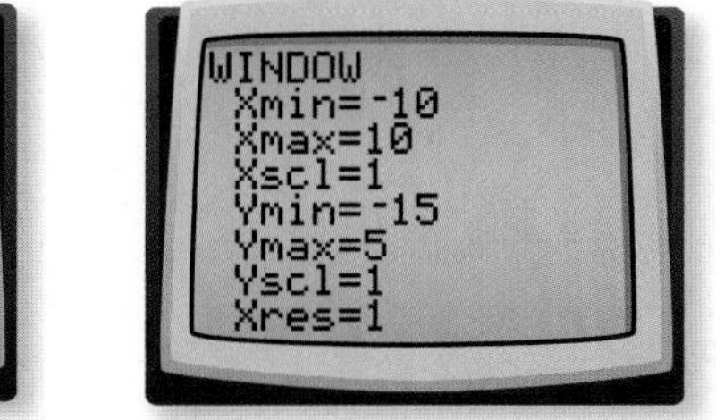

b. The word *local* is best shown in the graph in Part ai. Although the function has no minimum or maximum value, if the domain is restricted to $0 < x < 4$, there are both a maximum and minimum value of the function. These are called local maximum and minimum points because they are only the maximum or minimum for a small region surrounding the point itself.

c. The two given points are located on the graphs of the modeling functions in ways that place them between other points that are higher and lower, no matter how small a neighborhood you limit your eyes. The point (0, 0) might appear to be a minimum point. However, any cubic function model that captures the peak and valley of the Section I Design will have a graph that, when extended to the left of $x = 0$, will continue going down below $y = 0$.

d. The points (0, 25) and (5, 10) are not local max/min points of the function model graph of the Section II Design for reasons similar to those given in the answer to Part c. The graph of any good quartic model will continue up to the left of (0, 25) and to the right of (5, 10) so that those points will not appear at all special as local max/min points of the graphs.

6 **a.** Answers will vary but will probably include only linear functions. Some students may suggest exponential functions, but these are not polynomial functions.

b. A quadratic function will have either a local maximum or local minimum point. That point will also be the max/min point for the quadratic function.

Unit 5

7 To explore the graphs of higher degree polynomial functions, it is helpful to use computer software that accepts function definitions like $f(x) = ax^3 + bx^2 + cx + d$, allows you to move "sliders" controlling the values of a, b, c, and d, and quickly produces corresponding graphs.

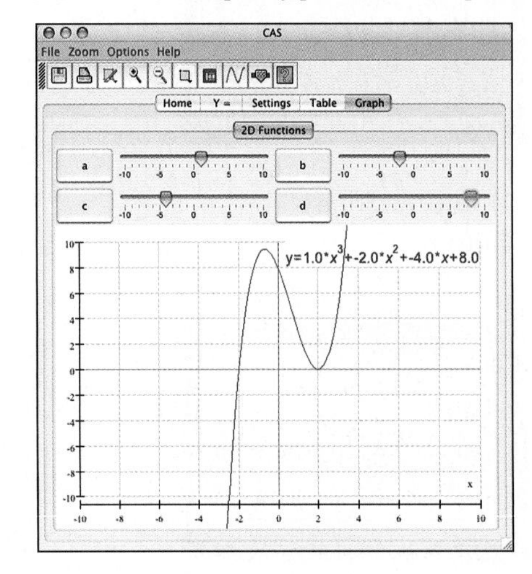

a. How many local maximum and/or local minimum points do you think there can be on the graph of a cubic polynomial function?

b. Test your conjecture in Part a by graphing cubic polynomial functions $p(x) = a_3x^3 + a_2x^2 + a_1x + a_0$ for various sets of values for the coefficients a_3, a_2, a_1, and a_0. You might start with examples like these.

$$y = x^3 - 9x$$
$$y = x^3 - 6x^2 + 12x - 3$$
$$y = -x^3 + 4x + 2$$

Then modify those examples to test other cases.

c. How many local maximum and/or local minimum points do you think there can be on the graph of a quartic polynomial?

d. Test your conjecture in Part c by graphing quartic polynomial functions $p(x) = a_4x^4 + a_3x^3 + a_2x^2 + a_1x + a_0$ for various combinations of values for the coefficients a_4, a_3, a_2, a_1, and a_0. You might start with examples like these.

$$y = x^4 - 9x^2 + 2$$
$$y = -x^4 - 8x^3 - 32x^2 - 32x + 5$$
$$y = -x^4 - 4x^3 + 4x^2 + 16x$$

Then modify those examples to test other cases.

e. What seems to be the connection between the degree of a polynomial and the number of local maximum and/or local minimum points on its graph? Test your conjecture by exploring graphs or tables of values for some polynomial functions of even higher degree like $p(x) = x^5 - 5x^3 + 4x$ and $q(x) = x^5 + x^3 + x + 4$.

7 **TECHNOLOGY NOTE** This problem could be completed as a whole-class interactive discussion or by making a computer with *CPMP-Tools* available per group.

Be sure that students make conjectures before exploring the number of local maximum and/or local minimum points. Alternatively, students can use graphing calculators or use the TI Transformation Graphing application as described on page T323.

a. Student conjectures may vary.

b. There can be zero or two local maximum *and* local minimum points (one maximum and one minimum) on the graph of a cubic function.

c. Student conjectures may vary.

d. There can be one or three local maximum and local minimum points on the graph of a quartic function.

e. The highest possible number of local maximum or local minimum points seems to be one less than the degree of the polynomial. (Some students may observe that if the degree n of a polynomial is even, then the number of max/min points could be any positive odd number less than n. If the degree n is odd, then the number of max/min points could be any positive even number less than n.)

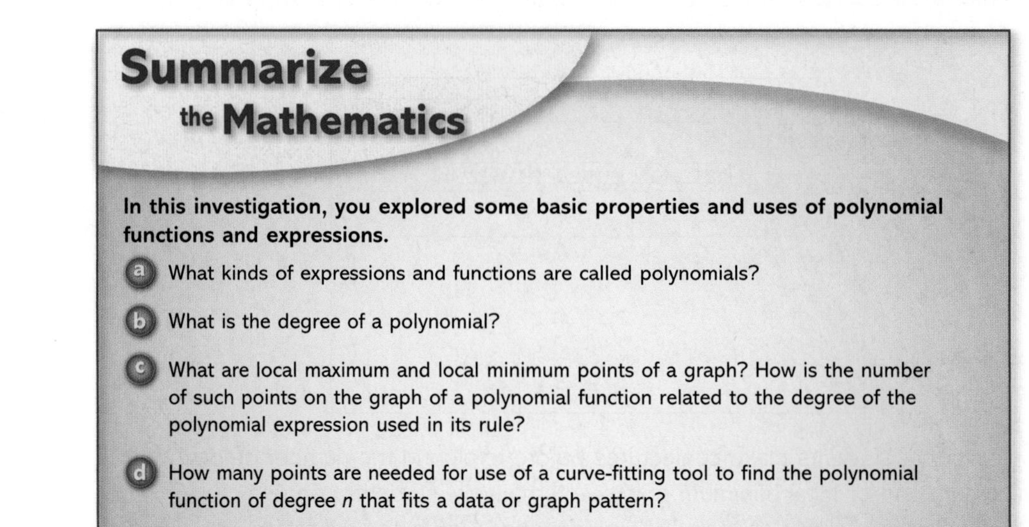

Summarize the Mathematics

In this investigation, you explored some basic properties and uses of polynomial functions and expressions.

a. What kinds of expressions and functions are called polynomials?

b. What is the degree of a polynomial?

c. What are local maximum and local minimum points of a graph? How is the number of such points on the graph of a polynomial function related to the degree of the polynomial expression used in its rule?

d. How many points are needed for use of a curve-fitting tool to find the polynomial function of degree n that fits a data or graph pattern?

Be prepared to explain your ideas to the class.

Check Your Understanding

Use what you have learned about polynomial functions to help complete the following tasks.

a. Consider the functions $f(x) = 2x^3 + 8x^2 + 3x - 2$ and $g(x) = x^4 - 8x^3 + 16x^2 + 4$.

- **i.** Identify the degree of each function.
- **ii.** Estimate coordinates of the local maximum and/or local minimum points on graphs of the functions.

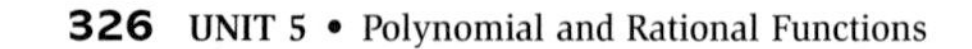

Unit 5

Summarize the Mathematics

a Any algebraic expression of the form $a_nx^n + a_{n-1}x^{n-1} + \cdots + a_1x + a_0$ is a polynomial expression. Any function with rule in the form $f(x) = a_nx^n + a_{n-1}x^{n-1} + \cdots + a_1x + a_0$ is a polynomial function.

b The degree of a polynomial is the greatest exponent that occurs in the polynomial, assuming that the coefficient of that term is not zero.

c A local maximum of a polynomial function is a "peak" on the graph (the highest value of the function on some interval around this "peak"). A local minimum of a polynomial function is a "valley" on the graph (the lowest value of the function on some interval around this "valley"). The number of local maximum or local minimum points is always less than the degree of the polynomial expression.

d When using a curve-fitting program to find the regression equation for a polynomial function of degree n, one needs $n + 1$ data points. But more data points would likely provide a better model.

Teaching Resources

Transparency Master 3.

UNIT 5 *Polynomial and Rational Functions*

Summarize the Mathematics

In this investigation, you explored some basic properties and uses of polynomial functions and expressions.

a What kinds of expressions and functions are called polynomials?

b What is the degree of a polynomial?

c What are local maximum and local minimum points of a graph? How is the number of such points on the graph of a polynomial function related to the degree of the polynomial expression used in its rule?

d How many points are needed for use of a curve-fitting tool to find the polynomial function of degree n that fits a data or graph pattern?

Be prepared to explain your ideas to the class.

COLLABORATION PROMPT
Identify the questions you asked each other that helped develop understanding of an idea.

Check Your Understanding

a. **i.** $f(x)$ is a polynomial function of degree 3 (cubic), while $g(x)$ is a polynomial function of degree 4 (quartic).

ii.

$f(x)$ has a local maximum at approximately $(-2.46, 9.26)$ and a local minimum at approximately $(-0.20, -2.30)$. $g(x)$ has a local maximum at $(2, 20)$ and local minimums (also global minimums) at $(0, 4)$ and $(4, 4)$.

b. Find a function whose graph models the following coaster track design.

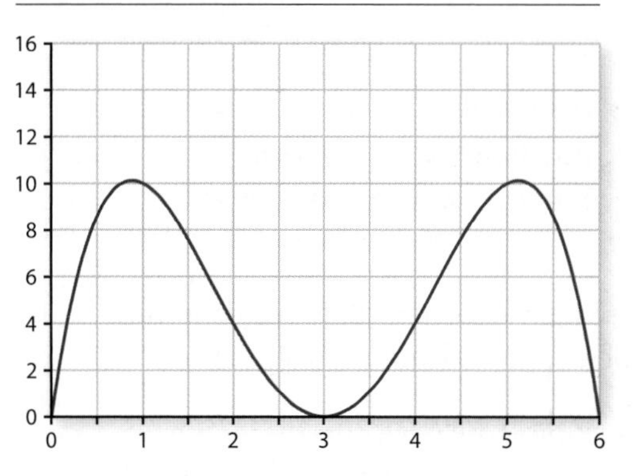

Investigation 2 Addition, Subtraction, and Zeroes

From early in your mathematical studies, you have learned how to perform arithmetic operations on numbers. As it turns out, you can do just about any operation with algebraic expressions that you can do with numbers. In this investigation, you will begin exploration of arithmetic operations on polynomials. As you work through the problems, look for answers to these questions:

How can the rules for polynomial functions $f(x)$ and $g(x)$ be combined to give rules for $f(x) + g(x)$ and $f(x) - g(x)$?

How are the degrees of expressions being added or subtracted related to the degree of the result?

How is the degree of a polynomial related to the number of zeroes for the function?

Adding and Subtracting Polynomials When a small music venue books a popular band, like *Ice and Fire*, business prospects of the event depend on how the ticket prices are set. For example, if the ticket price is set at x dollars, income and expenses might be estimated as follows.

Ticket sale income:
$t(x) = -25x^2 + 750x$

Snack bar income:
$s(x) = 7{,}500 - 250x$

Concert operating expense:
$c(x) = 4{,}750 - 125x$

Snack bar operating expense:
$b(x) = 2{,}250 - 75x$

b. One possible function is $f(x) = -0.5x^4 + 6x^3 - 22.5x^2 + 27x$. It is the quartic regression equation found using points (0, 0), (1, 10), (3, 0), (5, 10), and (6, 0).

Investigation 2 Addition, Subtraction, and Zeroes

In this investigation, students will continue working with polynomial expressions and functions, learning how to combine them by addition and subtraction. They will look for a pattern relating the degrees of components to the degree of the sum or difference of two polynomials and a pattern relating the degree of a polynomial expression to the number of zeroes of the corresponding function.

The computational work with polynomials is sometimes quite tedious and not attractive to less mathematically inclined students. Access to a computer algebra system (CAS) will help many students deal with deep mathematics while not getting bogged down in computational details. Thus, if you have not already introduced a CAS like the TI-89, TI-Nspire, or *CPMP-Tools* to your class, you might want to take some time out to do that at this point. You will want to show them how to enter expressions and define functions and alert them to the quirky but powerful CAS property that treats expressions like **ax** as a single variable with two-letter name.

Launch

It might make sense to launch the investigation by having students look at the given income and operating expense functions and then share their thoughts about Problem 1 Part a. Since these functions will be used often in subsequent investigations of the unit, it is important that students have some comfortable feeling for why they might make sense and how they relate ticket price to probable income and expenses.

Push students to think about how ticket price affects income and snack bar sales and why the given rules are plausible predictive models. You might ask students to sketch graphs of each function and to explain why the shape makes sense in the context and, in the case of the last three function rules, what each parameter tells about the relationship. For example $s(x) = 7{,}500 - 250x$ predicts that each dollar increase in ticket price will reduce snack bar income by $250. It makes sense that with higher ticket prices there will be fewer customers and less business at the snack bar or also that with higher ticket prices customers will have less money to spend at the snack bar.

1. Before each show, the manager uses the functions $t(x)$ and $s(x)$ to estimate total income.

   a. Why does it make sense that each source of income—ticket sales and snack bar sales—might depend on the price set for tickets?

   b. What income should the manager expect from ticket sales alone if the ticket price is set at $12? What income from snack bar sales? What income from the two sources combined?

   c. What rule would define the function $I(x)$ that shows how combined income from ticket sales and snack bar sales depends on ticket price? Write a rule for $I(x)$ that is in simplest form for calculation.

   d. How does the degree of $I(x)$ compare to the degrees of $t(x)$ and $s(x)$?

2. The manager also uses the functions $c(x)$ and $b(x)$ to estimate total operating expenses.

   a. Why does it make sense that each source of expense—concert operation and snack bar operation—might depend on the price set for tickets?

   b. What expense should the manager expect from concert operations alone if the ticket price is set at $12? What expense from snack bar operations? What expense from the two sources combined?

   c. What rule would define the function $E(x)$ that shows how combined expense from concert and snack bar operations depends on ticket price? Write a rule for $E(x)$ that is in simplest form for calculation.

   d. How does the degree of $E(x)$ compare to the degrees of $c(x)$ and $b(x)$?

3. Consider next the function $P(x)$ defined as $P(x) = I(x) - E(x)$.

   a. What does $P(x)$ tell about business prospects for the music venue?

   b. Write two equivalent rules for $P(x)$.

   - one that shows the separate expressions for income and operating expenses
   - another that is in simplest form for calculation

   Check your work with a CAS and resolve any differences in the results.

   c. How does the degree of $P(x)$ compare to that of $I(x)$ and of $E(x)$?

   d. Compare $E(x) - I(x)$ to $I(x) - E(x)$. What caution does this result suggest in using subtraction to find the difference of quantities represented by polynomial functions?

328 UNIT 5 • Polynomial and Rational Functions

1 **a.** The number of people attending a concert will almost always depend upon ticket price, so it follows that income from ticket sales and income from snack bar sales will also depend upon the ticket price.

b. $t(12) = 5{,}400$
$s(12) = 4{,}500$
total income $= \$9{,}900$

c. $I(x) = -25x^2 + 500x + 7{,}500$

d. The degree of $I(x)$ equals the larger of the two degrees of the summands.

2 **a.** Student ideas will vary about why operating expense will depend on price for tickets. But they should connect ticket price to number of customers and thus to expense items like number of ticket sellers, ticket takers, ushers, security people, and workers at the concession stand.

b. $c(12) = 3{,}250$
$b(12) = 1{,}350$
total combined operating expense $= \$4{,}600$

c. $E(x) = 7{,}000 - 200x$

d. The degree of $E(x)$ equals the degrees of the summands.

3 **a.** $P(x)$ is the profit that will be made (from all sources of income minus expenses) as a function of ticket price.

b. • $P(x) = (-25x^2 + 500x + 7{,}500) - (7{,}000 - 200x)$ shows income and operating expenses separately. Some students might actually recommend breaking each income and expense source down even further to show the contribution of each source.

• $P(x) = -25x^2 + 700x + 500$ is a more efficient rule, computationally. The TI-89 CAS calculation is shown below.

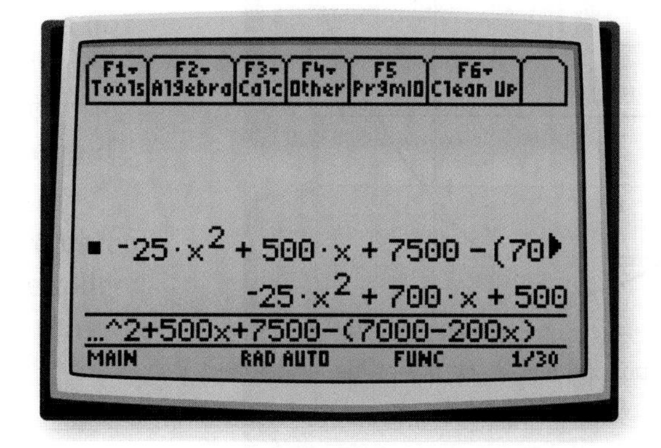

c. The degree of $P(x)$ is 2 which is the highest degree of $I(x)$ (degree of 2) and $E(x)$ (degree of 1).

d. $E(x) - I(x) = 25x^2 - 700x - 500$. This indicates the subtraction of polynomials is not commutative. Rather, for two polynomials m and n, $m - n = -(n - m)$.

Unit 5

5 The functions $f(x) = x^3 - 6x^2 + 9x$ and $g(x) = x^4 - 10x^3 + 32x^2 - 38x + 25$ could be used to model patterns in the roller coaster designs at the beginning of this lesson.

a. Graph and find the zeroes of $f(x)$.

b. Graph and find the zeroes of $g(x)$.

c. What might the zeroes represent in the roller coaster scenario?

6 Now consider possible connections between the degree of a polynomial and the number of zeroes of the related function. It might be helpful to use function graphing software that provides "sliders" to adjust coefficients and show the corresponding graphs.

a. What are the possible numbers of zeroes for linear functions? Make sketches that represent your ideas.

b. What are the possible numbers of zeroes for quadratic functions? Make sketches that represent your ideas.

c. Explore tables and graphs of several functions with rules in the form

$$f(x) = a_3x^3 + a_2x^2 + a_1x + a_0 \quad (a_3 \neq 0)$$

to discover the possible numbers of zeroes for cubic polynomial functions. Make sketches of results that illustrate your ideas.

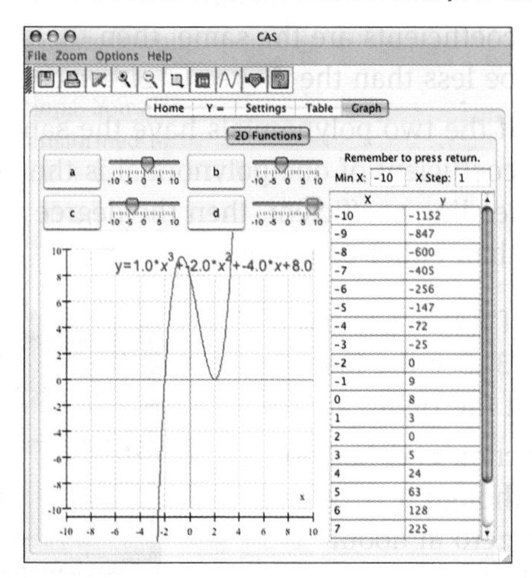

d. Explore tables and graphs of functions with rules in the form

$$g(x) = a_4x^4 + a_3x^3 + a_2x^2 + a_1x + a_0 \quad (a_4 \neq 0)$$

to discover the possible numbers of zeroes for quartic polynomials. Make sketches of results that illustrate your ideas.

330 UNIT 5 • Polynomial and Rational Functions

1 **a.** The number of people attending a concert will almost always depend upon ticket price, so it follows that income from ticket sales and income from snack bar sales will also depend upon the ticket price.

b. $t(12) = 5{,}400$
$s(12) = 4{,}500$
total income = \$9,900

c. $I(x) = -25x^2 + 500x + 7{,}500$

d. The degree of $I(x)$ equals the larger of the two degrees of the summands.

2 **a.** Student ideas will vary about why operating expense will depend on price for tickets. But they should connect ticket price to number of customers and thus to expense items like number of ticket sellers, ticket takers, ushers, security people, and workers at the concession stand.

b. $c(12) = 3{,}250$
$b(12) = 1{,}350$
total combined operating expense = \$4,600

c. $E(x) = 7{,}000 - 200x$

d. The degree of $E(x)$ equals the degrees of the summands.

3 **a.** $P(x)$ is the profit that will be made (from all sources of income minus expenses) as a function of ticket price.

b.
- $P(x) = (-25x^2 + 500x + 7{,}500) - (7{,}000 - 200x)$ shows income and operating expenses separately. Some students might actually recommend breaking each income and expense source down even further to show the contribution of each source.
- $P(x) = -25x^2 + 700x + 500$ is a more efficient rule, computationally.

The TI-89 CAS calculation is shown below.

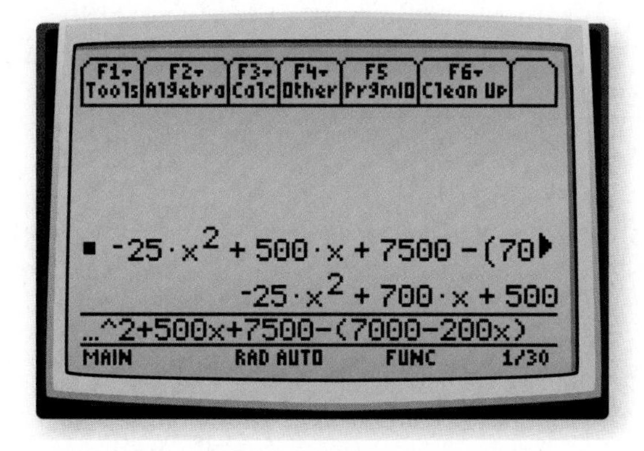

c. The degree of $P(x)$ is 2 which is the highest degree of $I(x)$ (degree of 2) and $E(x)$ (degree of 1).

d. $E(x) - I(x) = 25x^2 - 700x - 500$. This indicates the subtraction of polynomials is not commutative. Rather, for two polynomials m and n, $m - n = -(n - m)$.

Unit 5

Unit 5

4 In your analysis of business prospects for a concert by *Ice and Fire,* you used common sense to combine polynomials by addition and subtraction. You probably noticed a connection between the degree of a sum or difference of polynomials and the degrees of the polynomials being combined.

a. Test your ideas about the degree of the sum or difference of polynomials by finding the simplest rules for the sum and difference of each pair of functions given below. Compare your results with those of your classmates and resolve any differences.

i. $f(x) = 3x^3 + 5x - 7$ and $g(x) = 4x^3 - 2x^2 + 4x + 3$

ii. $f(x) = 3x^3 + 4x^2 + 5$ and $g(x) = -3x^3 - 2x^2 + 5x$

iii. $f(x) = x^4 + 5x^3 - 7x + 5$ and $g(x) = 4x^3 - 2x^2 + 5x + 3$

iv. $f(x) = x^4 + 5x^3 - 7x + 5$ and $g(x) = 4x^3 + 5x$

v. $f(x) = 6x^4 + 5x^3 - 7x + 5$ and $g(x) = 6x^4 + 5x$

b. Explain in your own words.

i. how to find the simplest rule for the sum or difference of two polynomials

ii. how the degree of the sum or difference of two polynomials is related to the degrees of the polynomials being combined

Zeroes of Polynomial Functions In your previous work with linear and quadratic polynomial functions, you discovered that answers to many important questions are found by solving equations. You also discovered that linear and quadratic equations can be transformed to equivalent forms that look like $a_1x + a_0 = 0$ or $a_2x^2 + a_1x + a_0 = 0$, respectively.

Solving these equations requires finding values of x that are called **zeroes** of the related functions $f(x) = a_1x + a_0$ and $g(x) = a_2x^2 + a_1x + a_0$. For example, the zeroes of $g(x) = x^2 + 5x - 6$ are -6 and 1 because $g(-6) = 0$ and $g(1) = 0$. The zeroes locate the x-intercepts of the graphs of the functions.

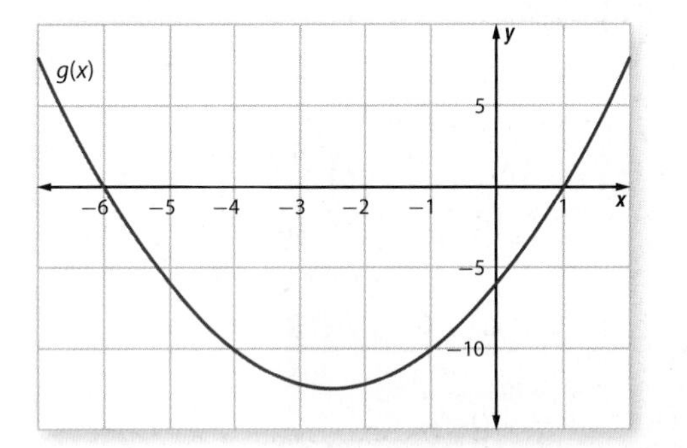

The next problems explore the possibilities for zeroes of higher degree polynomial functions.

4 **a.** **i.** $f(x) + g(x) = 7x^3 - 2x^2 + 9x - 4$; degree 3
$f(x) - g(x) = -x^3 + 2x^2 + x - 10$; degree 3

ii. $f(x) + g(x) = 2x^2 + 5x + 5$; degree 2
$f(x) - g(x) = 6x^3 + 6x^2 - 5x + 5$; degree 3

iii. $f(x) + g(x) = x^4 + 9x^3 - 2x^2 - 2x + 8$; degree 4
$f(x) - g(x) = x^4 + x^3 + 2x^2 - 12x + 2$; degree 4

iv. $f(x) + g(x) = x^4 + 9x^3 - 2x + 5$; degree 4
$f(x) - g(x) = x^4 + x^3 - 12x + 5$; degree 4

v. $f(x) + g(x) = 12x^4 + 5x^3 - 2x + 5$; degree 4
$f(x) - g(x) = 5x^3 - 12x + 5$; degree 3

b. **i.** When adding (or subtracting) two polynomials, add (or subtract) the coefficients of corresponding terms and these sums (or differences) will be the coefficients in the sum (or difference) of the two polynomials.

ii. The degree of a sum or difference of two polynomials is the largest degree of the two component polynomials except for two special cases.

(1) If the two polynomials have the same degree and the leading coefficients are the same, then the degree of the *difference* will be less than the degree of either component.

(2) If the two polynomials have the same degree and the leading coefficient of one polynomial is the opposite of the other leading coefficient, then the degree of the *sum* will be less than either component.

5 **a.** Zeroes of $f(x)$ are at $x = 0$ and $x = 3$. See the first screen at the right.

b. The function $g(x)$ has no zeroes, though it is very close to zero at about $x = 4.25$. See the second screen at the right.

c. The zeroes might represent points at which the roller coaster touches or runs along the ground.

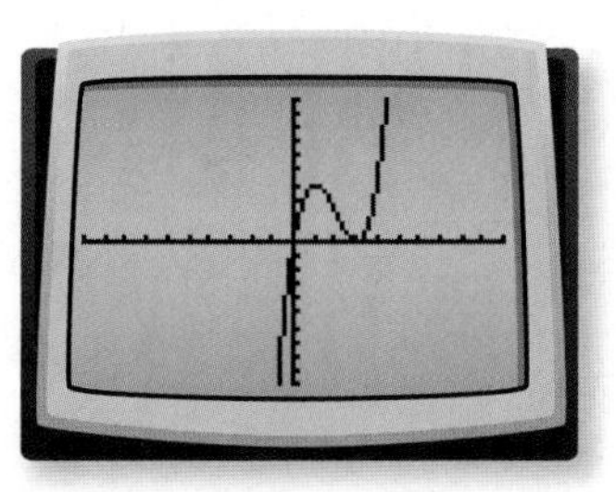

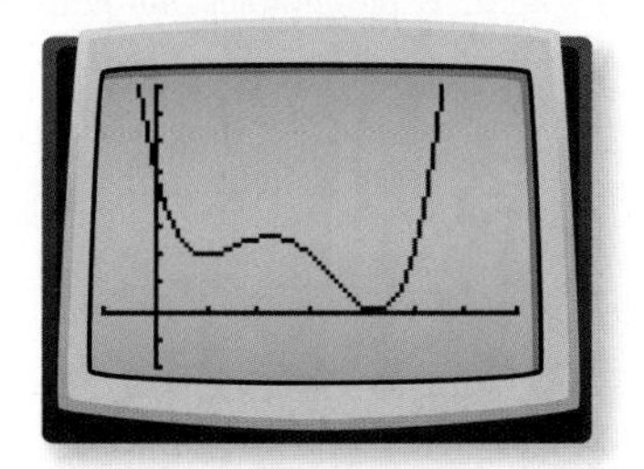

INSTRUCTIONAL NOTE
You may wish to ask each student to check only one part with the CAS.

INSTRUCTIONAL NOTE
You may wish to have a mini-summary after most students have completed work on Problem 4. The next several problems address a different important aspect of polynomials.

INSTRUCTIONAL NOTE
The screens in the solutions for Problem 5 are for your information. Students are not asked to sketch the functions. They will likely estimate the zeroes using the Trace feature. Other options include using technology capabilities to calculate zeroes.

5 The functions $f(x) = x^3 - 6x^2 + 9x$ and $g(x) = x^4 - 10x^3 + 32x^2 - 38x + 25$ could be used to model patterns in the roller coaster designs at the beginning of this lesson.

a. Graph and find the zeroes of $f(x)$.

b. Graph and find the zeroes of $g(x)$.

c. What might the zeroes represent in the roller coaster scenario?

6 Now consider possible connections between the degree of a polynomial and the number of zeroes of the related function. It might be helpful to use function graphing software that provides "sliders" to adjust coefficients and show the corresponding graphs.

a. What are the possible numbers of zeroes for linear functions? Make sketches that represent your ideas.

b. What are the possible numbers of zeroes for quadratic functions? Make sketches that represent your ideas.

c. Explore tables and graphs of several functions with rules in the form

$$f(x) = a_3x^3 + a_2x^2 + a_1x + a_0 \quad (a_3 \neq 0)$$

to discover the possible numbers of zeroes for cubic polynomial functions. Make sketches of results that illustrate your ideas.

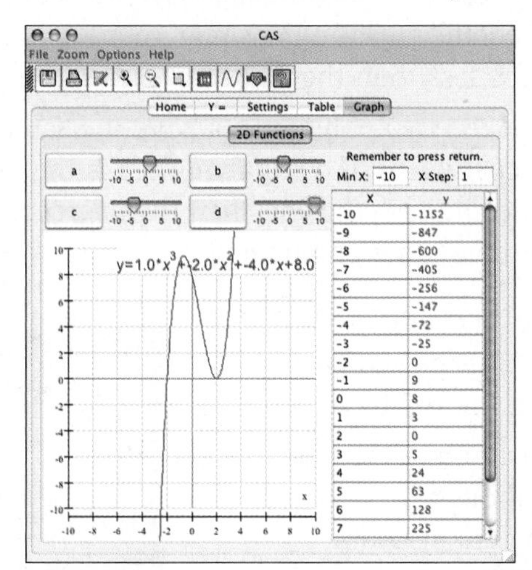

d. Explore tables and graphs of functions with rules in the form

$$g(x) = a_4x^4 + a_3x^3 + a_2x^2 + a_1x + a_0 \quad (a_4 \neq 0)$$

to discover the possible numbers of zeroes for quartic polynomials. Make sketches of results that illustrate your ideas.

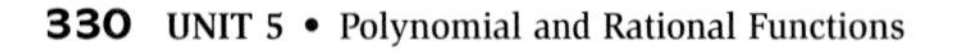

6 **TECHNOLOGY NOTE** Student exploration of this problem will be much more fruitful if they use their graphing calculators or, even better, function graphing software that allows use of sliders to change coefficients and then immediately reflects those changes in the graph. See the notes on pages T323 and T325.

NOTE Solutions to Problem 5 are on page T329.

a. A linear function can have 0, 1, or infinitely many (when $y = 0$) zeroes.

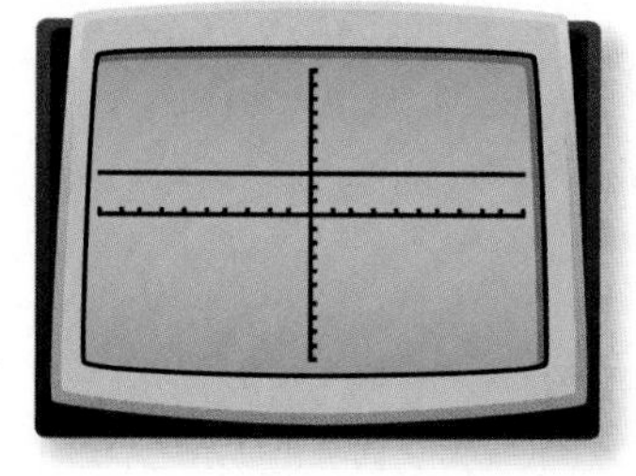
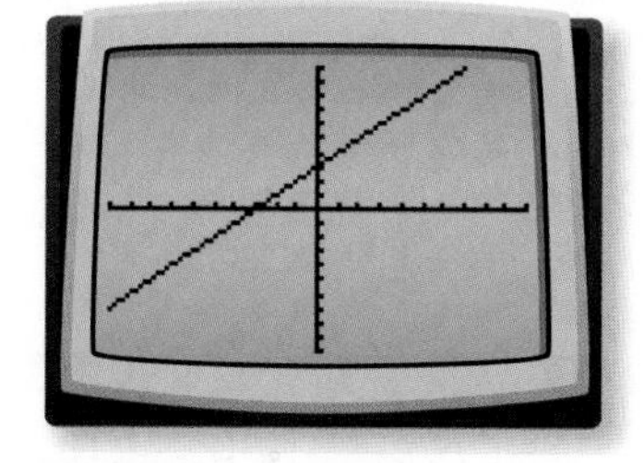

b. A quadratic function can have 0, 1, or 2 zeroes.

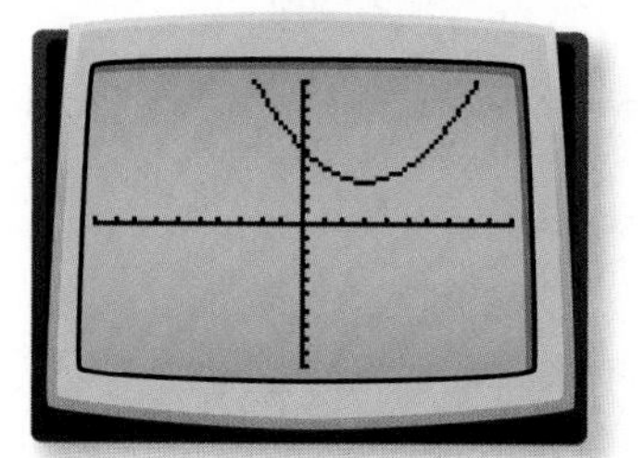
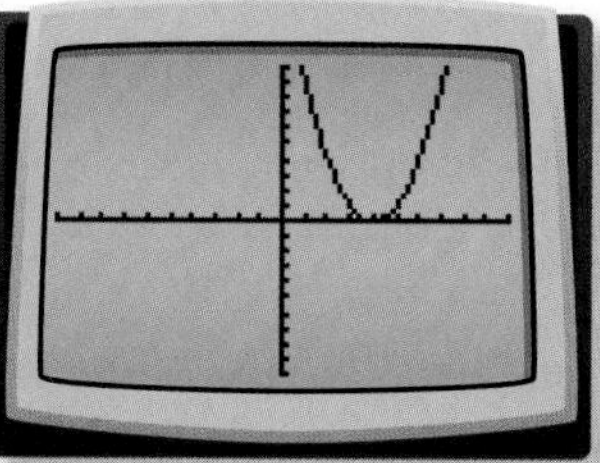
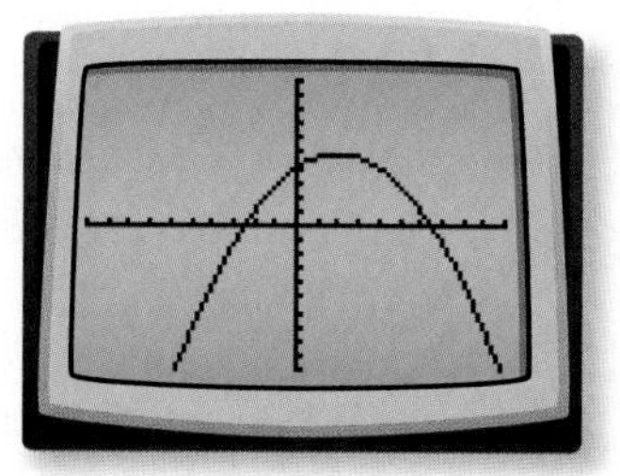

c. A cubic function can have 1, 2, or 3 zeroes.

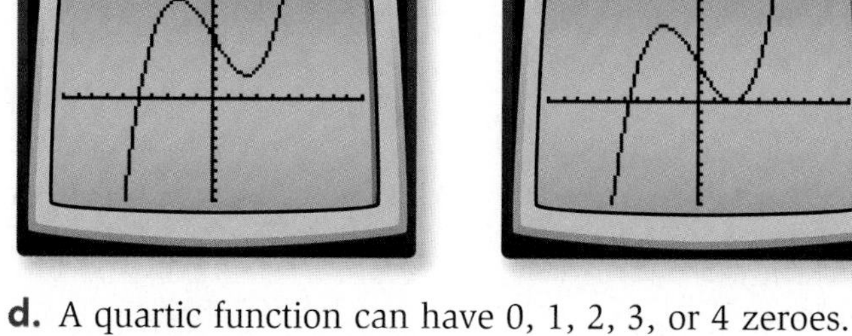

d. A quartic function can have 0, 1, 2, 3, or 4 zeroes.

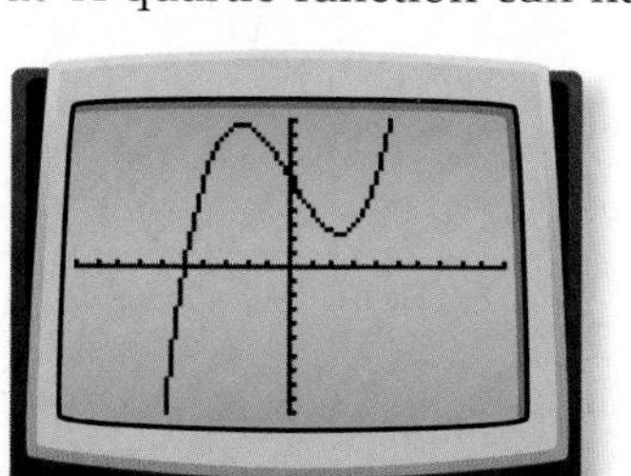
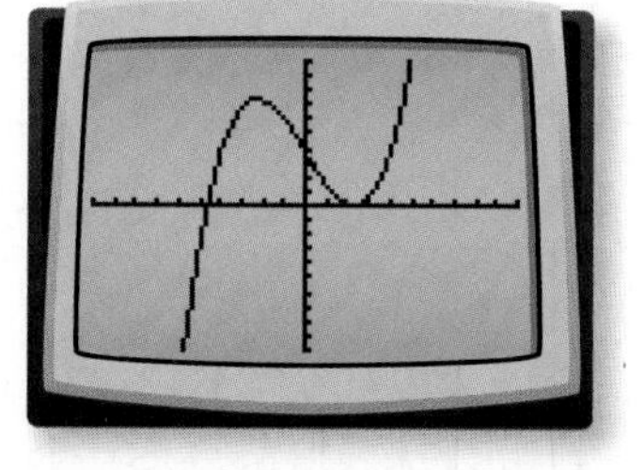
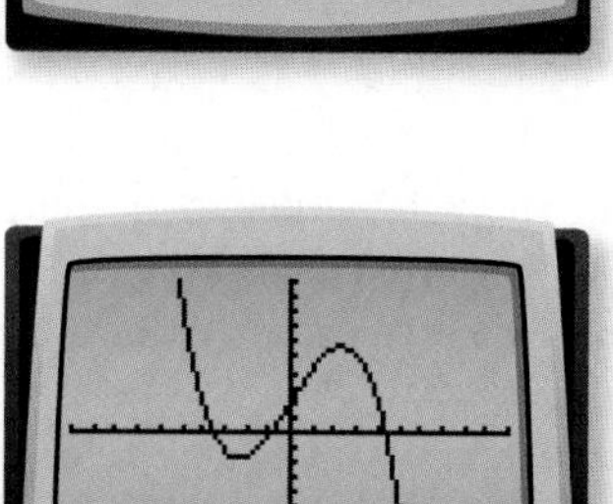
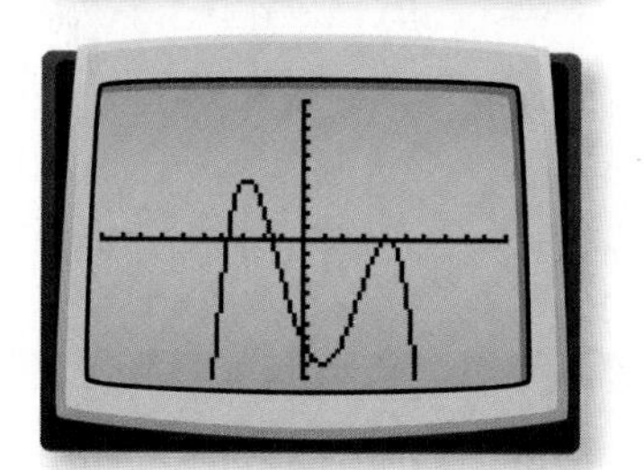
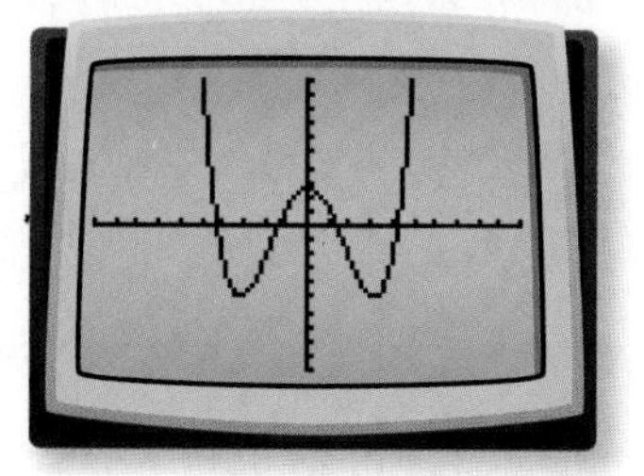

e. How does the degree of a polynomial seem to be related to the number of zeroes of the related polynomial function? Test your conjecture by studying graphs of some polynomial functions of degrees five and six.

Remember: When checking to see if a mathematical idea is correct, you should explore many different examples to see how, if at all, some example might be constructed that disproves the conjecture. Here again, it might be helpful to use computer software that accepts function definitions like $f(x) = ax^3 + bx^2 + cx + d$ and allows you to move "sliders" controlling the values of a, b, c, and d to quickly produce corresponding graphs.

Summarize the Mathematics

In this investigation, you explored addition and subtraction of polynomials and zeroes of polynomial functions.

a. What steps should one follow in finding a simplest rule for the sum or difference of two polynomials?

b. How is the degree of the sum or difference of two polynomials related to the degrees of the polynomials being combined?

c. What does the degree of a polynomial tell you about the possible number of zeroes for the corresponding polynomial function?

Be prepared to explain your ideas to the class.

Check Your Understanding

Consider the following polynomial functions.

$$f(x) = x^3 - 16x$$
$$g(x) = 16x^2 - 8x^3 + x^4$$
$$h(x) = x^4 - 8x^3 + 16x^2 + 4$$

a. For each function, (1) identify its degree, (2) sketch its graph, and (3) find its zeroes.

b. Find expressions in standard polynomial form for $f(x) + g(x)$ and $f(x) - g(x)$.

c. Find the degrees of these polynomials.

i. $g(x) - h(x)$

ii. $h(x) - f(x)$

Unit 5

e. The number of zeroes of a polynomial function is less than or equal to the degree of the related polynomial. In the case of a polynomial of odd degree, the function must have at least one zero. In the case of a polynomial of even degree, there can be no zeroes.

Summarize the Mathematics

a When adding (or subtracting) two polynomials, add (or subtract) the coefficients of corresponding terms and these sums (or differences) will be the coefficients of corresponding terms in the sum (or difference) of the two polynomials.

b The degree of the sum (or difference) of two polynomials will always be less than or equal to the higher degree of the polynomials being added (or subtracted).

c The number of zeroes of a polynomial function is less than or equal to the degree of the corresponding polynomial. In the case of a polynomial of odd degree, the function must have at least one zero. In the case of a polynomial of even degree, there can be no zeroes.

Teaching Resources

Student Master 5.

UNIT 5 *Polynomial and Rational Functions*

Summarize the Mathematics

In this investigation, you explored addition and subtraction of polynomials and zeroes of polynomial functions.

a What steps should one follow in finding a simplest rule for the sum or difference of two polynomials?

b How is the degree of the sum or difference of two polynomials related to the degrees of the polynomials being combined?

c What does the degree of a polynomial tell you about the possible number of zeroes for the corresponding polynomial function?

Be prepared to explain your ideas to the class.

MATH TOOLKIT
Explain what the degree of a polynomial tells you about the possible number of zeroes for the corresponding function.

Unit 5

Check Your Understanding

a. $f(x)$ has degree 3 and zeroes at $x = -4$, 0, and 4.

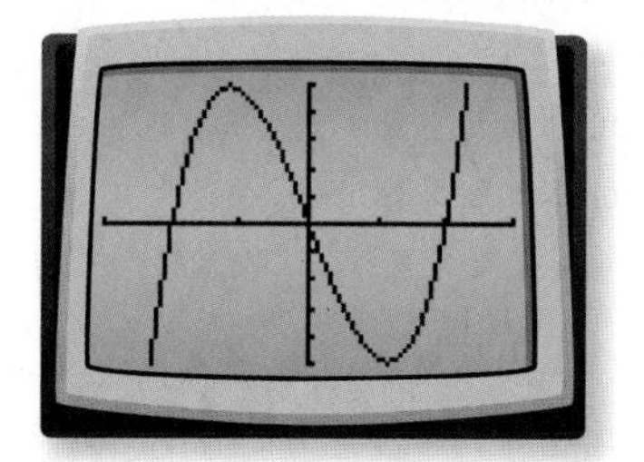

$g(x)$ has degree 4 and zeroes at $x = 0$ and 4.

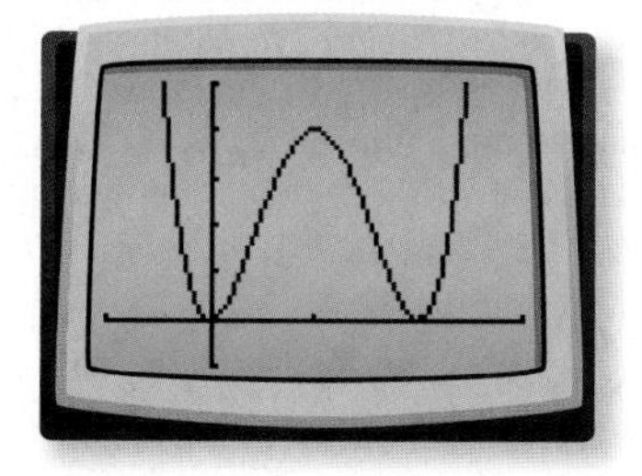

$h(x)$ has degree 4 and no zeroes.

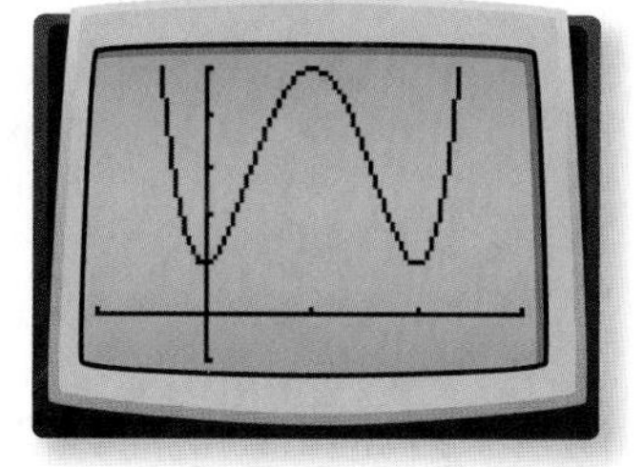

b. $f(x) + g(x) = x^4 - 7x^3 + 16x^2 - 16x$
$f(x) - g(x) = -x^4 + 9x^3 - 16x^2 - 16x$

c. **i.** 0

ii. 4

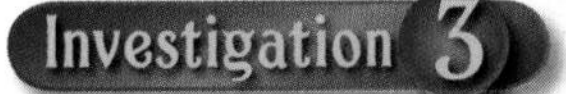

Investigation 3 Zeroes and Products of Polynomials

In earlier work with quadratic functions, you saw how both factored and expanded expressions for function rules provide useful information. For example, the two parabolas that make up the "M" in the following diagram can be created by graphing $f(x) = -x^2 + 6x$ and $g(x) = -x^2 + 14x - 40$.

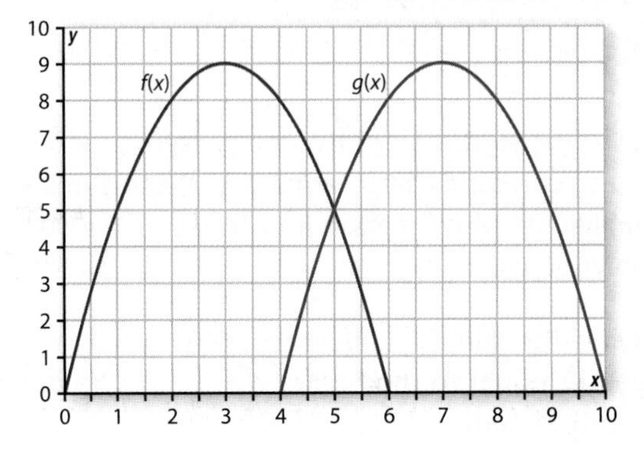

You have learned that the rules for those functions can be used to determine the location of maximum points, lines of symmetry, and y-intercepts of the graphs.

The function rules can be expressed in equivalent factored forms $f(x) = -x(x - 6)$ and $g(x) = -(x - 4)(x - 10)$. Those forms easily reveal the x-intercepts of the graphs.

Your work in this investigation will reveal strategies for working with factors and products of other polynomials. Look for answers to these questions:

How are the zeroes of a polynomial function related to the zeroes of its factors?

How can a product of polynomial factors be expanded to standard form?

How is the degree of a product of polynomials related to the degrees of the factors?

1 Analyze the following quadratic functions by using algebraic reasoning with the standard polynomial and factored forms of their rules.

a. $h(x) = x^2 + 4x$

b. $j(n) = -n^2 + n + 6$

c. $k(x) = (2x - 1)(x + 5)$

For each function:

i. write the rule in both standard polynomial and factored form.

ii. show how to use the factored form to find zeroes of the function and x-intercepts of its graph.

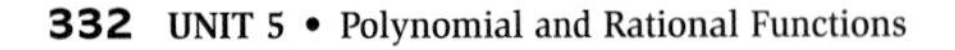

Investigation 3 Zeroes and Products of Polynomials

In this investigation, students will use the factored form of a polynomial function to determine its zeroes and use factors to construct a polynomial function with prescribed zeroes. They will then develop procedures for multiplying polynomials.

DIFFERENTIATION Multiplication of polynomials is generally a more complex operation than addition or subtraction, and it is not especially important for all students to become proficient in the (largely bookkeeping) process. For this reason, the material is presented in three sections, two of which might not be essential for all students or which you might choose as places to encourage use of a CAS.

It might still be important for all students to see how the multiplication, like that for products of two linear factors that students have dealt with in earlier courses, relies on repeated application of the distributive property. This connection is suggested by analogy to multiplication of multi-digit whole numbers where the place value plays a similar role to the various powers of the variable in a polynomial. This point is highlighted in several of the Connections tasks in the On Your Own set.

INSTRUCTIONAL NOTE
It might make sense to suggest that students divide the work on this problem and then share their results.

1 **a.** **i.** $h(x) = x^2 + 4x = x(x + 4)$

ii. Zeroes of the function are the zeroes of the linear factors, which are $x = 0$ and $x = -4$. So, the x-intercepts are $(0, 0)$ and $(-4, 0)$.

iii. The line of symmetry of a parabola is a vertical line that crosses the x-axis midway between the two x-intercepts. In this case, that implies that the line of symmetry of the graph of $h(x)$ is $x = -2$. The minimum point occurs when $h(-2) = -4$ or at $(-2, -4)$. The y-intercept $(0, 0)$ can be found by substituting 0 for x in the rule for $h(x)$.

iv. If the standard polynomial form of a quadratic function is $h(x) = ax^2 + bx + c$, the line of symmetry is $x = \frac{-b}{2a}$; the maximum or minimum point is $\left(\frac{-b}{2a}, h\left(\frac{-b}{2a}\right)\right)$; the graph has a minimum if $a > 0$ and a maximum if $a < 0$; the y-intercept is $(0, c)$. In this case, $\frac{-b}{2a} = -2$; $h\left(\frac{-b}{2a}\right) = -4$; $a = 1$ implies a minimum point; and the y-intercept is $(0, 0)$.

b. **i.** $j(n) = -n^2 + n + 6 = -(n - 3)(n + 2)$

ii. Zeroes of the function are the zeroes of the linear factors, which are $n = 3$ and $n = -2$. So, the n-intercepts are $(-2, 0)$ and $(3, 0)$.

iii. The line of symmetry of the graph of $j(n)$ is $n = 0.5$. The maximum point occurs when $j(0.5) = 6.25$ or at $(0.5, 6.25)$. The y-intercept $(0, 6)$ can be found by substituting 0 for n in the rule for $j(n)$.

iv. In this case, $\frac{-b}{2a} = 0.5$; $h\left(\frac{-b}{2a}\right) = 6.25$; a being negative implies a maximum point; and $c = 6$ implies that the y-intercept is $(0, 6)$.

c. **i.** $k(x) = (2x - 1)(x + 5) = 2x^2 + 9x - 5$

ii. Zeroes of the function are the zeroes of the linear factors which are $x = 0.5$ and $x = -5$. So, the x-intercepts are $(-5, 0)$ and $(0.5, 0)$.

iii. show how to use the factored form and information about the x-intercepts to find the line of symmetry, the maximum or minimum point, and the y-intercept of the graph.

iv. show how to use the standard polynomial form to locate the line of symmetry, maximum or minimum point, and y-intercept of the graph.

2 Next, consider the function $q(x) = x(x - 3)(x + 5)$.

a. What are the zeroes of $q(x)$?

b. Use reasoning like what you apply with products of two linear factors to write a rule for $q(x)$ in standard polynomial form. Record steps in your work so that someone else could check your reasoning.

c. Identify the degree of $q(x)$. How could you have predicted that property of the polynomial before any algebraic multiplication?

d. Graph $q(x)$ and label the x-intercepts, y-intercept, and local maximum and local minimum points with their coordinates.

3 The graph below is that of a cubic polynomial $c(x)$.

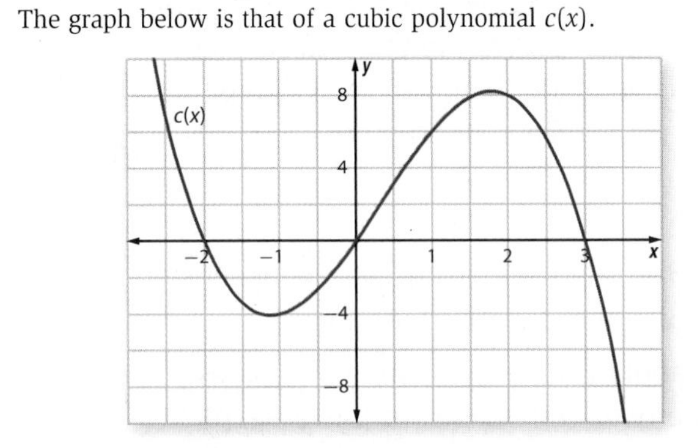

a. Use information from the graph to write a possible rule for $c(x)$. Express the rule in equivalent factored and standard polynomial forms.

b. Compare the overall shape of the graph, the local max/min points, and intercepts of the graph produced by your rule to the given graph. Adjust the rule if needed to give a better fit.

4 Look back at your work on Problems 1–3 to develop conjectures about answers to the following questions. In each case, be prepared to give other specific examples illustrating your idea.

a. How can you tell the zeroes of a polynomial function when its rule is written as a product of linear factors?

b. How can you tell the degree of a polynomial function when its rule is written as a product of linear factors?

c. Which properties of a polynomial function and its graph are shown best when the rule is written as a product of linear factors? When the rule is written in standard form?

iii. The line of symmetry of the graph of $k(x)$ is $x = -2.25$. The maximum point occurs when $k(-2.25) = -15.125$ or at $(-2.25, -15.125)$. The y-intercept $(0, -5)$ can be found by substituting 0 for x in the rule for $k(x)$.

iv. In this case, $\frac{-b}{2a} = -2.25$; $k\left(\frac{-b}{2a}\right) = -15.125$; $a = 2$ implies a minimum point; and $c = -5$ implies that the y-intercept is $(0, -5)$.

2 **a.** The zeroes are $x = 0, 3, -5$.

b. $q(x) = x^3 + 2x^2 - 15x$

c. The degree is 3, a fact that could have been guessed by noticing that the expression is a product of three linear factors.

d.

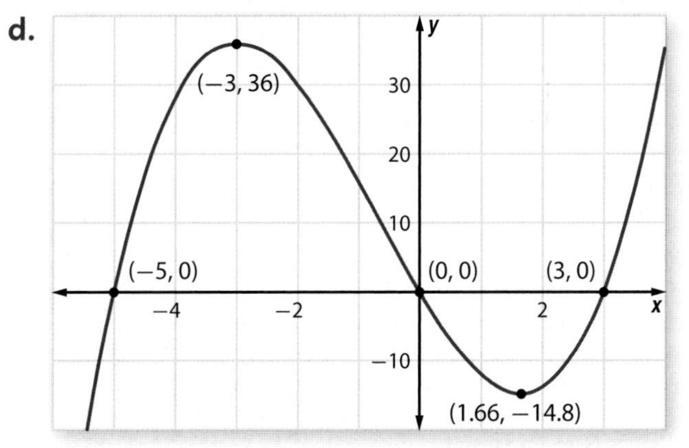

3 **a.** Using information about the zeroes alone, one might suggest $c(x) = (x + 2)(x)(x - 3) = x^3 - x^2 - 6x$.

b. In fact, the function used to produce the graph was the opposite of the conjecture in Part a: $c(x) = -x^3 + x^2 + 6x$.

INSTRUCTIONAL NOTE
Problem 3 should be done without technology.

4 **a.** The zeroes of a polynomial function written as a product of linear factors can be determined by finding zeroes of each linear factor since a product is 0 if and only if at least one of the factors is 0.

b. The degree of a product of linear factors will be the number of such linear factors occurring in the product.

c. When a polynomial is written in factored form, it is easiest to figure out the zeroes of the function. When it is in standard form, it is easiest to see the y-intercept and, by noticing the lead coefficient and degree, to determine the end behavior of the graph.

SCOPE AND SEQUENCE
This is a topic that will be pursued more thoroughly in later investigations and in Course 4, Unit 3, *Algebraic Functions and Equations.*

"Advanced" Multiplication Early in your experience with variables and expressions, you learned that the Distributive Property of Multiplication over Addition guarantees correctness of statements like $3(x + 4) = 3x + 12$. More recently, you have used the distributive property to expand products of binomials like $(2x + 4)(x - 3) = (2x + 4)x - (2x + 4)3 = 2x^2 + 4x - 6x - 12 = 2x^2 - 2x - 12$.

5 Suppose that you were asked to expand the product $(2x + 1)(3x^2 + 2x + 4)$.

a. How could you adapt the algorithm for finding the product of two binomials to find the desired product of polynomial factors? What standard polynomial form result does it give in this case?

b. Compare the zeroes of the factors $p(x) = 2x + 1$ and $q(x) = 3x^2 + 2x + 4$ and the product $p(x)q(x)$ in Part a.

6 When students in a *Core-Plus Mathematics* class in Denver, Colorado, were challenged to multiply a quadratic expression and a cubic expression, one group started like this.

$$(3x^2 + 4x - 10)(x^3 - 2x + 1) = 3x^5 - 6x^3 + 3x^2 + \cdots$$

a. Do you think they were on the right track? Explain your reasoning.

b. Based on what you know about the distributive, commutative, and associative properties, write the complete product in the form $a_nx^n + a_{n-1}x^{n-1} + a_{n-2}x^{n-2} + \cdots + a_1x + a_0$. You might choose to find the result using a CAS and then figure out why it works that way, or use your own reasoning first and check that a CAS gives the same result.

c. What strategy would you recommend for keeping track of results in the process of multiplying two such nonlinear polynomials?

d. Identify the degree of the product polynomial. How could you figure this out before carrying out any multiplication?

e. The zeroes of $f(x) = 3x^2 + 4x - 10$ are approximately 1.28 and -2.61, and the zeroes of $g(x) = x^3 - 2x + 1$ are approximately 1, 0.62, and -1.62. Are those values of x also zeroes of the product function $(3x^2 + 4x - 10)(x^3 - 2x + 1)$? Check by substituting the possible zeroes in the polynomial produced by your work on Part b.

7 Write the following products in standard polynomial form. Identify the degree of each product. Explain how that degree is related to the degrees of the factors.

a. $(x - 4)(x^4 - 3x^2 + 2)$

b. $(x^5 + 7)(-2x^2 + 6x - 1)$

c. $(x^6 - 5x^5 + 3x^4 + 7x^3 - 6x^2 + 2x - 8)(x^2 + 7x + 12)$

Repeated Zeroes You may have noticed that in Problems 1–7, each first-degree polynomial function had one zero, each second-degree polynomial function had two zeroes, and each third-degree polynomial function had three zeroes. As you discovered earlier in the case of quadratic functions, this correspondence of polynomial degree and function zeroes is not always the case.

334 UNIT 5 • Polynomial and Rational Functions

Unit 5

COMMON LEARNING CHALLENGE For almost all students, the fact that $p(x) = (x - 3)(x + 4)$ and has zeroes at $x = -4$ and $x = 3$ is counterintuitive. There seems to be something hardwired in human brains that expects the zeroes to be at $x = -3$ and $x = 4$. We do not know of a foolproof way to avert this common error. But pointing out the common mistake and getting students to talk about why it is an error and how to think correctly about it is likely to help some students.

This topic will be thoroughly revisited in Course 4, Unit 1, *Families of Functions*. There, students need to confront the similar counterintuitive fact that the graph of $f(x - a)$ is produced by translating the graph of $f(x)$ to the right a units and the graph of $f(x + a)$ by translating $f(x)$ to the left a units.

5 **a.** Students might suggest a variety of ways of keeping track that each term of the first expression is multiplied times each term of the second. Any correct procedure should yield the polynomial product $6x^3 + 7x^2 + 10x + 4$, which is of degree 3.

b. $p(x) = (2x + 1)$ has zero $-\frac{1}{2}$.

$q(x) = (3x^2 + 2x + 4)$ has no zeroes.

$p(x)q(x) = (2x + 1)(3x^2 + 2x + 4) = 6x^3 + 7x^2 + 10x + 4$

The function that represents this product is a cubic function with one x-intercept at $x = -\frac{1}{2}$ as shown on the graph below.

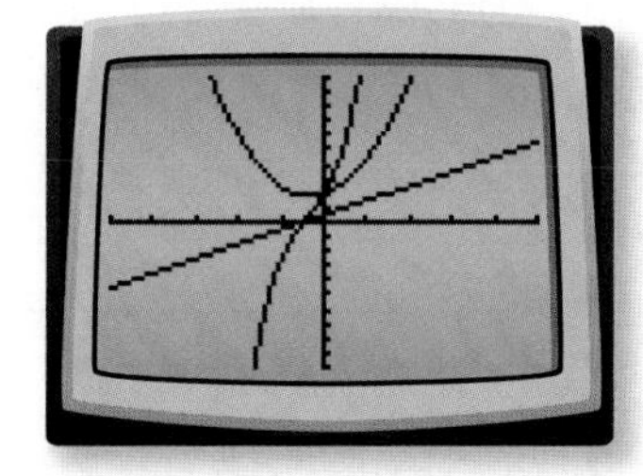

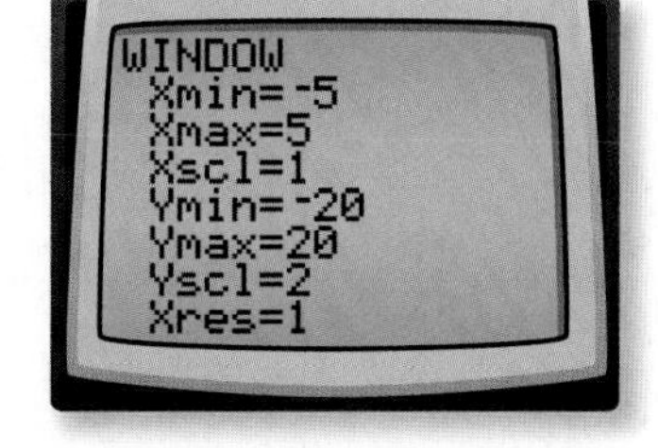

DIFFERENTIATION
Problems 5–9 on polynomial multiplication might be considered mostly for the mathematically inclined students to do by hand and for those with less interest, aptitude, or prior achievement to do with aid of a CAS.

6 **a.** It looks as if they were starting by multiplying each term of the second factor by $3x^2$. The next move might be to multiply each term of the second factor by $4x$ and then each term of that second factor by -10.

b. $3x^5 + 4x^4 - 16x^3 - 5x^2 + 24x - 10$, which is verified below.

F1 F2 Algebra F3 Calc F4 Other F5 PrgmIO F6 Clean Up

■ expand$((3 \cdot x^2 + 4 \cdot x - 10) \cdot (x^3 - 2 \cdot x + 1))$

$3 \cdot x^5 + 4 \cdot x^4 - 16 \cdot x^3 - 5 \cdot x^2 + 24 \cdot x - 10$

MAIN RAD EXACT FUNC 1/30

c. Student responses will vary and could include charts, arrows, recording results on several lines or using some other organizational tool. They might choose to mimic the algorithm layout for "long" multiplication of numbers. Connection Task 16 might suggest that to some students.

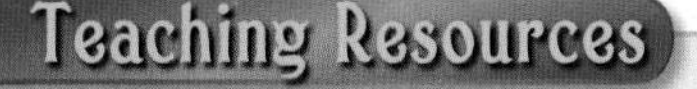

Transparency Master 6.

UNIT 5 *Polynomial and Rational Functions* — Technology Tip TI-89

Multiplying Polynomials

d. The degree of the product polynomial is 5, which could be derived by adding the degrees of the component polynomials. This uses the basic rule for finding the exponent of a product with the same base.

e. The zeroes of the product function are the zeroes of $f(x)$ and $g(x)$. Using $f(x) \cdot g(x) = 3x^5 + 4x^4 - 16x^3 - 5x^2 + 24x - 10$, students can check the tables to note that the y value for each of the 5 zeroes is approximately zero. Students might quite reasonably argue that there is no need to do the substitution because if the factored and expanded form of the expressions are truly equivalent, they will have the same zeroes.

Unit 5

DIFFERENTIATION
You might choose to allow some students to use a CAS for Part c or to check their results with a CAS.

7 Students should indicate that the degree of the product is the sum of the degrees of the factors.

a. $x^5 - 4x^4 - 3x^3 + 12x^2 + 2x - 8$; degree is 5

b. $-2x^7 + 6x^6 - x^5 - 14x^2 + 42x - 7$; degree is 7

c. $x^8 + 2x^7 - 20x^6 - 32x^5 + 79x^4 + 44x^3 - 66x^2 - 32x - 96$; degree is 8

8 **a.** $r(x) = x^2 - 6x + 9$ has degree 2.
$s(x) = x^3 + 9x^2 + 27x + 27$ has degree 3.

b. Each function has only one zero, $x = 3$ for $r(x)$ and $x = -3$ for $s(x)$.

c. The product has two zeroes, one from each factor.

d. $r(x)$ $s(x)$

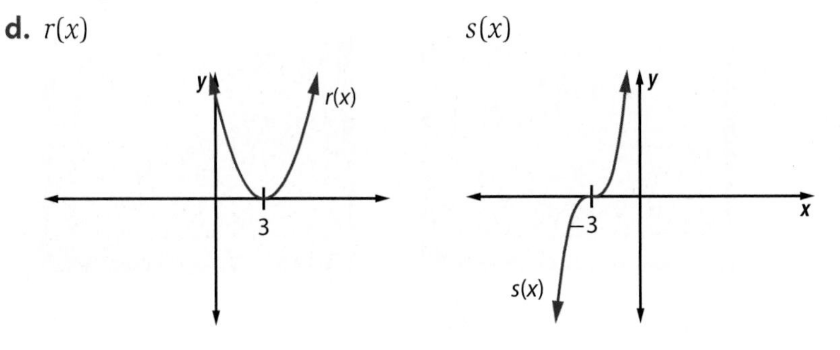

$p(x) = r(x)s(x)$

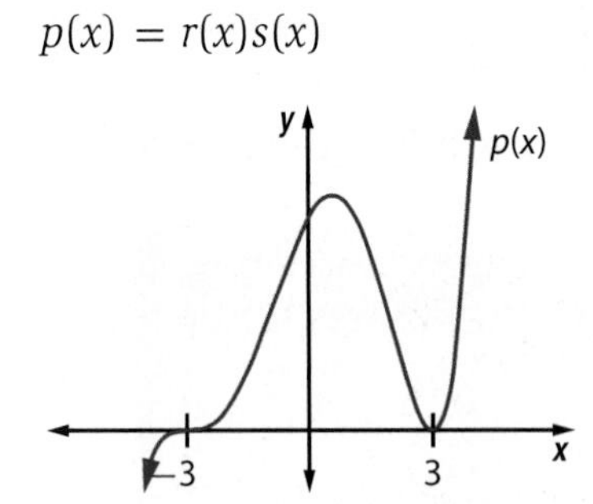

Teacher Notes

8 Consider the functions $r(x)$ and $s(x)$, where $r(x) = (x - 3)^2$ and $s(x) = (x + 3)^3$.

a. Expand the expressions that define $r(x)$ and $s(x)$. Identify the degree of each polynomial.

b. How many zeroes do $r(x)$ and $s(x)$ each have?

c. How many zeroes does the product $p(x) = r(x)s(x)$ have?

d. Use sketches of the respective function graphs to illustrate your responses in Parts b and c.

9 Consider the function $t(x) = (x - 3)(x + 4)^2$.

a. Expand the expression that defines $t(x)$. Identify the degree of the resulting polynomial.

b. What are the zeroes of $t(x)$?

c. Sketch a graph of $t(x)$ to show that the number of zeroes and the degree of the polynomial are not the same. Explain why that happens.

Summarize the Mathematics

In this investigation, you discovered connections between factors, zeroes, and the expanded form of polynomial functions.

a How is the degree of a product of polynomials determined by the degrees of its factors?

b What strategies can be used to find the standard form of a product of polynomials?

c How are the zeroes of a polynomial function related to the zeroes of its factors?

d In what cases will the degree of a polynomial function not equal the number of its zeroes?

Be prepared to explain your ideas to the class.

Check Your Understanding

Use your understanding of polynomial multiplication to complete these tasks.

a. Rewrite the following products in standard form
$a_nx^n + a_{n-1}x^{n-1} + a_{n-2}x^{n-2} + \cdots + a_1x + a_0$.
Identify the degree of each result. Explain how that degree is related to the degrees of the factors.

i. $f(x) = (x^2 - 5x + 6)(x - 4)$

ii. $g(x) = (-2x^2 + 6x - 1)(x^5 + 7)$

b. What are the zeroes of the function $h(x) = (x^2 - 5x + 6)(2x - 7)$?

c. What are the zeroes of the function $j(x) = (x + 3)^2(2x - 5)$?

d. Write rules for quadratic and cubic polynomial functions that each have zeroes at $x = 5$ and $x = -2$ only.

9 **a.** $t(x) = x^3 + 5x^2 - 8x - 48$; degree = 3

b. There are two zeroes, $x = 3$ and -4.

c. As shown in the graph, the number of zeroes is not the same as the degree of the related polynomial because the function does not cross the x-axis at -4. Instead, it simply "bounces off."

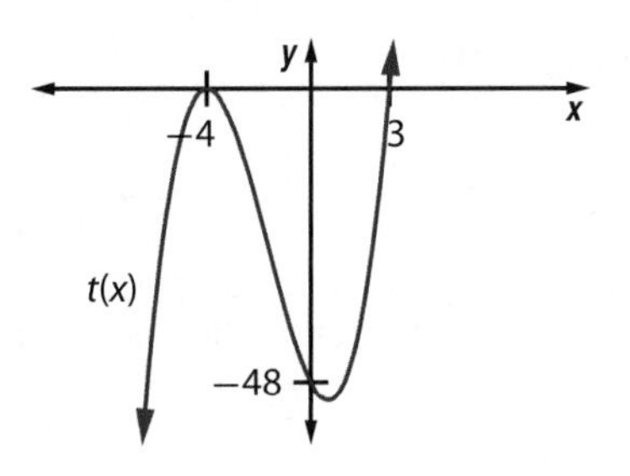

NOTE Solutions to Problem 8 are on page T334A.

DIFFERENTIATION
Students do not need to know the terms *repeated zeroes* or *double root* at this point. However, they may point out that there are really three linear factors of $t(x)$. But two of the factors are identical and therefore have the same zero.

Unit 5

Summarize the Mathematics

a The degree of the product of two or more polynomials is given by the sum of the degree of all of the factors.

b The distributive property is the key principle in finding the standard form of a product of two polynomials. Organizational strategies for this multiplication may differ among students, but using a CAS is also an option.

c The zeroes of factors of a polynomial will also be the zeroes for the corresponding polynomial function.

d The number of zeroes of a polynomial function will not equal the degree of the polynomial in cases where the graph of the function has a local maximum point on or below the x-axis or a local minimum point on or above the x-axis. This will be seen in symbolic form by repeated linear factors or in factors of degree greater than one that cannot be written as linear factors.

Teaching Resources

Transparency Master 7.

UNIT 5 *Polynomial and Rational Functions*

Summarize the Mathematics

In this investigation, you discovered connections between factors, zeroes, and the expanded form of polynomial functions.

a How is the degree of a product of polynomials determined by the degrees of its factors?

b What strategies can be used to find the standard form of a product of polynomials?

c How are the zeroes of a polynomial function related to the zeroes of its factors?

d In what cases will the degree of a polynomial function not equal the number of its zeroes?

Be prepared to explain your ideas to the class.

MATH TOOLKIT
Explain the relationship among the degree of a product of polynomials, the degrees of its factors, the zeroes of a polynomial function, and the zeroes of its factors.

Check Your Understanding

a. **i.** $f(x) = x^3 - 9x^2 + 26x - 24$; degree $3 = 2 + 1$

ii. $g(x) = -2x^7 + 6x^6 - x^5 - 14x^2 + 42x - 7$; degree $7 = 2 + 5$

b. $x = 3, 2, 3.5$

c. $x = -3, 2.5$

d. $f(x) = (x - 5)(x + 2)$ is perhaps the simplest example of a quadratic function with those zeroes; $g(x) = (x - 5)^2(x + 2)$ or $h(x) = (x - 5)(x + 2)^2$ will be simple cubic functions with the desired zeroes.

INSTRUCTIONAL NOTE
Students should be able to complete this task without use of technology.

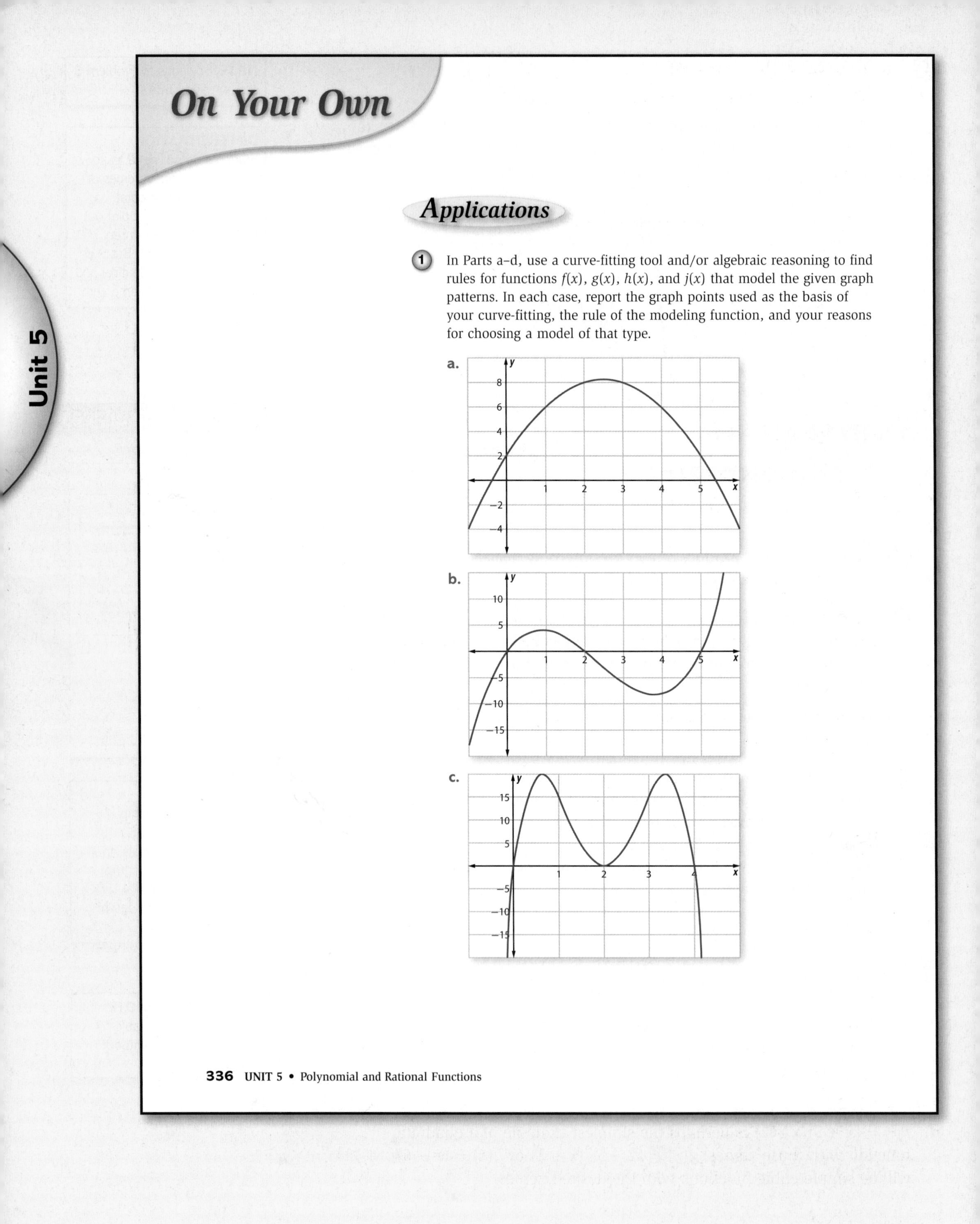
Unit 5

On Your Own

Applications

1 In Parts a–d, use a curve-fitting tool and/or algebraic reasoning to find rules for functions $f(x)$, $g(x)$, $h(x)$, and $j(x)$ that model the given graph patterns. In each case, report the graph points used as the basis of your curve-fitting, the rule of the modeling function, and your reasons for choosing a model of that type.

a.

b.

c.

336 UNIT 5 • Polynomial and Rational Functions

On Your Own

Applications

1. **a.** Points used: (0, 2), (5, 2), (2, 8), (3, 8)
   $y = -x^2 + 5x + 2$
   A quadratic rule would give one local maximum or local minimum for the domain shown.

   b. Points used: (0, 0), (2, 0), (5, 0), (1, 4)
   $y = x^3 - 7x^2 + 10x$
   A cubic model can give both a local maximum and local minimum.

   c. Points used: (0, 0), (0.6, 20), (2, 0), (3.4, 20), (4, 0)
   $y = -5x^4 + 40x^3 - 100x^2 + 80x$
   A quartic model can give three local max/min values.

d. 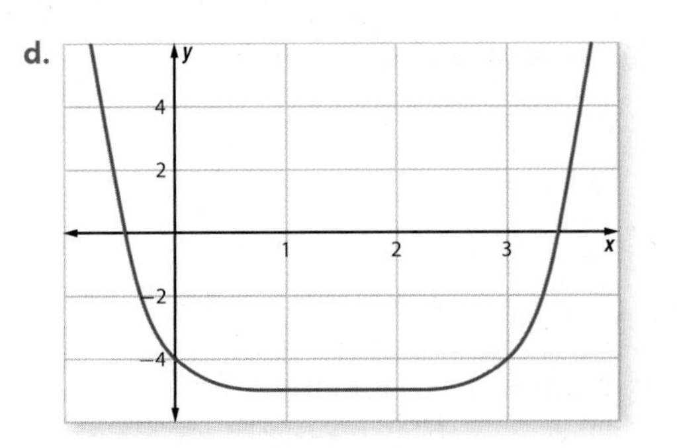

2. Graph each function and then calculate or estimate coordinates of all:
   - local maximum points.
   - local minimum points.
   - x-intercepts.
   - y-intercepts.

   a. $f(x) = 2x^2 + 4x + 1$
   b. $g(x) = x^3 + 2x^2 + 3x + 7$
   c. $h(x) = x^3 - 6x^2 + 12x - 8$
   d. $s(x) = x^4 - 8x^3 + 20x^2 - 16x$

3. For each algebraic expression:
   - write an equivalent expression in standard polynomial form.
   - identify the degrees of the expressions being combined and the degree of the result.

   a. $(2x^2 + 5x - 2) + (-2x^2 + 3x + 7)$
   b. $(2x^2 + 5x - 2) - (5x + 7)$
   c. $(-7x^3 + 6x^2 + 3x - 7) - (3x^4 + 7x^3 + 4x^2 - 3x + 2)$
   d. $(2x^2 + 3x - 7 + 5x^5 - 3x^4 - 7x^3) + (3x^5 + 2x^4 + 2x^3 + 4x^2 + 6x + 1)$
   e. $(5x^5 - 3x^4 + 2x^2 + 6x - 7) + (7x^3 - 2x^2 - 3x + 5)$

4. Without using a graph, table, or CAS, find all zeroes of these functions.

   a. $f(x) = (x - 3)(x + 4)$
   b. $g(x) = (x^2 - 9)x$
   c. $h(x) = (x^2 + 5)x^2$
   d. $s(t) = (t + 5)^2$

d. Points used: (−0.5, 0), (0, −4), (1, −5), (2, −5), (3, −4), (3.5, 0)
$y = 0.476x^4 - 2.857x^3 + 5.738x^2 - 4.357x - 4$
Since this graph is flatter near the minimum value, a quadratic function is not reasonable. But a function with even degree is a good choice.

2

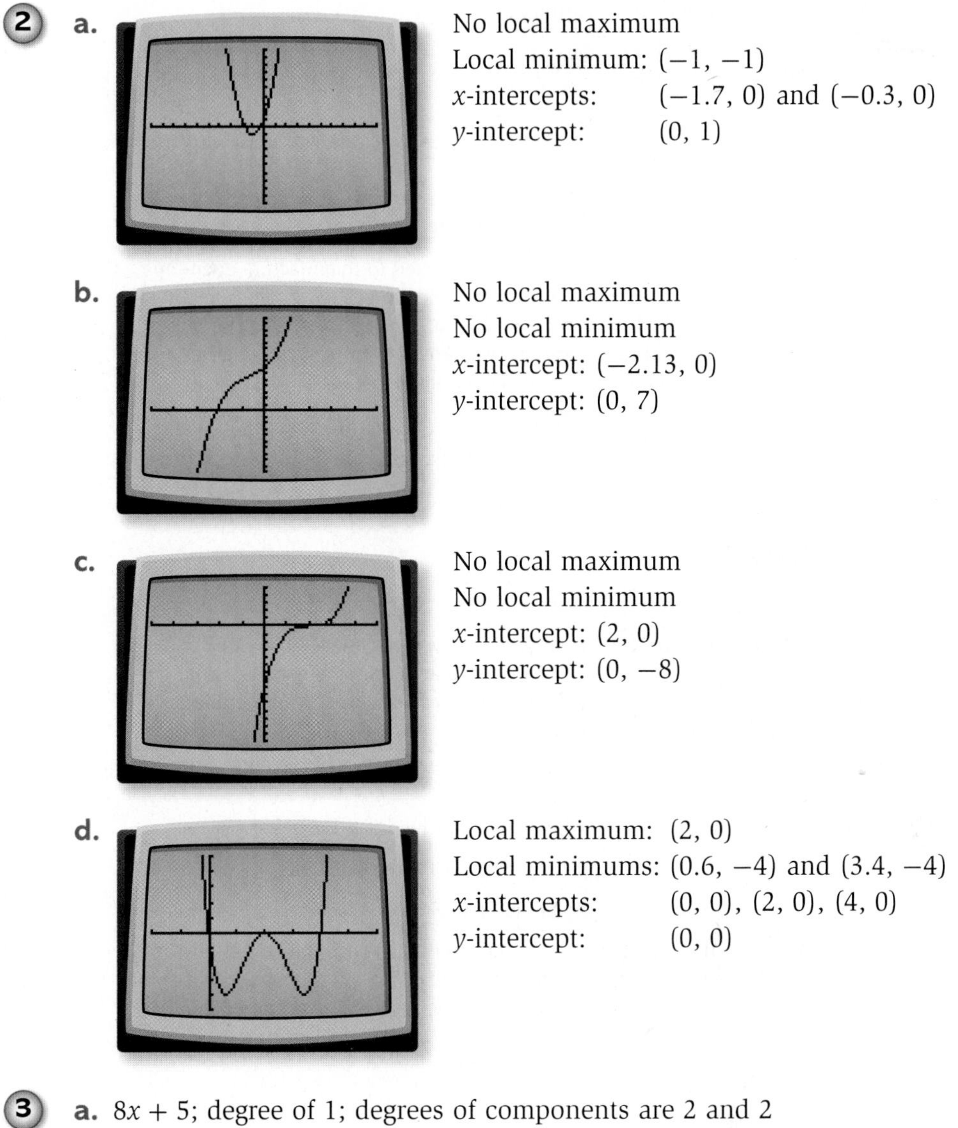

a. No local maximum
Local minimum: (−1, −1)
x-intercepts: (−1.7, 0) and (−0.3, 0)
y-intercept: (0, 1)

b. No local maximum
No local minimum
x-intercept: (−2.13, 0)
y-intercept: (0, 7)

c. No local maximum
No local minimum
x-intercept: (2, 0)
y-intercept: (0, −8)

d. Local maximum: (2, 0)
Local minimums: (0.6, −4) and (3.4, −4)
x-intercepts: (0, 0), (2, 0), (4, 0)
y-intercept: (0, 0)

3

a. $8x + 5$; degree of 1; degrees of components are 2 and 2

b. $2x^2 - 9$; degree of 2; degrees of components are 2 and 1

c. $-3x^4 - 14x^3 + 2x^2 + 6x - 9$; degree of 4; degrees of components are 3 and 4

d. $8x^5 - x^4 - 5x^3 + 6x^2 + 9x - 6$; degree of 5; degrees of components are 5 and 5

e. $5x^5 - 3x^4 + 7x^3 + 3x - 2$; degree of 5; degrees of components are 5 and 3

4

a. $x = 3, x = -4$

b. $x = 0, x = 3, x = -3$

c. $x = 0$

d. $t = -5$

On Your Own

5 For each algebraic expression:

- write an equivalent expression in standard polynomial form.
- identify the degrees of the expressions being combined and the degree of the result.

a. $(7x + 3)(x - 1)$

b. $(3x + 5)^2x^2$

c. $(2x^2 + 3x - 7)(3x + 7)$

d. $(7x^3 - 6x + 4)(2x^2 - 7)$

e. $(7x^3 + 2)(5x^2 + 3x - 8)$

f. $(-3x^4 + 2x^2 + 6x)(7x^3 - 2x^2 + 5)$

6 *Great Lakes Supply* has been contracted to manufacture open-top rectangular storage bins for small electronics parts. The company has been supplied with 30 cm × 16 cm sheets of material. The bins are made by cutting squares of the same size from each corner of a sheet, bending up the sides, and sealing the corners.

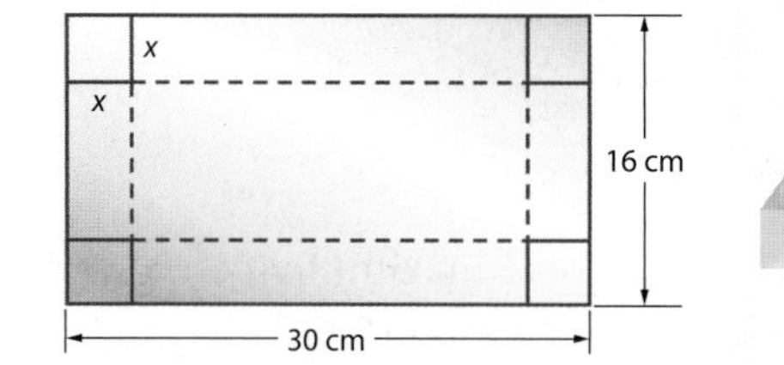

a. On centimeter graph paper, draw a rectangle 30 cm long and 16 cm wide. Cut equal-size squares from the corners of the rectangle. Fold and tape the sides as suggested above. Find the volume of your bin.

b. Write a rule expressing the volume V of a bin as a function of the length of the corner cutout x.

  i. What is the degree of the polynomial function?

  ii. What is a practical domain for the function?

  iii. Why must the graph of $V(x)$ have a local maximum point?

c. If the company is to manufacture bins with the largest possible volume, what should be the dimensions of the bins? What is the maximum volume?

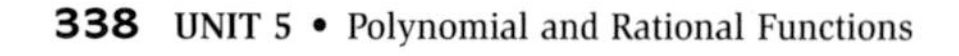

5 **a.** • $7x^2 - 4x - 3$

• Degrees of factors are both 1, product is of degree 2

b. • $9x^4 + 30x^3 + 25x^2$

• Degrees of factors are both 2, product is of degree 4

c. • $6x^3 + 23x^2 - 49$

• Degrees combined were 2 and 1, product is of degree 3

d. • $14x^5 - 61x^3 + 8x^2 + 42x - 28$

• Degrees combined were 2 and 3, product is of degree 5

e. • $35x^5 + 21x^4 - 56x^3 + 10x^2 + 6x - 16$

• Degrees combined were 2 and 3, product is of degree 5

f. • $-21x^7 + 6x^6 + 14x^5 + 23x^4 - 12x^3 + 10x^2 + 30x$

• Degrees combined were 3 and 4, product is of degree 7

6 **a.** Actual volume will vary. $V = \ell \cdot w \cdot h$

b. $V = (30 - 2x)(16 - 2x)x$

i. The degree is 3.

ii. The practical domain is $0 < x < 8$.

iii. $V(x)$ is a cubic function. In this case, it makes sense that there should be a local maximum point on the graph of $V(x)$ because of the conditions in the situation being modeled. If $x = 0$ or $x = 8$, then the box will have volume of 0. For values of x between 0 and 8, there will be positive volume. Given the possible shapes of graphs for a cubic function, there must be a local maximum on the interval (0, 8).

c. Dimensions of the box will be approximately 9.34 cm by 23.34 cm by 3.33 cm. The maximum volume is about 726 cm^3 when $x \approx 3.33$ cm.

7 The *Galaxy Sport and Outdoor Gear* company has a climbing wall in the middle of its store. Before the store opened for business, the owners did some market research and concluded that the daily number of climbing wall customers would be related to the price per climb x by the linear function $n(x) = 100 - 4x$.

a. According to this function, how many daily climbing wall customers will there be if the price per climb is \$10? What if the price per climb is \$15? What if the climb is offered to customers at no cost?

b. What do the numbers 100 and -4 in the rule for $n(x)$ tell about the relationship between climb price and number of customers?

c. What is a reasonable domain for $n(x)$ in this situation? That is, what values of x are plausible inputs for the function?

d. What is the range of $n(x)$ for the domain you specified in Part c? That is, what are the possible values of $n(x)$ corresponding to plausible inputs for the function?

e. If the function $I(x)$ tells how daily income from the climbing wall depends on price per climb, why is $I(x) = 100x - 4x^2$ a suitable rule for that function?

8 The function $e(x) = 2x + 150$ shows how daily operating expenses for the *Galaxy Sport* climbing wall (Task 7) depend on the price per climb x.

a. Write two algebraic rules for the function $P(x)$ that gives daily profit from the climbing wall as a function of price per climb, (1) one that shows how income and operating expense functions are used in the calculation of profit and (2) another that is in simpler equivalent form.

b. Find $P(5)$. Explain what this result tells about climbing wall profit prospects.

c. What is a reasonable domain for $P(x)$ in this problem situation?

d. What is the range of $P(x)$ for the domain you specified in Part c?

e. Write and solve an inequality that will find the climb price(s) for which *Galaxy Sport and Outdoor Gear* will not lose money on operation of the climbing wall.

f. Find the price(s) that will yield maximum daily profit from the climbing wall.

7 **a.** At a price of \$10, there will be 60 climbers. At a price of \$15, there will be 40 climbers. If the price is \$0, there will be 100 climbers.

b. The 100 indicates the number of climbers if the price is \$0. The -4 represents a loss of 4 of those climbers for every dollar increase in climb price.

c. A reasonable domain would be $0 \leq x \leq 25$.

d. The corresponding range would be $0 \leq n(x) \leq 100$.

e. Since the income would be the price per climb multiplied by the number of climbers, the rule can be expressed as $x(100 - 4x)$, which can be expanded to $100x - 4x^2$, which is the rule for $I(x)$.

8 **a.** **(1)** $P(x) = (100x - 4x^2) - (2x + 150)$
(2) $P(x) = -4x^2 + 98x - 150$

b. $P(5) = 240$; When the climb price is set at \$5, the climb will yield a profit of \$240.

c. A reasonable domain would be $0 \leq x \leq 25$.

d. The range would be $-200 \leq P(x) \leq 450.25$.

e. $-4x^2 + 98x - 150 \geq 0$ is true when $1.64 \leq x \leq 22.86$.

f. The maximum profit of \$450.25 occurs when the price per climb is \$12.25.

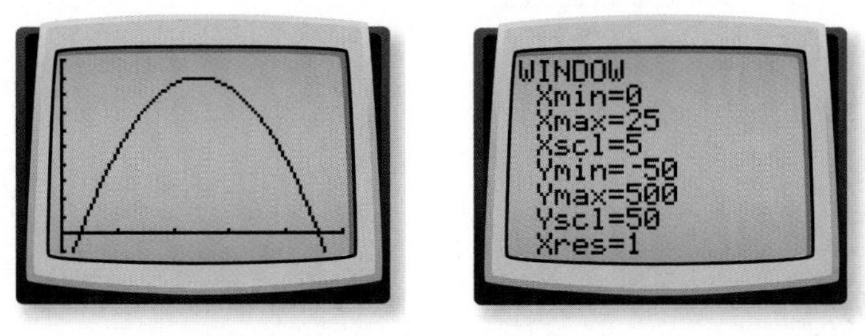

NOTE As a practical matter, the answers to Parts d–f need to be considered in relation to the problem condition that numbers of climb customers must be whole numbers. For a price of \$12.25, the number of customers will be 51. However, for calculated break-even prices of \$1.64 and \$22.86, the corresponding values of $n(x)$ are 93.44 and 8.56 customers. So, those break-even points are only approximate in practice.

On Your Own

Unit 5

Connections

9 Recall that graphs of quadratic polynomial functions of the form $f(x) = ax^2 + bx + c$ are called *parabolas*.

a. A basic geometric fact is that "two points determine a line." In general, how many points are needed to determine a parabola? Explain your reasoning.

b. Under what conditions, if any, will two points determine a parabola?

10 Evaluate each of these polynomial functions when $x = 10$.

$f(x) = 2x^2 + 3x + 7$

$g(x) = 5x^3 + x^2 + 5x + 4$

$h(x) = 3x^4 + 7x^3 + 9x^2 + 2x + 1$

$j(x) = 5x^5 + 3x^4 + 6x^3 + 2x^2 + 3x + 6$

a. Study the set of results. Explain why things turn out as they do in every case.

b. How does the pattern observed in Part a help to explain the arithmetic guideline that when adding numbers like 2,351.7 and 462.23, you should always "line up the decimal points"?

11 The following work illustrates one method for multiplying whole numbers.

$$\begin{array}{r} 5{,}283 \\ \underline{\times\ 25} \\ 15 \\ 400 \\ 1{,}000 \\ 25{,}000 \\ 60 \\ 1{,}600 \\ 4{,}000 \\ \underline{100{,}000} \\ 132{,}075 \end{array}$$

a. What products are represented by the numbers 15, 400, 1,000, … , 100,000?

b. Use a similar procedure to calculate $1{,}789 \times 64$, recording all of the individual products that must be summed to get the final result.

c. Why does the procedure give a correct result?

d. How does this method for arithmetic multiplication relate to the procedure for multiplying two polynomials?

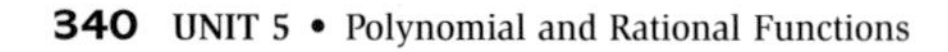

Connections

9 **a.** Three points are needed to determine a parabola. Students' explanations will likely be connected to their curve-fitting experience or testing to see if quadratic regression will produce a function for only two points.

b. If one point is known to be the vertex of the parabola, then symmetry can be used to find a third point. This point is the reflection image of the second point across the line of symmetry for the parabola.

10 $f(10) = 237$
$g(10) = 5{,}154$
$h(10) = 37{,}921$
$j(10) = 536{,}236$

a. Each answer is composed of digits where the leading coefficient is the first digit and the constant is the final digit and all other digits are in descending order of the power of the coefficient. This actually highlights the decimal place value system of our standard numeration scheme, single digits times powers of 10.

b. Student responses may vary but should include some notion of adding like terms in relation to adding digits in the same decimal place.

11 **a.** $15 = 3 \cdot 5$; $400 = 80 \cdot 5$; $1{,}000 = 200 \cdot 5$; $25{,}000 = 5{,}000 \cdot 5$;
$60 = 3 \cdot 20$; $1{,}600 = 80 \cdot 20$; $4{,}000 = 200 \cdot 20$; $100{,}000 = 5{,}000 \cdot 20$

b. $(9 \cdot 4) + (80 \cdot 4) + (700 \cdot 4) + (1{,}000 \cdot 4) + (9 \cdot 60) + (80 \cdot 60) + (700 \cdot 60) + (1{,}000 \cdot 60)$
$= (36 + 320 + 2{,}800 + 4{,}000) + (540 + 4{,}800 + 42{,}000 + 60{,}000)$
$= (7{,}156) + (107{,}340)$
$= 114{,}496$
$= 1{,}789 \cdot 64$

c. Since 1,789 can be expressed as $(1{,}000 + 700 + 80 + 9)$ and 64 can be expressed as $(60 + 4)$, the distributive property can be applied to yield the sum of 8 products.

d. Polynomials are sums of terms with different powers of the variable. This is like the sums of numbers as in Part c. Each part of one sum is multiplied times each part of the second sum (distributive property). Then, as with numbers, all these results are added. For the polynomial terms, only like terms can be added. The comparison is easiest to see if a polynomial arithmetic task is completed vertically. For example,

$$\begin{array}{r} 2x^2 + 3x + 7 \\ x - 1 \\ \hline -2x^2 - 3x - 7 \\ 2x^3 + 3x^2 + 7x \quad \\ \hline 2x^3 + 1x^2 + 4x - 7 \end{array}$$

Unit 5

Unit 5

12 In this task, you will explore related methods for multiplication of numbers and polynomials.

a. The following table shows a method of organizing work in multiplication of numbers like 314 × 27.

	3	1	4
2	6	2	8
7	21	7	28

i. Why is the result of this operation equal to 6,000 + 2,300 + 150 + 28?

ii. How are those partial products found from the table entries?

b. The next table shows a way of organizing the work involved in multiplying polynomials like $(7x^3 + 9x^2 + 2x + 1)$ and $(4x^2 + 3x + 5)$.

	7	9	2	1
4	28	36	8	4
3	21	27	6	3
5	35	45	10	5

i. What are the coefficients of each term in the result $\_x^5 + \_x^4 + \_x^3 + \_x^2 + \_x + \_$?

ii. How are the cell entries calculated?

iii. How are those cell entries combined to produce the coefficients of each term in the result? Why does that procedure give the desired result in each case?

13 Use the fact that $x^3 + 2x^2 - 11x - 12 = (x - 3)(x + 1)(x + 4)$ to solve the following inequalities. Express your solutions with inequality notation, number line graphs, and interval notation.

a. $x^3 + 2x^2 - 11x - 12 \geq 0$

b. $x^3 + 2x^2 - 11x - 12 < 0$

12 **a.** **i.** Since each number in either the top row or left column is really indicating a certain multiple of a certain power of 10, every other entry in the table is really a multiple of a power of 10 as well. Each cell's power of 10 is determined by adding the exponent on the corresponding power of 10 from the corresponding entries in the far left column and the top row. Cells with like powers of 10 can be added first to arrive at $6(10^3) + 23(10^2) + 15(10) + 28$ or, equivalently, $6{,}000 + 2{,}300 + 150 + 28$.

ii. These partial products are sums of entries on a 45° diagonal. This is the arrangement of products that correspond to the same power of 10.

b. **i.** The result is $28x^5 + 57x^4 + 70x^3 + 55x^2 + 13x + 5$.

ii. The cell entries are calculated by multiplying the bold number at the head of the cell's column by the bold number at the front of the cell's row.

iii. The top-left corner cell is the leading coefficient on the result. Then all other numbers are added on a diagonal from bottom left to top right to find the coefficients of successive terms. This method is only foolproof when there are entries in each cell (perhaps 0 in some) from the highest power to the constant term of each factor. This works for the same reason that the numeric version in Part a works. Cell entries on any diagonal correspond to terms with the same power of x.

13 Polynomial inequalities can be solved by finding zeroes of the corresponding polynomial function and then using graphic or algebraic reasoning to determine intervals on which the inequality is satisfied.

a. $x^3 + 2x^2 - 11x - 12 \geq 0$ on $[-4, -1] \cup [3, \infty)$. This can also be expressed as $-4 \leq x \leq -1$ or $3 \leq x < \infty$ and with the following number line graph.

−8 −6 −4 −2 0 2 4 6 8

b. $x^3 + 2x^2 - 11x - 12 < 0$ on $(-\infty, -4) \cup (-1, 3)$. This can also be expressed as $\infty < x < -4$ or $-1 < x < 3$ and with the following number line graph.

−8 −6 −4 −2 0 2 4 6 8

Reflections

14 One of the attractive features of polynomial models for data or graph patterns is the fact that evaluation of a polynomial requires only repeated use of three basic operations of arithmetic—addition, subtraction, and multiplication.

a. How does that make polynomials different and easier to use than some other types of functions that you have studied?

b. How do calculators and computers make that special feature of polynomials less important than it was before such technology was available?

15 Shown below are four polynomial functions, each written in expanded standard form and as a product of linear factors.

$f(x) = x^4 - 10x^3 + 35x^2 - 50x + 24 = (x - 1)(x - 2)(x - 3)(x - 4)$

$g(x) = x^4 - 7x^3 + 17x^2 - 17x + 6 = (x - 1)^2(x - 2)(x - 3)$

$h(x) = x^4 - 5x^3 + 9x^2 - 7x + 2 = (x - 1)^3(x - 2)$

$j(x) = x^4 - 4x^3 + 6x^2 - 4x + 1 = (x - 1)^4$

a. In which form is it easier to see the zeroes of the function?

b. In which form is it easier to see the y-intercept of the graph of the polynomial function?

c. How many zeroes do each of the four quartic polynomial functions have?

d. How does the collection of four functions help to explain why any polynomial function of degree n can have at most n distinct zeroes?

16 Graphs of quadratic polynomial functions have one basic shape—a parabola. For higher-degree polynomials, graphs of two polynomial functions of the same degree can have different shapes.

a. How does the basic shape of a quadratic polynomial function explain why quadratic functions can have 0, 1, or 2 zeroes?

b. Find a *cubic* (degree 3) polynomial function whose graph matches that shown in each case.

i.

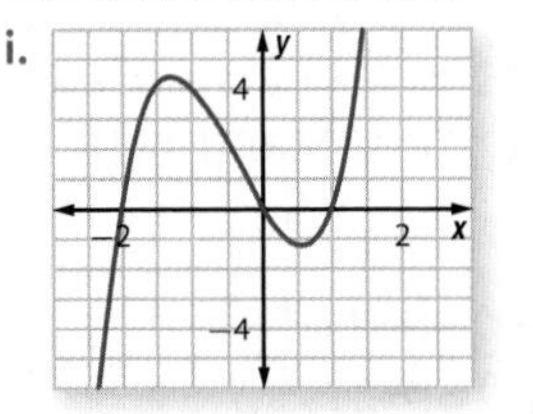

ii.

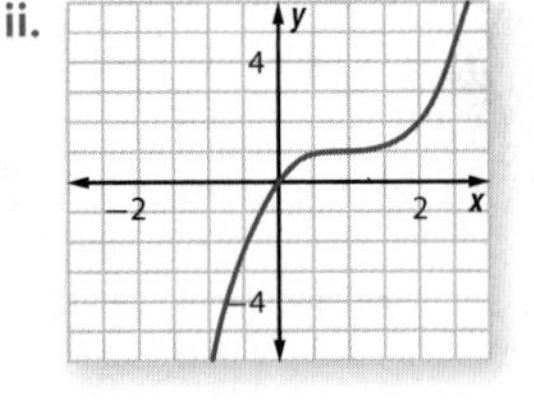

c. As each curve is shifted vertically, what happens to the number of zeroes of the corresponding function?

d. What are the possible numbers of zeroes for any cubic polynomial function? Explain your reasoning.

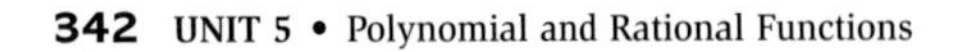

Reflections

14 **a.** Student responses will vary and should include comparisons to exponential and inverse variation functions and the ease of computation of values of polynomial functions at given points.

Typically, hand calculation division is much harder than the other three basic operations. Also, evaluation of roots and powers for non-integer exponents, logarithms, and trigonometric functions is not easy or even possible by hand.

b. Student responses will vary but should reference the advanced computational techniques of computers and calculators.

15 **a.** It is easier to see the zeroes in the factored form.

b. It is easier to see the y-intercept in the expanded standard form.

c. The functions have 4, 3, 2, and 1 zeroes, respectively.

d. A polynomial of degree 4 can be factored into no more than 4 distinct linear factors. And since each linear factor can have only one zero, there can be no more than 4 zeroes for the polynomial function.

16 **a.** The shape is always U-shaped, or parabolic. Thus, it will cross the x-axis 0, 1, or 2 times and have 0, 1, or 2 zeroes.

b. **i.** $f(x) = 2x(x + 2)(x - 1)$

ii. $f(x) = (x - 1)^3 + 1$

c. As the first function graph is shifted vertically, the numbers of zeroes goes from 3 to 2 to 1. The number of zeroes for the second function graph is always 1.

d. A cubic function can have 1, 2, or 3 zeroes. Since the end behavior is in opposite directions for a cubic function, the graph will cross the x-axis at least once. Two zeroes occur if one local maximum or local minimum is tangent to the x-axis. A graph with 3 zeroes is shown in the student text.

Extensions

17 You can work in many different ways to evaluate a polynomial function like

$$p(x) = 5x^5 + 3x^4 + 6x^3 + 2x^2 + 3x + 6$$

for some specific value of x. But to write a computer algorithm for that task, it is desirable to accomplish the work with a minimum number of instructions.

a. The following algorithm gives directions for evaluation of any polynomial. Follow the algorithm to evaluate $p(10)$. Use your calculator for the arithmetic.

Step 1. Enter the coefficient of the highest degree term.

Step 2. Multiply the result by x.

Step 3. Add the coefficient of the next lower degree term. (It might be zero.)

Step 4. If all coefficients have been used, go to Step 5. Otherwise, return to Step 2.

Step 5. Add the constant term and report the result.

b. Write this expression in equivalent standard polynomial form.

$$((((5x + 3)x + 6)x + 2)x + 3)x + 6$$

c. Use the algorithm in Part a to evaluate $f(x) = 4x^4 + 5x^3 + 7x^2 + 1x + 9$ when $x = 3$.

d. Write an expression like that in Part b that expresses the calculations involved in evaluating the polynomial $4x^4 + 5x^3 + 7x^2 + 1x + 9$ for any specific x. Then show why your alternative form is equivalent to the original.

18 A polynomial function $f(x)$ can have a *global maximum* or a *global minimum* value. A **global maximum** is a number M with the property that $f(x) \leq M$ for all values of x. A **global minimum** is a number m with the property that $f(x) \geq m$ for all values of x. For example, the quadratic function $f(x) = x^2 - 6$ has a global minimum at the point $(0, -6)$. The function $g(x) = -x^2 + 6x$ has a global maximum at $(3, 9)$.

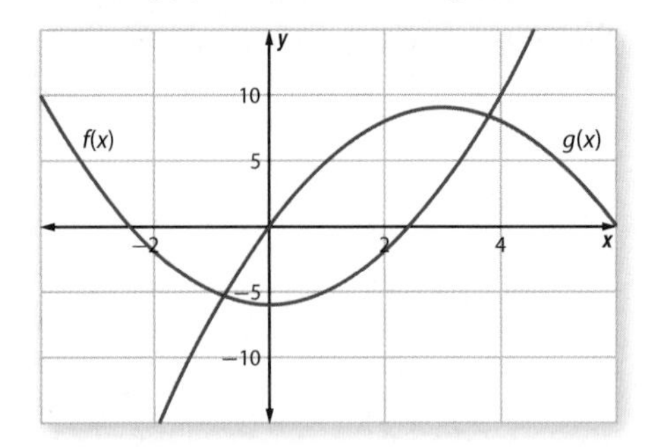

Extensions

17 **a.** When $x = 10$, $p(x) = 536{,}236$. The CAS work is below.

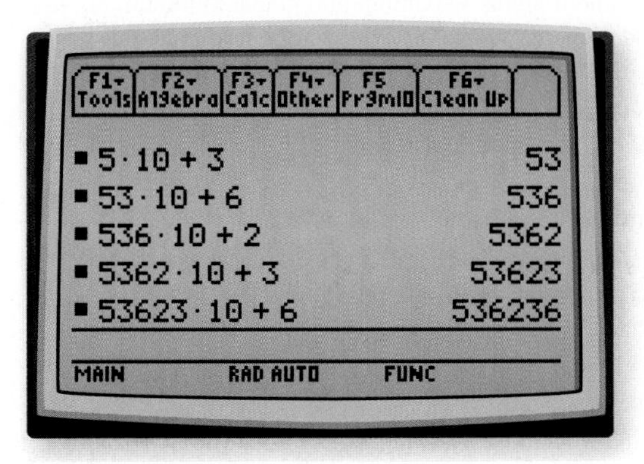

b. $5x^5 + 3x^4 + 6x^3 + 2x^2 + 3x + 6$

c. When $x = 3$, $f(x) = 534$. The CAS work is below.

F1 Tools F2 Algebra F3 Calc F4 Other F5 PrgmIO F6 Clean Up
4·3+5 17
17·3+7 58
58·3+1 175
175·3+9 534
MAIN RAD AUTO FUNC 4/30

d. $(((4x + 5)x + 7)x + 1)x + 9$, which can be expanded,

$$((4x^2 + 5x + 7)x + 1)x + 9 = (4x^3 + 5x^2 + 7x + 1)x + 9$$
$$= 4x^4 + 5x^3 + 7x^2 + x + 9$$

Unit 5

Use your experience with linear and quadratic functions and your explorations of graphs for cubic and quartic polynomials to answer these questions about global maximum and global minimum point possibilities. Be prepared to explain why you believe that your answers are correct.

a. Which polynomials of degree one, $p(x) = a_1x + a_0$, have global maximum or global minimum points?

b. Which polynomials of degree two, $p(x) = a_2x^2 + a_1x + a_0$, have global maximum or global minimum points?

c. Does the cubic polynomial function $g(x) = -x^3 + 6x^2 - 9x$ have a global maximum or global minimum?

d. Which polynomials of degree three, $p(x) = a_3x^3 + a_2x^2 + a_1x + a_0$, have global maximum or global minimum points?

e. Does the quartic polynomial function $h(x) = -x^4 + 2x^3 + 7x^2 - 8x - 12$ have a global maximum or global minimum?

f. Which polynomials of degree four, $p(x) = a_4x^4 + a_3x^3 + a_2x^2 + a_1x + a_0$, have global maximum or global minimum points?

19 When you first learned about division of whole numbers, you related that operation to multiplication by statements like "369 ÷ 3 = 123 because 3 × 123 = 369." You recorded the work to find a quotient in schemes that might have looked like this work.

$$\begin{array}{r} 123 \\ 3\overline{)369} \\ \underline{300} \\ 69 \\ \underline{60} \\ 9 \\ \underline{9} \end{array}$$

Apply your understanding and skill in division of whole numbers to find the quotients of polynomials in Parts a–d. It might help to organize your work in a style similar to what you learned to do with division of numbers, as shown in this example.

$$\begin{array}{r} x + 5 \\ x + 2\overline{)x^2 + 7x + 10} \\ \underline{x^2 + 2x} \\ 5x + 10 \\ \underline{5x + 10} \end{array}$$

a. $(x^2 + 11x + 28) \div (x + 7)$

b. $(x^2 + x - 12) \div (x - 3)$

c. $(x^3 + 7x^2 + 13x + 4) \div (x + 4)$

d. $(2x^3 + 13x^2 + 15x) \div (x^2 + 5x)$

344 UNIT 5 • Polynomial and Rational Functions

18 **NOTE** For all polynomials, the value of highest power term dominates all other terms eventually (for x of large absolute value). This means that for odd degree polynomials, there will be both large positive and large values; for even degree polynomials, either the values for large $|x|$ will both be positive or both negative (forcing a global minimum or global maximum).

a. $p(x)$ will only have a global maximum or global minimum point when $a_1 = 0$. In this case, $p(x)$ is a constant a_0, so the global maximum and global minimum are the same value, a_0. This value will be achieved for every x.

b. When $a_2 < 0$, the $p(x)$ will have a global maximum. When $a_2 > 0$, $p(x)$ will have a global minimum.

c. No, the function only has a local minimum and a local maximum.

d. The cubic function will not have a global minimum or global maximum value. This is the case for all odd-degree polynomials.

e. The function has a global maximum value of about 4 that occurs when $x \approx -1.56$ and when $x \approx 2.56$.

f. When $a_4 < 0$, the $p(x)$ will have a global maximum. When $a_4 > 0$, $p(x)$ will have a global minimum.

19 **a.**

$$\begin{array}{r|l} & x + 4 \\ x + 7 & x^2 + 11x + 28 \\ & \underline{x^2 + 7x} \\ & 4x + 28 \\ & \underline{4x + 28} \end{array}$$

b.

$$\begin{array}{r|l} & x + 4 \\ x - 3 & x^2 + x - 12 \\ & \underline{x^2 - 3x} \\ & 4x - 12 \\ & \underline{4x - 12} \end{array}$$

c.

$$\begin{array}{r|l} & x^2 + 3x + 1 \\ x + 4 & x^3 + 7x^2 + 13x + 4 \\ & \underline{x^3 + 4x^2} \\ & 3x^2 + 13x \\ & \underline{3x^2 + 12x} \\ & x + 4 \\ & \underline{x + 4} \end{array}$$

d.

$$\begin{array}{r|l} & 2x + 3 \\ x^2 + 5x & 2x^3 + 13x^2 + 15x \\ & \underline{2x^3 + 10x^2} \\ & 3x^2 + 15x \\ & \underline{3x^2 + 15x} \end{array}$$

20 In Investigation 3, you saw that if $(x - 3)$ is a factor of a polynomial function $q(x)$, then $q(3) = 0$.

a. Explain each step in the following proof of this general statement about polynomial functions.

If $(x - a)$ is a factor of $f(x)$, then $f(a) = 0$.

(1) If $(x - a)$ is a factor of $f(x)$, then $f(x) = (x - a)g(x)$, where $g(x)$ is a polynomial.

(2) If $f(x) = (x - a)g(x)$, then $f(a) = 0$.

b. Write the converse of the if-then statement in Part a.

c. Combine the proposition proven in Part a and its converse (which can also be proven) into a single if-and-only-if statement. That statement is called the **Factor Theorem**.

Review

21 Rewrite each expression in simplest form.

a. $6x^2 - 10x + 5x^2 + x + 8$

b. $2x + 5 - (8x - 1)$

c. $3(x + 1) + 2(x^2 + 7) - 7x$

d. $(-6x^2)(9x^3)$

22 Solve each quadratic equation or inequality without the use of technology.

a. $x^2 - 4x + 4 = 0$

b. $x^2 + 6x + 8 < 0$

c. $x^2 - 4x - 5 \geq 0$

d. $x^2 + 14x + 42 = -7$

23 Laboratory tests indicate that when planted properly, 6% of a particular type of seed fail to germinate. This means that out of every 100 seeds planted according to instructions, on the average six do not sprout. The laboratory has been developing a new variety of the seed in which only 1% fail to germinate. Suppose that in an experiment, ten seeds of each of the two types are planted properly.

a. Calculate the theoretical probability that at least one seed out of the ten will fail to germinate for each variety of seed.

b. Design and carry out a simulation to estimate the chance that if ten of the seeds with the 6% germination rate are planted, at least one will fail to germinate.

c. Design and carry out a simulation to estimate the chance that if ten of the new variety of the seed are planted, at least one will fail to germinate.

d. Compare the estimates from your simulations to your calculations in Part a.

20 **a.** **(1)** If $(x - a)$ is a factor of $f(x)$, then it must divide into $f(x)$ without a remainder, so $f(x)$ can be rewritten as $(x - a)g(x)$, where $g(x)$ is the quotient of $f(x)$ divided by $(x - a)$.

(2) $f(x) = (a - a)g(a) = 0 \cdot g(a) = 0$. Evaluating $f(a)$ gives $0 \cdot g(a) = 0$.

b. If, for polynomial function $f(x)$, $f(a) = 0$, then $(x - a)$ is a factor of $f(x)$.

c. **Factor Theorem:** The linear expression $(x - a)$ is a factor of a polynomial function $f(x)$ if and only if $f(a) = 0$.

Review

Just in Time

21 **a.** $11x^2 - 9x + 8$

b. $-6x + 6$

c. $2x^2 - 4x + 17$

d. $-54x^5$

22 In Course 3, Unit 2, *Inequalities and Linear Programming,* students learned to solve quadratic inequalities by factoring the inequality set equal to zero. Then they used the zeroes of the linear terms or corresponding functions to make a sketch and determine the solution. This method is shown in Part c.

a. $x = 2$

b. $-4 < x < -2$

c. $x^2 - 4x - 5 = 0$
$(x - 5)(x + 1) = 0$
$x = 5$ and $x = -1$
So, $x^2 - 4x - 5 \geq 0$ when $x \leq -1$ or $x \geq 5$.

d. $x = -7$

23 **a.** $1 - 0.94^{10} \approx 0.46$ and $1 - 0.99^{10} \approx 0.096$

b. Simulation designs can vary. One example would be to generate ten random numbers between 0 and 1 and count any number $0 \leq x \leq 0.06$ as a failure to germinate. Repeat the experiment many times. Then calculate the proportion of cases in which at least one failure to germinate occurs as an estimate of the probability of that event. When we ran 25 examples of this simulation, there was at least one failure to germinate 14 times or a proportion of 0.56.

c. The same sort of simulation can be used with any number $0 \leq x \leq 0.01$ considered a failure to germinate. When we ran 25 examples of this simulation, there was at least one failure to germinate only two times or a proportion of 0.08.

d. Comparisons will depend on simulation results. For our limited number of simulation trials (simulations tend to converge slowly), there were 0.56 vs 0.46 theoretical and 0.08 vs 0.096 theoretical in the two situations.

On Your Own

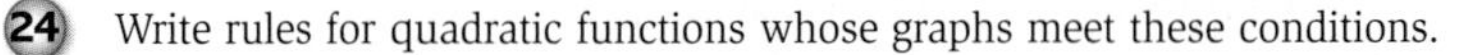

24 Write rules for quadratic functions whose graphs meet these conditions.

a. Opens up and has two x-intercepts

b. Opens down and has y-intercept $(0, -4)$

c. Opens up and the only x-intercept is $(5, 0)$

d. Has x-intercepts $(-2, 0)$ and $(6, 0)$

e. Opens up and has line of symmetry $x = 3$

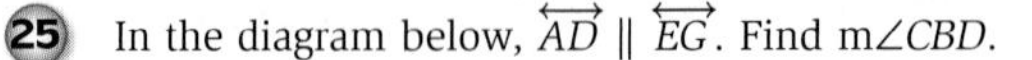

25 In the diagram below, $\overleftrightarrow{AD} \parallel \overleftrightarrow{EG}$. Find m$\angle CBD$.

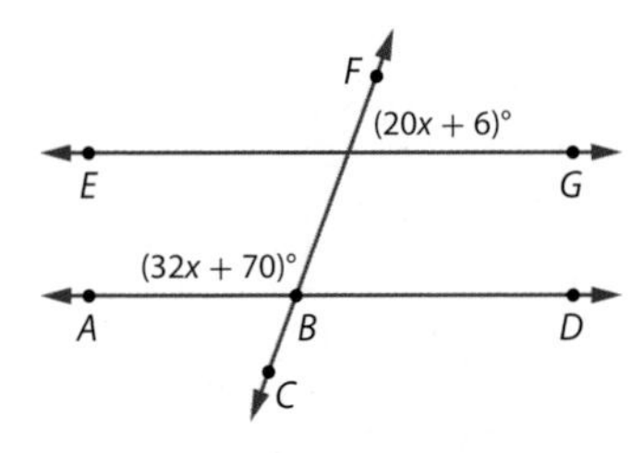

26 Rewrite each expression in equivalent simpler form with the smallest possible number under the radical sign.

a. $\sqrt{24}$

b. $\sqrt{48}$

c. $\sqrt{450}$

d. $\sqrt{\frac{8}{9}}$

e. $\frac{\sqrt{12}}{2}$

f. $\frac{\sqrt{60 + 3(5)}}{6}$

27 Write rules for linear functions whose graphs meet these conditions.

a. Slope 0.5 and y-intercept $(0, 4)$

b. Slope 1.6 and passing through $(2, 5)$

c. Passing through $(-2, 4)$ and $(6, 0)$

d. Parallel to the graph of $y = 2x + 3$ and passing through $(0, -3)$

28 Solve each of these quadratic equations by algebraic reasoning.

a. $x^2 + 7 = 23$

b. $3x^2 - 12 = 135$

c. $x^2 + 9 = 0$

d. $(x + 3)^2 = 19$

29 Expand each of these expressions to an equivalent standard form quadratic expression.

a. $(x + 5)(4x - 3)$

b. $(t + 8)(4 - t)$

c. $(x + 3)(x - 3)$

d. $(s - 7)^2$

e. $(3s + 2)^2$

f. $\left(y - \frac{5}{2}\right)^2$

346 UNIT 5 • Polynomial and Rational Functions

24 Answers will vary in the following general forms.

a. $y = (x - a)(x - b)$ where $a \neq b$.

b. $y = ax^2 + bx - 4$ where $a < 0$.

c. $y = a(x - 5)^2$ where $a > 0$.

d. $y = a(x - 6)(x + 2)$

e. Any quadratic function that opens up and has zeroes that are equidistant from 3 will have axis of symmetry $y = 3$. For example, $y = (x - 1)(x - 5)$. Another way of thinking about this is to write a rule in the form $y = ax^2 + bx + c$ such that $\frac{-b}{2a} = 3$ and $a > 0$. For example, $y = 2x^2 - 12x + 10$.

25 $134°$

26 **a.** $2\sqrt{6}$ **b.** $4\sqrt{3}$

c. $15\sqrt{2}$ **d.** $2\frac{\sqrt{2}}{3}$

e. $\sqrt{3}$ **f.** $\frac{5\sqrt{3}}{6}$

27 **a.** $y = 0.5x + 4$

b. $y = 1.6x + 1.8$

c. $y = -0.5x + 3$

d. $y = 2x - 3$

Just in Time

28 **a.** $x = \pm 4$ **b.** $x = \pm 7$

c. No solutions **d.** $x = -3 \pm \sqrt{19}$

Teaching Resources

Assessment Masters 8–13.

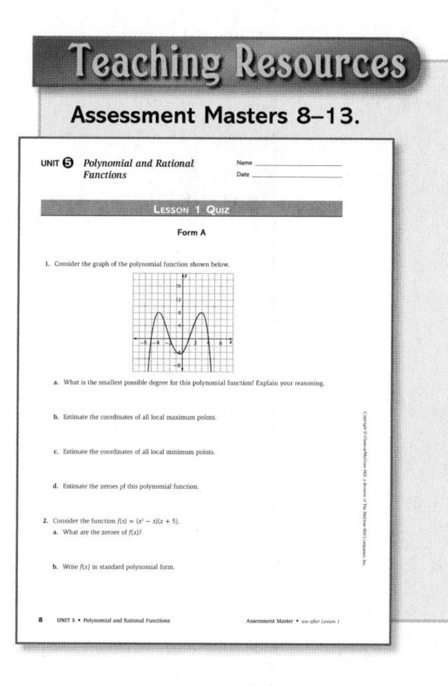
UNIT 5 Polynomial and Rational Functions
Name
Date
Lesson 1 Quiz
Form A
1. Consider the graph of the polynomial function shown below.
a. What is the smallest possible degree for this polynomial function? Explain your reasoning.
b. Estimate the coordinates of all local maximum points.
c. Estimate the coordinates of all local minimum points.
d. Estimate the zeroes of this polynomial function.
2. Consider the function $f(x) = (x^2 - x)(x + 5)$.
a. What are the zeroes of $f(x)$?
b. Write $f(x)$ in standard polynomial form.

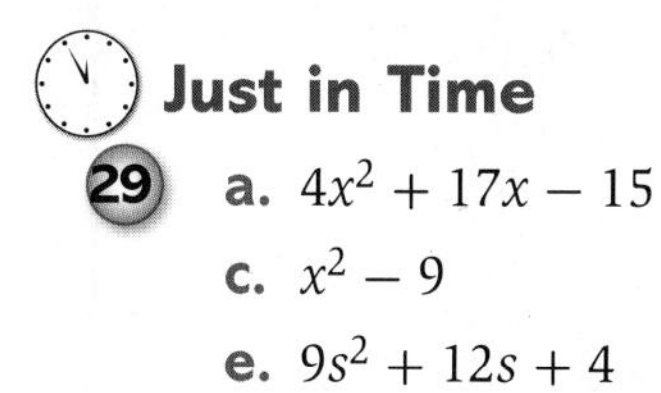

Just in Time

29 **a.** $4x^2 + 17x - 15$ **b.** $-t^2 - 4t + 32$

c. $x^2 - 9$ **d.** $s^2 - 14s + 49$

e. $9s^2 + 12s + 4$ **f.** $y^2 - 5y + \frac{25}{4}$

LESSON 2

Quadratic Polynomials

In the family of polynomial functions, the most useful are the simplest. In earlier work, you have used linear and quadratic polynomial functions to model and reason about a variety of business and scientific problems.

For example, in Lesson 1 of this unit, you analyzed business prospects for a concert promotion in which income was a quadratic function and operating expense was a linear function. Both depended on the price of tickets for the concert. The relationship of the two functions is shown below in the graph.

Concert Income and Operating Costs

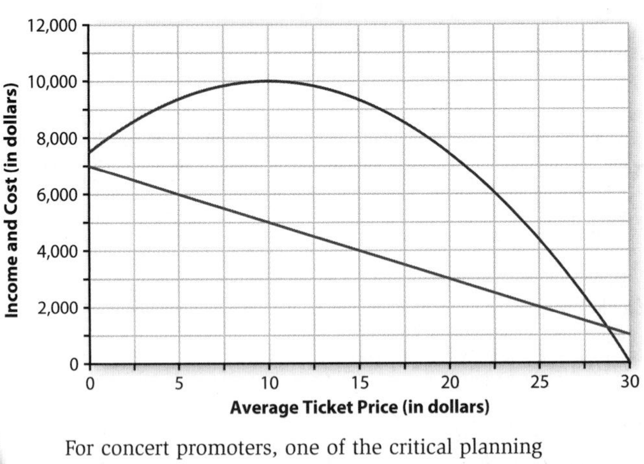

For concert promoters, one of the critical planning questions is estimating the break-even point(s) at which income from ticket sales and operating expenses are equal. In this case, that involves solving the equation $-25x^2 + 500x + 7{,}500 = 7{,}000 - 200x$.

Quadratic Polynomials

LESSON 2

Unit 5

This lesson focuses specifically on quadratic polynomials and finding the critical features of such functions.

The lesson is organized into two investigations. The first introduces students to the concept of "completing the square" and its uses. The second investigation focuses on the quadratic formula, leading to an informal introduction of complex numbers.

Lesson Objectives

- Express quadratic function rules in vertex form
- Use vertex form of quadratic expressions to solve quadratic equations and locate the vertex of parabolic graphs
- Use completing the square to prove the quadratic formula
- Use the quadratic formula to analyze solution possibilities for quadratic equations and indicate the rationale for extending the number system to include complex numbers

Lesson Launch

This TATS exercise should be one that serves primarily as a refresher of knowledge developed in earlier units that dealt with linear and quadratic functions, expressions, and equations. The setting connects back to problems in Lesson 1, but the mathematical ideas required to answer the questions posed here have been introduced in *Core-Plus Mathematics* Course 1, Unit 7, *Quadratic Functions* and in Course 2, Unit 5, *Nonlinear Functions and Equations*.

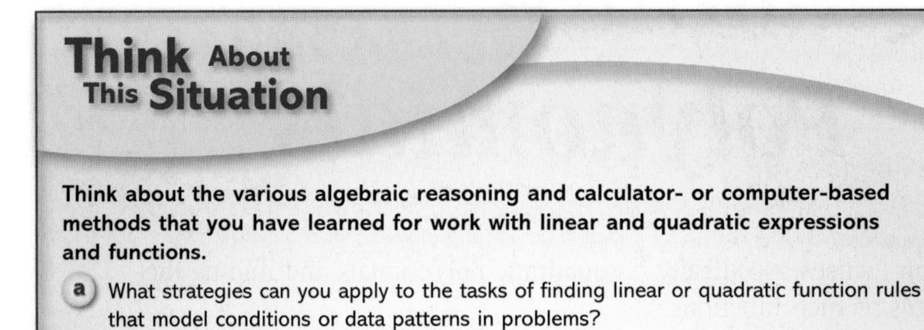

Think about the various algebraic reasoning and calculator- or computer-based methods that you have learned for work with linear and quadratic expressions and functions.

a What strategies can you apply to the tasks of finding linear or quadratic function rules that model conditions or data patterns in problems?

b What strategies can you apply to the tasks of solving linear or quadratic equations and inequalities?

c What strategies can you apply to find the maximum or minimum value of a quadratic function?

The investigations of this lesson will add to your toolkit of strategies for analyzing quadratic polynomials—writing quadratic expressions in new kinds of equivalent forms and using those expressions to solve equations and find max/min points on graphs of the corresponding functions.

Investigation 1 Completing the Square

When problems require solving quadratic equations, the simplest cases are those like $ax^2 + b = c$ that involve no linear term. You can solve such equations easily by reasoning like this.

$$\text{If } ax^2 + b = c, \text{ then } x^2 = \frac{c - b}{a}.$$

$$\text{So, } x = \pm\sqrt{\frac{c - b}{a}}.$$

It turns out that there are ways to transform every quadratic polynomial into an equivalent expression that has the general form $a(x - h)^2 + k$. This quadratic form, called the **vertex form**, gives easy-to-read information about the shape and location of the graph of the corresponding quadratic function. It also makes solution of quadratic equations easy.

As you work on the problems in this investigation, look for answers to these questions:

How does the vertex form of a quadratic function reveal the shape and location of its graph?

How can quadratic polynomials be expressed in vertex form?

As you work on these questions, keep in mind the fact that the general form $a(x - h)^2 + k$ includes examples like $-3(x + 6)^2 - 4$ where $a = -3$, $h = -6$, and $k = -4$.

348 UNIT 5 • Polynomial and Rational Functions

Think About This Situation

a Responses will vary but should include either algebraic reasoning from the conditions given, using a linear or quadratic curve-fitting tool, or experimenting with various specific possible function rules and adjusting to get better fits.

b Linear and quadratic equations can be solved by estimation using tables and graphs of the related functions or by algebraic reasoning that involves transforming the given equation and expressions into equivalent simpler forms. For linear equations, that generally means trying to isolate the variable on one side of the equation. For quadratic equations, students will have seen how to use factoring, reasoning similar to that applied to linear equations (when given equations are in the form $ax^2 + b = c$), or the quadratic formula (which they have used without proof earlier).

c To find the maximum or minimum point of a quadratic function, you can find the x-intercepts (provided they exist) of the parabola and calculate the x value which is halfway between these two points. At this midpoint, calculate the value of the function, and you will have the vertex point of the parabola.

Teaching Resources

Transparency Master 14.

UNIT 5 *Polynomial and Rational Functions*

Think About This Situation

Think about the various algebraic reasoning and calculator- or computer-based methods that you have learned for work with linear and quadratic expressions and functions.

a What strategies can you apply to the tasks of finding linear or quadratic function rules that model conditions or data patterns in problems?

b What strategies can you apply to the tasks of solving linear or quadratic equations and inequalities?

c What strategies can you apply to find the maximum or minimum value of a quadratic function?

COLLABORATION SKILL
Add a new perspective to the discussion.

Unit 5

Investigation 1 Completing the Square

In this investigation, students will be introduced to the vertex form of a quadratic expression $a(x - h)^2 + k$. This will help them to graph quadratic equations without the use of a graphing calculator or CAS. Although, there is a fair amount of algebra typically involved to get a quadratic expression in vertex form. It also provides an alternative strategy for solving quadratic equations.

Problems 1–3 guide students to discovery, statement, and justification of the information provided directly by quadratic expressions in the $a(x - h)^2 + k$ form. While it is natural to think of many different cases, depending on the signs of a, h, and k, it is standard in mathematical practice to express generalizations about the vertex form as $a(x - h)^2 + k$ rather than, for example, $a(x - h)^2 - k$. This will probably be awkward for many students, so be prepared to help them by reminding them how this form fits all cases if we just consider the possibility of both positive and negative values for a, h, and k.

Vertex Form of Quadratics To make use of quadratic polynomials in vertex form, you need to know how the parameters in those expressions are related to the shape and location of the corresponding function graphs.

1. First consider the question of how to find x- and y-intercepts on the graphs of quadratic functions with rules expressed in vertex form.

$$f(x) = a(x - h)^2 + k$$

To develop an answer to this question, you might analyze several specific examples like I–IV below and then make a conjecture. Then use algebraic reasoning to justify your conjecture. Or you might use more general algebraic reasoning to develop a conjecture and then test your ideas with the specific examples.

I. $g(x) = (x - 3)^2 - 16$ **II.** $j(x) = 3(x - 7)^2 - 12$

III. $m(x) = (x - 1)^2 + 25$ **IV.** $n(x) = -2(x + 6)^2 + 20$

a. What formula shows how to use values of a, h, and k to find coordinates for the x-intercepts on the graph of any function with rule in the form $f(x) = a(x - h)^2 + k$?

b. What formula shows how to use values of a, h, and k to find coordinates for the y-intercept on the graph of any function with rule in the form $f(x) = a(x - h)^2 + k$?

2. Consider next the question of how to locate maximum or minimum points on the graph of a quadratic function $f(x) = a(x - h)^2 + k$. Recall that this point is called the **vertex** of the graph. To develop an answer to this question, you might analyze several specific examples like I–IV below to make a conjecture. Then use algebraic reasoning to justify your conjecture. Or you might use more general algebraic reasoning to develop a conjecture and then test your ideas with the specific examples.

I. $r(x) = (x - 3)^2 + 5$ **II.** $s(x) = 3(x - 7)^2 - 4$

III. $t(x) = -2(x + 6)^2 + 3$ **IV.** $v(x) = -0.5(x + 5)^2 - 7$

a. How can you tell from the parameters a, h, and k when the graph of the function $f(x) = a(x - h)^2 + k$ will have a minimum point? When it will have a maximum point?

b. Consider the cases when the graph of the function has a minimum point.

i. For what value of x does the expression $a(x - h)^2 + k$ take on its smallest value?

ii. What is the y-coordinate of the corresponding point on the graph?

iii. What are the coordinates of the minimum point when $a > 0$?

c. Now consider the cases when the function has a maximum point.

i. For what value of x does the expression $a(x - h)^2 + k$ take on its largest possible value?

ii. What is the y-coordinate of the corresponding point on the graph?

iii. What are the coordinates of the minimum point when $a < 0$?

Launch

You might launch this investigation by asking students to record their personal hunches about the answers to Problems 1 and 2. That is, how do they think they might be able to use the parameters in the $y = a(x - h)^2 + k$ form of a quadratic function to locate the intercepts and max/min points on the corresponding graph? Then indicate that the problems will give them a chance to test, refine, and prove their ideas.

Since students will vary in their confidence about making such conjectures, it will probably be useful to reiterate the guidelines given in the stem of each problem. Students might choose to work out solutions to several specific examples (using a calculator where it seems likely to be helpful) and look for a general pattern in the results. Or, they might prefer to reason with the form $a(x - h)^2 + k$ to develop formulas and then check that their conjectured formulas give the correct results when applied to the specific illustrative examples.

Unit 5

1 **DIFFERENTIATION** Depending on the strength of your class, you might choose to give some additional scaffolding to Problem 1 by asking, "How do you find the x-intercept(s) of any graph?" and "How do you find the y-intercept of any graph?" and "How would you express each of those tasks as calculations and equations to be solved?"

a. $\left(h + \sqrt{\frac{-k}{a}}, 0\right)$ and $\left(h - \sqrt{\frac{-k}{a}}, 0\right)$ are the x-intercepts. This can be proven with algebraic reasoning as follows.

$$\text{If } a(x - h)^2 + k = 0,$$
$$\text{then } a(x - h)^2 = -k.$$
$$(x - h)^2 = \frac{-k}{a}$$
$$(x - h) = \pm\sqrt{\frac{-k}{a}}$$
$$x = h \pm \sqrt{\frac{-k}{a}}$$

b. $(0, ah^2 + k)$ is the y-intercept. This can be proven with algebraic reasoning as follows.

$$a(0 - h)^2 + k = a(-h)^2 + k$$
$$= ah^2 + k$$

The intercepts for the specific given examples are as follows.

I. x-intercepts: $(-1, 0)$ and $(7, 0)$
y-intercept: $(0, -7)$

II. x-intercepts: $(5, 0)$ and $(9, 0)$
y-intercept: $(0, 135)$

III. No x-intercepts
y-intercept: $(0, 26)$

IV. x-intercepts: $(-6 + \sqrt{10}, 0)$ and $(-6 - \sqrt{10}, 0)$
y-intercept: $(0, -52)$

INSTRUCTIONAL NOTE The formula in Problem 1 Part b is not one that is easily remembered, nor should it be.

2 **a.** If the lead coefficient a is positive, the function will have a minimum point. If that coefficient is negative, the function will have a maximum point.

You could confirm this by noticing that when the expression $a(x - h)^2 + k$ is expanded, ax^2 is the second-degree term. From earlier work with quadratics in standard polynomial form, you know that the sign of the coefficient of x^2 determines maximum or minimum value in the way described.

NOTE The remainder of the solutions for Problem 2 and Problem 3 are on page T350.

Unit 5

3 Your work on Problems 1 and 2 revealed a new way of thinking about max/min points and intercepts on graphs of quadratic functions. For example, the function $q(x) = x^2 - 10x + 24$ can be expressed as $q(x) = (x - 4)(x - 6)$ and also as $q(x) = (x - 5)^2 - 1$.

a. How would you use each of the three forms to find coordinates of the y-intercept on the graph of $q(x)$? Which approach seems most helpful?

b. How would you use each form to find coordinates of the x-intercepts on the graph of $q(x)$? Which approach seems most helpful?

c. How would you use each form to find coordinates of the maximum or minimum point on the graph of $q(x)$? Which approach seems most helpful?

Completing the Square You know from earlier work with quadratic expressions that there are useful patterns relating factored and expanded forms of those expressions. For any number n,

$$(x + n)^2 = x^2 + 2nx + n^2 \text{ and } (x - n)^2 = x^2 - 2nx + n^2.$$

The relationship between factored and expanded forms of such *perfect square* expressions is the key to finding vertex forms for quadratic function rules. Work on Problems 4–7 will give you some valuable insight into the process of finding vertex form expressions for quadratics.

4 Use the pattern relating expanded and factored forms of perfect square polynomials (where possible) to write factored forms of the expressions in Parts a–f. Use a CAS to check that your factored forms are equivalent to the corresponding expanded forms.

a. $x^2 + 6x + 9$

b. $x^2 + 10x + 25$

c. $x^2 + 8x + 12$

d. $x^2 - 10x + 25$

e. $x^2 + 5x + \frac{25}{4}$

f. $x^2 - 3x + \frac{9}{4}$

5 The challenge in transforming a given quadratic expression to an equivalent vertex form can be represented as a geometry problem. Study the following diagram. Find values of n, m, and k that make it possible to express the total area of the figure in two ways.

- as $(x + n)^2$
- as $x^2 + kx + m$

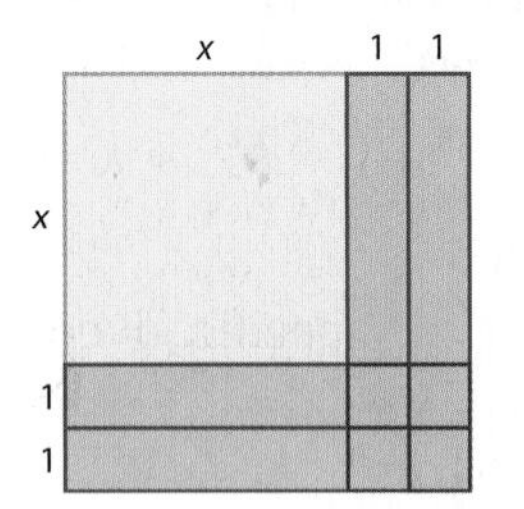

350 UNIT 5 • Polynomial and Rational Functions

b. **i.** When a is positive, the expression $a(x - h)^2$ is always non-negative. The sum of a non-negative quantity and k is always at least as large as k, and it equals k when $a(x - h)^2 = 0$ or $x = h$.

ii. The corresponding y value is $a(h - h)^2 + k = a(0) + k = k$.

iii. **I.** Min at $(3, 5)$ **II.** Min at $(7, -4)$

c. **i.** When a is negative, the expression $a(x - h)^2$ is always nonpositive. The sum of a nonpositive quantity and k is always at most as large as k, and it equals k when $a(x - h)^2 = 0$ or $x = h$.

ii. The corresponding y value is $a(h - h)^2 + k = a(0) + k = k$.

iii. **III.** Max at $(-6, 3)$ **IV.** Max at $(-5, -7)$

3 **a.** In all three forms, one substitutes 0 for x to find the y-coordinate of the y-intercept point. It is perhaps easiest to do with the standard form where the constant term reveals the y-intercept immediately. However, the factored form requires only a single multiplication after the substitution of 0 for x.

b. Of the three forms, the factored form probably reveals the x-intercepts most readily. From the vertex form, there is some calculation to perform to solve the equation $a(x - h)^2 + k = 0$. From the standard form, one needs either to factor the expression or apply the quadratic formula, both of which require some calculation beyond that necessary when the expression is already in factored form.

c. Problem 2 shows how to use the vertex form to find the maximum or minimum point of the quadratic directly. To use the factored form, we need to find both zeroes and then reason that the max/min point is on the vertical line midway between those zeroes. To use the standard form, students may remember the formula $x = \frac{-b}{2a}$ for finding the x-coordinate of the max/min point. In both the factored and standard form, there is an additional calculation to find the y-coordinate once the x-coordinate is determined. Thus, the vertex form reveals both coordinates of the vertex (h, k) most easily.

INSTRUCTIONAL NOTE Problems 4–9 develop strategies for transforming a given quadratic expression into vertex form, including several ways of visualizing the process with diagrams similar to what occurs in use of manipulatives like algebra tiles.

4 **a.** $(x + 3)^2$ **b.** $(x + 5)^2$

c. $(x + 2)(x + 6)$ **d.** $(x - 5)^2$

e. $\left(x + \frac{5}{2}\right)^2$ **f.** $\left(x - \frac{3}{2}\right)^2$

INSTRUCTIONAL NOTE The next two problems and Problem 9 at the end of the investigation develop ways of visualizing the completing the square process. To enhance that work, you might find it useful to visit the National Library of Virtual Manipulatives (nlvm.usu.edu/en/nav/vlibrary.html) and use the electronic algebra tiles there.

 $(x + 2)^2 = x^2 + 4x + 4$; so, $n = 2$, $k = 4$, and $m = 4$.

Unit 5

Unit 5

6 Now consider the expression $x^2 + 6x + 7$. The pieces of this expression can be represented with an "x by x" square, six "x by 1" rectangles, and seven unit squares.

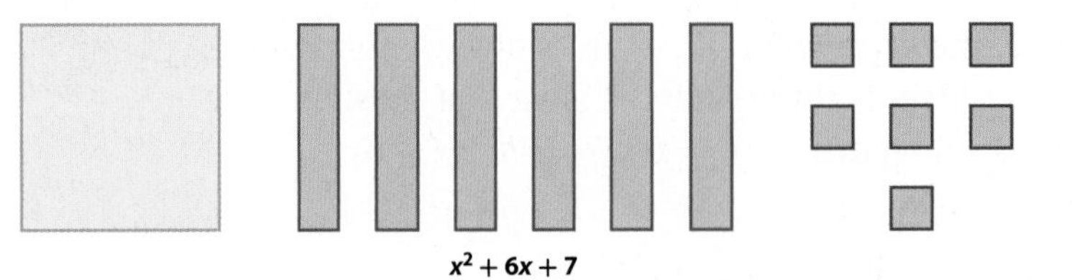

$x^2 + 6x + 7$

a. Why is it impossible to arrange the given squares and rectangles without overlapping to form one large square?

b. How could you produce the requested square if you were given some extra pieces or allowed to take away some pieces? What addition or subtraction would do the job most efficiently?

c. Explain how your answer to Part b illustrates the fact that $x^2 + 6x + 7 = (x + 3)^2 - 2$.

If a quadratic expression is not a perfect square (factorable to the form $(x \pm h)^2$), it is still possible to write an equivalent expression in the form $(x \pm h)^2 \pm k$. Your work in Problem 6 gives a picture that suggests the kind of algebraic operations that are required. Problem 7 asks you to adapt that reasoning to develop a symbol manipulation procedure.

7 Study the following example of the technique called **completing the square**. Explain the choice of "9" and why it was added and subtracted in different parts of the expression.

$$\begin{aligned} x^2 + 6x + 11 &= (x^2 + 6x + \_\_) + 11 \\ &= (x^2 + 6x + 9) - 9 + 11 \\ &= (x + 3)^2 + 2 \end{aligned}$$

Use similar reasoning to write the expressions in Parts a–f in vertex form.

a. $x^2 + 6x + 5$

b. $x^2 - 6x + 10$

c. $x^2 + 8x + 19$

d. $x^2 - 8x + 12$

e. $x^2 + 10x + 27$

f. $x^2 - 3x + 1$

8 How do the results of your work on Problems 6 and 7 suggest a strategy for writing any quadratic expression $x^2 + bx + c$ in equivalent vertex form $(x \pm h)^2 \pm k$?

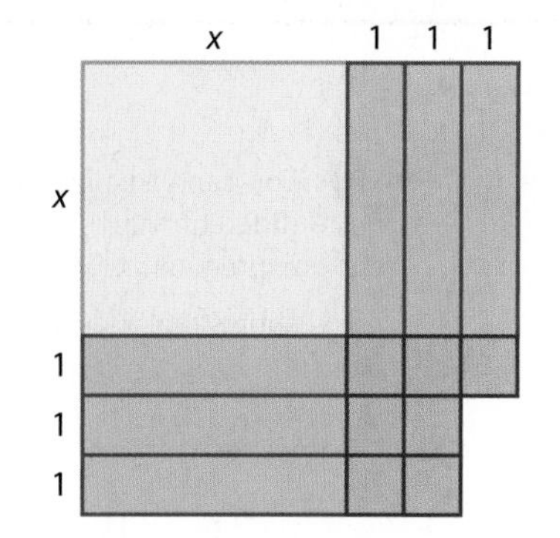

6 **a.** Responses may vary. Students will probably attempt to form an $(x + 3)$ by $(x + 3)$ square and find that there are not enough unit squares to fill in the larger square area as shown at the right.

b. Two extra unit squares will complete an $(x + 3)$ by $(x + 3)$ square.

c. Suppose students have an x by x piece, six x by 1 pieces, and seven 1 by 1 pieces. (This can be thought of as pieces with area sum of $x^2 + 6x + 7$.) They can almost make an $(x + 3)$ by $(x + 3)$ square, but they are two units short. Equivalently, if students make an $(x + 3)$ by $(x + 3)$ square and remove two unit squares, they are left with an area sum of $x^2 + 6x + 7$.

7 **a.** $(x + 3)^2 - 4$ **b.** $(x - 3)^2 + 1$

c. $(x + 4)^2 + 3$ **d.** $(x - 4)^2 - 4$

e. $(x + 5)^2 + 2$ **f.** $\left(x - \frac{3}{2}\right)^2 - \frac{5}{4}$

8 Any quadratic expression of the form $x^2 + bx + c$ can be written in the form $\left(x + \frac{b}{2}\right)^2 + \left(c - \left(\frac{b}{2}\right)^2\right) = \left(x + \frac{b}{2}\right)^2 + \left(c - \frac{b^2}{4}\right)$.

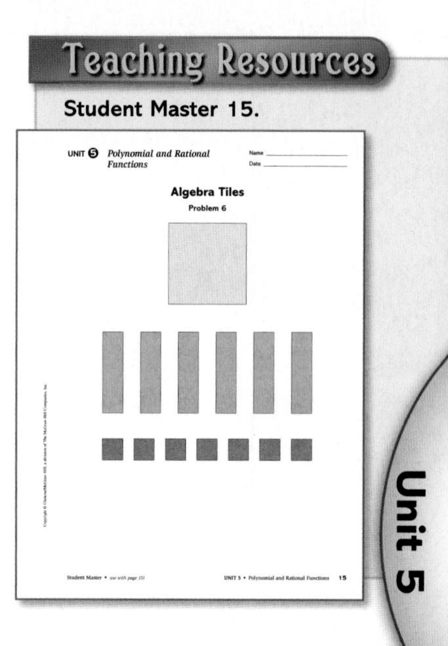

9 You can visualize the process of completing the square in a somewhat different way, if you focus attention on the first two terms of the given expression, $x^2 + bx$. Explain how the following proof without words shows that $x^2 + bx = \left(x + \frac{b}{2}\right)^2 - \left(\frac{b}{2}\right)^2$.

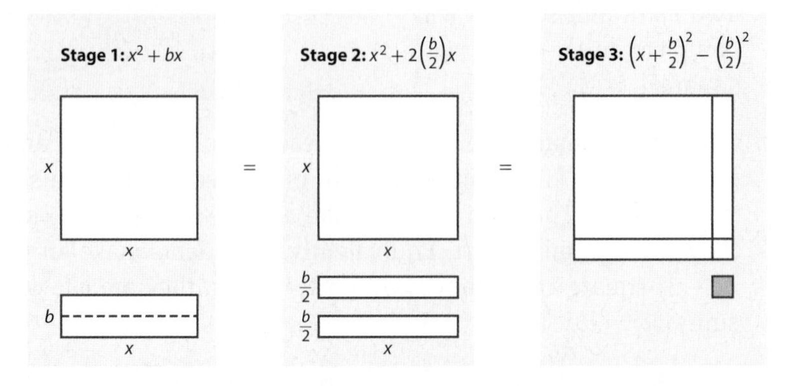

Summarize the Mathematics

In this investigation, you developed skill in transforming quadratic expressions in standard form to vertex form and in using that form to analyze the graphs of corresponding quadratic functions.

a How can the vertex form of a quadratic expression like $(x - h)^2 + k$ be used to locate the max/min point and intercepts on the graph of the corresponding quadratic function?

b What are key steps in transforming $x^2 + bx + c$ to vertex form?

Be prepared to explain your ideas to the class.

Check Your Understanding

Use your new completing-the-square skills to solve these problems.

a. Write the expression $x^2 - 2x - 5$ in equivalent vertex form.

b. Use the result of Part a to:

- **i.** solve $x^2 - 2x - 5 = 0$.
- **ii.** find coordinates of the minimum point on the graph of $f(x) = x^2 - 2x - 5$.
- **iii.** find coordinates of x- and y-intercepts on the graph of $f(x) = x^2 - 2x - 5$.

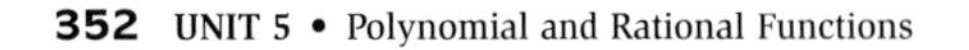

352 UNIT 5 • Polynomial and Rational Functions

9 In Stage 2, the bx piece is cut in half to form two $\frac{b}{2}x$ pieces. In Stage 3, the pieces are rearranged to attempt to form a square with sides of length $\left(x + \frac{b}{2}\right)$, but that square is missing a small square of side length $\frac{b}{2}$. Since the sum of the areas of the pieces equals the area of the sum of the pieces, $x^2 + bx = \left(x + \frac{b}{2}\right)^2 - \left(\frac{b}{2}\right)^2$.

Summarize the Mathematics

a The max/min point is always (h, k), the x-intercepts are $(h + \sqrt{-k}, 0)$ and $(h - \sqrt{-k}, 0)$, and the y-intercept is $(0, h^2 + k)$.

b The key steps are adding and subtracting $\left(\frac{b}{2}\right)^2$ and rewriting the terms of $x^2 + bx + \left(\frac{b}{2}\right)^2$ into a perfect square $\left(x + \frac{b}{2}\right)^2$.

Teaching Resources

Transparency Master 16.

UNIT 5 *Polynomial and Rational Functions*

Summarize the Mathematics

In this investigation, you developed skill in transforming quadratic expressions in standard form to vertex form and in using that form to analyze the graphs of corresponding quadratic functions.

a How can the vertex form of a quadratic expression like $(x - h)^2 + k$ be used to locate the max/min point and intercepts on the graph of the corresponding quadratic function?

b What are key steps in transforming $x^2 + bx + c$ to vertex form?

Be prepared to explain your ideas to the class.

16 UNIT 5 • Polynomial and Rational Functions   Transparency Master • use with page 352

Unit 5

COLLABORATION PROMPT

__________ added a new
(*name*)
perspective to our discussion by ... .

Check Your Understanding

a. $(x - 1)^2 - 6$

b. **i.** $(x - 1)^2 = 6$; $x - 1 = \pm\sqrt{6}$; $x = 1 \pm \sqrt{6}$

ii. Minimum point: $(1, -6)$

iii. x-intercepts: $(1 \pm \sqrt{6}, 0)$

y-intercept: $(0, -5)$

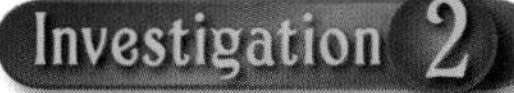

The Quadratic Formula and Complex Numbers

As you have seen in your previous studies, when problems require solving quadratic equations that cannot be factored easily, you can always turn to the *quadratic formula*. For instance, solutions for $3x^2 + 7x - 12 = 0$ are given by

$$x = \frac{-7}{2(3)} + \frac{\sqrt{7^2 - 4(3)(-12)}}{2(3)} \quad \text{and} \quad x = \frac{-7}{2(3)} - \frac{\sqrt{7^2 - 4(3)(-12)}}{2(3)}.$$

As you complete the problems in this investigation, look for answers to these questions:

How can the technique of completing the square be used to derive the quadratic formula?

How does use of the quadratic formula suggest the need for new kinds of numbers?

Proving and Using the Quadratic Formula The work that you have done to write quadratic expressions in vertex form is closely related to the quadratic formula that can be used to find solutions of any quadratic equation.

1. Consider the general form of a quadratic equation, $ax^2 + bx + c = 0$. The solutions of this equation are given by $x = \frac{-b}{2a} + \frac{\sqrt{b^2 - 4ac}}{2a}$ and $x = \frac{-b}{2a} - \frac{\sqrt{b^2 - 4ac}}{2a}$. Explain how each step in the following derivation of the quadratic formula is justified by properties of numbers and operations.

Start: If $ax^2 + bx + c = 0$ (and $a \neq 0$),

Step 1. Then $ax^2 + \frac{b}{a}x + \frac{c}{a} = 0$.

Step 2. $x^2 + \frac{b}{a}x + \frac{c}{a} = 0$

Step 3. $x^2 + \frac{b}{a}x = \frac{-c}{a}$

Step 4. $x^2 + \frac{b}{a}x + \frac{b^2}{4a^2} = \frac{-c}{a} + \frac{b^2}{4a^2}$

Step 5. $x^2 + \frac{b}{a}x + \frac{b^2}{4a^2} = \frac{b^2}{4a^2} + \frac{-c}{a}$

Step 6. $\left(x + \frac{b}{2a}\right)^2 = \frac{b^2}{4a^2} + \frac{-c}{a}$

Step 7. $\left(x + \frac{b}{2a}\right)^2 = \frac{b^2}{4a^2} + \frac{-4ac}{4a^2}$

Step 8. $\left(x + \frac{b}{2a}\right)^2 = \frac{b^2 - 4ac}{4a^2}$

Step 9. $x + \frac{b}{2a} = \frac{\sqrt{b^2 - 4ac}}{2a}$ or $x + \frac{b}{2a} = \frac{-\sqrt{b^2 - 4ac}}{2a}$

Step 10. So, $x = \frac{-b}{2a} + \frac{\sqrt{b^2 - 4ac}}{2a}$ or $x = \frac{-b}{2a} - \frac{\sqrt{b^2 - 4ac}}{2a}$.

Investigation 2 The Quadratic Formula and Complex Numbers

In this investigation, students will derive the quadratic formula and use it to solve quadratic equations and to analyze the various possibilities for real and complex solutions of those equations. There is more to come about complex numbers in the Course 4 pre-calculus track.

Launch

You might launch the examination of the quadratic formula proof by asking students to show how, in general, the vertex form of a quadratic leads to the solutions of the corresponding quadratic equation $(x - h)^2 + k = 0$ if $x = h \pm \sqrt{-k}$ and then suggesting that this is the key idea behind the quadratic formula and its proof. Give students some time to study the given steps of the proof in pairs and then have a full class discussion of the explanations for each step.

1

Step 1. Distributive property, or factoring out a common factor

Step 2. Since $a \neq 0$, the only way the product could equal zero is if the other factor is 0.

Step 3. Addition Property of Equality (adding $\frac{-c}{a}$ to both sides)

Step 4. Addition Property of Equality (adding $\left(\frac{b}{2a}\right)^2 = \frac{b^2}{4a^2}$ to both sides)

Step 5. Commutative Property of Addition (right-hand side)

Step 6. Substitution for the given expression by an equivalent perfect-square expression (left-hand side)

Step 7. Multiplication by 1 $\left(\text{in the form } \frac{4a}{4a}\right)$ to develop a common denominator prior to adding fractions (right-hand side)

Step 8. Addition of fractions with a common denominator

Step 9. Square root of both sides

Step 10. Addition property of equality (adding $\frac{-b}{2a}$ to both sides)

Unit 5

Teaching Resources

Student Master 17.

UNIT 5 Polynomial and Rational Functions

Proving the Quadratic Formula

Problem 1

Unit 5

2 The quadratic formula provides a tool for solving any quadratic equation by algebraic reasoning. But you have other helpful strategies available through use of technology.

a. How could you use calculator- or computer-generated tables of function values or graphs to estimate solutions for a quadratic equation like $3x^2 + 7x - 12 = 0$?

b. How could you use a computer algebra system (CAS) to solve $3x^2 + 7x - 12 = 0$?

c. Use the CAS available to you to solve $ax^2 + bx + c = 0$ for x and compare the CAS result to the quadratic formula derived in Problem 1.

3 Use the quadratic formula to solve each of the following equations. Report your answers in exact form, using radicals where necessary rather than decimal approximations. Check each answer by substituting the solution values for x back into the original equation.

a. $3x^2 + 9x + 6 = 0$

b. $3x^2 - 6 = -3x$

c. $2x^2 + x - 10 = 0$

d. $2x^2 + 5x - 1 = 0$

e. $x^2 + 2x + 1 = 0$

f. $x^2 - 6x + 13 = 0$

4 The solutions for quadratic equations in Problem 3 included several kinds of numbers. Some could be expressed as integers. But others could only be expressed as fractions or as irrational numbers involving radicals. One of the quadratic equations appears to have no solutions.

a. At what point in use of the quadratic formula do you learn whether the equation has two distinct solutions, only one solution, or no real number solutions?

b. If the coefficients of a quadratic equation are integers or rational numbers, at what point in use of the quadratic formula do you learn whether the solution(s) will be integers, rational numbers, or irrational numbers?

Complex Numbers In work on Problems 2 and 3, you discovered that some quadratic equations do not have real number solutions. For example, when you try to solve $x^2 - 6x + 13 = 0$, the quadratic formula gives

$$x = 3 + \frac{\sqrt{-16}}{2} \quad \text{and} \quad x = 3 - \frac{\sqrt{-16}}{2}.$$

If you ask a CAS to **solve(x^2-6*x+13=0,x)**, it is likely to return the disappointing result "false."

5 Sketch a graph of the function $f(x) = x^2 - 6x + 13$. Explain how it shows that there are no real number solutions for the equation $x^2 - 6x + 13 = 0$.

354 UNIT 5 • Polynomial and Rational Functions

2 **a.** Good estimates of solutions can be located by exploring tables or graphs of values of the function $y = 3x^2 + 7x - 12$. Using a table of values, find two successive x values for which one has a negative y value and the other has a positive y value. A zero of the function will be between these two x values, and the table can then be refined to better estimate the zero. On a graph, trace to find points where the graph crosses the x-axis. Zoom in if necessary.

b–c. The CAS results follow.

```
F1  F2▾     F3▾  F4▾   F5     F6▾
    Algebra Calc Other PrgmIO Clean Up
■ solve(3·x²+7·x−12=0,x)
        x = −(√193 + 7)/6   or   x = (√193 − 7)/6
■ solve(a·x²+b·x+c=0,x)
  x = (√(b²−4·a·c) − b)/(2·a)   or   x = −(√(b²−4·a·c) + ▸ /(2·a)
MAIN          RAD EXACT          FUNC 2/30
```

3 **a.** $x = -1$ or $x = -2$

b. $x = 1$ or $x = -2$

c. $x = 2$ or $x = -2.5$

d. $x = \frac{-5 \pm \sqrt{33}}{4}$

e. $x = -1$

f. $x = \frac{6 \pm \sqrt{-16}}{2}$ (No real solution is also an acceptable answer.)

4 **a.** When $b^2 - 4ac$ is greater than zero, there will be two distinct solutions. When $b^2 - 4ac$ is equal to zero, there will be only one solution. When $b^2 - 4ac$ is negative, you can tell there will be no real solutions.

b. When a, b, and c are integers or rational numbers and $b^2 - 4ac$ (the determinant) is positive but not a perfect square of an integer or rational number, the quadratic formula will yield a pair of irrational number solutions. If the discriminant is a positive perfect square, the equation will have two rational solutions. Sometimes, the rational solutions are integers, but it is not obvious, in general, when that occurs. $-b \pm \sqrt{b^2 - 4ac}$ must be divisible by $2a$ to have an integer solution.

NOTE Solutions to Problem 5 are on page T355.

The obstacle to solving $x^2 - 6x + 13 = 0$ appears with the radical $\sqrt{-16}$. Your prior experience with square roots tells you that *no* real number has -16 as its square. For thousands of years, mathematicians seemed to accept as a fact that equations like $x^2 - 6x + 13 = 0$ simply have no solutions. In general, a quadratic equation in the form $ax^2 + bx + c = 0$ has no real number solutions when the value of $b^2 - 4ac$, called the **discriminant** of the quadratic, is a negative number.

In the middle of the 16th century, Italian scholar Girolamo Cardano suggested all that was needed was a new kind of number. Cardano's idea was explored by mathematicians for several more centuries (often with strong doubts about using numbers with negative squares) until *complex numbers* became an accepted and well-understood tool for both pure and applied mathematics.

Girolamo Cardano

The obstacle to solving $x^2 - 6x + 13 = 0$ was removed by reasoning like this.

It makes sense that $\sqrt{-16}$ should equal $\sqrt{16(-1)}$.

But $\sqrt{16(-1)}$ should equal $\sqrt{16}\sqrt{-1}$.

So, $3 + \frac{\sqrt{-16}}{2}$ should equal $3 + \frac{4\sqrt{-1}}{2}$.

Or, the solutions for $x^2 - 6x + 13 = 0$ should be $x = 3 + 2\sqrt{-1}$ and $x = 3 - 2\sqrt{-1}$.

This kind of observation led mathematicians to develop what is now called the **complex number** system whose elements are in the form $\boldsymbol{a + b\sqrt{-1}}$ with a and b real numbers. The new number system contains all real numbers (the complex numbers for which $b = 0$). It also provides solutions to the problematic quadratic equations *and all other polynomial equations in the form p(x) = 0.*

Because $\sqrt{-1}$ was long considered an impossible or **imaginary number**, expressions of complex numbers are commonly written with $\sqrt{-1}$ replaced by the letter "i". So, $3 + 2\sqrt{-1}$ is written as $3 + 2i$. You will learn more about complex numbers in future studies.

6 Use the quadratic formula to show that each of these equations has complex number solutions with nonzero imaginary parts. Express those solutions in the form $a + bi$, where a and b are real numbers.

a. $x^2 - 10x + 29 = 0$

b. $4x^2 + 16 = 0$

c. $x^2 - 4x + 13 = 0$

d. $3x^2 - 18x + 30 = 0$

SCOPE AND SEQUENCE The following introduction to complex numbers is only intended to be a foreshadowing of developments that will occur in Course 4. Students are not expected to learn how to operate with complex numbers at this time. Although, there are some Extensions tasks that interested students might want to explore.

TECHNOLOGY NOTE
CAS software also solves equations over the complex numbers.

 Because the parabola lies entirely above the x-axis, as shown below, there are no real solutions.

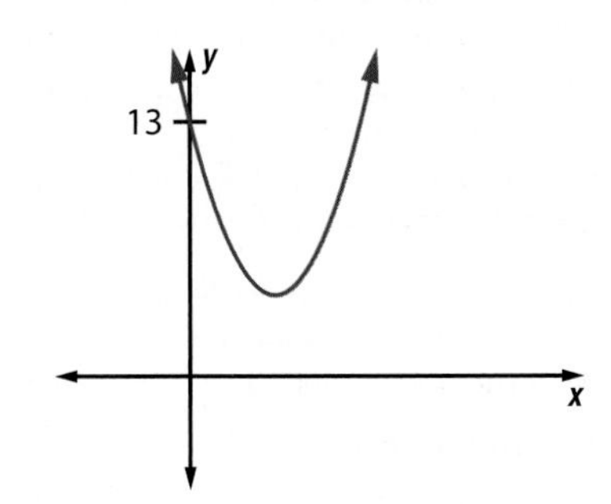

6 **a.** $5 + 2i$ and $5 - 2i$ **b.** $2i$ and $-2i$

c. $2 + 3i$ and $2 - 3i$ **d.** $3 + i$ and $3 - i$

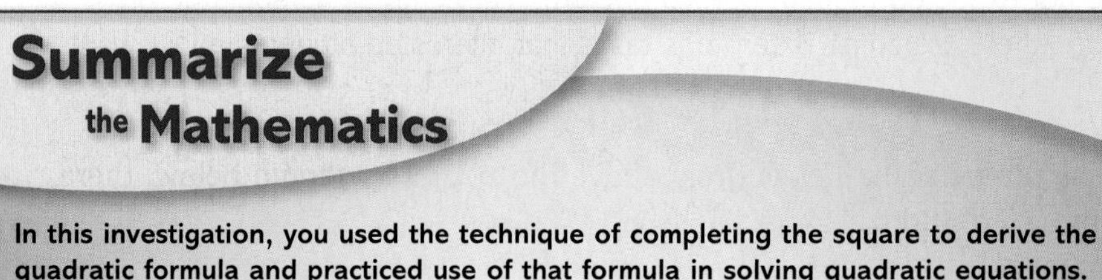

In this investigation, you used the technique of completing the square to derive the quadratic formula and practiced use of that formula in solving quadratic equations.

a. What is the quadratic formula for solving equations in the form $ax^2 + bx + c = 0$?

b. What does the value of the discriminant $b^2 - 4ac$ tell you about the number and type of solutions to the quadratic equation $ax^2 + bx + c = 0$?

c. How will the graph of $f(x) = ax^2 + bx + c$ tell when the quadratic equation $ax^2 + bx + c = 0$ has 2, 1, or 0 real number solutions? What will the graph tell about the value of the discriminant $b^2 - 4ac$?

Be prepared to explain your ideas to the class.

Check Your Understanding

Use the quadratic formula or other reasoning to solve each of the following equations. If the solutions are real numbers, identify them as integer, noninteger rational, or irrational numbers. Write nonreal complex number solutions in *standard form* $a + bi$.

a. $x^2 - 6x - 7 = 0$

b. $5x^2 - 6x + 2 = 0$

c. $6x^2 - 11x - 10 = 0$

d. $5(x - 3)^2 + 6 = 11$

356 UNIT 5 • Polynomial and Rational Functions

Summarize the Mathematics

a $x = \frac{-b}{2a} + \frac{\sqrt{b^2 - 4ac}}{2a}$ or $x = \frac{-b}{2a} - \frac{\sqrt{b^2 - 4ac}}{2a}$

b If a, b, and c are integers or other rational numbers, there will be rational number solutions if $b^2 - 4ac$ is the square of an integer or rational number. If $b^2 - 4ac$ is not a perfect square integer or rational number, the solutions will be irrational numbers. (The coefficients of a quadratic equation can be any real or complex numbers. However, in many situations, students will encounter only integers or rational numbers as coefficients.)

If $b^2 - 4ac$ is positive, there will be two solutions.
If $b^2 - 4ac$ is equal to zero, there will be one solution.
If $b^2 - 4ac$ is less than zero, there will be two complex solutions.

c If the graph crosses the x-axis, there will be two solutions. If the graph only touches the x-axis, there will be one solution. If the graph never touches the x-axis, there will be no real solutions.

If the graph crosses the x-axis at a rational number, then $b^2 - 4ac$ is a positive perfect square of a rational number. If the graph crosses at a nonrational number, then $b^2 - 4ac$ is a positive number but is not a perfect square of a rational number. If the graph only touches the x-axis, then $b^2 - 4ac = 0$. If the graph never crosses the x-axis, then $b^2 - 4ac$ is negative.

(It is also interesting that $x = \frac{-b}{2a}$ locates the max/min point of the graph of a quadratic, so $\frac{\sqrt{b^2 - 4ac}}{2a}$ tells the distance from that vertex x-coordinate to each of the zero points.)

Teaching Resources

Transparency Master 18.

UNIT 5 *Polynomial and Rational Functions*

Summarize the Mathematics

In this investigation, you used the technique of completing the square to derive the quadratic formula and practiced use of that formula in solving quadratic equations.

a What is the quadratic formula for solving equations in the form $ax^2 + bx + c = 0$?

b What does the value of the discriminant $b^2 - 4ac$ tell you about the number and type of solutions to the quadratic equation $ax^2 + bx + c = 0$?

c How will the graph of $f(x) = ax^2 + bx + c$ tell when the quadratic equation $ax^2 + bx + c = 0$ has 2, 1, or 0 real number solutions? What will the graph tell about the value of the discriminant $b^2 - 4ac$?

Be prepared to explain your ideas to the class.

Unit 5

MATH TOOLKIT
Record the quadratic formula. Provide an example of a quadratic equation that has no real solutions. Solve this equation over the complex number system.

Check Your Understanding

a. $x = 7$ or $x = -1$ (integers)

b. $x = \frac{3}{5} \pm \frac{1}{5}i$ (complex number)

c. $x = \frac{5}{2}$ or $x = \frac{-2}{3}$ (rational number)

d. $x = 4$ or $x = 2$ (integers)

On Your Own

Unit 5

Applications

1 Find coordinates of the max/min points, x-intercepts, and y-intercepts on graphs of these functions.

a. $f(x) = (x + 2)^2 - 9$

b. $g(x) = -(x - 2)^2 + 3$

c. $h(x) = (x - 5)^2 - 2$

d. $j(n) = (n + 7)^2 + 4$

2 In a *Punkin' Chunkin'* contest, the height (in feet) of shots from one pumpkin cannon is given by the function $h(t) = -16(t - 5)^2 + 425$. The height is in feet above the ground and the time is in seconds after the pumpkin leaves the cannon. Show how to use this function to answer questions about the height of the flying pumpkin.

a. At what height is the pumpkin released from the "chunker"?

b. At what time will the pumpkin hit the ground?

c. At what time does the pumpkin reach its maximum height and what is that height?

3 Consider the collection of squares and rectangles shown here.

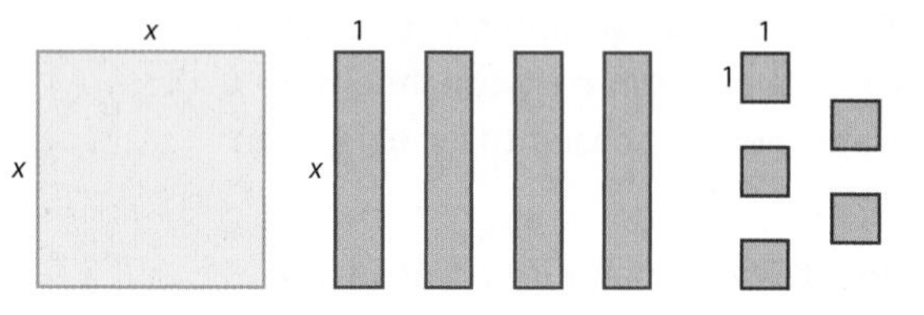

The four rectangles are congruent to each other, as are the five small squares.

a. What expression represents the total area of the ten figures?

b. Explain why the given shapes cannot be arranged to form a larger square without overlaps or gaps.

c. What is the minimal addition or subtraction of unit squares that will make it possible to arrange the new set of pieces to form a larger square?

d. Write an expression involving a binomial square to represent the area of the larger square formed by all the given pieces and the unit squares added or subtracted in Part c.

LESSON 2 • Quadratic Polynomials 357

On Your Own

Applications

1. **a.** Minimum point: $(-2, -9)$
   x-intercepts: $(-5, 0)$ and $(1, 0)$
   y-intercept: $(0, -5)$

   b. Maximum point: $(2, 3)$
   x-intercepts: $(2 \pm \sqrt{3}, 0)$
   y-intercept: $(0, -1)$

   c. Minimum point: $(5, -2)$
   x-intercepts: $(5 \pm \sqrt{2}, 0)$
   y-intercept: $(0, 23)$

   d. Minimum point: $(-7, 4)$
   x-intercepts: none
   y-intercept: $(0, 53)$

2. **a.** The pumpkin is released at a height of 25 feet. $h(0) = 25$

   b. The pumpkin hits the ground approximately 10.15 seconds after it is released. $-16(t - 5)^2 + 425 = 0$ at about 10.15 seconds.

   c. The maximum height of 425 feet is reached after 5 seconds.

3. **a.** $x^2 + 4x + 5$

   b. A square of side length $x + 2$ can be covered completely, yet one unit square will remain unused.

   c. If one unit square is subtracted, the pieces will exactly cover the square.

   d. $x^2 + 4x + 5 = (x + 2)^2 + 1$

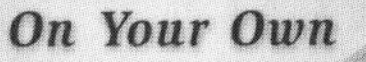

On Your Own

4 For each function, write the rule in vertex form and find coordinates of the max/min point on its graph.

a. $f(x) = x^2 + 12x + 11$ **b.** $g(x) = x^2 - 4x + 7$

c. $h(x) = x^2 - 18x + 74$ **d.** $j(s) = s^2 + 2s + 5$

5 Use the results of Task 4 to solve each of these equations.

a. $x^2 + 12x + 11 = 0$ **b.** $x^2 - 4x + 7 = 19$

c. $x^2 - 18x + 74 = 13$ **d.** $s^2 + 2s + 5 = 53$

6 Use the quadratic formula to solve each of these equations. If the solutions are real numbers, identify them as integer, noninteger rational, or irrational numbers. Write nonreal complex number solutions in standard form $a + bi$.

a. $2x^2 + 3x - 5 = 0$ **b.** $2x^2 + x - 3 = 0$

c. $3x^2 + x = 10$ **d.** $5x + x^2 + 10 = 0$

e. $x^2 + 9x - 10 = -24$ **f.** $3x^2 + 10 = 25$

7 Recall what you learned in Lesson 1 about factors of polynomials and zeroes of the corresponding polynomial functions. Use that knowledge to write quadratic equations in the form $ax^2 + bx + c = 0$ with two distinct solutions that:

a. are both integers.

b. include at least one fraction.

c. are both irrational numbers.

8 Use your knowledge of the quadratic formula to write quadratic equations with the indicated solutions.

a. exactly one real number solution

b. solutions that are complex numbers in the form $a + bi$, $a \neq 0, b \neq 0$

c. solutions that are imaginary numbers bi

9 The functions $I(x) = -25x^2 + 500x + 7{,}500$ and $E(x) = 7{,}000 - 200x$ give income and operating expenses as functions of average ticket price for a music concert. Use the quadratic formula to solve the equation $-25x^2 + 500x + 7{,}500 = 7{,}000 - 200x$ and find the ticket price(s) that will allow the promoters to break even on the event. That is, find the average ticket price that will make income equal to operating expenses.

358 UNIT 5 • Polynomial and Rational Functions

4 **a.** $f(x) = (x + 6)^2 - 25$
Minimum point: $(-6, -25)$

b. $g(x) = (x - 2)^2 + 3$
Minimum point: $(2, 3)$

c. $h(x) = (x - 9)^2 - 7$
Minimum point: $(9, -7)$

d. $j(s) = (s + 1)^2 + 4$
Minimum point: $(-1, 4)$

5 **a.** $(x + 6)^2 - 25 = 0$
$x + 6 = \pm\sqrt{25}$
$x = -6 \pm 5$
$x = -1$ or $x = -11$

b. $(x - 2)^2 + 3 = 19$
$x - 2 = \pm\sqrt{16}$
$x = 2 \pm 4$
$x = 6$ or $x = -2$

c. $(x - 9)^2 - 7 = 13$
$x - 9 = \pm\sqrt{20}$
$x = 9 \pm \sqrt{20}$

d. $(s + 1)^2 + 4 = 53$
$s + 1 = \pm\sqrt{49}$
$s = 6$ or $s = -8$

6 **a.** $x = 1, x = -\frac{5}{2}$; rational

b. $x = 1, x = -\frac{3}{2}$; rational

c. $x = \frac{5}{3}, x = -2$; rational

d. $x = \frac{-5}{2} \pm \frac{\sqrt{15}}{2}i$; complex

e. $x = -2, x = -7$; integer

f. $x = \pm\sqrt{5}$; irrational

7 Answers will vary. Examples are given below.

a. $x^2 + 10x + 24 = 0$

b. $2x^2 + 3x - 5 = 0$

c. $x^2 - 5 = 0$

8 Student-developed equations will vary.

a. The discriminant should be 0.

b. The quadratic should be in the form $mx^2 + nx + p$ with $n \neq 0$ and $n^2 - 4mp < 0$.

c. The quadratic should be in the form $mx^2 + nx + p$ with $n = 0$ and $n^2 - 4mp < 0$.

9 The ticket prices where the promoters will break even are at approximately −\$0.70 and \$28.70. Only the \$28.70 makes sense in this situation.

INSTRUCTIONAL NOTE
Task 9 offers an opportunity to use a common factor to lower the coefficients and make application of the quadratic formula easier.

Connections

10 There is a useful connection between the completing the square technique and coordinate equations for circles.

a. What are the center and radius for the circle with coordinate equation $(x - 5)^2 + (y - 7)^2 = 9$?

b. What are the center and radius for the circle with coordinate equation $(x + 5)^2 + (y + 7)^2 = 4$?

c. Write the equation in Part a without parentheses in the form $x^2 + y^2 + ax + by + c = 0$.

d. Write the equation in Part b without parentheses in the form $x^2 + y^2 + ax + by + c = 0$.

e. Use what you know about completing the square to write each of the following equations in a form that gives the center and radius of the circle. State the center and radius.

i. $x^2 + y^2 - 4x - 8y + 19 = 0$

ii. $x^2 + y^2 + 10x + 2y - 10 = 0$

iii. $x^2 + y^2 + 4y - 45 = 0$

iv. $x^2 + y^2 - 8x + 6y = 0$

11 Sketch graphs of these quadratic functions. Explain how the collection of graphs show that quadratic equations can have: (1) two real number solutions, (2) one repeated real number solution, or (3) no real number solutions.

a. $f(x) = x^2 - 4x - 5$

b. $g(x) = x^2 - 4x + 4$

c. $h(x) = x^2 - 4x + 6$

12 Solve each of these equations. Then compare the forms of the given equations and the procedures used to solve them.

a. $3m + 12 = 27$

b. $\begin{bmatrix} 3 & 1 \\ 5 & 2 \end{bmatrix} \begin{bmatrix} x \\ y \end{bmatrix} + \begin{bmatrix} 2 \\ 5 \end{bmatrix} = \begin{bmatrix} 4 \\ 7 \end{bmatrix}$

c. $3n^2 + 12 = 27$

13 The complex number system was constructed in stages that began with the set **W** of whole numbers {0, 1, 2, 3, 4, ... } and gradually introduced other important sets of numbers. Make a Venn diagram that illustrates the relationship among the following sets of numbers: whole numbers, integers, rational numbers, irrational numbers, real numbers, imaginary numbers, and complex numbers.

Connections

10 **a.** Center (5, 7); radius 3

b. Center (−5, −7); radius 2

c. $x^2 + y^2 + (-10)x + (-14)y + 65 = 0$

d. $x^2 + y^2 + 10x + 14y + 70 = 0$

e. **i.** $(x - 2)^2 + (y - 4)^2 = 1$
Center (2, 4); radius 1

ii. $(x + 5)^2 + (y + 1)^2 = 36$
Center (−5, −1); radius 6

iii. $x^2 + (y + 2)^2 = 49$
Center (0, −2); radius 7

iv. $(x - 4)^2 + (y + 3)^2 = 25$
Center (4, −3); radius 5

For the circle, the basic formula is $x^2 + y^2 = r^2$. This is justified by the Pythagorean Theorem or the distance formula because it says that the distance from any point on the circle to the origin (0, 0) is r. Moving the circle to the center (h, k) gives the formula $(x - h)^2 + (y - k)^2 = r^2$ because this equation says that the distance from any point (x, y) to the center (h, k) is r.

SCOPE AND SEQUENCE
The fact that $x - h$ represents moving to the right is always difficult for students. It will be tackled more patiently and thoroughly in *Families of Functions* in Course 4.

11 **a.** This graph shows how quadratic equations can have two solutions since it intersects the x-axis in two places.

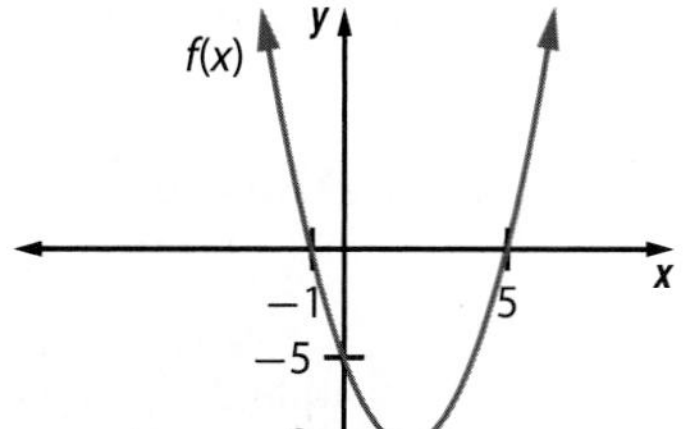

b. This graph shows how quadratic equations can have one repeated solution since it only touches the x-axis in one place.

c. This graph shows how quadratic equations can have only complex solutions since it never touches the x-axis.

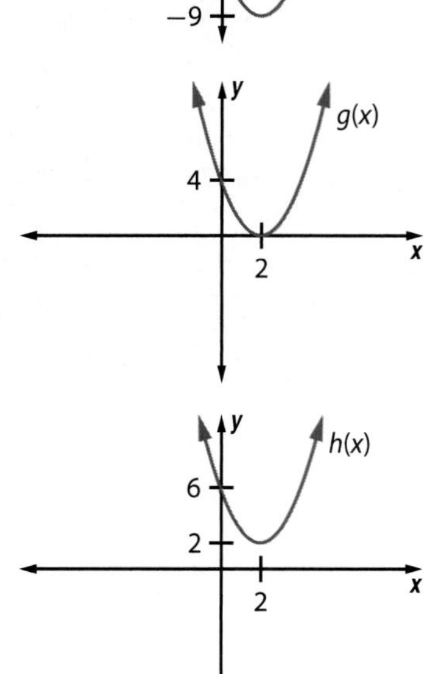

INSTRUCTIONAL NOTE
This task has been designed to highlight the similar structures and solution procedures in three quite different settings. All three have the general structure $AX + B = C$, and the solution approach is quite similar in all three.

12 **a.** $m = 5$
This equation can be solved by subtracting 12 from both sides and dividing each side by 3 since it is a linear equation in one variable.

b. $x = 2,\ y = -4$

$$\begin{bmatrix} 3 & 1 \\ 5 & 2 \end{bmatrix}\begin{bmatrix} x \\ y \end{bmatrix} + \begin{bmatrix} x \\ y \end{bmatrix}\begin{bmatrix} 2 \\ 5 \end{bmatrix} = \begin{bmatrix} 4 \\ 7 \end{bmatrix}$$

$$\begin{bmatrix} 3 & 1 \\ 5 & 2 \end{bmatrix}\begin{bmatrix} x \\ y \end{bmatrix} = \begin{bmatrix} 2 \\ 2 \end{bmatrix}$$

$$\begin{bmatrix} 3 & 1 \\ 5 & 2 \end{bmatrix}^{-1}\begin{bmatrix} 3 & 1 \\ 5 & 2 \end{bmatrix}\begin{bmatrix} x \\ y \end{bmatrix} = \begin{bmatrix} 3 & 1 \\ 5 & 2 \end{bmatrix}^{-1}\begin{bmatrix} 2 \\ 2 \end{bmatrix}$$

$$\begin{bmatrix} 1 & 0 \\ 0 & 1 \end{bmatrix}\begin{bmatrix} x \\ y \end{bmatrix} = \begin{bmatrix} 2 \\ -4 \end{bmatrix}$$

The form of this equation is $AX + B = C$ where A, B, and C are matrices. The multiplicative inverse of A is A^{-1}, so $X = A^{-1}[C - B]$. Recall that A^{-1} must be on the left of $[C - B]$.

c. $n = \pm\sqrt{5}$
Since this is a quadratic equation in one variable with no linear term, 12 is subtracted from each side, each side is divided by 3, and the equation is solved for n. Alternatively, the quadratic formula could be used, but that would disguise the similarity to Part a. This procedure has one more step than the procedure in Part a, taking the square root of both sides of the equation.

13

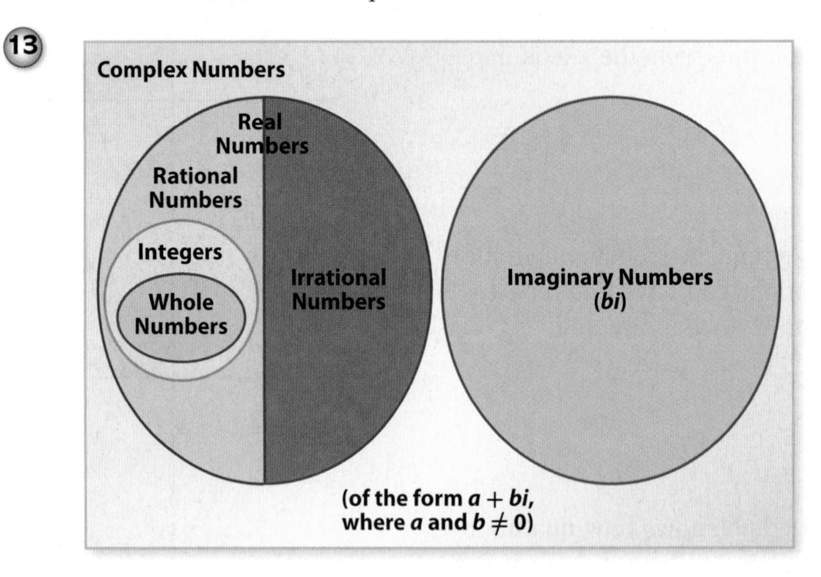

Teacher Notes

On Your Own

14. Each complex number can be represented in the form $a + bi$, where a and b are real numbers and i represents the imaginary $\sqrt{-1}$. At the turn of the 19th century, three different mathematicians, Caspar Wessel (1797), Jean Robert Argand (1806), and Carl Friedrich Gauss (1811), suggested that the complex numbers could be represented by points on a coordinate plane. The complex number $a + bi$ would correspond to the point with coordinates (a, b).

   a. On a single coordinate diagram, locate and label points corresponding to these complex numbers.

   $4 + 2i \qquad -2 + 3i \qquad -4 - 3i \qquad 2 - 3i$

   b. Use of commutative and associative properties of addition and combining "like terms" suggests a rule for addition of complex numbers, $(a + bi) + (c + di) = (a + c) + (b + d)i$. Use this rule to add the complex number $3 + 2i$ to each of the numbers in Part a.

   c. Using a second color, plot and label the points corresponding to your results in Part b. Then identify the geometric transformation that is accomplished by adding $3 + 2i$ to every complex number $a + bi$.

Reflections

15. When one student was asked to solve the quadratic equation $2x^2 + 12x = 5$, he wrote the factored form $2x(x + 6) = 5$ and concluded that the solutions are $x = 0$ and $x = -6$. What is the probable error in his thinking that led him to those incorrect answers?

16. You now know three different ways to express quadratic polynomials in equivalent forms—standard form, factored form, and vertex form.

   a. What do you see as the advantages of each form?

   b. Do you think that the value added by use of each different form is equal to the effort involved in transforming the original expression to a new form?

17. The creative team of *Conklin Brothers Circus* designed a cannon to shoot a human cannonball across the arenas where they operate. They judged that the height of the "cannonball" would be a quadratic function of time and wrote three different rules for the function (time in seconds and height in feet).

$$h(t) = -16t^2 + 32t + 48$$
$$h(t) = -16(t + 1)(t - 3)$$
$$h(t) = -16(t - 1)^2 + 64$$

   a. In what different ways could you convince yourself or others that the three different rules are mathematically equivalent?

360 UNIT 5 • Polynomial and Rational Functions

Unit 5

14 **a.**

$-2 + 3i$ | $4 + 2i$ | $-4 - 3i$ | $2 - 3i$

b. The parentheses can be removed to obtain $a + bi + c + di$. The middle two terms can be reordered by the Commutative Property of Addition to obtain $a + c + bi + di$. Parentheses can be reinserted to obtain $(a + c) + (bi + di)$. Finally, the distributive property can be applied to find $(a + c) + (b + d)i$.

$(4 + 2i) + (3 + 2i) = 7 + 4i$
$(-2 + 3i) + (3 + 2i) = 1 + 5i$
$(-4 - 3i) + (3 + 2i) = -1 - i$
$(2 - 3i) + (3 + 2i) = 5 - i$

c. Each original point has been shifted right 3 units and up 2 units to obtain the new points. This is a translation of the plane.

Reflections

15 The student is most likely very used to seeing quadratic equations in the form $ax^2 + bx + c = 0$ and did not notice or realize the significance of the difference when one side is not zero.

16 Student responses will vary.

a. They should comment on which basic pieces of information (zeroes, y-intercept, max/min points) can be obtained readily from each form. Some, like zeroes, are easiest to read from factored form. Some, like max/min points, are easiest to read from vertex form. Some, like y-intercepts, are easiest to read from standard form.

b. Students may think that the difficulty of transforming a standard quadratic form to factored or vertex form makes that work less than attractive, particularly if they can use technology to find the vertex of the quadratic function graph.

17 **a.** Student responses will vary but could include converting all forms of the function to standard form, comparing zeroes and y-intercepts, or converting all forms to vertex form. They might also create graphs and tables of all three forms and see whether or not they overlap each other. Of course, this is not a mathematically decisive strategy.

b. Which of the rules would be most helpful in answering each of these questions?

i. What is the maximum height of the "cannonball" and when will it occur in the flight?

ii. When would the "cannonball" hit the ground if the net collapsed while the flight was underway?

iii. At what height does the "cannonball" leave the end of the cannon?

18 How do you decide on an approach to solving a quadratic equation? What conditions influence your strategy choice in various situations?

19 One solution of a quadratic equation $ax^2 + bx + c = 0$ is $2 + 3i$. What is the other solution? Explain your reasoning.

Extensions

20 Of the two algebraic operations, expanding a product of linear factors is generally much easier than factoring a standard form quadratic. To understand factoring, you have to develop some skill in expanding products and in reversing that process.

Use algebraic reasoning to write each of these products in standard expanded form. Then check your results by using a CAS for the same work.

a. $(x + 4)(3x + 1)$

b. $(2x + 4)(x + 3)$

c. $(2x - 4)(5x + 3)$

d. $(x - 7)^2$

e. $(3x + 4)^2$

f. $(2x - 5)^2$

21 Use your experience in Task 20 to solve these quadratic equations by first writing the quadratic expression in equivalent form as a product of two linear factors.

a. $2x^2 + 7x + 3 = 0$

b. $5x^2 + 16x + 3 = 0$

c. $5x^2 + 17x = -6$

d. $6x^2 + 19x + 15 = 0$

e. $4x^2 - 12x + 9 = 0$

f. $9x^2 + 6x + 1 = 0$

22 Solve each of the following equations using factoring, where possible. Use a CAS to check your work.

a. $4x^2 + 12x + 9 = 0$

b. $9x^2 + 30x + 25 = 0$

c. $7x^2 - 18x + 11 = 0$

d. $9x^2 - 12x = -4$

e. $4x^2 + 10x + \frac{25}{4} = 0$

f. $4x^2 - 6x + \frac{9}{4} = 0$

b. **i.** The third rule is most helpful. The maximum height is 64 feet and will occur after one second.

ii. The second rule is most helpful. The cannonball would hit the ground after three seconds. (−1 second does not make sense here.)

iii. The first rule is most helpful. It leaves the cannon at a height of 48 feet.

18 Student answers will vary. They might comment on the pattern of coefficients and whether or not it reveals immediately how to factor or complete the square of a given standard form quadratic.

19 The other solution is $2 - 3i$. This must be true because the quadratic formula would give two complex number solutions from the discriminant.

Extensions

20 **a.** $3x^2 + 13x + 4$

b. $2x^2 + 10x + 12$

c. $10x^2 - 14x - 12$

d. $x^2 - 14x + 49$

e. $9x^2 + 24x + 16$

f. $4x^2 - 20x + 25$

21 **a.** $(2x + 1)(x + 3) = 0$

$x = -\frac{1}{2}$ or $x = -3$

b. $(5x + 1)(x + 3) = 0$

$x = -\frac{1}{5}$ or $x = -3$

c. $(5x + 2)(x + 3) = 0$

$x = -\frac{2}{5}$ or $x = -3$

d. $(2x + 3)(3x + 5) = 0$

$x = -\frac{3}{2}$ or $x = -\frac{5}{3}$

e. $(2x - 3)^2 = 0$

$x = \frac{3}{2}$

f. $(3x + 1)^2 = 0$

$x = -\frac{1}{3}$

22 **a.** $(2x + 3)^2 = 0$

$x = -\frac{3}{2}$

b. $(3x + 5)^2 = 0$

$x = -\frac{5}{3}$

c. $(7x - 11)(x - 1) = 0$

$x = \frac{11}{7}$ or $x = 1$

d. $(3x - 2)^2 = 0$

$x = \frac{2}{3}$

e. $\left(2x + \frac{5}{2}\right)^2 = 0$

$x = -\frac{5}{4}$

f. $\left(2x - \frac{3}{2}\right)^2 = 0$

$x = \frac{3}{4}$

On Your Own

23 When $a \neq 1$, quadratic functions in the form $f(x) = ax^2 + bx + c$ can still be transformed to equivalent vertex forms like $f(x) = m(x \pm n)^2 \pm d$.

a. Study the following example. Explain the choice of adding and subtracting 18 in two parts of the quadratic polynomial.

$$\begin{aligned} f(x) &= 2x^2 + 12x + 14 \\ &= 2(x^2 + 6x + \_\_) + 14 \\ &= 2(x^2 + 6x + 9) - 18 + 14 \\ &= 2(x + 3)^2 - 4 \end{aligned}$$

b. Use similar reasoning to write each function rule below in vertex form.

i. $f(x) = 3x^2 + 12x + 15$

ii. $g(x) = 5x^2 + 30x + 50$

iii. $h(x) = 2x^2 - 8x + 10$

iv. $j(x) = 4x^2 - 20x + 7$

c. How do the results of your work in Part b suggest a strategy for writing any quadratic function $f(x) = ax^2 + bx + c$ in equivalent vertex form $f(x) = m(x \pm n)^2 \pm d$?

24 Use the Factor Theorem (Extensions Task 20 in Lesson 1) to help explain why a cubic polynomial function has either zero or two nonreal complex number solutions.

25 Consider the ways that it would make sense to multiply complex numbers like $(3 + 2i)$ and $(4 + 7i)$.

a. If you think of the given complex numbers as linear expressions like $(3 + 2x)$ and $(4 + 7x)$, what would the product look like when expanded?

b. Because the letter i is the number for which $i^2 = -1$, the expression in Part a can be simplified. Write the product $(3 + 2i)(4 + 7i)$ in standard complex number form.

Review

26 Express each of these sums and differences as single fractions in simplest form.

a. $\frac{1}{3} + \frac{1}{6}$

b. $\frac{1}{2} - \frac{1}{8}$

c. $\frac{1}{4} + \frac{1}{3}$

d. $\frac{2}{3} - \frac{1}{2}$

e. $\frac{a}{b} + \frac{c}{d}$

Unit 5

362 UNIT 5 • Polynomial and Rational Functions

23 **a.** We need to add 9 to make $x^2 + 6x + \_\_$ a perfect square $(x + 3)^2$. Since $(x + 3)^2$ is multiplied by 2, 18 is added to the expression and so 18 must be subtracted to produce an expression equivalent to the original.

b. **i.** $f(x) = 3(x + 2)^2 + 3$

ii. $g(x) = 5(x + 3)^2 + 5$

iii. $h(x) = 2(x - 2)^2 + 2$

iv. $j(x) = 4\left(x - \frac{5}{2}\right)^2 - 18$

c. $ax^2 + bx + c = a\left(x + \frac{b}{2a}\right)^2 - \left(\frac{b^2 - 4ac}{4a}\right)$

24 A cubic function $f(x)$ has at least one real zero a since the end behavior is in opposite directions. So, $f(x) = (x - a)q(x)$. The function $q(x)$ is a quadratic function since its degree is two. So, $q(x)$ has two real solutions (or one duplicate solution) when $b^2 - 4ac \geq 0$. If $b^2 - 4ac < 0$, then there are two nonreal complex solutions, $\frac{-b}{2a} \pm \frac{\sqrt{b^2 - 4ac}}{2a}$.

25 **a.** The product would look like a quadratic polynomial $(12 + 29i + 14i^2)$.

b. $12 + 29i + 14i^2 = 12 + 29i + 14(-1) = -2 + 29i$.

Review

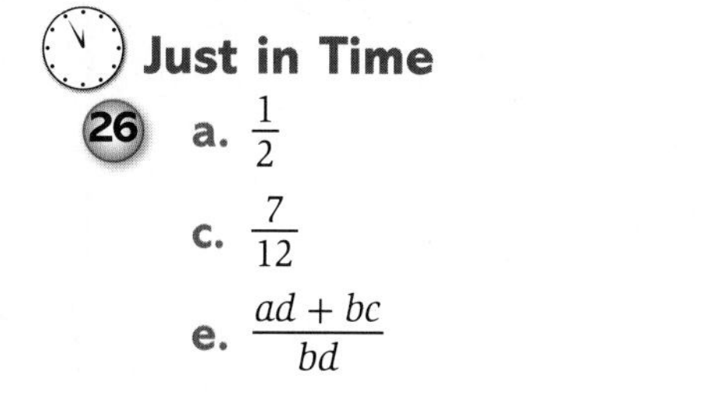

Just in Time

26 **a.** $\frac{1}{2}$

b. $\frac{3}{8}$

c. $\frac{7}{12}$

d. $\frac{1}{6}$

e. $\frac{ad + bc}{bd}$

Unit 5

27 Consider the following numbers.

$$\sqrt{100} \quad \frac{12}{5} \quad -5 \quad 2.2 \quad \sqrt{5}$$

$$\pi \quad 3.\overline{1} \quad \frac{1}{6} \quad \sqrt{2.25} \quad \sqrt[3]{27}$$

a. Which of the listed numbers are integers?

b. Which of the listed numbers are rational numbers?

c. Which of the listed numbers are irrational numbers?

d. Place the numbers in order from smallest to largest.

28 Find equivalent expanded forms for these expressions. Then use a CAS to check your reasoning. (*Remember*: The algebraic product mx must generally be entered as **m*x** in a CAS.)

a. $(x + n)^2$

b. $(mx + n)^2$

c. $(x + n)(x - n)$

d. $(mx + n)(mx - n)$

29 In the diagram at the right, $\overleftrightarrow{AB} \parallel \overleftrightarrow{DE}$.

a. Prove that $\triangle ABC \sim \triangle DEC$.

b. Find the lengths of $\overline{AC}$ and $\overline{DE}$.

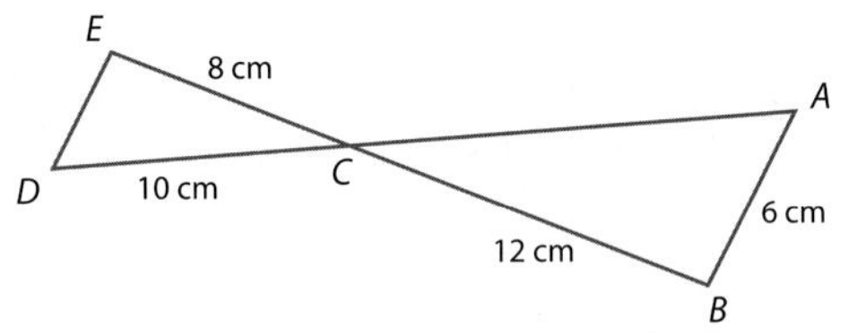

30 Without using a graphing calculator or a computer graphing tool, sketch a graph of each power function. Then check your ideas using technology.

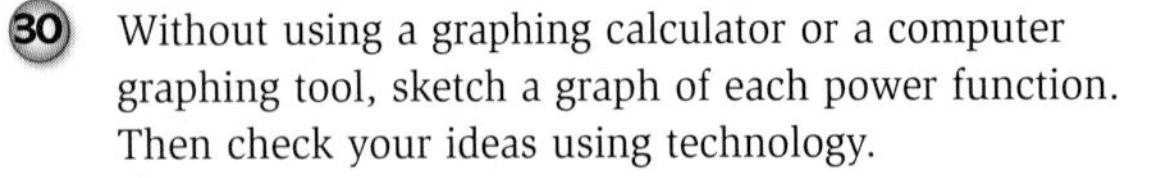

$$f(x) = \frac{3}{x} \qquad g(x) = \frac{3}{x^2}$$

a. What is the domain of $f(x)$? Of $g(x)$?

b. What is the range of $f(x)$? Of $g(x)$?

c. Describe the behavior of the graph of $f(x)$ as $|x|$ gets very large. As $|x|$ gets very small.

d. Describe the behavior of the graph of $g(x)$ as $|x|$ gets very large. As $|x|$ gets very small.

31 Simplify each algebraic expression.

a. $\frac{6x - 10}{2}$ **b.** $\frac{24 - 3x}{3}$ **c.** $\frac{x - 4}{x - 4}$

32 Consider the diagram below. Point P is on the terminal side of an angle θ in standard position. Find $\sin \theta$, $\cos \theta$, and $\tan \theta$.

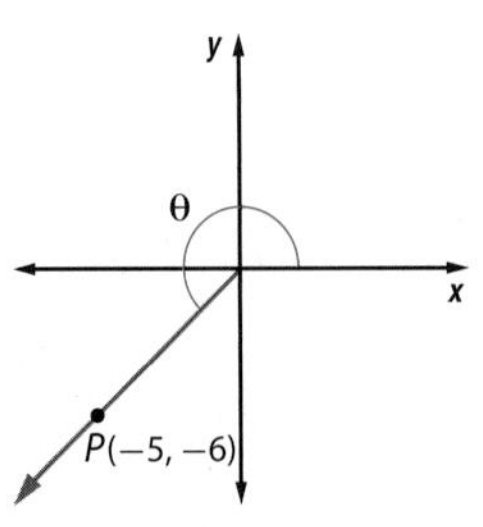

Just in Time

27 **a.** $\sqrt{100}, -5, \sqrt[3]{27}$

b. $\sqrt{100}, \frac{12}{5}, -5, 2.2, 3.\overline{1}, \frac{1}{6}, \sqrt{2.25}, \sqrt[3]{27}$

c. $\pi, \sqrt{5}$

d. $-5, \frac{1}{6}, \sqrt{2.25}, 2.2, \sqrt{5}, \frac{12}{5}, \sqrt[3]{27}, 3.\overline{1}, \pi, \sqrt{100}$

28 **a.** $x^2 + 2nx + n^2$ **b.** $m^2x^2 + 2mnx + n^2$

c. $x^2 - n^2$ **d.** $m^2x^2 - n^2$

29 **a.** Since $\overleftrightarrow{AB} \parallel \overleftrightarrow{DE}$, $\angle A \cong \angle D$ and $\angle B \cong \angle E$ by the Alternate Interior Angle Theorem. Thus, $\triangle ABC \sim \triangle DEC$ by the AA Similarity Theorem.

b. $\triangle ABC \sim \triangle DEC$ with a scale factor of $\frac{12}{8} = \frac{3}{2}$.

$\frac{AC}{DC} = \frac{AC}{10} = \frac{3}{2}$

$AC = 15$ cm

$\frac{AB}{DE} = \frac{6}{DE} = \frac{3}{2}$

$DE = 4$ cm

Just in Time

30

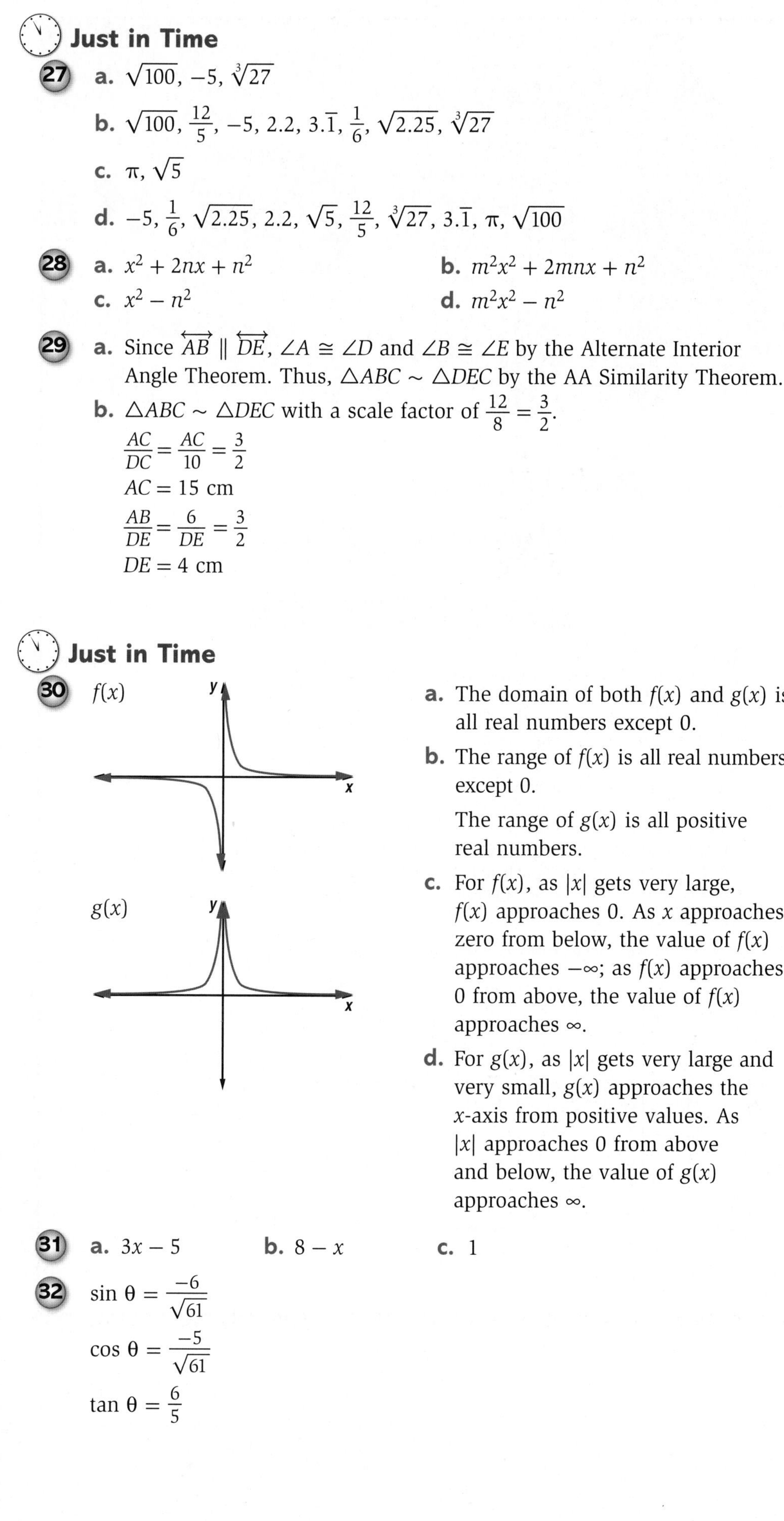

a. The domain of both $f(x)$ and $g(x)$ is all real numbers except 0.

b. The range of $f(x)$ is all real numbers except 0.

The range of $g(x)$ is all positive real numbers.

c. For $f(x)$, as $|x|$ gets very large, $f(x)$ approaches 0. As x approaches zero from below, the value of $f(x)$ approaches $-\infty$; as $f(x)$ approaches 0 from above, the value of $f(x)$ approaches ∞.

d. For $g(x)$, as $|x|$ gets very large and very small, $g(x)$ approaches the x-axis from positive values. As $|x|$ approaches 0 from above and below, the value of $g(x)$ approaches ∞.

31 **a.** $3x - 5$ **b.** $8 - x$ **c.** 1

32 $\sin \theta = \frac{-6}{\sqrt{61}}$

$\cos \theta = \frac{-5}{\sqrt{61}}$

$\tan \theta = \frac{6}{5}$

Teaching Resources

Assessment Masters 19–23.

UNIT 5 Polynomial and Rational Functions Name Date

LESSON 2 QUIZ

Form A

1. Consider the collection of squares and rectangles shown below.

a. What polynomial expression is represented by the squares and rectangles above?

b. Rearrange the squares and rectangles to help you write the complete square form of the polynomial expression. Draw your rearrangement below. Then write the complete square form of the polynomial expression. Show or explain your work.

2. Consider the quadratic function $f(x) = x^2 - 10x + 3$. Complete each task by algebraic reasoning alone. Show all of your work to support your answers.

a. Rewrite the function rule in vertex form.

b. Does the graph of this function have a maximum or a minimum? Determine the coordinates of the maximum or minimum point of the graph of this function.

Assessment Master • use after Lesson 2 UNIT 5 • Polynomial and Rational Functions 19

Unit 5

LESSON 3

Rational Expressions and Functions

How valuable is each customer to the bottom line of a business? In Lesson 1 of this unit, you discovered how income, expenses, and profits for a concert were functions of concert ticket price. It is possible to combine those functions to see how the profit from *each* ticket is related to the ticket price, giving a measure of each customer's value to the business.

The profit-per-ticket idea might seem simple, but the resulting function has some surprising properties. For example, if you focus only on income and expenses related to the concert itself (ignoring snack bar operations), the profit-per-ticket function has a graph that looks like the one below.

Profit per Ticket from Ticket Sales

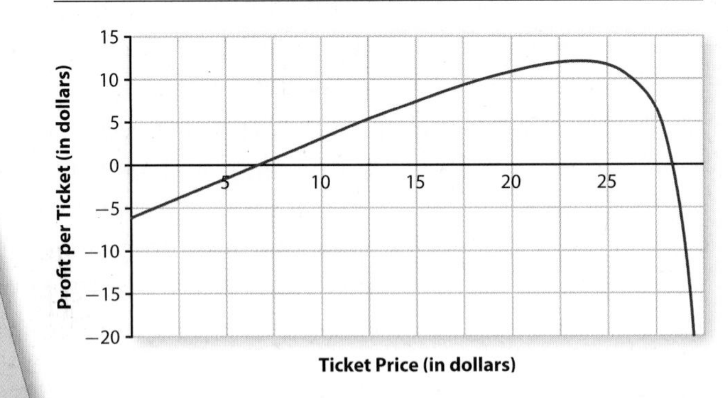

364 UNIT 5 • Polynomial and Rational Functions

Rational Expressions and Functions

LESSON 3

Unit 5

In problem-solving tasks that require comparison of quantities, there are two basic strategies for making those comparisons: subtraction and division. When comparison by division is the strategy that seems most informative in a situation, the resulting quantitative comparison is commonly expressed as a ratio, as a unit rate (e.g., miles per gallon, etc.), or as a percent.

This lesson extends students' prior experience with comparison by division using ratios, rates, and percents to comparison of polynomial functions in the same way. The result in such cases is a new kind of function called a rational function. The algebraic forms that provide rules for those functions are called rational expressions.

Students' prior work in *Core-Plus Mathematics* has given them some background for work with rational functions. In several earlier units, they have encountered inverse variation functions and they have seen the kind of table and graph patterns that arise in analysis of those relationships. In this lesson, students will consider the more complex patterns that occur when there are variable expressions in both numerator and denominator of an algebraic fraction.

The lesson is organized into four investigations. The first introduces students to rational functions as a way of modeling variation in the ratios that are often used to describe operation of a business like profit per customer (ticket), profit as a percent of income, and so on. Students explore the graph possibilities of rational functions, with special focus on vertical asymptotes and the questions about function domain that are connected to that rational function feature.

The second investigation focuses on reasons and techniques for simplifying rational expressions. It includes examples that illustrate common misconceptions students may have when simplifying rational expressions and cautions about changes in domain that can result from "canceling" common factors in numerator and denominator.

The third investigation focuses on addition and subtraction of rational expressions, both with and without a common denominator. In the fourth investigation, students focus on finding and simplifying products and quotients of rational functions.

The topic of algebraic fractions and rational functions is not conceptually or technically simple. This unit should be viewed as an introduction to both the important ideas and basic techniques for dealing with such algebraic tools. More extensive work in this area will occur in Course 4, Unit 1, *Families of Functions* and in Unit 3, *Algebraic Functions and Equations*.

DIFFERENTIATION Because the technical work with algebraic fractions is challenging, you might want to make use of computer algebra system tools for the more complex calculations. The most able students should aim at developing personal skill in manipulation of algebraic fractions. But many other students can still develop core conceptual understandings and use a CAS to perform many of the associated technical calculations.

Lesson Objectives

- Create rational functions to model problem situations
- Analyze graphs of rational functions and their asymptotes
- Simplify rational expressions
- Add, subtract, multiply, and divide rational expressions

CPMP-Tools

Shown below are two different windows that display the rational function students will explore in Investigation 1 of this lesson.

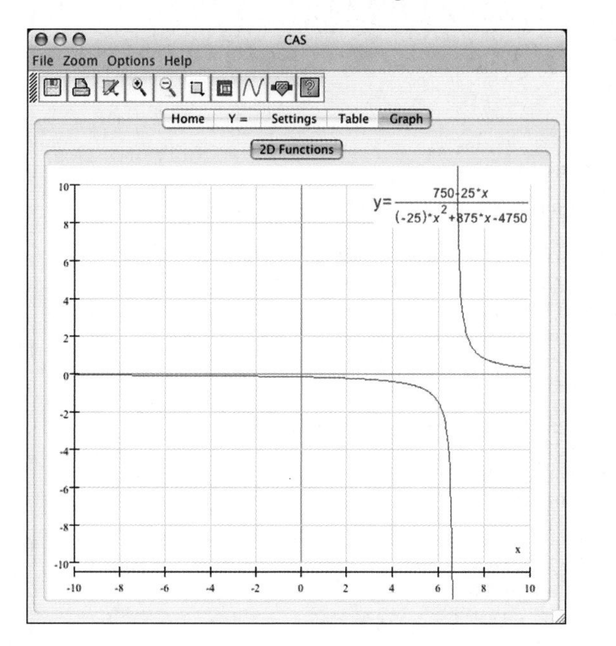

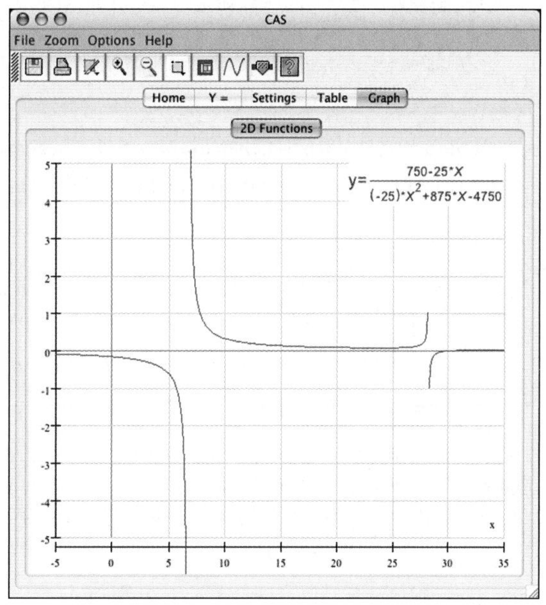

Unit 5

Unit 5

Examine the profit-per-ticket graph on the previous page.

a How would you describe the pattern of change in profit per ticket as ticket prices approach \$30?

b When the ticket price is set at \$15, the business plan predicts that 375 tickets will be sold. Total profit from ticket sales is predicted to be \$2,750. How would you calculate the profit per ticket sold when tickets are \$15? How is your answer shown in the graph?

c How would you find a rule for calculating profit per ticket at any ticket price?

The strange properties of the profit-per-ticket function result from the fact that it is a *rational function*, the quotient of two polynomials. In this lesson, you will explore the family of rational functions and learn how to use them as mathematical models of problem situations. You will learn the connections between rules and graphs for rational functions and how to simplify and combine the expressions in those rules.

Investigation 1 Domains and Graphs of Rational Functions

Information from analysis of the concert business led to the prediction that ticket sales and profit from concert operation alone (not including snack bar operations) would be related to average ticket price x (in dollars) by these rules.

Number of tickets sold: $n(x) = 750 - 25x$
Profit from ticket sales: $P_c(x) = -25x^2 + 875x - 4{,}750$

As you complete the following problems, look for answers to these questions:

How can polynomials like these be combined to give useful rational functions?

What are the important features of rational functions and their graphs?

1 Suppose that the concert promoters want to estimate the profit per ticket for various possible ticket prices.

a. What number of tickets, total profit, and profit per ticket would be expected:

i. if the average ticket price x is \$10?

ii. if the average ticket price x is \$20?

Lesson Launch

Since the notion of comparison by division is central to this entire lesson, it is important that students clearly understand the answers to the TATS questions before proceeding to the investigations. They should be able to connect with earlier experiences in which ratio or rate comparisons have been central.

Think About This Situation

a) The profit-per-ticket decreases sharply (in fact, becoming a loss) as ticket prices approach $30. (Without information about the total profit and number of tickets sold functions, it is not possible to explain why this is happening. That is the question that is pursued at the outset of Investigation 1.)

b) The profit per tickets sold will be calculated by dividing the total profit by the number of tickets sold. For the particular example given, that will be $2,750 \div 375 \approx \$7.33$ profit per tickets sold. From the graph, you find the profit per ticket (*y* value) for a ticket price of $15.

c) Students should suggest finding an expression for the total profit as a function of ticket price and dividing by the expression giving number of tickets sold at any given ticket price.

Teaching Resources

Transparency Master 24.

UNIT 5 *Polynomial and Rational Functions*

Think About This Situation

Examine the profit-per-ticket graph below.

a How would you describe the pattern of change in profit per ticket as ticket prices approach $30?

b When the ticket price is set at $15, the business plan predicts that 375 tickets will be sold. Total profit from ticket sales is predicted to be $2,750. How would you calculate the profit per ticket sold when tickets are $15? How is your answer shown in the graph?

c How would you find a rule for calculating profit per ticket at any ticket price?

Profit per Ticket from Ticket Sales

Profit per Ticket (in dollars)

Ticket Price (in dollars)

24 UNIT 5 • Polynomial and Rational Functions

Unit 5

Investigation 1 Domains and Graphs of Rational Functions

In this investigation, students will begin work with rational functions. Students will analyze situations using quotients of known functions as models of the variation that is involved. Students will also examine features in graphs of rational functions, including vertical asymptotes and the behavior of the rational function near these asymptotes. This graphical analysis is closely related to the consideration of function domain, since vertical asymptotes typically occur when the function in the denominator has a zero and the rational function is undefined.

Launch

You might launch this investigation directly from the TATS by indicating that knowledge of the various functions involved in the situation can be used to write and analyze a new function showing how profit per ticket is related to ticket price. Having an algebraic expression for this function will help in explaining the graph pattern observed in the TATS.

INSTRUCTIONAL NOTE
In the context for this introductory work, we are looking only at income and profit and profit per ticket for the concert itself, ignoring income and expenses for snack bar operation until Investigation 2.

1 **a. i.** 500 tickets will be sold.
The profit will be $1,500.
The profit per ticket will be $3.

ii. 250 tickets will be sold.
The profit will be $2,750.
The profit per ticket will be $11.

b. Write an algebraic rule for the function $R(x)$ giving profit per ticket when the ticket price is x dollars. Express your answer as an algebraic fraction.

A function with rule that is a fraction in which both numerator and denominator are polynomials is called a **rational function**. That is, a function $f(x)$ is a rational function if and only if its rule can be written in the form $f(x) = \frac{p(x)}{q(x)}$, where $p(x)$ and $q(x)$ are polynomial functions.

The profit-per-ticket function $R(x)$ that you developed in Problem 1 is a rational function. Like many other rational functions, its graph has several interesting and important features. To understand those properties, it helps to begin with analysis of the functions that are the numerator and the denominator of $R(x)$.

2 Sketch graphs of $n(x) = 750 - 25x$ and $P_c(x) = -25x^2 + 875x - 4{,}750$. Use the graphs to answer the following questions.

a. What is the practical domain of $n(x)$? That is, what prices x will give predicted numbers of tickets that make sense in the concert situation?

b. Estimate the ticket price for which profit from concert operation $P_c(x)$, excluding snack bar operations, is maximized. Find that profit.

3 Now turn to analysis of the profit-per-ticket function $R(x)$.

a. Graph $R(x)$ for x between 0 and 30.

b. Estimate the ticket price for which profit per ticket is maximized.

c. Why is the profit per ticket not maximized at the same ticket price that maximizes concert profit?

4 Something unusual happens in the graph of $R(x)$ near $x = 30$. Use a calculator or computer software to examine values of $R(x)$ when x is very close to 30, say, between 29 and 31 with increments of 0.1. If using a calculator, use **Dot** rather than **Connected** mode.

a. How does your technology tool respond to requests for $R(30)$? What does the response mean? Why does it make sense in this situation?

b. Describe the pattern of change in values of $R(x)$ as x approaches very close to 30 from below. Explain the trend by referring to the values of $P_c(x)$ and $n(x)$ that are used to calculate $R(x)$.

c. Describe the pattern of change in values for $R(x)$ as x approaches very close to 30 from above. Explain the trend by referring to the values of $P_c(x)$ and $n(x)$ for such x.

d. What is the theoretical domain of $R(x)$?

366 UNIT 5 • Polynomial and Rational Functions

b. $R(x) = \dfrac{-25x^2 + 875x - 4{,}750}{750 - 25x}$

2 **a.** The practical domain of $n(x)$ is $0 < x < 30$ because those are the only prices that give positive numbers of customers.

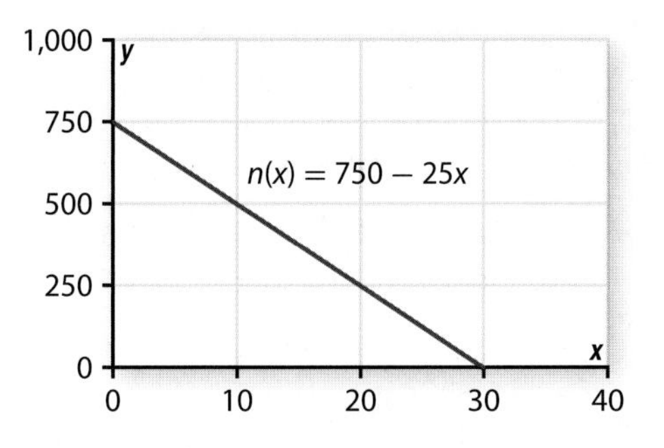

b. The maximum profit of $2,906.25 will occur when ticket prices are set at $17.50.

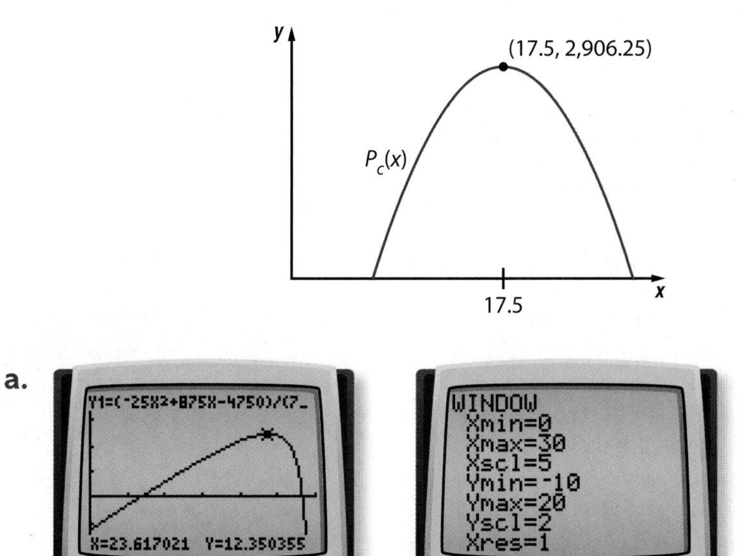

3 **a.**

Y1=(-25X²+875X-4750)/(7_
X=23.617021 Y=12.350355

WINDOW
Xmin=0
Xmax=30
Xscl=5
Ymin=-10
Ymax=20
Yscl=2
Xres=1

b. The profit per ticket reaches a maximum of approximately $12.35 when the ticket price is about $23.68.

c. Student responses will vary but should note that the ticket price for maximum profit per ticket is higher than that for maximum total profit. The higher ticket price means fewer concert customers. It is not unreasonable that the profit per ticket will be large when the number of tickets is small, as long as the concert is still making some positive profit.

NOTE The solution to Problem 4 is on page T367.

Domain and Asymptotes The unusual pattern of values for the profit-per-ticket function at and on either side of $x = 30$ can be explained by analyzing the domain of $R(x)$ and values of the numerator and denominator functions used to define $R(x)$. That is the sort of analysis required to understand any rational function and its graph.

5. Study this graph of the rational function $f(x) = \frac{x - 1}{x^2 - 2x - 3}$.

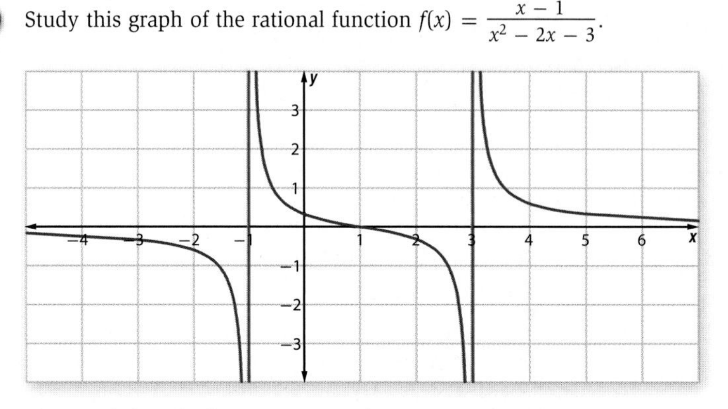

The graph has the lines $x = -1$ and $x = 3$ as **vertical asymptotes**. As values of x approach -1 from below, the graph suggests that values of $f(x)$ decrease without lower bound. As values of x approach -1 from above, the graph suggests that values of $f(x)$ increase without upper bound.

Describe the pattern of change in function values as x approaches 3.

6. Inspect values of $f(x) = \frac{x - 1}{x^2 - 2x - 3}$ in terms of values of the numerator $(x - 1)$ and values of the denominator $(x^2 - 2x - 3)$ to help answer these questions about the function and its graph.

a. How could you have located the x-intercept of the graph by examining the rational expression that defines $f(x)$?

b. How could you have located the two vertical asymptotes of the graph by studying the rational expression that defines $f(x)$?

c. What is the domain of $f(x)$—for what values of x can a value of $f(x)$ be calculated and for what values is it impossible to calculate $f(x)$? Explain how your answer to that question is related to your answer to the question in Part b.

d. The graph of $f(x)$ has the x-axis as a **horizontal asymptote**. As values of x decrease without lower bound and increase without upper bound, the graph of $f(x)$ gets closer and closer to the x-axis but never reaches it. How could you have located that horizontal asymptote of the graph by studying the rational expression that defines $f(x)$?

4 **a.** The table should display an error message for $R(30)$. This occurs because no tickets are sold when the ticket price is \$30 and division by zero is undefined.

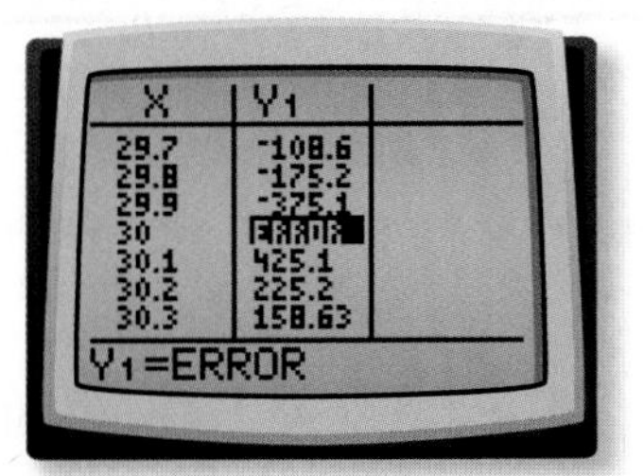

b. As x approaches 30 from below, the profit $P_c(x)$ becomes negative (at $x \approx 28$) and the number of tickets sold $n(x)$ becomes very small and positive. Therefore, $R(x)$ will be a very "large negative" number.

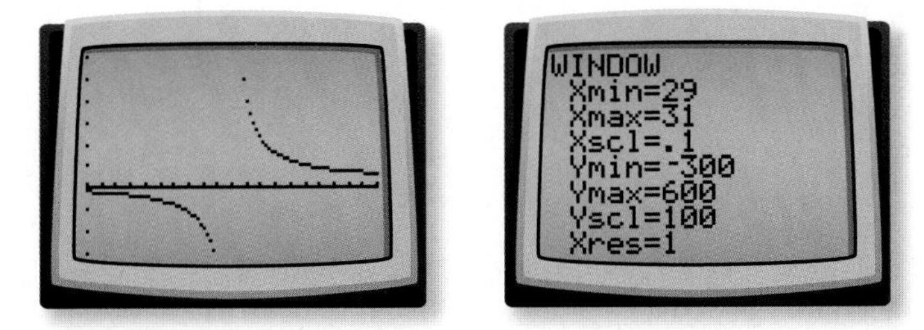

c. As x approaches 30 from above, the profit $P_c(x)$ remains negative and continues to decrease. However, $n(x)$ is also negative and decreasing but at a slower rate than $P_c(x)$. Therefore, $R(x)$ will approach positive infinity. (Technically, the values above $x = 30$ are not in the practical domain.)

d. The theoretical domain is all real numbers except 30.

5 As values of x approach 3 from below 3, the function values decrease rapidly approaching negative infinity. As values of x approach 3 from above 3, the function values approach positive infinity.

6 **a.** A fraction is zero when its numerator is zero (and the denominator is nonzero). In this case, $x - 1 = 0$ when $x = 1$.

b. Vertical asymptotes occur when the denominator of a fraction approaches 0 and the numerator approaches some finite value. The zeroes of the denominator in this case are $x = -1$ and 3.

c. The function rule defines a value for $f(x)$ except when the denominator is zero. That is, except when $x = -1$ or 3.

d. The horizontal asymptote can be recognized by realizing that as $|x| \rightarrow \infty$, the denominator of $f(x)$ grows in absolute value more rapidly than the numerator, since the denominator is a quadratic function and the numerator is a linear function. Thus, when calculating $f(x)$ for values such as $\pm 1{,}000$, the fraction decreases in absolute value approaching zero.

TECHNOLOGY NOTE
Again encourage students to use the **Dot** mode on calculators since the **Connected** mode gives an incorrect display of the function, appearing to produce values at points of discontinuity or to display the asymptotes.

INSTRUCTIONAL NOTE
The concept of *oblique* or *slant asymptote* occurs in a couple of parts of Problem 7, there is no need at this time to develop any techniques for finding the equations of those special graph effects. Students may notice the graphical effect. If not, you may wish to draw their attention to the effect and mention its name. Oblique asymptotes are addressed in Extensions Tasks 27 and 28.

7 For each of the following rational functions, use algebraic reasoning to:

- find coordinates of all x-intercepts and the y-intercept of its graph.
- find equations of all vertical and horizontal asymptotes.
- describe the domain of the function.
- sketch a graph on which you label intercepts and asymptotes.

Then check by examining a graph of the function, and correct your responses if necessary. Be prepared to explain how to avoid any errors you made.

a. $g(x) = \dfrac{3}{x - 2}$

b. $h(x) = \dfrac{2x + 3}{x^2 - 9}$

c. $j(x) = \dfrac{2x + 1}{3x}$

d. $k(x) = \dfrac{x^2 + 1}{x + 1}$

e. $m(x) = \dfrac{6x + 1}{3x + 5}$

f. $s(x) = \dfrac{2x^2 + 2x + 3}{x + 1}$

8 What strategies for analyzing features of a rational function and its graph are suggested by your work on Problems 1–7?

Concert Profit Prospects Reprise One of the important statistics used to describe the profitability of any business venture is the ratio of profit to income. For example, if a business earns profit of \$8 million on income from sales of \$100 million, it would report an 8% ratio of profit to income because $8 \div 100 = 8\%$.

Now recall the profit and income functions derived in analyzing the concert business. Profit from ticket sales for the concert (excluding snack bar operations) is a function of ticket price x with rule $P_c(x) = -25x^2 + 875x - 4{,}750$. Income from concert ticket sales is also a function of ticket price with rule $t(x) = -25x^2 + 750x$.

9 Consider the function $S(x)$ that gives the ratio of profit to income from concert ticket sales as a function of ticket price.

a. Write an algebraic rule for $S(x)$.

b. Will the graph of $S(x)$ have any vertical asymptotes? If so, where?

c. Sketch a graph of $S(x)$ for domain values from 0 to 30. Label the vertical asymptotes with their equations.

d. Describe the behavior of the profit-to-income function near each of the vertical asymptotes. Then use the rule for $S(x)$ to explain why that behavior occurs.

e. Estimate coordinates of any x-intercepts for $S(x)$. Explain what the x-intercepts tell about the concert profit-to-income ratio as a function of ticket price.

f. Estimate the ticket price that would maximize the profit to income ratio. Label that point on your graph of $S(x)$.

368 UNIT 5 • Polynomial and Rational Functions

7 **a.** $g(x) = \dfrac{3}{x-2}$

No x-intercepts

y-intercept: $\left(0, -\frac{3}{2}\right)$

Vertical asymptote: $x = 2$

Horizontal asymptote: $y = 0$

Domain: all reals except $x = 2$

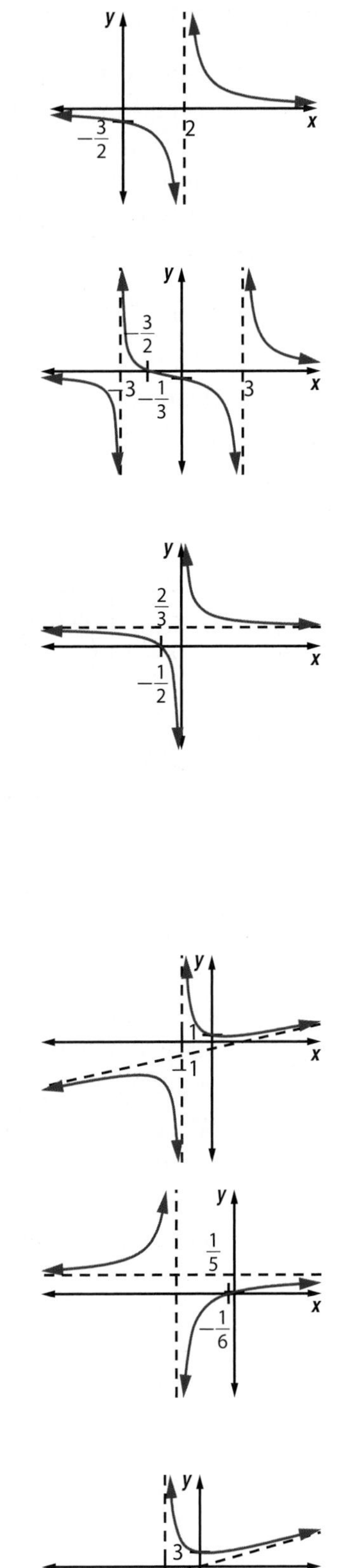

b. $h(x) = \dfrac{2x+3}{x^2-9}$

x-intercept: $\left(-\frac{3}{2}, 0\right)$

y-intercept: $\left(0, -\frac{1}{3}\right)$

Vertical asymptotes: $x = -3$ and $x = 3$

Horizontal asymptote: $y = 0$

Domain: all reals except $x = \pm 3$

c. $j(x) = \dfrac{2x+1}{3x}$

x-intercept: $\left(-\frac{1}{2}, 0\right)$

No y-intercept

Vertical asymptote: $x = 0$

Horizontal asymptote: $y = \frac{2}{3}$ (not so easy to detect; but if one splits the fraction into two parts, you can see that one part goes to 0 as x increases in absolute value while the other equals $\frac{2}{3}$ for all x)

Domain: all reals except $x = 0$

d. $k(x) = \dfrac{x^2+1}{x+1}$

No x-intercepts

y-intercept: $(0, 1)$

Vertical asymptote: $x = -1$ (and a slant or oblique asymptote $y = x - 1$)

Domain: all reals except $x = -1$

e. $m(x) = \dfrac{6x+1}{3x+5}$

x-intercept: $\left(-\frac{1}{6}, 0\right)$

y-intercept: $\left(0, \frac{1}{5}\right)$

Vertical asymptote: $x = -\frac{5}{3}$

Horizontal asymptote: $y = 2$

Domain: all reals except $x = -\frac{5}{3}$

f. $s(x) = \dfrac{2x^2+2x+3}{x+1}$

No x-intercepts

y-intercept: $(0, 3)$

Vertical asymptote: $x = -1$ (and slant or oblique asymptote $y = 2x$)

Domain: all reals except $x = -1$

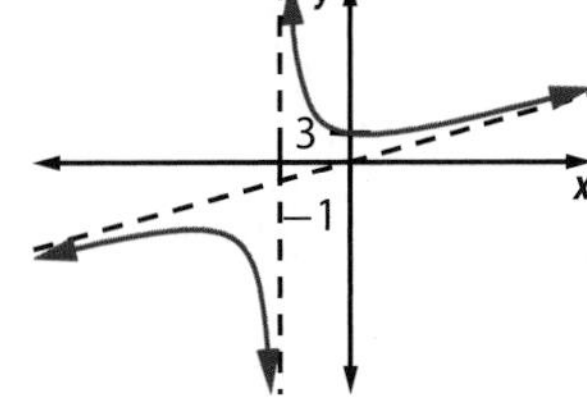

INSTRUCTIONAL NOTE You may wish to distribute parts of Problem 7 to different groups, for example, having each group do three parts.

DIFFERENTIATION You may choose to allow some students to use CAS or technology to find the zeroes.

8 Student answers will vary for this question, but they should include finding:

(1) x-intercepts by looking for zeroes of the numerator
(2) y-intercept by substituting $x = 0$
(3) vertical asymptotes by finding zeroes of the denominator
(4) horizontal asymptotes by looking to see what happens to the fraction as x grows large in absolute value
(5) domain limitations by finding zeroes of the denominator

9 **a.** $S(x) = \frac{P_c(x)}{t(x)} = \frac{-25x^2 + 875x - 4{,}750}{-25x^2 + 750x}$

b. The two vertical asymptotes occur at $x = 0$ and $x = 30$. The denominator can be factored to $-25x(x - 30)$.

c.

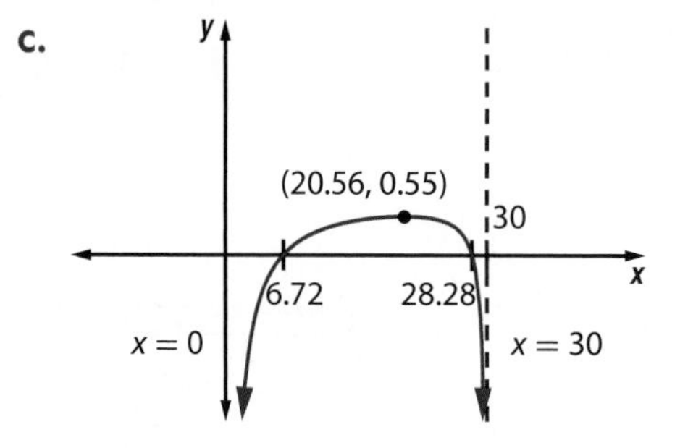

d. On the domain where the problem makes sense, $0 < x < 30$, $S(x)$ approaches negative infinity as x approaches either asymptote since, as x approaches either 0 or 30, the profit is a decreasing negative number while the income is positive and decreasing to zero. Therefore, the profit-to-income ratio must be negative and getting larger in absolute value.

e. The profit-to-income ratio is approximately zero when $x = 6.72$ and when $x = 28.28$, so the x-intercepts of the graph of $S(x)$ are approximately (6.72, 0) and (28.28, 0). These identify also the approximate zeroes of the profit function.

f. When tickets are sold for $20.56, the profit-to-income ratio will be a maximum of approximately 55%. Students might logically recommend setting the ticket price at a more round amount, such as $20.50, since that price also gives a profit-to-income ratio of approximately 55%.

Teacher Notes

Unit 5

Summarize the Mathematics

In this investigation, you derived and analyzed rules for two rational functions used to model conditions in operation of a concert business. Then you studied a variety of other rational functions to generalize strategies for finding critical points and sketching graphs.

a. What can cause a rational function to be undefined at particular values of x?

b. Describe the behavior of a rational function and its graph near vertical and horizontal asymptotes.

c. How can you analyze the numerator and denominator in a rational expression to locate zeroes of the corresponding rational function? The intercepts and asymptotes of its graph?

Be prepared to explain your ideas to the class.

Check Your Understanding

Use your understanding of rational functions to answer the following questions about the relationship of concert profit $P_c(x) = -25x^2 + 875x - 4{,}750$ to concert operating expenses $c(x) = 4{,}750 - 125x$.

a. Write an algebraic rule for the function $T(x)$, which gives the ratio of profit to operating expenses, that is, the number of dollars earned for every dollar spent by the concert promoters.

b. Find the location of all vertical asymptotes for $T(x)$. Describe the behavior of the function near those asymptotes. Explain why that behavior occurs.

c. What is a reasonable domain for $T(x)$ when it is being used to model conditions in the concert business?

d. At about what ticket price is the ratio of profit to operating expenses maximized?

Investigation 2 Simplifying Rational Expressions

When work on mathematical problems leads to fractions like $\frac{8}{12}$ or $\frac{12}{18}$ or $\frac{9}{15}$, you know that it is often helpful to replace each fraction by a simpler equivalent fraction. For example, $\frac{8}{12} = \frac{4 \cdot 2}{4 \cdot 3} = \frac{4}{4} \cdot \frac{2}{3} = 1 \cdot \frac{2}{3}$, so $\frac{8}{12} = \frac{2}{3}$.

As you work on the problems of this investigation, look for answers to these questions:

What principles and strategies help to simplify rational expressions?

What cautions must be observed when simplifying rational expressions?

Summarize the Mathematics

a The function will be undefined when the denominator is equal to zero.

b A line $x = k$ is a vertical asymptote if when values of x approach k as a limit, the values of y grow (or decrease) without bound. This makes the graph rise (or fall) rapidly near the vertical line but never quite reach the line.

A line $y = h$ is a horizontal asymptote if when values of x grow large in absolute value, the graph approaches the horizontal line as a limit but never quite reaches the line.

c To find zeroes of a rational function, look for zeroes of the numerator polynomial (as long as the denominator is not zero).

The x-intercepts are points with coordinates in the form $(x_0, 0)$ where x_0 is a zero of the numerator. To find the y-coordinate of the y-intercept, simply substitute 0 for x.

A rational function approaches either infinity or negative infinity near a vertical asymptote because the denominator is approaching zero, causing the function to take on either extremely large positive values or extremely "large negative" values. Thus, to locate vertical asymptotes of a rational function graph, look for zeroes of the denominator (assuming that the numerator is not simultaneously zero, in which case the point might be only a removable discontinuity, not the location of a vertical asymptote).

Teaching Resources

Transparency Master 25.

UNIT 5 *Polynomial and Rational Functions*

Summarize the Mathematics

In this investigation, you derived and analyzed rules for two rational functions used to model conditions in operation of a concert business. Then you studied a variety of other rational functions to generalize strategies for finding critical points and sketching graphs.

a. What can cause a rational function to be undefined at particular values of x?

b. Describe the behavior of a rational function and its graph near vertical and horizontal asymptotes.

c. How can you analyze the numerator and denominator in a rational expression to locate zeroes of the corresponding rational function? The intercepts and asymptotes of its graph?

Be prepared to explain your ideas to the class.

Transparency Master • use with page 369 UNIT 5 • Polynomial and Rational Functions 25

MATH TOOLKIT Without graphing the function $f(x) = \dfrac{3x - 1}{x^2 - 4}$, find the intercepts, the asymptotes, and the domain. Then sketch a graph of the function.

Check Your Understanding

a. $T(x) = \dfrac{P_c(x)}{c(x)} = \dfrac{-25x^2 + 875x - 4{,}750}{4{,}750 - 125x}$

b. There is only one vertical asymptote at $x = 38$. As x approaches 38 the expense function is positive but approaching 0 while the profit function is negative and decreasing. This causes the ratio of profit to expenses to approach negative infinity.

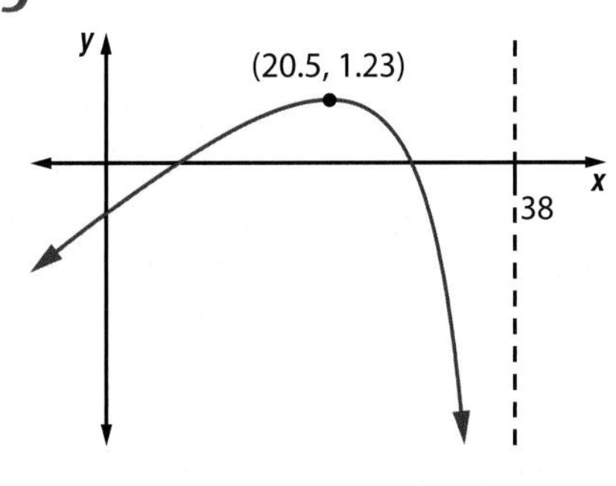

c. A reasonable domain would be $0 < x < 30$ because that is the practical domain of the numerator profit function. Beyond ticket price of \$30, there will be no attendance at the concert. Additionally, promoters will charge some positive price for the tickets.

d. For ticket prices near \$20.55, \$1.23 is earned for every \$1 spent. Here again, a ticket price of \$20.50 also gives \$1.23 earned for every \$1 spent.

Unit 5

1 Consider again the ticket sale income function $t(x) = -25x^2 + 750x$ and the function $n(x) = -25x + 750$, giving number of tickets sold. In both functions, x represents the price per ticket in dollars.

a. Write an algebraic rule for the rational function $U(x)$, giving income per ticket sold.

b. Examine the values of $U(x)$ for integer values of x from 0 to 30. Explain why the pattern in those results makes sense when you think about what the expressions in the numerator and denominator represent in the problem situation.

c. Factor both numerator and denominator of the expression defining $U(x)$. Then write the simpler rational expression that results from removing common factors.

d. How does the result in Part c relate to the pattern you observed in Part b?

e. When Rashid found the simplified expression called for in Part c, he said it is *equivalent* to the original rational expression. Flor said she did not think so, because the domain for $U(x)$ is different from that of the simplified expression. Who is correct?

2 Consider next the function $f(x) = \dfrac{x^2 + 2x - 15}{x^2 - 4x + 3}$.

a. Simplify $\dfrac{x^2 + 2x - 15}{x^2 - 4x + 3}$ by first factoring both the numerator and denominator. Let $g(x)$ be the new function defined by that simplified expression.

b. Study tables of values for $f(x)$ and $g(x)$ for integer values of x in the interval $[-10, 10]$. Find any values of x for which $f(x) \neq g(x)$. Explain why those inputs produce different outputs for the two functions.

c. Use a calculator or computer to draw graphs of $f(x)$ and $g(x)$ over the interval $[-10, 10]$. Compare the graphs.

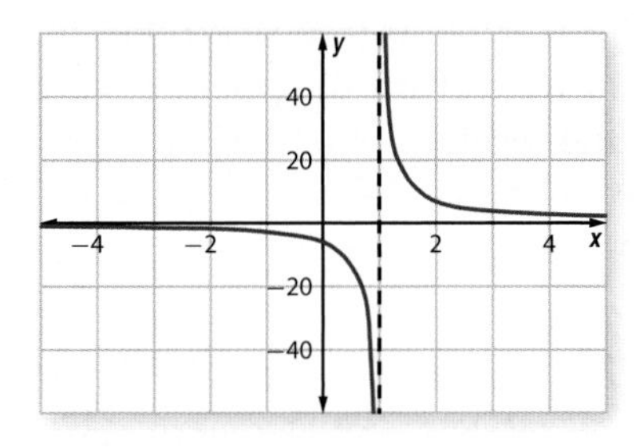

d. Now look again at tables of values for the two functions with smaller step sizes to see if you can explain why the differences observed in Part b do not seem to show up in the graphs.

3 For each of the following rational functions, use factoring to produce simpler and nearly equivalent rules. In each case, note any values of x for which the original and the simplified rules will not produce the same output values. Check your results by examining tables of values and graphs of the functions.

a. $f(x) = \dfrac{2x - 10}{x - 5}$

b. $g(x) = \dfrac{x + 3}{2x^2 + 6x}$

c. $h(x) = \dfrac{x^2 + 7x + 12}{x + 3}$

d. $j(x) = \dfrac{x^2 + 7x + 12}{x^2 + 5x + 6}$

370 UNIT 5 • Polynomial and Rational Functions

Investigation 2 Simplifying Rational Expressions

In this investigation, students will continue working with rational expressions, specifically simplifying the expressions to less complicated forms. It is important that students get the message that while some cancellation of common factors is suggested to simplify rational expressions, this can "oversimplify" the corresponding function by changing the domain in significant ways.

Launch

It will probably be useful to set up this investigation by asking students how they could simplify the fractions given in the introductory text. Encourage them to think of several different possible simplifications, not only the simplification to lowest possible terms. Then highlight the focal questions in this investigation of algebraic fraction simplification, especially alerting them to be on the lookout for ways that life with algebraic fractions is a bit more complex than arithmetic.

Unit 5

1 **a.** $U(x) = \dfrac{-25x^2 + 750x}{-25x + 750}$

b. It should become evident that $U(x) = x$ for almost every value of x. This makes sense because the total income from ticket sales divided by the number of tickets sold will be the price per ticket.

c. $U(x) = \dfrac{x(-25x + 750)}{-25x + 750} = x$

d. Since $U(x)$ reduces to x, the function values are the same as its corresponding domain value except at $x = 30$ where $U(x)$ is undefined.

e. Flor is correct, because the original expression yields an undefined value for $U(30)$, while the new expression indicates $U(30) = 30$. In order for two functions to be equivalent, the values of the functions must be equal for all values of the input.

2 **a.** $g(x) = \dfrac{x + 5}{x - 1}$

b. $f(x) = g(x)$ except when $x = 3$. The original function $f(x)$ is not defined for $x = 3$ because that value makes the denominator zero, but $g(x)$ is defined there.

c. The two functions differ in value only at $x = 3$, so it is almost impossible to detect the difference on graphs of them.

d. Looking at tables for $f(x)$ and $g(x)$ with smaller step sizes shows even more convincingly that the two functions are identical, except for $x = 3$.

TECHNOLOGY NOTE
Using a decimal window, such as **ZDecimal** on the TI calculators, allows you to observe removable discontinuities for these functions.

3 **a.** $f(x) = \dfrac{2x - 10}{x - 5}$ and $\hat{f}(x) = 2$ are identical except for $x = 5$, where $f(x)$ is not defined.

In this case, there is no vertical asymptote at $x = 5$, despite the fact that the denominator is 0 there. (This is due to the fact that both numerator and denominator have a factor of $(x - 5)$, making the point where $x = 5$ what is called a **removable discontinuity**. See Extensions Task 25. That is, if one were to defined $f(5) = 2$, the resulting function would be continuous. This example illustrates the point that a zero of the denominator of an algebraic fraction is not a guarantee of a vertical asymptote for its graph, although it does guarantee a discontinuity.)

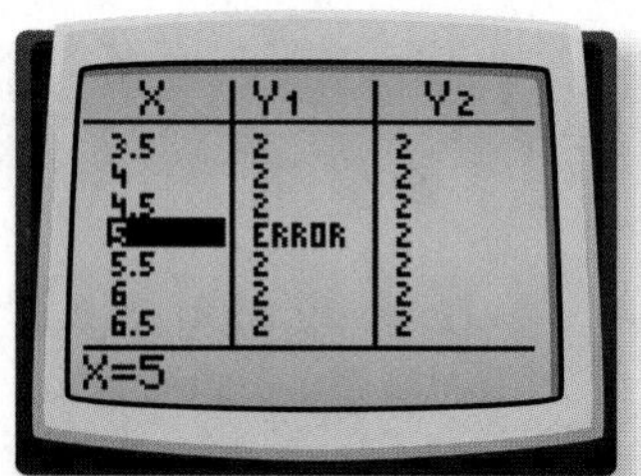

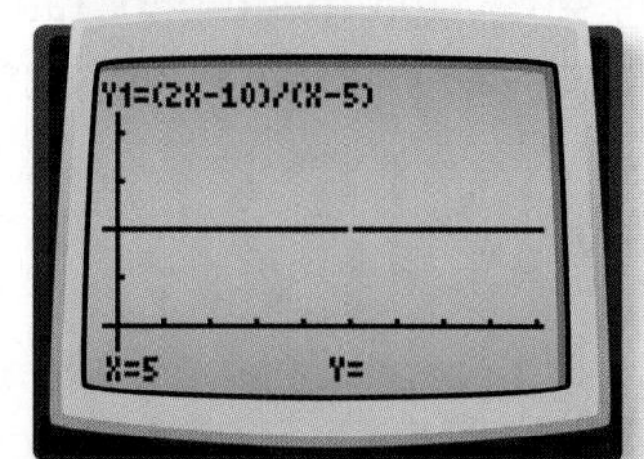

b. $g(x) = \dfrac{x + 3}{2x^2 + 6x}$ and $\hat{g}(x) = \dfrac{1}{2x}$ are identical except when $x = -3$, where $g(x)$ is undefined. Both functions are undefined for $x = 0$.

This is another case where a zero of the denominator does not guarantee an asymptote for the graph, because the problematic factor $(x + 3)$ is present in both the numerator and the denominator. The line $x = 0$ is a vertical asymptote.

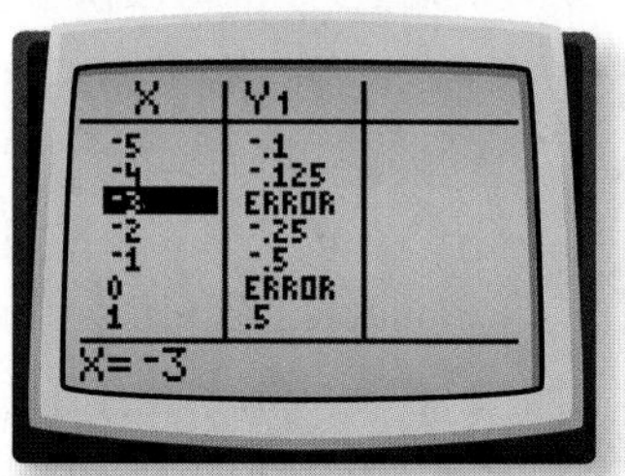

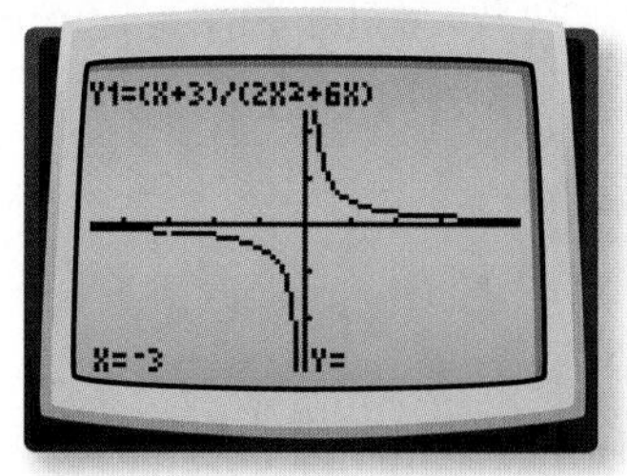

c. $h(x) = \dfrac{x^2 + 7x + 12}{x + 3}$ and $\hat{h} = x + 4$
are identical except when $x = -3$ where $h(x)$ is undefined.

The line $x = -3$ is not a vertical asymptote for the graph of $h(x)$.

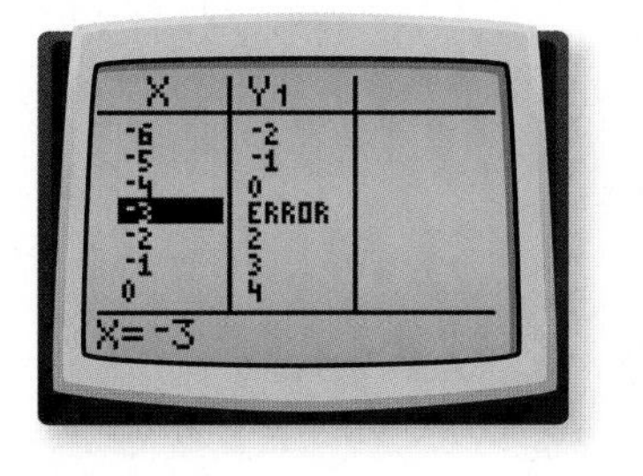

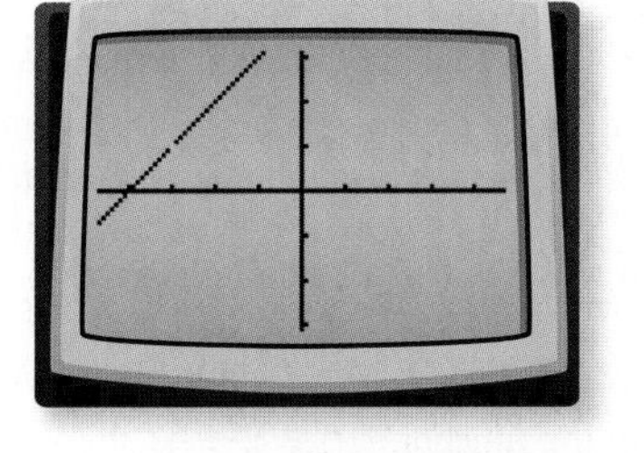

d. $j(x) = \dfrac{x^2 + 7x + 12}{x^2 + 5x + 6}$ and $\hat{j}(x) = \dfrac{x + 4}{x + 2}$
are identical except when $x = -3$ where $j(x)$ is undefined.

This is a case where one of the zeroes of the denominator determines a vertical asymptote $x = -2$, but the other does not.

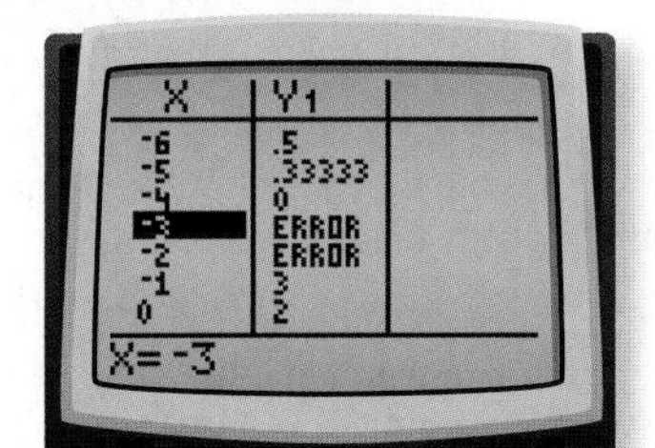

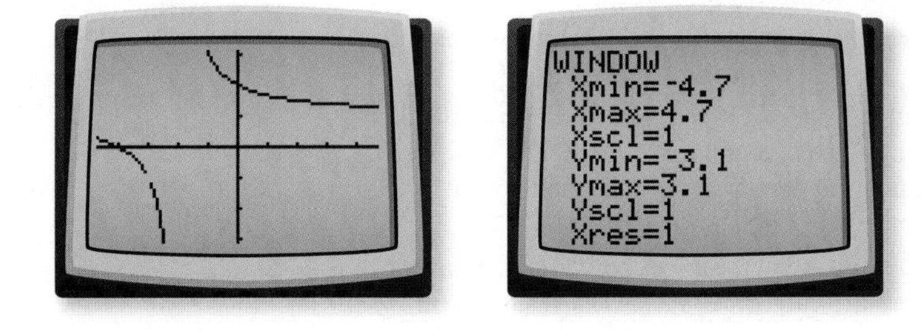

4 In Problem 3, you examined rational functions that had zeroes in the denominator but did not have the expected vertical asymptotes at some of those domain points. Study those examples and your simplifications again to formulate an answer to this question.

In what cases will a zero of the denominator in a rational function not indicate a vertical asymptote of its graph?

5 When you are faced with the task of simplifying rational expressions, you may be tempted to make some "cancellations" that do not produce nearly equivalent results. For example, when Arlen and Tara were faced with the function $s(t) = \frac{t + 9}{6t + 9}$, they produced what they thought were equivalent simpler expressions for the rule.

a. Arlen came up with $s_1(t) = \frac{1}{6}$. How could you show that this new function is quite different from the original? How could you help Arlen clarify his reasoning?

b. Tara came up with $s_2(t) = \frac{0}{6}$. How could you show that this new function is quite different from the original? How could you help Tara clarify her reasoning?

6 To check your skill and understanding in simplifying rational expressions, follow these steps on your own.

(1) Write an algebraic fraction in which both the numerator and the denominator are different linear expressions.

(2) Create another linear expression and multiply both numerator and denominator by that expression. Then expand the resulting numerator and denominator into standard form quadratic polynomials.

(3) Exchange the resulting rational expression with a classmate. See if you can find the quotient of linear expressions with which each began.

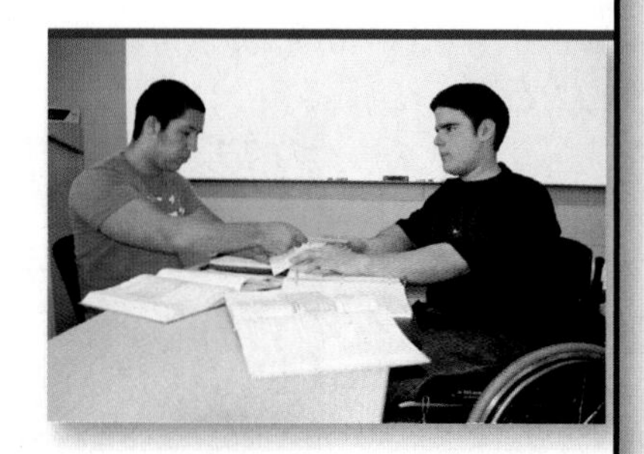

Summarize the Mathematics

In this investigation, you explored simplification of rational expressions.

a What is meant by simplifying rational expressions?

b For a given rational expression, what strategies can be applied to find another expression that is simpler but nearly equivalent to the original?

c What cautions must be observed when simplifying rational expressions?

Be prepared to explain your ideas to the class.

4 When $x = a$ is a zero of both the denominator and numerator of a rational function (with same multiplicity), the line $x = a$ will *not* be a vertical asymptote for the graph of that function.

COMMON ERROR The next problem is included to draw students' attention to some of the most common errors in work with fractions. Both mistaken calculations that students are asked to diagnose show cancellation of common terms from numerator and denominator, with two different errant ways of accounting for "what is left" after the cancellation. Perhaps the most effective way to highlight the errors is to ask students to think about similar work with arithmetic fractions and remember that cancellation in those situations is only allowed when it is possible to isolate a factor of 1 in the form $\frac{a}{a}$.

5 **a.** Student responses may vary as to how to explain the mistake but should include factoring of the numerator and denominator. Only common *factors* can be cancelled (because together they constitute a multiple of 1), not just any common numbers or terms.

The difference of the two expressions could be demonstrated by examining tables or graphs and noticing the many values of t for which the two expressions produce different outputs.

b. Once again, only common *factors* can be cancelled (because together they constitute a multiple of 1), not just any common numbers or terms. Also, cancellation of common factors does not mean that the cancelled terms are replaced by 0. Usually, the replacement is by a factor of 1.

The difference of the two expressions could be demonstrated by examining tables or graphs and noticing the many values of t for which the two expressions produce different outputs.

6 Students should check their partner's work on this problem.

Summarize the Mathematics

a Simplifying a rational expression includes removing all factors that are common to both the numerator and denominator.

b Both the numerator and denominator can be factored completely and common factors cancelled, leaving a simplified expression.

c Simplifying a rational expression will not change the function's vertical asymptotes but will remove other values for which the function is undefined because the denominator is undefined. Vertical asymptotes occur when there is a zero in the denominator that is not also a zero of the numerator. (They are called essential discontinuities of the rational function. See Extensions Task 25.)

When a factor of the denominator has a zero that is matched by a factor of the numerator (in same multiplicity), cancellation of the common factors will remove an undefined point of the function without noticeably changing the graph. (Such points are called removable discontinuities of the function. See Extensions Task 25.)

Teaching Resources

Transparency Master 26.

UNIT 5 *Polynomial and Rational Functions*

Summarize the Mathematics

In this investigation, you explored simplification of rational expressions.

a What is meant by simplifying rational expressions?

b For a given rational expression, what strategies can be applied to find another expression that is simpler but nearly equivalent to the original?

c What cautions must be observed when simplifying rational expressions?

Be prepared to explain your ideas to the class.

Unit 5

Unit 5

Check Your Understanding

Use your understanding of equivalent rational expressions to complete the following tasks.

a. The function $T(x) = \dfrac{-25x^2 + 875x - 4{,}750}{-125x + 4{,}750}$ compares concert profit to operating expenses.

i. Identify all values of x for which $T(x)$ is *undefined*.

ii. Explain why the expression defining $T(x)$ can be simplified to $\dfrac{x^2 - 35x + 190}{5x - 190}$.

iii. If the simplified expression in part ii were used to define a new function $K(x)$, would it have the same domain as $T(x)$?

b. Consider the expression $\dfrac{x^2 + 6x + 8}{x^2 - x - 6}$.

i. Identify all values of x for which this expression is undefined.

ii. Simplify the expression.

iii. Explain why simplifying this expression does or does not produce an expression with different undefined points than the original.

Investigation 3 Adding and Subtracting Rational Expressions

In Investigation 1, you derived the profit-per-ticket function $R(x) = \dfrac{-25x^2 + 875x - 4{,}750}{-25x + 750}$ for business at a concert venue. As you know, the concert promoters also make profit from sales at snack bars that operate before the concert and at intermissions. Including that profit source in the business calculations requires new operations on rational expressions and functions.

As you work on the problems of this investigation, look for answers to this question:

What principles and strategies guide addition and subtraction of rational expressions?

1 The concert promoter's business analysis suggests that total profit $P_b(x)$ from sale of snack bar items will be related to ticket price x by the function $P_b(x) = -175x + 5{,}250$.

a. Why does it make sense that profit from snack bar sales depends on ticket price?

b. Write and simplify a rule for the function $V(x)$ that gives the profit per ticket from snack bar sales. Remember that the number of people attending the concert is related to ticket price by the function $n(x) = -25x + 750$.

c. What are the values of $R(20)$, $V(20)$, and $R(20) + V(20)$? What do those values tell about the profit prospects for the whole concert event?

372 UNIT 5 • Polynomial and Rational Functions

Check Your Understanding

a. **i.** $T(x)$ is undefined when $x = 38$.

ii. -25 is factored out of both the numerator and denominator.

iii. The simplified function $k(x)$ will have the same domain as $T(x)$ because no zeroes of the denominator have been removed in the cancellation process.

b. **i.** The expression $\frac{x^2 + 6x + 8}{x^2 - x - 6}$ is undefined when $x = 3$ or $x = -2$.

ii. $\frac{(x + 2)(x + 4)}{(x - 3)(x + 2)} = \frac{x + 4}{x - 3}$

iii. $\frac{x + 4}{x - 3}$ is only undefined when $x = 3$ since $(x + 2)$ was factored out of both the numerator and denominator and cancelled. The graph $f(x) = \frac{x^2 + 6x + 8}{x^2 - x - 6}$ will have one vertical asymptote at $x = 3$ and be undefined at $x = -2$.

Unit 5

Investigation 3 Adding and Subtracting Rational Expressions

In this investigation, students will continue working with rational expressions and functions, developing understanding of when it makes sense to find the sum or difference of two given functions and strategies for combining the expressions involved and simplifying the result as appropriate.

It is relatively easy to add or subtract rational expressions with common denominators. But transforming given expressions to find a common denominator can be very complex work. At this point, we do not expect students to become proficient in doing those more difficult cases by hand. The task is easy for a CAS, so we recommend using that tool for all but the relatively straightforward cases. Once again, the more interested and able students will probably want to develop proficiency in doing this work by hand. But for many others, that technical skill is not important at this point. There will be more to come on rational expressions in Course 4.

Launch

You might find it useful to launch this investigation by reminding students that their work on the preceding investigation focused only on profits directly related to operation of the concert and did not include income and expenses related to snack bar operation. You could then recall from Investigation 1 the snack bar profit function and essentially ask students for answers to Problem 1 Part a. It might be useful to ask them what the numbers -175 and 5,250 represent about snack bar profit and why they might be reasonable. The 5,250 represents that if concert tickets are free, attendance will be large and the snack bar should do a good business. As ticket prices increase, attendance decreases and so will snack bar income and profit. In fact, the -175 suggests that each increase of \$1 in ticket price will reduce snack bar profits by \$175.

NOTE The solution to Problem 1 is on page T373.

2 When the concert promoters asked their business manager to find a function $W(x)$ that shows combined profit per ticket from ticket and snack bar sales, she suggested two possibilities.

$$W_1(x) = \frac{P_c(x)}{n(x)} + \frac{P_b(x)}{n(x)} \quad \text{and} \quad W_2(x) = \frac{P_c(x) + P_b(x)}{n(x)}$$

a. Using the algebraic expressions for each function involved, you get:

$$W_1(x) = \frac{-25x^2 + 875x - 4{,}750}{-25x + 750} + \frac{-175x + 5{,}250}{-25x + 750}$$

$$\text{and} \quad W_2(x) = \frac{-25x^2 + 700x + 500}{-25x + 750}.$$

How could you convince someone that both ways of calculating total profit per ticket are correct by:

i. reasoning about the meaning of each expression in the concert business situation?

ii. using what you know about addition of arithmetic fractions like $\frac{2}{5} + \frac{4}{5}$?

b. Which of the two expressions for total profit per ticket would be better for:

i. showing how each profit source contributes to total profit per ticket?

ii. calculating total profit per ticket most efficiently?

c. Find what you believe to be the expression that is most efficient for calculating $W(x)$. Use that expression to find the profit per ticket from *both* ticket and snack bar sales when the ticket prices are \$10, \$15, \$20, and \$25.

d. Estimate the ticket price that will yield maximum profit per ticket for:

i. the concert operation alone, $R(x)$.

ii. the snack bar operation alone, $V(x)$.

iii. the combination of concert and snack bar operations, $W(x)$.

3 Consider the following two rational functions.

$$f(x) = \frac{3x^2 + 5x - 2}{4x + 1} \quad \text{and} \quad g(x) = \frac{x^2 + 4x + 4}{4x + 1}$$

a. Evaluate $f(x)$, $g(x)$, and $f(x) + g(x)$ for a variety of values of x.

b. If $h(x) = f(x) + g(x)$, find what you believe to be the simplest algebraic rule for $h(x)$.

c. Use the rule from Part b to calculate $h(x)$ for the same values of x you used in Part a. Then compare the results with what you obtained in Part a.

1 a. Since the number of people who come to the concert is a function of ticket price and the profit from the snack bar should be a function of the number of people who attend, the snack bar profit ultimately depends on the price charged per ticket.

b. $V(x) = \dfrac{-175x + 5{,}250}{-25x + 750} = 7$

c. When the ticket price is \$20, R(20) = 11 indicates that profit per ticket from concert ticket sales is \$11. V(20) = 7 indicates that profit per ticket from concession stand sales is \$7. $R(20) + V(20) = 18$ indicates that total profit per ticket from the concert operation is \$18.

2 a. i. The total profit per ticket can be seen as the sum of the profit per ticket from ticket sales and the profit per ticket from snack bar sales. It can also be seen as the total profit from both ticket sales and concessions divided by the number of tickets sold.

ii. The expression for $W_1(x)$ is the sum of two fractions with a common denominator. Therefore, the numerators can be added to find the sum, which is the expression for $W_2(x)$.

b. i. The first expression would be best for showing each contribution to profit per ticket.

ii. The second expression would be best for efficiently calculating profit per ticket.

c. $W(10) = 10$, $W(15) = 14.33$, $W(20) = 18$, $W(25) = 19$. The most efficient expression for total profit per ticket would probably be something like this: $W(x) = \dfrac{x^2 - 28x - 20}{x - 30}$.

d. i. About \$23.68 (maximum profit per ticket of \$12.35)

ii. All ticket prices will yield the same profit per ticket (\$7).

iii. About \$23.68 (maximum profit per ticket of \$19.35)

3 a. Student responses will vary.

b. Students should conjecture that $h(x) = x + 2$. However, recognizing that the factor $(4x + 1)$ appears in the numerator of the combined fractions is not obvious. Students might not be able to do that factoring by themselves. If you use a CAS, it will automatically produce the simplified expression like this.

F1 Tools | F2 Algebra | F3 Calc | F4 Other | F5 Pr9mIO | F6 Clean Up

$\blacksquare\ \dfrac{3\cdot x^2+5\cdot x-2}{4\cdot x+1}+\dfrac{x^2+4\cdot x+}{4\cdot x+1}$ ▸

x + 2

...(4x+1)+(x^2+4x+4)/(4x+1)

MAIN DEG AUTO FUNC 1/30

c. The results should match except for $x = -\frac{1}{4}$. (Students might not have thought to check this value but will in Part d.)

d. If you simplify the algebraic fraction that results from adding $f(x)$ and $g(x)$, there is one value of x for which care must be exercised in work with $h(x) = f(x) + g(x)$.

i. What is that number? (*Hint:* Examine a table of values of $h(x)$ in increments of 0.25.)

ii. Why do you get different results from using a simplified rule for $h(x)$ and the given rules for $f(x)$ and $g(x)$?

4 Using the rules for $f(x)$ and $g(x)$ given in Problem 3, let $k(x) = f(x) - g(x)$.

a. Find a rule in simplest form for $k(x)$.

b. Check your answer to Part a by calculating $f(x) - g(x)$ and $k(x)$ for a variety of values of x.

c. How can you quickly tell that the numerator and denominator of $k(x)$ do not have a common factor?

Finding Common Denominators From your experiences with arithmetic, you know that addition and subtraction of fractions become more involved if the denominators are not the same. For example, to find the sum $\frac{2}{5} + \frac{7}{10}$, you first have to replace the addends with equivalent fractions having a common denominator. In this case, you might write $\frac{2}{5}$ as $\frac{4}{10}$ to get the sum $\frac{11}{10}$.

5 The same need for common denominators arises in work with algebraic fractions. And the strategies that work in dealing with numerical fractions can be applied to algebraic fractions as well. For example, consider $\frac{x+1}{x} + \frac{x+2}{x-1}$. Examine the results produced by a CAS shown below.

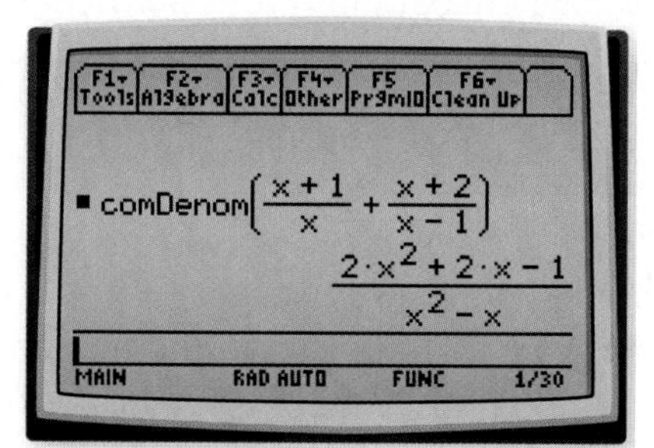

a. Explain why the denominator of $x^2 - x$ is correct.

b. Why is the numerator $2x^2 + 2x - 1$?

374 UNIT 5 • Polynomial and Rational Functions

d. **i.** The results do not match when $x = -0.25$.

ii. This discrepancy occurs because simplification of $h(x)$ caused the denominator to reduce to 1, losing any restriction on the domain of the function.

4 **a.** $k(x) = \dfrac{2x^2 + x - 6}{4x + 1}$

b. Student responses will vary but should verify the result from Part a.

c. The denominator has one factor $4x + 1$. The first term of the numerator is $2x^2$ and thus linear factors (if they exist) would have to look like $(4x + 1)\left(\frac{1}{4}x - ?\right)$, which would have a fractional middle term.

5 **a.** When you add two fractions with different denominators, one common denominator is the product of the two. In this algebraic fraction addition, the common denominator is $x(x - 1) = x^2 - x$.

b. Because $(x + 1)(x - 1) + (x + 2)x = 2x^2 + 2x - 1$

INSTRUCTIONAL NOTE
Some students may not be able to answer Part b at this point. If so, encourage them to come back to this part after they complete Problems 6 or 7.

Unit 5

6 Consider the following questions about airline flights from Chicago to Philadelphia and back. The cities are 678 miles apart. The return trip is scheduled to take almost half an hour longer than the flight from Chicago to Philadelphia because winds in the upper atmosphere almost always flow from west to east. Suppose the speed of the airplane without wind is s miles per hour, and the speed of the wind is 30 miles per hour from west to east.

a. Flight time is a function of distance and speed. Explain why the flight time from Chicago to Philadelphia is given by $f(s) = \frac{678}{s + 30}$ and the return time is given by $g(s) = \frac{678}{s - 30}$.

b. What information is given by values of $f(s) + g(s)$?

c. Explain why the rules for $f(s)$ and $g(s)$ can be replaced by

$$f(s) = \frac{678(s - 30)}{(s + 30)(s - 30)} \text{ and } g(s) = \frac{678(s + 30)}{(s - 30)(s + 30)}.$$

Why are those symbolic manipulations a useful idea?

d. Use the results in Part c to find a rule for $f(s) + g(s)$. Simplify it if possible.

e. Use the simplified rule for $f(s) + g(s)$ to find flight time for a round trip from Chicago to Philadelphia if the airplane's speed without wind is 310 miles per hour. Compare that result to the value of $f(310) + g(310)$.

7 Adapt the reasoning used in work on Problems 5 and 6 and what you know about adding arithmetic fractions with unlike denominators to write each of the following algebraic expressions in equivalent form as a single fraction. Then simplify each result as much as possible. Check your reasoning with a CAS.

a. $\frac{3x + 1}{5} + \frac{x + 4}{x}$

b. $\frac{5}{x - 1} + \frac{x + 1}{x}$

c. $\frac{x + 2}{x + 3} + \frac{x + 1}{2x - 6}$

d. $3x + 1 + \frac{x + 4}{x}$

8 The following display shows how the sum of two fractions is calculated by a CAS *without* use of the **comDenom** command. Use algebraic reasoning to show that this result is equivalent to that obtained in Problem 5.

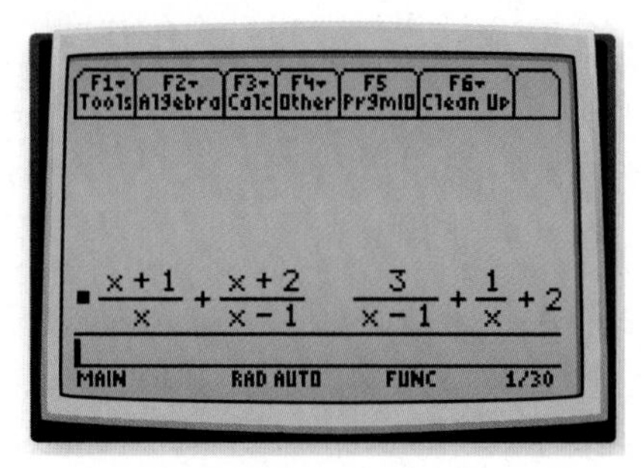

6 **a.** The time it takes to travel from one point to another can be found by dividing the distance between the two points by the speed at which you will travel. The speed at which you will travel to Philadelphia is $s + 30$ since the wind will help to carry the plane along, thus increasing its speed. The speed at which you will travel back to Chicago is $s - 30$ since the wind is working against the plane, slowing it down.

b. The time for the round trip is given by the values of $f(s) + g(s)$.

c. By the Multiplicative Identity property, any expression can be multiplied by 1 and remain unchanged. In the case of $f(s)$, 1 is expressed in the form $\frac{s - 30}{s - 30}$; 1 is expressed in the form $\frac{s + 30}{s + 30}$ in the case of $g(s)$. These manipulations have given $f(s)$ and $g(s)$ a common denominator.

(Some students might notice that there are some concerns about domain limitations for $s = \pm 30$. Actually, the $s = 30$ situation is the only one that would affect the practical problem since air speed of -30 miles per hour would not make sense. In fact, the function $g(s)$ has a vertical asymptote at $s = 30$, meaning that if the plane flies at a speed of 30 miles per hour into a 30 mile per hour headwind, it will make no progress and the trip will take "infinite" time.)

d. $f(s) + g(s) = \frac{1{,}356s}{(s + 30)(s - 30)}$, or $\frac{1{,}356s}{s^2 - 900}$

e. The round trip time would be approximately 4 hours 25 minutes if the plane were to travel at an average (still air) speed of 310 miles per hour in each direction. The trip from Chicago takes 1.99 hours; the return trip from Philadelphia takes 2.42 hours. The total of 4.41 hours is 4 hours 24.6 minutes.

7 **a.** $\frac{3x^2 + 6x + 20}{5x}$ **b.** $\frac{x^2 + 5x - 1}{x^2 - x}$

c. $\frac{3x^2 + 2x - 9}{2x^2 - 18}$ **d.** $\frac{3x^2 + 2x + 4}{x}$

8 One possible method to show equivalence is given.

$$\frac{3}{x-1} + \frac{1}{x} + 2 = \frac{3x}{x(x-1)} + \frac{(x-1)}{x(x-1)} + \frac{2(x)(x-1)}{x(x-1)}$$
$$= \frac{3x + x - 1 + 2x^2 - 2x}{x(x-1)}$$
$$= \frac{2x^2 + 2x - 1}{x^2 - 1}$$

INSTRUCTIONAL NOTE
Problem 8 does not need to be completed by all groups prior to the Summarize the Mathematics discussion.

Unit 5

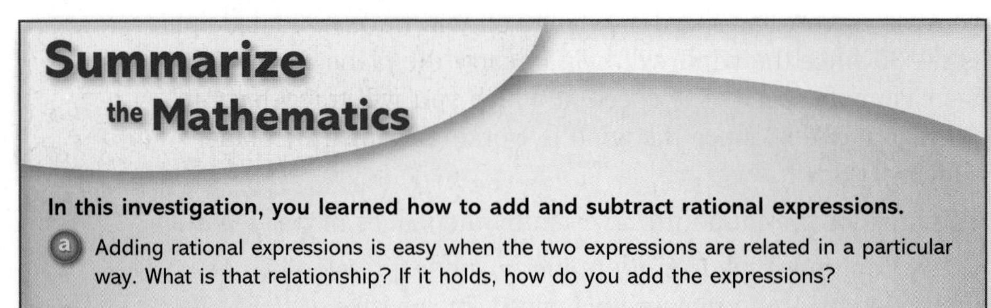

Summarize the Mathematics

In this investigation, you learned how to add and subtract rational expressions.

a. Adding rational expressions is easy when the two expressions are related in a particular way. What is that relationship? If it holds, how do you add the expressions?

b. If the most convenient relationship between rational expressions does *not* hold, what can you do to make addition or subtraction of the expressions possible?

Be prepared to explain your ideas to the class.

Unit 5

Check Your Understanding

Use your understanding of adding and subtracting rational expressions to find simplified rules for the sums and differences of functions in Parts a–c, where $f(x) = \frac{3x - 1}{4x}$, $g(x) = \frac{x - 5}{4x}$, and $h(x) = \frac{3x}{2x + 3}$.

a. $f(x) + g(x)$

b. $f(x) - g(x)$

c. $h(x) - g(x)$

Investigation 4 Multiplying and Dividing Rational Expressions

You have learned how to simplify, add, and subtract rational expressions, and you have seen how those operations are similar to operations with numerical fractions. The similarities continue, with some limitations, to multiplication and division.

As you work on the problems of this investigation, look for answers to these questions:

If the rules for two rational functions f(x) and g(x) are given, how can you calculate rules for the product and quotient of those functions?

What cautions must be observed when simplifying products and quotients of a rational expressions?

1 Give results, in simplest form, for these products of numerical fractions.

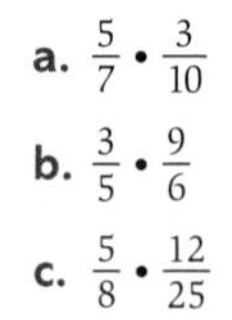

a. $\frac{5}{7} \cdot \frac{3}{10}$

b. $\frac{3}{5} \cdot \frac{9}{6}$

c. $\frac{5}{8} \cdot \frac{12}{25}$

376 UNIT 5 • Polynomial and Rational Functions

Summarize the Mathematics

a. Addition of rational expressions is easy when they have a common denominator. If this is the case, the numerators are added to find the result's numerator and the denominator of the sum or difference is the common denominator.

b. You can multiply one or both expressions by a form of the number 1 in order to obtain a common denominator. Then, proceed as stated above.

Check Your Understanding

a. $\dfrac{4x-6}{4x} = \dfrac{2(2x-3)}{4x} = \dfrac{2x-3}{2x}$

b. $\dfrac{2x+4}{4x} = \dfrac{2(x+2)}{4x} = \dfrac{x+2}{2x}$

c. $\dfrac{3x(4x)}{(2x+3)(4x)} - \dfrac{(x-5)(2x+3)}{4x(2x+3)} = \dfrac{10x^2+7x+15}{4x(2x+3)} = \dfrac{10x^2+7x+15}{8x^2+12x}$

Teaching Resources

Transparency Master 27.

UNIT 5 *Polynomial and Rational Functions*

Summarize the Mathematics

In this investigation, you learned how to add and subtract rational expressions.

a. Adding rational expressions is easy when the two expressions are related in a particular way. What is that relationship? If it holds, how do you add the expressions?

b. If the most convenient relationship between rational expressions does *not* hold, what can you do to make addition or subtraction of the expressions possible?

Be prepared to explain your ideas to the class.

Transparency Master • *use with page 376* UNIT 5 • Polynomial and Rational Functions 27

MATH TOOLKIT Combine and simplify the sum $\dfrac{2x-3}{2x} + \dfrac{2x-3}{2x}$.

Unit 5

Investigation 4 Multiplying and Dividing Rational Expressions

In this investigation, students will develop understanding of when it makes sense to combine rational functions and expressions through multiplication and division and how to perform the required algebraic operations. They will continue to develop skill in simplifying rational expressions. When an expression has been simplified, students must remember that they may have altered the domain of the function by canceling out common factors.

This investigation does not begin with an applied problem that naturally calls for multiplication or division of rational expressions, so you might have to motivate the work by simply noting that Investigation 3 developed algebraic fraction addition and subtraction using what we know about arithmetic fraction addition and subtraction. It makes mathematical sense to explore the same kind of connections for multiplication and division of algebraic fractions.

Launch

You might start by reminding students of some familiar situations in which multiplication and division are necessary. For instance, the area of a rectangle is obtained by multiplying the length and width. If the area and width are given, the length is found by division.

2 Suppose that $f(x) = \frac{x^2}{2}$ and $g(x) = \frac{12}{x}$.

a. If $h(x) = f(x) \cdot g(x)$, what do you think will be the simplest expression that gives correct values of $h(x)$ for all x?

b. Test your idea in Part a by comparing tables of values for $\left(\frac{x^2}{2}\right)\left(\frac{12}{x}\right)$ and for your proposed simpler expression to calculate $h(x)$. Use values of x in the interval $[-10, 10]$.

c. Test your idea in Part a by graphing $y = \left(\frac{x^2}{2}\right)\left(\frac{12}{x}\right)$ for values of x in the interval $[-10, 10]$ and then graphing $y = h(x)$, using your proposed simplified expression for $h(x)$.

d. What similarities and what differences between multiplication of numeric and algebraic fractions are suggested by the results of your work on Parts a–c?

3 Suppose that $f(x) = \frac{3x}{x - 2}$ and $g(x) = \frac{5x - 10}{x}$.

a. If $h(x) = f(x) \cdot g(x)$, what do you think will be the simplest expression that gives correct values of $h(x)$ for all x?

b. Test your idea in Part a by comparing tables of values for $\left(\frac{3x}{x - 2}\right)\left(\frac{5x - 10}{x}\right)$ and for your proposed simpler expression to calculate $h(x)$. Use values of x in the interval $[-10, 10]$.

c. Test your idea in Part a by graphing $y = \frac{3x}{x - 2} \cdot \frac{5x - 10}{x}$ for values of x in the interval $[-10, 10]$ and graphing $y = h(x)$, using your proposed simplified expression for $h(x)$.

d. What similarities and what differences between multiplication of numeric and algebraic fractions are suggested by the results of your work on Parts a–c?

4 The following work shows how Cho calculated the product $h(x) = f(x) \cdot g(x)$ in Problem 3.

$$\begin{aligned}\frac{3x}{x - 2} \cdot \frac{5x - 10}{x} &= \frac{3x(5x - 10)}{(x - 2)x} \\ &= \frac{15x^2 - 30x}{x^2 - 2x} \\ &= \frac{15x(x - 2)}{x(x - 2)} \\ &= 15\end{aligned}$$

a. Explain how Cho could have saved time by factoring and removing identical factors before expanding the numerator and denominator expressions.

b. What restrictions on the domain of $f(x)$ and $g(x)$ has Cho ignored? What are the consequences?

Unit 5

Then ask students questions like these, involving fractions.

"If length and width of a rectangle are $\frac{3}{4}$ feet and $\frac{20}{9}$ feet respectively, what is the area of that rectangle?"

"If a rectangle has area $\frac{20}{9}$ square feet and width $\frac{2}{3}$ feet, what is the length of that rectangle?"

Although it might be a cause for considerable delay in getting to algebraic fraction multiplication and division, it might be profitable to probe students' understandings of why those standard operations for arithmetic fractions work as they do. All too often, students who have not done fraction work recently have only a hazy and muddled recall of rules for those operations. They tend to combine and misapply some combinations of "cross-multiplication" and "invert and multiply" that they remember unreliably. In this sense, one of the greatest payoffs of dealing with algebraic fractions is one more review and analysis of rules for operating with arithmetic fractions.

1 **a.** $\frac{3}{14}$ **b.** $\frac{9}{10}$ **c.** $\frac{3}{10}$

2 **a.** $h(x) = 6x$ appears simplest.

b. The results should verify the formula from Part a except when $x = 0$. This is because the rule for $g(x)$ is not defined there, but the simplified product is.

c. The graphs should match because the removable discontinuity at $x = 0$ will be unobtrusive.

d. The key difference is that when simplifying a product of algebraic expressions, one has to worry about loss of discontinuities through change in the domain of the fraction result.

3 **a.** $\frac{(3)(x)}{(x-2)} \cdot \frac{5(x-2)}{(x)} = 15$ (Students will check their answers while completing Parts b and c.)

b. x cannot be equal to 0 or 2. If you evaluate the simplified expression at either of these values, the result will be 15. According to the original expression, the result should be undefined.

c. The graphs will be nearly identical, with only two imperceptible holes in the graph of the original at $x = 2$ and $x = 0$ where the original rule is undefined.

d. Multiplication of algebraic fractions is very much the same as that operation on arithmetic fractions, with the difference that simplification can lead to omission of undefined points.

4 **a.** $\frac{3x}{x-2} \cdot \frac{5x-10}{x} = \frac{15(x-2)x}{(x-2)x}$ reveals the simplification to 15 by canceling two factors of 1.

b. The restriction to $x \neq 2$ and $x \neq 0$ does not appear to be necessary in the simplified form, but those domain constraints are part of the original multiplication. (Those restrictions are, however, what are called "removable discontinuities" of the product function. By defining $h(x)$ to be 15 when $x = 0$ and when $x = 2$, the new function has the same limiting values as x approaches those two points.)

Unit 5

5. Simplify $\frac{x-2}{x^2-25} \cdot \frac{2x^2+11x+5}{6x-12}$ by first factoring and then removing common factors before expanding the products in the numerator and denominator. Check your answer with a CAS. Be careful to explain the values of x for which the simpler expression is not equivalent to the original.

6. Suppose that $f(x) = \frac{6}{x}$ and $g(x) = \frac{2}{3x}$.
   a. If $h(x) = f(x) \div g(x)$, what do think will be the simplest rule that gives correct values of $h(x)$?
   b. Test your idea in Part a by comparing tables of values for $\frac{6}{x} \div \frac{2}{3x}$ and for your proposed simpler expression to calculate $h(x)$. Use values of x in the interval $[-10, 10]$.
   c. Test your idea in Part a by graphing $y = \frac{6}{x} \div \frac{2}{3x}$ for values of x in the interval $[-10, 10]$ and then graphing $y = h(x)$, using your proposed simplified expression for $h(x)$.
   d. What similarities and what differences between division of numeric and algebraic fractions are suggested by the results of your work on Parts a–c?

7. Suppose that $f(x) = \frac{2x}{x^2-9}$ and $g(x) = \frac{5x^2}{2x-6}$.
   a. If $h(x) = f(x) \div g(x)$, what do you think will be the simplest rule that gives correct values of $h(x)$?
   b. Test your idea in Part a by comparing tables of values for $\frac{2x}{x^2-9} \div \frac{5x^2}{2x-6}$ and for your proposed simpler expression to calculate $h(x)$. Use values of x in the interval $[-10, 10]$.
   c. Test your idea in Part a by graphing $y = \frac{2x}{x^2-9} \div \frac{5x^2}{2x-6}$ for values of x in the interval $[-10, 10]$ and then graphing $y = h(x)$, using your proposed simplified expression for $h(x)$.
   d. What similarities and what differences between division of numeric and algebraic fractions are suggested by the results of your work on Parts a–c?

8. Consider the rational expression $\frac{6x^2+9x+8}{3x}$.
   a. Which of these expressions (if any) are equivalent to the original? How do you know?
      i. $2x + \frac{9x+8}{3x}$
      ii. $2x + 9x + 8$
      iii. $2x + 3 + \frac{8}{3x}$
   b. Check your answer to Part a by comparing graphs of the functions defined by each expression in the window $-5 \leq x \leq 5$ and $-10 \leq x \leq 20$.

378 UNIT 5 • Polynomial and Rational Functions

5 The simplified form is $\frac{2x + 1}{6x - 30}$ ($x \neq 5$); this can be obtained by recognizing that both numerator and denominator of the original product share common factors $(x + 5)$ and $(x - 2)$. The simplified expression ignores the limitation of the original to $x \neq 2$ and $x \neq -5$.

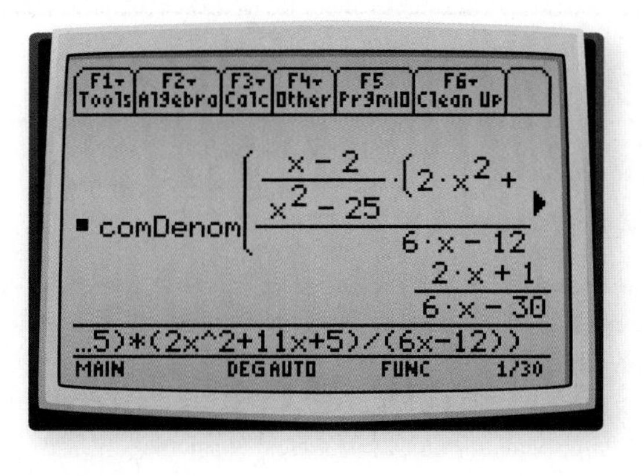

6 **a.** $h(x) = 9$

b. The results should verify the rule found in Part a, with the exception of $x \neq 0$. The domain of the original quotient has that limitation that is not apparent in the simplified form.

c. The graphs should match with the undetectable exception $x \neq 0$.

d. x cannot be equal to zero in the original, so a domain restriction has been lost by the simplification.

7 **a.** $h(x) = \frac{4}{5x^2 + 15x}$

b. The original and simplified functions agree on every integer x value from -10 to 10 except $x = 3$, which is an undefined point for the original quotient but not for the simplified expression. However, the quotient has a domain restriction $x \neq 0$ that was not present in either dividend or divisor.

c. Once again, the two graphs look indistinguishable because the only point at which their values differ, $x = 3$, leaves a removable discontinuity in the graph of the first expression.

d. Once again, simplification has removed a domain restriction in the resulting expression. Furthermore, division has introduced a domain restriction that did not apply to either dividend or divisor. This effect never happens with arithmetic fractions.

8 **a.** Expressions i and iii are "equivalent" to the original fraction, including the domain restriction $x \neq 0$ because all that has been done is to apply the general fraction identity $\frac{a}{c} + \frac{b}{c} = \frac{a + b}{c}$ in reverse and then simplify the results. In this case, the simplification does not result in change for the domain of definition of the result.

b. The graphs of expressions i and iii will agree with that of the original fraction but not that of expression ii, which is a straight line.

Unit 5

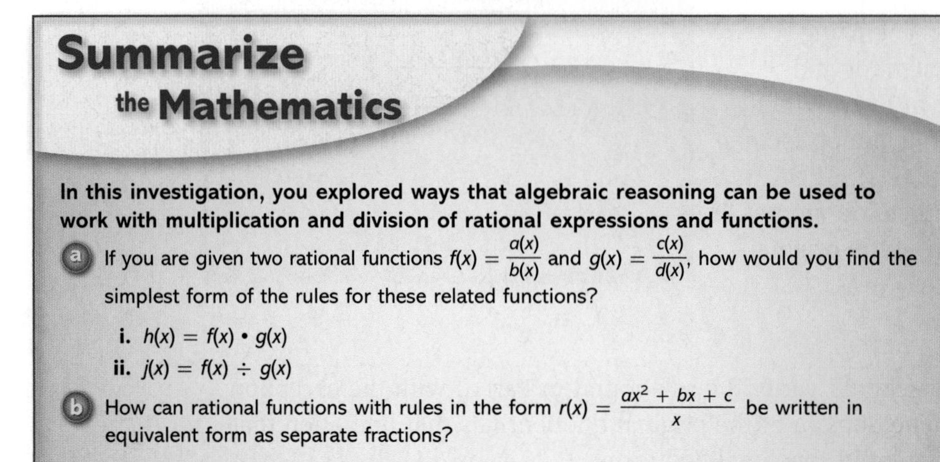

Summarize the Mathematics

In this investigation, you explored ways that algebraic reasoning can be used to work with multiplication and division of rational expressions and functions.

a If you are given two rational functions $f(x) = \frac{a(x)}{b(x)}$ and $g(x) = \frac{c(x)}{d(x)}$, how would you find the simplest form of the rules for these related functions?

i. $h(x) = f(x) \cdot g(x)$

ii. $j(x) = f(x) \div g(x)$

b How can rational functions with rules in the form $r(x) = \frac{ax^2 + bx + c}{x}$ be written in equivalent form as separate fractions?

Be prepared to explain your ideas to the class.

Unit 5

Check Your Understanding

Use your understanding of multiplication, division, and equivalent expressions to complete these tasks.

a. If $r(x) = \frac{x^2 + 3x - 10}{2x - 4}$ and $s(x) = \frac{3x - 6}{x - 2}$, find rules for the following expressed in simplest form.

i. $r(x) \cdot s(x)$

ii. $r(x) \div s(x)$

iii. $r(x) + s(x)$

iv. $r(x) - s(x)$

b. Write the rule for $y = \frac{3x - 5}{2x}$ in equivalent form as a sum of two separate fractions.

Summarize the Mathematics

a **i.** $h(x) = \dfrac{a(x)c(x)}{b(x)d(x)}$

ii. $j(x) = \dfrac{a(x)d(x)}{b(x)c(x)}$

If you return the factored forms of each function $a(x)$, $c(x)$, $b(x)$, and $d(x)$, you can look for identical factors in the numerator and denominator to remove. Once the rule is in simplest form, you can decide whether or not to multiply the remaining factors in the numerator and denominator.

b $r(x) = \dfrac{ax^2}{x} + \dfrac{bx}{x} + \dfrac{c}{x} = ax + b + \dfrac{c}{x}$

Check Your Understanding

a. **i.** $r(x) \cdot s(x) = \dfrac{3(x+5)}{2} = \dfrac{3x+15}{2}$

ii. $r(x) \div s(x) = \dfrac{x+5}{6}$

iii. $r(x) + s(x) = \dfrac{(x-2)(x+11)}{2(x-2)} = \dfrac{x+11}{2}$

iv. $r(x) - s(x) = \dfrac{(x-2)(x-1)}{2(x-2)} = \dfrac{x-1}{2}$

b. $y = \dfrac{3x}{2x} - \dfrac{5}{2x} = \dfrac{3}{2} - \dfrac{5}{2x}$

Teaching Resources

Transparency Master 28.

UNIT 5 *Polynomial and Rational Functions*

Summarize the Mathematics

In this investigation, you explored ways that algebraic reasoning can be used to work with multiplication and division of rational expressions and functions.

a If you are given two rational functions $f(x) = \frac{a(x)}{b(x)}$ and $g(x) = \frac{c(x)}{d(x)}$, how would you find the simplest form of the rules for these related functions?

i. $h(x) = f(x) \cdot g(x)$

ii. $j(x) = f(x) \div g(x)$

b How can rational functions with rules in the form $r(x) = \frac{ax^2 + bx + c}{x}$ be written in equivalent form as separate fractions?

Be prepared to explain your ideas to the class.

28 UNIT 5 • Polynomial and Rational Functions — Transparency Master • *use with page 379*

MATH TOOLKIT

Find $h(x) = \dfrac{f(x)}{g(x)}$. Describe the domain of $h(x)$ for $f(x) = \dfrac{x^2 - 3x - 4}{x + 3}$ and $g(x) = \dfrac{x^2 - 1}{x + 3}$.

Unit 5

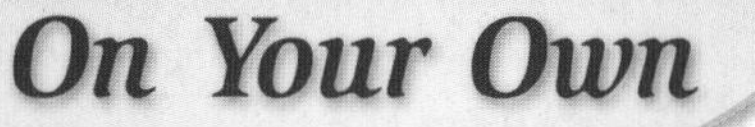

On Your Own

Applications

1. The Cannery designs and manufactures cans for packaging soups and vegetables. A&W Foods contracted with the Cannery to produce packaging for its store brand canned corn. Each can is to hold 500 cm^3 of corn. The company is interested in minimizing the cost of each can by minimizing the surface area of the can.

   a. Using the information below about the volume of the can, find a rational function $h(r)$ that gives the height h of the can as a function of the radius r of the can.

Volume of a Can	**Surface Area of a Can**
$V = \pi r^2 h$	$SA = 2\pi r^2 + 2\pi rh$

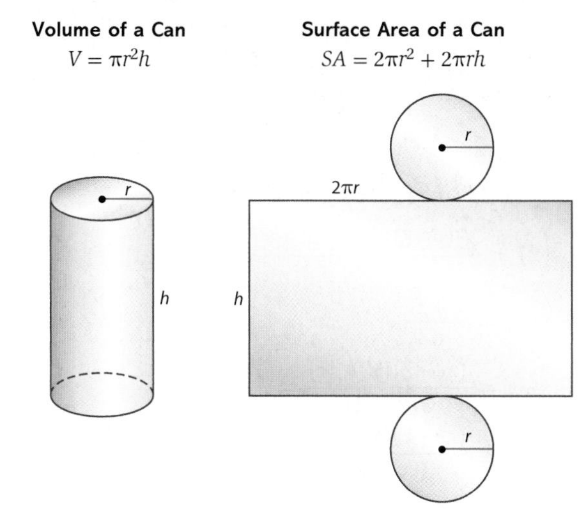

   b. Based on your results from Part a, write a function $S(r)$ to calculate the surface area of the can for any given radius r.

   c. Determine a practical domain for $S(r)$. Sketch a graph of the function on that domain. Identify any vertical asymptotes.

   d. Determine the minimum value of $S(r)$ on this practical domain. Give the radius and height of the can with minimum surface area to the nearest tenth of a centimeter.

380 UNIT 5 • Polynomial and Rational Functions

On Your Own

Applications

1 **a.** $h(r) = \frac{500}{\pi r^2}$

b. $S(r) = 2\pi r^2 + 2\pi r\left(\frac{500}{\pi r^2}\right) = 2\pi r^2 + \frac{1{,}000}{r}$

c. There is a vertical asymptote at $r = 0$. The practical domain is $0 < r < k$ where k is some upper bound of modest size (probably less than 20 for sure).

d. The minimum surface area of 348.7 cm^2 occurs when the radius is 4.3 cm. The height is 8.6 cm.

2 At the concert venue you have studied several times in this unit, concert attendance, snack bar income, operating expenses, and profit are all functions of the ticket price x.

- Concert attendance is given by $n(x) = 750 - 25x$.
- Snack bar income is given by $s(x) = 7{,}500 - 250x$.
- Snack bar operating expenses are given by $b(x) = 2{,}250 - 75x$.

a. Write two equivalent rules for the function $P_b(x)$ that gives snack bar profit as a function of ticket price. Give one rule that shows the separate expressions for calculating snack bar income and operating cost and another that is equivalent, yet easier to use in calculations.

b. For the rational functions described in parts i–iv:

- explain what they tell about the business situation.
- describe the theoretical and practical domains of the functions—the values of x for which a function output *can be* calculated and the values of x for which calculation of outputs makes sense in the problem situation.
- sketch graphs of each function, indicating any vertical asymptotes and enough of the graph so that its overall shape is clear.

i. $\dfrac{s(x)}{n(x)}$ **ii.** $\dfrac{b(x)}{n(x)}$

iii. $\dfrac{P_b(x)}{s(x)}$ **iv.** $\dfrac{b(x)}{s(x)}$

3 Simplify the rules for the rational functions defined in Task 2 as far as possible. In each case, check to see whether the domain of each simplified function rule is the same as that of the original.

4 When income from concert ticket and snack bar sales (Task 2) are combined, the functions that model the business situation are:

- Total income as a function of average ticket price is given by $I(x) = -25x^2 + 500x + 7{,}500$.
- Combined operating expenses for the concert and the snack bar is given by $E(x) = 7{,}000 - 200x$.
- The number of tickets sold is given by $n(x) = 750 - 25x$.

a. Write two equivalent rules for the function $P(x)$ that gives total profit as a function of ticket price. Give one rule that shows the separate expressions for calculating income and cost and another that is equivalent, yet easier to use in calculations.

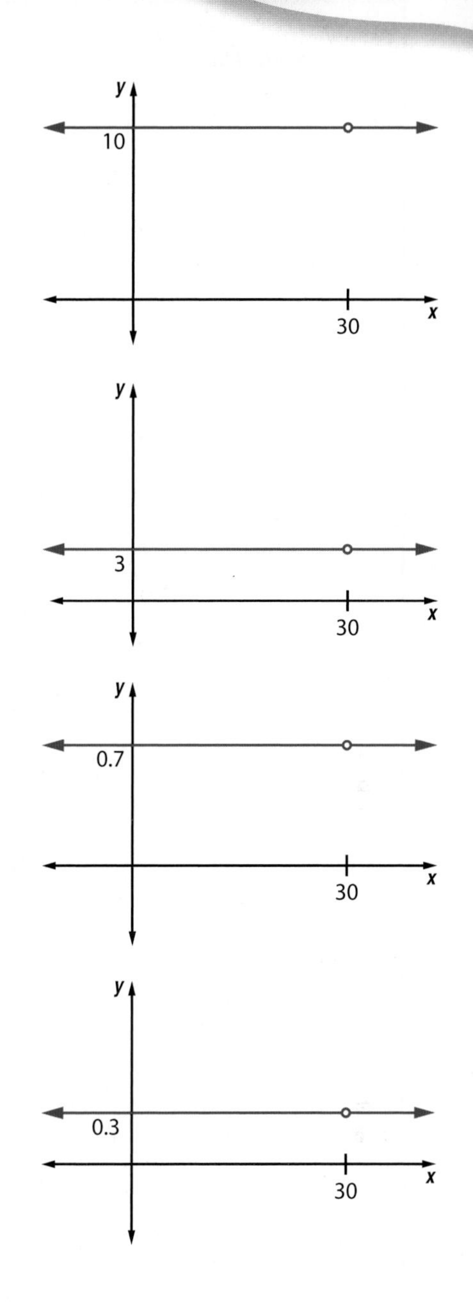

2 **a.** $P_b(x) = (7{,}500 - 250x) - (2{,}250 - 75x)$
$P_b(x) = 5{,}250 - 175x$

b. **i.** $\dfrac{s(x)}{n(x)} = \dfrac{7{,}500 - 250x}{750 - 25x}$

- Snack bar income per ticket
- The expression can be evaluated for all $x \neq 30$. It makes sense to consider $0 < x < 30$.
- No vertical asymptote; undefined at $x = 30$

ii. $\dfrac{b(x)}{n(x)} = \dfrac{2{,}250 - 75x}{750 - 25x}$

- Snack bar expenses per ticket
- The expression can be evaluated for all $x \neq 30$. It makes sense to consider $0 < x < 30$.
- No vertical asymptote; undefined at $x = 30$

iii. $\dfrac{P_b(x)}{s(x)} = \dfrac{5{,}250 - 175x}{7{,}500 - 250x}$

- Ratio of snack bar profit to income
- The expression can be evaluated for all $x \neq 30$. It makes sense to consider $0 < x < 30$.
- No vertical asymptote; undefined at $x = 30$

iv. $\dfrac{b(x)}{s(x)} = \dfrac{2{,}250 - 75x}{7{,}500 - 250x}$

- Ratio of snack bar expenses to income
- The expression can be evaluated for all $x \neq 30$. It makes sense to consider $0 < x < 30$.
- No vertical asymptote; undefined at $x = 30$

3 **a.** $\dfrac{s(x)}{n(x)} = 10$, when $x \neq 30$ **b.** $\dfrac{b(x)}{n(x)} = 3$, when $x \neq 30$

c. $\dfrac{P_b(x)}{s(x)} = \dfrac{7}{10}$, when $x \neq 30$ **d.** $\dfrac{b(x)}{s(x)} = \dfrac{3}{10}$, when $x \neq 30$

4 **a.** $P(x) = (-25x^2 + 500x + 7{,}500) - (7{,}000 - 200x)$
$P(x) = -25x^2 + 700x + 500$

ASSIGNMENT NOTE
Task 4 must be assigned before Task 5.

On Your Own

b. For the rational functions described in parts i–iv:

- explain what they tell about the business situation.
- describe the theoretical and practical domains of the functions—the values of x for which a function output *can be* calculated and the values of x for which calculation of outputs makes sense in the problem situation.
- sketch graphs of each function, indicating any vertical asymptotes and enough of the graph so that its overall shape is clear.

i. $\frac{P(x)}{I(x)}$ **ii.** $\frac{E(x)}{I(x)}$

iii. $\frac{P(x)}{n(x)}$ **iv.** $\frac{E(x)}{n(x)}$

5 Simplify the rules for the rational functions defined in Task 4 as far as possible. In each case, check to see whether the domain of the simplified function rule is the same as that of the original.

6 Describe the domains of these rational functions. Explain how you know that your answers are correct.

a. $f(x) = \frac{4x + 1}{3x + 2}$ **b.** $g(x) = \frac{5x + 10}{x + 2}$

c. $h(x) = \frac{x + 1}{x^2}$ **d.** $j(x) = \frac{x^2 + 3}{x^2 - 9}$

7 Simplify these algebraic fractions as much as possible. In each case, check to see whether the simplified expression is undefined for the same values of x as the original expression.

a. $\frac{4x + 12}{8x + 4}$ **b.** $\frac{4 - 3x}{6x - 8}$

c. $\frac{15x^2 + 6x}{3x^2}$ **d.** $\frac{4 + x^2}{16 - x^2}$

8 Write each of these sums and differences of rational expressions in equivalent form as a single algebraic fraction. Then simplify the result as much as possible.

a. $\frac{4x + 13}{x - 3} + \frac{x + 2}{x - 3}$ **b.** $\frac{3x + 7}{x - 2} - \frac{x + 5}{x - 2}$

c. $(x + 2) + \frac{x + 6}{x - 4}$ **d.** $\frac{3x^2 + 5x + 1}{x^2 - 25} - \frac{3x^2 + 4x - 4}{x^2 - 25}$

9 Write these products and quotients of rational expressions in equivalent form as single algebraic fractions. Then simplify the results as much as possible.

a. $\frac{2x}{x + 2} \cdot \frac{3x + 6}{x^2}$ **b.** $\frac{2x + 6}{x + 2} \cdot \frac{3x + 2}{x + 3}$

c. $\frac{x + 2}{x} \div \frac{3x + 6}{x^2}$ **d.** $\frac{2x}{x + 2} \div \frac{x^2}{2x + 4}$

10 Write each of these products and quotients of rational expressions in equivalent form as a single algebraic fraction. Then simplify the result as much as possible.

a. $\frac{2x + 4}{x^2 - 6x} \cdot \frac{x^2 - 36}{4x + 8}$ **b.** $\frac{x - 3}{7x} \cdot \frac{3x^2}{x^2 - 2x - 3}$

c. $\frac{x^2 - 4}{x^2 + 2x - 5} \div \frac{x + 2}{x^2 + 2x - 5}$ **d.** $\frac{2x^2 + 10x}{4x + 10} \div \frac{3x^2 + x}{9x + 3}$

382 UNIT 5 • Polynomial and Rational Functions

b. **i.** $\dfrac{P(x)}{I(x)} = \dfrac{-25x^2 + 700x + 500}{-25x^2 + 500x + 7{,}500}$

- Ratio of profit to income
- The expression can be evaluated for all $x \neq -10, 30$. It makes sense to consider $0 < x < 30$.
- There are vertical asymptotes at $x = -10$ and at $x = 30$.

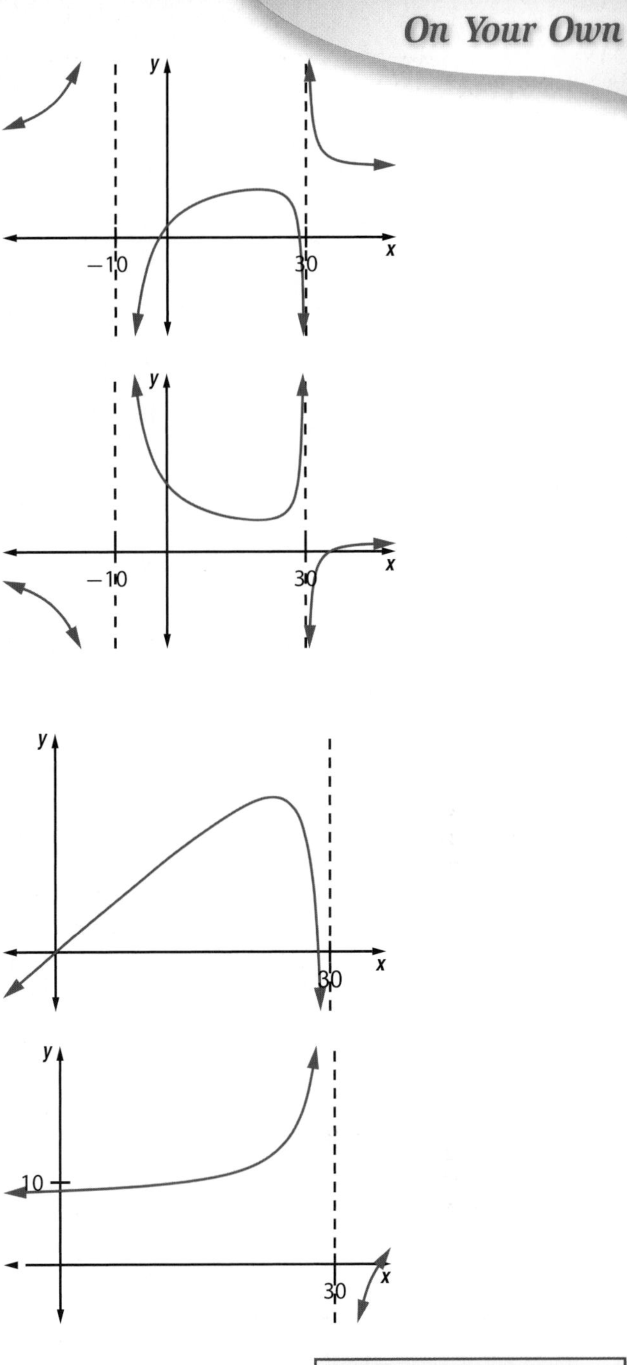

ii. $\dfrac{E(x)}{I(x)} = \dfrac{7{,}000 - 200x}{-25x^2 + 500x + 7{,}500}$

- Percentage of income that goes to pay expenses
- The expression can be evaluated for all $x \neq -10, 30$. It makes sense to consider $0 < x < 30$.
- There are vertical asymptotes at $x = -10$ and at $x = 30$.

iii. $\dfrac{P(x)}{n(x)} = \dfrac{-25x^2 + 700x + 500}{750 - 25x}$

- Profit per ticket
- The expression can be evaluated for all $x \neq 30$. It makes sense to consider $0 < x < 30$.
- There is a vertical asymptote at $x = 30$.

iv. $\dfrac{E(x)}{n(x)} = \dfrac{7{,}000 - 200x}{750 - 25x}$

- Expense per ticket
- The expression can be evaluated for all $x \neq 30$. It makes sense to consider $0 \leq x < 30$.
- There is a vertical asymptote at $x = 30$.

5

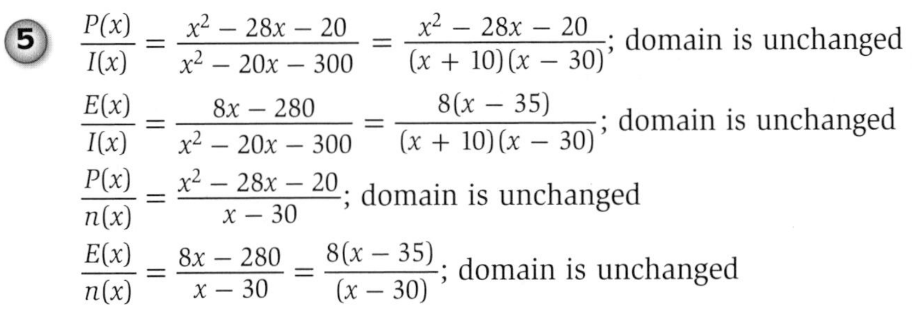

$\dfrac{P(x)}{I(x)} = \dfrac{x^2 - 28x - 20}{x^2 - 20x - 300} = \dfrac{x^2 - 28x - 20}{(x + 10)(x - 30)}$; domain is unchanged

$\dfrac{E(x)}{I(x)} = \dfrac{8x - 280}{x^2 - 20x - 300} = \dfrac{8(x - 35)}{(x + 10)(x - 30)}$; domain is unchanged

$\dfrac{P(x)}{n(x)} = \dfrac{x^2 - 28x - 20}{x - 30}$; domain is unchanged

$\dfrac{E(x)}{n(x)} = \dfrac{8x - 280}{x - 30} = \dfrac{8(x - 35)}{(x - 30)}$; domain is unchanged

INSTRUCTIONAL NOTE
In Task 5, all rational expressions reduce by a common integer factor and thus have no domain changes.

6 Restrictions on domains (x values) occur when the denominator is zero.

a. The domain of $f(x)$ is any x where $x \neq -\frac{2}{3}$ because $3\left(-\frac{2}{3}\right) + 2 = 0$.

b. The domain of $g(x)$ is any x where $x \neq -2$ because $(-2) + 2 = 0$.

c. The domain of $h(x)$ is any x where $x \neq 0$ because $0^2 = 0$.

d. The domain of $j(x)$ is any x where $x \neq -3$ and $x \neq 3$ because $x^2 - 9 = 0$ when $x = \pm 3$.

7 **a.** $\frac{x+3}{2x+1}$; undefined for same values of x.

b. $-\frac{1}{2}$; new expression is defined when evaluated at $x = \frac{4}{3}$, original was not.

c. $\frac{5x+2}{x}$; undefined for same values of x.

d. $\frac{4+x^2}{16-x^2}$; undefined for same values of x because it does not simplify.

8 **a.** $\frac{5x+15}{x-3} = \frac{5(x+3)}{x-3}$

b. $\frac{2x+2}{x-2} = \frac{2(x+1)}{x-2}$

c. $\frac{x^2-x-2}{x-4}$

d. $\frac{x+5}{x^2-25} = \frac{x+5}{(x+5)(x-5)} = \frac{1}{x-5}$

9 **a.** $\frac{6x(x+2)}{x^2(x+2)} = \frac{6}{x}$

b. $\frac{2(x+3)(3x+2)}{(x+2)(x+3)} = \frac{6x+4}{x+2}$

c. $\frac{x^2(x+2)}{3x(x+2)} = \frac{x}{3}$

d. $\frac{4x(x+2)}{x^2(x+2)} = \frac{4}{x}$

10 **a.** $\frac{2(x+2)(x+6)(x-6)}{4x(x-6)(x+2)} = \frac{x+6}{2x}$

b. $\frac{3x^2(x-3)}{7x(x-3)(x+1)} = \frac{3x}{7x+7}$

c. $\frac{(x+2)(x-2)(x^2+2x-5)}{(x^2+2x-5)(x+2)} = x - 2$

d. $\frac{2x(x+5)3(3x+1)}{2(2x+5)x(3x+1)} = \frac{3x+15}{2x+5}$

Teacher Notes

11 Write each of these rational expressions as a sum or difference of two or more algebraic fractions in simplest form.

a. $\dfrac{3x + 5}{x}$

b. $\dfrac{3x^2 + 5x}{x}$

c. $\dfrac{3x^2 - 9x + 12}{6x^2}$

d. $\dfrac{3x + 21}{x + 7}$

Connections

12 Look back at your work for Applications Task 1.

a. Record the height and radius of the can with minimum surface area in Part d.

b. Find the radius and height of the can with minimum surface area for cylindrical cans with these volumes: 236 cm^3, 650 cm^3, and 946 cm^3.

c. Plot (*optimal radius, optimal height*) for each of the cans in Parts a and b.

d. What relationship seems to exist between the optimal radius and height for a given volume?

13 In any right triangle ABC with right angle at C, the *tangent* of $\angle A$ is the ratio $\frac{a}{b}$.

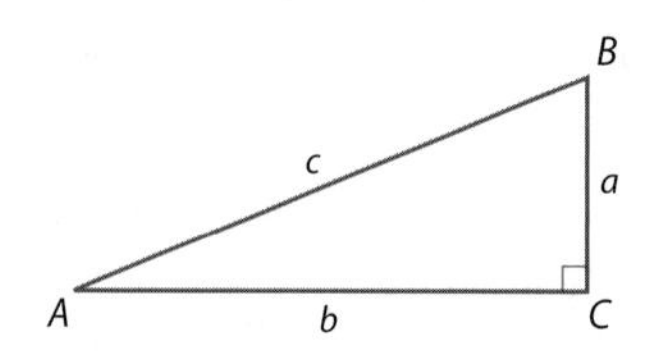

Use what you know about operations with fractions to prove that for any acute angle A,

$$\frac{\sin A}{\cos A} = \tan A.$$

14 Consider the function $r(x) = \dfrac{3(2)^x}{0.5(10)^x}$.

a. Is $r(x)$ a rational function?

b. When the function is graphed, are there any asymptotes? If so, give their location.

c. Show how the expression defining $r(x)$ can be written in a simpler form that shows the function family to which it belongs.

15 The graphs of these functions all have *horizontal asymptotes*, lines with equations in the form $y = a$.

$f(x) = 2^x$ $\qquad g(x) = 0.5^x + 3$ $\qquad h(x) = \dfrac{1}{x}$

$j(x) = \dfrac{1}{x^2}$ $\qquad k(x) = \dfrac{8x + 5}{2x}$ $\qquad m(x) = \dfrac{x^2 + 2x - 1}{x^2 + x - 2}$

Study graphs and rules of the given functions to identify equations of their horizontal asymptotes.

11 Answers may vary here. Answers below provide what seems to be the most obvious response to the given task.

a. $\frac{3x}{x} + \frac{5}{x} = 3 + \frac{5}{x}$

b. $\frac{3x^2}{x} + \frac{5x}{x} = 3x + 5$

c. $\frac{3x^2}{6x^2} - \frac{9x}{6x^2} + \frac{12}{6x^2} = \frac{1}{2} - \frac{3}{2x} + \frac{2}{x^2}$

d. $\frac{3(x+7)}{x+7} = 3(x \neq -7)$, or $\frac{3x}{x+7} + \frac{21}{x+7}$

Connections

12 **a.** The minimum surface area for a can with volume 500 cm^3 is approximately 348.7 cm^2 and has $r \approx 4.3$ cm and $h \approx 8.6$ cm.

b. The formulas for surface area and volume of a can are $S = 2\pi r^2 + 2\pi rh$ and $V = \pi r^2 h$, so the surface area formula can be rewritten as $S = 2\pi r^2 + \frac{2V}{r}$. The dimensions of cans with minimum surface area are:

$V = 236$ cm^3	$S \approx 211$ cm^2	$r \approx 3.35$ cm	$h \approx 6.7$ cm
$V = 650$ cm^3	$S \approx 416$ cm^2	$r \approx 4.7$ cm	$h \approx 9.4$ cm
$V = 946$ cm^3	$S \approx 533$ cm^2	$r \approx 5.3$ cm	$h \approx 10.7$ cm

c.

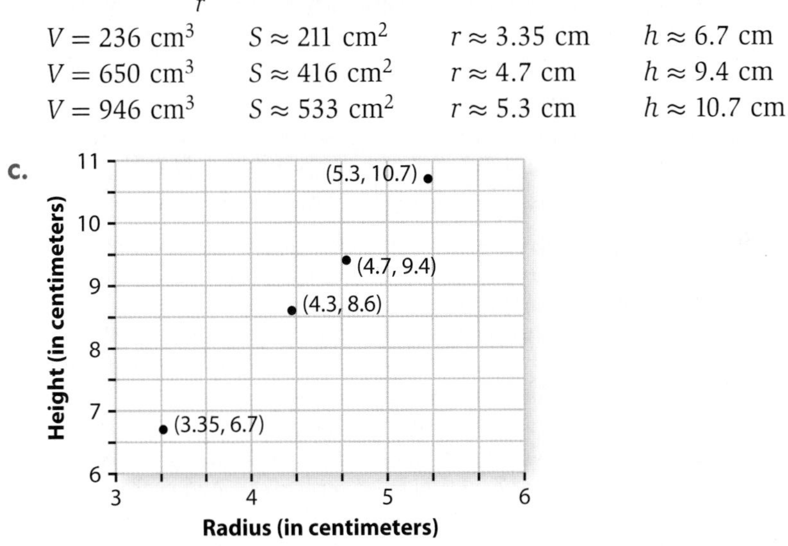

d. To minimize the surface area for a given volume, the height should be approximately twice the radius.

(Some cans are designed near the optimum, but many cans are not. The lip required to manufacture the can plays an important role and can be three times as thick as the other parts of the can.)

13 $\frac{\sin A}{\cos A} = \frac{\frac{a}{c}}{\frac{b}{c}} = \frac{a}{c} \cdot \frac{c}{b} = \frac{a}{b} = \tan A$

14 **a.** The function is not a rational function because neither the numerator nor the denominator is a polynomial.

b. There are no vertical asymptotes since $0.5(10)^x$ can never equal zero. However, the x-axis is a horizontal asymptote. This can be seen by rewriting the given expression as shown in Part c.

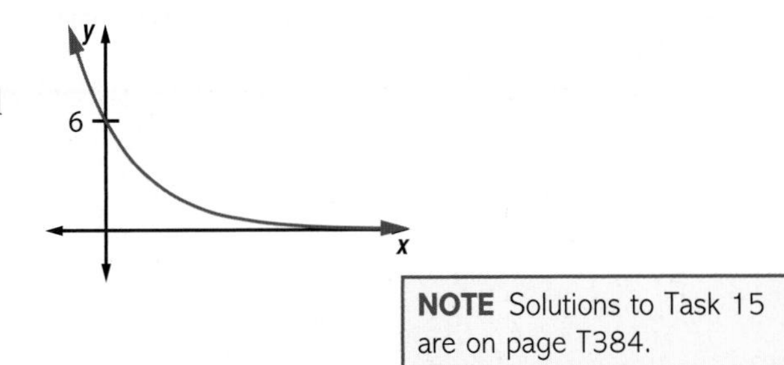

c. $r(x) = \frac{3(2)^x}{0.5(10)^x} = \frac{3}{0.5} \cdot \frac{2^x}{10^x} = 6\left(\frac{2}{10}\right)^x = 6(0.2)^x$

$r(x)$ is an exponential function.

NOTE Solutions to Task 15 are on page T384.

On Your Own

16 Explain procedures that are necessary to perform these operations on arithmetic fractions.

a. Simplify a fraction like $\frac{36}{60}$.

b. Find the sum or difference of two fractions like $\frac{3}{5}$ and $\frac{7}{5}$.

c. Find the sum or difference of two fractions like $\frac{3}{5}$ and $\frac{7}{4}$.

d. Find the product of two fractions like $\frac{3}{5}$ and $\frac{7}{4}$.

e. Find the quotient of two fractions like $\frac{3}{5}$ and $\frac{7}{4}$.

17 The time required to complete a 100-mile bicycle race depends on the average speed of the rider. The function $T(s) = \frac{100}{s}$ tells time in hours if speed is in miles per hour.

a. Identify the vertical and horizontal asymptotes for the graph of $T(s)$.

b. Explain what each asymptote says about the way race time changes as average rider speed changes.

18 The intensity of sound from some source like a music speaker or a lightning strike is inversely proportional to the square of the distance from source to receiver. For example, suppose that the intensity of sound at various distances from a nearby explosion is given by the function $I(d) = \frac{100}{d^2}$, where distance is measured in meters and sound intensity in watts per square meter.

a. Identify the vertical and horizontal asymptotes for the graph of $I(d)$.

b. Explain what each asymptote says about the way received sound intensity changes as distance from the source changes.

19 When the Holiday Out hotel chain was planning to build a new property, organizers bought land for $5,000,000, and their architect made building plans that would cost $10,000,000 for the lobby, restaurant, and other common facilities. The architect also said that construction costs would average an additional $75,000 per guest room.

a. What rule defines the function that relates total construction cost C to the number n of guest rooms in the hotel?

b. What rule defines the function $A(n)$ that gives average cost per guest room as a function of the number n of guest rooms in the hotel?

c. What are the theoretical domains of the total cost and average cost functions? What are reasonable practical domains to consider for those functions?

d. Sketch a graph of the average cost per guest room function. Identify the vertical and horizontal asymptotes of that graph. Explain what the asymptotes tell about the way average cost per room changes as the number of planned guest rooms changes.

384 UNIT 5 • Polynomial and Rational Functions

15 $f(x)$: $y = 0$ $g(x)$: $y = 3$ $h(x)$: $y = 0$
$j(x)$: $y = 0$ $k(x)$: $y = 4$ $m(x)$: $y = 1$

16 **a.** Find the largest integer that divides both 36 and 60 (12) and divide numerator and denominator by that integer.

b. Since the denominators are the same, the numerators are added and the denominator is the original value.

c. Express each fraction with the same denominator. Then proceed as in Part b.

d. Multiply the numerators and multiply the denominators. These products are the numerator and denominator of the result.

e. Multiply the dividend by the reciprocal of the divisor using the procedure in Part d.

17 For this answer, the domain is $s \geq 0$.

a. The asymptotes are at $s = 0$ (vertical) and $T(s) = 0$ (horizontal).

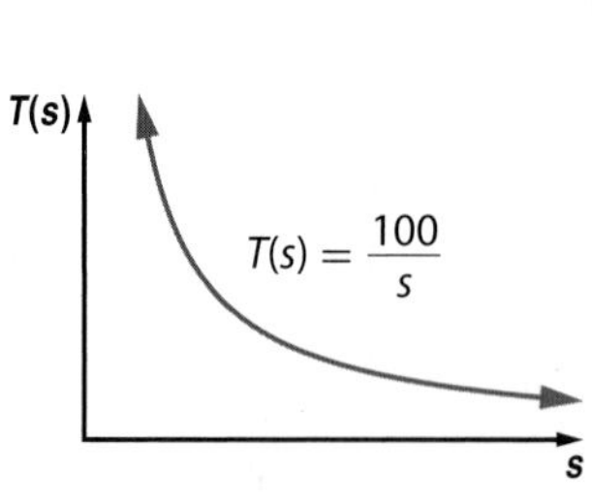

b. If the speed were to be zero ($s = 0$), it would take an infinite amount of time to finish the race. As the rider's speed approaches zero miles per hour, the time to finish the race grows without bound. On the other hand, as the racer's speed increases without bound, the time to complete the race decreases toward 0 hours.

18 For this answer, the domain is $d > 0$.

a. The asymptotes are at $d = 0$ and $I(d) = 0$.

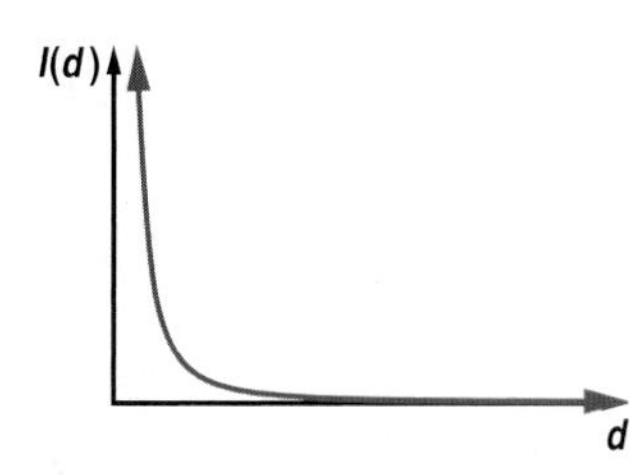

b. If the distance from the explosion is zero ($d = 0$), the intensity of the sound would be infinite. As the observer's distance from the explosion approaches 0 meters, the intensity of the sound grows without bound.
As the distance from the source increases, the intensity of the sound decreases toward a lower limit of 0.

19 **a.** $C(n) = 15{,}000{,}000 + 75{,}000n$

b. $A(n) = \dfrac{15{,}000{,}000 + 75{,}000n}{n}$

c. The domain of $C(n)$ is the set of all real numbers. The domain of $A(n)$ is the set of all numbers not equal to zero. It only makes sense to consider positive integers in this situation. Also, even the largest hotels seldom have more than a few thousand rooms.

d. There is a vertical asymptote at $n = 0$ (as the number of rooms approaches zero, the cost per room approaches infinity) and a horizontal asymptote at $C = 75{,}000$ (each room costs 75,000 even when the cost of the lobby and common areas per room approaches zero).

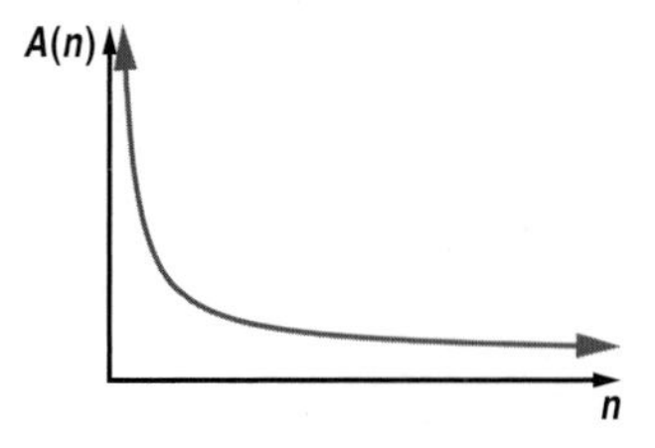

20 Rational functions arise naturally when working with similar triangles. Suppose that a long ladder is to be moved horizontally around a corner in a building with 8-foot hallways. The ladder can make it around the corner only if its length is less than all lengths L that satisfy the conditions of the diagram below.

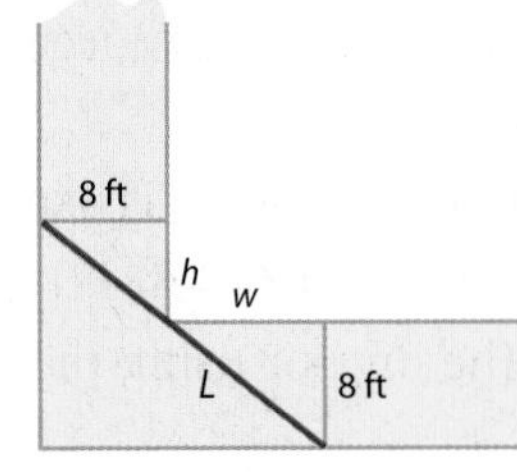

a. Using similar triangles, determine a relationship between h and w.

b. Write a function relating the distance L to the lengths h and w. Then use the relationship from Part a to write L as a function of h. (Ignore the thickness of the ladder.)

c. Determine the minimum value $L(h)$.

d. As the longest possible ladder moves through the corner, what angle is made with the walls? Explain how this angle is determined by the symmetry of the situation.

e. What is the minimum value of L if one of the hallways is 4 feet wide and the other is 8 feet wide?

Reflections

21 Why does the term *rational function* seem appropriate for any function that can be expressed as the quotient of two polynomials?

22 Suppose $f(x) = \frac{p(x)}{q(x)}$ is a rational function.

a. What can you conclude if $p(a) = 0$ and $q(a) \neq 0$?

b. What can you conclude if $q(a) = 0$ and $p(a) \neq 0$?

c. What can you conclude if $p(a) = 0$ and $q(a) = 0$?

23 What are some important things to remember and look for when:

a. analyzing the behavior of rational functions and their graphs?

b. simplifying rational expressions for functions?

c. adding or subtracting rational expressions and functions?

d. multiplying or dividing rational expressions and functions?

20 **a.** The two smaller right triangles are similar by the AA Similarity Theorem. The two acute angles formed by the object and the corner are complementary (assuming that the corner is a right angle). Similarly, the acute angles of each of the right triangles are complementary. So, the acute angle at the corner vertex of one triangle is the same measure as the acute angle of the other triangle that is not at the corner vertex. Alternatively, parallel lines and transversals could be used to justify the two triangles are similar. So, $\frac{8}{h} = \frac{w}{8}$.

b. To find the length of the object L, consider the diagram at the right that shows the right triangle formed by drawing the rectangle with sides of length h and w. Using the Pythagorean Theorem, $L^2 = (h + 8)^2 + (w + 8)^2$. From Part a, $w = \frac{64}{h}$. Thus, $L^2 = (h + 8)^2 + \left(\frac{64}{h} + 8\right)^2$. So, $L(h) = \sqrt{(h + 8)^2 + \left(\frac{64}{h} + 8\right)^2}$.

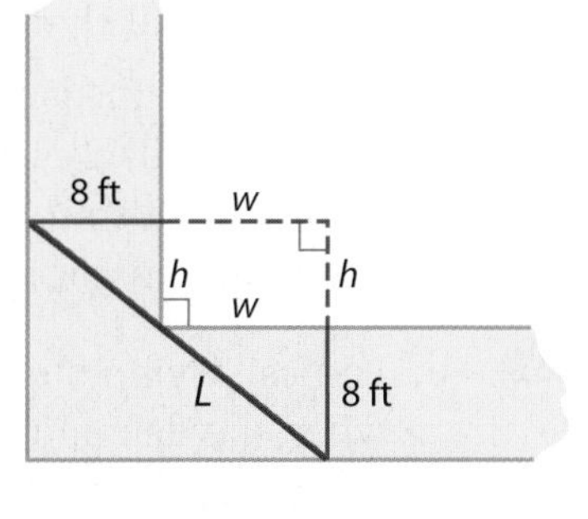

c. You can find the minimum of $L(h)$ by examining a table or graph of the function. The minimum occurs when h is 8. So, the minimum value of $L = \sqrt{512} \approx 22.6$ ft.

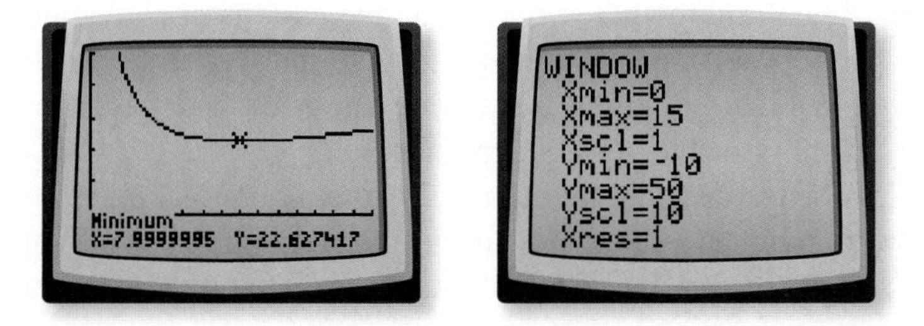

d. The corresponding value of k is also 8. Thus, the ladder would make 45° angles with each side of the corner and each outer side of the hall as it just fits through. The values of h and w equal to 8 ft make each triangle an isosceles right triangle, so the acute angles are all 45°.

e. The equations that will help find the length are $L^2 = (h + 4)^2 + (w + 8)^2$ and $\frac{4}{w} = \frac{h}{8}$. Then $L(h) = \sqrt{(h + 4)^2 + \left(\frac{32}{h} + 8\right)^2}$. The minimum length occurs at $h \approx 6.35$.

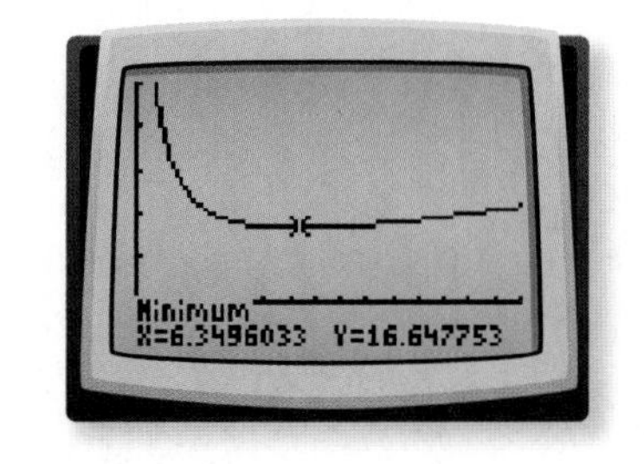

Thus, $L \approx \sqrt{(10.35)^2 + (13.04)^2} \approx 277.16 \approx 16.6$ ft.

Reflections

21 Student responses may vary but should include a reference to a *rational number* as a number that can be expressed as the quotient of two integers. Also, the root of "rational" is "ratio" which is a comparison of two numbers by division.

22 **a.** $f(a) = 0$

b. $f(a)$ is undefined, so a is not a domain value of $f(x)$. Also, the graph of $f(x)$ will likely have a vertical asymptote at $x = a$.

c. $f(a)$ is undefined, so a is not a domain value of $f(x)$. Also, the graph of $f(x)$ will likely have a hole (removable discontinuity) at $x = a$. (This depends on the multiplicity of the zero in the numerator and denominator.)

23 **a.** Vertical asymptotes will occur only when the denominator is 0. Even when the denominator is zero, some discontinuities of a rational function may not be clearly visible in a graph when the zero of the denominator is also a zero of the numerator.

b. Only common *factors* can be cancelled and the domain of the expression may be altered through these operations.

c. Two rational expressions can only be added or subtracted if their denominators are the same.

d. When multiplying two rational expressions, it sometimes helps to find common factors in numerators and denominators before multiplying. Once the multiplication is done, the result can be examined for common factors to reduce the result.

When dividing two rational expressions it is important to remember to invert the divisor. Again, it often helps to look for common factors in numerator and denominator before doing the required multiplication of numerators and denominators.

Teacher Notes

Extensions

24 Consider the function $f(x) = \dfrac{x^2 + x - 12}{x^2 - x - 6}$.

a. What are the values of x for which $f(x)$ is undefined?

b. Graph $f(x)$ to see whether there seem to be vertical asymptotes at the values of x for which $f(x)$ is undefined.

c. Let $\tilde{f}(x)$ be the function resulting from simplifying the expression for $f(x)$. For how many values of x is $\tilde{f}(x)$ undefined?

d. How many vertical asymptotes does the graph of $\tilde{f}(x)$ have? Where are they?

e. How do the graphs of $f(x)$ and $\tilde{f}(x)$ compare?

25 The function $f(x)$ in Task 24 is *undefined* at $x = 3$. The nearly identical function $\tilde{f}(x)$ with rule obtained by "simplifying" the rational expression for $f(x)$, is *defined* at $x = 3$. However, the graph of $f(x)$ has no vertical asymptote at $x = 3$. That fact is shown by drawing a "hole" in the graph where $x = 3$.

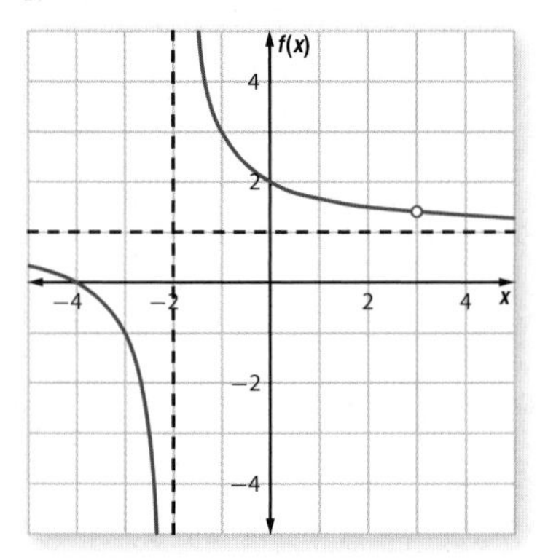

The function $f(x)$ is said to have a **removable discontinuity** at $x = 3$ because the discontinuity or break in the graph can be removed by simplifying the expression. As a result, 3 is in the domain of $\tilde{f}(x)$ but not in the domain of $f(x)$. However, the other value of x for which $f(x)$ is undefined gives rise to a vertical asymptote, a discontinuity that cannot be removed by simplification. Therefore, $f(x)$ is said to have an **essential discontinuity** at $x = -2$.

Determine the essential and removable discontinuities for each function in Parts a–d.

a. $f(x) = \dfrac{4x + 12}{8x + 4}$

b. $g(x) = \dfrac{5x + 10}{x + 2}$

c. $h(x) = \dfrac{15x^2 + 6x}{3x^2}$

d. $j(x) = \dfrac{x^2 + 3}{x^2 - 9}$

26 Consider $f(x) = \dfrac{20x^3 + 10x^2 - 150x}{20x^2 - 125}$.

a. Simplify the expression for $f(x)$.

b. Compare graphs of $f(x)$ and the function given by the simplified expression.

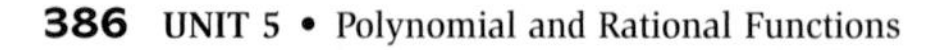

Extensions

24 **a.** $f(x)$ is undefined when $x = 3$ and when $x = -2$.

b. There is a vertical asymptote at $x = -2$ but not at $x = 3$.

c. It is undefined only when $x = -2$.

d. One vertical asymptote at $x = -2$

e. They appear to be the same. The only difference is the "hole" in the graph of $f(x)$ at $x = 3$.

25 **a.** Essential discontinuity at $x = -0.5$; no removable discontinuities

b. Removable discontinuity at $x = -2$; no essential discontinuities

c. There is an essential discontinuity at $x = 0$. (Students may say there is a removable discontinuity at $x = 0$. But here is a somewhat subtle point that even though the factor of x appears in both the numerator and denominator of the original fraction, it appears with greater multiplicity in the denominator, causing a vertical asymptote of $x = 0$.)

d. Essential discontinuities at $x = 3$ and $x = -3$; no removable discontinuities

26 **a.** $\frac{2x(x + 3)}{2x + 5}$

b. The graphs should appear identical with a vertical asymptote at $x = -2.5$.

INSTRUCTIONAL NOTE
Task 26 provides another opportunity for students to recognize the value of first finding common factors.

c. Give the values of x for which $f(x)$ is undefined. Classify each discontinuity as removable or essential. (See Task 25.)

d. What is the domain of $f(x)$?

e. What is the domain of the function derived by simplifying the expression for $f(x)$?

27 The graph of $R(x) = \frac{-25x^2 + 875x - 4{,}750}{750 - 25x}$ has what is called an **oblique asymptote**. The next diagram shows how the graph of $R(x)$ approaches the oblique asymptote $y = x - 5$.

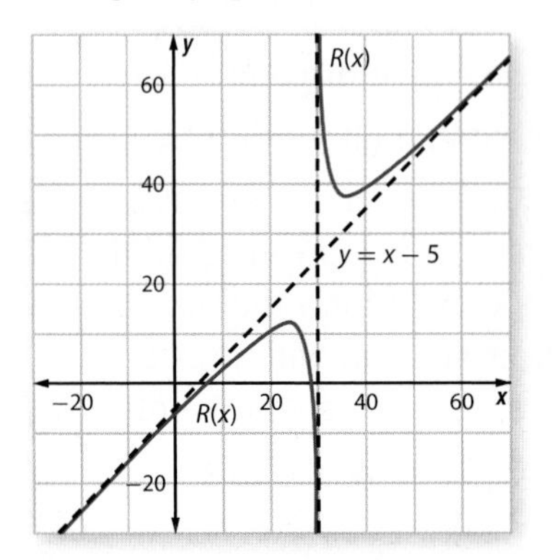

Use a spreadsheet or function table tool to examine values of $R(x)$ for very large values of x, say larger than 100, and then for "large negative" values of x.

a. Explain how your results illustrate the fact that as x approaches positive infinity, the graph of $R(x)$ gets arbitrarily close to the line $y = x - 5$, while remaining above it.

b. Explain how your results illustrate the fact that as x approaches negative infinity, the graph of $R(x)$ gets arbitrarily close to the line $y = x - 5$, while remaining below it.

28 Consider the function with rule $h(x) = 3x - 4 + \frac{5}{x}$.

a. What is the oblique asymptote for the graph of this function? How can you tell by analyzing values produced by the function rule when x is very large (approaches positive infinity) or very small (approaches negative infinity)?

b. How can the rule for $h(x)$ be given by an equivalent rational expression?

29 Suppose $f(x) = x - 3$ and $g(x) = \frac{6}{x - 2}$.

a. If you want to think of $f(x)$ as a rational function, what is its denominator?

b. What could you multiply that denominator by so it is the same as the denominator of $g(x)$?

c. Use your idea from Part b to find a rule for $f(x) - g(x)$ expressed with one simplified algebraic fraction.

c. $x = -2.5$ (essential) and $x = 2.5$ (removable)

d. The domain is the set of all x such that $x \neq \pm 2.5$.

e. The new domain is the set of all x such that $x \neq -2.5$.

27 a. As x gets very large, the numbers produced for $R(x)$ should remain larger than the corresponding values of $x - 5$, but they should approach those values very closely. For example, $R(100) \approx 95.571$, $R(200) \approx 195.24$, and $R(300) \approx 295.15$, all values slightly above $y = x - 5$.

b. As x decreases in value in the negative direction, results produced for $R(x)$ should remain smaller than the corresponding values of $x - 5$, but they should approach those values very closely. For example, $R(-100) \approx -105.3$, $R(-200) \approx -205.2$, and $R(-300) \approx -305.1$, all values slight below $y = x - 5$.

28 a. The oblique asymptote is $y = 3x - 4$. As x approaches positive or negative infinity, $\frac{5}{x}$ approaches zero, so the expression for $h(x)$ approaches $3x - 4$.

b. $h(x) = \frac{3x^2 - 4x + 5}{x}$

29 a. 1

b. $(x - 2)$

c. $\frac{x^2 - 5x}{x - 2}$

d. Check your answer to Part c by graphing the simplified algebraic fraction and the function $y = (x - 3) - \frac{6}{x - 2}$.

e. The graph of $y = (x - 3) - \frac{6}{x - 2}$ has an oblique asymptote. Which form of the difference expression makes it easier to identify the equation of that asymptote, the expression $(x - 3) - \frac{6}{x - 2}$ or your answer to Part c? Be prepared to explain your reasoning.

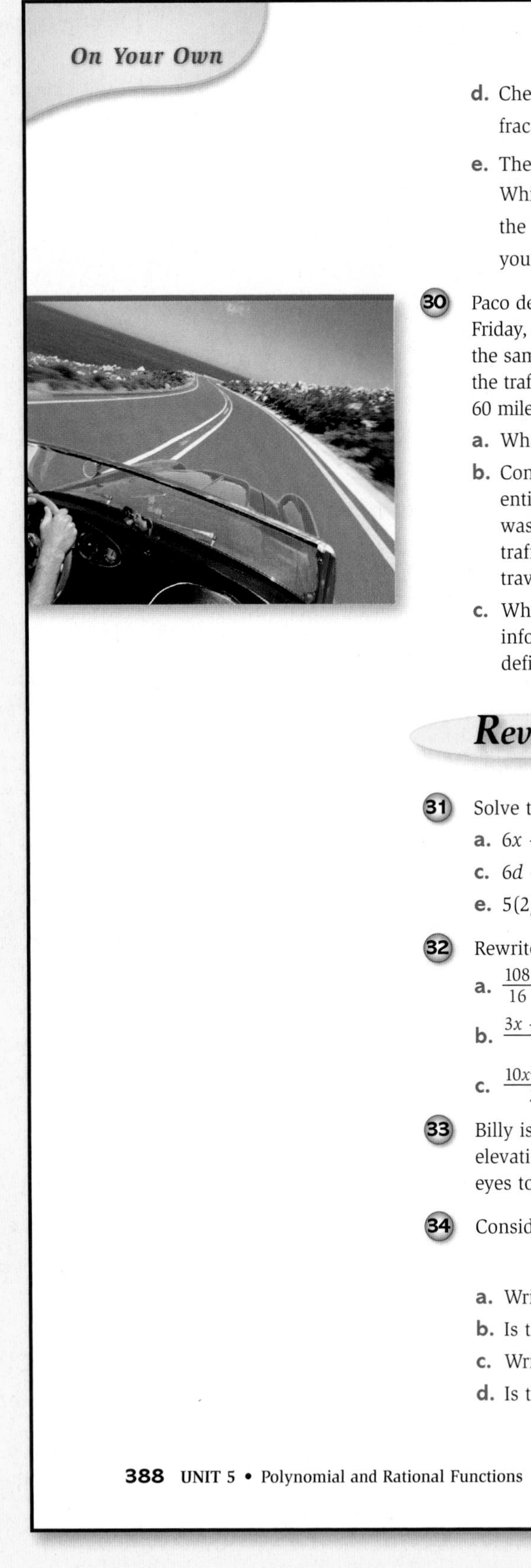

30 Paco decided to spend the weekend at the local beach. He left on Friday, and his average speed was only 30 miles per hour. He took the same route home but was able to wait until Tuesday when the traffic was lighter. For the return trip, his average speed was 60 miles per hour.

a. What was Paco's average speed for the entire trip?

b. Consider the similar situation of Tory's trip to the beach. The entire trip took her two hours. For the first hour, her average speed was 60 miles per hour. During the second hour, she encountered traffic, so her average speed was 30 miles per hour for that hour of travel. What was Tory's average speed for the entire trip?

c. What information regarding Tory's trip is different from the information about Paco's trip? Which situation is in line with your definition of "average"?

Review

31 Solve these equations.

a. $6x - 14 = 16$

b. $12c + 18 = 24$

c. $6d + 5 = 4d + 7$

d. $7x + 4 = 9x + 13$

e. $5(2f - 3) + 6 = 10f - 9$

f. $5(2x + 5) = 10x + 15$

32 Rewrite each expression in a simpler equivalent form.

a. $\frac{108}{16}$

b. $\frac{3x + 12}{3}$

c. $\frac{10x^2 - 8}{24}$

33 Billy is standing 80 feet from the base of a building. The angle of elevation to the top of the building is 35°. If the distance from Billy's eyes to the ground is five feet, how tall is the building?

34 Consider the following statement.

The diagonals of a rhombus are perpendicular.

a. Write this statement in if-then form.

b. Is this a true statement? Explain your reasoning.

c. Write the converse of this statement.

d. Is the converse of this statement true? Explain your reasoning.

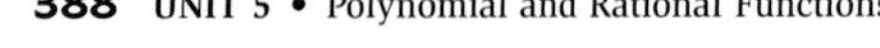

d. The graphs are identical.

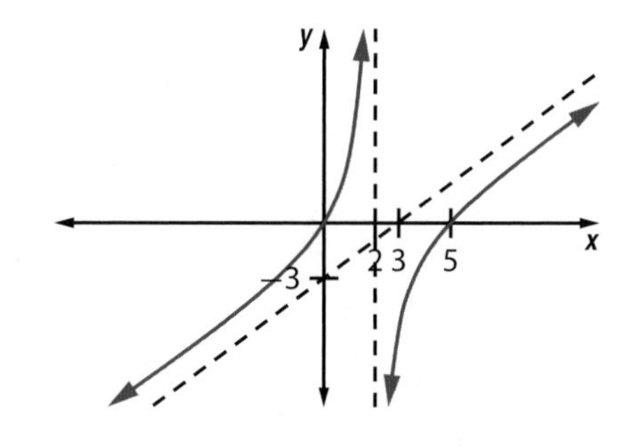

e. The expression $(x - 3) - \frac{6}{x - 2}$ makes it easier to identify the oblique asymptote at $y = x - 3$ because as x gets large in absolute value the term $\frac{6}{x - 2}$ approaches 0.

30 **a.** Average speed is 40 miles per hour. The surprising thing about this problem is that the answer is independent of the distance traveled, and you do not need to know the distance traveled. One way to reason to the answer could start with the fact that average speed equals total distance divided by total time. Letting d equal one way distance, we have the following algebraic reasoning.

$$\begin{aligned} \textit{average speed} &= \frac{\textit{total distance}}{\textit{total time}} \\ &= \frac{2d}{\frac{d}{30} + \frac{d}{60}} \\ &= \frac{2d}{\frac{2d}{60} + \frac{d}{60}} \\ &= \frac{2d}{\frac{3d}{60}} \\ &= \frac{120d}{3d} \\ &= 40 \end{aligned}$$

b. Tory's average speed is 45 miles per hour, $\left(\frac{60 + 30}{2}\right)$.

c. Tory's average speed is much easier to find because we are able to figure the total distance (90 miles) and total time (2 hours) readily. In Paco's case, neither the distance nor time is known, so it is very tempting to simply mistakenly average 60 and 30 to get his average speed.

Review

31 **a.** $x = 5$ **b.** $c = \frac{1}{2}$

c. $d = 1$ **d.** $x = -4.5$

e. True for all values of f **f.** No solution

Just in Time

32 **a.** $\frac{27}{4}$

b. $x + 4$

c. $\frac{5x^2 - 4}{12}$

33 $\tan 35° = \frac{h}{80}$

$h \approx 56$ ft

So, the building is approximately 61 ft tall.

34 **a.** One way to state this in if-then form is: If a polygon is a rhombus, then the diagonals are perpendicular.

b. The statement is true.

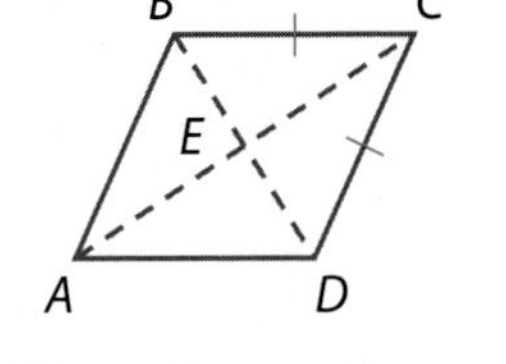

The proofs that students offer will vary, depending on what properties of a rhombus they remember and take as usable in the argument. One path that students might take is as follows.

By definition, all sides of a rhombus are the same length. Every rhombus is a parallelogram, and the diagonals of a parallelogram bisect each other. So, $\triangle BEC \cong \triangle DEC$ by the SSS congruence condition. Thus, $\angle BEC \cong \angle CED$ and since $m\angle BEC + m\angle CED = 180°$, we can conclude that $m\angle BEC = m\angle CED = 90°$. Thus, the diagonals are perpendicular.

c. One way to state a converse for the given proposition would be: If the diagonals of a quadrilateral are perpendicular, then the quadrilateral is a rhombus.

(The use of "quadrilateral" is not explicit in the original statement, but its use allows us to make an unambiguous converse. For theorems that are not stated in precise if-then form, it is often the case that "converse" is not well-defined.)

d. The converse in Part c is not true. The diagonals of kites are perpendicular and kites are not rhombuses.

Teacher Notes

35 Solve these equations for x.

a. $2^x = 8$

b. $2^x = \frac{1}{16}$

c. $10^x = 10{,}000$

d. $10^x = 0.0000001$

36 Express each of these sums or differences as a single fraction in simplest form.

a. $\frac{1}{8} + \frac{5}{8}$

b. $\frac{4}{5} - \frac{2}{3}$

c. $\frac{1}{3} + \frac{5}{6}$

d. $\frac{3}{10} - \frac{7}{6}$

e. $\frac{2}{x} + \frac{3}{4}$

37 Sketch the solution set for each system of inequalities.

a. $\begin{cases} 3x + 6y \geq 12 \\ y \leq -5x + 10 \end{cases}$

b. $\begin{cases} y > x^2 \\ y < x + 2 \end{cases}$

38 Suppose that Elizabeth rolls two regular dice and finds the sum of the numbers that are showing.

a. What is the probability that the sum is even or greater than 8?

b. What is the probability that the sum is even and greater than 8?

c. If she rolls the dice twice what is the probability that the sum is greater than 8 on both rolls?

39 Express each of these fraction products and quotients as a single fraction in simplest form.

a. $\frac{1}{2} \cdot \frac{1}{3}$

b. $\frac{2}{3} \div \frac{4}{5}$

c. $\frac{3}{4} \cdot \frac{2}{3}$

d. $\frac{2}{3} \div \frac{1}{2}$

e. $\frac{a}{b} \cdot \frac{c}{d}$

40 In $\triangle ABC$ and $\triangle DEF$, $\angle B$ and $\angle E$ are right angles. In each case below, decide whether the given information is sufficient to conclude that $\triangle ABC \cong \triangle DEF$. If so, explain why. If not, give a counterexample.

a. $\overrightarrow{AC} \cong \overrightarrow{DF}$; $\angle C \cong \angle F$

b. $\angle A \cong \angle D$; $\angle C \cong \angle F$

c. $\overrightarrow{AC} \cong \overrightarrow{DF}$; $\overrightarrow{AB} \cong \overrightarrow{DE}$

41 Triangle ABC is an isosceles triangle with $AB = BC$.

a. If $m\angle B = 138°$, find $m\angle C$ and $m\angle A$.

b. If $AC = 16$ cm, find the perimeter and the area of $\triangle ABC$.

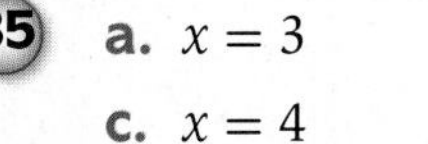
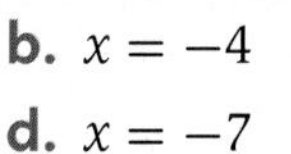

35 a. $x = 3$ b. $x = -4$
c. $x = 4$ d. $x = -7$

Just in Time

36 a. $\frac{3}{4}$ b. $\frac{2}{15}$
c. $\frac{7}{6}$ d. $-\frac{13}{15}$
e. $\frac{3x + 8}{4x}$

37 a.

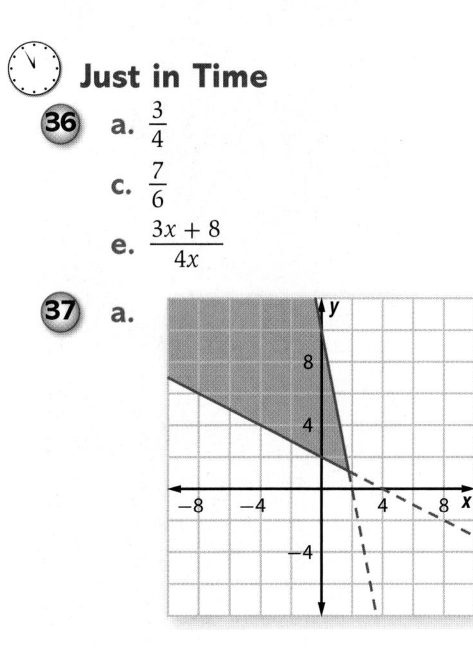

b.

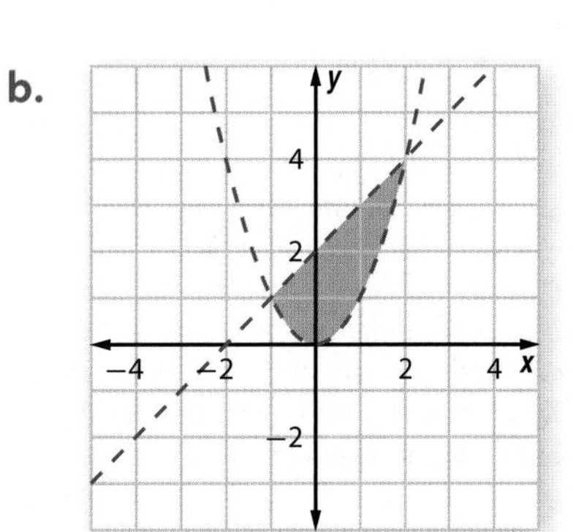

38 a. $P(even) = \frac{18}{36}$
$P(odd\ and\ greater\ than\ 8) = \frac{6}{36}$
$\frac{18}{36} + \frac{6}{36} = \frac{24}{36} = \frac{2}{3}$
b. $\frac{4}{36} = \frac{1}{9}$
c. $\left(\frac{10}{36}\right)^2 = \frac{25}{324}$

Just in Time

39 a. $\frac{1}{6}$ b. $\frac{5}{6}$ c. $\frac{1}{2}$
d. $\frac{4}{3}$ e. $\frac{ac}{bd}$

Just in Time

40 a. $\triangle ABC \cong \triangle DEF$ (HA or ASA)
b. Not congruent; Counterexamples should be similar triangles with scale factor not equal to 1.
c. $\triangle ABC \cong \triangle DEF$ (HL or SSS)

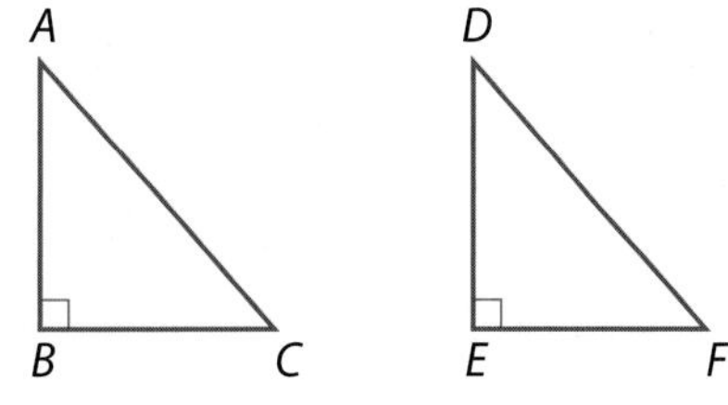

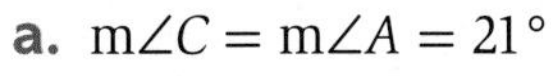

Just in Time

41 a. $m\angle C = m\angle A = 21°$
b. Students should use right triangle trigonometry to find the altitude and length of the other two congruent sides. The altitude is approximately 3.07 cm and the length of each of the congruent sides is approximately 8.57 cm. Therefore, the perimeter is approximately 33.14 cm. The area is approximately 24.56 cm^2.

B
138°
h
21°
A
8
8
C

Teaching Resources

Assessment Masters 29–34.

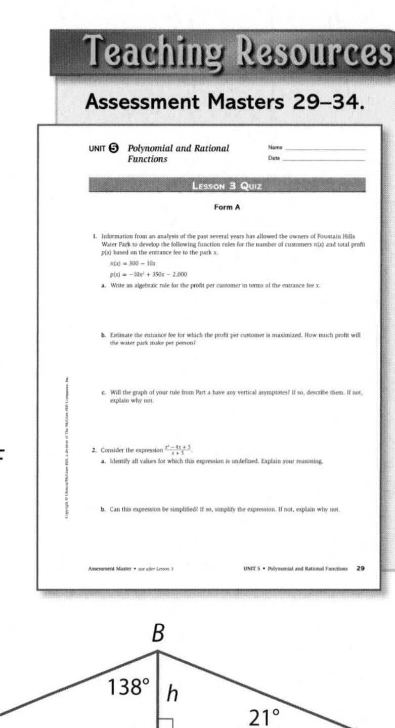

Looking Back

The lessons of this unit extended your knowledge and skill in work with algebraic functions and expressions in three ways. First, you learned how to use polynomials that go beyond linear and quadratic functions and expressions to model data and graph patterns that are more complex than the familiar straight lines and parabolas. You discovered ways of predicting the shape of polynomial function graphs from analysis of their rules—especially the number of local maximum and local minimum points and the number of zeroes—and ways of combining polynomials by addition, subtraction, and multiplication.

Second, you revisited quadratic functions and expressions to learn about completing the square to produce vertex forms for their rules. You learned how to use the vertex form to locate maximum and minimum points on the graphs of quadratic functions and how to solve equations by algebraic reasoning. You also studied the way that completing the square can be used to prove the quadratic formula for solving equations.

Finally, you explored properties and applications of rational functions and expressions. You learned how to identify undefined points of algebraic fractions and asymptotes of their graphs. You explored simplification of algebraic fractions and the ways that cautious use of such algebraic work can provide insights into functions and the problems they model. Then you learned how to combine rational functions and expressions by addition, subtraction, multiplication, and division.

The following tasks give you an opportunity to review and to put your new knowledge of polynomial and rational functions to work in some new contexts.

390 UNIT 5 • Polynomial and Rational Functions

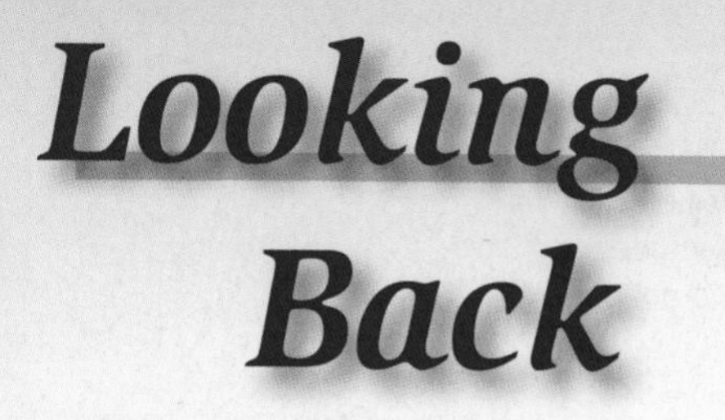

Looking Back

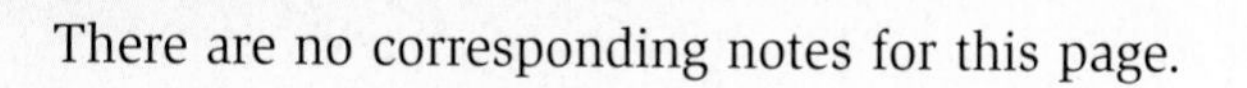

LESSON 4

There are no corresponding notes for this page.

1. Cassie and Cliff decided to start a company called Maryland Web Design that would help individuals build personal sites on the World Wide Web. Cassie sketched out a possible logo for their company on graph paper. Cliff thought it looked like a graph of two polynomial functions, so he drew in a pair of axes.

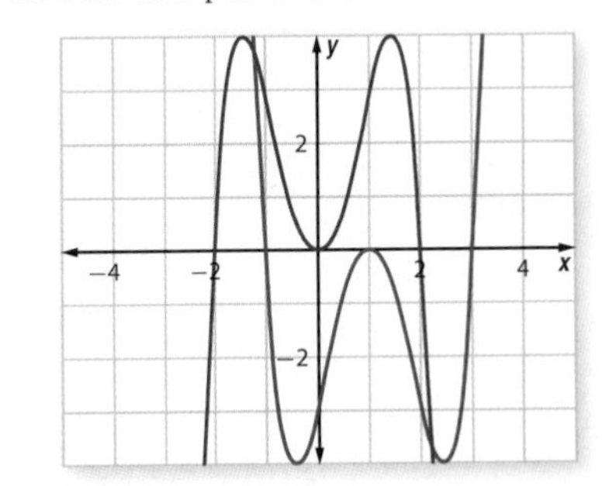

a. What is the smallest possible degree of each polynomial function?

b. Write possible functions to describe the curves Cassie drew. Use $M(x)$ to describe the curve that looks like the letter M and $W(x)$ to describe the curve that looks like the letter W.

2. Cassie and Cliff decided that their company would specialize in designing Web logs, or "blogs." Since production of any blog requires about the same amount of programming time, each customer could be charged the same price.

Cassie and Cliff also estimated that the number of customers in a year would be related to the price by $n(x) = 600 - 2x$, where x is the price charged per blog.

Production of each blog will require about \$200 in programmer labor. To get started in business, they bought a computer for \$2,000.

a. Write rules for the following functions, simplifying where possible.

i. Annual income from blog designs $I(x)$ if the price is x dollars per blog

ii. Annual production costs for blog designs $C(x)$ if the price is x dollars per blog

iii. Annual profit from the business $P(x)$ if the price is x dollars per blog

iv. Profit per customer $P_c(x)$ if the price is x dollars per blog

1 **a.** 4

b. $M(x) = -x^4 + 4x^2$ and $W(x) = x^4 - 4x^3 + 2x^2 + 4x - 3$ work well, but students might have some others if they used some different points to represent key features of the graphs.

2 **INSTRUCTIONAL NOTE** Have groups check their answers to Part a before going ahead to the rest of the task so that they are not using incorrect functions as they look for optimal income, profit, and profit per blog points. Part aii is the one most likely to be missed. To find expense as a function of price, we need to add the fixed cost of $2,000 to the product $200n(x)$, which takes account of the $200 per blog labor expense and the number of blog orders as a function of price per blog.

a. **i.** $I(x) = 600x - 2x^2$

ii. $E(x) = 122{,}000 - 400x$

iii. $P(x) = (600x - 2x^2) - (122{,}000 - 400x) = -2x^2 + 1{,}000x - 122{,}000$

iv. $P_c(x) = \dfrac{-2x^2 + 1{,}000x - 122{,}000}{600 - 2x} = \dfrac{x^2 - 500x + 61{,}000}{x - 300}$

Unit 5

b. What would be reasonable domains for the functions in Part a?

c. For what blog prices would the following functions be maximized?

i. Income $I(x)$

ii. Profit $P(x)$

iii. Profit per customer $P_c(x)$

d. What price would you recommend that Cassie and Cliff charge per blog? Explain your reasoning.

3 Find results of these algebraic operations. Express each answer in the equivalent form that would be simplest for evaluation at any specific value of x.

a. $(3x^4 + 5x^3 - 7x^2 + 9x - 1) + (2x^4 + 4x^2 + 6x + 8)$

b. $(3x^5 + 5x^3 - 7x^2 + 9x - 1) - (2x^4 + 4x^3 + 6x + 8)$

c. $(7x^2 + 9x - 1)(2x + 3)$

4 Look back at the graphs that look like an M and a W in Task 1.

a. Write and check the fit of models for the M whose function rules have these properties.

i. A product of linear factors that has zeroes at −2, 0, and 2

ii. A product of linear factors with zeroes at −2 and 2 and a repeated zero at $x = 0$

b. Write and check the fit of models for the W whose function rules have these properties.

i. A product of linear factors that has zeroes at −1, 1, and 3

ii. A product of linear factors with zeroes at −1 and 3 and a repeated zero at $x = 1$

c. Expand the products in Parts a and b that appear to give the best matches for the M and W drawings. Compare the resulting polynomials to the results produced in your work on Task 1. Reconcile any differences.

5 Express the quadratic function $f(x) = x^2 - 12x + 11$ in two ways, as the product of two linear factors and in vertex form. Then show how both forms can be used to find coordinates of these points on the graph of $y = f(x)$.

a. x-intercept(s)

b. y-intercept

c. maximum or minimum point

392 UNIT 5 • Polynomial and Rational Functions

b. The functions above should be considered for positive (integer) values of x where $n(x) > 0$. This occurs when $0 < x < 300$.

c. **i.** \$150 (Income is \$45,000. But profit is negative because the price that attracts so many customers is below operating expenses.)

ii. \$250 (profit is \$3,000)

iii. \$268 (profit per blog is \$36.75)

d. Student responses will vary but should include a comparison of the three results from Part c.

3 **a.** $5x^4 + 5x^3 - 3x^2 + 15x + 7$

b. $3x^5 - 2x^4 + x^3 - 7x^2 + 3x - 9$

c. $14x^3 + 39x^2 + 25x - 3$

4 **a.** **i.** $(x + 2)x(x - 2)$, which is actually a cubic that does not match the M shape well at all.

ii. $(x + 2)x^2(x - 2)$, which is a reflection across the x-axis of what one wants for an M. Simply writing $-(x + 2)x^2(x - 2)$ gives a very good model.

b. **i.** $(x + 1)(x - 1)(x - 3)$ is a cubic that does not match the W well at all.

ii. $(x + 1)(x - 1)^2(x - 3)$ matches the W very well.

c. The expanded products are $M(x) = x^4 - 4x^2$ or $M(x) = -x^4 + 4x^2$ for the reflection that models the M better and $W(x) = x^4 - 4x^3 + 2x^2 + 4x - 3$. If students did Task 1 by choosing representative points and using quartic regression, they will probably not have as simple a set of coefficients. On the other hand, they probably did not have to do the reflection in the x-axis to get the suitable rule modeling the M.

5 $(x^2 - 12x + 11) = (x - 11)(x - 1) = (x - 6)^2 - 25$

a. The x-intercepts are (11, 0) and (1, 0), a fact that is most obvious in the factored form where one simply sets each linear factor equal to 0, making the product 0.

To use the vertex form for that task requires some algebraic manipulation like this.

$$\begin{aligned} (x - 6)^2 - 25 &= 0 \\ (x - 6)^2 &= 25 \\ x - 6 &= \pm 5 \\ x &= 6 \pm 5 \end{aligned}$$

b. The y-intercept is (0, 11), a fact that is obvious in the standard polynomial form. To find this point from the factored form, one has to substitute 0 for x and get $(-11)(-1) = 11$. The vertex form requires substitution of 0 for x and evaluation of $(-6)^2 - 25$.

c. The minimum point $(6, -25)$ can be read directly from the vertex form. To get the same information from the factored form, one needs to find the average of the two zeroes and then evaluate the function at that x value.

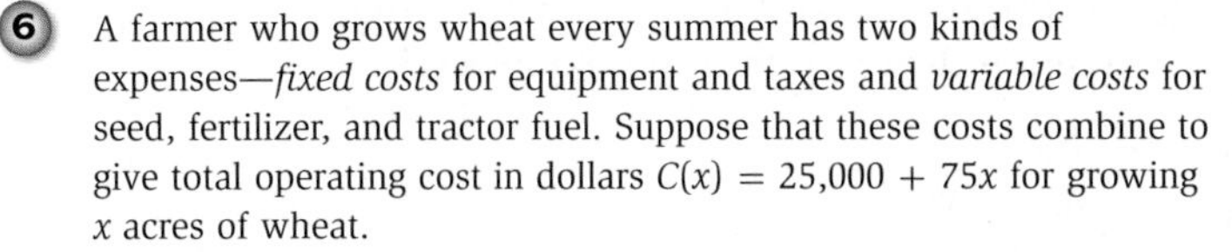

6 A farmer who grows wheat every summer has two kinds of expenses—*fixed costs* for equipment and taxes and *variable costs* for seed, fertilizer, and tractor fuel. Suppose that these costs combine to give total operating cost in dollars $C(x) = 25{,}000 + 75x$ for growing x acres of wheat.

a. What is a rule for the function $c(x)$ that gives the operating cost per acre on that farm?

b. The function giving operating cost per acre has a horizontal asymptote. Explore values of $c(x)$ as x increases to discover the equation of that asymptote.

c. Sketch a graph of $c(x)$. Explain what it shows about the way that operating cost per acre changes as the number of acres planted increases. In particular, explain what the horizontal asymptote tells about the relationship between number of acres planted and operating cost per acre.

7 Suppose that the wheat farmer in Task 6 can expect income of about $125 per acre.

a. What functions give total profit $P(x)$ and profit per acre $p(x)$ from planting x acres of wheat?

b. How many acres of wheat must the farmer plant to break even on the crop?

c. Sketch a graph of the profit per acre function $p(x)$ for $0 < x < 2{,}000$. What seems to be the horizontal asymptote for this graph? What does it tell about the relationship between profit per acre and number of acres planted?

8 Consider the functions $f(x) = \frac{2x + 7}{x^2 - 4}$ and $g(x) = \frac{x + 5}{x^2 - 4}$.

a. Sketch graphs of each function. Identify any asymptotes.

b. Describe the domains of the two functions.

c. Calculate expressions in simplest form for these combinations of $f(x)$ and $g(x)$.

i. $f(x) + g(x)$

ii. $f(x) - g(x)$

iii. $f(x)g(x)$

iv. $f(x) \div g(x)$

6 **a.** Cost per acre:

$c(x) = \dfrac{25{,}000 + 75x}{x}$

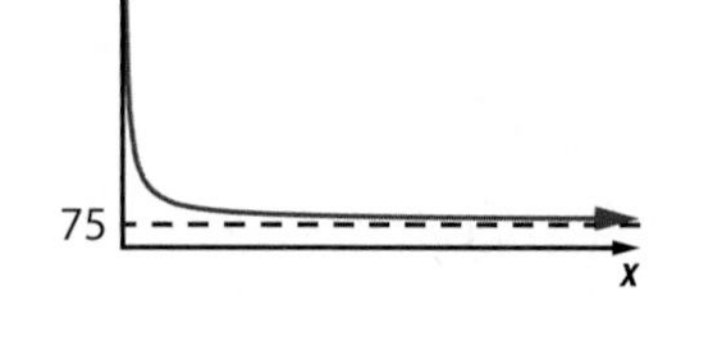

b. $y = 75$

c. As the number of acres increases, the operating cost per acre approaches the $75 cost per acre of seed, fertilizer, and fuel.

7 **a.** Total profit: $P(x) = 125x - C(x) = 50x - 25{,}000$

Profit per acre: $p(x) = \dfrac{50x - 25{,}000}{x}$

b. 500 acres of wheat must be planted to break even. $P(x) = 0$ when $x = 500$.

c. The horizontal asymptote seems to be at $y = 50$. As the number of acres increases, the profit per acre is negative at first and then approaches but does not reach a maximum of $50 per acre.

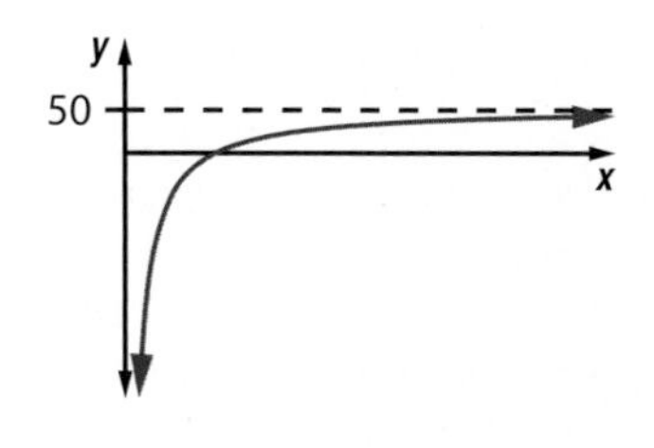

8 **a.** Graphs of the two functions will look like this.

$f(x) = \dfrac{2x + 7}{x^2 - 4}$ $\quad\quad$ $g(x) = \dfrac{x + 5}{x^2 - 4}$

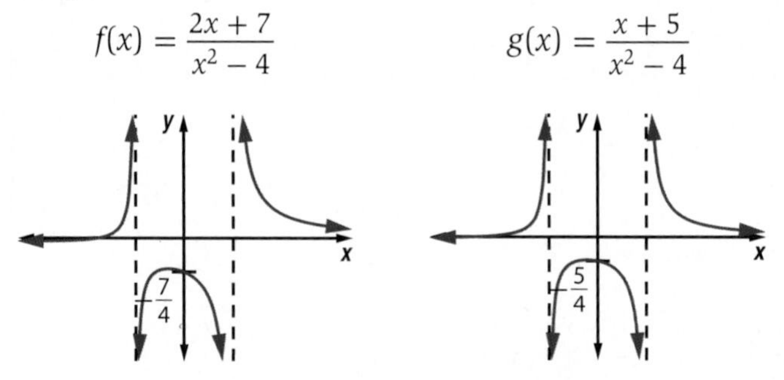

There are vertical asymptotes at $x = \pm 2$ and a horizontal asymptote at $y = 0$ for both functions.

b. The domains of both functions are $x \neq \pm 2$.

c. **i.** $f(x) + g(x) = \dfrac{3x + 12}{x^2 - 4}$

ii. $f(x) - g(x) = \dfrac{x + 2}{(x + 2)(x - 2)} = \dfrac{1}{x - 2}$

iii. $f(x)g(x) = \dfrac{2x^2 + 17x + 35}{x^4 - 8x^2 + 16}$

iv. $f(x) \div g(x) = \dfrac{2x + 7}{x + 5}$

Unit 5

Unit 5

Summarize the Mathematics

In this unit, you modeled problem situations using polynomial and rational functions and developed an understanding of some of the properties of those families of functions. You also learned how to add, subtract, and multiply polynomials and rational expressions.

a. What kinds of functions are called:
   - **i.** polynomial functions?
   - **ii.** rational functions?

b. Describe how you can determine:
   - **i.** the degree of a polynomial.
   - **ii.** local maximum or local minimum points on the graph of a polynomial function.
   - **iii.** the zeroes of a polynomial function.
   - **iv.** the sum or difference of two polynomials.
   - **v.** the product of two polynomials.

c. What is the vertex form of a quadratic function?
   - **i.** What are the advantages and disadvantages of using this form?
   - **ii.** How would you transform any quadratic expression in the form $ax^2 + bx + c$ into vertex form?

d. For questions that call for solving quadratic equations $ax^2 + bx + c = 0$, how can you tell the number and kind of solutions from the value of the discriminant $b^2 - 4ac$?

e. When working with rational expressions and functions, describe:
   - **i.** when an expression will be undefined.
   - **ii.** when the graph of a function will have a vertical asymptote.
   - **iii.** when the graph of a function will have a horizontal asymptote.
   - **iv.** strategies you can use to simplify the expression for a function.
   - **v.** when two rational expressions can be added or subtracted and how you would go about performing the addition or subtraction.
   - **vi.** how multiplication or division of two rational expressions can be performed.

Be prepared to share your examples and descriptions with the class.

✓ *Check Your Understanding*

Write, in outline form, a summary of the important mathematical concepts and methods developed in this unit. Organize your summary so that it can be used as a quick reference in future units and courses.

394 UNIT 5 • Polynomial and Rational Functions

Summarize the Mathematics

a

i. An expression of the form $a_nx^n + a_{n-1}x^{n-1} + \cdots + a_1x + a_0$ is a polynomial expression. A function with rule in the form $f(x) = a_nx^n + a_{n-1}x^{n-1} + \cdots + a_1x + a_0$ is a polynomial function.

ii. An expression of the form $\frac{p}{q}$, where p and q are polynomial expressions, is a rational expression. A function of the form $f(x) = \frac{p(x)}{q(x)}$ is a rational function if and only if $p(x)$ and $q(x)$ are polynomial functions.

b

i. The degree is the largest exponent in the polynomial expression.

ii. Use a calculator's max/min feature or estimate the location of the local max/min points by tracing a graph or scanning entries in a table of function values. In the case of a quadratic polynomial function, the equation could be converted to vertex form and the coordinates of the vertex can be read from the form directly.

iii. Zeroes of a polynomial function can be estimated by scanning a table of values or tracing a graph of the function. They can be found exactly by use of a CAS solve command. If the polynomial is written as a product of linear factors, zeroes of the whole function can be determined by finding zeroes of each factor. For quadratic polynomials, in particular, the quadratic formula can be used to identify zeroes.

iv. The coefficients of like terms are added or subtracted to find the new coefficients of those terms.

v. The distributive property is applied completely so that each term in the first polynomial is multiplied by each term in the second. These products are all added to find the resulting product of the two polynomials, generally combining like terms to get simpler standard form.

c A quadratic expression in the form $a(x - h)^2 + k$ is said to be in vertex form.

i. The vertex is easily identified, but the x- and y-intercepts require computation and algebraic manipulation. (Of course, it is not generally trivial to put a given quadratic in vertex form.)

ii. $a\left(x - \frac{b}{2a}\right)^2 + c - \frac{b^2}{4a}$

d When using the quadratic formula, there will be two real solutions if the discriminant is positive, one real solution if the discriminant is 0, and two complex solutions if the discriminant is negative. The distinction between rational and irrational solutions depends on the nature of the coefficients a, b, and c. When they are rational numbers, the solutions of the equation will be rational only when the discriminant is the square of a rational number. In all other cases, the solutions will be irrational.

Teaching Resources

Transparency Masters 35–36.

UNIT 5 *Polynomial and Rational Functions*

Summarize the Mathematics

In this unit, you modeled problem situations using polynomial and rational functions and developed an understanding of some of the properties of those families of functions. You also learned how to add, subtract, and multiply polynomials and rational expressions.

a What kinds of functions are called:

i. polynomial functions?

ii. rational functions?

b Describe how you can determine:

i. the degree of a polynomial.

ii. local maximum or local minimum points on the graph of a polynomial function.

iii. the zeroes of a polynomial function.

iv. the sum or difference of two polynomials.

v. the product of two polynomials.

c What is the vertex form of a quadratic function?

i. What are the advantages and disadvantages of using this form?

ii. How would you transform any quadratic expression in the form $ax^2 + bx + c$ into vertex form?

Transparency Master • use with page 394 UNIT 5 • Polynomial and Rational Functions 35

Unit 5

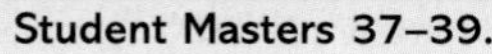

Student Masters 37–39.

UNIT 5 *Polynomial and Rational Functions*

UNIT SUMMARY

Assessment Masters 40–57.

UNIT 5 *Polynomial and Rational Functions*

UNIT TEST

Form A

Student Masters 58–59.

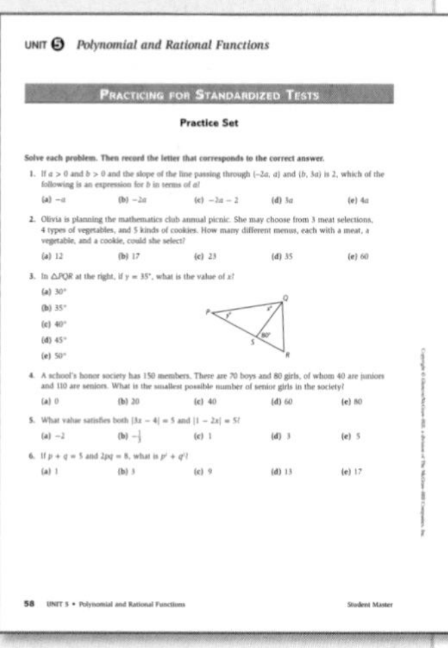
UNIT 5 *Polynomial and Rational Functions*

PRACTICING FOR STANDARDIZED TESTS

Practice Set

Solve each problem. Then record the letter that corresponds to the correct answer.

1. If $a > 0$ and $b > 0$ and the slope of the line passing through $(-2a, a)$ and $(b, 3a)$ is 2, which of the following is an expression for b in terms of a?
   (a) $-a$ (b) $-2a$ (c) $-2a - 2$ (d) $3a$ (e) $4a$
2. Olivia is planning the mathematics club annual picnic. She may choose from 3 meat selections, 4 types of vegetables, and 5 kinds of cookies. How many different menus, each with a meat, a vegetable, and a cookie, could she select?
   (a) 12 (b) 17 (c) 23 (d) 35 (e) 60
3. In $\triangle PQR$ at the right, if $y = 35°$, what is the value of x?
   (a) 30° (b) 35° (c) 40° (d) 45° (e) 50°
4. A school's honor society has 150 members. There are 70 boys and 80 girls, of whom 40 are juniors and 110 are seniors. What is the smallest possible number of senior girls in the society?
   (a) 0 (b) 20 (c) 40 (d) 60 (e) 80
5. What value satisfies both $|3x - 4| = 5$ and $|1 - 2x| = 5$?
   (a) -2 (b) $-\frac{1}{3}$ (c) 1 (d) 3 (e) 5
6. If $p + q = 5$ and $2pq = 8$, what is $p^2 + q^2$?
   (a) 1 (b) 3 (c) 9 (d) 13 (e) 17

58 UNIT 5 • Polynomial and Rational Functions Student Master

e When working with rational expressions and functions:

- **i.** The function will be undefined when the denominator is equal to zero.
- **ii.** The function will have a vertical asymptote when the denominator is equal to zero and the numerator is not.
- **iii.** The function will have a horizontal asymptote if when values of x grow large in absolute value, the graph approaches the horizontal line as a limit but never quite reaches the line.
- **iv.** Factor both the numerator and the denominator and remove common factors.
- **v.** The sum or difference of two rational expressions can be written in a simpler combined form when the component expressions have been written in forms with common denominator. Once a common denominator is obtained, the numerators are added or subtracted and the result is the numerator of the sum or difference.
- **vi.** In the case of multiplication, the numerators are multiplied and the denominators are multiplied to get the resulting numerator and denominator of the product. In the case of division, the dividend is multiplied by the reciprocal of the divisor.

Check Your Understanding

You may wish to have students use the Teaching Master, *Polynomial and Rational Functions* Unit Summary, to help them organize the information. Above all, this should be something that is useful to the individual student.

Practicing for Standardized Tests

Each Practicing for Standardized Tests master presents 10 questions in the multiple-choice format of test items similar to how they often appear in standardized tests. Answers are provided below.

Answers to Practice Set 5

1. (a)	**2.** (e)	**3.** (d)	**4.** (c)	**5.** (d)
6. (e)	**7.** (d)	**8.** (d)	**9.** (c)	**10.** (d)

Teacher Notes

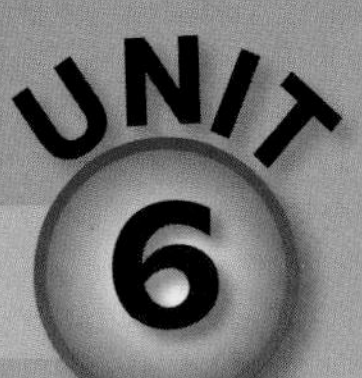

Circles and Circular Functions

Circles are the most symmetric of all two-dimensional shapes. As a result, a circle has many interesting properties whose investigation continues to develop visual thinking and reasoning abilities. From another perspective, the rotation of a circle is key to the utility of wheels, circular saws, pulleys and sprockets, center-pivot irrigation, and other mechanisms that involve circles. The motion of the circle as it rotates is a special case of periodic change that can be modeled and analyzed using trigonometric or circular functions.

In this unit, you will learn about and prove properties of special lines and angles as they relate to circles. You will analyze circular motion, both how its power can be harnessed and multiplied in pulley and sprocket systems and how trigonometric functions model the motion. The key ideas will be developed through work on problems in two lessons.

Lessons

1 ***Properties of Circles***

State and prove properties of tangents to circles, chords, arcs, and central and inscribed angles. Interpret and apply these properties.

2 ***Circular Motion and Periodic Functions***

Analyze pulley and sprocket systems in terms of their transmission factor, angular velocity, and linear velocity. Use sine and cosine functions of angles and radians to model circular motion and other periodic phenomena.

Unit 6

UNIT 6

CIRCLES AND CIRCULAR FUNCTIONS

Unit Overview

This unit focuses on consequences of the complete symmetry of circles. The progression of the treatment of circles began in the coordinate plane in Course 2, Unit 3, *Coordinate Methods*. Then in Course 2, Unit 7, *Trigonometric Methods*, the sine, cosine, and tangent functions were defined based on a point on the terminal side of an angle in standard position. This unit draws on and extends the idea of circles to circular motion.

Overall, this unit helps students extend their understanding of proof in geometric settings and broaden their understanding and application of important geometric and trigonometric concepts. Again, students are frequently asked to explore relationships, make conjectures, and reason deductively to verify these conjectures. Synthetic proofs, mainly based on congruent triangles, and coordinate proofs are constructed and compared. Topics developed include: properties of chords, tangent lines, and central and inscribed angles of circles; linear and angular velocity; and functions modeling periodic change.

Since the rotation of circles is key to the functioning of wheels, pulleys, and sprockets, applications involving these devices are drawn upon in the unit. Such circular motion is a special case of periodic change. The mathematical description of periodic change uses the sine and cosine functions of trigonometry and a new unit of angle measure called radians.

Unit Objectives

- State, prove, and apply various properties of a line tangent to a circle, central angles, chords, arcs, and radii of a circle
- State, prove, and apply the Inscribed Angle Theorem and the property that angles that intercept the same or congruent arcs are congruent
- Analyze situations involving pulleys or sprockets to determine angular velocity and linear velocity
- Use sines and cosines to model aspects of circular motion and other periodic phenomena using both degrees and radians

CPMP-Tools

Custom tools developed for this unit help students visualize and understand the relationships among the measures of central angles, inscribed angles, and the arcs that they intercept, and the relationship between radian and degree measures of angles. Sample sketches have been developed related to tangents, chord lengths, circular motion, and the relationship between the measures of an inscribed angle and an angle intercepting the same arc that is exterior to the circle (Lighthouse). Some sketches can be used to launch investigations as noted in the *Teacher's Guide*.

CPMP-Tools

Course Tools Algebra Geometry Statistics Discrete Math Help

Interactive
Coordinate Geometry
Synthetic Geometry
Explore Similar Triangles
Explore Angles and Arcs
Explore Radians

CPMP-T

CPMP-Tools is a suite of *Algebra, Geometry, Statistics*, and *Discrete Math* software tools designed for and integrated with the *Core-Plus Mathematics* curriculum.

This material is based upon work supported by the National Science Foundation under Grant No. ESI-0137718. Opinions expressed are those of the authors and do not necessarily reflect the views of the National Science Foundation.

CPMP-Tools © 2006–2008, B. A. Keller, Michigan State University and Core-Plus Mathematics Project, Western Michigan University (www.wmich.edu/cpmp) comes with ABSOLUTELY NO WARRANTY.

This suite of tools is built upon several open source projects.. Please see the Licensing information in the Help menu for further details and credits.

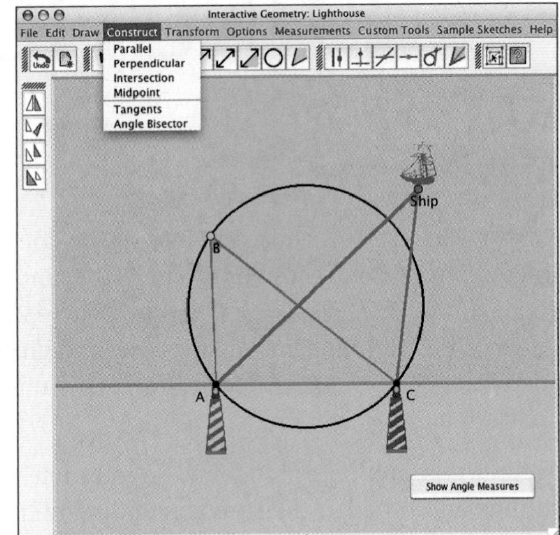

Unit 6

Unit 6 Planning Guide

Lesson Objectives	On Your Own Assignments*	Suggested Pacing	Materials
Lesson 1 ***Properties of Circles*** • Determine and prove that a line tangent to a circle is perpendicular to the radius at the point of tangency and that the two tangent segments to a circle from the same external point are congruent • State, prove, and apply the relationships among the measures of central angles, their chords, and their arcs • State, prove, and apply the properties relating a radius, a chord, and the midpoint and perpendicular bisector of the chord • State, prove, and apply the Inscribed Angle Theorem and the property that angles that intercept the same or congruent arcs are congruent	**After Investigation 1:** A1, A2, C12 or C13, R18 or R19, E24, Rv30–Rv34 **After Investigation 2:** Choose two of A3–A7, C14, C15, R20, R21, choose one of E25–E27, Rv35–Rv37 **After Investigation 3:** A8, A9 or A10, A11, C16, C17, R22 or R23, E28 or E29, Rv38–Rv40	5 days (including assessment)	• Compasses, straightedges, rulers, protractors, graph paper • "Explore Angles and Arcs" custom tool in *CPMP-Tools* • "Tangents to Circles," "Lighthouse," and "Chord Lengths in Circles" sketches in *CPMP-Tools* • Unit Resources
Lesson 2 ***Circular Motion and Periodic Functions*** • Analyze situations involving pulleys or sprockets to study angular velocity and linear velocity • Use sine and cosine functions to describe rotations of circular objects • Use radian and degree measures to measure angles and rotations • Define sine and cosine as functions of real numbers and analyze the resulting periodic graphs • Use the sine and cosine functions to model periodic patterns of change in various physical phenomena	**After Investigation 1:** A1, choose one of A2–A4, C13, R20 or R21, E27 or E28, Rv34–Rv36 **After Investigation 2:** A5, A6, C14 or C15, E29, Rv37–Rv39 **After Investigation 3:** A7 or A8, A9, C16 or C17, R22, R23, E30, Rv40 **After Investigation 4:** A10, A11 or A12, C18 or C19, choose two of R24–R26, choose one of E31–E33, Rv41–Rv43	9 days (including assessment)	• Protractors, rulers, and compasses • Manila file folders, pipe cleaners, dental floss or string • "Explore Radians" custom tool and "Ferris Wheel" sketch in *CPMP-Tools* • Unit Resources
Lesson 3 ***Looking Back*** • Review and synthesize the major objectives of the unit		2 days (including assessment)	• Unit Resources

** When choice is indicated, it is important to leave the choice to the student.*

Note: *It is best if Connections tasks are discussed as a whole class after they have been assigned as homework.*

LESSON 1

Properties of Circles

In Course 2 of *Core-Plus Mathematics*, you explored some properties of a circle and its center, radius, and diameter. You also learned how to determine the equation of a circle in a coordinate plane.

Circles are the most symmetric of all geometric figures. This symmetry makes them both beautiful and functional. Below, on the left, is a circle-based decorative design from the Congo region of Africa. On the right is a diagram of a circular barbeque grill.

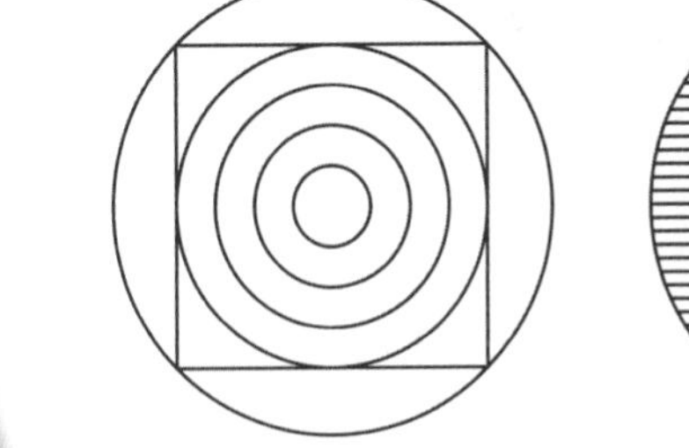

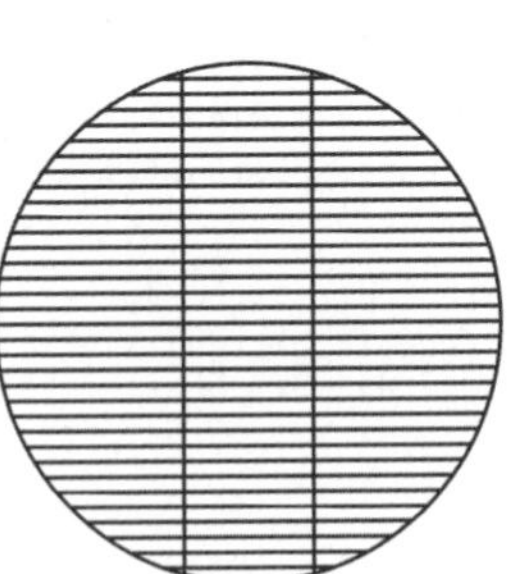

Unit 6

Properties of Circles

LESSON 1

This lesson continues the geometry story, building on the three Course 1 and Course 2 geometry units and particularly on geometric proof begun in earlier units in Course 3. Tangent lines to circles are explored in order to show that they are perpendicular to the radius of the circle at the point of tangency. The various properties of the tangent segments to a circle from an exterior point are also explored and proved. Chords, arcs, central angles, and their interconnections are the topic of the second investigation. Properties involving midpoints of chords, radii to those midpoints, and the perpendicular bisector of a chord are proved, using reasoning from coordinates and from congruent triangles. The inscribed angle theorem and its proof by cases is the main topic of the third investigation. Throughout the lesson, these properties are applied, sometimes along with trigonometric methods, to calculate segment and angle measures.

Lesson Objectives

- Determine and prove that a line tangent to a circle is perpendicular to the radius at the point of tangency and that the two tangent segments to a circle from the same external point are congruent
- State, prove, and apply the relationships among the measures of central angles, their chords, and their arcs
- State, prove, and apply the properties relating a radius, a chord, and the midpoint and perpendicular bisector of the chord
- State, prove, and apply the Inscribed Angle Theorem and the property that angles that intercept the same or congruent arcs are congruent

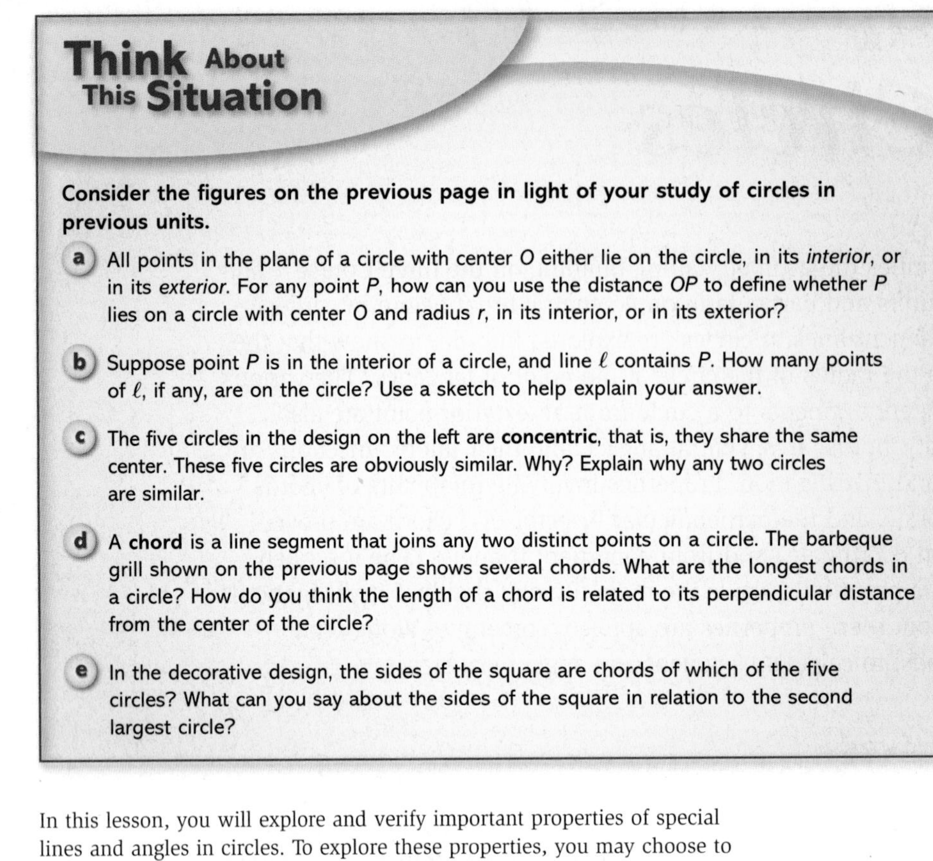

Think About This Situation

Consider the figures on the previous page in light of your study of circles in previous units.

a All points in the plane of a circle with center O either lie on the circle, in its *interior*, or in its *exterior*. For any point P, how can you use the distance OP to define whether P lies on a circle with center O and radius r, in its interior, or in its exterior?

b Suppose point P is in the interior of a circle, and line ℓ contains P. How many points of ℓ, if any, are on the circle? Use a sketch to help explain your answer.

c The five circles in the design on the left are **concentric**, that is, they share the same center. These five circles are obviously similar. Why? Explain why any two circles are similar.

d A **chord** is a line segment that joins any two distinct points on a circle. The barbeque grill shown on the previous page shows several chords. What are the longest chords in a circle? How do you think the length of a chord is related to its perpendicular distance from the center of the circle?

e In the decorative design, the sides of the square are chords of which of the five circles? What can you say about the sides of the square in relation to the second largest circle?

In this lesson, you will explore and verify important properties of special lines and angles in circles. To explore these properties, you may choose to use compass and straightedge, paper folding, measuring, or geometry software. To reason about these properties, you will use congruent triangles, symmetry, coordinate methods, and trigonometric methods. The properties of circles you derive in the first lesson form a basis for the second lesson, which is the study of circular motion and how it is modeled.

Investigation 1 Tangents to a Circle

As you learned in Course 2, lines that touch a circle in exactly one point are said to be **tangent** to the circle. Tangent lines have great practical importance. For example, many satellites orbit Earth collecting and transmitting data that is crucial for the operation of modern communication systems. The sketch on the next page shows tangent lines to the circle of the equator from a satellite at point S. These tangent lines can help to determine the range of the satellite's signal.

Think About This Situation

a A point P in the plane of the circle lies (i) on the circle with center O if and only if $OP = r$, (ii) in the interior of the circle with center O if and only if $OP < r$, and (iii) in the exterior of the circle if and only if $OP > r$.

b The line will intersect the circle in two points, one on each side of the point P in the interior of the circle.

c Each pair of circles maps one to the other by a size transformation with the center of the circles a common center and scale factor equal to the ratio of their radii. Any two circles are similar because one circle can be translated so the circles are concentric and then one maps to the other by a size transformation. (The composition of the translation and size transformation is a similarity transformation.)

d The longest chords in a circle are its diameters. As a chord moves farther away from the center of a given circle, it becomes shorter.

e The sides of the square are chords of the largest circle. They appear to be tangent to the second largest circle.

f The equation is $(x - h)^2 + (y - k)^2 = r^2$.

Teaching Resources

Transparency Master 1.

UNIT 6 *Circles and Circular Functions*

Think About This Situation

Consider the figures below in light of your study of circles in previous units.

a All points in the plane of a circle with center O either lie on the circle, in its *interior*, or in its *exterior*. For any point P, how can you use the distance OP to define whether P lies on a circle with center O and radius r, in its interior, or in its exterior?

b Suppose point P is in the interior of a circle, and line ℓ contains P. How many points of ℓ, if any, are on the circle? Use a sketch to help explain your answer.

c The five circles in the design on the left are **concentric**, that is, they share the same center. These five circles are obviously similar. Why? Explain why any two circles are similar.

d A **chord** is a line segment that joins any two distinct points on a circle. The barbeque grill below shows several chords. What are the longest chords in a circle? How do you think the length of a chord is related to its perpendicular distance from the center of the circle?

e In the decorative design, the sides of the square are chords of which of the five circles? What can you say about the sides of the square in relation to the second largest circle?

Transparency Master • *use with page 397* UNIT 6 • Circles and Circular Functions 1

ASSUMPTION We will assume the Circle Construction Postulate: Given any point O and any positive number r, a circle may be constructed with center O and radius r. You may or may not want to discuss this with your students. Most students will accept it with little question.

Unit 6

Investigation 1 Tangents to a Circle

Students begin by examining the use of tangents to circles. They then explore the connection between a line tangent to a circle and the radius drawn to the point of tangency, and finally construct an if-and-only-if proof of the perpendicularity of the tangent and radius. Similarly, they explore and conjecture about the congruence of the tangent segments from an exterior point. A proof involving congruent triangles is constructed. Finally, these theorems are used with the Pythagorean Theorem and trigonometric methods to determine measures of segments and angles from given measures.

Launch

You may wish to launch this investigation with an interactive class discussion of the "Tangents to Circles" sample sketch in *CPMP-Tools*. The ideas from Problem 1 could be discussed. Treating the four parts of the problem separately would not be necessary. Then students could be asked individually to do Problem 2, using the proof support handout if needed, and compare responses with a partner.

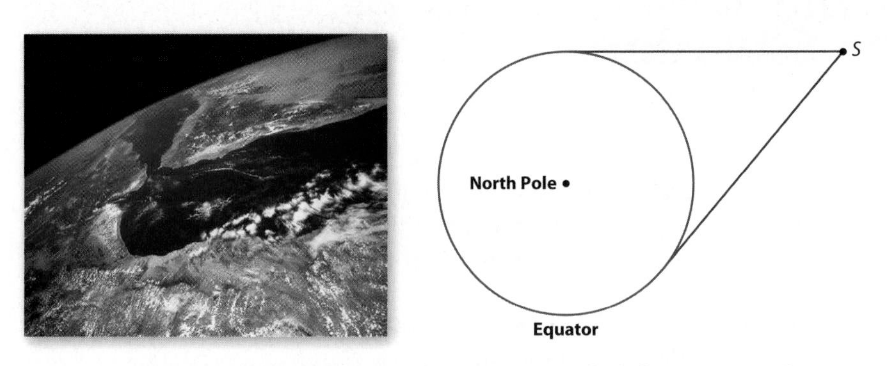

As you work on problems in this investigation, look for answers to the following question:

What are important properties of tangents to a circle, and how can they be verified?

1 **Tangent at a Point on a Circle** Use a compass, straightedge and protractor, paper folding, or the "Tangents to Circles" sample sketch to investigate properties of a line that is tangent to a circle.

a. Draw a circle like the one at the right with center O and a convenient radius r. Draw a tangent line touching the circle at just one point, A. Point A is called the *point of tangency*. Draw segment $\overline{OA}$. Relative to r, how long is $\overline{OA}$?

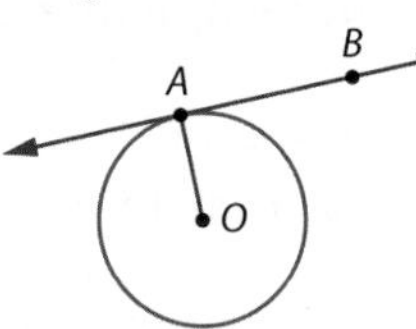

b. Suppose B is any point on the tangent line other than A, the point of tangency. Relative to r, how long is $\overline{OB}$? Is B in the interior or exterior of the circle?

c. Find the measure of the angle made by $\overline{OA}$ and the tangent line. Compare your finding with that of others. Write a conjecture about a tangent line and the radius drawn to the point of tangency.

d. Is the converse of your conjecture in Part c also true? If you think so, write your conjecture in if-and-only-if form.

2 As with any if-and-only-if statement, proof of your conjecture in Problem 1 Part d requires an argument in both directions.

a. One direction is the following:

If a radius is perpendicular to a line at a point where the line intersects the circle, then the line is tangent to the circle at that point.

Students at Peninsula High School wrote the following steps for a proof. Provide reasons that support each of the statements.

Unit 6

398 UNIT 6 • Circles and Circular Functions

1. a. $OA = r$, because by definition, $\overline{OA}$ is a radius of the circle.

   b. $OB > r$; B is in the exterior of the circle.

   c. The measure of the angle made by the radius and the tangent line is 90°. A line tangent to a circle is perpendicular to the radius drawn to the point of tangency.

   d. The converse of the conjecture is also true. A line is tangent to a circle if and only if the line is perpendicular to the radius drawn to the point of tangency.

2. a. (1) Given

   (2) Two points determine a unique segment.

   (3) Definitions of right triangle and hypotenuse

   (4) The longest side of a right triangle is the hypotenuse. (Pythagorean Theorem)

   (5) Any point that is more than r units from O is in the exterior of the circle (from TATS).

   (6) Definition of tangent to a circle: it has been shown that no other point on ℓ is also on the circle.

Teaching Resources

Student Masters 2–3.

UNIT 6 *Circles and Circular Functions* Name ______ Date ______

Tangent Relationships

Problem 2

2. As with any if-and-only-if statement, proof of your conjecture in Problem 1 Part d requires an argument in both directions.

   a. One direction is the following:

   If a radius is perpendicular to a line at a point where the line intersects the circle, then the line is tangent to the circle at that point.

   Students at Peninsula High School wrote the following steps for a proof. Provide reasons that support each of the statements.

   Given: Point A on both line ℓ and circle with center O with $\overline{OA} \perp \ell$

   Prove: Line ℓ is tangent to the circle with center O, that is, ℓ intersects the circle only in point A.

   (1) $\overline{OA}$ is a radius. $\overline{OA} \perp \ell$ at point A.

   (2) Let B be any point on line ℓ other than A. Draw $\overline{OB}$.

   (3) $\triangle BAO$ is a right triangle with hypotenuse $\overline{OB}$.

   (4) $OB > OA$

   (5) Point B is in the exterior of the circle with center O.

   (6) Line ℓ is tangent to the circle with center O.

   b. What is the converse of the statement proved in Part a?

   c. You are asked to prove the converse in Extensions Task 25. After your conjecture is proved in both directions, it is an if-and-only-if theorem. The theorem should be the same as the statement of the conjecture that you wrote for Problem 1 Part d. If necessary, adjust that statement to make it an accurate statement of the theorem. Add the theorem to your toolkit to use as needed in later problems.

2 UNIT 6 • Circles and Circular Functions   Student Master • use with pages 398 and 399

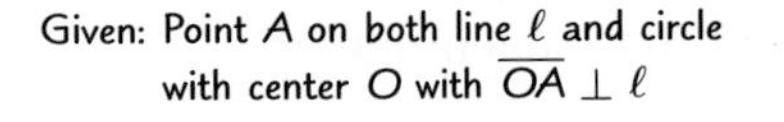

Given: Point A on both line ℓ and circle with center O with $\overline{OA} \perp \ell$

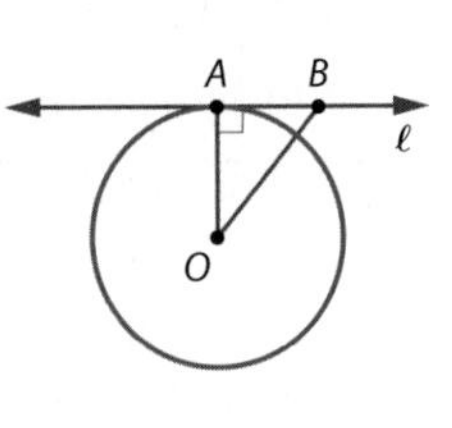

Prove: Line ℓ is tangent to the circle with center O, that is, ℓ intersects the circle only in point A.

(1) $\overline{OA}$ is a radius. $\overline{OA} \perp \ell$ at point A

(2) Let B be any point on line ℓ other than A. Draw $\overline{OB}$.

(3) $\triangle BAO$ is a right triangle with hypotenuse $\overline{OB}$.

(4) $OB > OA$

(5) Point B is in the exterior of the circle with center O.

(6) Line ℓ is tangent to the circle with center O.

b. What is the converse of the statement proved in Part a?

c. You are asked to prove the converse in Extensions Task 24. After your conjecture is proved in both directions, it is an if-and-only-if theorem. The theorem should be the same as the statement of the conjecture that you wrote for Problem 1 Part d. If necessary, adjust that statement to make it an accurate statement of the theorem. Add the theorem to your toolkit to use as needed in later problems.

3 Refer to the figure shown at the right.

a. If line ℓ is tangent to circle O at point A, the radius of the circle is 4 inches, and $AB = 3$ inches, what is length BO? Explain why.

b. If $AB = 5$ cm, $AO = 12$ cm, and $BO = 13$ cm, why is it correct to conclude that line ℓ must be tangent to the circle at point A?

4 **Tangents from a Point not on a Circle** Given a circle centered at O, here is an algorithm for using a compass and straightedge to construct tangent lines to the circle from a point P in the exterior of the circle.

Step 1. Draw $\overline{OP}$ and then construct its midpoint M.

Step 2. Construct the circle with center M and radius $\overline{OM}$. Label the points of intersection of the two circles A and B.

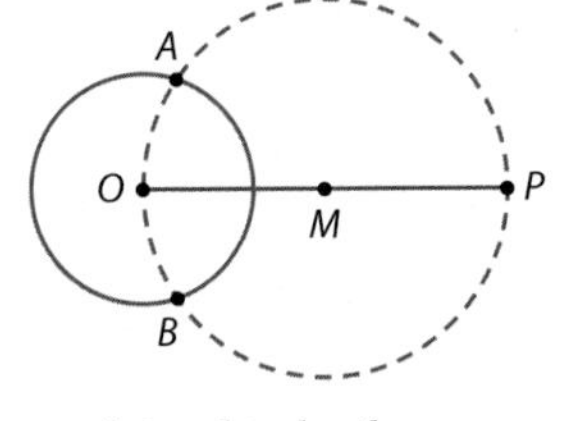

Step 3. Draw lines $\overleftrightarrow{PA}$ and $\overleftrightarrow{PB}$. These are claimed to be the tangent lines to the circle with center O through point P.

a. On a sheet of paper, draw a large circle with center O and a point P in the exterior of the circle. Use the above algorithm to construct tangent lines to the circle with center O from point P.

b. To verify that this construction works, draw radii $\overline{OA}$ and $\overline{OB}$ and segments $\overline{PA}$ and $\overline{PB}$ on your copy of the figure from Part a. How do you know that $\overleftrightarrow{PA}$ and $\overleftrightarrow{PB}$ are tangent to the circle with center O?

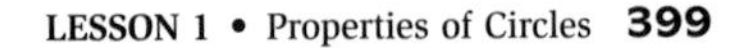

b. If a line is tangent to a circle, then the line is perpendicular to the radius at the point of tangency; $\overline{OA} \perp \ell$.

c. A line is tangent to a circle if and only if the line is perpendicular to the radius drawn to the point of tangency.

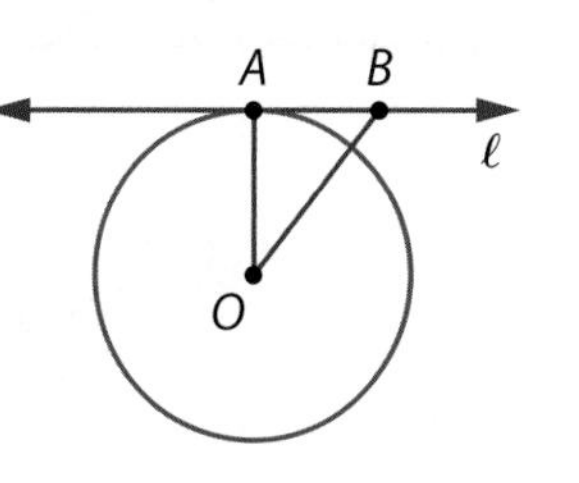

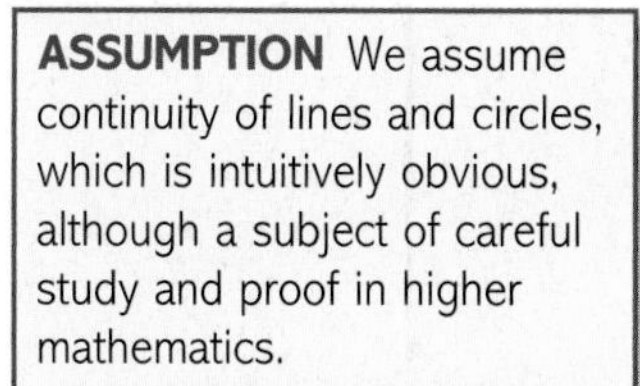
ASSUMPTION We assume continuity of lines and circles, which is intuitively obvious, although a subject of careful study and proof in higher mathematics.

3 **a.** $BO = 5$ inches by the Pythagorean Theorem. The theorem in Part b states that ℓ and $\overline{OA}$ are perpendicular, so we know that $\triangle OAB$ is a right triangle.

b. Note that $13^2 = 5^2 + 12^2$, so by the converse of the Pythagorean Theorem $\angle BAO$ is a right angle. By the theorem in Part b, it follows that ℓ is tangent to the circle at point A.

4 **INSTRUCTIONAL NOTE** In Problem 4, students will need to know how to use a compass and straightedge to construct a midpoint. See Unit 1 pages 33–34, and in this unit, Review Task 31 (page 417) and Problem 3 Part a (page 402). Also, students may not remember that an angle inscribed in a semicircle is a right angle. Do not remind them until they have done their best to solve the problem themselves.

a. Students should apply the algorithm for the construction of a tangent to a circle.

b. Angles PAO and PBO are each inscribed in a semicircle (in this case, half the circle with center M), so they are right angles. By definition, radii $\overline{OA}$ and $\overline{OB}$ are perpendicular to lines $\overleftrightarrow{PA}$ and $\overleftrightarrow{PB}$, respectively, at points A and B on the circle. Therefore, $\overleftrightarrow{PA}$ and $\overleftrightarrow{PB}$ are tangent to the circle centered at O.

Teaching Resources

Student Master 4.

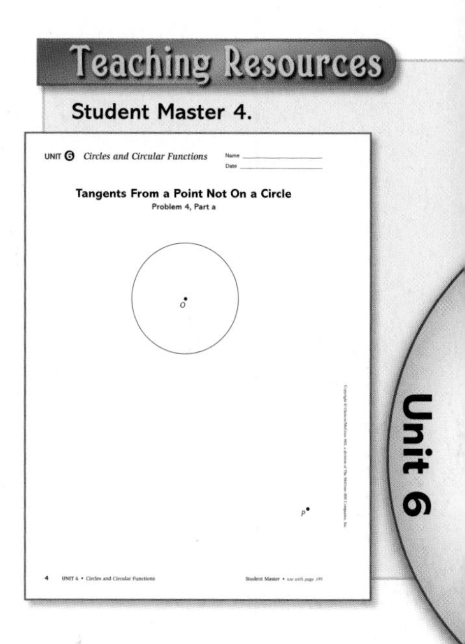

UNIT 6 Circles and Circular Functions
Name
Date
Tangents From a Point Not On a Circle
Problem 4, Part a
Unit 6

5 Now suppose you are given that $\overline{PA}$ and $\overline{PB}$ are tangent to a circle centered at O. To help prove that $\overline{PA} \cong \overline{PB}$, *auxiliary* line segments $\overline{OA}$, $\overline{OB}$, and $\overline{OP}$ are drawn in the figure.

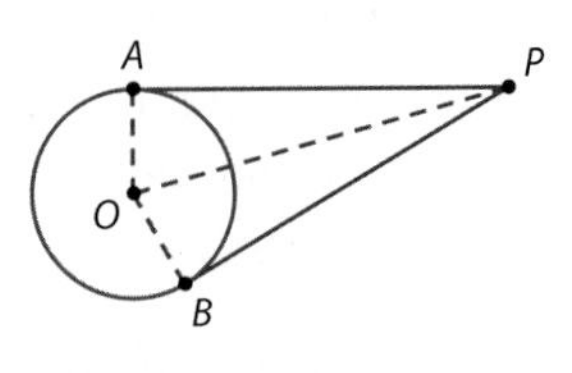

a. How could you use congruent triangles to prove that $\overline{PA} \cong \overline{PB}$?

b. How could you use the Pythagorean Theorem to show that $\overline{PA} \cong \overline{PB}$?

c. State in words the theorem you have proved about tangents drawn to a circle from an exterior point.

Summarize the Mathematics

In this investigation, you proved and applied some important properties of tangents to a circle.

a Make a list summarizing the properties of tangents that you proved.

b Some mathematics books define a tangent to a circle with center O at point A to be a line perpendicular to radius $\overline{OA}$ at point A. With that definition, would a tangent line necessarily intersect the circle in exactly one point? Why or why not?

c If point A is any point on a circle with center O, is there always a unique line that is tangent to the circle at point A? Explain.

Be prepared to compare your responses with those of others.

Check Your Understanding

The last three problems of this investigation suggest how to determine measures related to tangents to a circle from an exterior point, such as a satellite orbiting Earth. Suppose a satellite is located in space at point S. In its view of Earth in the plane of the equator, the angle between the lines of sight at S is 50°. The radius of Earth is 3,963 miles.

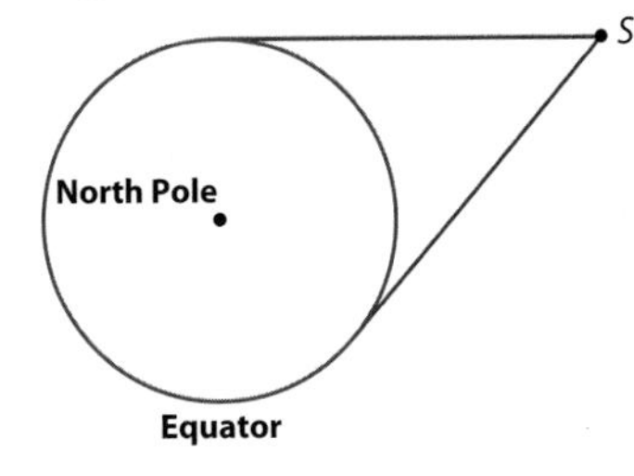

a. What is the distance from S to the horizon along the equator, that is, the length of a tangent from S to Earth's surface along the equator?

b. How high is the satellite S above Earth's surface, that is, the length of a segment S to the closest point on Earth's surface along the equator?

400 UNIT 6 • Circles and Circular Functions

5 **a.** $\angle PAO$ and $\angle PBO$ are right angles because tangent lines are perpendicular to radii drawn to the points of tangency. $AO = BO$ because radii of a circle are equal. PO equals itself. Therefore, $\triangle APO \cong \triangle BPO$ (HL Congruence Theorem). Thus, $\overline{PA} \cong \overline{PB}$ (CPCTC).

b. Since $\triangle PAO$ and $\triangle PBO$ are right triangles and $AO = BO$, $AP = \sqrt{OP^2 - OA^2} = \sqrt{OP^2 - OB^2} = BP$ (Pythagorean Theorem).

c. Segments drawn tangent to a circle from an exterior point are congruent.

Summarize the Mathematics

a A line is tangent to a circle if and only if the line is perpendicular to the radius drawn to the point of tangency. The tangent segments drawn to a circle from an exterior point are congruent.

b Yes, because the theorem in Problem 2 is if-and-only-if. In other words, if a line is perpendicular to a radius at a point on the circle, then the line is tangent to the circle; that is, the line intersects the circle in exactly one point.

c Yes. The unique line tangent to a circle with center O at a point A on the circle is the unique line that is perpendicular to the radius $\overline{OA}$ at point A.

Teaching Resources

Transparency Master 5.

UNIT 6 *Circles and Circular Functions*

Summarize the Mathematics

In this investigation, you proved and applied some important properties of tangents to a circle.

a Make a list summarizing the properties of tangents that you proved.

b Some mathematics books define a tangent to a circle with center O at point A to be a line perpendicular to radius $\overline{OA}$ at point A. With that definition, would a tangent line necessarily intersect the circle in exactly one point? Why or why not?

c If point A is any point on a circle with center O, is there always a unique line that is tangent to the circle at point A? Explain.

Be prepared to compare your list and reasoning with those of others.

Transparency Master • use with page 400 UNIT 6 • Circles and Circular Functions 5

MATH TOOLKIT
Students should add the two properties of tangents from STM Part a to their list of properties and theorems.

Unit 6

Check Your Understanding

a. In the figure, $OT = OE = 3{,}963$ miles, $\angle STO$ is a right angle, and $m\angle TSO = 25°$. (Since $\triangle PSO \cong \triangle TSO$, $m\angle TSO = \frac{1}{2}m\angle PST = 25°$.)

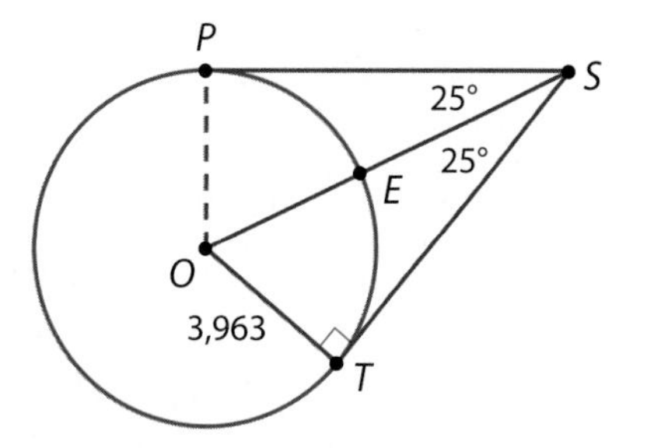

$$\tan 25° = \frac{OT}{ST} = \frac{3{,}963}{ST}$$

So, $ST = \dfrac{3{,}963}{\tan 25°} \approx 8{,}499$ miles.

b. $SE = OS - OE = OS - 3{,}963$

$OS = \sqrt{8{,}499^2 + 3{,}963^2} \approx 9{,}378$ miles

So, $SE \approx 9{,}378 - 3{,}963 = 5{,}415$ miles.

Investigation 2 Chords, Arcs, and Central Angles

As noted at the beginning of this lesson, a **chord** of a circle is a line segment that joins two points of the circle. Any diameter is a chord, but chords may also be shorter than a diameter.

Wheel covers come in a wide range of designs. One wheel cover option is pictured on the left below. Some companies manufacture wheel covers according to buyers' design specifications, as for example, the figure on the right below. Each segment in the design represents a wire that forms a chord that must be at least 3 inches from the center of the wheel cover.

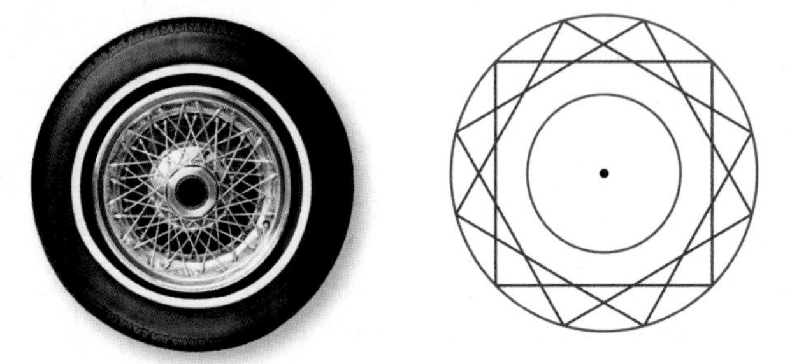

As you work on the problems of this investigation, look for answers to the following questions:

What are important properties of chords, arcs, and central angles of a circle?

How can these properties be proved and applied?

Relating Central Angles, Chords, and Arcs A **central angle** of a circle is an angle of measure less than 180° with vertex at the center of the circle and sides along radii of the circle. In the diagram below, $\angle AOB$ is a central angle and $\overline{AB}$ is the *corresponding chord*.

Each central angle splits a circle into two arcs. In the diagram, the arc $\widehat{ACB}$ that lies in the interior of the central angle is called a **minor arc**. The other arc $\widehat{ADB}$ is called a **major arc**. The simple arc notation $\widehat{AB}$ is used to indicate the minor arc corresponding to the central angle $\angle AOB$.

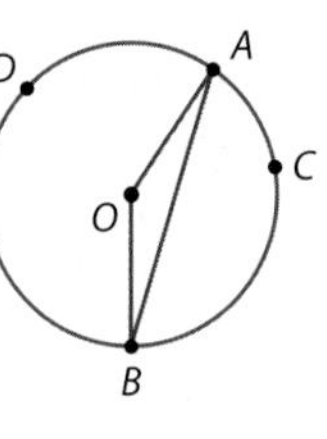

Arcs are commonly measured in degrees. The degree measure of a minor arc is equal to the measure of the corresponding central angle. The degree measure of a major arc is 360 minus the measure of the corresponding minor arc.

1. Suppose that in the diagram above $m\angle AOB = 160°$.
   a. What is $m\widehat{ACB}$, the measure of the minor arc $\widehat{ACB}$?
   b. What is $m\widehat{ADB}$, the measure of the major arc $\widehat{ADB}$?
   c. Make a copy of the sketch showing possible locations of a point X so that $m\widehat{AX} = 90°$?

Investigation 2 Chords, Arcs, and Central Angles

This investigation defines chords, arcs, and central angles. Connections between these are explored, including the properties involving a radius containing the midpoint of a chord and the connection between the length of a chord and its distance from the center of the circle. Coordinate and synthetic proofs are explored and compared in Connections Task 14.

Properties developed are:

- The degree measure of a minor arc and the degree measure of its corresponding central angle are the same.
- A line through the center of a circle bisects a chord if and only if the line is perpendicular to the chord.
- If one chord in a circle is longer than another, then the longer chord is closer to the center of the circle.

MATH NOTE This material uses the convention that central angles are less than 180°. Thus, the arc subtended by a central angle is the minor arc, unless the major arc is directly specified.

1 **a.** $m\widehat{ACB} = 160°$

b. $m\widehat{ADB} = 360° - 160° = 200°$

c. The two possible locations are shown at the right.

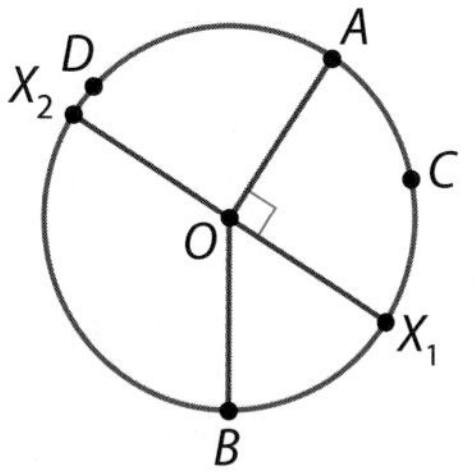

A
D
X_2
C
O
X_1
B

2 **a.** $AB = CD$ is given. Since all radii of a circle are equal, $AO = CO$ and $BO = DO$. So, $\triangle ABO \cong \triangle CDO$ (SSS) and $m\angle AOB = m\angle COD$ (CPCTC). Thus, $m\widehat{AB} = m\widehat{CD}$ by the definition of arc measure.

b. Given that $m\widehat{AB} = m\widehat{CD}$, it follows by definition that $m\angle AOB = m\angle COD$. Since all radii of a circle are equal, $AO = CO$ and $BO = DO$. So, $\angle ABO \cong \angle CDO$ (SAS) and $AB = CD$ (CPCTC).

c. *The measures of two minor arcs are equal if and only if the lengths of their corresponding chords are equal.*

Unit 6

2 By definition, two arcs have the same measure if and only if their central angles are congruent. But what about the corresponding chords? Consider chords $\overline{AB}$ and $\overline{CD}$ and their central angles pictured at the right.

a. Suppose $AB = CD$. Prove that $m\angle AOB = m\angle COD$ and $m\widehat{AB} = m\widehat{CD}$.

b. Suppose $m\widehat{AB} = m\widehat{CD}$. Prove that $AB = CD$.

c. Summarize in an if-and-only-if statement what you have proved in Parts a and b.

3 **Relationships between Chords** Some other interesting properties of chords can be explored with compass-and-straightedge constructions.

a. Divide the work on these three constructions among your classmates so that each person completes one of the constructions. All three constructions should be done carefully, beginning with a large copy of the figure at the right.

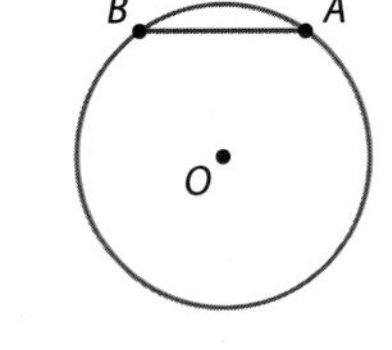

i. Construct the midpoint M of chord $\overline{AB}$. Draw line $\overleftrightarrow{OM}$.

ii. Construct line p, the perpendicular bisector of chord $\overline{AB}$.

iii. Construct line ℓ perpendicular to chord $\overline{AB}$ through point O.

b. Compare lines $\overleftrightarrow{OM}$, p, and ℓ that you and your classmates constructed. How are they alike? How are they different?

c. Based on your findings in the first two constructions, complete the following conjectures.

i. If a line contains the center of a circle and the midpoint of a chord, then ____________.

ii. The perpendicular bisector of a chord of a circle contains ____________.

iii. If a line through the center of a circle is perpendicular to a chord, then ____________.

You are asked to prove these conjectures in the On Your Own tasks.

4 The properties of chords that you explored in this investigation combined with trigonometric methods allow you to find measures of various angles and segments in circles. Suppose that a given circle has radius 6 inches.

a. What is the length of a chord that has a central angle of 115°?

b. What is the measure of the arc of a chord that is 8 inches long? What is the perpendicular distance from the center of the circle to the chord?

c. The perpendicular distance from the center of the circle to a chord is 4 inches. What is the length of the chord? What is the measure of its central angle?

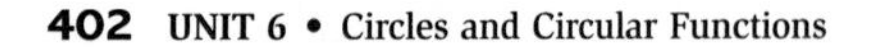

402 UNIT 6 • Circles and Circular Functions

3 **a. i–ii.**

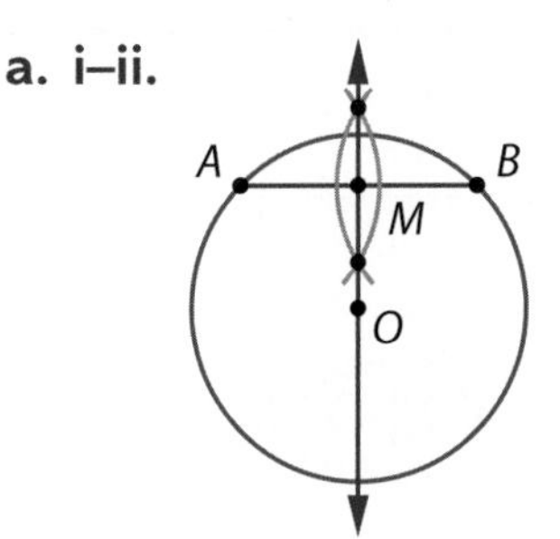

iii.

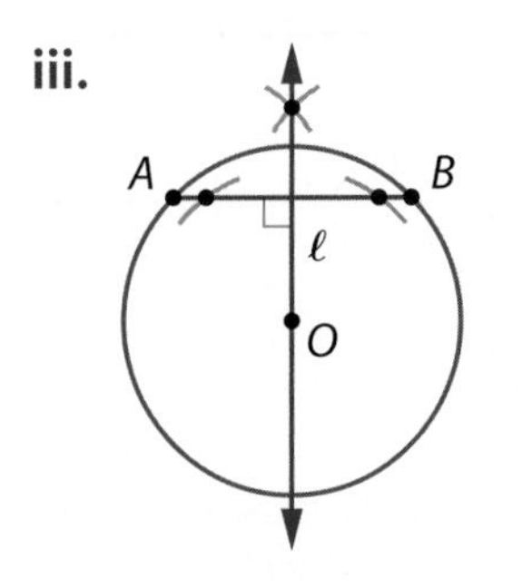

b. The resulting lines in each construction are the same line, although the steps in the constructions in Part aiii are not the same as in the other two constructions.

c. **i.** If a line contains the center of a circle and the midpoint of a chord, then the line is perpendicular to the chord. So, the line is the perpendicular bisector of the chord.

ii. The perpendicular bisector of the chord of a circle contains the center of the circle.

iii. If a line through the center of a circle is perpendicular to a chord, then the line contains the midpoint of the chord and is the perpendicular bisector of the chord.

4 **a.** Use the fact that a radius drawn perpendicular to the chord bisects the chord and the central angle, and let x be the length of the chord.

$$\sin 57.5° = \frac{\frac{c}{2}}{6} = \frac{c}{12}$$

$$c = 12 \sin 57.5° \approx 10.1 \text{ in.}$$

b. Let θ be the measure of the central angle. Then

$$\sin \frac{\theta}{2} = \frac{4}{6}$$

$$\frac{\theta}{2} = \sin^{-1}\left(\frac{4}{6}\right) \approx 41.8°$$

$$\theta \approx 83.6°$$

Therefore, the measure of the arc is 83.6°.

The perpendicular distance d from the center of the circle to the chord can be found by using the Pythagorean Theorem: $d = \sqrt{20} \approx 4.5$ in.

c. Let $\frac{c}{2}$ be half the length of the chord. Then

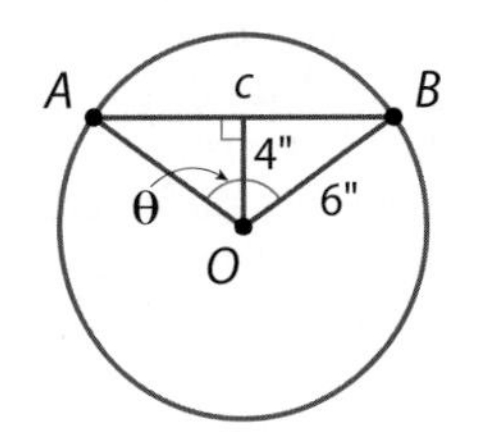

$$\left(\frac{c}{2}\right)^2 = 6^2 - 4^2 = 20$$

$$\frac{c}{2} = \sqrt{20} \text{ in.}$$

The length of the chord is $2\sqrt{20} \approx 8.94$ in.

Let θ be the measure of the central angle.

$$\cos \frac{\theta}{2} = \frac{4}{6}$$

$$\frac{\theta}{2} = \cos^{-1}\left(\frac{4}{6}\right) \approx 48.2°$$

$$\theta \approx 96.4°$$

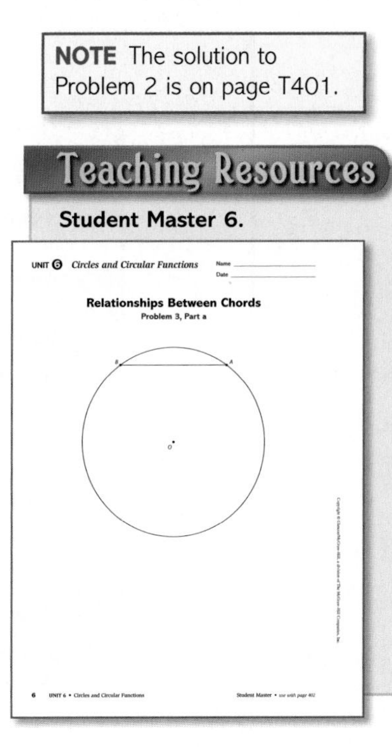

NOTE The solution to Problem 2 is on page T401.

Teaching Resources

Student Master 6.

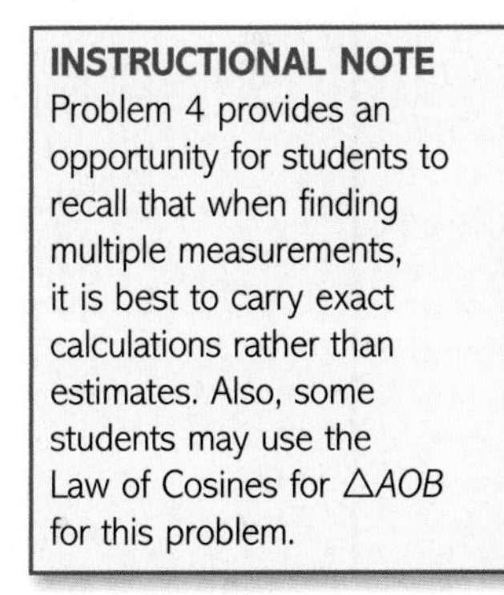

INSTRUCTIONAL NOTE
Problem 4 provides an opportunity for students to recall that when finding multiple measurements, it is best to carry exact calculations rather than estimates. Also, some students may use the Law of Cosines for $\triangle AOB$ for this problem.

Unit 6

Summarize the Mathematics

In this investigation, you explored and justified some interesting and useful properties of chords in the same or congruent circles.

a. Describe how minor and major arcs are determined, named, and measured.

b. Summarize how a chord, its minor arc, and its central angle are related.

c. Complete the following if-and-only-if statement that summarizes two theorems explored in this investigation: A line through the center of a circle bisects a chord if and only if ________.

d. If you know the radius of a circle and the length of a chord that is shorter than the diameter, describe how you can determine the measure of the central angle of the chord.

Be prepared to share your responses and thinking with the class.

Check Your Understanding

The designer wheel cover shown at the right has diameter 12 inches. The wires (chords) that are shown are all of equal length.

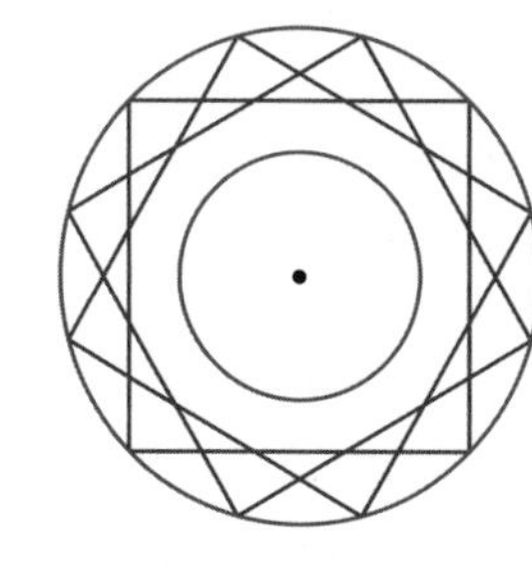

a. What is the length of each of the wire chords?

b. More wire chords can be added to the design, but none can come closer than 3 inches to the center of the wheel cover.

  i. What is the longest possible wire chord that can be added to this design?

  ii. What is the measure of the central angle of one of these longest wire chords?

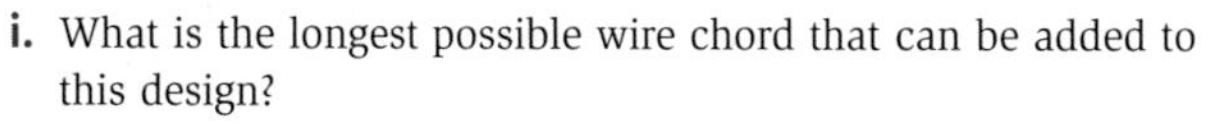

Investigation 3 Angles Inscribed in a Circle

Angle measurements and circular arcs are used as navigation aids for ships cruising in dangerous waters. For example, if a stretch of water off two lighthouses holds hazards like rocks, reefs, or shallow areas, the navigation charts might include a circle that passes through the two lighthouses and contains the hazards. It turns out that by carefully tracking the angle determined by the two lighthouses and a ship, its captain can stay safely outside the hazardous area.

Summarize the Mathematics

a A major or minor arc is determined by two points on a circle. These two points, such as A and B, are used to name the minor arc $\overset{\frown}{AB}$. The minor arc is less than a semicircle. A major arc is typically named using a third point that is between A and B on the arc that is larger than a semicircle. For example, $\overset{\frown}{ACB}$. The degree measure of a minor arc and its central angle are the same. The degree measure of the major arc is 360 minus the degree measure of the minor arc (or its central angle).

b The measure of the chord's minor arc is equal to the measure of its central angle. The greater the measure of the central angle (up to 180°), the longer the chord.

c A line through the center of a circle bisects a chord if and only if the line is perpendicular to the chord.

d You can use trigonometry as follows. If x is the length of the chord, θ is its central angle and r is the radius, then $\sin \frac{\theta}{2} = \frac{\frac{x}{2}}{r} = \frac{x}{2r}$. So, $\frac{\theta}{2} = \sin^{-1}\left(\frac{x}{2r}\right)$.

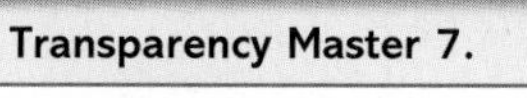

Transparency Master 7.

UNIT 6 Circles and Circular Functions

Summarize the Mathematics

In this investigation, you explored and justified some interesting and useful properties of chords in the same or congruent circles.

a. Describe how minor and major arcs are determined, named, and measured.

b. Summarize how a chord, its minor arc, and its central angle are related.

c. Complete the following if-and-only-if statement that summarizes two theorems explored in this investigation: A line through the center of a circle bisects a chord if and only if ______.

d. If you know the radius of a circle and the length of a chord that is shorter than the diameter, describe how you can determine the measure of the central angle of the chord.

Be prepared to share your responses and thinking with the class.

Transparency Master • UNIT 6 • Circles and Circular Functions 7

MATH TOOLKIT Students should provide themselves illustrative examples to show the relationships among a chord, its minor arc, and its central angle. They should also add the theorem from STM Part b to their theorem list.

Unit 6

Check Your Understanding

a. The wire chords are sides of squares whose vertices lie on the circle. The central angle of one of these chords measures 90°, one-fourth of the circle. Therefore, the chord is the hypotenuse of an isosceles right triangle with radii of the circle as legs. Therefore, the length of a chord c can be found as follows:

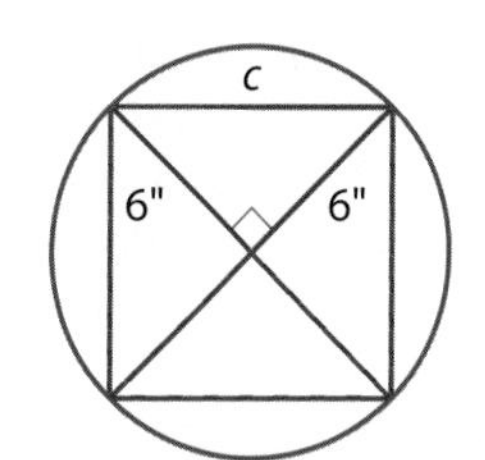

$c^2 = 6^2 + 6^2 = 72$

$c = \sqrt{72} \approx 8.5$ in.

b. i. Half the chord will be a leg of a triangle whose hypotenuse is 6 inches and the other leg is 3 inches. Thus,

$\left(\frac{c}{2}\right)^2 = 6^2 - 3^2 = 27$

$\frac{c}{2} = \sqrt{27}$

$c = 2\sqrt{27} \approx 10.4$ in.

c
3"
6"
6"

ii. If the central angle is θ, then $\cos \frac{\theta}{2} = \frac{1}{2}$, $\frac{\theta}{2} = 60°$, and $\theta = 120°$.

INSTRUCTIONAL NOTE Some students may recognize the 30°-60° right triangle relationship in Part bii and use that to determine the central angle measure. If not, you may wish to reference this at the summary so students watch for it in future tasks.

The key to this navigation strategy is the relationship between *inscribed angles* and arcs of circles. As you work on the problems of this investigation, look for answers to the following questions:

What is an inscribed angle in a circle?

How is the measure of an inscribed angle related to the arc it intercepts?

1 Make a drawing like that on the sketch below or use the "Lighthouse" sample sketch in *CPMP-Tools* to see how m$\angle ASC$ tells whether the ship is inside, outside, or on the circle of hazardous water.

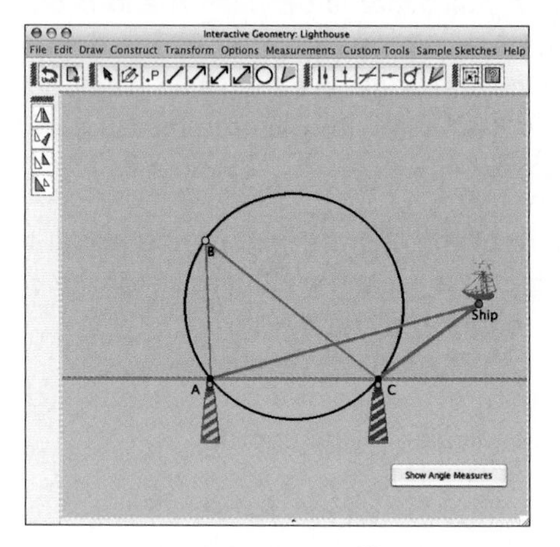

a. First find the approximate measure of $\overset{\frown}{AC}$.

b. What seems to be true of m$\angle ASC$ when the ship is right on the boundary of the circle of hazardous water?

c. What seems to be true of m$\angle ASC$ when the ship is inside the circle of hazardous water?

d. What seems to be true of m$\angle ASC$ when the ship is outside the circle of hazardous water?

e. As captain of the ship, how could you use sighting instruments to keep safely outside the circle of hazardous water?

Inscribed Angles and Intercepted Arcs When the ship is located on the boundary of the region of hazardous water, the angle determined by the two lighthouses and the ship is called an **inscribed angle** in the circle. In general, if points A, B, and C are on the same circle, then those points determine three inscribed angles in that circle.

404 UNIT 6 • Circles and Circular Functions

Investigation 3 Angles Inscribed in a Circle

This investigation develops two main properties of inscribed angles, the Inscribed Angle Theorem (the measure of an inscribed angle is half that of the intercepted arc) and the congruence of inscribed angles that intercept the same arc. The former theorem is proved by cases, an important proof technique. Some practical applications and further consequences of these theorems are explored.

TECHNOLOGY NOTE When students are using the "Lighthouse" sample sketch, encourage them to explore the relative measures of $\angle B$ and $\angle S$ for various positions of the ship in the interior of the circle. Students might notice that when $\angle S$ is at the center, it is twice the measure of $\angle B$. Using the relationship that the $m\overset{\frown}{AC}$ is equal to the measure of its central angle, students might make the connection that the measure of inscribed $\angle B$ is also half the measure of intercepted $\overset{\frown}{AC}$. It is not necessary that this relationship be observed at this point, since it comes up in Problem 2.

As long as the computers are in use, you may wish to have students use the "Explore Angles and Arcs" custom tool in *CPMP-Tools* and complete Problem 5 Parts a and b. They will then have the conjecture to prove after Problem 4.

Alternatively, you could launch this investigation as a whole class discussion using the "Lighthouse" sample sketch.

1
- **a.** The measure of arc $\overset{\frown}{AC}$ is approximately 77.32°.
- **b.** When S is on the boundary of the circle, $m\angle ASC \approx 38.66°$, or half of $m\overset{\frown}{AC}$.
- **c.** When S is inside the circle, $m\angle ASC > 38.66°$.
- **d.** When S is outside the circle, $m\angle ASC < 38.66°$.
- **e.** The sighting instruments could be used to monitor the measure of $\angle ASC$. The key to avoiding the hazards is to make sure that $m\angle ASC$ is always less than or equal to 38.66°.

Unit 6

2 In the figures below, inscribed angle $\angle ABC$ is said to **intercept $\widehat{ADC}$** where $\widehat{ADC}$ consists of points A and C and all points on the circle O that lie in the interior of $\angle ABC$. Your goal is to explore the connection between the measures of inscribed angle $\angle ABC$ and its intercepted arc $\widehat{ADC}$.

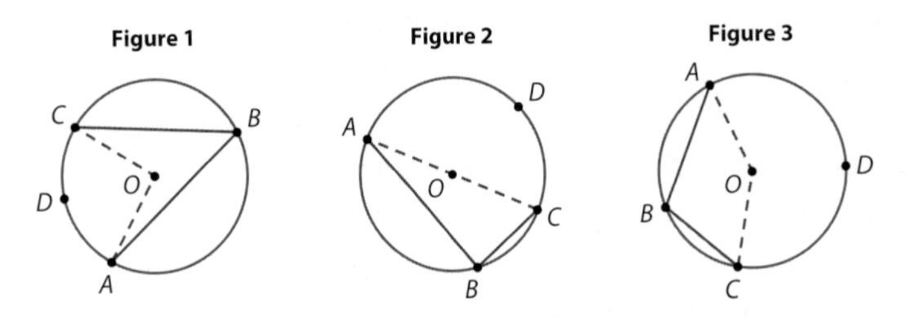

a. When $\widehat{ADC}$ is a semicircle, as in Figure 2, what is $m\angle ABC$? How do the measures of $\angle ABC$ and $\widehat{ADC}$ compare?

b. Using the "Explore Angles and Arcs" custom tool or by drawing several diagrams, consider multiple instances of Figure 1 where $\angle B$ is an acute angle on the circle. Does the same relationship between the measures of an acute inscribed angle and its intercepted arc that you noted in the case of the inscribed right angle seem to hold?

c. In Figure 3 above, $\angle ABC$ is an obtuse inscribed angle. Its intercepted arc is *major arc* $\widehat{ADC}$. How can the measure of major arc $\widehat{ADC}$ be determined if you know $m\angle AOC$? Use the "Explore Angles and Arcs" custom tool to explore the relationship between the measure of obtuse inscribed angle $\angle ABC$ and its intercepted arc $\widehat{ADC}$.

d. Write a conjecture about how the measure of an inscribed angle and the measure of its intercepted arc are related.

3 You noted in Problem 2 Part a that $m\widehat{ADC} = 180°$ when $m\angle B = 90°$. You also noted in Part c that when the measure of the inscribed angle is more than 180°, you can find the measure of the major arc by subtracting the measure of the minor arc from 360°. This means that to prove the important conjecture, "The measure of an angle inscribed in a circle is half the measure of its intercepted arc," it is sufficient to prove it for acute $\angle B$. To do this, we need to break this case into three smaller cases *all* where $\angle B$ is an *acute* angle as shown in the figures below.

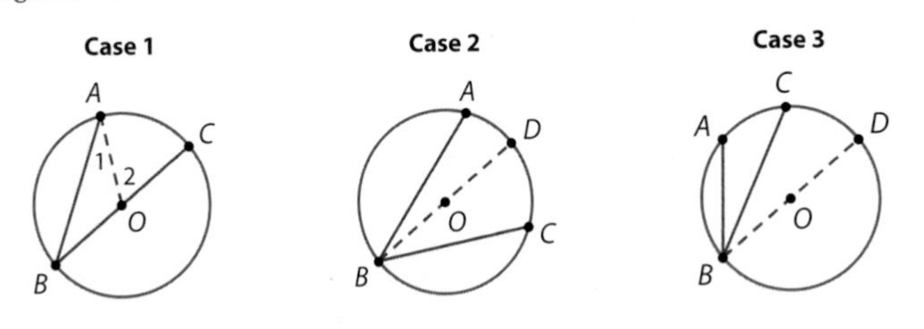

a. These cases differ from one another according to the location of the inscribed angle relative to center O. Explain this difference.

Unit 6

2 **a.** $\angle ABC$ is inscribed in a semicircle, so $m\angle ABC = 90°$.
$m\angle ABC = \frac{1}{2} m\widehat{ADC}$

b. Students should verify that when $\angle B$ is an acute inscribed angle, it is half the measure of its intercepted arc.

c. The measure of major arc $\widehat{ADC}$ is $360° - m\widehat{AC} = 360° - m\angle AOC$. Using the "Explore Angles and Arcs" custom tool, students should find that the measure of the inscribed angle is half the measure of its intercepted arc, which is now a major arc; $m\angle ABC = \frac{1}{2} m\widehat{ADC}$.

d. **Inscribed Angle Theorem** The measure of an inscribed angle of a circle is half the measure of its intercepted arc.

3 **a.** In Case 1, the center O of the circle is on a side of the inscribed angle. In Case 2, O is in the interior of the inscribed angle. In Case 3, O is in the exterior of the inscribed angle.

b. A *proof by cases* strategy for proving this conjecture is to prove it for Case 1 first. Then use that result to prove it for the other two cases. Why would carrying out this strategy successfully constitute a complete proof of the conjecture?

4 In Case 1, one side of the inscribed angle contains the center O of the circle. Study the following proof by students at Holland High School of the conjecture in Problem 3. Give a reason why each of the statements is correct.

Proof of Case 1:

Center O lies on $\overline{BC}$. Draw radius $\overline{AO}$.	(1)
In $\triangle AOB$, $\overline{AO} \cong \overline{BO}$.	(2)
$m\angle ABC = m\angle 1$	(3)
$m\angle 2 = m\angle ABC + m\angle 1$	(4)
$m\angle 2 = 2(m\angle ABC)$	(5)
$m\angle 2 = m\widehat{AC}$	(6)
$2(m\angle ABC) = m\widehat{AC}$	(7)
$m\angle ABC = \frac{1}{2}(m\widehat{AC})$	(8)

The proof of Case 1 shows that whenever one side of an inscribed angle is a diameter of the circle, its measure is half the measure of its intercepted arc. In Applications Task 8, you will be asked to prove Cases 2 and 3. Assuming all three cases are proved, record the **Inscribed Angle Theorem** in your toolkit.

Angles Intercepting the Same Arc Think back to the introduction of this investigation and the problem of assuring that a ship navigates outside of a circle of hazardous water. Suppose that a captain wants to steer his ship along the boundary of that circle.

5 Use the "Explore Angles and Arcs" custom tool to see how, if at all, the measure of $\angle ABC$ changes as the ship moves.

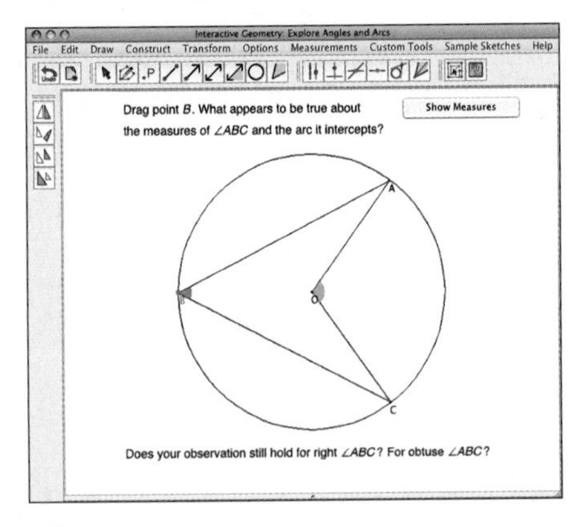

a. Keeping $m\widehat{AC}$ constant, drag the vertex B on the circle always keeping it on the same side of $\widehat{AC}$. How does the measure of $\angle B$ change as you move it to various locations on the circle?

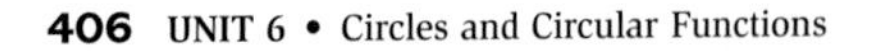

406 UNIT 6 • Circles and Circular Functions

b. Center O is either on a side of the inscribed angle, in the angle's interior, or in its exterior. There are no other possible locations of O. So, if you prove the conjecture for these three cases, it is proved for all inscribed angles.

4. (1) In this case, $\overline{BC}$ is a diameter which by definition contains O.
   (2) Radii of the same circle are congruent.
   (3) Base angles of an isosceles triangle are congruent.
   (4) Exterior Angle Theorem for Triangles
   (5) Substitution [3, 4]
   (6) Definition of arc measure
   (7) Substitute $2(m\angle ABC)$ from Step 5 into Step 6 for $m\angle 2$.
   (8) Divide both sides of the equation by 2.

5. **a.** The measure of $\angle B$ is constant, always equal to half of $m\widehat{AC}$.

b. Now change the measure of $\widehat{AC}$ by dragging point A or point C. Then drag vertex B again. Make a conjecture about the measures of inscribed angles that intercept the same arc.

c. How could the Inscribed Angle Theorem be used to prove this result?

Summarize the Mathematics

In this investigation, you explored the connection between an inscribed angle and its intercepted arc.

a Summarize the two main properties that you considered in this investigation. How were these properties used to help the captain of the ship avoid the hazardous area?

b If $\angle ABC$ is inscribed in a semicircle, what is the measure of its intercepted arc? What is the measure of $\angle ABC$?

c A central angle and an inscribed angle intercept the same arc. How are the measures of the angles related?

Be prepared to explain your responses to the class.

Check Your Understanding

In the diagram below, $\overline{BD}$ is a diameter of the circle with center O. Points A, B, C, and D are on the circle.

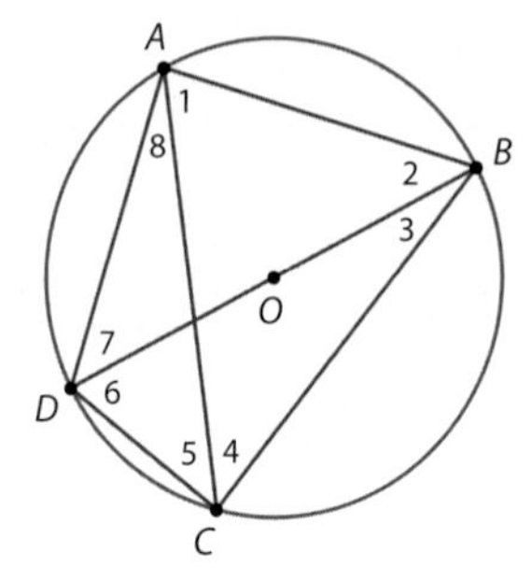

a. If $m\widehat{AB} = 100°$, find the measures of as many of the numbered angles as possible.

b. Given the two measures $m\angle 1 = 55°$ and $m\angle 2 = 50°$, find the measures of the four minor arcs $\widehat{AB}$, $\widehat{BC}$, $\widehat{CD}$, and $\widehat{DA}$.

b. By dragging A or C, you will change $m\widehat{AC}$. But given the new measure of $\widehat{AC}$, $m\angle B$ will equal half that measure no matter where you drag B as long as it is on the same side of A and C on the circle.

c. For any two locations of B on the same side of A and C on the circle, say B_1 and B_2, $m\angle AB_1C = m\angle AB_2C$.

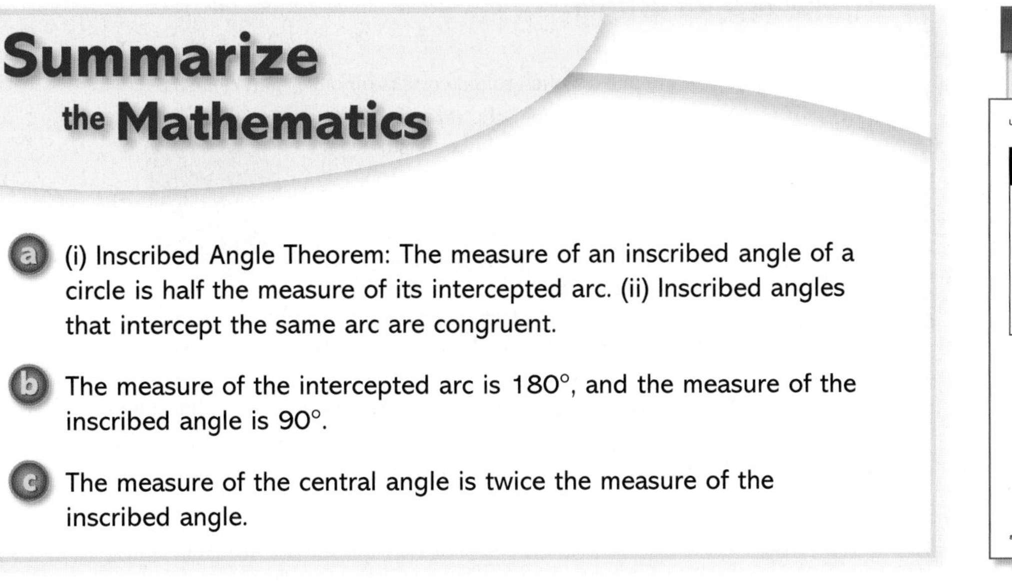

Summarize the Mathematics

a (i) Inscribed Angle Theorem: The measure of an inscribed angle of a circle is half the measure of its intercepted arc. (ii) Inscribed angles that intercept the same arc are congruent.

b The measure of the intercepted arc is 180°, and the measure of the inscribed angle is 90°.

c The measure of the central angle is twice the measure of the inscribed angle.

Teaching Resources

Transparency Master 8.

UNIT 6 *Circles and Circular Functions*

Summarize the Mathematics

In this investigation, you explored the connection between an inscribed angle and its intercepted arc.

a Summarize the two main properties that you considered in this investigation. How were these properties used to help the captain of the ship avoid the hazardous area?

b If $\angle ABC$ is inscribed in a semicircle, what is the measure of its intercepted arc? What is the measure of $\angle ABC$?

c A central angle and an inscribed angle intercept the same arc. How are the measures of the angles related?

Be prepared to explain your thinking to the class.

MATH TOOLKIT Students should include the Inscribed Angle Theorem in their list of theorems.

INSTRUCTIONAL NOTE Although this solution does not use arc addition, students may use it since it is an extension of segment addition.

Check Your Understanding

a. By direct application of the Inscribed Angle Theorem, $m\angle 4 = 50°$ and $m\angle 7 = 50°$. Because $\overline{BD}$ is a diameter, $m\angle DCB = 90°$ and $m\angle 5 = 40°$. Since $\angle 2$ intercepts $\widehat{AB}$, it is the same measure as $\angle 5$ which also intercepts $\widehat{AD}$. Thus, $m\angle 2 = 40°$.

$m\angle 2 = 40°$
$m\angle 4 = 50°$
$m\angle 5 = 40°$
$m\angle 7 = 50°$

b. By direct application of the Inscribed Angle Theorem, $m\widehat{BC} = 110°$ and $m\widehat{DA} = 100°$. Since $m\angle 1 + m\angle 8 = 90°$, $m\angle 8 = 35°$ and $m\widehat{CD} = 70°$.
$m\angle 5 = \frac{1}{2}m\widehat{DA} = 50°$ and $m\angle 4 + m\angle 5 = 90°$, so $m\angle 4 = 40°$ and $m\widehat{AB} = 80°$.

$m\widehat{AB} = 80°$
$m\widehat{BC} = 110°$
$m\widehat{CD} = 70°$
$m\widehat{DA} = 100°$

Unit 6

On Your Own

Applications

1 Furniture makers often round corners on tables and cabinets.

a. In the figure at the right, the lower-left corner is to be rounded, using a circle with a radius of 2 inches. Lines $\overleftrightarrow{AB}$ and $\overleftrightarrow{CB}$ will be tangent to the circle. When the corner is rounded, point B will be cut off and points A and C will lie on the circular arc. Explain how to apply tangent theorems to locate the center of the circle that rounds the corner. Sketch the rounded corner.

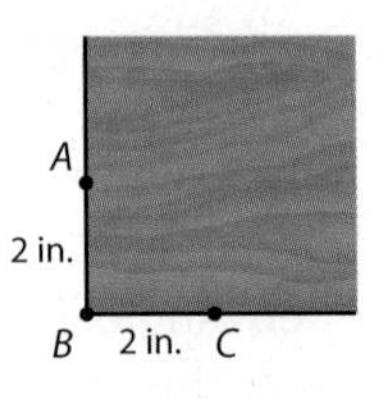

b. Determine the distance from point B to the center of the circle.

c. As shown in the figure, point B is equidistant from points A and C. When this corner is rounded as described in Part a, this illustrates a tangent theorem. Which one?

2 Prove the following direct result (*corollary*) of the theorem about tangent segments from a point exterior to a circle.

In the figure at the right, two tangent segments, $\overline{PA}$ and $\overline{PB}$, are drawn to the circle with center O from exterior point P. What ray appears to be the bisector of $\angle APB$? Prove your answer.

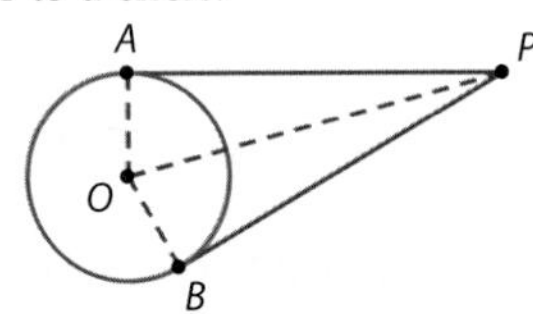

3 Suppose a circle with center O has radius 10 inches, P is a point in the exterior of the circle, and the tangent segments to the circle from point P are $\overline{AP}$ and $\overline{BP}$.

a. If point P is 18 inches from the center of the circle, determine the length of $\overline{AP}$ and the measure of $\angle APB$.

b. If $m\angle APB = 48°$, determine the distances OP, AP, and BP.

4 Prove the three conjectures from Investigation 2, Problem 3.

a. *If a line contains the center of a circle and the midpoint of a chord, then the line is perpendicular to the chord.*

b. *The perpendicular bisector of the chord of a circle contains the center of the circle.*

c. *If a line through the center of a circle is perpendicular to a chord, then the line contains the midpoint of the chord.*

Unit 6

408 UNIT 6 • Circles and Circular Functions

On Your Own

Applications

1 **a.** Draw lines perpendicular to the edges of the corner at points A and C, respectively. Their point of intersection is the center of the circle used to round the corner.

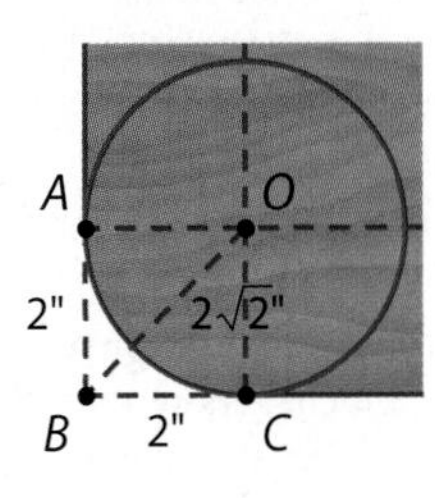

b. $\overline{BO}$ is the diagonal of a square; $BO = \sqrt{8} = 2\sqrt{2}$ inches.

c. The tangent segments to a circle from an exterior point are congruent.

2 $\overline{PO}$ appears to be the bisector of $\angle APB$.

Proof: $AP = BP$ (congruent tangent segments from an exterior point), $OA = OB$ (radii of the same circle), and $\overline{OP}$ is a common side of $\triangle AOP$ and $\triangle BOP$. So, $\triangle AOP \cong \triangle BOP$ (SSS). Thus, $\angle APO \cong \angle BPO$ (CPCTC). By definition, $\overrightarrow{PO}$ is the bisector of $\angle APB$.

3 **a.** $PA = \sqrt{OP^2 - OA^2} = \sqrt{18^2 - 10^2} = \sqrt{224} \approx 15.0$ inches $\approx \sqrt{OP^2 - OB^2} = PB$

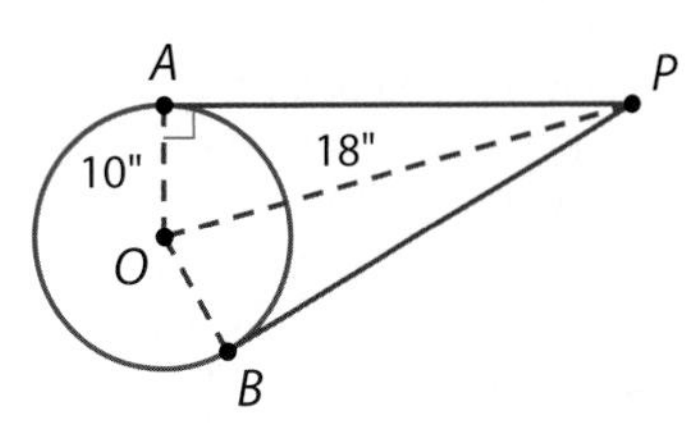

Find m$\angle APB$.

$\sin \angle APO = \frac{10}{18}$, so m$\angle APO \approx 33.75°$

m$\angle APB \approx 67.5°$.

b. Because $\triangle PAO \cong \triangle PBO$, m$\angle APO =$ m$\angle BPO = \frac{1}{2}(48°) = 24°$. Using trigonometry in these right triangles,

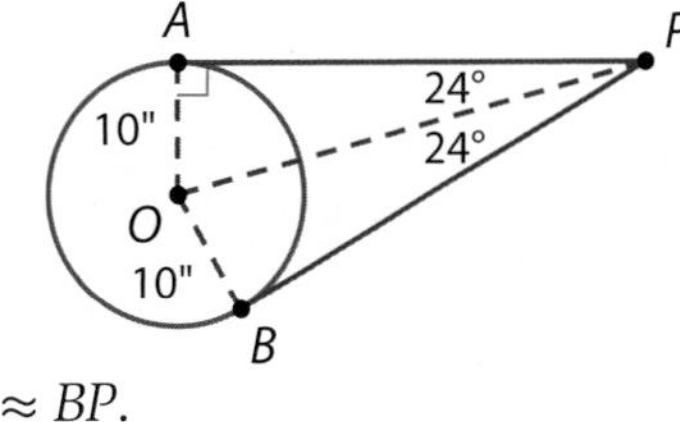

$\sin 24° = \frac{10}{OP}$, so $OP = \frac{10}{\sin 24°} \approx 24.6$ inches.

$\tan 24° = \frac{10}{AP}$, so $AP = \frac{10}{\tan 24°} \approx 22.5$ inches $\approx BP$.

Or using the Pythagorean Theorem,

$BP = \sqrt{OP^2 - OB^2} = \sqrt{(24.6)^2 - 10^2} \approx 22.5$ inches

4 **a.** *If a line contains the center of a circle and the midpoint of a chord, then the line is perpendicular to the chord.*

Given chord $\overline{AB}$ with midpoint M in circle with center O. Radii are equal, so $AO = BO$. $AM = BM$ by definition of midpoint, and $MO = MO$. Therefore, $\triangle AMO \cong \triangle BMO$ (SSS). Since $\angle AMO \cong \angle BMO$ and these angles form a linear pair, they are both right angles. By definition, $\overline{OM} \perp \overline{AB}$.

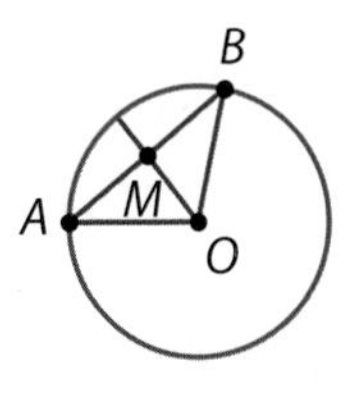

b. *The perpendicular bisector of the chord of a circle contains its center.*

A point is equidistant from the endpoints of a line segment if and only if it lies on the perpendicular bisector of a line segment. Since $\overline{AO}$ and $\overline{BO}$ are radii of the same circle, $AO = BO$. Therefore, point O lies on the perpendicular bisector of chord $\overline{AB}$.

NOTE The solution to Problem 4 Part c is on page T409.

5 At the beginning of this lesson, you explored some properties of the decorative design from the Congo region of Africa pictured below. In this design, there are five concentric circles and square *ABCD*. The vertices of *ABCD* lie on the largest circle; that is, the square is inscribed in the largest circle. The sides of the square are tangent to the second largest circle; that is, the square is circumscribed about the second largest circle. In this task, you will continue to explore this design.

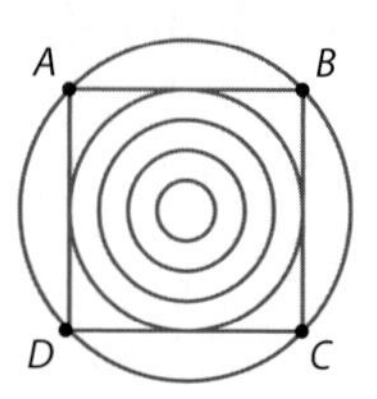

a. Suppose the radius of the smallest circle is 0.2 inches. The radii of the next three circles in increasing size are 0.2 inches more than the previous one. What is the length of a side of square *ABCD*?

b. What is the radius of the largest circle?

c. What is $m\widehat{AB}$? What is $m\widehat{ABC}$? What is the measure of major arc $\widehat{ABD}$?

d. Suppose point *E* is the point of tangency of $\overline{AB}$ to the second largest circle. Why must *E* also be the midpoint of $\overline{AB}$?

6 A broken piece of a circular plate shaped like the picture at the right is dug up by an archaeologist, who would like to describe the plate's original appearance and size.

a. Explain how to use one of the theorems that you proved in this lesson to find the location of the center of the plate.

b. Once you find the center, how could you find the circumference of the circular plate?

7 Eighteen equally spaced pins form a "circle" on the geoboard below. The measure of the diameter of circle *O* is 10 cm, and *M* is the midpoint of $\overline{AD}$.

Find the following measures:

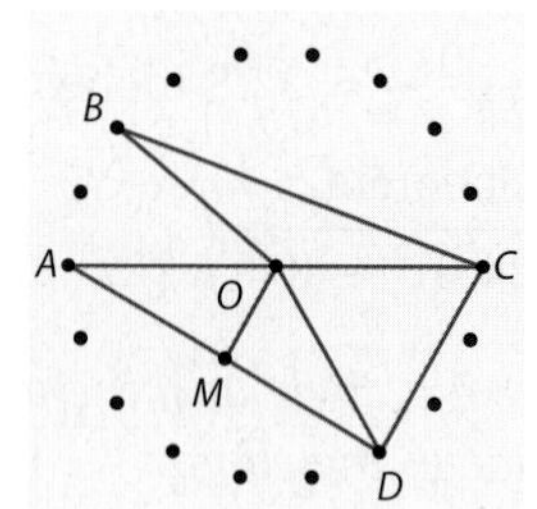

a. $m\widehat{AB}$

b. $m\widehat{BC}$

c. *BO*

d. *BC*

e. *CD*

f. $m\angle OMA$

c. **Given:** A circle with center O and $\overline{AB} \perp \overline{OP}$
Prove: P is the midpoint of chord $\overline{AB}$.

$\overline{OA} \cong \overline{OB}$ (radii of same circle)
$\overline{OP} \cong \overline{OP}$ (segment congruent to itself)
$\triangle AOP$ and $\triangle BOP$ are right triangles ($\overline{AB} \perp \overline{OP}$)
$\triangle AOP \cong \triangle BOP$ (hypotenuse-leg)
So, $\overline{AP} \cong \overline{BP}$ (CPCTC) and P is the midpoint of $\overline{AB}$.

5 **a.** The radius of the second largest circle is 0.8 inches and is equal to half the length of a side of a square which must be 1.6 inches.

b. Its radius is half the length of the diagonal of the square which is $0.8\sqrt{2} \approx 1.1$ in.

c. 90°; 180°; 270°

d. The line from the center to point E is perpendicular to $\overline{AB}$, because the sides of the square are tangent to the second largest circle. Side $\overline{AB}$ is also a chord of the largest circle, and the perpendicular from the center of a circle to a chord contains the midpoint of the chord. So, E is the midpoint of $\overline{AB}$ as well as the point of tangency.

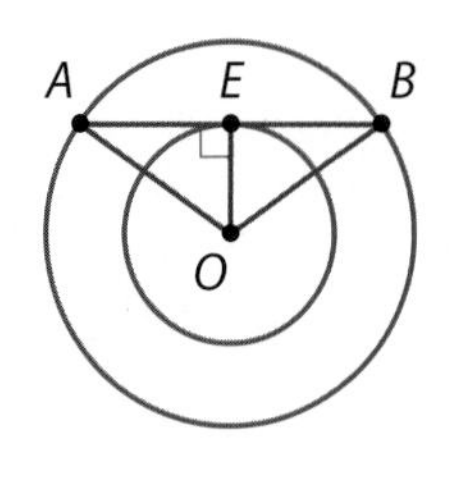

6 **a.** Consider two chords of the arc of the circular plate that is intact. Draw their perpendicular bisectors. They intersect at the center of the plate.

b. The radius is the distance from the center to any point on the intact arc, and the circumference is 2π times the radius.

7 **a.** $m\widehat{AB} = 40°$

b. $m\widehat{BC} = 140°$

c. $BO = 5$ cm

d. $BC \approx 9.4$ cm (Law of Cosines)

e. $CD = 5$ ($\triangle OCD$ is equilateral.)

f. $m\angle OMA = 90°$

Unit 6

8 Case 2 and Case 3 of the Inscribed Angle Theorem in Investigation 3, Problem 3 are shown below. In each figure, $\overline{BD}$ is a diameter. Assume these two basic properties.

Angle Addition Postulate:
If P is in the interior of $\angle ABC$, then $m\angle ABP + m\angle PBC = m\angle ABC$.

Arc Addition Postulate:
If P is on $\widehat{AC}$, then $m\widehat{AP} + m\widehat{PC} = m\widehat{APC}$.

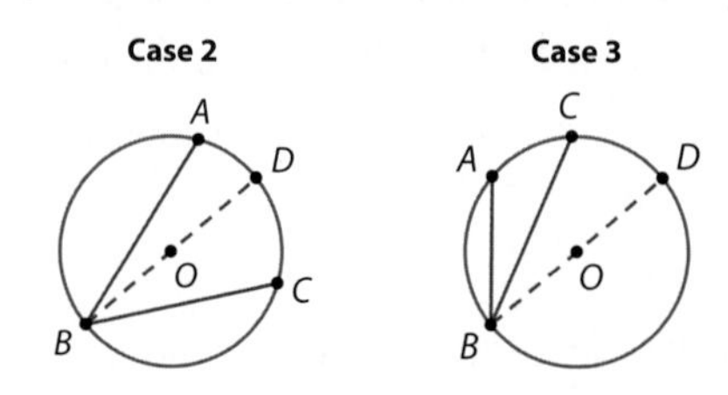

a. Prove Case 2: center O is in the interior of inscribed angle $\angle ABC$.

b. Prove Case 3: center O is in the exterior of inscribed angle $\angle ABC$.

9 As you saw in Investigation 3, to protect ships from dangerous rocks as they approach a coastline, the rocks in an area near shore are charted and a circle that contains all of them is drawn. The circle passes through two lighthouses at A and C. The measure of any inscribed angle that intercepts $\widehat{AC}$, such as $\angle ABC$ is called the *horizontal danger angle*.

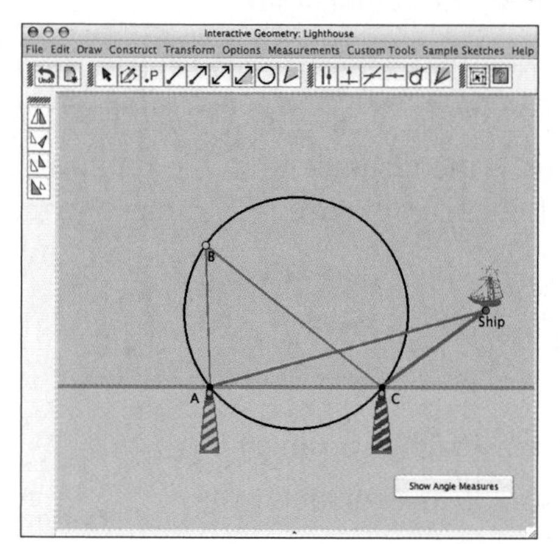

a. What is the measure of $\widehat{AC}$ in terms of the horizontal danger angle?

b. Suppose the lighthouses at A and C are 0.6 miles apart, and the horizontal danger angle is 35°. What is the radius of the hazardous water circle?

c. What is the perpendicular distance from the center of the hazardous water circle to shore?

10 A quadrilateral is inscribed in a circle if each vertex is a point on the circle. Prove the theorem:

If a quadrilateral is inscribed in a circle, then its opposite angles are supplementary.

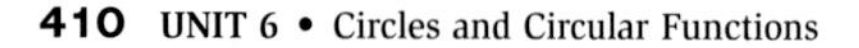

8 a. **Case 2:**

Since $\overline{BD}$ is a diameter of the circle, $m\angle ABD = \frac{1}{2}m\widehat{AD}$ and $m\angle CBD = \frac{1}{2}m\widehat{CD}$ as proved in Case 1. Using the Angle Addition and Arc Addition properties and the distributive property, $m\angle ABC = \frac{1}{2}m\angle ABD + \frac{1}{2}m\angle CBD = \frac{1}{2}m\widehat{AD} + \frac{1}{2}m\widehat{DC} = \frac{1}{2}m\widehat{AC}$.

b. **Case 3:**

Since $\overline{BD}$ is a diameter of the circle, $m\angle ABD = \frac{1}{2}m\widehat{AD}$ and $m\angle CBD = \frac{1}{2}m\widehat{CD}$ as proved in Case 1. By the Angle Addition property, $m\angle ABD = m\angle CBD + m\angle ABC$. Subtracting gives $m\angle ABC = m\angle ABD - m\angle CBD = \frac{1}{2}m\widehat{AD} - \frac{1}{2}m\widehat{CD} = \frac{1}{2}m\widehat{AC}$.

The last step uses the Arc Addition property, the distributive property, and the Subtraction Property of Equality.

9 a. The measure of $\widehat{AC}$ is twice the measure of the horizontal danger angle.

b. Let O be the center of the circle and $\overline{OD}$ be the perpendicular segment from O to chord $\overline{AC}$, so D is midpoint of $\overline{AC}$. Since the measure of the inscribed horizontal danger angle is 35°, $m\widehat{AC} = 70°$. In right triangle ADO, $m\angle AOD = \frac{1}{2}m\angle AOC = 35°$ and $AD = 0.3$ miles. Using trigonometry, $\sin 35° = \frac{0.3}{AO}$, so radius $AO = \frac{0.3}{\sin 35°} \approx 0.5$ miles.

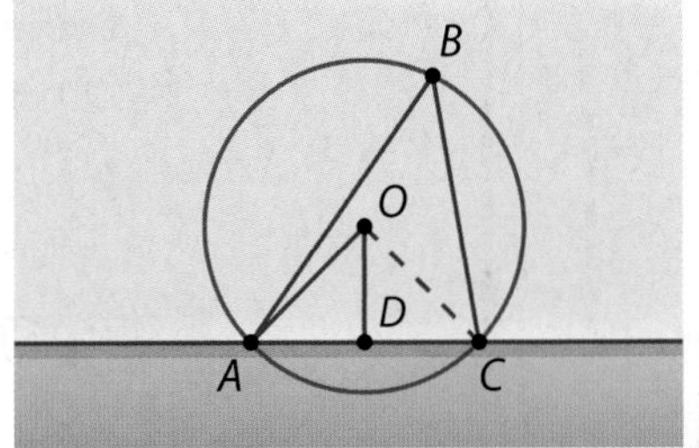

c. The required distance is OD in the figure. By the Pythagorean Theorem, $OD^2 \approx 0.5^2 - 0.3^2$, so $OD \approx 0.4$ miles. Alternatively, $\tan 35° = \frac{AD}{OD}$, so $OD \approx 0.4$ miles.

10 In the figure at the right,

$m\angle D = \frac{1}{2}m\widehat{ABC}$ and $m\angle B = \frac{1}{2}m\widehat{ADC}$.

$$m\angle D + m\angle B = \frac{1}{2}(m\widehat{ABC} + m\widehat{ADC})$$
$$= \frac{1}{2}(360°)$$
$$= 180°$$

$\angle D$ and $\angle B$ are supplementary. The same argument holds for the other pair of opposite angles.

TERMINOLOGY NOTES

A quadrilateral that is inscribed in a circle is called a *cyclic quadrilateral.* A theorem that follows directly from another, like this from the Inscribed Angle Theorem, is called a *corollary.*

11 Suppose $\triangle ABC$ is inscribed in a circle with diameter $\overline{BC}$ and $\overleftrightarrow{DE}$ is tangent to the circle at point C.

a. Prove that $m\angle A = m\angle BCE$ and $m\angle B = m\angle DCA$.

b. $\angle DCA$ and $\angle BCE$ are angles formed by a chord of a circle and a tangent line at the endpoint of the chord. $\angle DCA$ intercepts minor arc $\widehat{AC}$, and $\angle BCE$ intercepts semicircle $\widehat{BC}$. Using Part a, what is the relationship between the measures of these angles and of their intercepted arcs? Why?

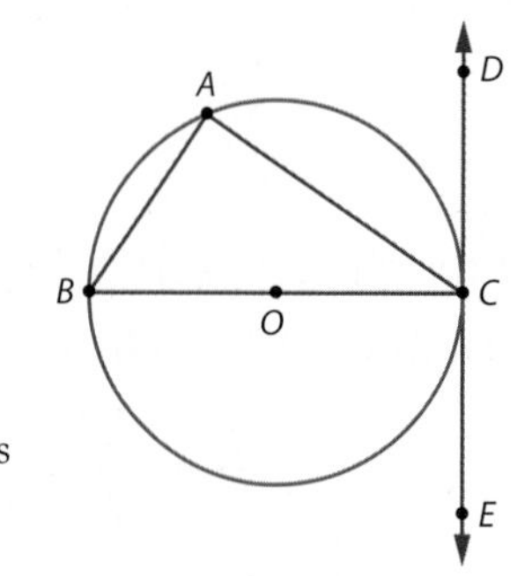

c. In Part b, you justified the relationship between the measure of an angle formed by a chord and a tangent at an endpoint of the chord and its intercepted arc for acute angle $\angle DCA$ and right $\angle BCE$. Does the same relationship hold true for obtuse angle $\angle ACE$ and its intercepted arc $\widehat{ABC}$? Justify your answer.

d. Parts a, b, and c prove a theorem about the measures of angles formed by a chord of a circle and a tangent line at the endpoint of the chord. Write the theorem and add it to your toolkit.

Connections

12 The *interior* and *exterior of a circle* are defined in terms of the circle's radius and center. Consider these ideas from a coordinate perspective.

a. A circle with radius r is centered at the origin. If $P(x, y)$ is any point in the coordinate plane, what conditions must x and y satisfy in each case below?

i. P is on the circle.

ii. P is in the interior of the circle.

iii. P is in the exterior of the circle.

b. Two overlapping circles shown at the right are centered at (0, 0) and (3, 0), respectively. They are inscribed in the rectangle as shown. What inequalities must x and y satisfy if $P(x, y)$ is in each of the following locations in the diagram?

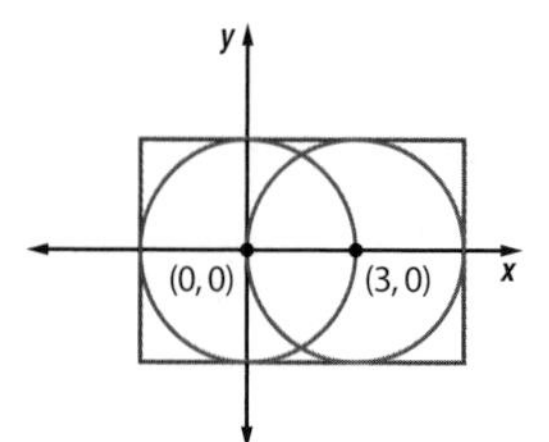

i. Inside the rectangle

ii. Inside the left circle but not the right one

iii. Inside both circles

iv. Inside the rectangle but in the exterior of both circles

11 **a.** **Prove:** $m\angle BAC = m\angle BCE$

Note that $\angle BCE$ is a right angle (radius at point of tangency) and $\angle BAC$ is a right angle (inscribed in a semicircle), so $m\angle BAC = m\angle BCE$.

Prove: $m\angle ABC = m\angle DCA$

$m\angle ACB + m\angle ABC = 90°$ and $m\angle ACB + m\angle DCA = 90°$ (acute angles of right triangles). So, $m\angle ACB + m\angle DCA = m\angle ACB + m\angle ABC$ and thus $m\angle DCA = m\angle ABC$ (Subtraction Property of Equality).

b. The measures of $\angle DCA$ and $\angle BCE$ are half the measures of their respective intercepted arcs, because each is equal in measure to an inscribed angle that intercepts the same arc.

c. Yes, the measure of $\angle ACE$ is half that of its intercepted arc $\widehat{ABC}$.

Justification:

(1) $m\angle ACE = m\angle ACB + m\angle BCE$ (angle addition)

(2) $m\widehat{ABC} = m\widehat{AB} + m\widehat{BC}$ (arc addition)

(3) $m\widehat{ABC} = \frac{1}{2}m\angle ACB + \frac{1}{2}m\angle BCE$ (substitute angle measures for arc measures of acute $\angle ACB$ and right $\angle BCE$ as proved in Part b)

(4) So, $m\widehat{ABC} = \frac{1}{2}m\angle ACE$ (angle addition).

A second justification:

(1) $m\widehat{AC} + m\widehat{ABC} = 360°$, so $\frac{1}{2}(m\widehat{AC}) + \frac{1}{2}(m\widehat{ABC}) = 180°$. (Part b)

(2) $m\angle DCA + m\angle ACE = 180°$ (linear pair)

(3) $\frac{1}{2}(m\widehat{AC}) + \frac{1}{2}(m\widehat{ABC}) = m\angle DCA + m\angle ACE$ (equate Steps 1 and 2)

(4) $m\angle DCA = \frac{1}{2}(m\widehat{AC})$. So, $\frac{1}{2}(m\widehat{AC}) + \frac{1}{2}(m\widehat{ABC}) = m\angle DCA + m\angle ACE$ (substitution).

(5) Thus, $m\angle ACE = \frac{1}{2}(m\widehat{ABC})$ (subtracting $\frac{1}{2}(m\widehat{AC})$ from both sides).

d. *The measure of an angle formed by a chord of a circle and a tangent line at the endpoint of the chord is equal to half the measure of its intercepted arc.* (Tangent-secant Theorem)

INSTRUCTIONAL NOTE
A line that intersects a circle in two points is called a **secant** of the circle. The theorem in this task is sometimes written in terms of angles formed by a secant line and a tangent line.

Connections

12 **a.** **i.** $x^2 + y^2 = r^2$

ii. $x^2 + y^2 < r^2$

iii. $x^2 + y^2 > r^2$

b. **i.** $-3 < x < 6$ and $-3 < y < 3$, since each circle has radius 3.

ii. $x^2 + y^2 < 9$ and $(x - 3)^2 + y^2 \geq 9$

iii. $x^2 + y^2 < 9$ and $(x - 3)^2 + y^2 < 9$

iv. $-3 < x < 6$ and $-3 < y < 3$ and $x^2 + y^2 > 9$ and $(x - 3)^2 + y^2 > 9$

13 Symmetrical circular black-and-white designs, called Lunda-designs, are used in the Lunda region of Angola. The basis for some of these designs is the left-hand figure. Two of the completed designs are to the right of that figure.

a. In the figure on the left, suppose the radii are extended to the common center of the concentric circles. Twenty-four central angles of equal measures would be formed.

- **i.** What is the measure of each central angle?
- **ii.** Choose one central angle that intercepts nine different circles. What are the degree measures of these arcs?

b. In the basis figure on the left, suppose the radius of the innermost concentric circle is 1 cm. As the circles increase in size, their radii are 2 cm, 3 cm, 4 cm, and so on.

- **i.** What size transformation takes the smallest circle to the largest? The second smallest to the third largest? The second largest to the fifth smallest?
- **ii.** What is the circumference of the largest circle? What is the length of each arc (of the largest circle) intercepted by the congruent central angles?

c. Describe the symmetries of the middle design above.

d. Describe the symmetries of the design on the right above.

e. Use an enlarged copy of the base design to create an interesting figure that has rotational symmetry of only 120° and 240°.

14 Two groups of students suggested the following proof plans for this conjecture.

If a line through the center of a circle is perpendicular to a chord, then it bisects the chord.

a. Use the following proof plan as a guide to write a proof for this conjecture.

Synthetic Proof Plan—Draw the figure at the right, where $\overline{OM}$ is perpendicular to chord $\overline{AB}$. $\triangle AMO$ and $\triangle BMO$ are congruent right triangles. So, $\overline{MA} \cong \overline{MB}$. Then consider the case when $\overline{AB}$ is a diameter of the circle.

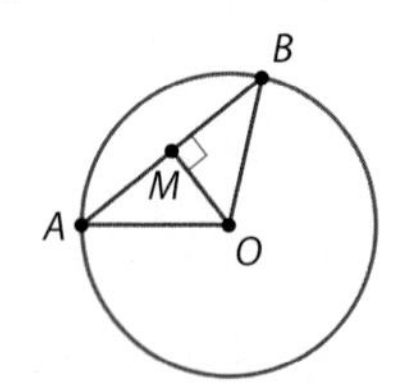

412 UNIT 6 • Circles and Circular Functions

13 **a.** **i.** Each central angle measures $360° \div 24 = 15°$.

ii. To each central angle, there corresponds an arc of each circle. All these arcs measure 15°, although the larger the circle the longer the arc.

b. **i.** The size transformation centered at the common center of the circles with scale factor 9.

Same center, with scale factor $\frac{7}{2} = 3.5$.

Same center, with scale factor $\frac{5}{8} = 0.625$.

ii. The circumference of the largest circle is $2\pi(9) = 18\pi \approx 56.5$ cm. Each arc length is $\frac{18\pi}{24} = \frac{3\pi}{4} \approx 2.4$ cm.

c. The middle design has rotational symmetries of 90°, 180°, and 270° about its center.

d. The design on the right has rotational symmetries of 60°, 120°, 180°, 240°, and 300° about its center.

e. Figures will vary but must have only symmetries of 120° and 240° about the center.

14 **a.** Assume $\overline{AB}$ is not a diameter and $\overleftrightarrow{OM}$ is perpendicular to $\overline{AB}$. Radii $\overline{AO}$ and $\overline{BO}$ are congruent. $\overline{MO}$ is a common side for right triangles $\triangle AMO$ and $\triangle BMO$. $\triangle AMO \cong \triangle BMO$ (HL), so $\overline{AM} \cong \overline{BM}$ (CPCTC). This means that $\overleftrightarrow{OM}$ bisects chord $\overline{AB}$. If $\overline{AB}$ is a diameter, then O is its midpoint and O is on $\overleftrightarrow{OM}$, so $AO = BO$ and $\overleftrightarrow{OB}$ bisects $\overline{AB}$.

b. Yes, the center of any circle can be the origin of a coordinate system. Furthermore, there is always a line that is perpendicular to a chord from the center (origin), and that line can be named the x-axis with the positive direction toward the chord. Once the origin and x-axis are established, the y-axis is the line through the origin perpendicular to the x-axis.

The x-coordinate of B is a, because $\overline{AB}$ is perpendicular to the x-axis. The equation of the circle is $x^2 + y^2 = r^2$, where r is the radius of the circle. So for a point on the circle with x-coordinate equal to a, $a^2 + y^2 = r^2$. Thus, $y = \pm\sqrt{r^2 - a^2}$. Since A has a positive y-coordinate b, $b = \sqrt{r^2 - a^2}$. Therefore, the y-coordinate of B is $-\sqrt{r^2 - a^2} = -b$, and A and B are both a distance b from the x-axis.

c. Answers will depend on student preferences.

NOTE If you assign this task, give the students a copy of the basic figure in the Teaching Masters.

Teaching Resources

Student Master 9.

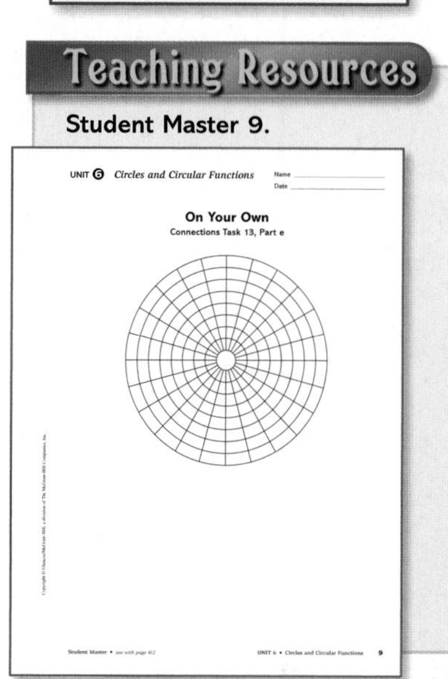

Unit 6

TERMINOLOGY NOTE
A *synthetic* proof uses postulates, theorems, and definitions that do not make use of coordinates. An analytic proof uses coordinates and coordinate properties.

INSTRUCTIONAL NOTE
Students may want to argue from the picture that the missing coordinate is $-b$. Be sure they understand the argument here that uses the equation of the circle.

b. The other group decided to write a coordinate proof plan as outlined below. Use their proof plan as a guide to help write an analytic proof for this conjecture.

Analytic Proof Plan—Draw a coordinate axis. Place the center of the circle at the origin and the x-axis perpendicular to chord $\overline{AB}$. Then explain why this placement can be done for any chord. Label point $A(a, b)$ and explain why the x-coordinate of B must be a. Then, reason from the equation of a circle to find the y-coordinate of point B. Finally, show that A and B are the same distance from the x-axis and so the x-axis bisects chord $\overline{AB}$.

c. Which proof, the synthetic or the analytic one, was easier for you to understand? Why?

15 *All-Star Baseball* is a fantasy game that simulates the batting records of current and former all-star baseball players by dividing a circular disk into *sectors* representing hits of various types, walks, strikeouts, fly outs, and ground outs. The ratio of the measure of the central angle of each sector on a particular all-star player's disk to 360° is proportional to his hitting records. For example, a player who hit a double 6% of the times that he batted will have a "double" sector of (0.06)(360°), or 21.6°. When it is his turn to bat in *All-Star Baseball*, a player's disk is fitted on a random spinner. The spinner is spun, and the sector to which the arrow points when it stops determines the outcome of the player's time at bat.

a. Would you expect a player's average hitting performance over a large number of "at-bats" in *All-Star Baseball* to approximate his actual batting record? Why or why not?

b. Babe Ruth was one of the greatest home-run hitters in baseball history. In 1927, he hit 60 home runs, the single season record for many years. He made 691 appearances at bat that year.

- **i.** How many degrees would Ruth's home-run sector for 1927 be in *All-Star Baseball*?
- **ii.** When Babe Ruth (1927 disk) comes to bat in *All-Star Baseball*, what is the probability that he will hit a home run?

c. During the 2007 season, Alex (A-Rod) Rodriguez hit 54 home runs, the most in major league baseball that year. The home run sector on A-Rod's 2007 disk begins at the terminal side of 76.3° and ends at the terminal side of 103.7°.

- **i.** How many times did A-Rod come to bat in 2007?
- **ii.** When Alex Rodriguez (2007 disk) comes to bat in *All-Star Baseball*, what is the probability that he will hit a home run?

NOTE Solutions to Problem 14 Parts b and c are on page T412.

15 **a.** Yes, the Law of Large Numbers in probability theory implies that the proportions of types of hits of a player over a large number of times "at bat" in *All-Star Baseball* will approximate their corresponding proportions in reality.

b. **i.** Ruth's home-run sector would be $\left(\frac{60}{691}\right)(360°) \approx 31.3°$.

ii. The probability that Ruth will hit a home run is $\frac{60}{691} \approx 0.087$.

c. **i.** A-Rod's home-run sector is $103.7° - 76.3° = 27.4°$. Because the sector is proportional to his actual home run probability, $\frac{27.4}{360} = \frac{54}{x}$, where x is the number of times that A-Rod came to bat in 2007. Solving for x:

$$27.4x = (54)(360)$$

$$x \approx 709$$

Due to rounding errors, this answer is slightly off. Alex Rodriguez actually came to bat 708 times in 2007.

ii. Using 709, the computed times at bat for A-Rod, the probability that he will hit a home run is $\frac{54}{709} \approx 0.076$.

16 **a.** Students should plot $A(1, 6)$, $B(6, 1)$, and $C(-2, -3)$ on graph paper.

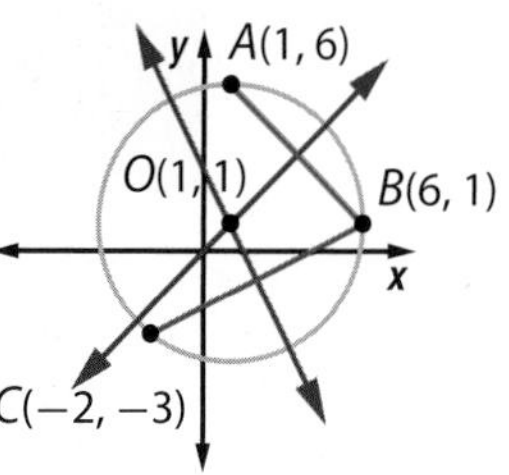

b. The perpendicular bisector of $\overline{AB}$ has slope 1, that is, the negative reciprocal of $\frac{6-1}{1-6} = -1$. It contains the midpoint (3.5, 3.5) of $\overline{AB}$. Thus, its equation is $y = x$. The perpendicular bisector of $\overline{BC}$ has slope -2, that is, the negative reciprocal of $\frac{1-(-3)}{6-(-2)} = \frac{1}{2}$. It contains the midpoint $(2, -1)$ of $\overline{BC}$. Its equation is $y = -2x + 3$. The point of intersection of the two perpendicular bisectors is found by solving $x = -2x + 3$, so $x = 1$ and, substituting in $y = x$, it follows that $y = 1$. The center of the desired circle is $O(1, 1)$.

The radius of the circle is the distance from the center O to any point on the circle, say, $A(1, 6)$. The x-coordinate of both A and O is 1, so the distance then is $6 - 1 = 5 = r$.

c. The equation of the circle is $(x-1)^2 + (y-1)^2 = 25$.

d. The length of chord $\overline{AC}$ is $\sqrt{(1-(-2))^2 + (6-(-3))^2} = \sqrt{90} \approx 9.5$ units.

e. Use the Law of Cosines to find the angle of $\triangle AOB$ between two sides of length 5 and opposite a side of length $\sqrt{90}$.

$(\sqrt{90})^2 = 5^2 + 5^2 - 2(5)(5)\cos\angle AOC$; $\cos\angle AOC = -\frac{40}{50} = -0.805$; $m\angle AOC \approx 143°$.

The measure of inscribed angle $\angle ABC$ is half the measure of the central angle $\angle AOC$, or about 71.5°. (Note $m\angle AOC$ and $m\angle ABC$ will be slightly larger if 9.5 is used instead of $\sqrt{90}$.)

Unit 6

16 A circle in a coordinate plane contains points $A(1, 6)$, $B(6, 1)$, and $C(-2, -3)$.

a. Plot these points on graph paper.

b. Find the coordinates of the center O. What is the radius of the circle?

c. What is the equation of the circle?

d. What is the length of chord $\overline{AC}$?

e. What is the measure of $\angle AOC$? What is the measure of $\angle ABC$?

17 Water wheels are frequently used to generate energy and distribute water for irrigation. The water wheel pictured below operates in a river in the Guangxi Province of China.

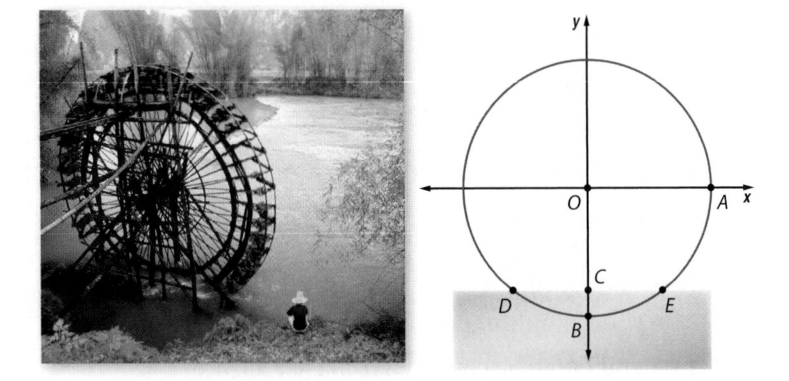

In the diagram at the right above, the 30-foot diameter water wheel has been positioned on a coordinate system so that the center of the wheel is the origin and the wheel reaches 3 feet below water level. As the wheel rotates, it takes 12 seconds for point A on the circumference of the wheel to rotate back to its starting position.

a. What are the coordinates of the other labeled points?

b. At its current position, how far is point A from the surface of the water?

c. If the wheel rotates counterclockwise, through what angle does point A rotate to first reach the water at D? How many seconds does it take A to first reach the water?

d. The surface of the water forms a chord $\overline{DE}$. What is the measure of $\widehat{DE}$? What is the length of chord $\overline{DE}$?

e. What is the measure of inscribed angle $\angle DAE$?

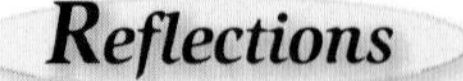

Reflections

18 Describe how to use a compass and straightedge to construct a line tangent to a circle at a point on the circle. This construction is based on a theorem from this lesson. Which one?

414 UNIT 6 • Circles and Circular Functions

17 **a.** Since the radius of the circle is 15 feet and the water level is 3 feet above the wheel, points are located as follows: $C(0, -12)$, $A(15, 0)$, and $B(0, -15)$. Note that point D is at water level, so the y-coordinate of D is -12. In right triangle $\triangle DOC$, the length of the hypotenuse $\overline{DO}$ is 15 feet and the length of the leg $\overline{OC}$ is 12 feet. By the Pythagorean Theorem, $DC = 9$ feet, so the coordinates of D are $(-9, -12)$. Similarly, the coordinates of E are $(9, -12)$.

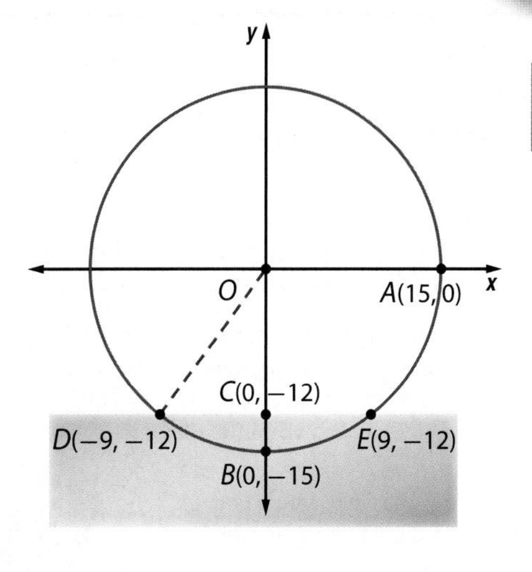

b. Point A is 12 feet above the surface of the water.

c. Major arc $\widehat{AD}$ has measure $270° - m\angle DOC$, $CO = 12$ feet and $DO = 15$ feet. So in right triangle $\triangle DOC$, $m\angle DOC = \cos^{-1}\left(\frac{12}{15}\right) \approx 36.9°$. Thus, $m\angle AOD = 270° - 36.9° \approx 233.1°$. It takes $\frac{233.1}{360}(12) \approx 7.8$ seconds for A to first reach water at point D.

d. Since $m\angle DOC \approx 36.9°$ and the circle is symmetric across the y-axis, it follows that $m\angle DOE = m\widehat{DE} = 2(36.9°) = 73.8°$. Since the x-coordinate of D is -9 and that of E is 9, it follows that $DE = 18$ feet.

e. $m\angle DOE = m\widehat{DE} = 73.8°$; $m\angle DAE = \frac{1}{2}(m\widehat{DE}) = 36.9°$

NOTE The solution to Task 16 is on page T413.

Reflections

18 Draw the line through the point on the circle and the center of the circle. At the point on the circle, construct a line perpendicular to the line through the center. The perpendicular line is tangent to the circle. This is based on the following theorem: *A line is tangent to a circle if and only if it is perpendicular to the radius drawn to the point of tangency.*

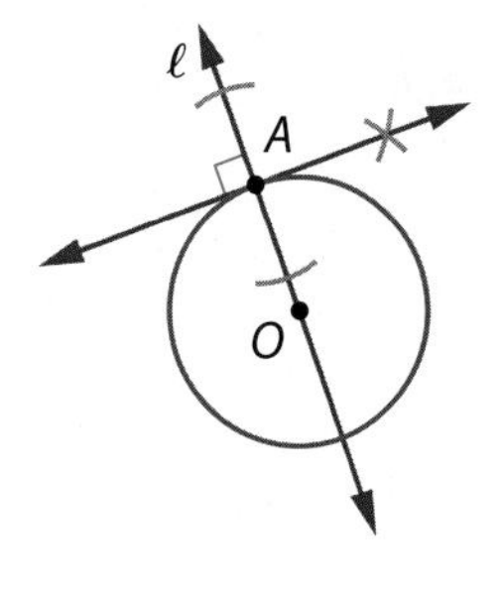

19 The road is tangent to the wheels and the chain is tangent to the crankset and to the rear sprocket.

19 Give some examples of tangents to a circle that are evident in bicycle design and use.

20 Summarize the theorems that relate a chord, its midpoint, and the center of a circle. Draw a figure. Explain why these theorems follow from the fact that a circle is symmetric about any line through its center.

21 Use your knowledge about degree measures of arcs and central angles to consider the following questions related to linear measure and area measure. Suppose an irrigation sprinkling system waters an agricultural field as shown in the diagram.

a. What is the area of the watered section of the field which is a sector of the circle with radius 15 meters?

b. If the farmer wishes to fence in this section of field, what length of fencing would be needed?

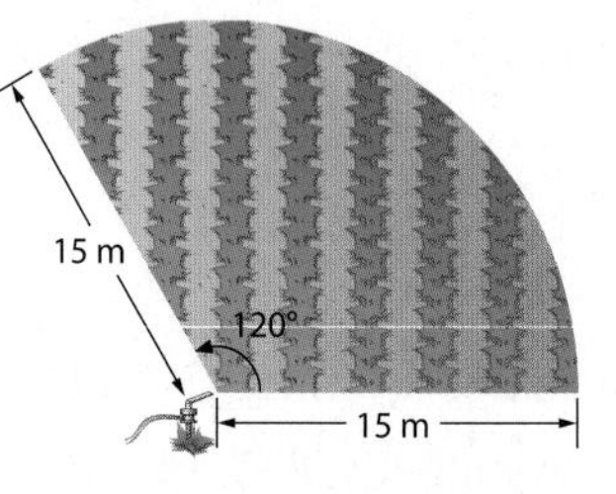

22 Arcs of circles can be measured in degrees as you did in Investigation 2 or in linear measures as when finding the circumference of a circle.

a. In the circle with center O, $AO = 4"$, and $m\angle AOB = 120°$, find $m\widehat{AB}$ in degrees and the length of $\widehat{AB}$ in inches.

b. Is the following statement true or false? Explain.

Arcs that have the same degree measure also have the same linear measure.

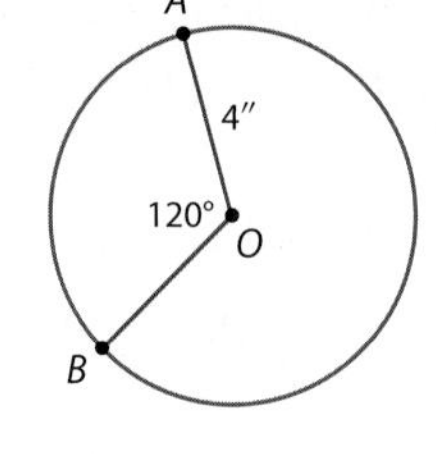

23 How does the arc intercepted by an acute, right, or obtuse central angle of a circle compare to a semicircle of the same circle? Of different circles?

Extensions

24 Prove: *If a line is tangent to a circle, then the line is perpendicular to the radius at the point of tangency.* You may use the following two facts.

- If a line contains an interior point of a circle, then it intersects the circle in two points.
- The shortest distance from a point to a line is the length of the perpendicular segment.

25 The following is a variation of an ancient Chinese problem. When the stem of a water lily is pulled up so it is vertical, the flower is 12 centimeters above the surface of the lake. When the lily is pulled to one side, keeping the stem straight, the blossom touches the water at a point 22 centimeters from where the vertical stem cuts the surface. The figure at the right is not drawn to scale; the center of the circle has been placed on the bed of the pond. What is the depth x of the water?

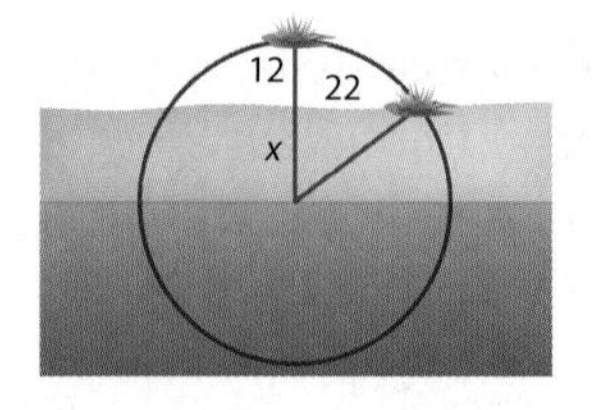

20 (1) A line through the center of a circle bisects a chord if and only if the line is perpendicular to the chord.

(2) The perpendicular bisector of a chord contains the center of a circle.

To see why theorem (1) follows from the symmetry of the circle about line ℓ through the center, note that if $\ell \perp \overline{AB}$, then reflection across ℓ maps A to a point on the circle and on $\overleftrightarrow{AB}$ so that point must be B. By the definition of line reflection, A and its image B are equidistant from ℓ, so ℓ bisects $\overline{AB}$. Conversely, if ℓ contains O and bisects $\overline{AB}$, then ℓ contains two points that are equidistant from A and B. This means that ℓ must be the perpendicular bisector of $\overline{AB}$. That $\ell \perp \overline{AB}$ can also be shown using congruent triangles.

To show (2) using the circle's symmetry, simply note that since the center of the circle is equidistant from any two points on the circle, the center of the circle lies on the perpendicular bisector of any chord.

NOTE The solution to Task 19 is on page T414.

21 **a.** $\frac{120°}{360°}\pi(15)^2 \approx 236$ square meters

b. $2(15) + \frac{1}{3}(2\pi)(15) = 30 + 10\pi \approx 61.5$ meters

INSTRUCTIONAL NOTE
Task 21 Part b is an example where the context suggests rounding 61.416 meters up to 61.5 or 62 meters to allow enough fencing.

22 **a.** $m\widehat{AB} = m\angle AOB = 120°$. The circumference of the circle is $2\pi(4) \approx 25.1$ in., so the length of $\widehat{AB}$ is about one-third of 25.1, or 8.4 in.

b. In general, the statement is false. It is only true for arcs of the same or congruent circles.

23 In the same circle, an arc intercepted by a right central angle equals half of a semicircle, that is, a quarter circle. The arc intercepted by an acute central angle is less than a quarter circle, and the arc intercepted by an obtuse central angle is more than a quarter circle but less than a semicircle. In the same circle, these relationships apply to both degree measures and lengths of the arcs. In different circles, the degree measures of the arcs are related as described above, but the relationship between the lengths of the arcs depends on the relative lengths of the radii of the two circles.

Unit 6

Extensions

24 **Given:** ℓ is tangent to circle with center O at point A.

Prove: $\overline{OA} \perp \ell$

No point on ℓ is in the interior of the circle, since only one point of ℓ lies on the circle. Every point B on ℓ except A is in the exterior of the circle, so $OB > r = OA$. Thus, OA is the shortest distance from O to line ℓ. So, $\overline{OA} \perp \ell$. (Unit 3, Review Task 37, page 226)

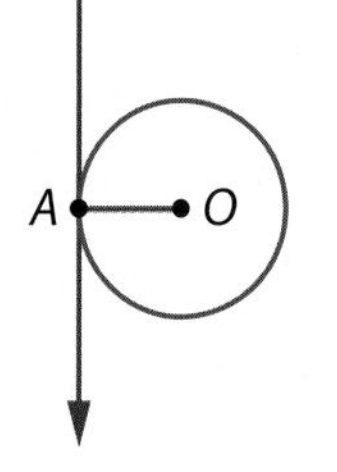

MATH TOOLKIT NOTE
With the proof in Extensions Task 24 and the one in Investigation 1, students can add the following theorem to their toolkit. A line is tangent to a circle iff it is perpendicular to the radius at the point of tangency.

25 In the figure in the student book, notice the right triangle with legs of length x and 22. The hypotenuse is the length of the stem of the water lily, $x + 12$. Use the Pythagorean Theorem.

$$(x + 12)^2 = x^2 + 22^2$$
$$x^2 + 24x + 144 = x^2 + 484$$
$$24x = 340$$
$$x \approx 14.2 \text{ cm}$$

On Your Own

26 A familiar pattern in mathematics is to explore, conjecture, and then prove or disprove the conjecture.

a. If two chords of the same circle have different lengths, which is closer to the center of the circle? Explore figures like the one on the right in which one chord, $\overline{CD}$, is longer than the other, $\overline{AB}$. How are their perpendicular distances from the center, ON and OM, related? Write a conjecture.

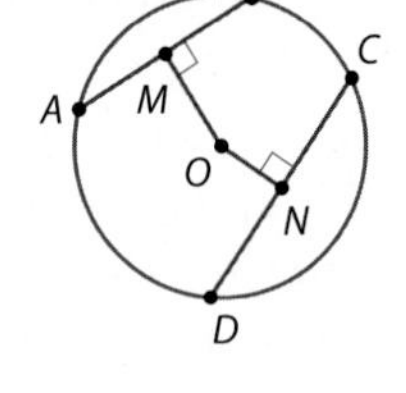

b. Using right triangles $\triangle AOM$ and $\triangle DON$, prove your conjecture.

27 Circles and similar triangles provide the foundation for a compass-and-straightedge construction of the square root of the length of any segment. The construction algorithm is given below.

Step 1. Segments of length 1 and x are given. Draw a segment that is greater than $x + 1$. Label one endpoint A.

Step 2. On this segment, mark point B with your compass so that $AB = x$. Then mark point C so that $BC = 1$.

Step 3. Construct the midpoint of $\overline{AC}$. Label the midpoint O. Draw the circle centered at O with radius $OA = OC$.

Step 4. Construct the line perpendicular to $\overline{AC}$ at point B. Label the point D at which the perpendicular line intersects the upper semicircle. Then $BD = \sqrt{x}$, as you will prove in Parts b and c below.

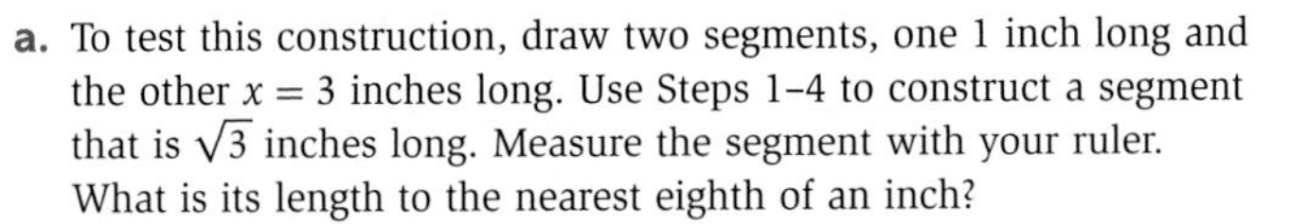

a. To test this construction, draw two segments, one 1 inch long and the other $x = 3$ inches long. Use Steps 1–4 to construct a segment that is $\sqrt{3}$ inches long. Measure the segment with your ruler. What is its length to the nearest eighth of an inch?

b. To justify this construction, draw segments $\overline{AD}$ and $\overline{CD}$. What kind of angle is $\angle ADC$?

c. Show that $\triangle ABD$ is similar to $\triangle DBC$. Then $\frac{x}{BD} = \frac{BD}{1}$. What is the length of $\overline{BD}$ in terms of x?

Unit 6

416 UNIT 6 • Circles and Circular Functions

26 **a.** Students' conjectures should be something like this: If one chord in a circle is longer than another, then the longer chord is closer to the center of the circle.

b. A possible proof follows:

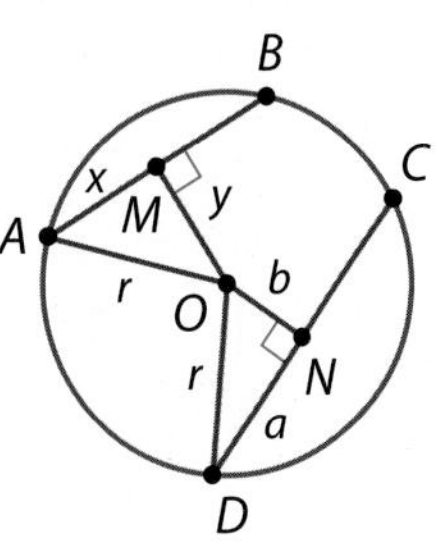

Assumptions: $AB < CD$, $AB > 0$, $CD > 0$, $\overline{OM} \perp \overline{AB}$, and $\overline{ON} \perp \overline{CD}$.

Then M is the midpoint of $\overline{AB}$ and N is the midpoint of $\overline{CD}$.

Proof: Half the length of chord $\overline{AB}$, x, is less than half the length of chord $\overline{CD}$, a, since $AB < CD$. So, $x^2 < a^2$. Using the Pythagorean Theorem, $x^2 + y^2 = r^2$ and $a^2 + b^2 = r^2$, so $x^2 + y^2 = a^2 + b^2$. Since one leg of right $\triangle AMO$ (x) is shorter than one leg of $\triangle DNO$ (a), and the hypotenuses are the same length (r), it follows that the second leg (y) of $\triangle AMO$ must be longer than the second leg (b) of $\triangle DNO$. This means that the shorter chord $\overline{AB}$ is farther from the center of the circle than the longer chord $\overline{CD}$.

Alternate Proof: $\frac{1}{2}AB < \frac{1}{2}CD$ or $AM < DN$ (since AB and CD are positive). It follows that $AM^2 < DN^2$ and so $DN^2 - AM^2 > 0$. By the Pythagorean Theorem, $OA^2 = OM^2 + AM^2$ and $OD^2 = ON^2 + DN^2$. But $OA = OD$ (equal radii), so the two equations can be equated: $OM^2 + AM^2 = ON^2 + DN^2$. Then $OM^2 - ON^2 = DN^2 - AM^2$ and $DN^2 - AM^2 > 0$, so $OM^2 - ON^2 > 0$, which means that $OM^2 > ON^2$. Since OM and ON are both positive, $OM > ON$.

27 **a.** If the student carries out the construction accurately, the length should be about 1.7 inches.

b. $\angle ADC$ is a right angle because it is inscribed in a semicircle.

c. Both triangles $\triangle ABD$ and $\triangle DBC$ are right triangles with right angle at B. Since $\angle ADC$ is also a right angle, $m\angle ADB = 90° - m\angle BDC$. But in right triangle $\triangle DBC$, $m\angle BCD = 90° - m\angle BDC$. By substitution, $m\angle ADB = m\angle BCD$ and triangles $\triangle ABD$ and $\triangle DBC$ are similar by AA. It follows that $\frac{x}{BD} = \frac{BD}{1}$, so $BD^2 = x$ and $BD = \sqrt{x}$.

Unit 6

28 The theorems about angles and chords can help justify interesting conjectures about products of lengths of segments that intersect circles.

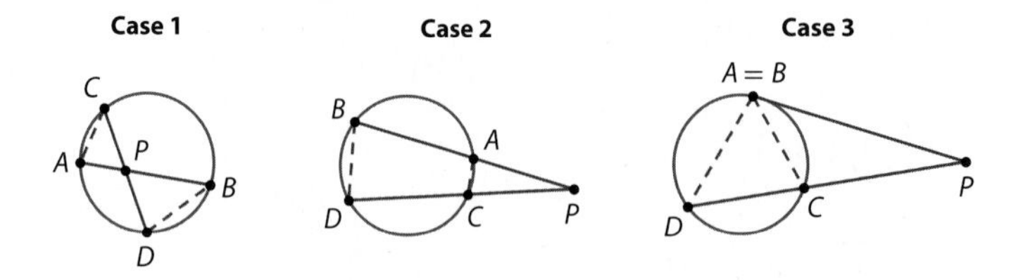

a. The "Chord Lengths in Circles" sample sketch is designed to help you see that for each case above, $PA \times PB = PC \times PD$. Use the sketch to consider multiple instances of each case.

b. In each case shown above, show that $\triangle ACP$ is similar to $\triangle DBP$.

c. Show that the result in Part a implies that $PA \times PB = PC \times PD$. To what does this equation reduce in Case 3?

29 The result at the right is called Keith's Corollary, named for the high school student who discovered it (although it is not a direct result of any theorem). *ABCD* is an arbitrary quadrilateral inscribed in a circle. Each of its four angles is bisected, and the bisectors intersect the circle at the points *E*, *F*, *G*, and *H*.

Prove that *EFGH* is a rectangle. *Hint:* Show that the angles of *EFGH* are right angles by using the facts that opposite angles of quadrilateral *ABCD* are supplementary (see Applications Task 10) and that two inscribed angles intercepting the same arc have equal measure.

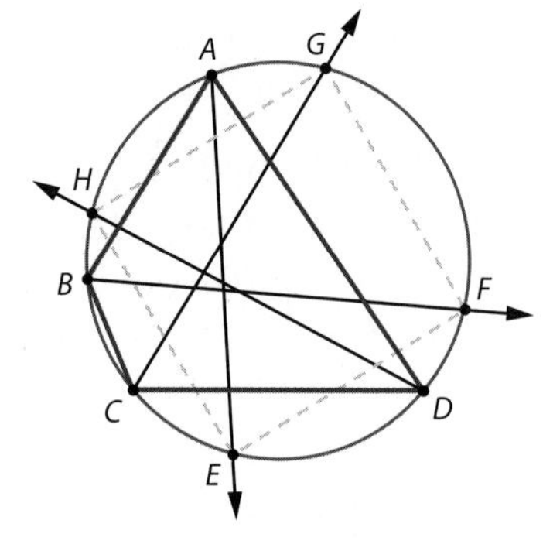

Review

30 Write each expression in standard polynomial form.

a. $(3x^3 + 4x^2 - 5x) + (9x^2 - 3x + 12)$

b. $(x^5 - x^3 - 2x - 1) - (5x^5 - x^3 + 5x + 10)$

c. $(x^2 + 3x)(x - 2)$

d. $\dfrac{4x^3 - 2x^2 + 8x}{2x}$

31 Use a compass and straightedge to complete the following constructions.

a. Draw a line segment $\overline{AB}$ and construct its perpendicular bisector. Label the midpoint of $\overline{AB}$ as *M*.

b. Draw a line ℓ and mark a point *P* on the line. Construct the line that contains *P* and is perpendicular to line ℓ.

c. Draw a line ℓ and mark a point *P* that is not on the line. Construct the line that contains *P* and is perpendicular to line ℓ.

INSTRUCTIONAL NOTE
Case 1 represents two chords; Case 2 represents two secants; and Case 3 represents a tangent and secant.

28 **a.** Students should use the "Chord Lengths in Circles" sample sketch to dynamically change chord lengths and observe the resulting product values.

b. On the left, $\angle APC \cong \angle BPD$, because they are vertical angles. $\angle ACP \cong \angle DBP$, because they are inscribed angles that intercept the same arc. Therefore, $\triangle ACP \sim \triangle DBP$ (AA).

In the case in the middle, $\angle P \cong \angle P$ and $m\angle ACP = 180° - m\angle ACD = m\angle ABD$ using the linear pair property and opposite angles in a cyclic quadrilateral. Therefore, $\triangle ACP \sim \triangle DBP$ (AA).

In the case on the right, $\angle APC \cong \angle BPD$, because they are the same angles. $m\angle BDP = \frac{1}{2}m\widehat{BC}$ by the Inscribed Angle Theorem. $m\angle CAP = \frac{1}{2}m\widehat{BC}$ because the angle formed by a chord and a tangent equals half the intercepted arc. (This was proved in Applications Task 11 on page 411.) Therefore, $\triangle ACP \sim \triangle DBP$ by AA.

c. The similarity conclusion in each case implies that $\frac{PA}{PD} = \frac{PC}{PB}$. Multiplying gives the required result: $PA \times PB = PC \times PD$. In the case on the right, points A and B coincide so $PA^2 = PC \times PD$.

29 To show that $\angle GHE$, for example is a right angle, note that $m\angle GHE = m\angle GHD + m\angle DHE$. Since $\angle GHD$ and $\angle GCD$ intercept the same arc, $m\angle GHD = m\angle GCD$. Similarly, $m\angle DHE = m\angle DAE$. Now in quadrilateral $ABCD$, $m\angle C = 2m\angle GCD$ and $m\angle A = 2m\angle DAE$ (since $\overrightarrow{CG}$ bisects $\angle C$ and $\overrightarrow{AE}$ bisects $\angle A$). Also, $m\angle C + m\angle A = 180°$ since $\angle C$ and $\angle A$ are opposite angles in a cyclic quadrilateral.

Thus, $90° = \frac{1}{2}m\angle C + \frac{1}{2}m\angle A = m\angle GCD + m\angle DAE$. Substituting the equal angle measures, we obtain $90° = m\angle GHD + m\angle DHE = m\angle GHE$. The other angles of quadrilateral $GHEF$ can be shown to be right angles in a similar way. Therefore, $GHEF$ is a rectangle.

Review

30 **a.** $3x^3 + 13x^2 - 8x + 12$ **b.** $-4x^5 - 7x - 11$

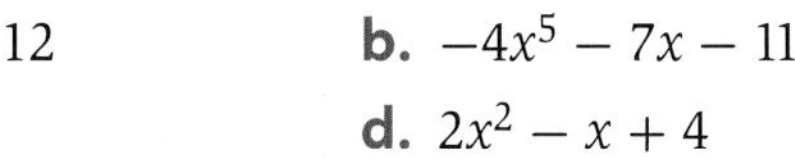

c. $x^3 + x^2 - 6x$ **d.** $2x^2 - x + 4$

Just in Time

31 **a.** **b.** **c.**

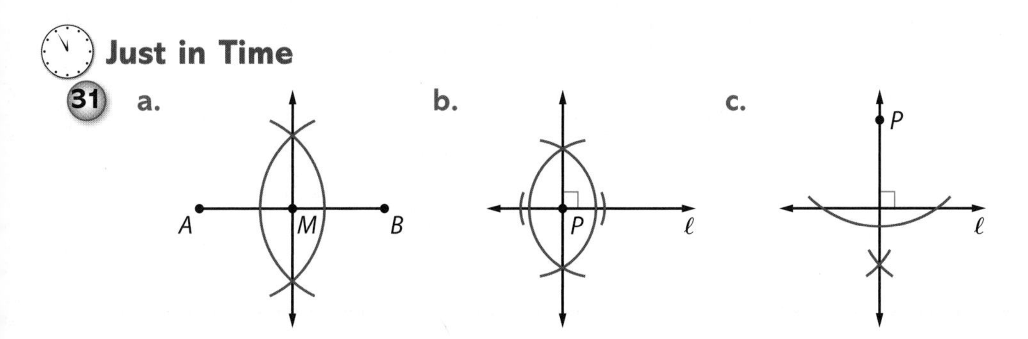

Unit 6

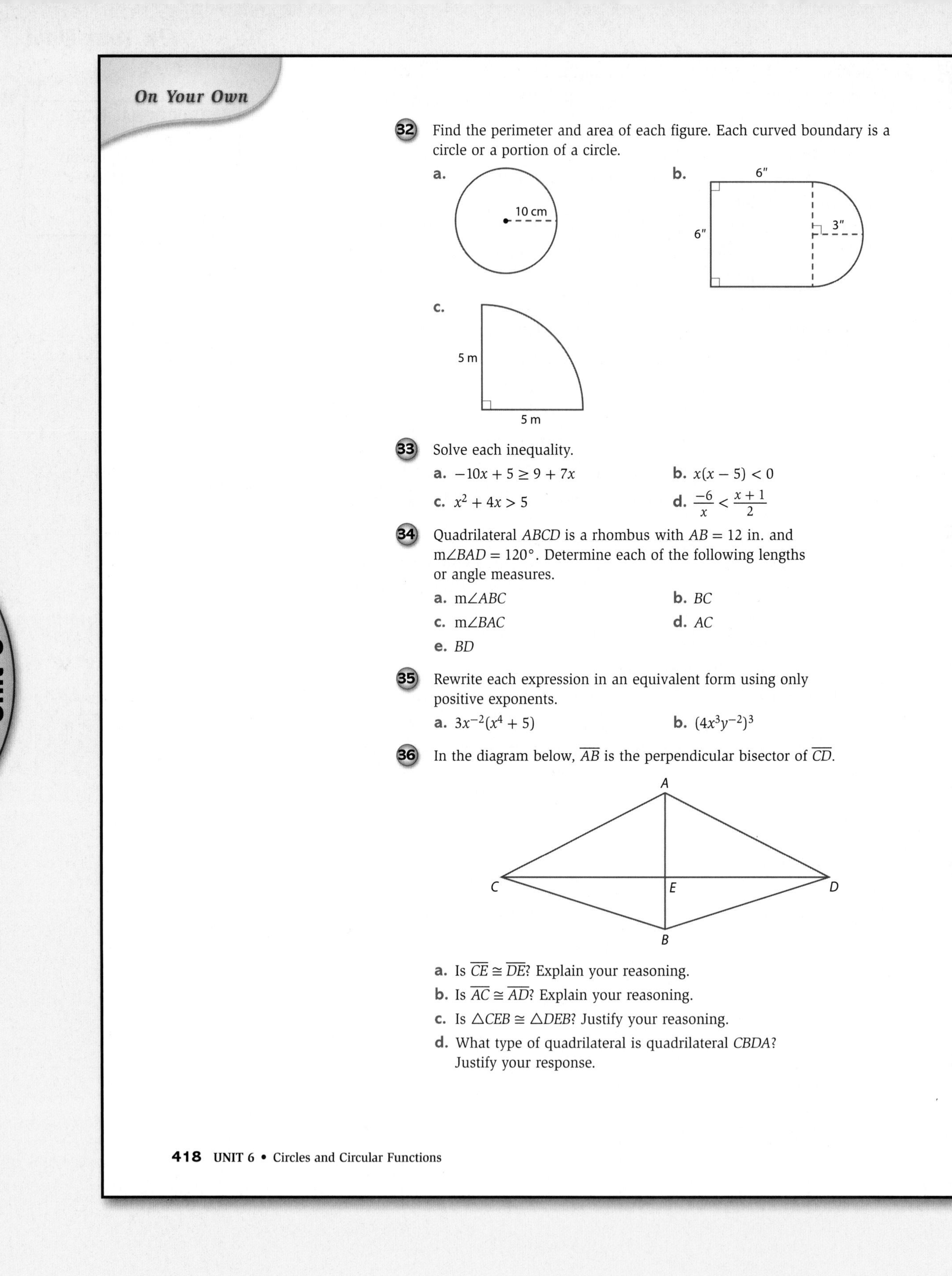

32 Find the perimeter and area of each figure. Each curved boundary is a circle or a portion of a circle.

a.

b.

c.

33 Solve each inequality.

a. $-10x + 5 \geq 9 + 7x$

b. $x(x - 5) < 0$

c. $x^2 + 4x > 5$

d. $\frac{-6}{x} < \frac{x + 1}{2}$

34 Quadrilateral *ABCD* is a rhombus with $AB = 12$ in. and $m\angle BAD = 120°$. Determine each of the following lengths or angle measures.

a. $m\angle ABC$

b. BC

c. $m\angle BAC$

d. AC

e. BD

35 Rewrite each expression in an equivalent form using only positive exponents.

a. $3x^{-2}(x^4 + 5)$

b. $(4x^3y^{-2})^3$

36 In the diagram below, $\overline{AB}$ is the perpendicular bisector of $\overline{CD}$.

a. Is $\overline{CE} \cong \overline{DE}$? Explain your reasoning.

b. Is $\overline{AC} \cong \overline{AD}$? Explain your reasoning.

c. Is $\triangle CEB \cong \triangle DEB$? Justify your reasoning.

d. What type of quadrilateral is quadrilateral *CBDA*? Justify your response.

418 UNIT 6 • Circles and Circular Functions

Just in Time

32 **a.** $P = 20\pi \text{ cm} \approx 62.83 \text{ cm}$; $A = \pi(10^2) = 100\pi \approx 314 \text{ cm}^2$

b. $P = 18 + 3\pi \approx 27.42$ in.; $A = 6^2 + 0.5\pi(5)^2 = 36 + 4.5\pi \approx 50.14 \text{ in}^2$

c. $P = 10 + \frac{5\pi}{2} \approx 17.85$ m; $A = 0.25\pi(5)^2 = 6.25\pi \approx 19.63 \text{ m}^2$

33 **INSTRUCTIONAL NOTE** Care must be taken when solving inequalities with a variable in the denominator. In Part d, the inequality would be reversed when $x < 0$. This task should remind students of the value of visualizing the inequality as two functions $y_1 = \frac{-6}{x}$ and $y_2 = \frac{x+1}{2}$. Since y_1 is an inverse variation function and y_2 is a linear function with positive slope and y-intercept at $\frac{1}{2}$, the solution is $x > 0$ as shown below.

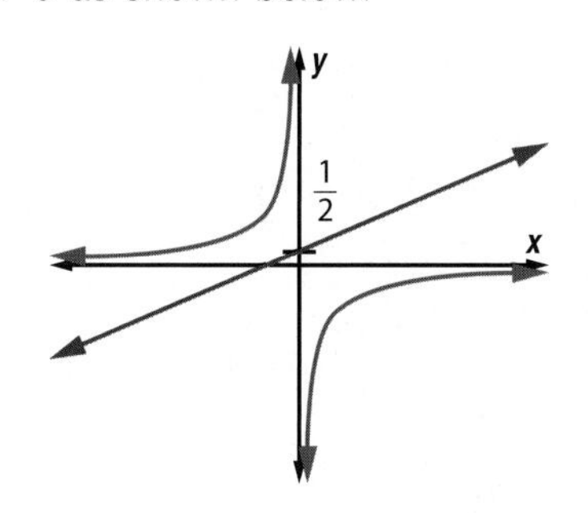

a. $x \leq -\frac{4}{17}$

b. $0 < x < 5$

c. $x < -5$ or $x > 1$

d. $x > 0$

34 **a.** $m\angle ABC = 60°$

b. $BC = 12$ in.

c. $m\angle BAC = 60°$

d. $AC = 12$ in.

e. $BD = 2\sqrt{12^2 - 6^2} \approx 20.8$ in.

35 **a.** $3x^2 + \frac{15}{x^2}$

b. $\frac{64x^9}{y^6}$

36 **a.** Yes, because $\overline{AB}$ bisects $\overline{CD}$

b. Yes. Students might remember that any point on the perpendicular bisector of a segment is equidistant from the endpoints of the segment. If they do not remember this, they can reason that $\triangle AEC \cong \triangle AED$ by the SAS congruence condition and thus $\overline{AC} \cong \overline{AD}$.

c. Yes. Students can use the SSS or SAS congruence conditions to justify this congruence.

d. Quadrilateral *CBDA* is a kite since it has two distinct pairs of congruent consecutive sides.

37 Solve each equation.

a. $2(3x) = 96$

b. $3x^2 = 96$

c. $3 + x^2 = 96$

d. $3 + 2x = 96$

e. $3(2x) = 96$

f. $(3 + x)^2 = 96$

38 Find the missing side lengths in each right triangle.

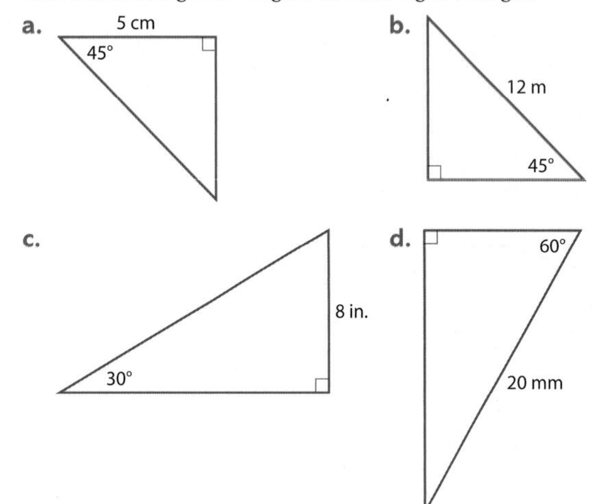

39 If $f(x) = 2x^2 + 11x - 6$, $g(x) = x^2 - 9$, and $h(x) = f(x) \cdot g(x)$, find each of the following.

a. $h(-2)$

b. The degree of $h(x)$

c. All zeroes of $h(x)$

d. The factored form of $h(x)$

e. The y-intercept of $h(x)$

40 Suppose the terminal side of an angle in standard position with measure θ contains the indicated point. Find $\sin \theta$, $\cos \theta$, and $\tan \theta$. Then find the measure of θ to the nearest degree.

a. $P(3, 4)$

b. $P(3, -4)$

c. $P(-3, 4)$

d. $P(0, -5)$

37 a. $x = 16$
b. $x = \pm\sqrt{32} = \pm 4\sqrt{2}$
c. $x = \pm\sqrt{93}$
d. $x = 46.5$
e. $x = 16$
f. $x = -3 \pm \sqrt{96} = -3 \pm 4\sqrt{6}$
$x \approx 6.8$ or $x \approx -12.8$

Just in Time

38

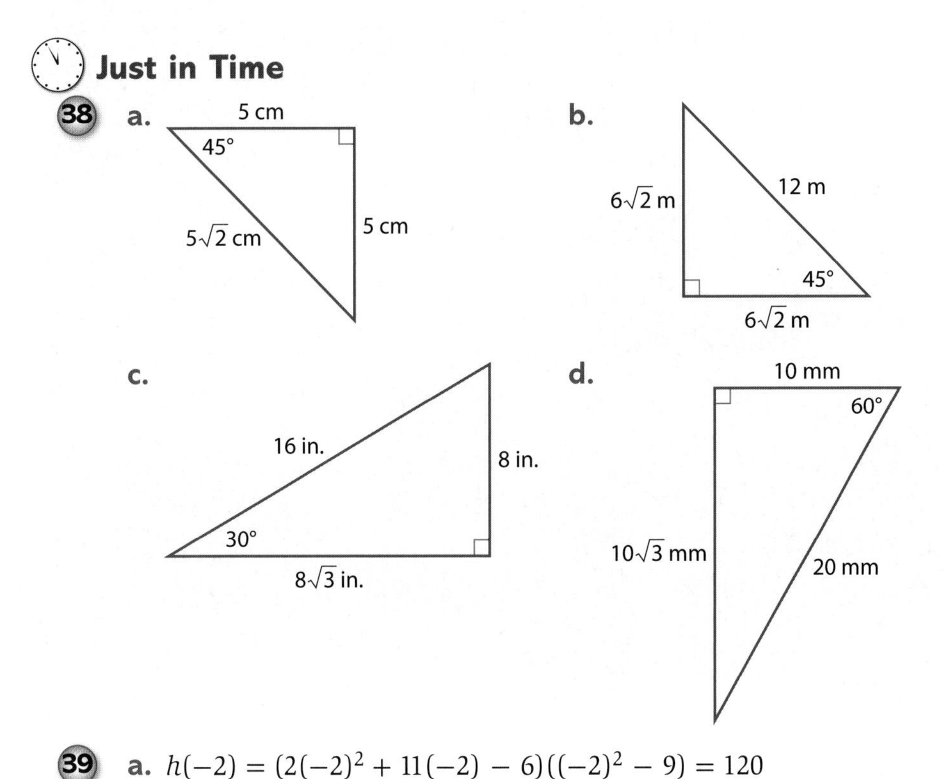

39 a. $h(-2) = (2(-2)^2 + 11(-2) - 6)((-2)^2 - 9) = 120$
b. 4
c. $x = 3,\ x = -3,\ x = -6,\ x = \frac{1}{2}$
d. $h(x) = (2x - 1)(x + 6)(x - 3)(x + 3)$
e. $(0, 54)$

Just in Time

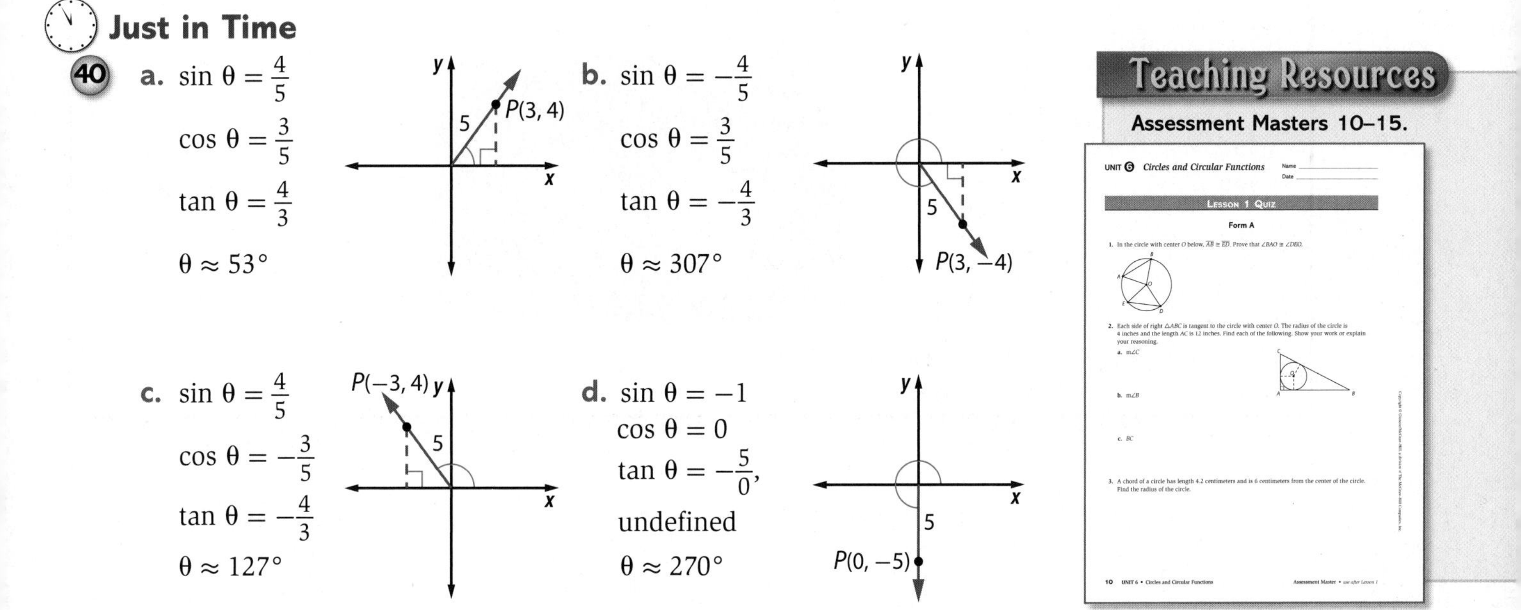

40 a. $\sin\theta = \frac{4}{5}$
$\cos\theta = \frac{3}{5}$
$\tan\theta = \frac{4}{3}$
$\theta \approx 53°$

b. $\sin\theta = -\frac{4}{5}$
$\cos\theta = \frac{3}{5}$
$\tan\theta = -\frac{4}{3}$
$\theta \approx 307°$

c. $\sin\theta = \frac{4}{5}$
$\cos\theta = -\frac{3}{5}$
$\tan\theta = -\frac{4}{3}$
$\theta \approx 127°$

d. $\sin\theta = -1$
$\cos\theta = 0$
$\tan\theta = -\frac{5}{0}$,
undefined
$\theta \approx 270°$

Teaching Resources

Assessment Masters 10–15.

LESSON 2

Circular Motion and Periodic Functions

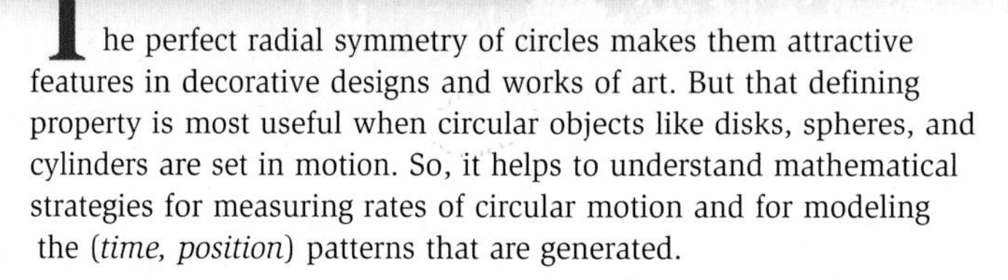

The perfect radial symmetry of circles makes them attractive features in decorative designs and works of art. But that defining property is most useful when circular objects like disks, spheres, and cylinders are set in motion. So, it helps to understand mathematical strategies for measuring rates of circular motion and for modeling the (*time, position*) patterns that are generated.

For example, the instrument panel on a high performance car usually contains both a speedometer and a tachometer. The speedometer shows forward speed in miles or kilometers per hour; the tachometer shows revolutions per minute (rpm) by the engine crankshaft.

420 UNIT 6 • Circles and Circular Functions

Circular Motion and Periodic Functions

In the previous lesson, students learned some properties of circles and special lines and angles in circles. These properties follow mainly from a circle's rotational and reflection symmetry about its center. This symmetry also leads to many important practical and mathematical applications of circular shapes. The lesson begins with a study of linear and angular velocity of pulleys and sprockets and then moves on to connect rotations and the circular (sine and cosine) functions, radian measure for angles, and applications to modeling of periodic patterns of change over time.

In Investigation 1, students work with models of pulleys and sprockets to determine angular and linear velocities and transmission factors from one pulley or sprocket to another.

The problems of Investigation 2 link the sine and cosine function to rotations of circular objects. This investigation begins by connecting the right triangle ratios of sine and cosine to coordinates of points on a circle. Tracking the patterns of change in (x, y) coordinates of points moving on the circumference of a Ferris wheel leads to the familiar sinusoidal graphs associated with the periodic sine and cosine functions.

Radian measure of angles is developed in problems of Investigation 3, and links are established between degree, radian, and revolution measures of rotation. This investigation closes with analysis of the "wrapping function" that suggests a way of thinking about sin t and cos t as functions of real numbers.

In Investigation 4, students analyze variations on the basic sine and cosine functions and their graphs, with special attention to amplitude, period, frequency, and y-displacement. These tools are used to work with models of pendulum motion, seasons of the year, and alternating electrical current.

Lesson Objectives

- Analyze situations involving pulleys or sprockets to study angular velocity and linear velocity
- Use sine and cosine functions to describe rotations of circular objects
- Use radian and degree measures to measure angles and rotations
- Define sine and cosine as functions of real numbers and analyze the resulting periodic graphs
- Use the sine and cosine functions to model periodic patterns of change in various physical phenomena

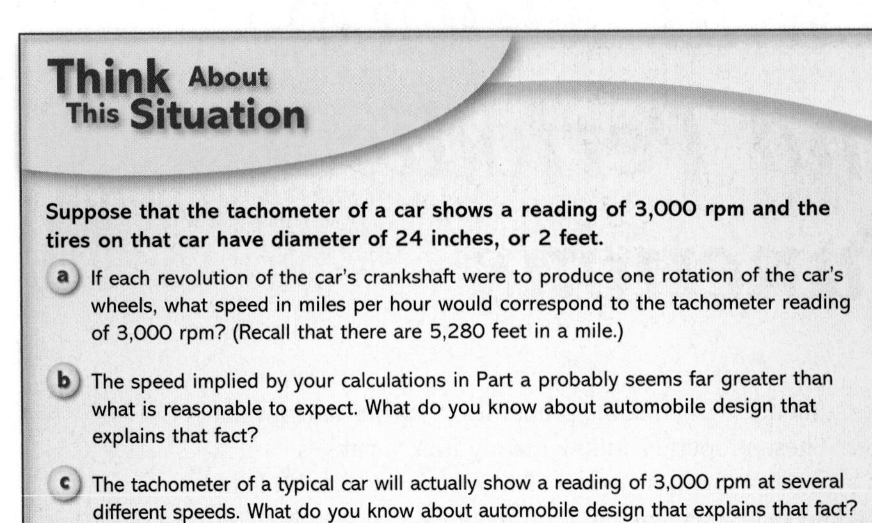

Think About This Situation

Suppose that the tachometer of a car shows a reading of 3,000 rpm and the tires on that car have diameter of 24 inches, or 2 feet.

a If each revolution of the car's crankshaft were to produce one rotation of the car's wheels, what speed in miles per hour would correspond to the tachometer reading of 3,000 rpm? (Recall that there are 5,280 feet in a mile.)

b The speed implied by your calculations in Part a probably seems far greater than what is reasonable to expect. What do you know about automobile design that explains that fact?

c The tachometer of a typical car will actually show a reading of 3,000 rpm at several different speeds. What do you know about automobile design that explains that fact?

The investigations of this lesson develop strategies for measuring the velocity of circles rotating about axes and rolling along tangent lines. Trigonometric functions are then used to model the relationship between time and position of points on such rotating objects. Finally, those functions are used to describe the *periodic variation* of other phenomena like seasons of the year, pendulums, ocean tides, and alternating electrical current.

Unit 6

Investigation 1 Angular and Linear Velocity

There are two common measures of circular motion. The angle of rotation about the center of a circle in a unit of time is called its **angular velocity**. It is commonly measured in units like revolutions per minute. The distance traveled by each point on the circle in a unit of time is called its **linear velocity**. It is commonly measured in units like miles per hour or meters per second. As you work on the problems in this investigation, look for answers to the following questions:

How are angular and linear velocity related in circular motion?

How do mechanical systems connect the motion of driver and follower circles?

Lesson Launch

The TATS questions will help you to assess the informal knowledge that students bring to this lesson and to introduce key ideas that will be explored throughout the lesson. You might want to give students some time to produce answers to the questions in Parts a–c and then share their results and the thinking that led to those results. Many students might not know anything about automotive transmissions, but it seems highly likely that a few will and can give some explanation of the results from calculations relating tachometer and speedometer readings.

Think About This Situation

a If the car's crankshaft of 3,000 rpm translated directly to 3,000 revolutions of the car's wheels, the car would travel $3{,}000(2\pi) \approx 18{,}850$ feet per minute, or 1,130,973 feet per hour, or 214 miles per hour.

b A speed of 214 miles per hour is unlikely for any place except the Indianapolis Motor Speedway. The fact that crankshaft rotations do not translate one-to-one into rotations of the wheels is explained by the operation of engine transmissions that operate in general like the gears of multi-speed bicycles (studied in the first investigation to follow immediately).

c The fact that tachometer readings are not surefire indicators of car speed is again explained by existence of a power transmission mechanism between the engine and the wheel axle. Students with experience on multi-speed bicycles might comment that you can experience slow pedaling in a low gear or a high gear, all depending on how fast your wheels are turning.

The mathematical factors that allow one to predict the relationship of connected turning circles will be analyzed in the coming investigation.

Teaching Resources

Transparency Master 16.

UNIT 6 *Circles and Circular Functions*

Think About This Situation

Suppose that the tachometer of a car shows a reading of 3,000 rpm and the tires on that car have diameter of 24 inches, or 2 feet.

a If each revolution of the car's crankshaft were to produce one rotation of the car's wheels, what speed in miles per hour would correspond to the tachometer reading of 3,000 rpm? (Recall that there are 5,280 feet in a mile.)

b The speed implied by your calculations in Part a probably seems far greater than what is reasonable to expect. What do you know about automobile design that explains that fact?

c The tachometer of a typical car will actually show a reading of 3,000 rpm at several different speeds. What do you know about automobile design that explains that fact?

16 UNIT 6 • Circles and Circular Functions — Transparency Master • use with page 421

Unit 6

Investigation 1 Angular and Linear Velocity

When Investigation 1 has been completed, students should be able to explain the concepts of angular and linear velocity and how those variables are related in circular motion. They should also be able to analyze the relationships of angular and linear velocities in systems where rotating circles like pulleys and sprockets are connected by belts or chains.

The ratio of angular velocities for two *linked* pulleys or sprockets is the reciprocal of the ratio of the sizes (diameters/radii/circumferences) of the two pulleys. That is, in general, the larger pulley rotates slower than the smaller. This is a useful scientific understanding for students to have, so time spent thinking about how these things work should be time well spent.

Bicycle Gear Ratios One familiar example of a transmission connecting moving circles is the gear mechanism used in bicycles. For example, suppose that a mountain bike is set up so that the pedal sprocket in use has 42 teeth and the rear-wheel sprocket in use has 14 teeth of the same size.

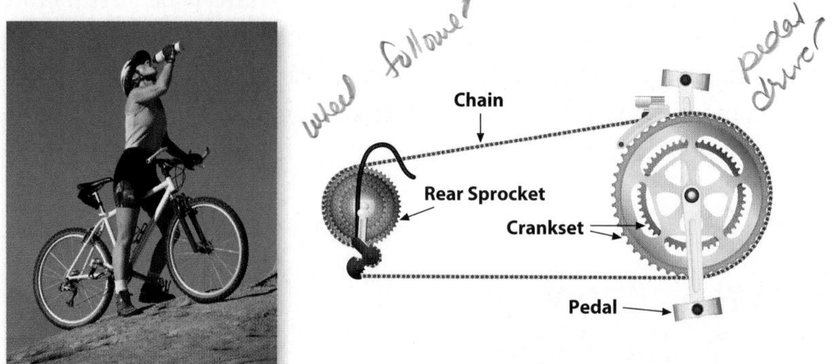

1. Consider the given "teeth per sprocket" information above.
   a. What does this information tell you about the circumferences of the two sprockets?
   b. Suppose that the rider is pedaling at an angular velocity of 80 revolutions per minute.
      i. What is the angular velocity of the rear sprocket?
      ii. What is the angular velocity of the rear wheel?

2. Suppose that the wheels on the mountain bike have a radius of 33 centimeters.
   a. How far does the bike travel for each complete revolution of the 14-tooth rear sprocket?
   b. How far does the bike travel for each complete revolution of the front pedal sprocket?
   c. If the rider pedals at an angular velocity of 80 rpm, how far will she travel in one minute?
   d. How long will the rider need to pedal at 80 rpm to travel 2 kilometers?

3. In the connection between the pedal and rear sprockets of a bicycle, the pedal sprocket is called the **driver** and the rear sprocket is called the **follower**.
   a. Write rules that express the relationships between angular velocities of the driver v_d and follower v_f when the bicycle gears are set in the following ways.
      i. Driver sprocket with 30 teeth and follower sprocket with 15 teeth
      ii. Driver sprocket with 20 teeth and follower sprocket with 30 teeth
   b. Which of the gear settings in Part a will make pedaling harder for the rider? Why?

422 UNIT 6 • Circles and Circular Functions

(1) **a.** The pedal sprocket has three times the circumference of the rear sprocket (at the given setting).

b. **i.** The rear sprocket rotates at 240 rpm.

ii. Since the rear sprocket is attached directly to the wheel (in a non-slip condition), the rear wheel will also rotate at 240 rpm.

(2) **a.** One revolution of the rear sprocket will cause 1 revolution of the wheel which has circumference $2\pi r = 66\pi$ cm, or about 207 cm.

b. Each revolution of the pedal sprocket will cause 3 revolutions of the rear sprocket and rear wheel. So, that means 198π cm, or about 622 cm.

c. Angular velocity of 80 rpm will cause the bike to cover $80(622) = 49{,}760$ cm in one minute. This figure is much more easily understood if converted to other larger units of measure such as meters; in this case, about 498 meters.

d. To cover 2 kilometers, the rider will need to pedal at 80 rpm for about 4 minutes, because 2 km = 200,000 cm and $200{,}000 \div 49{,}760 \approx 4.02$.

(3) **a.** Driver and follower relationships can be expressed in a variety of equivalent equations. Only one is given in each part here; the one that expresses follower speed as a function of driver speed.

i. $v_f = 2v_d$

ii. $v_f = \frac{2}{3}v_d$

b. The gear settings in Part ai will make pedaling harder. One revolution of the 30-teeth driver sprocket will spin the 15-teeth follower sprocket (and thus bike wheel) through 2 revolutions. But it takes 3 revolutions of the 20-teeth driver sprocket to move the bike wheel through 2 revolutions. The work accomplished by pedaling one revolution of the larger sprocket is greater than the work accomplished by pedaling one revolution of the smaller sprocket, so it requires greater effort by the cyclist when using the larger sprocket.

Crankshafts and Transmissions Many internal combustion engines have pistons that move up and down, causing a cylindrical crankshaft to rotate. The crankshaft *driver* then transfers power to the *follower* wheels but also to other parts of the engine. For example, in many cars, a belt connects the crankshaft to pulleys that drive the fan and the alternator. When the engine is running, the fan cools the radiator while the alternator generates electrical current.

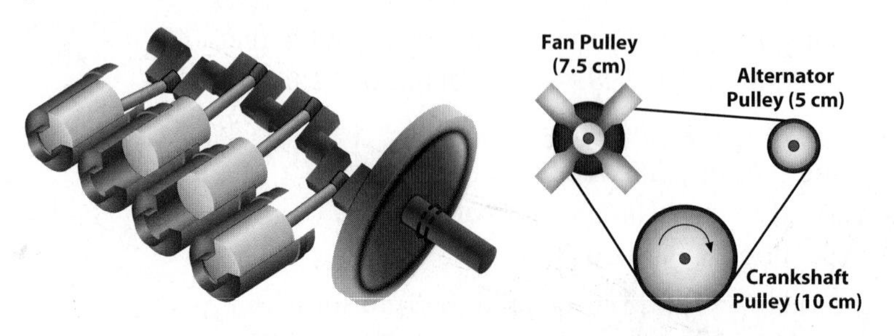

4. The pulley diameters from the diagram above allow us to compare angular velocities of the crankshaft, alternator, and fan pulleys. If the crankshaft makes one complete revolution:
   a. how many revolutions will the alternator pulley make?
   b. how many revolutions will the fan pulley make?

5. Write rules expressing the relationships of angular velocities for the driver v_d and follower v_f in case the crankshaft is the driver and:
   a. the alternator pulley is the follower.
   b. the fan pulley is the follower.

6. Suppose that the crankshaft (with diameter 10 cm) of the car is rotating with angular velocity of 1,500 rpm.
   a. Calculate the linear velocities in centimeters per minute of points on the edge of each pulley.
      i. crankshaft
      ii. alternator
      iii. fan
   b. Explain why the pattern of your answers in Part a makes sense if one thinks about how the belt and pulley mechanism operates.

INSTRUCTIONAL NOTE The problems about driver and follower angular velocities seem like an excellent setting for a "mathematical moral lesson" about regularly asking oneself, "Does this answer make sense?" The reciprocal relationship between diameters and angular velocities of linked pulleys or gears makes it easy to unthinkingly do some calculation and have the wrong answer. Thus, for instance, in Part aii of Problem 3, it is tempting to write the equation $v_f = 1.5v_d$. However, if you stop to think, this states that the follower wheel will rotate faster than the smaller driver. That does not make physical sense, so one is pressed to rethink and come up with the correct formula.

The next problems deal with angular and linear velocities in automobile engines. Many students might have very little understanding of how these engines work. So, you might suggest that in preparation for work on the "Crankshafts and Transmissions" segment of this investigation, they ask someone they know to show them what things look like "under the hood" of a car. You might visit the Wikipedia entry under "crankshaft" and show the graphics that you find. This entry should show an animated cutaway view of how the pistons of an engine move up and down to turn a crankshaft.

4. **a.** Each revolution of the crankshaft causes 2 revolutions of the alternator pulley since their circumferences are in that ratio (assuming the belt does not slip as it causes each pulley to turn).

   b. The fan will make $\frac{10}{7.5} = 1\frac{1}{3}$ revolutions for each turn of the crankshaft.

5. **a.** $v_f = 2v_d$

   b. $v_f = \frac{4}{3}v_d$

6. **a.** The linear velocities for a crankshaft with angular velocity 1,500 rpm are:

   i. Crankshaft: $1{,}500(10\pi) \approx 47{,}124$ cm (about 470 meters, or more than one quarter of a mile in each minute)

   ii. Alternator: $3{,}000(5\pi) \approx 47{,}124$ cm

   iii. Fan: $2{,}000(7.5\pi) \approx 47{,}124$ cm

   b. The fact that all three linear velocities turned out the same (albeit with different diameters and different angular velocities) is explained by the fact that it is a single belt that is turning all three pulleys. Assuming no slippage of the belt, every centimeter that the belt moves when impelled by the crankshaft cause it to move the fan and alternator pulleys the one centimeter.

Summarize the Mathematics

In this investigation, you studied angular and linear velocities—important concepts in the design and analysis of connections between rotating circular objects.

a. What do angular and linear velocity measurements tell about the motion of a circular object?

b. What are some common units of measurement for angular velocity? For linear velocity?

c. How can you use information about the radii of two connected sprockets or pulleys to determine the relationship between their angular and linear velocities?

d. If you know the angular velocity and radius of a rotating circular object, how can you determine the linear velocity of points on its circumference?

Be prepared to discuss your responses with the class.

Check Your Understanding

Because power plants that burn fossil fuels are known to increase atmospheric carbon dioxide, many countries are turning to alternative, cleaner sources of electric power. In some places, it makes sense to construct pollution-free wind farms like that pictured below.

a. Suppose that a wind turbine has blades that are 100 feet long and an angular velocity of 2.5 rpm. What is the linear velocity of points at the tip of each blade?

b. Suppose a wind turbine connects a driver pulley with diameter 6 feet to a follower pulley with diameter 4 feet. What is the angular velocity of the follower pulley when the angular velocity of the driver is 3 rpm?

424 UNIT 6 • Circles and Circular Functions

Summarize the Mathematics

a The angular velocity tells the spin rate of a circular object in revolutions per unit of time. The linear velocity tells the distance traveled by a point on the circumference of the circular object in units of length per unit of time. (Linear motion need not be in a straight line path, but the linear velocity tells how far a point object would move if its path were straightened out.)

b Common units of angular velocity are revolutions per second or minute (and, as students will see in subsequent investigations, degrees or radians of rotation per unit of time). Units of linear velocity are the common units like feet per second, kilometers or miles per hour, and so on.

c If two pulleys or sprockets are linked by a non-slipping belt or chain, their linear velocities will be the same. Their angular velocities depend on their relative radii, diameters, or circumferences. In general, the larger pulley or sprocket will have slower angular velocity than the linked smaller pulley or sprocket. The ratio of angular velocities is the reciprocal of the ratio of their radii (or diameters or circumferences).

d Linear velocity is equal to the product of angular velocity (in revolutions per unit of time) and circumference of the circular object.

Check Your Understanding

a. The circumference of the circle traced by the tip of the wind turbine blade is $2\pi(100)$, or 200π. At an angular velocity of 2.5 rpm, the tip of each blade is moving at a linear velocity of 500π, or about 1,570 feet per minute. That is equivalent to about 18 miles per hour. (This is a speed that is generally surprising to observers when they see what seems to be very languid, or slow, motion of wind turbine blades.)

b. The follower pulley moves at a greater angular velocity than the larger driver pulley. In fact, it moves 1.5 times as fast to make 4.5 rpm when the driver is rotating at 3 rpm.

PROMOTING MATHEMATICAL DISCOURSE

Teaching Resources

Transparency Master 17.

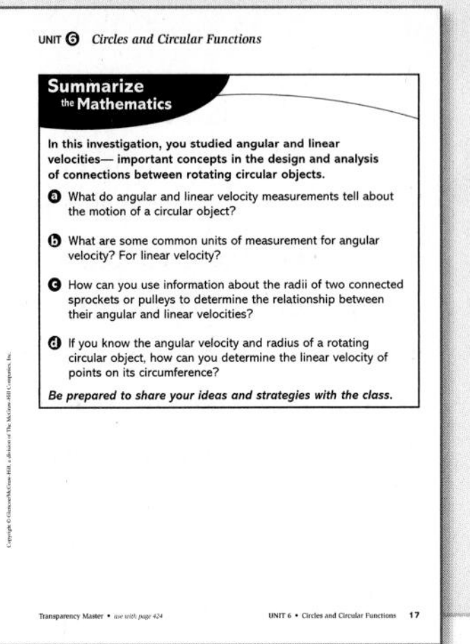

UNIT 6 *Circles and Circular Functions*

Summarize the Mathematics

In this investigation, you studied angular and linear velocities— important concepts in the design and analysis of connections between rotating circular objects.

a What do angular and linear velocity measurements tell about the motion of a circular object?

b What are some common units of measurement for angular velocity? For linear velocity?

c How can you use information about the radii of two connected sprockets or pulleys to determine the relationship between their angular and linear velocities?

d If you know the angular velocity and radius of a rotating circular object, how can you determine the linear velocity of points on its circumference?

Be prepared to share your ideas and strategies with the class.

Transparency Master • use with page 424 UNIT 6 • Circles and Circular Functions 17

MATH TOOLKIT Students should write definitions for the new terms in this investigation—angular velocity and linear velocity. If students have been identifying other mechanical applications of pulley systems, you may wish to have them use their applications to illustrate these concepts.

Promoting Mathematical Discourse

Summarize the Mathematics, *page 424*

Teacher: In this investigation, you studied angular and linear velocity. Some of you told us that you had some experience with these concepts prior to this formal study with go-cart building and bicycle use. These concepts are important in the design and analysis of rotating circular objects. Talk for a couple of minutes with a partner about the following questions: "What do angular velocity measurements tell you about the motion of a circular object and what are common measurements for angular velocity?" Then consider the same questions for linear velocity. *(The teacher listens as students discuss these questions and then he asks for student thinking, starting with angular velocity.)*

Karen: Angular velocity tells you how fast something is spinning. We said it can be measured by counting the number of times it goes completely around, from a starting point, say in a minute or second.

Placido: Yeah, revolutions per minute, rpms, like for car transmissions.

Teacher: Aahil, what does linear velocity tell you and how is it measured?

Aahil: It tells you the distance traveled around a circle. This is like the circumference, or part of the circumference, or many circumferences around. Just like with straight line distance, it is measured in feet, meters, or something else like that but it has time with the measurement too. So, like feet per second or meters per minute.

Teacher: Anyone have something to add about angular and linear velocity? *(No one does.)* Then using the ideas from our discussion, take a couple of minutes to summarize our discussion in your Math Toolkit notes. Focus on what the two concepts tell you and how they are measured. You may wish to add an example or diagram with your notes.

Teacher: Now let's consider Parts c and d of the STM. Take a couple of minutes to discuss these two parts with a partner, and be ready to discuss your response. *(Students are given a couple of minutes. Then they are asked for their thinking.)*

Asha: We decided that when two pulleys are connected, their linear velocity is the same. Each time one pulley goes around, the other one does, too. The size of the circle has nothing to do with the linear velocity. It seems a little strange to me because I usually think of "velocity" as how fast something is going, but linear velocity is really how far something has traveled—like a point on the circle—in a certain amount of time. I have to keep reminding myself about that.

Teacher: Interesting, Asha. Does someone else have a way to think about linear velocity that they wish to share? Ritchie?

Ritchie: I keep myself from being confused by thinking about the word "linear." I think about measuring along a line—distance that is—like straightening out the circumference to measure it. Actually, the circumference is measured in linear units, so we are just including the time factor. Distance traveled around the circle per unit of time.

Hadeeqah: I connect linear velocity to driving my car. I don't always go straight, but the speed is miles per hour (distance per hour).

Teacher: So, does it make sense then that two connected pulleys or sprockets have the same linear velocity even if they have quite different radii? *(Students agree.)* Then how can you use information about the length of the radii of the two connected circular objects to determine their angular velocities? Help us understand how you think about this idea as you respond. Sam, how did you and Marie think about this?

Sam: We said that the larger circle would have slower angular velocity since when the smaller circle goes around once, the larger circle has not completed a revolution, so it is slower. We made a picture of the pulleys. Here, let me draw it. We traced around the smaller pulley and then estimated a trace around the larger pulley that matches the smaller circumference. In our example, we made the larger circle with twice the radius of the smaller circle. Then we could quickly think about the fact that the larger circle had half the angular velocity of the smaller circle. So, when the larger circle has twice the radius of the smaller circle, it has half the angular velocity.

Constance: We did something like that but went from the larger circle to the smaller circle. Whichever way you think about it, the ratio of the radii and the ratio of the angular velocities are reciprocals.

Teacher: Now suppose that you are given the diameters or the circumferences of the two pulleys rather than the radii. What can you say about the ratio of the angular velocities? Nyla?

Nyla: It is the same. I mean, it is again the reciprocal relationship. For two circles, the ratio of radii, diameters, and circumferences is the same for all three. If the radius of the larger circle is twice the smaller, then the diameter and circumference of the larger one is also twice the smaller one.

Unit 6

Teacher: If you know the angular velocity and radius of a rotating circular object, how can you find the linear velocity? Tina, what did you and Mark decide?

Tina: You need to find the circumference of the circle using $2\pi r$ and then multiply that by the revolutions per minute or second.

Teacher: Tina, please write that product on the board for us using the words "linear velocity" and "angular velocity." *(She writes "linear velocity = angular velocity × 2πr.")* Now take a couple of minutes to add the ideas we have discussed about finding the linear velocity as Tina has indicated and also the relationship between the radii and the angular and linear velocities of two connected pulley's in your Math Toolkit. Use diagrams if you wish. For homework for this investigation, please complete the Check Your Understanding task and also A1, one of A2–A4, C13, R20 or R21, and E27 or E28. In addition, do Review Tasks 34–36. Have the CYU and Review tasks done to check with others tomorrow. If there are questions, we will address them. The other tasks will be due on Wednesday.

Investigation 2 Modeling Circular Motion

The Ferris wheel was invented in 1893 as an attraction at the World Columbian Exhibition in Chicago, and it remains a popular ride at carnivals and amusement parks around the world. The wheels provide a great context for study of circular motion.

Ferris wheels are circular and rotate about the center. The spokes of the wheel are radii, and the seats are like points on the circle. The wheel has horizontal and vertical lines of symmetry through the center of rotation. This suggests a natural coordinate system for describing the circular motion. As you work on the problems in this investigation, look for an answer to the following question:

How can the coordinates of any point on a rotating circular object be determined from the radius and angle of rotation?

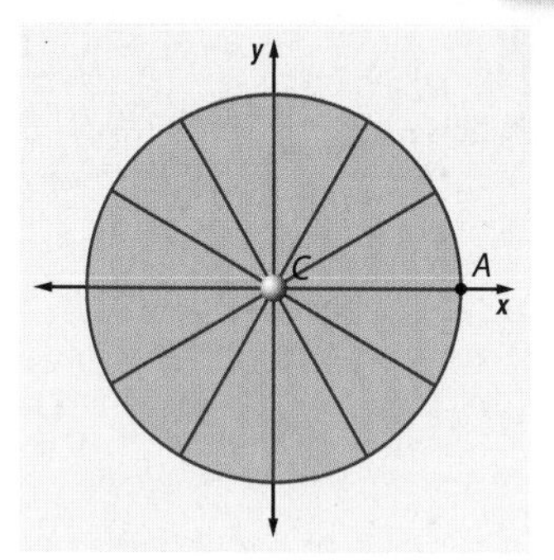

Coordinates of Points on a Rotating Wheel To aid your thinking about positions on a rotating circle, it might be helpful to make a Ferris wheel model that uses a disk to represent the wheel with x- and y-coordinate axes on a fixed backboard.

Connect the disk to the coordinate axis backboard with a fastener that allows the disk to turn freely while the horizontal and vertical axes remain fixed in place.

1. Imagine that a small Ferris wheel has radius 1 decameter (about 33 feet) and that your seat is at point A when the wheel begins to turn counterclockwise about its center at point C.
   - **a.** How does the x-coordinate of your seat change as the wheel turns?
   - **b.** How does the y-coordinate of your seat change as the wheel turns?

2. Find angles of rotation between 0° and 360° that will take the seat from point A to the following special points.
   - **a.** Maximum and minimum distance from the horizontal axis
   - **b.** Maximum and minimum distance from the vertical axis
   - **c.** Points with equal x- and y-coordinates
   - **d.** Points with opposite x- and y-coordinates

When a circle like that modeling the Ferris wheel is placed on a rectangular coordinate grid with center at the origin (0, 0), you can use what you know about geometry and trigonometry to find the x- and y-coordinates of any point on the circle.

Investigation 2 Modeling Circular Motion

This investigation develops ways that the sine and cosine functions from trigonometry can be used to track the position of a point on the circumference of a circular object as that object rotates about a point. The main result is that if you imagine horizontal and vertical axes through the center of a rotating circle with radius r, the (x, y) coordinates, or the distances from the point P on the circle to the two axes, will be given by $(r \cos \theta, r \sin \theta)$ where θ is the directed angle determined by P, the origin, and the positive x-axis.

You might choose to launch the investigation by showing a picture (or perhaps an animation) of a Ferris wheel and asking students to recount some of their experiences with such a ride. For example, you might ask:

How many of you have ridden on a Ferris wheel?

For those who have, how high was the top of the wheel?

What was the scariest part of the ride?

Do you remember whether the wheel turned in a clockwise or counterclockwise direction?

The last question is a trick, intended to raise an important point for the subsequent investigation. In fact, whether the wheel is turning in a clockwise or counterclockwise direction is entirely a matter of your point of view. From one side, it will appear to move one direction and from the other side, it will move in the opposite direction. This point is raised because Ferris wheel motion will be used to introduce mathematical rotations and circular functions, and standard practice in mathematics orients circular motion to start from the positive x-axis and turn in a counterclockwise direction (perhaps to deal with as many problems as possible in the first graphing quadrant where both coordinates of points are positive numbers).

You can conclude this scene-setting discussion by pointing out the focus question of the investigation and encouraging students to build the sort of model Ferris wheel described in the text. A Student Master is provided, which can be connected to a rectangular piece of poster board with a brad.

After students work on Problems 1 and 2 for a short time, have a class discussion of their ideas before launching into the next problems that require recall and use of the basic definitions for sine and cosine.

TECHNOLOGY NOTE
You might want to make use of the "Ferris Wheel" sample sketch in *CPMP-Tools* for this investigation.

INSTRUCTIONAL NOTE You will notice that the first Ferris wheel used for illustrative purposes in this investigation is said to have a radius of 1 decameter. While this is a rarely used unit in the metric measurement system, it has the virtue for this particular investigation that it is a plausible size for a small Ferris wheel (perhaps one for young children) and it allows use of a unit circle for the calculation of (x, y) coordinates. Then the coordinates are simply $(\cos \theta, \sin \theta)$. In subsequent problems, we extend the ideas to deal with circles of other radii. But it seems desirable at this introductory point to avoid the complication of a multiplicative constant.

Teaching Resources

Student Master 18.

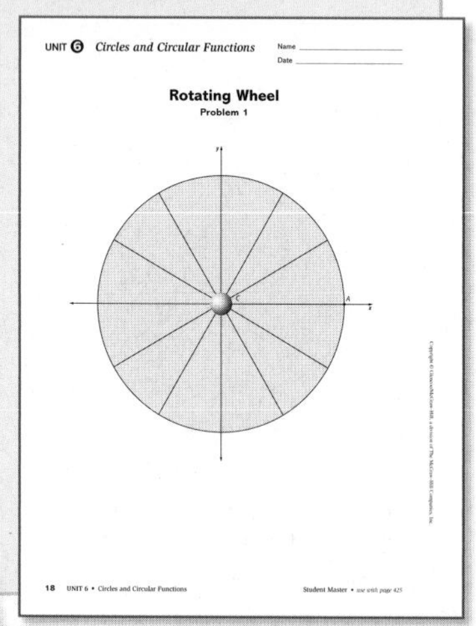

1 **a.** As the wheel turns, the x-coordinate of the seat decreases (slowly at first and then more rapidly) to 0 when the seat is at its maximum height and then becomes negative (rapidly at first and then more slowly) until it reaches its minimum value of -1. Then the value of x begins to increase (slowly at first and then more rapidly), reaching 0 when the seat is at its lowest point. The value of x then becomes positive and increases (rapidly at first and then more slowly), reaching 1 when the seat returns to its starting position at $(1, 0)$.

b. As the wheel turns, the y-coordinate of the seat increases (rapidly at first and then more slowly) to 1 when the seat reaches its maximum height and then decreases (slowly at first and then more rapidly) until it reaches its minimum non-negative value of 0. Then the value of y continues to decrease (rapidly at first and then more slowly), reaching -1 when the seat is at its lowest point. The value of y then begins increasing (slowly at first and then more rapidly), reaching 0 when the seat returns to its starting position at $(1, 0)$.

2 **a.** Maximum distance from horizontal axis: 90° and 270°
Minimum distance from horizontal axis: 0°, 180°, and 360°

b. Maximum distance from vertical axis: 0°, 180°, and 360°
Minimum distance from vertical axis: 90° and 270°

c. Points with equal x- and y-coordinates: 45° and 225°

d. Points with opposite x- and y-coordinates: 135° and 315°

INSTRUCTIONAL NOTE The solutions to Problem 3 are direct applications of the definitions of the trigonometric functions for all four quadrants, as shown below. If students have difficulty, refer them to their list of Key Geometric Ideas. Be sure that students' answers make sense when viewed on a diagram showing the angles and the *x*- and *y*-axes. You may need to make some judgments and adjustments for your particular class, depending on what they remember from their Course 2 work and subsequent Review tasks involving this definition.

Definitions of trigonometric functions, $0° \leq \theta \leq 360°$

sine of $\theta = \sin \theta = \frac{y}{r}$

cosine of $\theta = \cos \theta = \frac{x}{r}$

tangent of $\theta = \tan \theta = \frac{y}{x}$ $(x \neq 0)$

3 The coordinates of points after any rotation of $\theta°$ will be given by $(\cos \theta, \sin \theta)$ for any angle or rotation of $\theta°$.

a. $\left(\frac{\sqrt{3}}{2}, \frac{1}{2}\right) \approx (0.87, 0.5)$

b. $(0.34, 0.94)$

c. $(0, 1)$

d. $\left(-\frac{1}{2}, \frac{\sqrt{3}}{2}\right) \approx (-0.5, 0.87)$

e. $(-0.77, 0.64)$

f. $(-1, 0)$

g. $(-0.77, -0.64)$

h. $(0, -1)$

i. $(0.64, -0.77)$

4

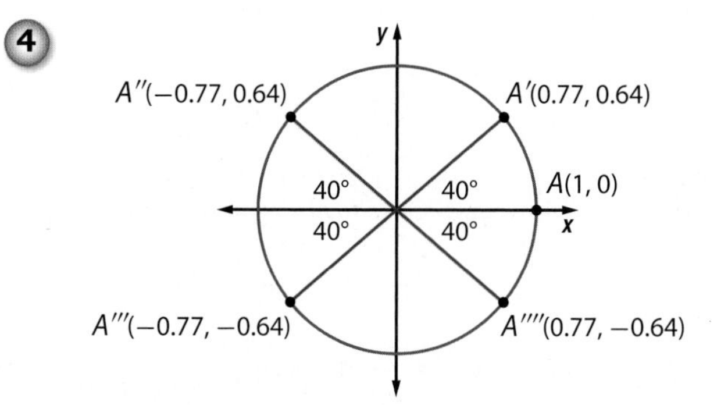

Reflections across the *x*- and *y*-axes as shown in the diagram allow you to decide that:

Rotation Size	Location of Seat
140°	$A''(-0.77, 0.64)$
220°	$A'''(-0.77, -0.64)$
320°	$A''''(0.77, -0.64)$

Any rotations of 360° plus the angles in the table above will end at the same location. (Some students may mention symmetry about the line $y = x$ which gives coordinates for locations with reference angles of 50°.)

5 **a.** $P(x, y) = (\cos \theta, \sin \theta)$

b. $P(x, y) = (r \cos \theta, r \sin \theta)$ when the circle has radius r.

INSTRUCTIONAL NOTE
You might want to ask students why some of the same absolute values appeared in the answers to Problem 3. It is because several of the pairs of points involved are located in symmetric positions with respect to the axes.

3. Find coordinates of points that tell the location of the Ferris wheel seat that begins at point $A(1, 0)$ when the wheel undergoes the following rotations. Record the results on a sketch that shows a circle and the points with their coordinate labels.

a. $\theta = 30°$	**b.** $\theta = 70°$	**c.** $\theta = 90°$
d. $\theta = 120°$	**e.** $\theta = 140°$	**f.** $\theta = 180°$
g. $\theta = 220°$	**h.** $\theta = 270°$	**i.** $\theta = 310°$

4. When the Ferris wheel has rotated through an angle of 40°, the seat that started at $A(1, 0)$ will be at about $A'(0.77, 0.64)$. Explain how the symmetry of the circle allows you to deduce the location of that seat after rotations of 140°, 220°, 320°, and some other angles as well.

5. Suppose that $P(x, y)$ is a point on the Ferris wheel model with $m\angle PCA = \theta$ in degrees.

   a. What are the coordinates x and y?

   b. How will the coordinate values be different if the radius of the circle is r decameters?

6. With your calculator or computer graphing program set in degree mode, graph the functions $\cos \theta$ and $\sin \theta$ for $0° \leq \theta \leq 360°$. Compare the patterns in those graphs to your ideas in Problems 1 and 2 and to the results of your work on Problem 3.

7. How will the x- and y-coordinates of your seat on the Ferris wheel change during a second complete revolution? How will those patterns be represented in graphs of the coordinate functions for $360° \leq \theta \leq 720°$?

Summarize the Mathematics

In this investigation, you explored the connection between circular motion and the cosine and sine functions.

a Think about the motion of a point on a wheel that starts at (1, 0) and undergoes counterclockwise rotation about the center of the wheel.

i. Describe the pattern of change in the *x*-coordinate of the point as the wheel makes one complete revolution.

ii. Describe the pattern of change in the *y*-coordinate of the point as the wheel makes one complete revolution.

b How are the patterns of change in coordinates extended as the wheel continues to turn counterclockwise through more revolutions?

c Explain how trigonometry can be used to model circular motion.

Be prepared to discuss your responses with the class.

Unit 6

426 UNIT 6 • Circles and Circular Functions

6 **INSTRUCTIONAL NOTE** It is probably useful to have a discussion about how the given graphs do or do not represent the patterns of change that the students described in their responses to Problem 1. In particular, do the graphs show the right maximum and minimum points, intercepts, and intervals of rapid and slower change?

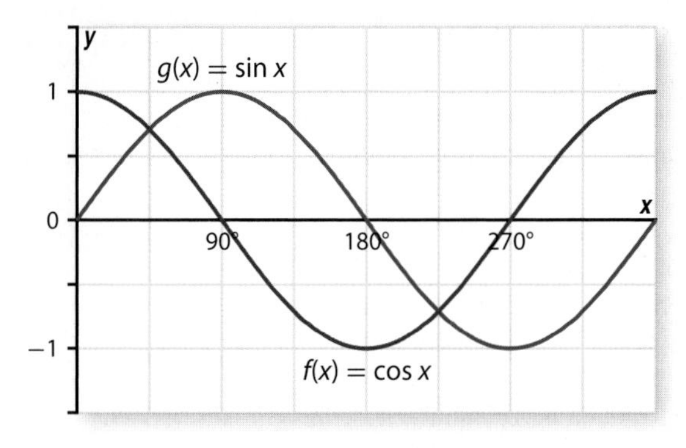

7 The patterns of change in the x- and y-coordinates on the interval $360° \leq \theta \leq 720°$ should be identical to those on the interval $0° \leq \theta \leq 360°$. The graphs of the two functions for $360° \leq \theta \leq 720°$ should be identical in shape to those on the interval $0° \leq \theta \leq 360°$, just a horizontal translation of $(x + 360, y)$.

NOTE Solutions to Problems 3–5 are on page T425B.

Summarize the Mathematics

a **i.** Initially, the x-coordinate or directed distance from the vertical axis begins at its maximum, decreases slowly, then decreases faster until it reaches 0 after a 90° rotation. Then the x-coordinate decreases to -1, rapidly at first and then more slowly until it is the minimum value -1 after a 180° rotation (another 90°). Then the process reverses itself, with the x-coordinate increasing back to 0 after a 270° rotation (another 90°), and finally to the maximum value of 1 after one full revolution of 360°.

ii. Initially, the y-coordinate or directed distance from the horizontal axis increases rapidly starting at 0, then continues to increase but at a slower rate until it reaches its maximum 1 above the center of the circle after a 90° rotation. Then the process reverses itself until the y-coordinate is 0 after a 180° rotation (another 90°). Next, the y-coordinate decreases from 0 to -1, rapidly at first, and then more slowly as the point nears the minimum value of -1 after a 270° rotation (another 90°). The y-coordinate then increases back to 0, its original value after one full revolution of 360°.

b The patterns of change in coordinates repeat in cycles or periods of 360° for each revolution of the wheel.

c If r is the radius of the circle and θ is the measure of the angle of rotation, then $r \cos \theta$ is the x-coordinate and $r \sin \theta$ is the y-coordinate of a point on the circle.

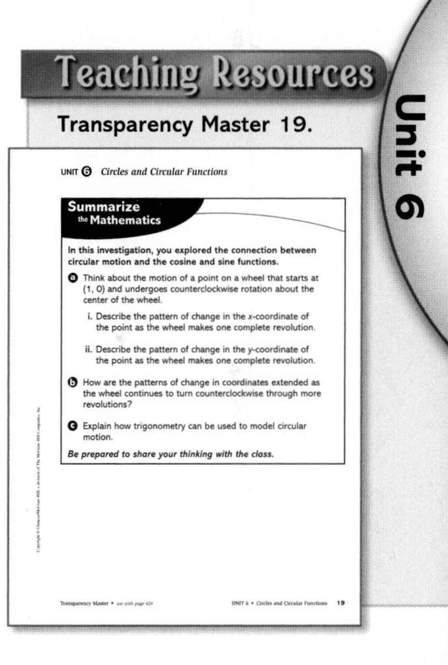
Teaching Resources

Transparency Master 19.

UNIT 6 *Circles and Circular Functions*

Summarize the Mathematics

In this investigation, you explored the connection between circular motion and the cosine and sine functions.

a Think about the motion of a point on a wheel that starts at (1, 0) and undergoes counterclockwise rotation about the center of the wheel.

i. Describe the pattern of change in the x-coordinate of the point as the wheel makes one complete revolution.

ii. Describe the pattern of change in the y-coordinate of the point as the wheel makes one complete revolution.

b How are the patterns of change in coordinates extended as the wheel continues to turn counterclockwise through more revolutions?

c Explain how trigonometry can be used to model circular motion.

Be prepared to share your thinking with the class.

Transparency Master • *use with page 426* UNIT 6 • Circles and Circular Functions 19

Unit 6

MATH TOOLKIT Students should write a general explanation of how trigonometric ratios can be used to locate vertical and horizontal distances on a circle if you know the radius of the circle and the measure of the angle. Illustrate the explanation using a right triangle like the ones modeled in the Ferris wheel application.

Check Your Understanding

At the Chelsea Community Fair, there is a Ferris wheel with a 15-meter radius. Suppose the Ferris wheel is positioned on an x-y coordinate system as in Problem 1.

a. Danielle is on a seat to the right of the vertical axis halfway to the highest point of the ride. Make a sketch showing the wheel, x- and y-axes through the center of the wheel, and her starting position.

b. Find the x- and y-coordinates of Danielle's seat after the wheel has rotated counterclockwise through an angle of $56°$. Through an angle of $130°$.

c. Write expressions that give Danielle's position relative to the x- and y-axes for any counterclockwise rotation of θ in degrees from her starting point.

d. Suppose the wheel turns at one revolution every minute. Describe in several different ways the location of Danielle's seat at the end of 50 seconds.

Investigation 3 Revolutions, Degrees, and Radians

The degree is the most familiar unit of measurement for angles and rotations. However, it is common in scientific work to measure angles and rotations in *radians*, a unit that directly connects central angles, arcs, and radii of circles. As you work on the problems of this investigation, look for answers to the following questions:

How are angles measured in radians?

How are radians related to other units of measure for angles and rotations?

Radian Measurement Every central angle in a circle intercepts an arc on the circle. The length of that arc is some fraction of the circumference of the circle. This is the key to linking length and angle measurement with radian measure.

1 To see how a *radian* is defined, collaborate with classmates to conduct the following experiment.

a. The diagram at the right represents three concentric circles with center O and radii varying from 1 to 3 inches. Points B_1, B_2, B_3, and O are collinear.

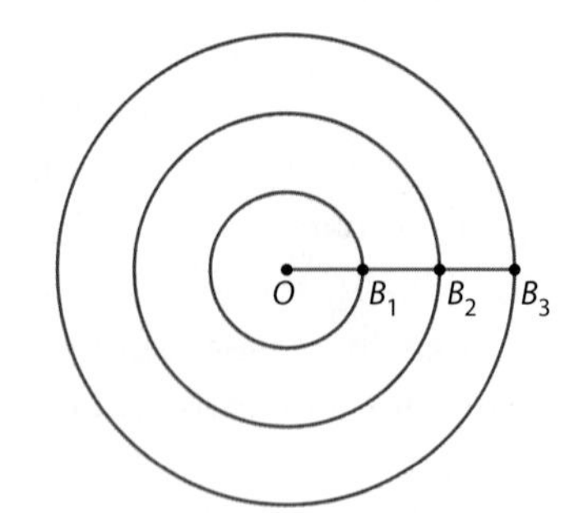

On a full-size copy of the diagram, for each circle:

- wrap a piece of string along the circle counterclockwise from point B_n to a second point A_n so that the length of $\widehat{A_nB_n}$ is equal to the radius of the circle with radius $\overline{OB_n}$.
- draw $\angle A_nOB_n$ and measure it in degrees.
- record the circle radius and the measure of $\angle A_nOB_n$.

Check Your Understanding

a. When Danielle is halfway to the top, she has revolved 90° from the bottom where she boarded; her position is on the horizontal line and 15 meters from the vertical line.

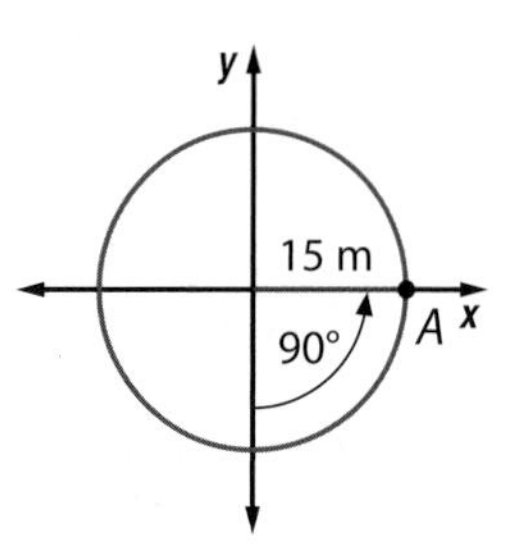

b. x-coordinates: $15 \cos 56° \approx 8.39$ m
$15 \cos 130° \approx -9.64$ m
y-coordinates: $15 \sin 56° \approx 12.44$ m
$15 \sin 130° \approx 11.49$ m

c. $15 \cos \theta°$ represents the x-coordinate or directed distance from the vertical axis. $15 \sin \theta°$ represents the y-coordinate or directed distance from the horizontal axis.

d. In 50 seconds, she will rotate $\frac{50}{60} = \frac{5}{6}$ of a full revolution. Therefore, she will rotate $\frac{5}{6} \cdot 360° = 300°$. Her seat will be at an angle 60° below horizontal and moving upward. The coordinates of her position are $(15 \cos 300°, 15 \sin 300°)$, so she is $15 \cos 300° = 7.5$ meters from the vertical axis and $15 \sin 300° \approx -12.99$, or 12.99 meters below the horizontal axis.

Unit 6

Investigation 3 Revolutions, Degrees, and Radians

Although radian measure is the standard in mathematical practice and the natural link to trigonometric functions defined on the real line and complex plane, students tend to find the notion of a radian difficult to grasp. Thus, in this investigation, students do some hands-on experiments designed to reveal the connection among central angles, arc length, and circle radii. This is followed by a number of problems designed to help students connect the new way of measuring angles with angle measure and rotations that are more familiar.

In Problem 3, students are expected to make the logical connection that if it takes 2π radii to wrap around the circumference of any circle and if each of the arcs on the circle of length one radius has central angle 1 radian, then it takes 2π radians to equal an angle of 360°, or one complete revolution. It is important that students see that this is true for all circles.

The investigation closes with development of the wrapping function that connects the real number line with the cosine and sine functions as they are used to provide coordinates of points on a unit circle. This definition of cosine and sine as functions of real numbers is applied in the next investigation to create models of periodic variation over time.

MATHEMATICAL NOTE
Degrees and radians are two ways to measure angles. Although their definitions are motivated differently, they essentially differ only by scale, so either can be used as the domain of trigonometric functions. Radians are more convenient in calculus, since, for example, the derivative of the sine function is the cosine function in radians. For more on this, see Reflections Task 23 and Extensions Task 30.

Launch

You may wish to launch the investigation by remarking that the problems will reveal an important new way of measuring angles and connect that measurement strategy to degree measure, rotations, and trigonometric functions. Then provide student groups with an actual size copy of the concentric circle drawing in the text, a ruler, and some flexible linear object like a piece of string, pipe cleaner, or tape measure. Ask them to respond to the questions of Problem 1.

NOTE The remainder of the launch ideas and the solution to Problem 1 Part a are on page T428.

Examine the resulting data and describe any interesting patterns you observe.

b. What is the approximate degree measure of the central angle you would expect to be determined by a 15-cm arc in a circle with a radius of 15 cm?

c. Suppose a circle with center O has radius r. What would you expect to be the approximate degree measure of $\angle AOB$ if $\widehat{AB}$ is r units long?

A **radian** is the measure of any central angle in a circle that intercepts an arc equal in length to the radius of the circle. To use radian measure effectively in reasoning about angles and rotations, it helps to develop number sense about how radian measures are related to degrees and revolutions.

That is the goal of the next several problems and the "Explore Radians" custom tool in *CPMP-Tools*.

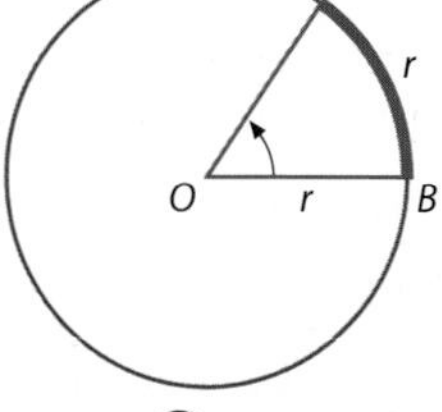
A
r
O
r
B

length $\widehat{AB} = r =$ radius
m$\angle AOB = 1$ radian

2 Think about how you measure angles in radians.

a. In a circle with center O, radius 5 centimeters, and $\angle AOB$ intercepting $\widehat{AB}$ of length 10 cm, what are the radian and approximate degree measures of $\angle AOB$?

b. In a circle with center O, radius 8 meters, and $\angle AOB$ intercepting $\widehat{AB}$ of length 24 meters, what are the radian and approximate degree measures of $\angle AOB$?

3 One formula for calculating the circumference of a circle is $C = 2\pi r$. Analyze the ways that Khadijah and Jacy used that fact to find the radian measure equivalent to 120°.

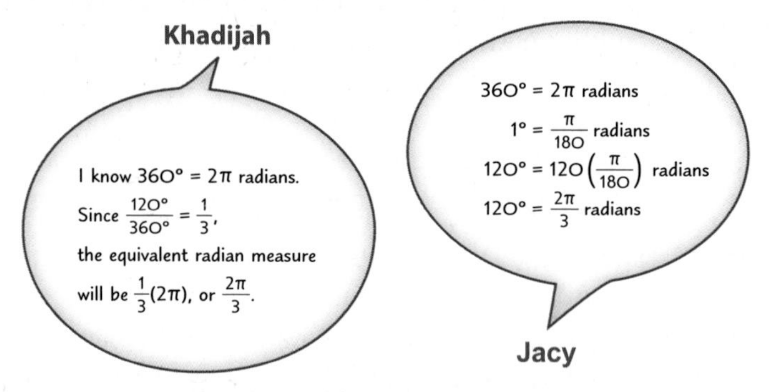
Khadijah
I know $360° = 2\pi$ radians.
Since $\frac{120°}{360°} = \frac{1}{3}$,
the equivalent radian measure
will be $\frac{1}{3}(2\pi)$, or $\frac{2\pi}{3}$.
$360° = 2\pi$ radians
$1° = \frac{\pi}{180}$ radians
$120° = 120\left(\frac{\pi}{180}\right)$ radians
$120° = \frac{2\pi}{3}$ radians
Jacy

a. How do you think Khadijah would find the radian measure equivalent to 30°?

b. How do you think Jacy would find the radian measure equivalent to 30°?

c. Which method, Khadijah's or Jacy's, do you find easiest to use?

Discuss answers to Problem 1 before introducing the definition of radian. Press students to explain why it is reasonable that the points marking off arcs of one radius length are collinear, determining the same central angle. They should be able to draw on their understanding of size transformations and similarity to explain that result.

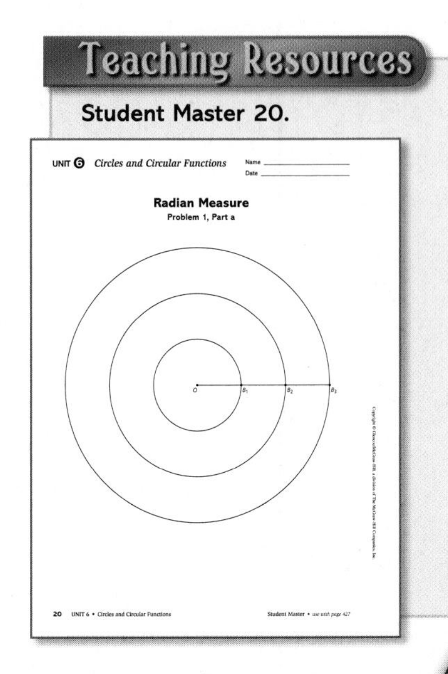

1 **a.** All three points A_1, A_2, and A_3 are collinear, so all three central angles $\angle A_nOB_n$ have the same measure. Although one radius measure or one radian is approximately 57.3°, students are likely to come up with measurements between 55° and 60°. You might press them to explain why 60° is too large—this would imply that the circumference of a circle is 6 radius lengths, but we know that it is in fact 2π, or about 6.28 radius lengths. Similarly, 55° is too small because $360° \div 55° = 6.55$ and we know that the circumference of a circle is not as large as 6.55 radius lengths. In fact, this line of reasoning could lead students (by a strategy of successive approximation) to a good estimate of the degree equivalent of one radian. $\frac{360}{x}r = 2\pi r$ when $x = \frac{360}{2\pi}$, so $x \approx 57.3$.

b. A 15-centimeter arc in a circle of radius 15 cm should again have degree measure between 55 and 60 (the same as those in Part a).

c. In general, all arcs of length r (on circles of radius r) will have the same degree measure. This follows from the fact that all circles with common center are similar. That is, a circle with radius r is related by a size transformation with scale factor r to the unit circle.

INSTRUCTIONAL NOTE As indicated above, you will probably want to have a class discussion of work on Problem 1 before moving ahead to the rest of the investigation. You can conclude that discussion by reviewing the definition of radian following Problem 1 and then asking students to work ahead. If students have access to *CPMP-Tools* software, you can direct them to work with it outside of class.

A bit of history can be introduced here. The division of a circle into 360 units (degrees) is attributed to the Babylonians who were quite accomplished mathematicians and astronomers over 4,000 years ago. Their number system had a base of 60. For a brief time in the 19th century, Napoleon declared an angle measure in which a unit was $\frac{1}{100}$th of a full revolution. Although metric measures survived for length, area, and volume, Napoleon's proposal did not survive for angle measure.

2 **a.** $\angle AOB$ has radian measure 2 and degree measure about 114.6.

b. $\angle AOB$ has radian measure 3 and degree measure about 171.9.

3 **a.** Khadijah would use $360° = 2\pi$, $\frac{30°}{360°} = \frac{1}{12}$, and $\frac{1}{12}(2\pi) = \frac{\pi}{6}$ radians.

b. Jacy would use $1° = \frac{\pi}{180}$ radians, so $30° = 30\left(\frac{\pi}{180}\right) = \frac{\pi}{6}$ radians.

c. Opinions may differ.

Unit 6

d. How do you think Khadijah would reason to find the degree measure equivalent to $\frac{\pi}{4}$ radians?

e. How do you think Jacy would reason to find the degree measure equivalent to $\frac{\pi}{4}$ radians?

4 Use any method you prefer to determine the equivalent angle measures in Parts a–c.

a. Find the measures in radians and revolutions equivalent to these degree measures.

i. 90° **ii.** 150° **iii.** 75° **iv.** 210°

b. Find the measures in degrees and revolutions equivalent to these radian measures.

i. $\frac{\pi}{3}$ **ii.** $\frac{5\pi}{4}$ **iii.** $\frac{\pi}{5}$ **iv.** $\frac{11\pi}{6}$

c. Complete a copy of the following table to show equivalent revolution, degree, and radian measurements. Save the table as a reference for later use.

Revolution/Degree/Radian Equivalents

Revolutions	0	?	?	?	?	?	?	?	?	?	?	?	?	?	?	?	1
Degrees	0	30	?	?	90	?	135	150	?	210	?	240	270	300	315	?	360
Radians	?	?	$\frac{\pi}{4}$	$\frac{\pi}{3}$	?	$\frac{2\pi}{3}$	?	?	π	?	$\frac{5\pi}{4}$	?	?	?	?	$\frac{11\pi}{6}$	?

5 Once again, consider the information provided by an engine tachometer.

a. The tachometer of a particular SUV traveling in overdrive on a level road at a speed of 60 mph reads about 2,100 rpm. Find the equivalent angular velocity in degrees per minute and in radians per minute.

b. The idle speed of the SUV is about 1,000 rpm. Find the equivalent angular velocity in degrees per minute and in radians per minute.

c. Suppose that the SUV engine has an angular velocity of $6{,}000\pi$ radians per minute.

i. What rpm reading would the tachometer show?

ii. What is the degrees-per-minute equivalent of that angular velocity?

To develop your understanding and skill in use of radian measures for angles and rotations, you might find it helpful to work with the "Explore Radians" custom tool in *CPMP-Tools*. This software shows angles, asks you to estimate the radian and degree measures of those angles, and then checks your estimates numerically and visually.

Unit 6

d. Khadijah might reason $\frac{\pi}{4}$ is $\frac{2\pi}{8}$, which is $\frac{1}{8}$ of 2π, and $\frac{1}{8}$ of 360° is 45°.

e. Jacy might reason $360° = 2\pi$ radians, so 1 radian $= \frac{180}{\pi}$ degrees.
Then $\frac{\pi}{4}$ radians $\cdot \frac{180 \text{ degrees}}{\pi \text{ radians}} = 45°$.

4 Students may use either method from Problem 3. Parts aiii and biii will not be used in the table in Part c.

a. **i.** $90° = \frac{\pi}{2}$ radians, or $\frac{1}{4}$ revolution

ii. $150° = \frac{5\pi}{6}$ radians, or $\frac{5}{12}$ revolution

iii. $75° = \frac{15\pi}{36}$ radians, or $\frac{15}{72}$ revolution

iv. $210° = \frac{7\pi}{6}$ radians, or $\frac{7}{12}$ revolution

b. **i.** $\frac{\pi}{3} = 60°$, or $\frac{1}{6}$ revolution

ii. $\frac{5\pi}{4} = 225°$, or $\frac{5}{8}$ revolution

iii. $\frac{\pi}{5} = 36°$, or $\frac{1}{10}$ revolution

iv. $\frac{11\pi}{6} = 330°$, or $\frac{11}{12}$ revolution

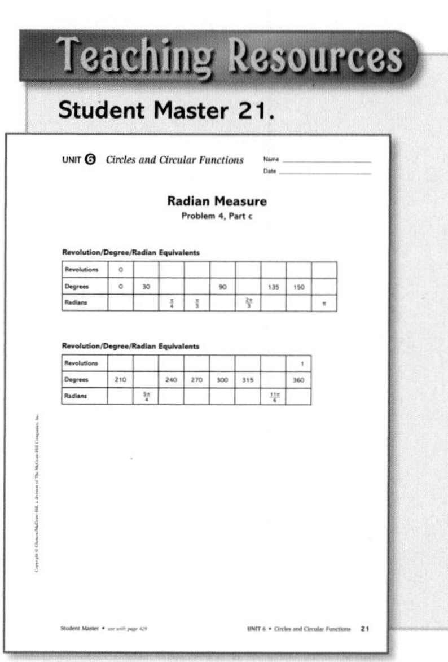
Teaching Resources

Student Master 21.

UNIT 6 *Circles and Circular Functions* Name ____ Date ____

Radian Measure

Problem 4, Part c

Revolution/Degree/Radian Equivalents

Revolutions	0								
Degrees	0	30			90		135	150	
Radians			$\frac{\pi}{4}$	$\frac{\pi}{3}$		$\frac{2\pi}{3}$			π

Revolution/Degree/Radian Equivalents

Revolutions								1
Degrees	210		240	270	300	315		360
Radians		$\frac{5\pi}{4}$					$\frac{11\pi}{6}$	

c. **Revolution/Degree/Radian Equivalents**

Revolutions	0	$\frac{1}{12}$	$\frac{1}{8}$	$\frac{1}{6}$	$\frac{1}{4}$	$\frac{1}{3}$	$\frac{3}{8}$	$\frac{5}{12}$	$\frac{1}{2}$	$\frac{7}{12}$	$\frac{5}{8}$	$\frac{2}{3}$	$\frac{3}{4}$	$\frac{5}{6}$	$\frac{7}{8}$	$\frac{11}{12}$	1
Degrees	0	30	45	60	90	120	135	150	180	210	225	240	270	300	315	330	360
Radians	0	$\frac{\pi}{6}$	$\frac{\pi}{4}$	$\frac{\pi}{3}$	$\frac{\pi}{2}$	$\frac{2\pi}{3}$	$\frac{3\pi}{4}$	$\frac{5\pi}{6}$	π	$\frac{7\pi}{6}$	$\frac{5\pi}{4}$	$\frac{4\pi}{3}$	$\frac{3\pi}{2}$	$\frac{5\pi}{3}$	$\frac{7\pi}{4}$	$\frac{11\pi}{6}$	2π

Unit 6

5 **a.** 2,100 rpm $= 360 \cdot 2{,}100 = 756{,}000$ degrees per minute
2,100 rpm $= 2\pi \cdot 2{,}100 = 4{,}200\pi$ radians per minute
$\approx 13{,}195$ radians per minute

b. 1,000 rpm $= 360 \cdot 1{,}000 = 360{,}000$ degrees per minute
1,000 rpm $= 2\pi \cdot 1{,}000 = 2{,}000\pi$ radians per minute
$\approx 6{,}283$ radians per minute

c. **i.** $6{,}000\pi$ radians per minute $= \frac{6{,}000\pi}{2\pi} = 3{,}000$ rpm

ii. 3,000 rpm $= 360 \cdot 3{,}000 = 1{,}080{,}000°$ per minute

Linking Angular and Linear Motion The mathematical appeal of radian measure lies in the way that it enables use of linear measurement ideas and tools to produce meaningful measurement of angles and rotations. For example, suppose that you wanted to measure $\angle AOB$ and the only available tool was a tape measure marked off in inches.

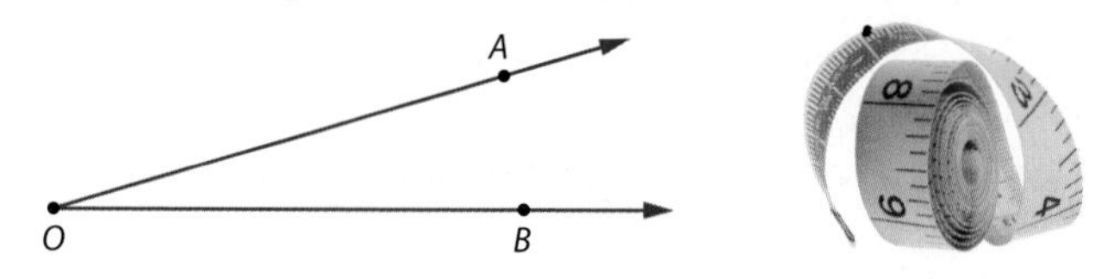

To measure the angle in radians, you could draw a circle with center O and radius equal to the unit segment on the tape measure. Then wrap the tape measure around the circle, starting where $\overline{OB}$ meets the circle and noting the point on the tape measure where $\overline{OA}$ meets the circle.

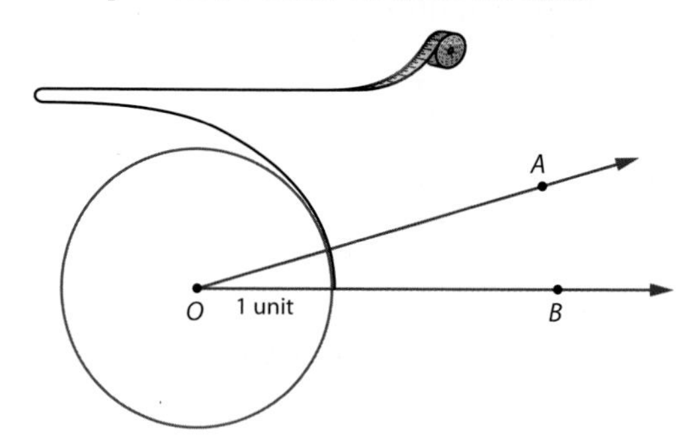

The arc length indicated on the tape measure will be the radian measure of the angle.

The mathematical description of what you have done to measure the angle in radians is to wrap a number line around a circle. If you imagine continuing that wrapping of a number line around a circle (in both directions from the original point of contact), the result is a correspondence between points on the number line and points on the circle.

If you imagine the angle and the circle located on vertical and horizontal coordinate axes, each point has x- and y-coordinates—the cosine and sine of the measure of the angle, respectively. In this way, it is possible to define these trigonometric functions with domain all real numbers.

6 Consider first the cosine function, the correspondence between points on the number line and the x-coordinates of points on the unit circle.

a. What pattern of change would you expect in values of the cosine function as the positive number line is wrapped in a counterclockwise direction around the unit circle starting at $(1, 0)$? How would that pattern appear in a plot of $(t, \cos t)$ values?

b. What pattern of change would you expect in values of the cosine function as the negative real number line is wrapped in a clockwise direction around the unit circle starting at $(1, 0)$? How would that pattern appear in a plot of $(t, \cos t)$ values?

Unit 6

430 UNIT 6 • Circles and Circular Functions

INSTRUCTIONAL NOTE The following development of the *wrapping function* begins with a fairly long discussion of how mathematicians think about the connection between radian measure, the trigonometric functions cosine and sine, and the real number line. Since this section of the investigation will probably require a significant segment of class time on its own, you will probably want to have a summarizing discussion of the results from the revolutions/degrees/radians work before moving ahead.

Then you could launch this next work by indicating that the goal ahead is to find a way to think about cosine and sine as functions with real number domains—just like the linear, exponential, power, polynomial, and rational functions that have been studied in earlier work. The wrapping metaphor suggests attaching to each point of a number line the values of cos *x* and sin *x*, then unwinding the number line and at each point of the now straight *x*-axis plotting points corresponding to the values of cos *x* and sin *x* that have been attached by the wrapping. With that introduction, probably accompanied by reference to the given graphic or something similar, you can set the students to work on Problems 6 and 7.

To avoid possible confusion with *x* as a variable in the (*x*, *y*) coordinates of points on the unit circle, we have introduced the letter *t* to label the independent variable. You might point out that out, indicating the rationale of avoiding confusion by multiple use of *x* and that *t* will often be used to represent *time* as an independent variable.

6 **a–d.** The graphs will look like those below.

e. The suggested limits on the independent variable were multiples of 2π because the cosine function repeats its pattern of values in periods (term to be defined technically shortly) of length 2π.

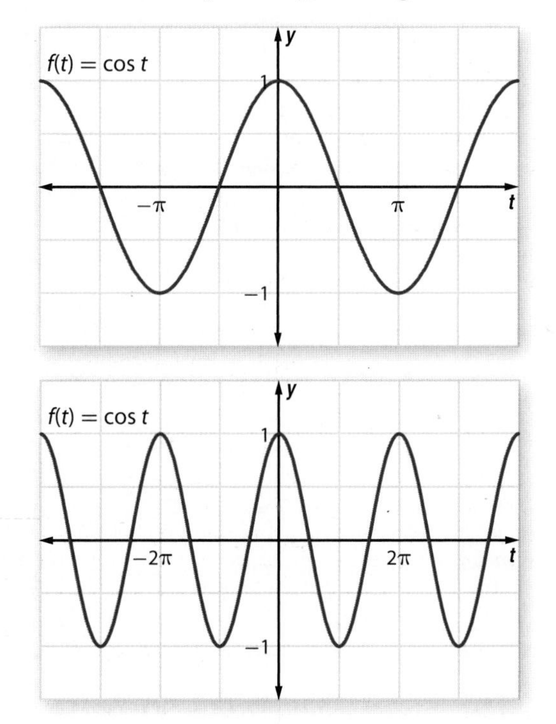

INSTRUCTIONAL NOTE
Press students to answer Parts a and b in Problems 6 and 7 with informal sketches before turning to their graphing tools.

c. Set your graphing calculator or computer software in radian mode. Graph cos t for $-2\pi \leq t \leq 2\pi$ to test your ideas in Parts a and b.

d. What would you expect to appear in the graphing window if the lower and upper bounds for t were reset to $-4\pi \leq t \leq 4\pi$?

e. Why were the suggested upper and lower bounds for the graphing windows multiples of 2π?

7 Consider next the sine function, the correspondence between points on the number line and the y-coordinates of points on the unit circle.

a. What pattern of change would you expect in values of the sine function as the positive number line is wrapped in a counterclockwise direction around the unit circle starting at (1, 0)? How would that pattern appear in a plot of (t, *sin* t) values?

b. What pattern of change would you expect in values of the sine function as the negative real number line is wrapped in a clockwise direction around the unit circle starting at (1, 0)? How would that pattern appear in a plot of (t, *sin* t) values?

c. Set your graphing calculator or computer software in radian mode. Graph sin t for $-2\pi \leq t \leq 2\pi$ to test your ideas in Parts a and b.

d. What would you expect to appear in the graphing window if the lower and upper bounds for t were reset to $-4\pi \leq t \leq 4\pi$?

e. In Parts c and d, the upper and lower bounds given for the graphing windows are multiples of 2π. What are advantages of this form?

Summarize the Mathematics

In this investigation, you learned about measuring angles using radians. The radian is a unit for measuring angles that is useful because it connects length and angular measurement.

a Describe how to draw an angle that measures 1 radian.

b How are angle measurements in revolutions, radians, and degrees related to each other?

c If an angle has measure r in radians, d in degrees, and v in revolutions what rule expresses:

- **i.** r as a function of d?
- **ii.** r as a function of v?
- **iii.** d as a function of r?
- **iv.** v as a function of r?

d How are the cosine and sine functions defined for radian measures or real numbers? How are the resulting numeric and graphic patterns of values for those functions similar to or different from those when the functions are defined for degrees?

Be prepared to discuss your responses with the class.

7 **a–d.** The graphs will look like those below.

e. The suggested limits on the independent variable were multiples of 2π because the sine function repeats its pattern of values in periods of length 2π.

NOTE Solutions to Problem 6 Parts c–e are on page T430.

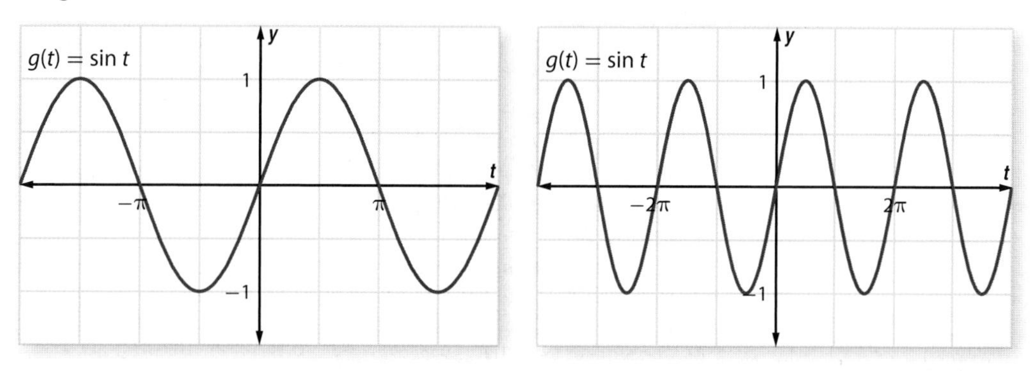

Summarize the Mathematics

a Responses may vary, but students should describe an arc equal in length to the radius and indicate that the central angle intercepted by that arc has measure 1 radian.

b 1 revolution $= 2\pi$ radians $= 360°$

c
i. $r = \frac{d}{57.3}$

ii. $r = 2\pi v$

iii. $d = 57.3r$

iv. $v = \frac{r}{2\pi}$

d The cos t and sin t functions are defined as the x- and y-coordinates of points on a unit circle located by measuring (in radians) an arc of length t from the point (1, 0). The patterns of function values for cosine and sine defined on radians or degrees are basically the same. One is just a one-dimensional stretch $(x, y) \rightarrow \left(\frac{\pi x}{180}, y\right)$ of the other (degrees graph to radians graph).

Teaching Resources

Transparency Master 22.

UNIT 6 *Circles and Circular Functions*

Summarize the Mathematics

In this investigation, you learned about measuring angles using radians. The radian is a unit for measuring angles that is useful because it connects length and angular measurement.

a Describe how to draw an angle that measures 1 radian.

b How are angle measurements in revolutions, radians, and degrees related to each other?

c If an angle has measure r in radians, d in degrees, and v in revolutions what rule expresses:

i. r as a function of d?

ii. r as a function of v?

iii. d as a function of r?

iv. v as a function of r?

d How are the cosine and sine functions defined for radian measures or real numbers? How are the resulting numeric and graphic patterns of values for those functions similar to or different from those when the functions are defined for degrees?

Be prepared to share your descriptions and reasoning with the class.

Unit 6

MATH TOOLKIT
Ask students to write a description and draw a diagram showing the concept of radian measure. Also, have them make a table of equivalent measures for angles using radians expressed as fractions of π and in degrees. (See Problem 4 Part c of Investigation 3.) This resource should be available for reference until the radian measures become familiar.

Check Your Understanding

Suppose that one of the wind turbines shown in the Check Your Understanding of Investigation 1 has a driver pulley with 6-foot diameter attached by a belt to a follower pulley with 4-foot diameter.

a. If the driver pulley turns at 3 revolutions per minute:

- **i.** what is the angular velocity of the driver pulley in radians per minute?
- **ii.** what is the angular velocity of the follower pulley in radians per minute?

c. Suppose that economic use of the wind turbine to generate electric power requires the follower pulley to turn at a rate of 90π radians per minute. How fast, in radians per minute, must the driver pulley turn to accomplish this rate?

d. Draw sketches and use geometric reasoning to find exact values of the sine and cosine functions when the input values are the following radian measures or real numbers. Check your answers using technology or the table you completed in Problem 4.

i. $\frac{3\pi}{4}$ **ii.** π **iii.** $\frac{7\pi}{6}$ **iv.** $\frac{5\pi}{3}$

Investigation 4 Patterns of Periodic Change

Tracking the location of seats on a spinning Ferris wheel shows how the cosine and sine functions can be used to describe rotation of circular objects. Wrapping a number line around a circle shows how the radius of the circle can be used to measure angles, arcs, and rotations in radians and how the cosine and sine can be defined as functions of real numbers. In both cases, the resulting functions had repeating graph patterns that are called *sinusoids*.

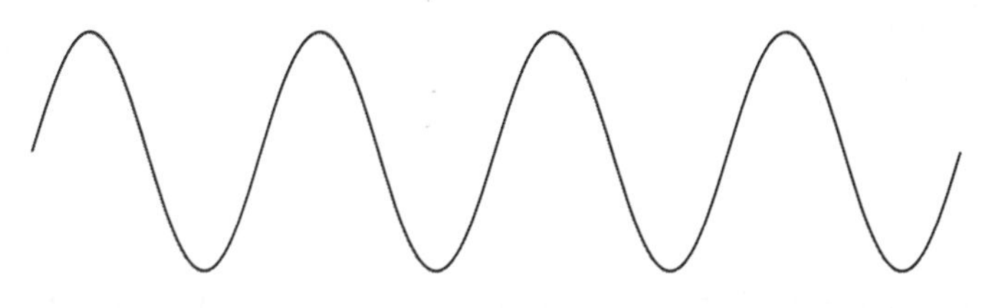

Many important variables that change over time have sinusoidal graphs. As you work on the problems of this investigation, look for answers to the following question:

How can the cosine and sine functions be modified to represent the variety of important patterns of periodic change?

432 UNIT 6 • Circles and Circular Functions

Check Your Understanding

a. **i.** $3(2\pi) = 6\pi$ radians per minute

ii. $\left(\frac{6}{4}\right)(3)(2\pi) = 9\pi$ radians per minute

b. 90 radians per minute is 10 times the angular velocity of the driver pulley found in Part ai. So, the driver pulley must turn at 60π radians per minute.

c. Students should make a sketch for each part and use geometric reasoning to obtain exact values.

i. $\left(\cos \frac{3\pi}{4}, \sin \frac{3\pi}{4}\right) = \left(-\frac{\sqrt{2}}{2}, \frac{\sqrt{2}}{2}\right)$

ii. $(\cos \pi, \sin \pi) = (-1, 0)$

iii. $\left(\cos \frac{7\pi}{6}, \sin \frac{7\pi}{6}\right) = \left(-\frac{\sqrt{3}}{2}, -\frac{1}{2}\right)$

iv. $\left(\cos \frac{5\pi}{3}, \sin \frac{5\pi}{3}\right) = \left(\frac{1}{2}, -\frac{\sqrt{3}}{2}\right)$

Investigation 4 Patterns of Periodic Change

Now that students have an idea about the shape of circular functions, they will investigate the more general functions $y = a \sin bx + c$ and $y = a \cos bx + c$ in greater detail. Students will look at how changes in amplitude and period express themselves in the equations and graphs of sine and cosine curves and how those variations on the basic cosine and sine functions are useful in modeling a variety of periodic patterns.

The investigation will be greatly facilitated if students have access to the CAS in *CPMP-Tools* or other software that has the capability of changing parameters and viewing corresponding graphs. See Problem 7.

1 **a.** The maximum for $\cos \theta$ is 1 and the minimum is -1. The maximum for $1.5 \cos \theta$ is 1.5 and the minimum is -1.5.

i. Maximum values for both functions occur when $\theta = 0°$ and at integer multiples of 360°. Minimum values of both functions occur when $\theta = 180°$ and at all other odd integer multiples of 180°.

ii. Maximum values for both functions occur when $\theta = 0$ radians and at integer multiples of 2π radians. Minimum values of both functions occur when $\theta = \pi$ radians and at all odd integer multiples of π radians.

b. Both $\cos \theta$ and $1.5 \cos \theta$ intersect the θ-axis at the same points.

i. The functions intersect the θ-axis at $\theta = 90°$ and at $\theta = 90° + 180n°$ for any integer n.

ii. The functions intersect the θ-axis at $\theta = \frac{\pi}{2}$ radians and at $\theta = \frac{\pi}{2} + \pi n$ radians for any integer n.

c. The maximum for $\sin \theta$ is 1 and the minimum is -1. The maximum for $1.5 \sin \theta$ is 1.5 and the minimum is -1.5.

i. Maximum values for both functions occur when $\theta = 90°$ and at $\theta = 90° + 360n°$ for any integer n. Minimum values of both functions occur when $\theta = 270°$ and at $\theta = 270° + 360n°$ for any integer n.

Unit 6

A Family of Ferris Wheels The Ferris wheel that you analyzed during work on Investigation 2 had a radius of one decameter and an unspecified angular velocity. To model the motion of wheels with different radii and to account for different rates of rotation, it is necessary to construct functions that are variations on the basic cosine and sine functions.

1. If a Ferris wheel has radius 1.5 decameters (15 meters), the functions $1.5 \cos \theta$ and $1.5 \sin \theta$ give x- and y-coordinates after rotation of θ for a seat that starts at (1.5, 0). Compare the graphs of these new coordinate functions with the graphs of the basic cosine and sine functions.
   a. Find the maximum and minimum points of the graphs of $\cos \theta$ and $1.5 \cos \theta$ when:
      i. θ is measured in degrees.
      ii. θ is measured in radians.
   b. Find the θ-axis intercepts of the graphs of $\cos \theta$ and $1.5 \cos \theta$ when:
      i. θ is measured in degrees.
      ii. θ is measured in radians.
   c. Find the maximum and minimum points of the graphs of $\sin \theta$ and $1.5 \sin \theta$ when:
      i. θ is measured in degrees.
      ii. θ is measured in radians.
   d. Find the θ-axis intercepts of the graphs of $\sin \theta$ and $1.5 \sin \theta$ when:
      i. θ is measured in degrees.
      ii. θ is measured in radians.
   e. How would the maximum and minimum points and the θ-axis intercept change if the Ferris wheel being modeled had radius a and the coordinate functions were $a \cos \theta$ and $a \sin \theta$?

2. When riding a Ferris wheel, customers are probably more nervous about their height above the ground than their distance from the vertical axis of the wheel. Suppose that a large wheel has radius 25 meters, the center of the wheel is located 30 meters above the ground, and the wheel starts in motion when seat S is at the "3 o'clock" position.

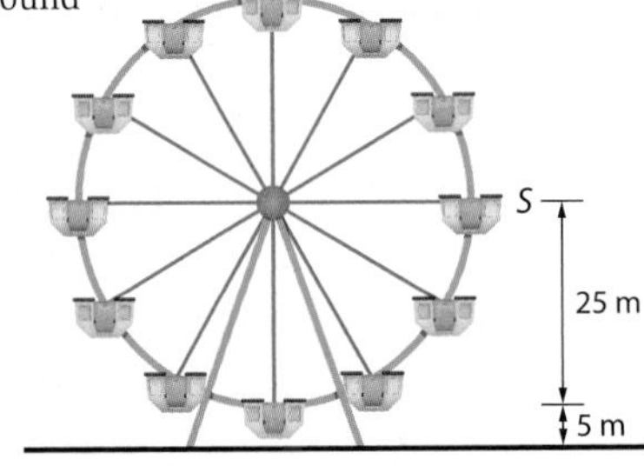

   a. Modify the sine function to get a rule for $h(\theta)$ that gives the *height* of seat S in meters after rotation of θ. Compare the graph of this height function with the graph of $\sin \theta$.
   b. Find the maximum and minimum points on the graphs of $\sin \theta$ and $h(\theta)$ when:
      i. θ is measured in degrees.
      ii. θ is measured in radians.

Unit 6

ii. Maximum values for both functions occur when $\theta = \frac{\pi}{2}$ radians and when $\theta = \frac{\pi}{2} + 2\pi n$ radians for any integer n. Minimum values of both functions occur when $\theta = \frac{3\pi}{2}$ radians and when $\theta = \frac{3\pi}{2} + 2\pi n$ radians for any integer n.

d. Both sin θ and 1.5 sin θ intersect the θ-axis at the same points.

i. The functions intersect the θ-axis at $\theta = 0°$ and at $\theta = 180n°$ for any integer n.

ii. The functions intersect the θ-axis at $\theta = 0$ radians and at $\theta = \pi n$ radians for any integer n.

e. Multiplying the cosine function or the sine function by a nonzero constant a will change the maximum and minimum values by a factor of a but will have no effect on the location of points where the graphs intersect the horizontal or θ-axis.

NOTE Solutions to Problem 1 Parts a–ci are on page T432.

INSTRUCTIONAL NOTE The rule for $h(\theta)$ is written in standard notation in Problem 2 Part a. Students might be uncertain about the order of operations implied by that form. To make the notational convention clear, you might point out that sin θ is really shorthand for a function sin(θ), so to evaluate the expression 25 sin θ + 30, you find sin(θ) first, then multiply by 25, and then add 30.

2 **a.** $h(\theta) = 25 \sin \theta + 30$ will give the height after rotation of any angle θ.

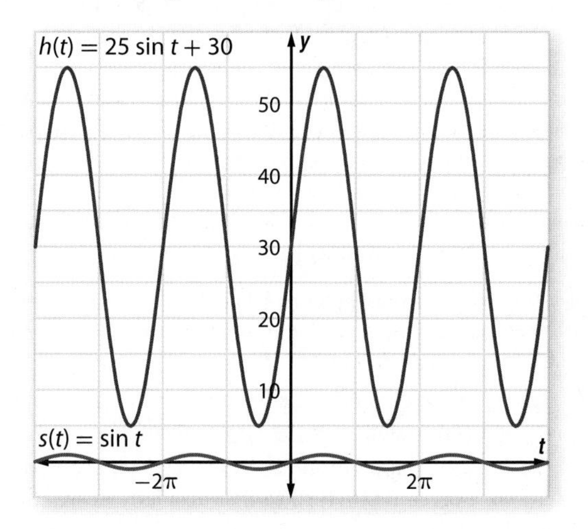

b. The maximum and minimum values of sin θ are 1 and −1, respectively. The maximum and minimum values of and $h(\theta) = 25 \sin \theta + 30$ are 55 and 5, respectively.

i. Maximum values for both functions occur when $\theta = 90°$ and at $\theta = 90° + 360n°$ for any integer n. Minimum values of both functions occur when $\theta = 270°$ and at $\theta = 270° + 360n°$.

ii. Maximum values for both functions occur when $\theta = \frac{\pi}{2}$ radians and when $\theta = \frac{\pi}{2} + 2\pi n$ radians for any integer n.
Minimum values of both functions occur when $\theta = \frac{3\pi}{2}$ radians and when $\theta = \frac{3\pi}{2} + 2\pi n$ radians.

Unit 6

c. Find the θ-axis intercepts on the graphs of $\sin \theta$ and $h(\theta)$.

d. How would the maximum and minimum points and the θ-axis intercept change if the Ferris wheel being modeled had radius a and its center was c meters above the ground? Why is $c > a$?

Functions with sinusoidal graphs all have patterns that repeat as values of the independent variable increase. Functions that have that kind of repeating pattern are called **periodic functions**. The **period** is the length of the shortest interval of values for the independent variable on which the repeating pattern of function values occurs. If a periodic function has maximum and minimum values, half the absolute value of the difference between those values is called its **amplitude**. In addition to the change in amplitude of $\sin \theta$ used to model Ferris wheel motion, the graph of $h(\theta)$ appears to involve a shift of that graph upward. That upward shift of 30 meters is called the ***y*-displacement**.

3 The functions $\cos \theta$, $\sin \theta$, $1.5 \cos \theta$, $1.5 \sin \theta$, and $h(\theta)$ all have the same period. Find that common period and the amplitude of each function when:

a. θ is measured in degrees.

b. θ is measured in radians.

4 How are the period and the amplitude of $f(\theta) = a \cos \theta + c$ and $g(\theta) = a \sin \theta + c$ related to the values of the numbers a and c?

Period and Frequency In various problems of this lesson, you have seen how to find the location of points on a rotating circle from information about the starting point and the angle of rotation. For actual rotating wheels, it is much easier to measure elapsed *time* than the *angle* of rotation. The link between these two variables is *angular velocity*.

For constant angular velocity, the angle of rotation varies directly with the elapsed time. So, it is often convenient to describe the location of points on a wheel as a function of time. Because radian measure connects points on a number or time line axis to points on a circle with a common unit of measurement, it is customary to use radian measure in analyzing circular motion as a function of time.

5 Suppose that the height of a Ferris wheel seat changes in a pattern that can be modeled by the function $h(t) = 25 \sin t + 30$, where time is in minutes and height is in meters.

a. What are the period and amplitude of $h(t)$? What do those values tell about motion of the Ferris wheel?

b. If a seat starts out in the "3 o'clock" position, how long will it take the seat to first return to that position? At what times will it revisit that position?

c. What is the angular velocity of this wheel:

i. in revolutions per minute? (This is also called the **frequency** of the periodic motion.)

ii. in degrees per minute?

iii. in radians per minute?

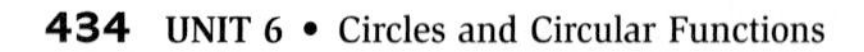
434 UNIT 6 • Circles and Circular Functions

Unit 6

c. The graph of sin θ intersects the θ-axis where described in Problem 1. The graph of $h(\theta)$ does not intersect the θ-axis at all.

d. The function modeling height of a seat on the new Ferris wheel would have rule $h(\theta) = a \sin \theta + c$. The maximum and minimum heights would be $c + a$ and $c - a$ respectively, but they would occur at the same values of θ as sin θ itself. There would be no θ-axis intercepts because c must be greater than a or the wheel would not rotate.

3 a. The period of all four functions is 360°. The amplitude of the function is the coefficient on the trigonometric function, either 1 or 1.5.

b. The period of all four functions is 2π radians. The amplitudes are unaffected by change of units for θ.

4 The period is unaffected by the parameters a and c, they have the effect of stretching and/or sliding the graphs in the vertical direction. The value of a changes the amplitude by a factor of $|a|$, but c does not affect amplitude because it has the effect of translating a graph up or down vertically.

INSTRUCTIONAL NOTE
Students might be puzzled by the use of $|a|$, since all examples so far have involved $a > 0$. There are some times when a negative multiplier is useful. The graphs are reflections across the θ-axis of the original function graphs.

5 a. Period of $h(t)$ is 2π minutes, or about 6 minutes 17 seconds. This means that this large wheel makes one complete revolution in a bit more than 6 minutes. The amplitude of $h(t)$ is 25, meaning that the wheel has radius 25 meters.

b. The seat first returns to the starting "3 o'clock" position after 6.28 minutes and at intervals of 6.28 minutes thereafter.

c. i. $\frac{1}{6.28} = 0.16$ rpm ii. $\frac{360}{6.28} = 57.3$ degrees per minute

iii. $\frac{2\pi}{2\pi} = 1$ radian per minute

6 a. $h(t) = 15 \sin 0.5t + 17$:

Start height: 17 meters
Amplitude: 15 meters is radius of wheel
Period: $4\pi \approx 12.57$ minutes is time for one revolution
Angular velocity/frequency: $\frac{1}{4\pi} \approx 0.08$ rpm

b. $h(t) = 24 \cos 2t + 27$:

Start height: 51 meters
Amplitude: 24 meters is radius of wheel
Period: $\pi \approx 3.14$ minutes is time for one revolution
Angular velocity/frequency: $\frac{1}{\pi} \approx 0.32$ rpm

c. $h(t) = 12 \sin 1.5t + 13$:

Start height: 13 meters
Amplitude: 12 meters is radius of wheel
Period: $\frac{4\pi}{3} \approx 4.2$ minutes is time for one revolution
Angular velocity/frequency: $\frac{1}{\frac{4\pi}{3}} \approx 0.24$ rpm

d. $h(t) = -12 \cos t + 14$:

Start height: 2 meters
Amplitude: 12 meters is radius of wheel
Period: $2\pi \approx 6.28$ minutes is time for one revolution
Angular velocity/frequency: $\frac{1}{2\pi} \approx 0.16$ rpm

INSTRUCTIONAL NOTE
Problem 6 asks students to explore effects of several parameters in modifying the basic cosine and sine functions. For efficiency, it might be most productive to divide the work on the four parts among different groups in your class or different individuals in groups and then have each present its findings for discussion by the class.

TECHNOLOGY NOTE
If you have a few computers available, groups could use *CPMP-Tools* CAS software when they reach Problem 7 Part b. Once all groups have had an opportunity to explore the effects of the parameters, ideas could be summarized in a class discussion.

6 Suppose that the height (in meters) of seats on different Ferris wheels changes over time (in minutes) according to the functions given below. For each function:

- find the height of the seat when motion of the wheel begins.
- find the amplitude of $h(t)$. Explain what it tells about motion of the wheel.
- find the period of $h(t)$. Explain what it tells about motion of the wheel.
- find the angular velocity of the wheel in revolutions per minute—the frequency of $h(t)$.

a. $h(t) = 15 \sin 0.5t + 17$ **b.** $h(t) = 24 \cos 2t + 27$

c. $h(t) = 12 \sin 1.5t + 13$ **d.** $h(t) = -12 \cos t + 14$

7 In Problems 5 and 6, you analyzed properties of functions with rules in the general form

$$h(t) = a \sin bt + c \quad \text{and} \quad h(t) = a \cos bt + c.$$

a. How do each of the values a, b, and c seem to affect the graphs of the functions?

b. Check your ideas by reasoning about the function rules and by graphing examples with a calculator or by using the parameter variation capability of *CPMP-Tools* CAS. Be sure your answer accounts for both positive and negative values of a and c.

Modeling Periodic Change over Time Variations of the basic cosine and sine functions can be used to model the patterns of change in many different scientific and practical situations. The next three problems ask you to analyze familiar situations.

8 Pendulums are among the simplest but most useful examples of periodic motion. Once set in motion, the arm of the pendulum swings left and right of a vertical axis. The angle of displacement from vertical is a periodic function of time that depends on the length of the pendulum and its initial release point.

Suppose that the function $d(t) = 35 \cos 2t$ gives the displacement from vertical (in degrees) of the tire swing pendulum shown at the right as a function of time (in seconds).

a. What are the amplitude, period, and frequency of $d(t)$? What does each tell about the motion of the swing?

b. If the motion of a different swing is modeled by $f(t) = 45 \cos \pi t$, what are the amplitude, period, and frequency of $f(t)$? What does each tell about the motion of that swing?

c. Why does it make sense to use variations of the circular function $\cos t$ to model pendulum motion?

d. What function $g(t)$ would model the motion of a pendulum that is released from a displacement of 18° right of vertical and swings with a frequency of 0.25 cycles per second (a period of 4 seconds)?

7 **a.** The value of a stretches (or shrinks) the graph by a factor of $|a|$; the value of b changes the period and frequency—making the period longer if $b < 1$ and making it shorter if $b > 1$; the value of c is the y-displacement of the graph (after vertical and horizontal stretching and shrinking).

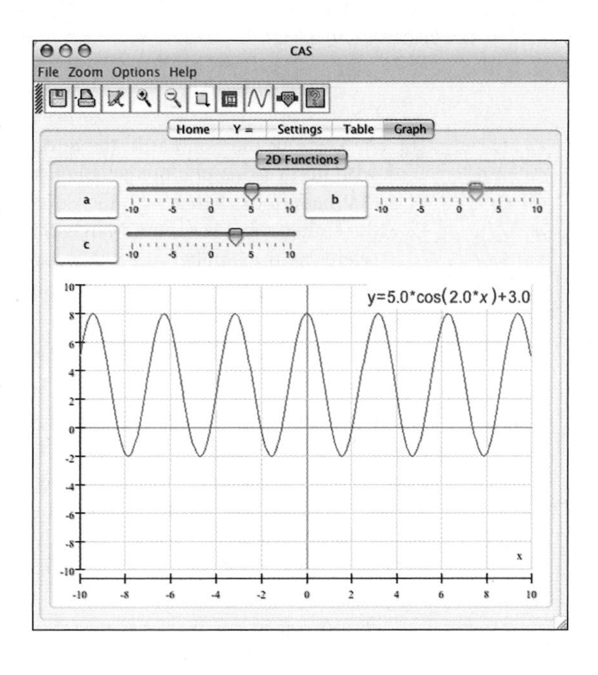

Negative values of a cause reflection of the graph across the horizontal t-axis.

Negative values of c cause the graph to slide downward.

b. The stretching effect of a makes sense because you are essentially multiplying each y value by a factor of a. The vertical sliding effect of c makes sense because you are essentially adding the same number to each y value. The counterintuitive effect of the value of b can be rationalized by thinking that a value of $b > 1$ essentially speeds up time and makes the function run through its periodic pattern more quickly. Values of $b < 1$ essentially slow down the passage of time and make the function run through its periodic pattern more slowly.

NOTE The solution to Problem 6 is on page T434.

8 **a.** The amplitude is 35 and it tells that the pendulum swings from 35° right of vertical to 35° left of vertical.

The period is π seconds and it tells that it takes about 3.14 seconds for the tire to swing from right to left and back.

The frequency is $\frac{1}{\pi}$ and it tells that the swing makes about 0.32 complete swings per second. Converting this to a more natural unit, it would be about 19 swings per minute.

b. The amplitude of this different swing is 45 and it tells that pendulum swings from 45° right of vertical to 45° left of vertical.

The period is 2 seconds and it tells that it takes 2 seconds for the tire to swing from right to left and back.

The frequency is $\frac{1}{2}$ and it tells that the swing makes about 0.5 complete swings per second. Converting this to a more natural unit, it would be 30 swings per minute.

c. Cosine is the natural function to begin with because motion of a pendulum, like a swing, usually begins when the pendulum is pulled to its maximum deflection from vertical. Cosine has its maximum value when $t = 0$.

d. $g(t) = 18 \cos \frac{\pi}{2}t$

Unit 6

9 At every location on Earth, the number of hours of daylight varies with the seasons in a predictable way. One convenient way to model that pattern of change is to measure time in days, beginning with the spring equinox (about March 21) as $t = 0$. With that frame of reference, the number of daylight hours in Boston, Massachusetts is given by $d(t) = 3.5 \sin \frac{2\pi}{365}t + 12.5$.

a. What are the amplitude, period, and frequency of $d(t)$? What do those values tell about the pattern of change in daylight during a year in Boston?

b. What are the maximum and the minimum numbers of hours of daylight in Boston? At what times in the year do they occur?

c. If the function giving the number of daylight hours in Point Barrow, Alaska, had the form $f(t) = a \sin bt + c$, how would you expect the values of a, b, and c to be related to the corresponding numbers in the rule giving daylight hours in Boston?

d. Why does it make sense that the function giving daylight hours at points on Earth should involve the circular function $\sin t$?

10 Oscilloscopes are common scientific instruments for display of the periodic variation in pressure and electronic waves that carry sound and light. For example, the function

$$V(t) = 170 \sin 120\pi t$$

gives the voltage in a standard alternating current electrical line as a function of time in seconds.

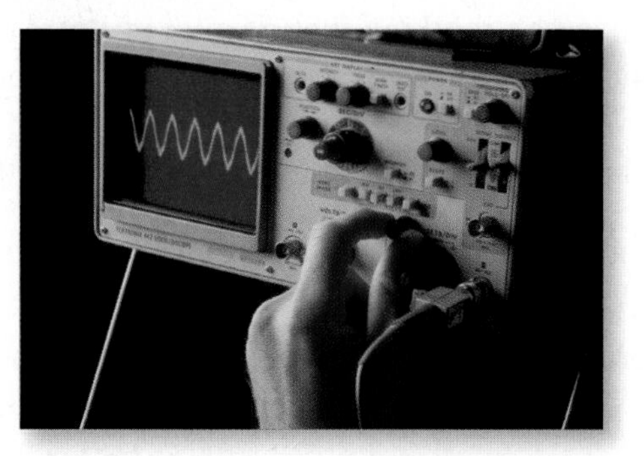

a. What maximum and minimum voltage are implied by the function $V(t)$?

b. What period and frequency are implied by the rule for $V(t)$? (That standard frequency is called **one Hertz**.)

436 UNIT 6 • Circles and Circular Functions

9 **a.** The amplitude is 3.5 meaning that the range from shortest to longest daylight hours is 7 hours over the year.

The period is 365 meaning that the pattern of change in daylight hours repeats every 365 days.

Frequency is $\frac{1}{365}$ meaning that each day represents $\frac{1}{365}$ parts of a full cycle.

b. The maximum number of daylight hours is 16 hours and it occurs about 91 days after the spring equinox, or June 21.

The minimum number of daylight hours is 9 and it occurs about 273 days after the spring equinox, or December 21.

c. Since Point Barrow is in the far north of Earth, one would expect greater variation in the number of daylight hours but the same period. There are days that are almost completely dark and others that are almost completely light. So, the amplitude a would be greater for the Point Barrow model than the Boston model. Since the period is the same, 365 days, b would be the same as in the model for Boston. The values of a and c for the Point Barrow model would probably be nearly equal and about 12.

d. It makes sense that daylight hours should be modeled by a circular function because the Earth is nearly a sphere and its orbit around the Sun is nearly a circle.

10 **a.** Maximum voltage is 170 volts and minimum is −170 volts.

b. The period is $\frac{1}{60}$ seconds and frequency is 60 cycles per second, or 60 Hz.

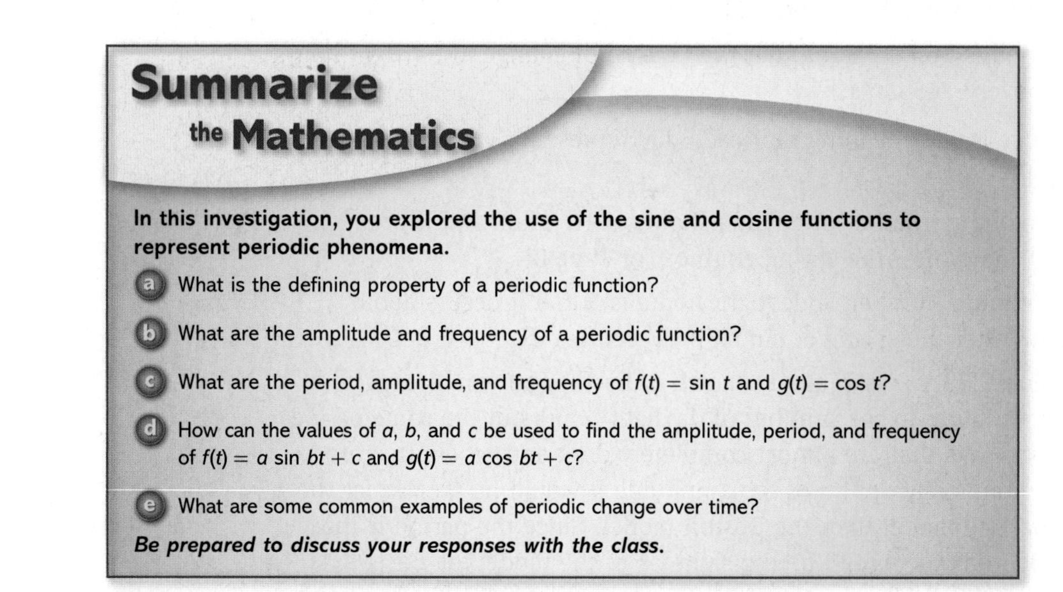

Summarize the Mathematics

In this investigation, you explored the use of the sine and cosine functions to represent periodic phenomena.

a. What is the defining property of a periodic function?

b. What are the amplitude and frequency of a periodic function?

c. What are the period, amplitude, and frequency of $f(t) = \sin t$ and $g(t) = \cos t$?

d. How can the values of a, b, and c be used to find the amplitude, period, and frequency of $f(t) = a \sin bt + c$ and $g(t) = a \cos bt + c$?

e. What are some common examples of periodic change over time?

Be prepared to discuss your responses with the class.

Check Your Understanding

Portions of periodic graphs are shown below with windows $-4\pi \leq x \leq 4\pi$ and $-6 \leq y \leq 6$. Without using technology, match each graph to one of the given functions. (Not all function rules will be used.) In each case, explain the reason for your choice.

I $y = 3 \sin x$	II $y = 3 \cos x$	III $y = 3 + \sin x$
IV $y = -3 \sin x$	V $y = -3 \cos x$	VI $y = \sin 3x$

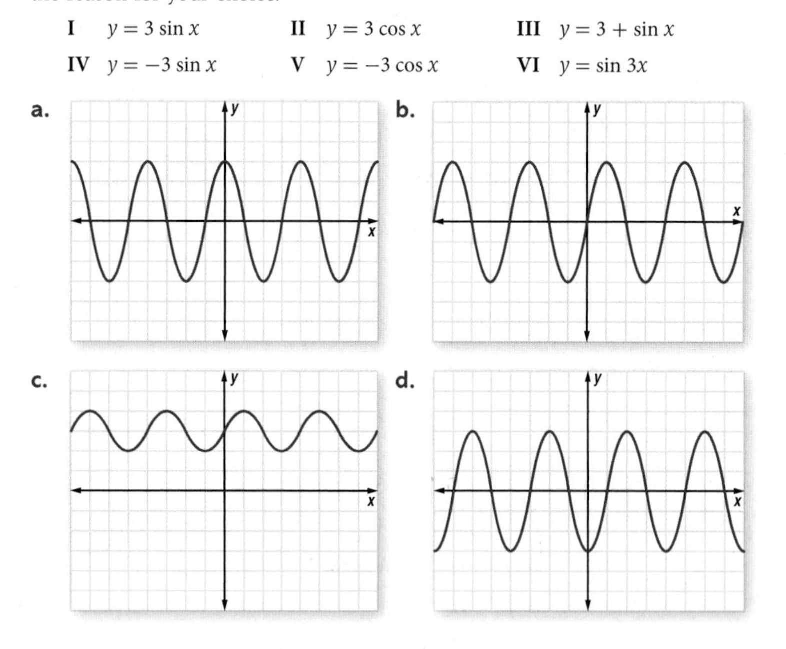

Unit 6

ADDITIONAL RESOURCES The examples students have studied in problems of this investigation show key properties and uses of the sine and cosine functions when they are used to model periodic change over time. To see other examples and to experiment with rules in the form $a \cos bt + c$ and $a \sin bt + c$, they may find it interesting to visit the Web site:
mathdemos.gcsu.edu/mathdemos/sinusoidapp/sinusoidapp.html

Summarize the Mathematics

a Periodic change refers to a pattern of change in the y values of a relationship between two variables that repeats itself over every x-interval of a given length.

b The amplitude is one half the positive difference between minimum and maximum values of the function. The frequency is the rate per unit of time at which the function repeats its basic pattern.

c Both the cosine and sine function have period 2π, amplitude 1, and frequency $\frac{1}{2\pi}$.

d For both functions, the amplitude is $|a|$, the period is $\frac{2\pi}{b}$, and the frequency is $\frac{b}{2\pi}$. The parameter c is the y-displacement and does not affect amplitude, period, or frequency.

e Examples in this lesson have included rotation of a Ferris wheel, swing of a pendulum, changes in hours of daylight during a year, and voltage in an alternating current circuit. Students should be encouraged to think of others.

Teaching Resources

Transparency Master 23.

UNIT 6 *Circles and Circular Functions*

Summarize the Mathematics

In this investigation, you explored the use of the sine and cosine functions to represent periodic phenomena.

a. What is the defining property of a periodic function?

b. What are the amplitude and frequency of a periodic function?

c. What are the period, amplitude, and frequency of $f(t) = \sin t$ and $g(t) = \cos t$?

d. How can the values of a, b, and c be used to find the amplitude, period, and frequency of $f(t) = a \sin bt + c$ and $g(t) = a \cos bt + c$?

e. What are some common examples of periodic change over time?

Be prepared to discuss your responses with the class.

Transparency Master • *use with page 437* UNIT 6 • Circles and Circular Functions 23

MATH TOOLKIT Students should write examples of a sine and a cosine function and sketch graphs of the functions. Then label the graphs with the amplitude, period, frequency, and y-displacement. Finally, explain how those four values are related to the function rule.

Unit 6

Check Your Understanding

a. II: $y = 3 \cos x$ The amplitude is 3, and the graph looks like $y = \cos x$ with a maximum of 3.

b. I: $y = 3 \sin x$ The amplitude is 3, and the graph looks like $y = \sin x$ with a maximum of 3.

c. III: $y = 3 + \sin x$ The graph is simply $y = \sin x$ shifted up 3 units.

d. V: $y = -3 \cos x$ The graph looks like the graph in Part a reflected across the x-axis.

On Your Own

Applications

1. Lena's mountain bike has 21 speeds. To get started, she shifts gears so that the chain connects the 42-tooth crankset with a 28-tooth rear-wheel sprocket.

   a. If Lena pedals at 40 rpm, at what rate do the rear sprocket and wheel turn?

   b. If Lena pedals at 40 rpm, how far will she travel in one minute if her bike has tires with 66-cm diameters?

   c. What is the relationship between the angular velocities of the pedal sprocket v_p and the rear wheel sprocket v_w?

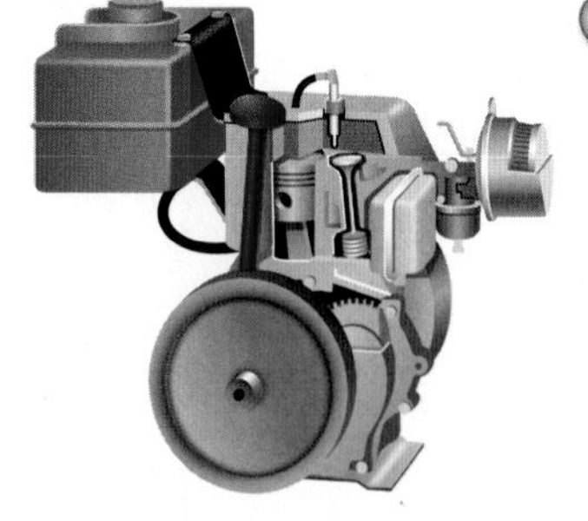

2. In go-carts, the engine driver sprocket is attached to a follower sprocket on the rear axle by a belt. These sprockets can have many different diameters depending upon course demands and safety.

   a. Sketch the situation in which an engine sprocket with a 7-cm diameter drives a rear-axle sprocket with a 10-cm diameter.

   b. Suppose that the engine is turning at 1,620 rpm.

      i. Find the angular velocity of the rear axle.

      ii. Find the go-cart's speed, in cm per minute and km per hour, if the rear wheels have a diameter of 28 cm.

   c. When rounding corners, a speed of 30 km per hour or less is needed to reduce lateral sliding. What engine speed in rpm is optimal?

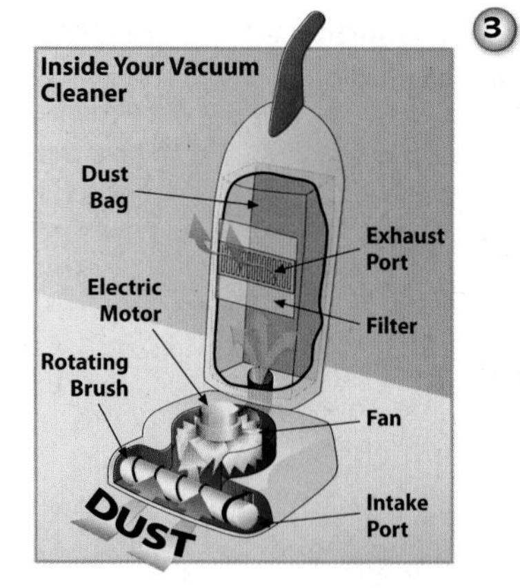

3. The operation of most vacuum cleaners depends on circular motion at several points in the vacuuming process. In one vacuum cleaner model, the rotating brush is 1.5 inches in diameter and is driven by a rubber belt attached to a driver pulley on the motor. The driver pulley is 0.5 inches in diameter. The belt is attached with a half twist, so that the rotating brush and the driver rotate in opposite directions.

   a. The rotating brush is designed to help pull dust from the floor into the vacuum cleaner. Should the rotating brush be turning clockwise or counterclockwise? Explain.

   b. Sketch this pulley system.

   c. What are the circumferences of the driver pulley and the rotating brush?

   d. How far does a point on the edge of the rotating brush travel in one revolution of the driver?

   e. If the driver pulley is turning 600 rpm, how fast is the rotating brush turning?

   f. Write a rule that shows the relationship between angular velocities of the engine drive shaft v_D and the rotating brush v_B.

438 UNIT 6 • Circles and Circular Functions

On Your Own

Applications

1 **a.** The rear sprocket turns at $40 \cdot \frac{3}{2} = 60$ rpm.

b. $60 \text{ rpm} \cdot \pi \cdot 66 \text{ cm} \approx 12{,}440.7 \text{ cm}$
$\approx 124.4 \text{ m}$

c. $v_w = 1.5v_p$ or $v_p = \frac{2}{3}v_w$

2 **a.**

7 cm   10 cm

b. **i.** Angular velocity of rear axle: $\frac{7}{10} \cdot 1{,}620 \text{ rpm} = 1{,}134 \text{ rpm}$

ii. Diameter (in km): 0.00028 km
Circumference (in km): 0.00028π km
Speed: $1{,}134 \text{ rpm} \cdot 0.00028\pi \text{ km/revolution}$
$\approx 0.998 \text{ km/min} \cdot 60 \text{ min/hr}$
$\approx 59.9 \text{ km/hr}$

This speed is 99,800 cm/min, not a very useful unit choice.

c. $x \text{ rpm} \cdot 0.00028\pi \frac{\text{km}}{\text{rev}} \cdot 60 \frac{\text{min}}{\text{hr}} = 30 \frac{\text{km}}{\text{hr}}$

$x \text{ rpm} \approx 568.4$ rpm for the wheel

Multiply by $\frac{10}{7}$ to get the engine speed of approximately 812 rpm.

3 **a.** Depending on the perspective, the rotating brush can be turning in either a clockwise direction or a counterclockwise direction. Either way, it brushes the dust backwards as the vacuum cleaner moves forward. See the arrows at the rotating brush in the sketch of the vacuum cleaner.

b.

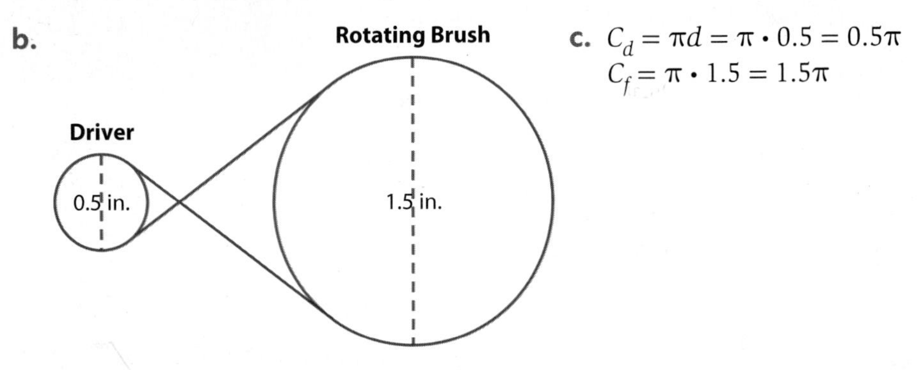

c. $C_d = \pi d = \pi \cdot 0.5 = 0.5\pi$
$C_f = \pi \cdot 1.5 = 1.5\pi$

d. The point travels a distance equal to the circumference of the driver, that is, 0.5π or approximately 1.57 inches, but in the direction opposite the direction of rotation of the driver.

e. 200 rpm; the brush (follower) rotates at $\frac{1}{3}$ times the rate of the driver and in the opposite direction.

f. $v_B = \frac{1}{3}v_D$

INSTRUCTIONAL NOTE
You may need to remind students that to change centimeters per minute to kilometers per minute. First, divide by 100 to change to meters and then by 1,000 to change to kilometers. Therefore, $15{,}000\pi$ cm per minute = 0.15π kilometers per minute. To change kilometers per minute to kilometers per hour, multiply by 60 min/hr.

4. The crankshaft of a particular automobile engine has an angular velocity of 1,500 rpm at 30 mph. The crankshaft pulley has a diameter of 10 cm, and it is attached to an air conditioner compressor pulley with a 7-cm diameter and an alternator pulley with a 5-cm diameter.

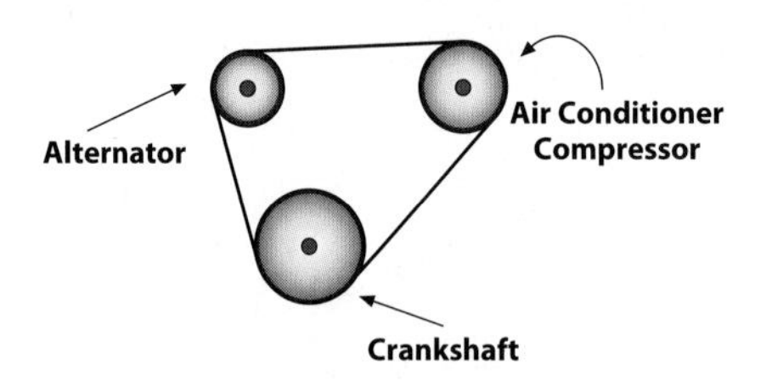

a. At what angular velocities do the compressor and alternator turn?

b. The three pulleys are connected by a 60-cm belt. At a crankshaft rate of 1,500 rpm, how many times will the belt revolve through its 60-cm length in one minute?

c. Most belts do not show significant wear until each point of the belt has traveled about 20,000 kilometers. How long can the engine run at 1,500 rpm before the belt typically would show wear?

5. One of the scarier rides at carnivals and amusement parks is provided by a long rotating arm with riders in capsules on either end. Of course, the capsules not only move up and down as the arm rotates, but they spin other ways as well.

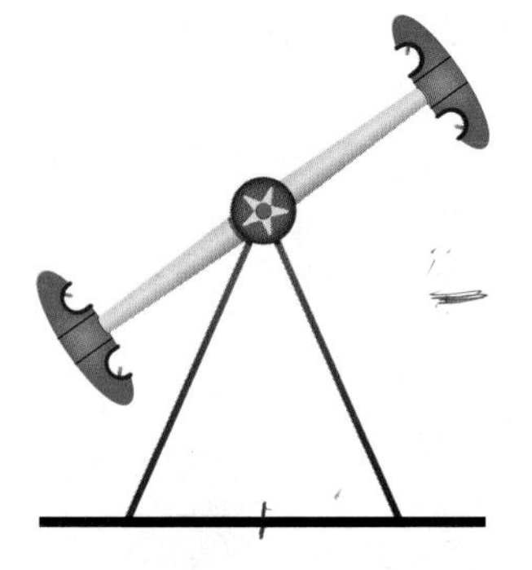

Suppose that the arm of one such ride is 150 feet long and that you get strapped into one of the capsules when it is at ground level. Assume simple rotating motion and treat the capsule as a single point. Find your height above the ground when the arm has made the following rotations counterclockwise from its starting vertical position.

a. 20°
b. 45°
c. 85°
d. 90°
e. 120°
f. 180°
g. 270°
h. 300°
i. 340°

6. Radio direction and ranging (radar) is one of the most widely used electronic sensing tools. Most of us probably know about radar from its applications in measuring speed of baseball pitches and automobiles. But it is also an invaluable tool in navigation and weather forecasting.

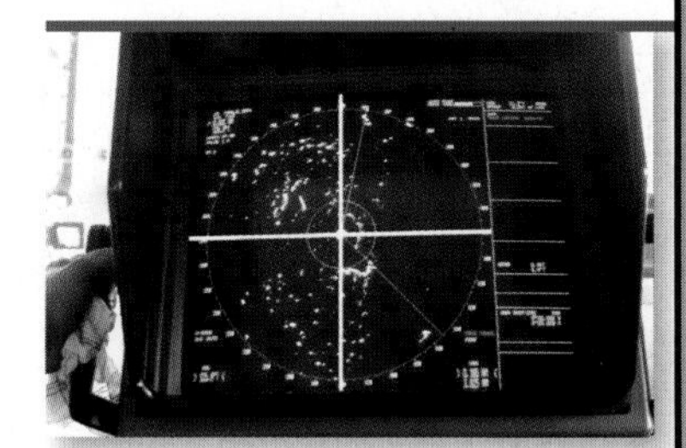

In those applications, the echoes to a rotating transmitter/receiver are displayed as blips on a scope. Each blip is located by distance and angle.

To describe locations of radar blips by distance east/west and north/south of the radar device, the (*distance, angle*) information needs to be converted to rectangular (x, y) coordinates.

Find the (x, y) coordinates of radar blips located by the following (*distance, angle*) data.

a. (30 km, 40°)
b. (20 km, 160°)
c. (70 km, 210°)
d. (15 km, 230°)
e. (45 km, 270°)
f. (40 km, 310°)

4 **a.** The 10-cm pulley turns at 1,500 rpm since it is attached to the crankshaft. The transmission factor to the compressor pulley is $\frac{10}{7}$, so this pulley has angular velocity equal to $\frac{10}{7} \cdot 1{,}500 \approx 2{,}142.9$ rpm. The alternator pulley turns at $2 \cdot 1{,}500 = 3{,}000$ rpm.

b. The circumference of the crankshaft pulley is 10π, so its linear velocity is $1{,}500 \cdot 10 \cdot \pi = 15{,}000\pi$ cm per minute. To find the number of times the 60-cm belt revolves, divide:

$$\frac{15{,}000\pi}{60} = 250\pi \approx 785 \text{ times}$$

c. From Part b, the belt travels $15{,}000\pi$ cm each minute. Therefore, 0.15π kilometers per minute $= 9\pi$ kilometers per hour. (The belt travels 9π kilometers each hour of continuous running.) To determine the hours needed to reach 20,000 km, divide 20,000 by 9π:
$\frac{20.000}{9\pi} \approx 707.4$ hours. This is approximately 29.5 days of nonstop driving. (At 30 mph, you will travel about 21,220 miles.)

5 The height of the rotating capsule is $75 \sin (270° + \theta) + 75$, or $75 \sin (\theta - 90°) + 75$. The answers below are rounded to the nearest tenth of a foot.

a. 4.5

b. 22.0

c. 68.5

d. 75

e. 112.5

f. 150

g. 75

h. 37.5

i. 4.5

6 **a.** (23, 19.3)

b. (−18.8, 6.8)

c. (−60.6, −35)

d. (−9.6, −11.5)

e. (0, −45)

f. (25.7, −30.6)

7 A rack-and-pinion gearset is used in the steering mechanism of most cars. The gearset converts the rotational motion of the steering wheel into the linear motion needed to turn the wheels, while providing a gear reduction that makes it easier to turn the wheels. As shown in the sketch below, when you turn the steering wheel, the gear (pinion) spins, moving the rack. The tie rod at the end of the rack connects to the steering arm on the spindle of each wheel.

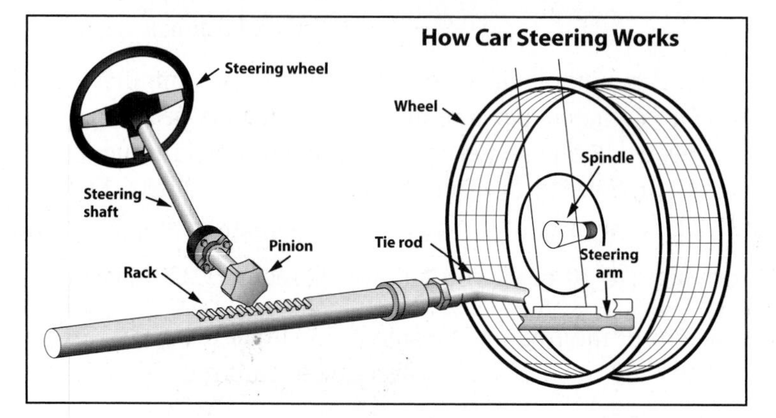

a. The steering ratio is the ratio of how far you turn the steering wheel to how far the wheels turn. For example, a steering ratio of 18:1 means you must turn the steering wheel 18° in order to turn the front wheels 1°. A higher steering ratio such as 20:1 means you have to turn the steering wheel more to get the wheels to turn through a 1° angle, but less effort is required because of "gearing down." Would you expect lighter, sportier cars to have higher or lower steering ratios than larger cars and trucks? Explain.

b. Suppose the steering ratio of a car is 18:1.

i. Through how many degrees will the front wheels turn if the steering wheel is turned a complete revolution?

ii. Suppose the maximum turn of the front wheels is 75°. How many revolutions of the steering wheel are needed to make the maximum turn?

8 A circle of radius r centimeters has a circumference of $2\pi r$ centimeters.

a. Suppose a point A on the circle rotates through an angle of p radians. What is the length of the arc traversed by the point?

b. Suppose a point A on the circle rotates at p radians per minute. Find the linear velocity of the point.

c. Suppose a circle with radius 10 cm has an angular velocity of 80 radians per second. Find the linear velocity of a point A on the circle.

d. Suppose a point on a circle with radius 10 cm has linear velocity of 30π cm per second. Find the angular velocity of the point.

e. Explain how to convert an angular velocity v (in radians per second) for a circle of radius r centimeters into the linear velocity of a point on the circle.

440 UNIT 6 • Circles and Circular Functions

7 a. Because of their lesser weight, sporty cars require less gearing down to turn the steering wheel. Therefore, they would generally have lower steering ratios.

b. i. The front wheel will turn $\frac{360°}{18} = 20°$ if the steering wheel is turned through a complete revolution.

ii. Since $75° = 3(20°) + 15°$, the steering wheel must turn through 3 revolutions plus $\frac{3}{4}$ of a fourth revolution.

8 a. The length of the arc is pr cm.

b. The linear velocity is pr cm/min.

c. Each radian intercepts an arc of length $r = 10$ cm, so the angular velocity is $80 \cdot 10 = 800$ cm/sec.

d. The circumference of the circle is $2 \cdot 10 \cdot \pi = 20\pi$. So in one second, the point moves through an angle of $\frac{30\pi}{20\pi} \cdot 360°$, or $\frac{30\pi}{20\pi} \cdot 2\pi$ radians. Therefore, the angular velocity of the point is 3π radians/sec, or 540°/sec.

e. In one second, a point moving at an angular velocity of v radians/sec will travel vr centimeters. Therefore, the linear velocity of the point is the product of the angular velocity and the radius of the circle, that is, vr cm/sec.

9 Degree measure of angles is more familiar to you than radian measure. But the difference between the two is just a matter of scale. That is, $1° = \frac{\pi}{180}$, or about 0.0175 radians, and 1 radian $= \left(\frac{180}{\pi}\right)°$, or about 57.3°. The following tasks may help you better understand radians.

a. Each of the following is the radian measure of an angle in standard position. Give the quadrant in which the terminal side of each angle lies.

i. 5 **ii.** -5

iii. $-\frac{4\pi}{3}$ **iv.** $\frac{7\pi}{3}$

b. The measure of an angle in standard position is p radians, and the angle's terminal side is in the second quadrant. In what quadrant is the terminal side of an angle with each of the following radian measures? Give all possibilities and explain.

i. $p + 2\pi$ **ii.** $p - \frac{\pi}{2}$

iii. $p + 9\pi$ **iv.** $p - 2$

10 Many variations on the sine and cosine functions are also periodic functions.

a. Find the amplitude, period, and y-displacement for each of the following functions.

i. $y = 2 \cos(-x) + 3$

ii. $y = -3 \sin 0.1x + 5$

iii. $y = 12 \sin 3x - 8$

b. Suppose data from a periodic variable are fit well by a function of the form $y = a \cos bx + c$ where $a < 0$ and $b > 0$. A plot of the data suggests a y-displacement of -5, amplitude of 7, and period of 6π. Write a function rule for this data.

11 The center of a Ferris wheel in an amusement park is 7 meters above the ground and the Ferris wheel itself is 12 meters in diameter. The wheel turns counterclockwise at a constant rate and takes 20 seconds to make one complete revolution.

a. Yolanda and her friend enter their seat when it is directly below the wheel's center. Sketch a graph that you would expect to show their height above the ground during one minute at full rotational speed, starting from the entry point.

b. Make a table of values for the radian measure t and the height $h(t)$ of Yolanda's seat above the ground at 5 second intervals for the one-minute ride.

c. Use the data pairs in Part b to sketch a graph of the height $h(t)$ as a function of time t. Compare this graph to the one you drew by hand in Part a?

d. Is this function periodic? If so, what is its period? What is its amplitude?

9 **a.** **i.** IV **ii.** I **iii.** II **iv.** I

b. **i.** The terminal side of $p + 2\pi$ is the same as that of p, so it is in Quadrant II.

ii. The terminal side of $p - \frac{\pi}{2}$ is a 90° clockwise rotation from that of p, so it is in Quadrant I.

iii. The terminal side of $p + 9\pi$ is two complete counterclockwise rotations of that of p plus π more, so it is in Quadrant IV.

iv. Since 2 radians is about 114.6°, the terminal side of $p - 2$ could be in either Quadrant I (if $p > 114.6°$) or in Quadrant IV (if $p < 114.6°$).

10 **a.** **i.** Amplitude is 2; period is 2π; y-displacement is 3

ii. Amplitude is 3; period is 20π; y-displacement is 5

iii. Amplitude is 12; period is $\frac{2\pi}{3}$; y-displacement is -8

b. $y = 7 \cos\left(\frac{1}{3}x\right) - 5$

11 **a.**

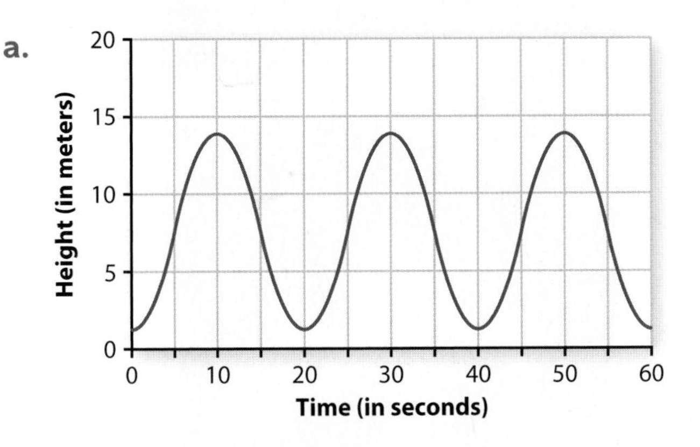

b. Using 5-second increments, the table would be as follows:

x	0	5	10	15	20	25	30	35	40	45	50	55	60
y	1	7	13	7	1	7	13	7	1	7	13	7	1

c.

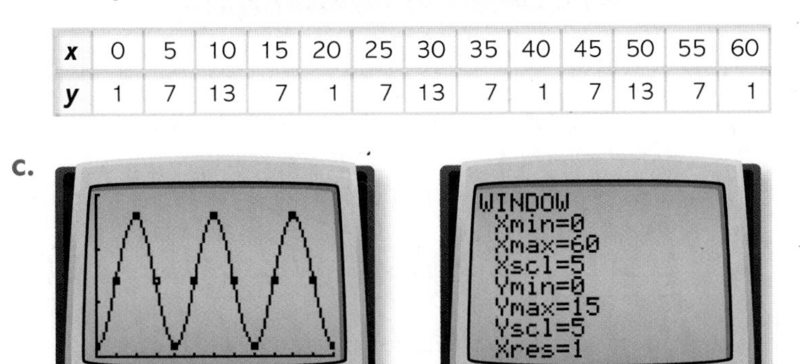

d. The graph is periodic. The period is 20 seconds, which is $\frac{1}{3}$ minute, or 1 revolution. The minimum is 1 m, and the maximum is 13 m, so the amplitude is 6.

e. Several functions that students predicted would fit the data in Part b are given below. In each case, $\frac{\pi}{10}$ is angular velocity in radians per second, t is time in seconds, and $h(t)$ is height in meters. Determine if any are good fits for the data.

   i. $h(t) = 6 \sin \frac{\pi t}{10} + 7$

   ii. $h(t) = -6 \cos \frac{\pi t}{10} + 7$

   iii. $h(t) = -6 \sin \frac{\pi}{10}(t + 5) + 7$

   iv. $h(t) = 6 \cos \frac{\pi t}{10} + 7$

12 Suppose that you are trying to model the motion of a clock pendulum that moves as far as 5 inches to the right of vertical and swings with a period of 2 seconds.

a. Find variations of $d(t) = \cos t$ that fit the conditions for each part below.

   i. A modeling function whose values range from -5 to 5 and has a period of 2π

   ii. A modeling function that has a period of 2 and whose values range from -1 to 1

   iii. A modeling function that has a period of 2 and whose values range from -5 to 5

b. How are the numbers in the function for Part aiii related to the motion of the pendulum you are modeling?

c. Graph the function that models the motion of the clock pendulum. Identify the coordinates of the t-intercepts and minimum and maximum points of the graph.

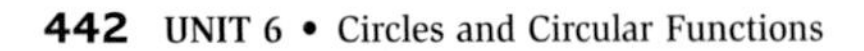

e. $h(t) = -6 \cos\left(\frac{\pi t}{10}\right) + 7$ and $h(t) = -6 \sin\left(\frac{\pi(t + 5)}{10}\right) + 7$ both fit the data.

12 **a.** **i.** $d(t) = 5 \cos t$

ii. $d(t) = \cos \pi t$

iii. $d(t) = 5 \cos \pi t$

b. The pocket watch follows a path that begins 5 inches to the right from the vertical, so the initial value of the function should be 5. Since $\cos 0°$ is 1, $5 \cos 0°$ is 5. The two-second period requires the watch to stop and reverse direction every second, so the value of $\cos Bx$ should be -1 when $x = 1$. This is accomplished when $B = \pi$, or $180°$. So, the desired model for the motion of the watch is $y = 5 \cos \pi x$. (This model ignores the effect of gravity.)

c. The graph follows:

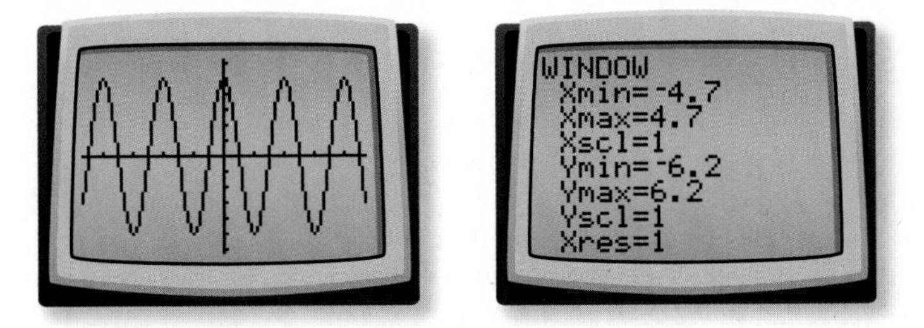

The coordinates of the t-intercepts on the interval shown are $(-4.5, 0)$, $(-3.5, 0)$, $(-2.5, 0)$, $(-1.5, 0)$, $(-0.5, 0)$, $(0.5, 0)$, $(1.5, 0)$, $(2.5, 0)$, $(3.5, 0)$, and $(4.5, 0)$.

The maximum value of the function is 5, and the coordinates for the maximum points are $(-4, 5)$, $(-2, 5)$, $(0, 5)$, $(2, 5)$, and $(4, 5)$.

The minimum value of the function is -5, and the coordinates of the minimum points are $(-3, -5)$, $(-1, -5)$, $(1, -5)$, and $(3, -5)$.

Connections

13 Some automobile manufacturers are beginning to use an automatic, continuously-variable transmission (CVT) based on segments of cones. A simplified model is shown below. It consists of two 10-centimeter segments of right cones. The diameters of the circular ends are given. These partial cones form the basis for a *variable-drive* system, in which either partial cone can be moved laterally (left and right) along a shaft.

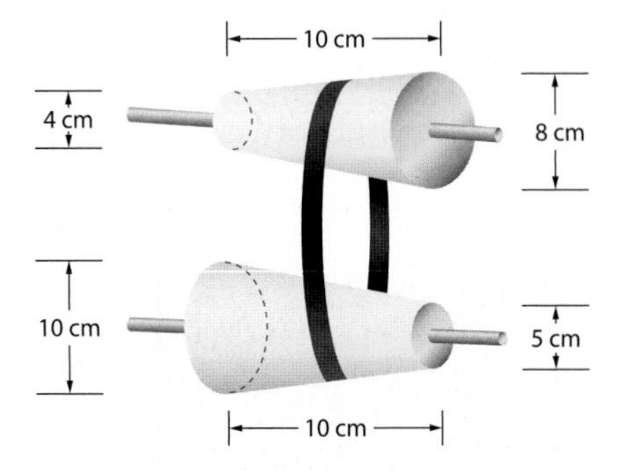

a. When two pulleys are connected by a chain or belt, their angular velocities are related. The number by which the angular velocity of the driver pulley is multiplied to get the angular velocity of the follower pulley is called the **transmission factor** from driver to follower. For example, in the figure above, the transmission factor for the top cone (driver) to the bottom cone (follower) is $\frac{6}{7.5} = 0.8$. Explain why.

b. If the upper shape is the driver, what are the maximum and minimum transmission factors?

c. Suppose the belt is halfway between the two circular ends of the upper shape. If the lower shape is permitted to move laterally, what range of transmission factors is possible?

d. Describe a position of the cones for which the transmission factor is 1.

14 In Connections Task 13, you considered transmission factors. The transmission factor for pulley A to pulley B can be denoted in function notation as **tf(*AB*)**. Assume A has radius r_1 and B has radius r_2.

a. What does tf(*BA*) represent?

b. Express tf(*AB*) in terms of the radii of A and B. Similarly, express tf(*BA*).

c. If the circumference of A is C_1 and the circumference of B is C_2, express tf(*AB*) in terms of C_1 and C_2.

d. Using the formula for the circumference of a circle, rewrite your expression in Part c as one involving only radii (r_1 or r_2). Is this result consistent with Part b? Why or why not?

e. Suppose B turns through an angle of $b°$ whenever A turns through an angle of $a°$. Express tf(*AB*) in terms of a and b.

Connections

13 **a.** For the placement of the belt in the figure, the diameter of the driver is 6 cm and the diameter of the bottom cone is 7.5 cm. The ratio of the angular velocity of the driver to the angular velocity of the follower is the reciprocal of the diameters: $\frac{v_d}{v_f} = \frac{7.5}{6}$. So, $v_d = \frac{7.5}{6}v_f$ and $\frac{6}{7.5}v_d = v_f$. Thus, the transmission factor is 0.8.

b. The maximum is $\frac{8}{5} = 1.6$. The minimum is $\frac{4}{10} = 0.4$.

c. At a position halfway between a 4-cm radius circle and an 8-cm radius circle, the cross section is a 6-cm circle. Thus, the driver pulley has a radius of 6 cm. Moving the lower partial cone gives radii from 5 to 10 cm. The transmission factors, therefore, range from $\frac{6}{5}$ to $\frac{6}{10}$.

d. The transmission factor is 1 when the belt runs between locations on both pulleys that have equal radii. If the upper cone has the belt halfway between the ends, the radius is 6. The lower cone has a radius of 6 cm when the belt is $\frac{1}{5}$ the distance from the 5-cm end. Many other answers are possible.

14 **a.** tf(BA) represents the transmission factor from pulley B to pulley A.

b. $\text{tf}(AB) = \frac{r_1}{r_2}$; $\text{tf}(BA) = \frac{r_2}{r_1}$

c. $\text{tf}(AB) = \frac{C_1}{C_2}$

d. $\frac{C_1}{C_2} = \frac{2\pi r_1}{2\pi r_2} = \frac{r_1}{r_2}$; It is consistent. Since the circumferences of circles are proportional to the radii, the ratios are equal.

e. $\text{tf}(AB) = \frac{a}{b}$

15 **INSTRUCTIONAL NOTE** The connection of matrices to rotations was developed in Course 2, Unit 3, *Coordinate Methods*. It seems quite possible that students will not remember this topic in any technical detail, so it will probably be useful to discuss and show sketches of the special half-turn matrix example in the text to show how it produces the correct results.

a. The given matrix fits the form of a rotation of 180° because $\cos 180° = -1$ and $\sin 180° = 0$.

b. The matrix for a rotation of 30° will be $\begin{bmatrix} \frac{\sqrt{3}}{2} & -\frac{1}{2} \\ \frac{1}{2} & \frac{\sqrt{3}}{2} \end{bmatrix} \approx \begin{bmatrix} 0.87 & -0.5 \\ 0.5 & 0.87 \end{bmatrix}$.

Multiplying this matrix times each of the column matrices $\begin{bmatrix} 1 \\ 0 \end{bmatrix}$, $\begin{bmatrix} \frac{1}{2} \\ \frac{\sqrt{3}}{2} \end{bmatrix}$, and $\begin{bmatrix} 1 \\ 0 \end{bmatrix}$ gives the results on page T444.

15 **Rotation Matrices** In earlier study of coordinate geometry, you discovered that results of several special rotations can be produced by matrix multiplication. For example, for any point $P(x, y)$, the matrix product $\begin{bmatrix} -1 & 0 \\ 0 & -1 \end{bmatrix}\begin{bmatrix} x \\ y \end{bmatrix} = \begin{bmatrix} -x \\ -y \end{bmatrix}$. So, the matrix $\begin{bmatrix} -1 & 0 \\ 0 & -1 \end{bmatrix}$ represents a rotation of 180° or half-turn about the origin. In general, multiplication by a matrix in the form $\begin{bmatrix} \cos\theta & -\sin\theta \\ \sin\theta & \cos\theta \end{bmatrix}$ represents a counterclockwise rotation of $\theta°$ about the origin.

a. How does the matrix $\begin{bmatrix} -1 & 0 \\ 0 & -1 \end{bmatrix}$ for a rotation of 180° fit the general form for rotation matrices?

b. Write the matrix for a counterclockwise rotation of 30°. Then use matrix multiplication to find the images of the following special points on the unit circle and use geometric reasoning to prove that the matrix multiplication has produced the correct rotation images of the points.

i. (1, 0) **ii.** $\left(\frac{1}{2}, \frac{\sqrt{3}}{2}\right)$ **iii.** (0, 1)

16 An angle of 1 radian is shown in standard position below.

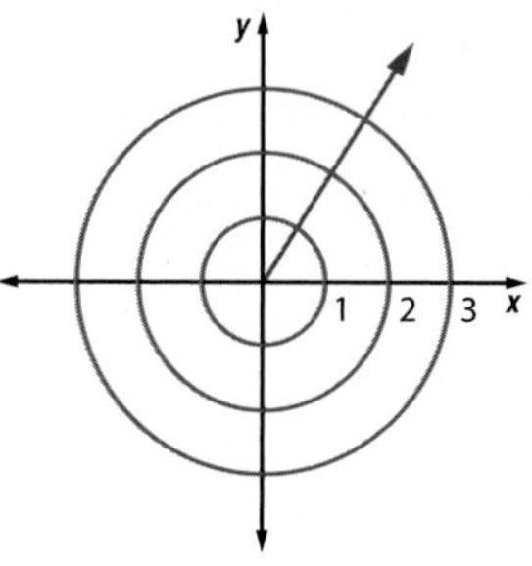

a. What is the length of the arc in the circle of radius 1 traversed by rotating through 1 radian?

b. What transformation takes the circle of radius 1 to that of radius 2? What transformation takes the circle of radius 3 to the circle of radius 2?

c. What are the lengths of the arcs in the circles of radii 2 and 3 traversed by rotating through an angle of 1 radian? Explain why this answer makes sense using the transformations in Part b.

17 In Course 2 Unit 7, *Trigonometric Methods*, you used properties of special right triangles to determine the trigonometric ratios for angles of 30°, 45°, and 60°. You also found the values of these ratios for 0° and 90°.

a. Complete the table at the right giving the sine and cosine of the radian equivalent of each of these angles.

t (in radians)	sin t	cos t
0		
	$\frac{1}{2}$	
$\frac{\pi}{4}$		$\frac{\sqrt{2}}{2}$
	$\frac{\sqrt{3}}{2}$	
$\frac{\pi}{2}$		

b. In this lesson, you learned that the sine and cosine functions can be used to model the motion of a circle with radius 1 centered at the origin. Sketch this circle and mark the points that lie on the terminal side of each of the five angles in the table. Write the coordinates of each point.

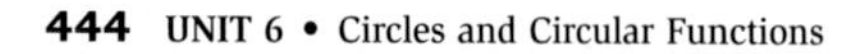

i. $\begin{bmatrix} \frac{\sqrt{3}}{2} \\ \frac{1}{2} \end{bmatrix}$; These coordinates determine a 30°-60° right triangle in the first graphing quadrant, so the point is the image of (1, 0) after rotation of 30°.

ii. $\begin{bmatrix} \frac{1}{2} \\ \frac{\sqrt{3}}{2} \end{bmatrix}$; These coordinates determine a 30°-60° right triangle in the first graphing quadrant, so the point is the image of $\left(\frac{\sqrt{3}}{2}, \frac{1}{2}\right)$ after rotation of 30°.

iii. $\begin{bmatrix} \frac{1}{2} \\ \frac{\sqrt{3}}{2} \end{bmatrix}$; These coordinates determine a 30°-60° right triangle in the second graphing quadrant, so the point is the image of (0, 1) after rotation of 30°.

NOTE An instructional note and the solutions to Task 15 begin on page T443.

16 **a.** By the definition, the length of the arc is the length of the circle's radius, or 1 unit.

b. A size transformation centered at the origin with scale factor 2 takes the circle of radius 1 to that of radius 2. A size transformation centered at the origin with scale factor $\frac{2}{3}$ takes the circle of radius 3 to that of radius 2.

c. The lengths of the arcs are 2 units and 3 units, respectively. This follows from the definition of radian, which is a central angle that intercepts an arc whose length is the radius. The transformation in Part b with scale factor $\frac{2}{3}$ takes the circle of radius 3 to the circle of radius 2, and scales the arcs of length 3 to arcs of length 2 and the radii of length 3 to radii of length 2.

17 **a.**

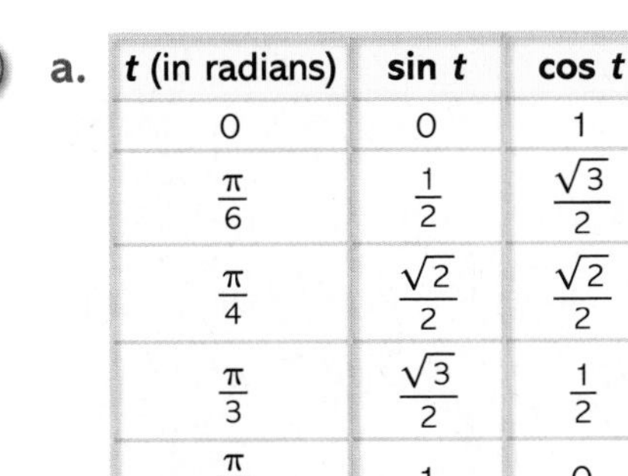

t (in radians)	sin *t*	cos *t*
0	0	1
$\frac{\pi}{6}$	$\frac{1}{2}$	$\frac{\sqrt{3}}{2}$
$\frac{\pi}{4}$	$\frac{\sqrt{2}}{2}$	$\frac{\sqrt{2}}{2}$
$\frac{\pi}{3}$	$\frac{\sqrt{3}}{2}$	$\frac{1}{2}$
$\frac{\pi}{2}$	1	0

INSTRUCTIONAL NOTE Some students may list coordinates as (sin *t*, cos *t*) since the columns in the table are in that order. Emphasize that (cos *t*, sin *t*) is the correct order.

b.

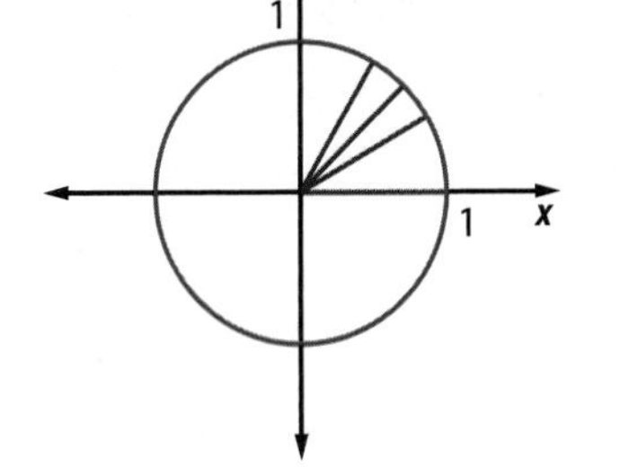

The coordinates of the points common to the circle and the terminal side of an angle x are (cos t, sin t), so the coordinates of the marked points can be written using the table in Part a.

Unit 6

c. The terminal sides of angles measuring 0 and $\frac{\pi}{2}$ radians each lie on one of the coordinate axes. There are two other angles between 0 and 2π radians whose terminal sides lie on an axis. What are the radian measures of these angles? What are the sine and cosine of each angle?

d. In Part b, you used geometric reasoning to calculate cosine and sine of three angles with terminal side in the first quadrant. Use those results and symmetry of the circle to find the cosine and sine of nine more angles—three with terminal side in Quadrant II, three with terminal side in Quadrant III, and three with terminal side in Quadrant IV.

e. In which quadrants are the sines of angles positive? Negative? Answer the same questions for the cosine.

18 Strip or frieze patterns are used in architecture and interior design. The portions of frieze patterns below are from the artwork on pottery of the San Ildefonso Pueblo, New Mexico.

a. What aspects of the graphs of the sine and cosine functions are similar to these strip patterns?

b. What is the shortest nonzero distance you could translate the graph of $y = \sin x$ so that it would map onto itself? Answer the same question about the graph of $y = \cos x$.

c. What symmetries do the graphs of $y = \sin x$ and $y = \cos x$ have? Describe any line of reflection or center and angle of rotation involved in each symmetry.

19 Use the language of geometric transformations to describe the relationships between the graphs of the following pairs of functions.

a. $-\cos t$ and $\cos t$

b. $5 + \sin t$ and $\sin t$

c. $5 \cos t$ and $\cos t$

Reflections

20 A popular amusement park ride for young children is the carousel or merry-go-round. A typical carousel consists of a circular platform with three circles of horses to ride, an inner circle, a middle circle, and an outer circle.

Children and sometimes adults ride these horses as the carousel goes round and round. In which circle should a child ride for the slowest ride? For the fastest ride? Why?

c. π and $\frac{3\pi}{2}$; $\sin \pi = 0$;
$\cos \pi = -1$; $\sin \frac{3\pi}{2} = -1$;
$\cos \frac{3\pi}{2} = 0$

d.

t (in radians)	sin t	cos t
$\frac{2\pi}{3}$	$\frac{\sqrt{3}}{2}$	$-\frac{1}{2}$
$\frac{3\pi}{4}$	$\frac{\sqrt{2}}{2}$	$-\frac{\sqrt{2}}{2}$
$\frac{5\pi}{6}$	$\frac{1}{2}$	$-\frac{\sqrt{3}}{2}$
$\frac{7\pi}{6}$	$-\frac{1}{2}$	$-\frac{\sqrt{3}}{2}$
$\frac{5\pi}{4}$	$-\frac{\sqrt{2}}{2}$	$-\frac{\sqrt{2}}{2}$
$\frac{4\pi}{3}$	$-\frac{\sqrt{3}}{2}$	$-\frac{1}{2}$
$\frac{5\pi}{3}$	$-\frac{\sqrt{3}}{2}$	$\frac{1}{2}$
$\frac{7\pi}{4}$	$-\frac{\sqrt{2}}{2}$	$\frac{\sqrt{2}}{2}$
$\frac{11\pi}{6}$	$-\frac{1}{2}$	$\frac{\sqrt{3}}{2}$

e. The sine is positive in Quadrants I and II and negative in Quadrants III and IV. The cosine is positive in Quadrants I and IV and negative in Quadrants II and III.

18 **a.** Both strip patterns have translational symmetry and so are periodic. The first pattern has vertical line symmetry with axis of any vertical line through a minimum or maximum point.

The second pattern has glide reflection symmetry. It also has 180° rotational symmetry about the midpoints of the longest and shortest vertical segments as shown at the right. Variations of the sine and cosine functions have analogues of all these symmetries.

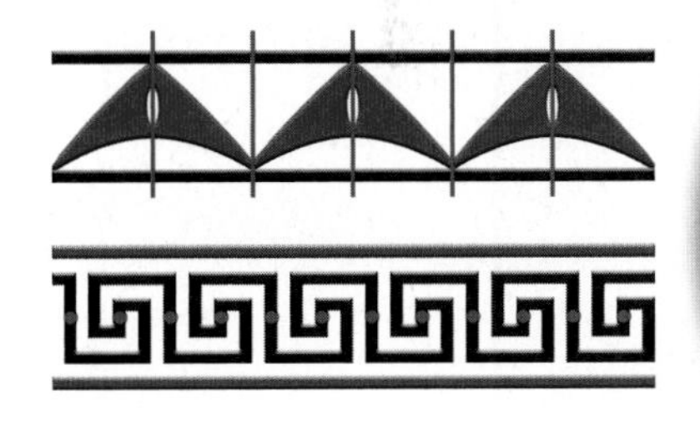

b. 360° or 2π for both sine and cosine

c. The graphs of $y = \sin x$ and $y = \cos x$ have:

(1) 180° rotational symmetry about any point that is an x-intercept.

(2) glide reflection symmetry: translate 180°, or π radians, parallel to the x-axis and then reflect across the x-axis.

(3) line symmetry across any vertical line through a maximum or minimum point.

19 **a.** The graph of $-\cos t$ is a reflection of the graph of $\cos t$ across the t-axis.

b. The graph of $5 + \sin t$ is a translation of the graph of $\sin t$ upward 5 units.

c. The graph of $5 \cos t$ is a stretch of the graph of $\cos t$ by a factor of 5 units away from the t-axis.

Reflections

20 Although the angular velocity is the same for a horse in any circle, a horse in the inner circle has less linear velocity as the wheel turns. This is true because of the inner circle's smaller circumference. The linear velocity of the outer circle is greatest, so you will be moving fastest if you ride in the outer circle of horses.

21 Read the cartoon below. Using mathematical ideas that you developed in Investigation 1, write a paragraph explaining to Calvin how two points on a record can move at two different speeds.

22 Karen wishes to evaluate sin 25° using her calculator. She presses SIN 25) ENTER. The calculator displays the screen below. What indicates that there must be an error? What do you think the error is?

23 According to Morris Kline, a former Professor of Mathematics at New York University, "The advantage of radians over degrees is simply that it is a more convenient unit. ... The point involved here is no different from measuring a mile in yards instead of inches."

Why do you think Kline believes the radian is a "more convenient unit"? (Source: Morris Kline, *Mathematics for Liberal Arts*, Addison Wesley, 1967. page 423)

24 If you have ever ridden a Ferris wheel that was rotating at a constant rate, you know that at some positions on the wheel, you feel like you are falling or rising faster than at other points on the wheel. As the wheel rotates counterclockwise, your directed distance to the horizontal axis through the center of the wheel is $r \sin \theta$, where r is the radius of the Ferris wheel. Examine the graph of the sine function.

a. Near what values of θ in radians is the sine function increasing most rapidly? Decreasing most rapidly?

b. Where on the wheel are you located when the sine function is increasing most rapidly? Decreasing most rapidly?

c. Explain what your answers in Parts a and b may have to do with your feelings of falling or rising when you ride a Ferris wheel.

Unit 6

446 UNIT 6 • Circles and Circular Functions

21 Student responses will vary but should include the idea that linear velocity is equal to angular velocity times circumference. Furthermore, since the points are moving at the same number of revolutions per minute (which is angular velocity) and the circumference of an inner circle will be less than the circumference of an outer circle, it must be that the linear velocity of a point on the smaller circle will be less than the linear velocity of a point on the larger circle.

22 The value given by the calculator cannot be correct, because 25° is located in Quadrant I, and the values of sine in that quadrant are all positive. The calculator is probably in radian mode instead of degree mode.

23 The difference between degree measure and radian measure is just a matter of scale, that is, $1° = \frac{\pi}{180}$, or about 0.0175 radians, and 1 radian $= \left(\frac{180}{\pi}\right)^{\circ}$, or about 57.3°. For an exploration of the scale difference, see Applications Task 9. One aspect of the convenience of radians is explored in Extensions Task 30. In that task, students learn that the limit of $\frac{\sin x}{x}$ is 1 in radians, but the same limit is $\frac{\pi}{180}$ in degrees. This is a special case of an important convenience. In radians, the derivative of the sine is the cosine and the derivative of the cosine is the negative of the sine. In degree mode, these derivatives would include $\frac{\pi}{180}$, or a decimal approximation, as coefficient.

24 **a.** The sine function is increasing most rapidly near 0 radians or, in general, near integral multiples of 2π. It is decreasing most rapidly near π or, in general, angles with measures of the form $\pi + 2\pi n$, where n is any integer.

b. When the sine function is increasing most rapidly, you are located on your way up, passing through the horizontal axis of the wheel, and continuing your motion toward the top of the wheel. When the sine function is decreasing most rapidly, you are on the other side of the wheel, descending toward the horizontal axis of the wheel, and continuing your motion toward the bottom of the wheel.

c. The feelings of falling faster or rising faster occur at these respective points on the Ferris wheel. In fact, you are falling or rising faster than when you are at, or very near, the top of the wheel or the bottom of the wheel where, not surprisingly, the sine function is increasing or decreasing very slowly.

25 In previous courses, you have studied various functions—linear, exponential, power, polynomial, and trigonometric. It is helpful to think about each "family" of functions in terms of basic symbolic rules and their corresponding graphs.

a. Make a general sketch of the graph of each function below. Label the x- and y-intercepts. In each case, assume $a > 1$.

i. $y = ax$ **ii.** $y = a^x$ **iii.** $y = ax^2$

iv. $y = ax^3$ **v.** $y = \frac{a}{x}$ **vi.** $y = \frac{a}{x^2}$

vii. $y = a \sin x$ **viii.** $y = a \cos x$

b. If you are given a graph, what characteristics would you look for to identify the graph as a member of each family in Part a?

26 The *biorhythm* theory asserts that a person's biological functioning is controlled by three inner rhythms which begin at birth: physical, emotional, and intellectual. These rhythms vary sinusoidally with time. Biorhythm graphs are used by athletes as well as industrial firms to predict potential "good" or "bad" performance days for a person. Use the labeled graphs below to determine the period of each biorhythm.

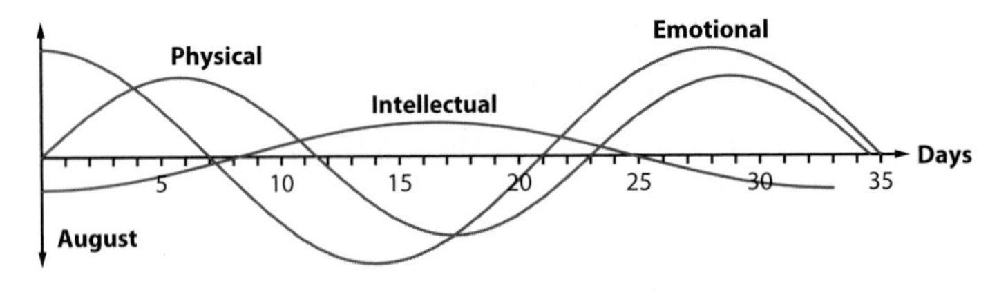

a. Physical **b.** Emotional **c.** Intellectual

d. According to biorhythm theory, when a cycle is near a high point, a person can perform well in an activity requiring the corresponding biological functioning. Similarly, low points in the cycle are associated with times of low performance. What date(s) would be best for a person to run a 10-km race?

Extensions

27 When two rotating circles are linked in a driver/follower relationship, the **transmission factor** from driver to follower can be expressed as the ratio of angular velocities $\frac{v_f}{v_d}$. One model of a 21-speed mountain bike has a pedal crankset of 3 sprockets with 48, 40, and 30 teeth; the bike has 7 sprockets for the rear wheel with 30, 27, 24, 21, 18, and 12 teeth.

a. What is the largest transmission factor available for this bicycle? What is the smallest?

a. **i.** $y = ax$ **ii.** $y = a^x$

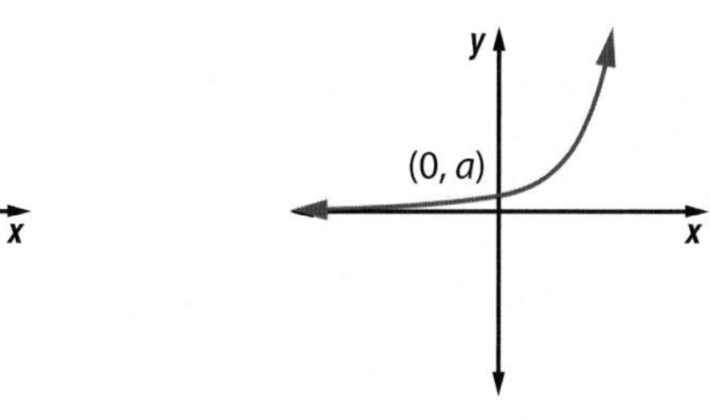

iii. $y = ax^2$ **iv.** $y = ax^3$

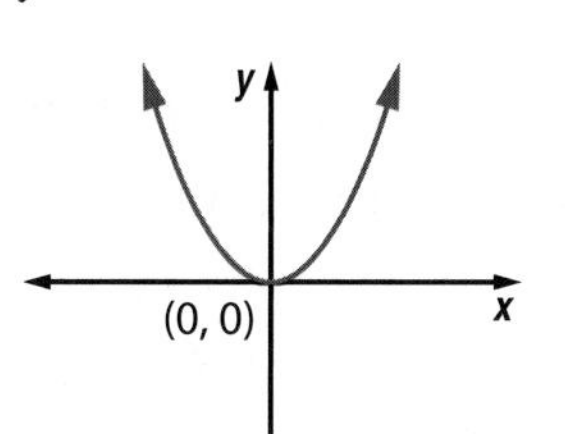

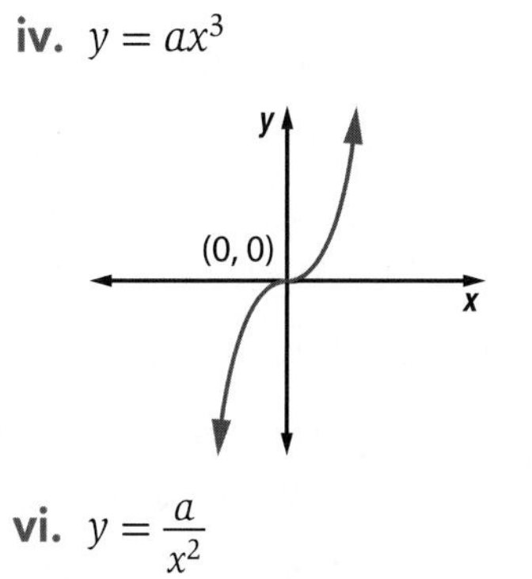

v. $y = \frac{a}{x}$ **vi.** $y = \frac{a}{x^2}$

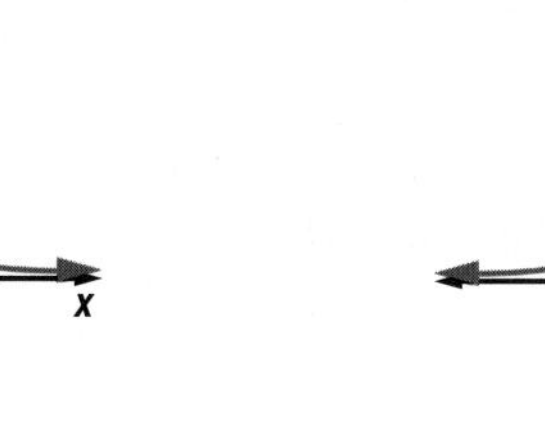

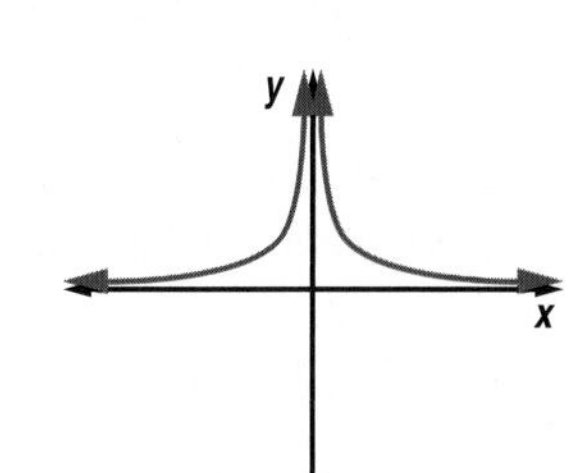

vii. $y = a \sin x$

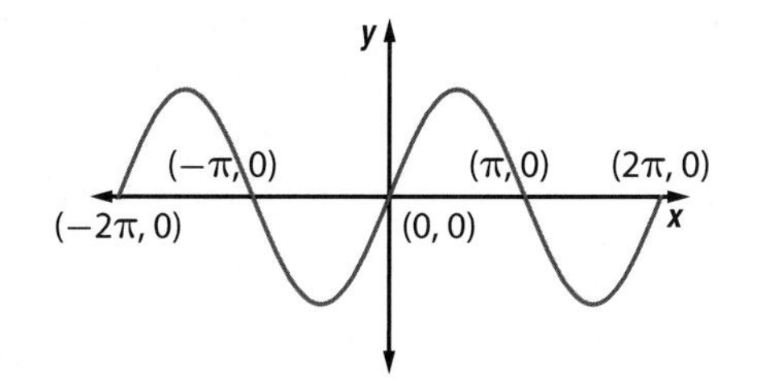

viii. $y = a \cos x$

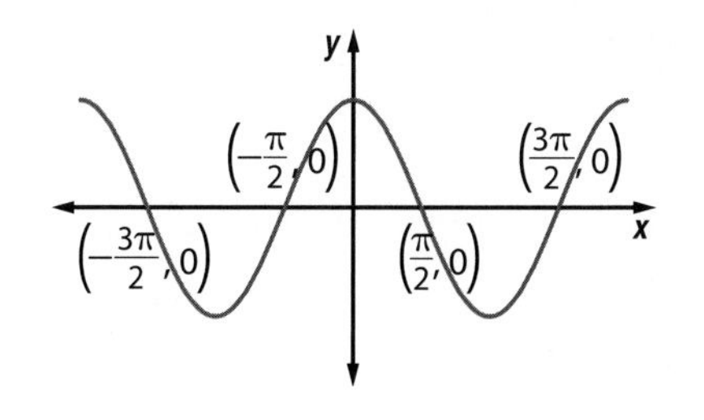

b. **i.** Functions in the family $y = ax$ $(a > 1)$ will have linear graphs with positive slope.

ii. Functions in the family $y = a^x$ $(a > 1)$ will have graphs that are asymptotic to the x-axis for $x < 0$ and increases rapidly for $x > 0$.

iii. Functions in the family $y = ax^2$ $(a > 1)$ will have graphs that are parabolas opening upward.

iv. Functions in the family $y = ax^3$ $(a > 1)$ will have graphs that are increasing, curved down to the left of 0 and curved up to the right of 0, and passing through (0, 0).

v. Functions in the family $y = \frac{a}{x}$ $(a > 1)$ will have graphs that are asymptotic to both axes, values only in Quadrants I and III and decreasing as x increases.

vi. Functions in the family $y = \frac{a}{x^2}$ $(a > 1)$ will have graphs that are asymptotic to both axes, values only in Quadrants I and II, increasing to the left of 0 and decreasing to the right of 0.

vii. Functions in the family $y = a \sin x$ $(a > 1)$ will have sinusoidal graphs that pass through the origin.

viii. Functions in the family $y = a \cos x$ will have sinusoidal graphs that pass through $(0, a)$.

26 **a.** Physical: 23 days

b. Emotional: 28 days

c. Intellectual: 33 days

d. The best dates to run a race would be when physical rhythms are high, about August 6 and August 28.

Extensions

27 **a.** The largest transmission factor occurs when the pedal sprocket is largest and the rear sprocket is smallest. In this case, that ratio is $\frac{48}{12} = 4$. The smallest meets the opposite condition $\frac{30}{30} = 1$.

Teacher Notes

b. Suppose on a cross-country ride, you can maintain an angular velocity of 70 rpm for the pedal sprocket. What is the fastest that you can make the rear wheel turn?

c. The radius of a mountain bike tire is about 33 cm.

i. What is the linear velocity of the rear wheel when the pedal sprocket turns at 70 rpm and the transmission factor is greatest possible?

ii. What is the linear velocity of the rear wheel when the pedal sprocket turns at 70 rpm and the transmission factor is least?

28 In the figure at the right, $\overline{AE}$ and $\overline{BD}$ are tangent to both circles. The point of intersection of the two tangents lies on the line containing the centers of the circles.

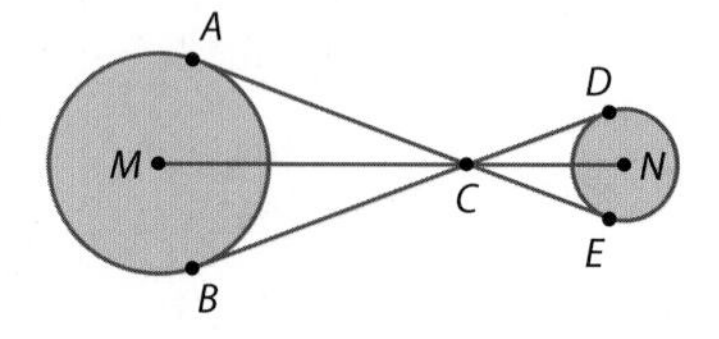

a. Draw the radii to the points of tangency in each circle. The result should be four triangles that are similar to one another. Explain why?

b. Suppose the radius of the larger circle is 8 cm, the radius of the smaller circle is 4 cm, and the distance between the centers is 30 cm. Use similar triangles to determine the length of a common tangent segment.

c. Suppose the circles represent pulleys with a belt going around the pulleys as indicated by the common tangents. Given the measures in Part c, determine the length of the belt.

In this task, you will explore a shape that is different in form from a circle but can serve a similar design function.

a. Make a cardboard model of this shape as follows.

Step 1. Construct an equilateral triangle of side length 6 cm.

Step 2. At each vertex, place a compass and draw the arc of a circle with radius 6 cm that gives the two other vertices. When all three pairs of vertices have been joined by these arcs, you have a rounded triangle-like figure, known as a *Reuleaux triangle* (pronounced re-low).

Step 3. Carefully cut out the Reuleaux triangle.

b. Draw a pair of parallel lines 6 cm apart, and place the edge of a ruler along one of the lines. Place your cardboard Reuleaux triangle between the lines and roll it along the edge of the ruler. Note any unusual occurrences.

c. Conduct library or Internet research on the Wankel engine. How is it related to your model?

d. Investigate the concept of *shapes of constant width*. What are two other examples of such shapes?

Unit 6

448 UNIT 6 • Circles and Circular Functions

b. $70 \times 4 = 280$ rpm

c. **i.** 280 rpm $\times\ 66\pi \approx 58{,}057$ cm/min, or about 581 meters/min, or about 35 km/hr.

ii. The smallest transmission factor is 1. Each revolution of the pedal sprocket means 1 rotation of the rear sprocket and wheel, or movement of 66π cm. Thus, 70 rpm translates into about 14,514 cm per minute, or about 145 meters per minute, or about 8.7 km per hour.

28 **a.** See the figure on the right. Angles A, B, D, and E are right angles since they are formed by a radius and a tangent line at the point of tangency. Note that $\triangle ACM \cong \triangle BCM$ and $\triangle DCN \cong \triangle ECN$ (SSS Congruence Theorem). $\angle ACM \cong \angle ECN$ since they are vertical angles. So, $\triangle ACM \sim \triangle ECN$ (AA Similarity Theorem). Thus, the four triangles are similar to one another. Some pairs are similar with scale factor of 1.

b. $\overline{AE}$ is one of the two common tangents. Let $CM = x$. Then $CN = 30 - x$. By similar triangles, $\frac{AM}{EN} = \frac{CM}{CN}$. Substituting, $\frac{8}{4} = \frac{x}{30 - x}$. Therefore, $240 - 8x = 4x$, so $12x = 240$ and $CM = x = 20$ cm. It follows that $CN = 30 - 20 = 10$ cm. Now apply the Pythagorean Theorem in $\triangle ACM$ and $\triangle ECN$.

$$AC^2 = CM^2 - AM^2$$
$$AC = \sqrt{20^2 - 8^2} = \sqrt{336} \approx 18.3 \text{ cm}$$

By similar triangles, $\frac{DN}{AM} = \frac{CE}{AC}$, so $\frac{4}{8} = \frac{CE}{18.3}$; $CE = 9.2$ cm. Therefore, the length of common tangent $\overline{AE}$ is $AE = AC + CE \approx 27.5$ cm.

c. The belt's length is the sum of the two common tangents, or 55 cm, plus the portion of the circumference of each circle that the belt is touching. Determine the latter by first finding the common measure of central angles AMB and DNE using trigonometry.

$$m\angle AMC = m\angle BMC = \cos^{-1}\frac{8}{20} \approx 66.4°$$

Therefore, $m\angle AMB \approx 132.8°$. Also by similar triangles, $m\angle DNE \approx 132.8°$. The length of the belt touching the larger circle is:

$$\frac{360 - 132.8}{360} \cdot (2\pi \cdot 8) \approx 31.7 \text{ cm.}$$

It follows by similar triangles that the length of the belt touching the smaller circle is half of this result or about 15.9 cm. The total length of the belt is:

$$31.7 + 15.9 + 2(27.5) = 102.6 \text{ cm.}$$

29 **a.** Students should construct a model similar to the Reuleaux triangle shown here.

b. The shape always touches both lines as it rolls along.

c. The Wankel engine is based on the shape shown here.

d. The *NCTM 1979 Yearbook*, Chapter 18 Applications of Curves of Constant Width, is a good resource for students. A circle and a five-sided shape similar to the Reuleaux triangle are two other shapes of constant width.

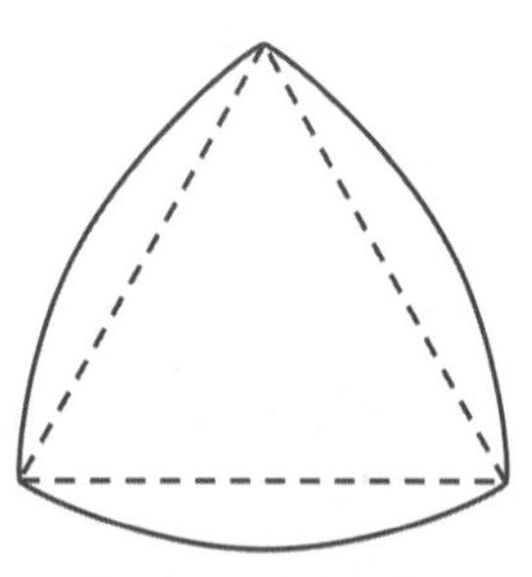

Reuleaux triangle

30 An important idea in calculus involves the ratio $\frac{\sin x}{x}$ for values of x close to 0. Make a table with columns headed x and $\frac{\sin x}{x}$.

a. Using radian mode, complete one table for $x = 1, 0.5, 0.25, 0.1, 0.01, 0.001$, and 0.0001. What appears to be happening to $\frac{\sin x}{x}$ as x approaches 0 in radian mode?

b. Using degree mode, complete a second table with the same headings and same values of x. What appears to be happening to $\frac{\sin x}{x}$ as x approaches 0 in degree mode?

c. Compare your results in Parts a and b to the difference in scale of degrees and radians. Do you see any connection?

31 The electronic pattern of simple sounds, such as those you can view on an oscilloscope, are modeled by trigonometric functions of the form $y = a \sin bt$ or $y = a \cos bt$, where b is expressed in radians per second and t is time in seconds. The period of a sound wave relates to the frequency or number of waves that pass a point each second. The greater the frequency (or shorter the period) of the sound wave, the higher the pitch of the sound.

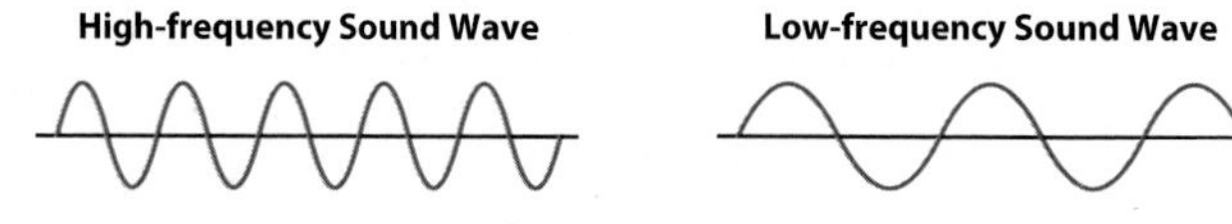

The amplitude $|a|$ represents loudness. The greater the amplitude of the wave, the louder the sound. A good example of a simple sound is the sound produced by a piano tuning fork.

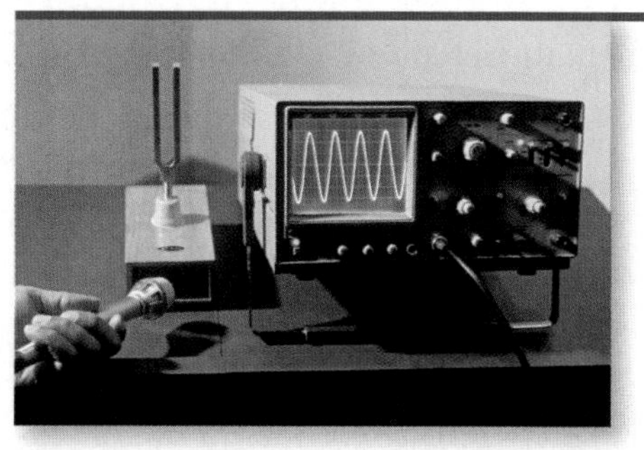

a. The middle C tuning fork oscillates at 264 cycles per second. This is called its frequency. How many radians per second is this?

b. Write a function rule that models the sound of middle C when a is 1.

c. What is the period of the function? How is it related to the frequency of 264 cycles per second?

d. Graph four cycles of the function. If you use 0 for the minimum x value, what should you use for the maximum value?

e. The C note two octaves above middle C has a frequency of 1,056 cycles per second. Model this sound with a function rule. What is the period?

f. The C note that is one octave below middle C has a frequency of 132 cycles per second. Model this sound with a function rule. Graph the function in the same viewing window with the middle C graph from Part b. What do you think is the frequency of the C note one octave above middle C?

30 **a.** Using radian mode, it appears that the ratio is approaching 1 as x approaches 0. The last value $\frac{\sin 0.0001}{0.0001} \approx 0.9999999983$.

b. Using degree mode, it appears that the ratio is approaching 0.0174532925. This is also the decimal approximation of $\frac{\pi}{180}$.

c. The ratio in Part b approaches the ratio of radians to degrees. In calculus, the limit of this ratio is the derivative of the sine function at $x = 0$ or the slope of the tangent line to the sine graph at 0. In radians, the slope is 1, but in degrees it is a much smaller number (about 0.174532925) because the sine curve in degrees has period 360 while in radians the period is a little over 6 (2π, to be exact). In general, in radians the derivative of the sine is the cosine, while in degrees the derivative of the sine is $\frac{\pi}{180}$ times the cosine. As Morris Kline noted, "The advantage of radians over degrees is simply that it is a more convenient unit ..." (see Reflections Task 23).

31 **a.** 264 cycles per second $= 264 \cdot 2\pi = 528\pi$ radians per second

b. $y = 1 \cdot \sin$ (264 cycles/sec $\cdot$ 2π radians per cycle)$x = \sin 528\pi x$, where x is in seconds.

c. The period is $\frac{1}{264}$ seconds. The period is the reciprocal of the frequency.

d. One cycle will occur in $\frac{1}{264}$ seconds. Windows may vary. To show four cycles, use Xmax $= \frac{4}{264}$, Xmin $= 0$, Ymax $= 1.5$, and Ymin $= 1.5$.

e. $y = \sin$ (1,056 cycles/sec $\cdot$ 2π radians/cycle)$x = \sin 2{,}112\pi x$, where x is in seconds. The period is $\frac{1}{1{,}056}$ seconds.

f. $y = \sin$ (132 cycles/sec $\cdot$ 2π radians per cycle)$x = \sin 264\pi x$
See the graphs below.

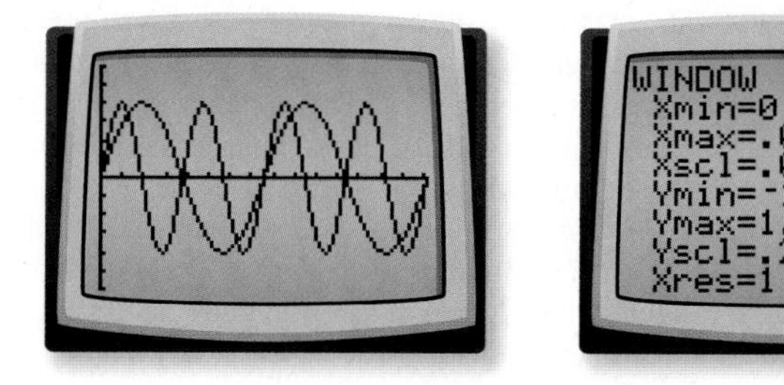

Since middle C shows 4 cycles on this segment and one octave below middle C shows 2 cycles, it seems reasonable that one octave above will show 8 cycles. Since the frequency of middle C is 264 cycles per second and one octave above shows twice the cycles in the same interval, the frequency of one octave above should be 528 cycles per second.

INSTRUCTIONAL NOTE
Students who have completed this problem might be intrigued by the following questions: "What can you see when you look at the graphs of the models for middle C, low C, and the C two octaves above middle C?" (The periods of all the C graphs are multiples of each other. The frequency of the C one octave above middle C is 528 cycles per second.)

On Your Own

32 In this lesson, you learned that the distance from a point on a circle of radius r to the vertical axis of the circle is given by $y = r \cos x$. Similarly, the distance to the horizontal axis of the circle is $y = r \sin x$.

Another way to describe circular motion is to use *parametric equations*, which you will study more fully in Course 4. With parametric equations, a third variable t is introduced, and the x- and y-coordinates of points on the circle are written as separate functions of t.

For an introductory look at this idea for a circle of radius 5 centimeters, set your calculator or computer software to parametric mode and use degrees. Set the viewing window so that t varies from 0 to 360 in steps of 5, x varies from -9 to 9, and y varies from -6 to 6. Then in the functions list, enter $X_T = 5 \cos t$ and $Y_T = 5 \sin t$ as the first pair of functions.

a. Graph and trace values for $t = 30, 60, 90$, and so on.

b. What physical quantity does X_T represent? What physical quantity does Y_T represent?

c. What measurement does t represent? What are the units of t?

d. How much does t change in one revolution of the circle?

e. If one revolution of the circle takes 20 seconds, what is the angular velocity of a point on the circle in units of t per second?

f. What is the linear velocity of a point on the circle in meters per second?

g. What parametric equations would represent circular motion on a circle with a radius of 3 centimeters? Enter them as the second pair of parametric equations in your calculator's function list.

h. Graph at the same time the equations for circles with radii of 3 and 5 cm. (On some calculators, you need to set the mode for simultaneous graphs.) Watch carefully.

- **i.** If the circles both turn with the same angular velocity, on which circle does a point have the greater linear velocity?
- **ii.** What is the linear velocity of the slower point?

33 AM and FM radio stations broadcast programs at various frequencies. The frequency f of a periodic function is the number of cycles per unit of time t. Radio signals broadcast by a given station transmit sound at frequencies that are multiples of 10^3 cycles per second (kilohertz, kHz) or 10^6 cycles per second (megahertz, MHz).

AM radio stations broadcast at frequencies between 520 and 1,610 kHz. An AM radio station broadcasting at 675 kHz sends out a **carrier signal** whose function rule and graph are of the form shown in the diagram below.

Carrier Wave

$y = A_0 \sin (2\pi f \cdot t)$

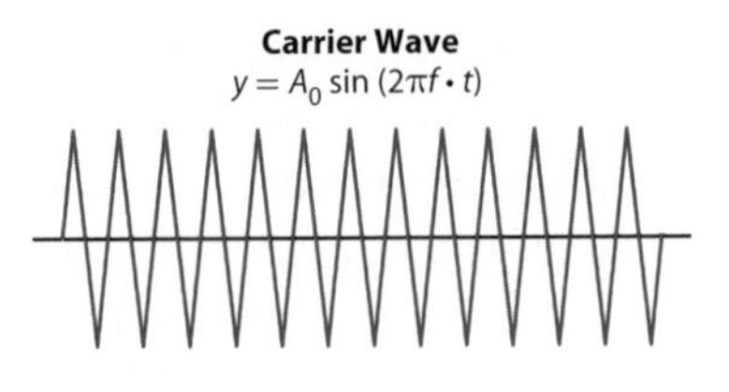

450 UNIT 6 • Circles and Circular Functions

Unit 6

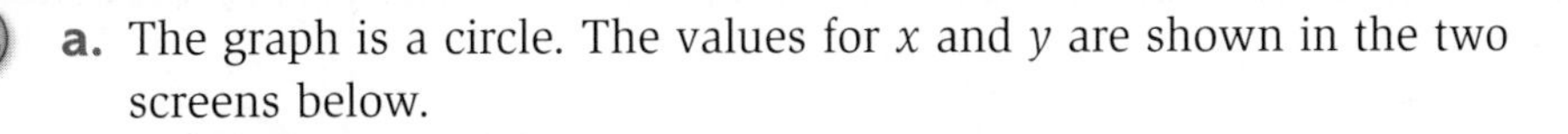

32 **a.** The graph is a circle. The values for x and y are shown in the two screens below.

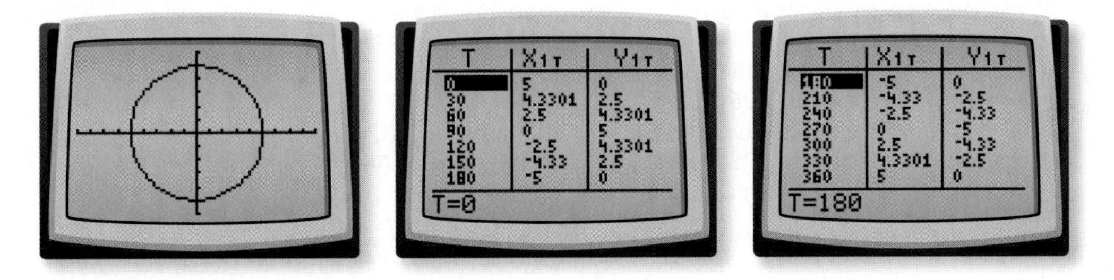

b. X_T represents a point's directed distance from the vertical line going through the center of the circle. Y_T represents a point's directed distance from the horizontal line going through the center of the circle.

c. t represents the measure in degrees of the angle in standard position, that is, measured counterclockwise from the "3 o'clock" position.

d. t goes from 0° to 360° in one revolution.

e. $\frac{360°}{1 \text{ rev}} \cdot \frac{1 \text{ rev}}{20 \text{ sec}} = \frac{360°}{20 \text{ sec}} = 18°$ per sec

f. $\textit{linear velocity} = \frac{\textit{circumference of 1 rev}}{\textit{time for 1 rev}} = \frac{5 \cdot 2\pi \text{ cm}}{20 \text{ sec}} = \frac{10\pi \text{ cm}}{20 \text{ sec}} =$

$\frac{\pi}{2}$ cm/sec ≈ 1.57 cm/sec. Or, using Part e, *linear velocity* =

$\frac{18°}{360°} \cdot 2\pi \cdot 5 = \frac{180\pi \text{ cm}}{360 \text{ sec}} = \frac{\pi}{2}$ cm/sec.

g. $X_T = 3 \cos t$

$Y_T = 3 \sin t$

h. **i.** The point on the 5-cm radius wheel has the greater linear velocity.

ii. The slower point has linear velocity of $\frac{3 \cdot 2\pi \text{ cm}}{20 \text{ sec}} \approx 0.94$ cm/sec.

To transmit program sounds of varying frequencies, an AM station varies or "modulates" the amplitude of the carrier signal. The initials AM refer to **amplitude modulation**. An amplitude-modulated signal has a function rule and graph of the form shown below. Note that the period, and therefore, the frequency, of the carrier wave is left unchanged. The variable amplitude $A_0(t)$ is itself a sinusoidal function representing the broadcast programming.

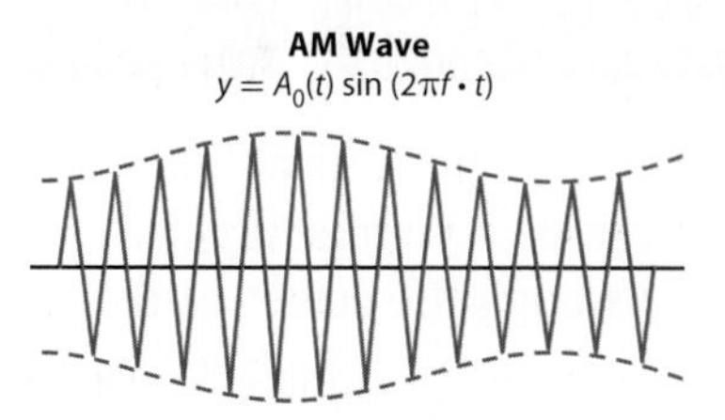

FM radio stations broadcast at frequencies between 87.8 and 108 MHz. An FM (**frequency modulation**) station transmits program sounds by varying the frequency of the carrier signal while keeping the amplitude constant. A frequency-modulated signal has a function rule and graph of the form shown below. The variable frequency $f(t)$ is itself a sinusoidal function representing the broadcast programming.

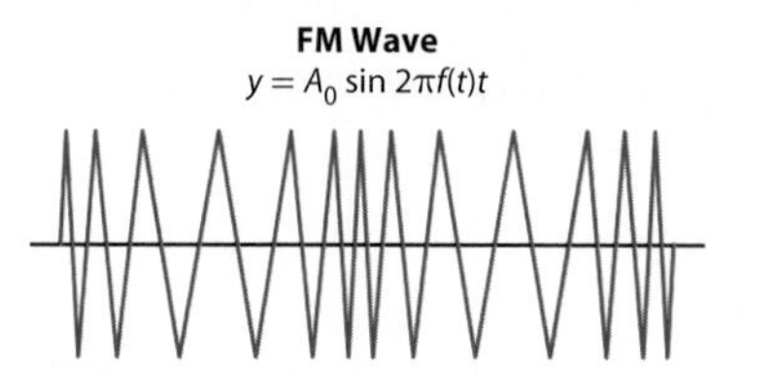

a. A radio station operates at a frequency of 98.5 MHz.

  i. Is the station AM or FM?

  ii. What position on your radio dial would you tune to receive the signals broadcast by this station?

b. Write a function rule for the carrier signal of a radio station that broadcasts at a frequency of 610 kHz. What is the period of the carrier wave for this station?

c. Write a function rule in terms of its variable frequency $f(t)$ for the carrier signal of a radio station that broadcasts at a frequency of 104.1 MHz. What is the period of the carrier wave for this station?

Review

34 Use what you know about the relationships between different units of measurement to complete the following.

a. 7.5 ft = _____ in. = _____ yd

b. 1,780 mm = _____ cm = _____ m

c. 1 yd^2 = _____ ft^2 = _____ in^2

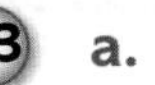

a. i. FM

ii. 98.5 FM

b. $y = A_0(t) \sin 2\pi(610{,}000)t = A_0(t) \sin 1{,}220{,}000\pi t$

$period = \frac{2\pi}{1{,}220{,}000\pi} = \frac{1}{610{,}000} \approx 1.64 \times 10^{-6}$ seconds

c. $y = A_0 \sin (2\pi f(t) \cdot t)$

$period = \frac{2\pi}{2\pi f(t)} = \frac{1}{f(t)}$ seconds

NOTE Each FM frequency gets 0.2 MHz. So, station 104.1 is represented by its center frequency and has 0.1 MHz "play" on either side. Thus, there is no signal overlap with neighboring stations. Therefore, the FM wave's frequency component $f(t)$ could be something like $f(t) = 100{,}000 \sin 2\pi t + 104{,}100{,}000$, where MHz have been converted to Hz and 100,000 is the ± 0.1 MHz around the central frequency for the FM station.

Review

Just in Time

a. 7.5 ft = 90 in. = 2.5 yd

b. 1,780 mm = 178 cm = 1.78 m

c. 1 yd^2 = 9 ft^2 = 1,296 in^2

35 Use algebraic reasoning to find the coordinates of the maximum or minimum point, the x-intercept(s), and the y-intercept of each function.

a. $f(x) = -(x - 5)^2 + 7$

b. $g(x) = x^2 + 6x - 1$

36 Use properties of quadrilaterals to place the special types of quadrilaterals (parallelogram, rectangle, square, rhombus, kite, trapezoid, isosceles trapezoid) in the correct region of Venn diagrams similar to the one below.

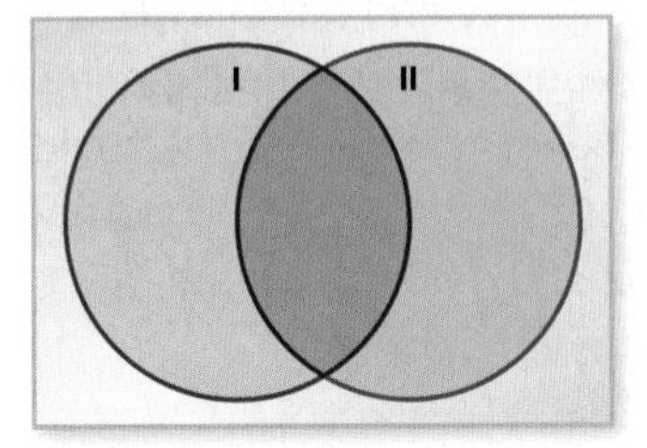

a. **I** Both pairs of opposite sides are parallel.
II Has at least one line of symmetry.

b. **I** Each diagonal divides the figure into two congruent triangles.
II Both diagonals are the same length.

37 Solve each equation for the indicated variable.

a. $C = 2\pi r$ for r

b. $A = \frac{1}{2}h(b_1 + b_2)$ for b_2

c. $E = mc^2$ for c

d. $d = \frac{m}{v}$ for v

38 Suppose that a machine fills bottles of water so that the distribution of the amounts of water in the bottles is normal, with a mean of 16 fluid ounces and a standard deviation of 0.1 ounces.

a. Draw a sketch of the amount of water in the bottles. Include a scale on the horizontal axis.

b. What percentage of the bottles will have less than 16.2 ounces of water in them?

c. What percentage of the bottles will have at least 15.9 ounces of water in them?

39 Using the diagram at the right, determine, for each set of conditions, whether the conditions imply that any pairs of lines are parallel. If so, indicate which lines are parallel.

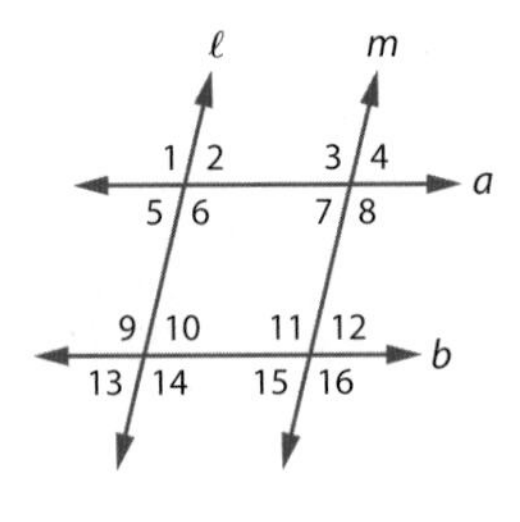

a. $m\angle 9 = m\angle 11$

b. $m\angle 13 = m\angle 7$

c. $m\angle 3 = m\angle 16$

d. $m\angle 1 + m\angle 12 = 180°$ and $m\angle 9 = m\angle 11$

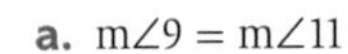

Unit 6

35 **a.** Maximum point: (5, 7)
x-intercepts: $(5 + \sqrt{7}, 0)$, $(5 - \sqrt{7}, 0)$
y-intercept: $(0, -18)$

b. Minimum point: $(-3, -10)$
x-intercepts: $(-3 + \sqrt{10}, 0)$, $(-3 - \sqrt{10}, 0)$
y-intercept: $(0, -1)$

36 **a.**

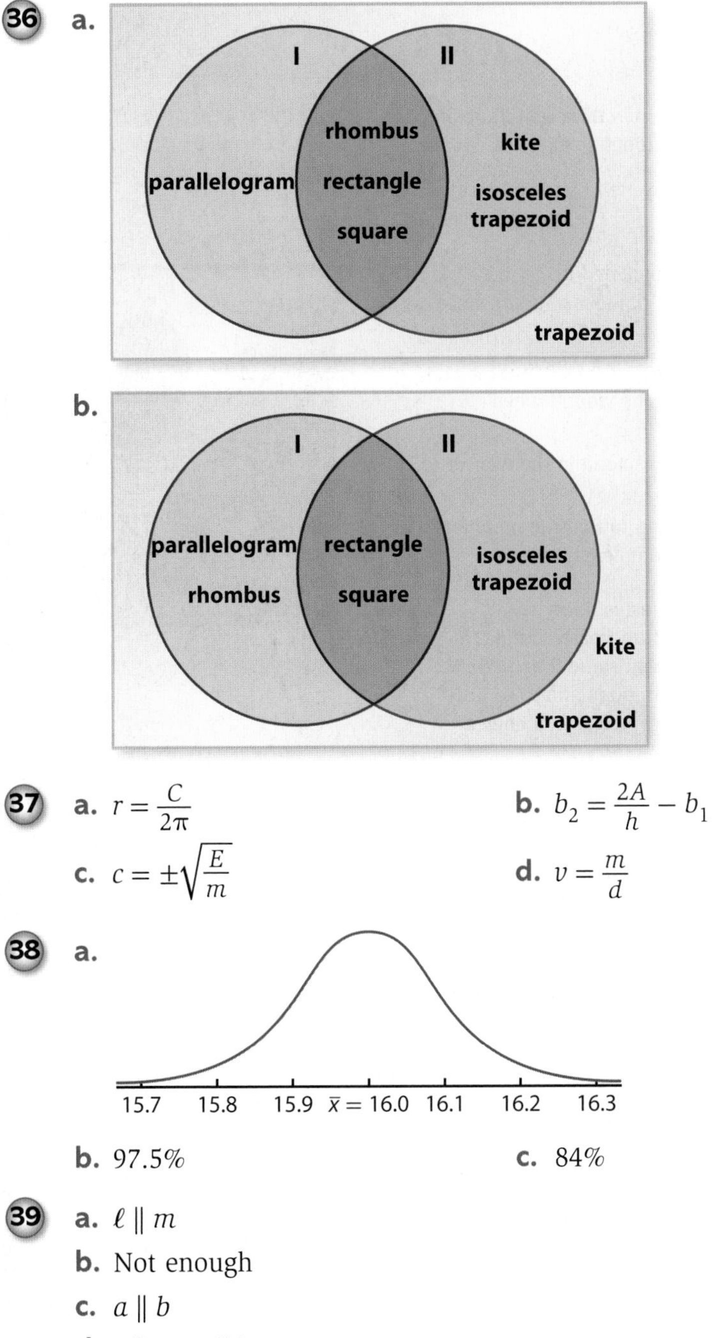

b.

37 **a.** $r = \frac{C}{2\pi}$

b. $b_2 = \frac{2A}{h} - b_1$

c. $c = \pm\sqrt{\frac{E}{m}}$

d. $v = \frac{m}{d}$

38 **a.**

b. 97.5%

c. 84%

39 **a.** $\ell \parallel m$

b. Not enough

c. $a \parallel b$

d. $\ell \parallel m$; $a \parallel b$

40 Simplify each algebraic fraction as much as possible.

a. $\dfrac{16x + 12}{3x + 15}$

b. $\dfrac{x^2 - 9x}{x^2 - 81}$

c. $\dfrac{x^2 + 8x + 15}{x^2 + 2x - 3}$

d. $\dfrac{x - 1}{4x - 4}$

41 Use each *NOW-NEXT* rule to produce a table of values that illustrates the pattern of change from the start value through 5 stages of change.

a. $NEXT = NOW + 2.5$, starting at 3

b. $NEXT = \frac{1}{2}NOW - 50$, starting at 450

42 The number of bacteria in a wound can be modeled using the function $N(t) = 3(8^t)$, where t represents the number of hours since the wound occurred.

a. Evaluate and explain the meaning of $N(2)$.

b. How many bacteria were introduced into the wound when it occurred?

c. How long does it take for the number of bacteria in the wound to double?

d. Write a *NOW-NEXT* rule that could be used to find the number of bacteria present after any number N of complete hours.

43 Between July 1, 2006, and July 1, 2007, the fastest growing metropolitan area in the United States was Palm Coast, Florida. It had an annual growth rate of 7.2%. During that same time period, the Youngstown, Ohio, area saw a decrease in population of 1%. (Source: www.census.gov/Press-Release/www/releases/archives/population/009865.html)

a. The population of Palm Coast was 82,433 on July 1, 2006. What was its approximate population on July 1, 2007?

b. The population of the Youngstown, Ohio, area was 576,602 on July 1, 2006. What was its approximate population on July 1, 2007?

c. Which of these *NOW-NEXT* rules could be used to help calculate the population of the Youngstown, Ohio, area in future years if this rate of decline continues? All rules have a starting value of 576,602.

- $NEXT = 0.01NOW$
- $NEXT = 0.99NOW$
- $NEXT = NOW - 0.01NOW$
- $NEXT = NOW + 0.01NOW$

40 **a.** Cannot be simplified but could be factored: $\dfrac{4(4x + 3)}{3(x + 5)}$

b. $\dfrac{x}{x + 9}$

c. $\dfrac{x + 5}{x - 1}$

d. $\dfrac{1}{4}$

Just in Time

41 **a.**

NOW	*NEXT*
0	3
1	5.5
2	8
3	10.5
4	13
5	15.5

b.

NOW	*NEXT*
0	450
1	175
2	37.5
3	−31.25
4	−65.625
5	−82.8125

Just in Time

42 **a.** $N(2) = 192$. After 2 hours there are 192 bacteria present in the wound.

b. 3 bacteria

c. $\frac{1}{3}$ hour, or 20 minutes

d. $NEXT = NOW \times 8$, starting at 3

Just in Time

43 **a.** $1.072(82{,}433) \approx 88{,}368$ people

b. $0.99(576{,}602) \approx 570{,}836$ people

c. The correct rules are $NEXT = 0.99NOW$ and $NEXT = NOW - 0.01NOW$, both starting at 576,602.

Unit 6

Teaching Resources

Assessment Masters 24–29.

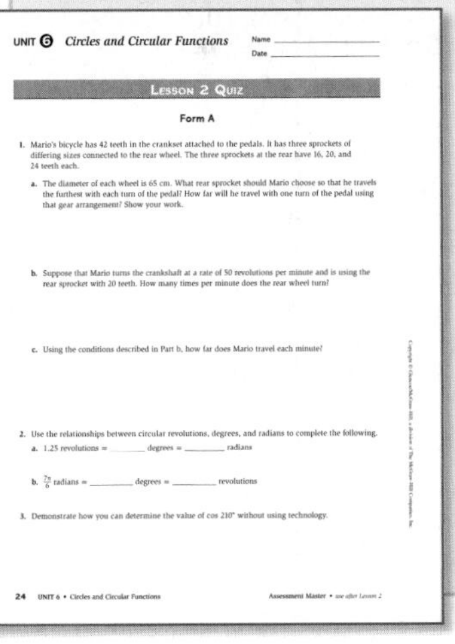

UNIT 6 *Circles and Circular Functions* Name ________ Date ________

LESSON 2 QUIZ

Form A

1. Mario's bicycle has 42 teeth in the crankset attached to the pedals. It has three sprockets of differing sizes connected to the rear wheel. The three sprockets at the rear have 16, 20, and 24 teeth each.
   a. The diameter of each wheel is 65 cm. What rear sprocket should Mario choose so that he travels the furthest with each turn of the pedal? How far will he travel with one turn of the pedal using that gear arrangement? Show your work.
   b. Suppose that Mario turns the crankshaft at a rate of 50 revolutions per minute and is using the rear sprocket with 20 teeth. How many times per minute does the rear wheel turn?
   c. Using the conditions described in Part b, how far does Mario travel each minute?
2. Use the relationships between circular revolutions, degrees, and radians to complete the following.
   a. 1.25 revolutions = ________ degrees = ________ radians
   b. $\frac{7\pi}{6}$ radians = ________ degrees = ________ revolutions
3. Demonstrate how you can determine the value of cos 210° without using technology.

24 UNIT 6 • Circles and Circular Functions Assessment Master • use after Lesson 2

Lesson 3 Looking Back

In this unit, you explored and proved important properties of special lines and angles in circles. To reason about these properties, you drew on methods that used congruent triangles, symmetry, coordinate geometry, and trigonometry. You then built on these circle properties by embarking on a study of characteristics and applications of revolving circles. Your study of circular motion began with a study of pulleys and gears, moved to linear and angular velocity, introduced radian angle measure, and culminated with the study of the sine and cosine functions and their role in modeling aspects of circular motion and other periodic phenomena.

The following tasks will help you review, pull together, and apply what you have learned.

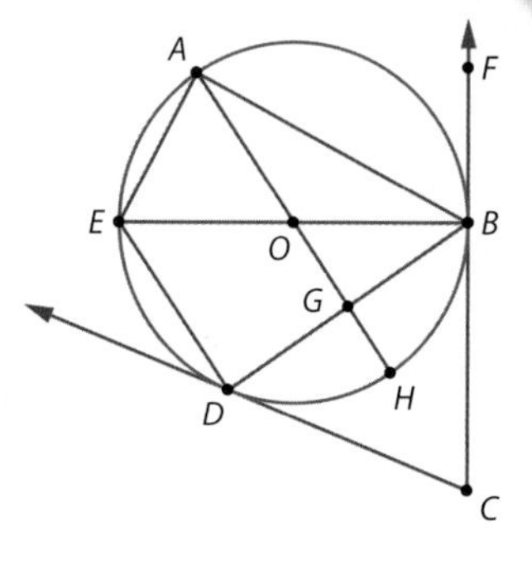

1. A circle with center O has diameters $\overline{BE}$ and $\overline{AH}$. Rays $\overrightarrow{CB}$ and $\overrightarrow{CD}$ are tangent to the circle at points B and D, respectively, and G is the midpoint of chord $\overline{BD}$.

   a. Explain why $m\angle EAB = m\angle EBC = m\angle AGB$.

   b. Suppose $m\widehat{AED} = 124°$ and $m\angle ABF = 62°$. Find the degree measures of $\angle AED$, $\angle BCD$, and $\widehat{DE}$. Explain your reasoning.

2. For each of the following statements, prove the statement if it is true or give a counterexample if it is false.

   a. The midpoint of the common chord of two circles that intersect in two points lies on the line through the centers of the circles.

   b. If inscribed angle $\angle ABC$ in a circle with center O measures $120°$, then central angle $\angle AOC$ measures $120°$.

   c. The angle bisector of any angle inscribed in a circle contains the center of the circle.

   d. If the line through the midpoints of two chords of a circle contains the center of the circle, then the chords are parallel.

Unit 6

454 UNIT 6 • Circles and Circular Functions

Looking Back

INSTRUCTIONAL NOTE There are often several different ways to arrive at correct answers to these measurement questions. Encourage students to compare their different methods.

1. The following justifications are examples. There are other ways to determine many of these measures.

   a. All three angles are right angles: $m\angle BDE = 90°$ because it is inscribed in a semicircle; $m\angle EBC = 90°$ because it is formed by a radius and a line tangent to the circle; and $m\angle AGB = 90°$ because it is formed by a chord and a line through the center of the circle.

   b. The measure of $\widehat{ABD}$ is $360° - 124° = 236°$, so by the Inscribed Angle Theorem, $m\angle AED = 118°$. The measure of $\widehat{AB}$ is $2(m\angle ABF) = 124°$, so the measure of $\widehat{BHD}$ is $236° - 124° = 112°$ and $m\angle CBD = m\angle BCD = 56°$. $m\angle BCD = 180° - 112° = 68°$ by the Angle Sum Theorem for Triangles. The measure of $\widehat{DE}$ is $180° - m\widehat{BHD} = 68°$.

2. **a.** This statement is true. Consider the common chord as a chord of just one of the circles. In that circle, the radius is perpendicular to the chord at its midpoint. The same can be said for the radius of the second circle. Since there is a unique perpendicular to a line at a point on the line, the two radii are collinear, forming the line through the centers, and the midpoint of the chord is on that line.

   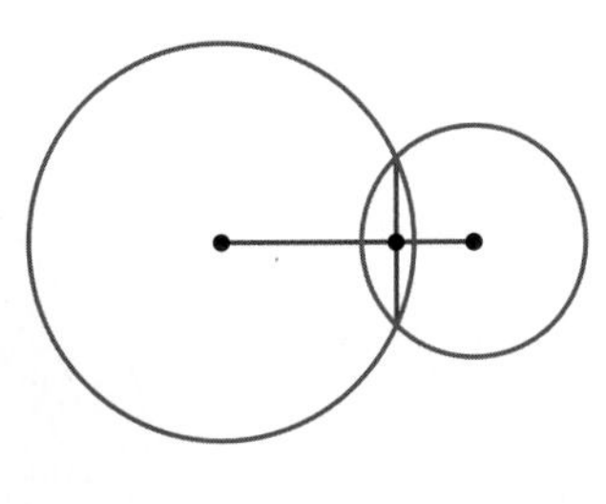

   b. This statement is true. The measure of the arc intercepted by inscribed angle $\angle ABC$ is twice $m\angle ABC$ or 240°. Thus, inscribed angle $\angle ABC$ intercepts major arc $\widehat{AC}$, but central angle $\angle AOC$, by definition, measures less than 180°. So, central angle $\angle AOC$ intercepts minor arc $\widehat{AC}$ whose measure is $360° - 240° = 120°$. By definition, $m\angle AOC = m\widehat{AC} = 120°$.

   c. The diagram at the right provides a counterexample.

   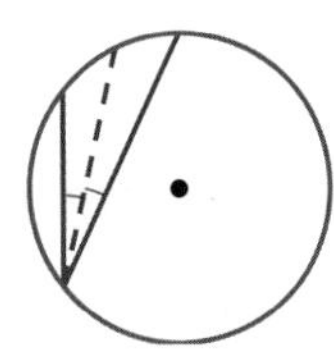

NOTE The solution to Task 2 Part d is on page T455.

3 *Wheel of Fortune* has been the most popular game show in the history of television. On the show, three contestants take turns spinning a large wheel similar to the one at the right. The result determines how much that contestant wins as she or he progresses toward solving a word, phrase, or name puzzle. The wheel is divided into 24 sectors of equal size, each corresponding to a dollar value or some other outcome.

a. If the wheel spins through 3.8 counterclockwise revolutions, what is the degree measure of the angle through which the wheel spins?

b. What is the measure of the minimum positive angle that is *coterminal* with (has the same terminal side as) the angle in Part a?

c. Suppose the wheel starts at the center of the "Bankrupt" sector and spins through 1,055°. Will it stop at "Bankrupt"? Describe the intervals of angle measures that will return the wheel to the "Bankrupt" sector.

Imagine a coordinate system superimposed on the wheel of fortune with its origin at the center of the wheel. Suppose a contestant spins the wheel releasing it at the "3 o'clock" position on the coordinate system, and the wheel completes 2.8 revolutions in 20 seconds.

d. What is the angular velocity in revolutions per second? In radians per second?

e. If the wheel is 10 feet in diameter, what is the average linear velocity in feet per second of a point on the edge of the wheel?

f. What are the coordinates of the release point when the wheel stops at the end of 20 seconds? Explain your reasoning.

4 The Thames River passes through the heart of London, England. Ships entering that part of the river need to pass under a number of bridges like the famous Tower Bridge. The height of the Tower Bridge above the river (in meters) varies over time (in hours following high tide) according to $d(t) = 12 + 3.4 \cos 0.5t$.

a. What are the maximum and minimum distances from the bridge to the river?

b. What are the period and amplitude of variation in distance from the bridge to the river?

c. How often in one day does the distance from bridge to river complete a full cycle from maximum to minimum and back to maximum?

d. This statement is false, in general. As a counterexample, consider two diameters of a circle. A diameter is a chord. The common midpoint of the two diameters is the center of the circle, so any line ℓ through the center of the circle contains both midpoints, yet the diameters are not parallel. (If the given chords are not diameters, the statement would be true because both chords would be perpendicular to the diameter that contains the midpoints of the chords.)

3 a. $3.8(360°) = 1{,}368°$

b. $-0.2(360°) = -72°$

c. There are 24 equal intervals, so each sector is determined by a central angle of 15°. A rotation of 1,055° is 25° short of three full rotations of the wheel. Thus, it will not bring the wheel back to the "Bankrupt" sector. Spins of $360n \pm 7.5°$ will return the wheel to the "Bankrupt" sector for any integer n.

d. Its average angular velocity was $\frac{2.8}{20} = 0.14$ revolutions per second. This is $0.14(2\pi) \approx 0.88$ radians per second.

e. The circumference of the wheel is 10π feet, so its average linear velocity on this spin was $\frac{2.8(10\pi)}{20} \approx 4.4$ ft/sec.

f. 2.8 revolutions $= 5.6\pi$ radians, so the coordinates of the release point when the wheel stops are $(10 \cos 5.6\pi, 10 \sin 5.6\pi) \approx (3.09, -0.95)$.

4 a. The maximum distance is 15.4 meters.
The minimum distance is 8.6 meters.

b. The period is 4π hours, or about 12.6 hours.
The amplitude is 3.4 meters.

c. The frequency of the height function is a bit less than 2. This is calculated by dividing the number of hours in a day by the period of the function, $24 \div 4\pi \approx 1.9$. Those who live near tidal waters will recognize that the high and low tides do not occur at the same time each day. Instead, they "advance" about an hour each day.

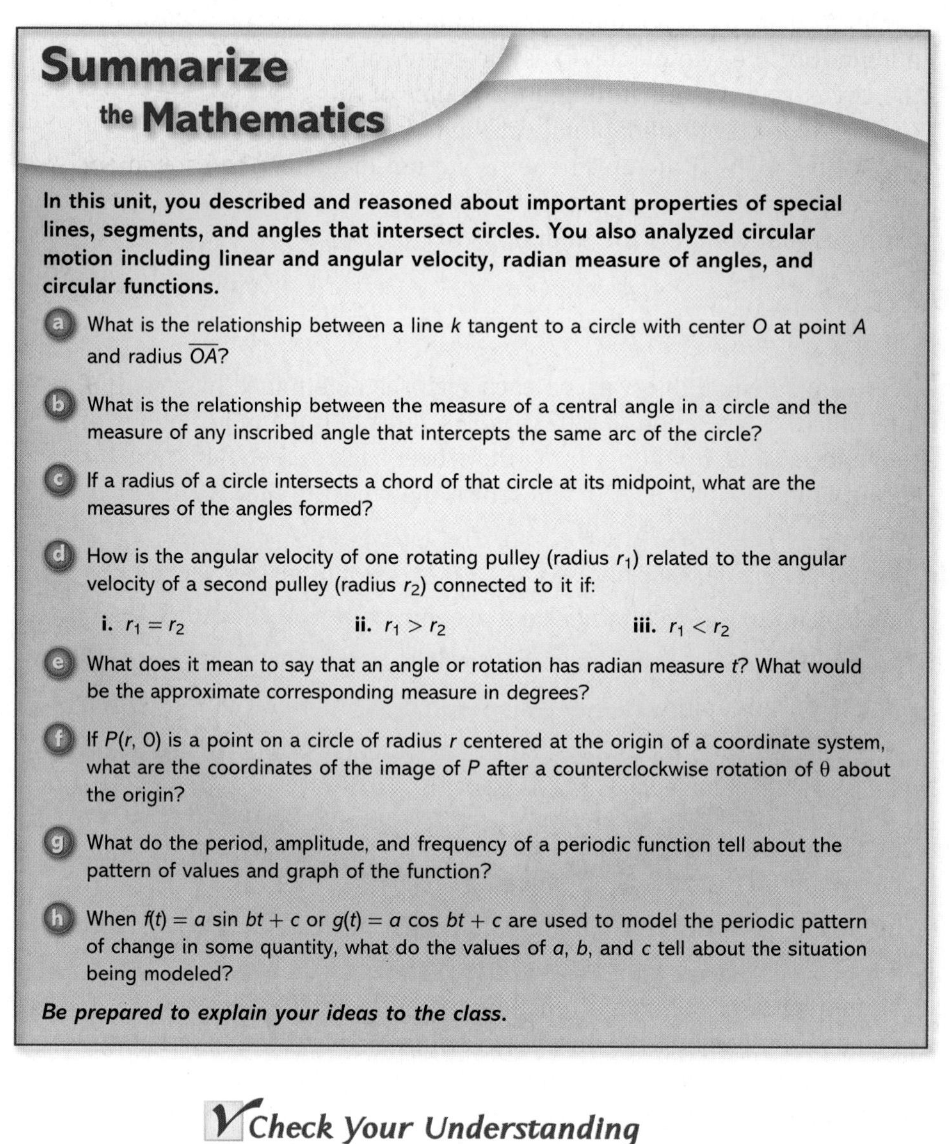

Summarize the Mathematics

In this unit, you described and reasoned about important properties of special lines, segments, and angles that intersect circles. You also analyzed circular motion including linear and angular velocity, radian measure of angles, and circular functions.

a. What is the relationship between a line k tangent to a circle with center O at point A and radius $\overline{OA}$?

b. What is the relationship between the measure of a central angle in a circle and the measure of any inscribed angle that intercepts the same arc of the circle?

c. If a radius of a circle intersects a chord of that circle at its midpoint, what are the measures of the angles formed?

d. How is the angular velocity of one rotating pulley (radius r_1) related to the angular velocity of a second pulley (radius r_2) connected to it if:

i. $r_1 = r_2$ **ii.** $r_1 > r_2$ **iii.** $r_1 < r_2$

e. What does it mean to say that an angle or rotation has radian measure t? What would be the approximate corresponding measure in degrees?

f. If $P(r, 0)$ is a point on a circle of radius r centered at the origin of a coordinate system, what are the coordinates of the image of P after a counterclockwise rotation of θ about the origin?

g. What do the period, amplitude, and frequency of a periodic function tell about the pattern of values and graph of the function?

h. When $f(t) = a \sin bt + c$ or $g(t) = a \cos bt + c$ are used to model the periodic pattern of change in some quantity, what do the values of a, b, and c tell about the situation being modeled?

Be prepared to explain your ideas to the class.

✓ Check Your Understanding

Write, in outline form, a summary of the important mathematical concepts and methods developed in this unit. Organize your summary so that it can be used as a quick reference in future units and courses.

456 UNIT 6 • Circles and Circular Functions

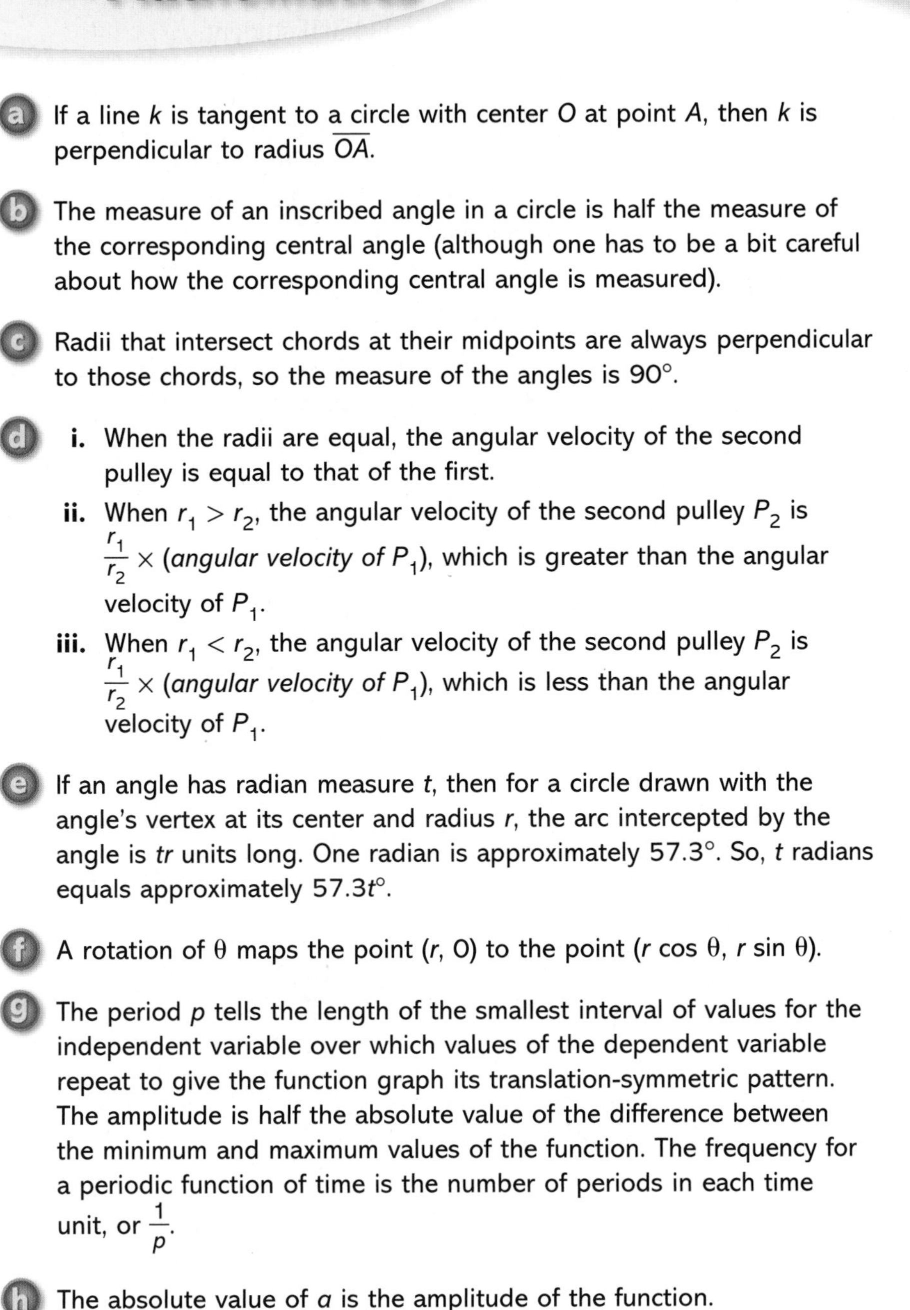

Summarize the Mathematics

a. If a line k is tangent to a circle with center O at point A, then k is perpendicular to radius $\overline{OA}$.

b. The measure of an inscribed angle in a circle is half the measure of the corresponding central angle (although one has to be a bit careful about how the corresponding central angle is measured).

c. Radii that intersect chords at their midpoints are always perpendicular to those chords, so the measure of the angles is 90°.

d.
- **i.** When the radii are equal, the angular velocity of the second pulley is equal to that of the first.
- **ii.** When $r_1 > r_2$, the angular velocity of the second pulley P_2 is $\frac{r_1}{r_2} \times$ (*angular velocity of* P_1), which is greater than the angular velocity of P_1.
- **iii.** When $r_1 < r_2$, the angular velocity of the second pulley P_2 is $\frac{r_1}{r_2} \times$ (*angular velocity of* P_1), which is less than the angular velocity of P_1.

e. If an angle has radian measure t, then for a circle drawn with the angle's vertex at its center and radius r, the arc intercepted by the angle is tr units long. One radian is approximately 57.3°. So, t radians equals approximately $57.3t°$.

f. A rotation of θ maps the point $(r, 0)$ to the point $(r \cos \theta, r \sin \theta)$.

g. The period p tells the length of the smallest interval of values for the independent variable over which values of the dependent variable repeat to give the function graph its translation-symmetric pattern. The amplitude is half the absolute value of the difference between the minimum and maximum values of the function. The frequency for a periodic function of time is the number of periods in each time unit, or $\frac{1}{p}$.

h. The absolute value of a is the amplitude of the function.

The value of b is used to adjust the basic period of 2π for sine and cosine to produce functions with shorter or longer periods. The value of b is related to the period p by the equivalent equations $bp = 2\pi$, $b = \frac{2\pi}{p}$, and $p = \frac{2\pi}{b}$.

The value of c is used to adjust the values of the basic sine and cosine functions up or down by a constant amount when the periodic variation being modeled oscillates around c rather than 0.

Teaching Resources

Transparency Masters 30–31.

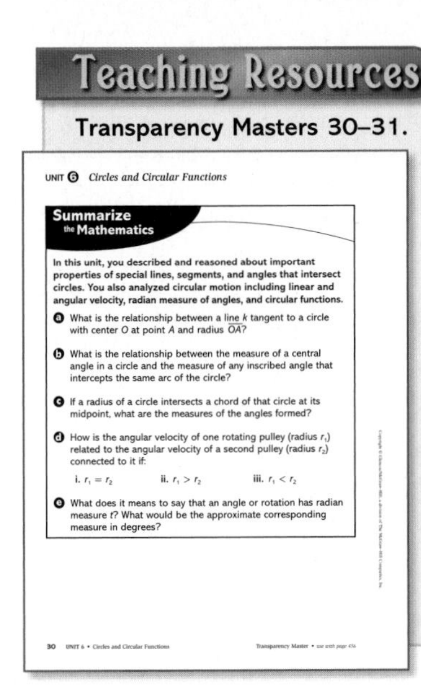

UNIT 6 *Circles and Circular Functions*

Summarize the Mathematics

In this unit, you described and reasoned about important properties of special lines, segments, and angles that intersect circles. You also analyzed circular motion including linear and angular velocity, radian measure of angles, and circular functions.

a. What is the relationship between a line k tangent to a circle with center O at point A and radius $\overline{OA}$?

b. What is the relationship between the measure of a central angle in a circle and the measure of any inscribed angle that intercepts the same arc of the circle?

c. If a radius of a circle intersects a chord of that circle at its midpoint, what are the measures of the angles formed?

d. How is the angular velocity of one rotating pulley (radius r_1) related to the angular velocity of a second pulley (radius r_2) connected to it if:

i. $r_1 = r_2$ ii. $r_1 > r_2$ iii. $r_1 < r_2$

e. What does it mean to say that an angle or rotation has radian measure t? What would be the approximate corresponding measure in degrees?

Unit 6

Teaching Resources

Student Masters 32–33.

Assessment Masters 34–54.

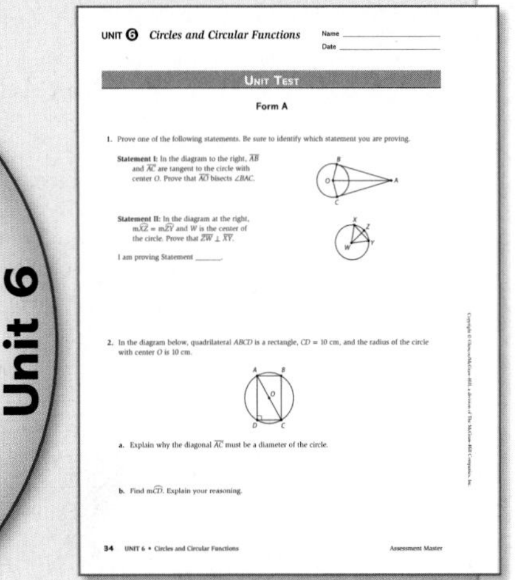

UNIT 6 *Circles and Circular Functions* Name ______ Date ______

UNIT TEST

Form A

1. Prove one of the following statements. Be sure to identify which statement you are proving.

Statement I: In the diagram to the right, $\overline{AB}$ and $\overline{AC}$ are tangent to the circle with center O. Prove that $\overline{AO}$ bisects $\angle BAC$.

Statement II: In the diagram at the right, $m\widehat{XZ} = m\widehat{ZY}$ and W is the center of the circle. Prove that $\overline{ZW} \perp \overline{XY}$.

I am proving Statement ______.

2. In the diagram below, quadrilateral $ABCD$ is a rectangle, $CD = 10$ cm, and the radius of the circle with center O is 10 cm.

a. Explain why the diagonal $\overline{AC}$ must be a diameter of the circle.

b. Find $m\widehat{CD}$. Explain your reasoning.

34 UNIT 6 • Circles and Circular Functions Assessment Master

Student Masters 55–56.

Unit 6

Check Your Understanding

You may wish to have students use the Teaching Master, *Circles and Circular Functions* Unit Summary, to help them organize the information. Above all, this should be something that is useful to the individual student.

Practicing for Standardized Tests

Each Practicing for Standardized Tests master presents 10 questions in the multiple-choice format of test items similar to how they often appear in standardized tests. Answers are provided below.

Answers to Practice Set 6

1. (b)	**2.** (b)	**3.** (d)	**4.** (e)	**5.** (d)
6. (b)	**7.** (b)	**8.** (a)	**9.** (b)	**10.** (a)

Teacher Notes

Recursion and Iteration

In previous units, you have used equations, tables, and graphs to investigate linear, exponential, polynomial, and periodic patterns of change. You have used coordinates and matrices to model geometric change in position, size, and shape. In many situations, it is also important to understand step-by-step sequential change, such as yearly change in population or hourly change in antibiotic concentration after taking medication.

Recursion and iteration are powerful tools for studying sequential change. You have already used recursion and iteration when you used *NOW-NEXT* rules to solve problems. In this unit, you will study sequential change more fully. The concepts and skills needed are developed in the following three lessons.

Lessons

1 *Modeling Sequential Change Using Recursion and Iteration*

Represent and solve problems related to sequential change, using subscript and function notation and technological tools, such as spreadsheets.

2 *A Recursive View of Functions*

Analyze linear, exponential, and polynomial functions from a recursive point of view, specifically through the study of arithmetic and geometric sequences and finite differences tables.

3 *Iterating Functions*

Investigate the general process of iterating functions, and completely analyze the behavior of linear functions when they are iterated, including an analysis of slope to identify attracting and repelling fixed points.

Recursion and Iteration

Unit Overview

Although the words "recursion" and "iteration" have not yet been explicitly used in *Core-Plus Mathematics*, they represent a key theme in the curriculum, primarily as seen so far in terms of work with *NOW-NEXT* rules. Recursion and iteration are powerful tools for representing and solving problems related to sequential change. *Sequential change* is step-by-step change, such as population change year-by-year. *Recursion* is the method of describing a given step in a sequential process in terms of previous steps. *Iteration* is the process of repeating the same procedure or computation over and over again.

This unit formalizes the development of recursion and iteration while exploring some common applications, like compound interest, and related topics, such as arithmetic and geometric sequences. The major topics in this unit are recursive formulas (also called recurrence relations, recurrences, or difference equations), arithmetic and geometric sequences, arithmetic and geometric sums, finite differences, and function iteration (which implicitly includes function composition). The unit also provides a review of linear, exponential, and polynomial functions.

In a sense, this unit is mainly about recursive formulas of the form $A_n = rA_{n-1} + b$. Such recursive formulas can be called *combined recursive formulas* because they are a combination of the basic recursive formulas that give rise to arithmetic and geometric sequences. Recursive formulas of this form have several different names in discrete mathematics texts. For example, they are also called affine recurrence relations or first-order linear difference equations with constant coefficients. In Lesson 1, real-world situations are modeled with combined recursive formulas. In Lesson 2, students investigate combined recursive formulas with $r = 1$, producing arithmetic sequences, and combined recursive formulas with $b = 0$, producing geometric sequences. In Lesson 3, the emphasis is on iterating linear functions, which corresponds to sequentially evaluating combined recursive formulas.

Unit Objectives

- Use iteration and recursion as tools to represent, analyze, and solve problems involving sequential change
- Formalize and consolidate previous study of *NOW-NEXT* rules, particularly through the use of subscript notation and the introduction of recursive formulas
- Understand and apply arithmetic and geometric sequences and series
- Understand and apply finite differences tables
- Explore function iteration and, in the process, informally introduce function composition
- Understand and apply recursive formulas, particularly combined recursive formulas of the form $A_n = rA_{n-1} + b$
- Review linear, exponential, and polynomial models from a recursive perspective

CPMP-Tools

The spreadsheet software in *CPMP-Tools* can be used to examine sequences and (*term number, sequence value*) scatterplots. The "Function Iteration" custom tool has been developed to use with Lesson 3. In addition, the data analysis software can be used with finite differences tables to find function formulas for certain sequences once a constant finite difference is found to determine the power of the associated polynomial function.

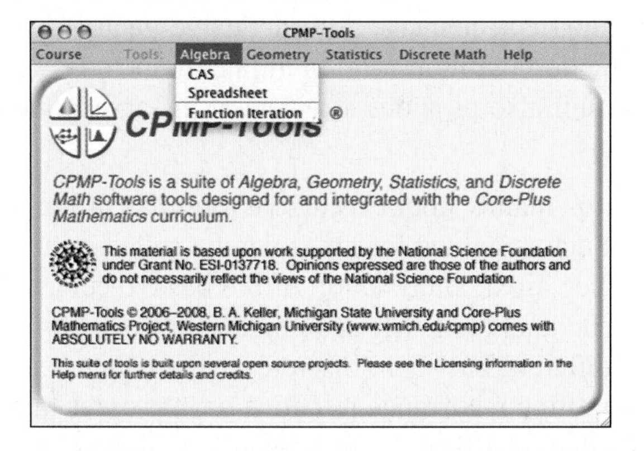

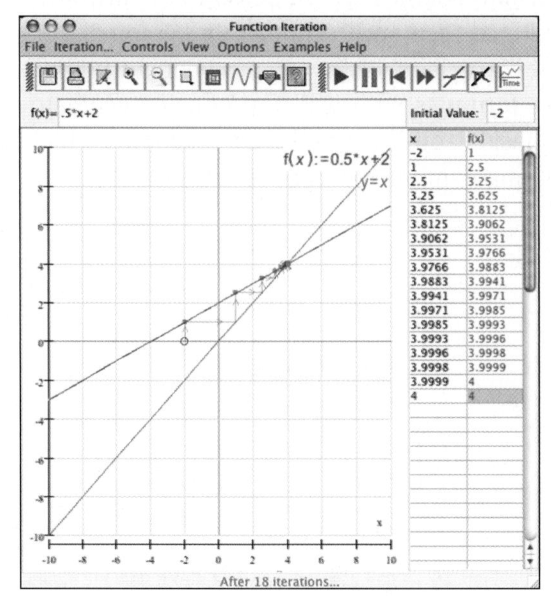

Unit 7 Planning Guide

Lesson Objectives	On Your Own Assignments*	Suggested Pacing	Materials
Lesson 1 ***Modeling Sequential Change Using Recursion and Iteration*** • Use iteration and recursion to model real-world situations involving sequential change • Understand the basic concepts of recursive formulas, particularly those of the form $A_n = A_{n-1} + b$ • Understand the effects of changing certain parameters on the long-term behavior of recursive formulas and the situations they model • Use subscript notation and spreadsheet software to represent formulas that use the words *NOW* and *NEXT* and to take advantage of this notation and spreadsheet software to analyze recursive formulas more efficiently	**After Investigation 1:** A1, A2, A3ab, Rv21–Rv24 **After Investigation 2:** A3c–e, A4 or A5, A6, choose one of C7, C8, or C10, choose one of R11–R13, R14, choose one of E15–E20, Rv25, Rv26	4 days (including assessment)	• Unit Resources • *CPMP-Tools* or other spreadsheet software
Lesson 2 ***A Recursive View of Functions*** • Understand arithmetic sequences and their connections to linear functions, using recursive formulas, function formulas, and applications • Understand geometric sequences and their connections to exponential functions, using recursive formulas, function formulas, and applications • Understand and apply arithmetic and geometric series (sums of sequences) • Use finite differences tables to find function formulas for certain recursive formulas and to describe the connection between such tables and polynomial functions • Use linear, exponential, and polynomial functions to model discrete situations	**After Investigation 1:** A1, A2, A3 or A4, C9, C10, R16, E21, Rv27–Rv30 **After Investigation 2:** A5, A6, C11, C12 or C13, C14 or C15, R18 or R19, E21, E22, Rv30–Rv33 **After Investigation 3:** A7, A8, choose one of E23–E25, Rv34, Rv35	6 days (including assessment)	• Unit Resources
Lesson 3 ***Iterating Functions*** • Iterate functions and describe the resulting patterns, the long-term behavior in particular • Describe the connection between function iteration and recursive formulas • Analyze long-term behavior when iterating linear functions, using graphical iteration, numerical iteration, and algebraic methods, including fixed point analysis and connections to slope	**After Investigation 1:** A1, A2 or A3, C8, C9, choose one of R13–R15, Rv22–Rv25 **After Investigation 2:** Choose one of A4–A6, A7, C10 and C11 or C11 and C12, R16, R17, choose one of E18–E21, Rv26, Rv27	5 days (including assessment)	• Unit Resources • *CPMP-Tools* "Function Iteration" custom tool
Lesson 4 ***Looking Back*** • Review and synthesize the major objectives of the unit		2 days (including assessment)	• Unit Resources

** When choice is indicated, it is important to leave the choice to the student.*

Note: *It is best if Organizing tasks are discussed as a whole class after they have been assigned as homework.*

LESSON 1

Modeling Sequential Change Using Recursion and Iteration

Wildlife management has become an increasingly important issue as modern civilization puts greater demands on wildlife habitat. Tracking annual changes in the size of wildlife population is essential to effective management. In previous units, you have used *NOW-NEXT* rules or formulas to model situations involving sequential change. Now you will examine sequential change more fully.

458 UNIT 7 • Recursion and Iteration

LESSON 1

Modeling Sequential Change Using Recursion and Iteration

Throughout *Core-Plus Mathematics*, students have informally worked with recursion and iteration, using *NOW-NEXT* rules. This lesson begins more formal study of recursion. In particular, *NOW-NEXT* formulas are represented with subscript notation, function notation, and with spreadsheet software. In the process, combined recursive formulas of the form $A_n = rA_{n-1} + b$ are studied.

Lesson Objectives

- Use iteration and recursion to model real-world situations involving sequential change
- Understand the basic concepts of recursive formulas, particularly those of the form $A_n = A_{n-1} + b$
- Understand the effects of changing certain parameters on the long-term behavior of recursive formulas and the situations they model
- Use subscript notation and spreadsheet software to represent formulas that use the words *NOW* and *NEXT* and to take advantage of this notation and spreadsheet software to analyze recursive formulas more efficiently

Lesson Launch

This launch sets up the context for the investigation, generates some student interest, and foreshadows some of the key ideas, particularly the ideas of sequential change and long-term behavior.

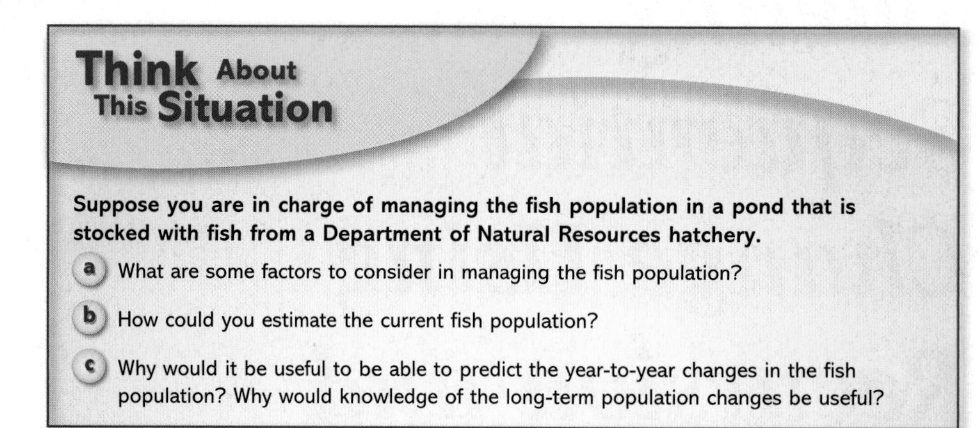

Think About This Situation

Suppose you are in charge of managing the fish population in a pond that is stocked with fish from a Department of Natural Resources hatchery.

a. What are some factors to consider in managing the fish population?

b. How could you estimate the current fish population?

c. Why would it be useful to be able to predict the year-to-year changes in the fish population? Why would knowledge of the long-term population changes be useful?

In this unit, you will use recursion and iteration to represent and solve problems related to sequential change, such as year-to-year change in a population or month-to-month change in the amount of money owed on a loan. You will use subscript notation and function notation. Spreadsheet software will be used to help with the analysis.

Investigation 1 Modeling Population Change

The first step in analyzing sequential change situations, like the fish population situation, is to build a mathematical model. As you work on the problems of this investigation, look for answers to this question:

How can you construct and use a mathematical model to help you analyze a changing fish population?

As you have seen before, a typical first step in mathematical modeling is simplifying the problem and deciding on some reasonable assumptions. Three factors that you may have listed in the Think About This Situation discussion are initial fish population in the pond, annual growth rate of the population, and annual restocking amount, that is, the number of fish added to the pond each year. For the rest of this investigation, use just the following assumptions.

- There are 3,000 fish currently in the pond.
- 1,000 fish are added at the end of each year.
- The population decreases by 20% each year (taking into account the combined effect of all causes, including births, natural deaths, and fish being caught).

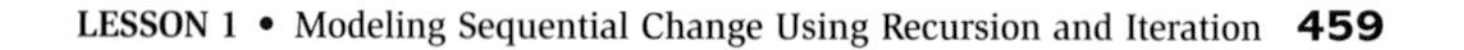

Think About This Situation

a Factors include size of the pond, distance from the hatchery, weather, personnel, equipment, money, regulations, food supply, general pond ecology, size of fish population, restocking amount, catch rate, birthrate, death rate, and predators. Students may suggest other factors.

b You might estimate the current population by catch-and-release sampling (for example, catch 100 fish, tag and release them, and then catch another 100 to see what proportion is tagged). You could also use a fishing sonar device.

c It would be useful to predict year-to-year and long-term changes so that short-term and long-term plans could be made for such things as budgets, times and seasons of operation, staffing, and many of the other factors listed in Part a.

Teaching Resources

Transparency Master 1.

UNIT 7 *Recursion and Iteration*

Think About This Situation

Suppose you are in charge of managing the fish population in a pond that is stocked with fish from a Department of Natural Resources hatchery.

a What are some factors to consider in managing the fish population?

b How could you estimate the current fish population?

c Why would it be useful to be able to predict the year-to-year changes in the fish population? Why would knowledge of the long-term population changes be useful?

Transparency Master • *use with page 459* UNIT 7 • Recursion and Iteration 1

Investigation 1 Modeling Population Change

The main focus of the unit in general and this investigation in particular is to examine the behavior of recursive formulas, starting with the familiar *NOW-NEXT* rules. This investigation is frequently a delight for students and teacher alike, as it is both practical and puzzling. Your students may be surprised to discover that the long-term population of the fish pond is not dependent on the starting population but only on the die-off rate and the restocking amount.

There should be some discussion of rounding in this investigation since the population must be a whole number of fish. Some students may think that rounding up does not make sense since, for example, 0.57 fish does not give another whole fish. However, you may want to discuss that these numbers are estimates and that it really may not matter if answers are rounded up or down.

1. Using these assumptions, build a mathematical model to analyze the population growth in the pond as follows.

   a. Estimate of the population after one year. Estimate the population after two years. Describe how you computed these estimates. What additional details did you assume to get the answers that you have?

   b. Assume that the population decreases by 20% *before* the 1,000 new fish are added. Also assume that the population after each year is the population *after* the 1,000 new fish are added. Are these the assumptions you used to compute your answers in Part a? If not, go back and recompute using these assumptions. Explain why these assumptions are reasonable. These are the assumptions you will use for the rest of this analysis.

   c. Write a formula using the words *NOW* and *NEXT* to model this situation as specified in Part b.

   d. Use the formula from Part c and the last-answer feature of your calculator or computer software to find the population after seven years. Explain how the keystrokes or software features you used correspond to the words *NOW* and *NEXT* in the formula.

2. Now think about the patterns of change in the long-term population of fish in the pond.

   a. Do you think the population will grow without bound? Level off? Die out? Make a quick guess about the long-term population. Compare your guess to those made by other students.

   b. Determine the long-term population by continuing the work that you started in Part d of Problem 1.

   c. Explain why the long-term population you have determined is reasonable. Give a general explanation in terms of the fishing pond ecology. Also, based on the assumptions above, explain mathematically why the long-term population is reasonable.

   d. Does the fish population change faster around year 5 or around year 25? How can you tell?

3. What do you think will happen to the long-term population of fish if the initial population is different but all other conditions remain the same? Make an educated guess. Then check your guess by finding the long-term population for a variety of initial populations. Describe the pattern of change in long-term population as the initial population varies.

4. Investigate what happens to the long-term population if the annual restocking amount changes but all other conditions are the same as in the original assumptions. Describe as completely as you can the relationship between long-term population and restocking amount.

Unit 7

460 UNIT 7 • Recursion and Iteration

1 **a.** The most common answer from students for the population after one year is likely to be 3,400 fish. However, some students might possibly get 2,400 or 3,200, depending on whether the computation for the 20% reduction is done before or after the restocking occurs, and whether the final population for each year is computed before or after the restocking occurs. For example, if students reduce the population by 20% *after* the restocking occurs, then the population they would compute after one year would be $0.8(3{,}000 + 1{,}000) = 3{,}200$. If they reduce the population by 20% *before* the restocking occurs and also compute the final population *before* the restocking occurs, then the population they would compute after one year would be $0.8(3{,}000) = 2{,}400$. The assumptions made in these two examples (which students in actual classes have made) are not as reasonable as the assumptions given in the student text for Part b.

b. The population after one year under these assumptions is $0.8(3{,}000) + 1{,}000 = 3{,}400$.

It seems more sensible to assume that the 20% decrease happens over the course of a year, then at the end of the year 1,000 fish are added, and the final population for the year is the population after the reduction and the restocking have occurred. Students should explain why these are more reasonable assumptions.

c. $NEXT = 0.8NOW + 1{,}000$, or $NEXT = NOW - 0.2NOW + 1{,}000$, starting at 3,000.

d. There will be 4,580.57, or approximately 4,580 fish after 7 years.

Students should explain the keystrokes or software features they used so that they know how the calculator or computer procedure relates to the *NOW-NEXT* representation and the situation. For example, *NOW* corresponds to the number (of fish) currently displayed on the calculator screen. *NOW* also corresponds to the "last-answer" feature; it is the answer you have now. *NEXT* corresponds to the number displayed after a calculation.

2 **a.** The results of the long-term analysis can be surprising. Students should make conjectures based on their current computations and their intuition. You will probably have students who think the population will grow without bound and others who think it will level off. It is not possible for the pond not to have any fish in it since 1,000 fish are added each year.

KEY IDEA Mathematical modeling is an important skill for students to develop. In this problem, they need to carefully consider the assumptions that they use in order to compute the population and find the *NOW-NEXT* formula that models the situation.

INSTRUCTIONAL NOTE
This situation is primarily analyzed using a recursive model. An explicit formula (e.g., a $y =$ rule) is somewhat complex and is not expected here. Explicit formulas are investigated in the On Your Own tasks beginning with Connections Task 7 on page 472.

TECHNOLOGY NOTE
Spreadsheets will be used in the next investigation. If your students are already using spreadsheets here, that is fine. If not, using the last-answer feature of a graphing calculator is the best tool to use for now.

DIFFERENTIATION
In Problems 2–5, all students should investigate population patterns numerically, using technology. Some students may choose, or you may encourage some students, to also look for algebraic rules that describe and explain the patterns.

b. The long-term population levels out at 5,000. Students can determine this population by repeating the necessary calculations using technology, as in Part d of Problem 1.

c. This long-term population seems reasonable in terms of reaching a point at which the pond ecology is in balance (for example, neither too much nor too little food). More precisely, students should be able to reason about the long-term population using the given assumptions. Encourage them to examine the assumptions and think about how they determine the long-term population. Students should reason and discuss until they get a good explanation. For example, they may say that the population will level out when the restocking amount (1,000) is the same as the amount lost due to the decrease rate. This will happen at a population of 5,000 since 20% of 5,000 is 1,000. Some students may use this reasoning to set up and solve an equation. That is, the long-term population must be a number L such that $0.2L = 1{,}000$, which means that $L = 5(1{,}000) = 5{,}000$.

d. The fish population changes faster around year 5 than around year 25. It changes most quickly in the beginning, and then it levels off and has small changes when the population gets close to 5,000. Students should compare population changes from years 4 to 5, years 5 to 6, years 24 to 25, and years 25 to 26. They may refer to rate of change.

3 Students may conjecture that the long-term population will be different if the initial population is different. Surprisingly, this is not the case. The long-term population will always be 5,000, no matter what the initial population is. If the initial population is smaller than 5,000, the population will increase (more rapidly at the beginning) to 5,000. If the initial population is greater than 5,000, the population will decrease (more rapidly at the beginning) to 5,000.

INSTRUCTIONAL NOTE
In Problems 4 and 5, encourage students to be as specific as possible when describing relationships. During the STM discussion of Part d, students who have been quite specific in their analysis can be asked to report their thinking.

4 Long-term population and restocking amount are directly proportional. For example, if the restocking amount quadruples, so does the long-term population. Students may notice that the long-term population is always 5 times the restocking amount. They might explain this as follows. The population will level out when the restocking amount is the same as the amount lost due to the decrease rate. Thus, the long-term population must be a number L such that $D \cdot L = A$, where D is the decrease rate and A is the restocking amount. This formula clearly shows that the restocking amount (A) and the long-term population (L) are proportional. Furthermore, when $D = 0.2$, then $0.2L = A$, and so $L = 5A$.

Teacher Notes

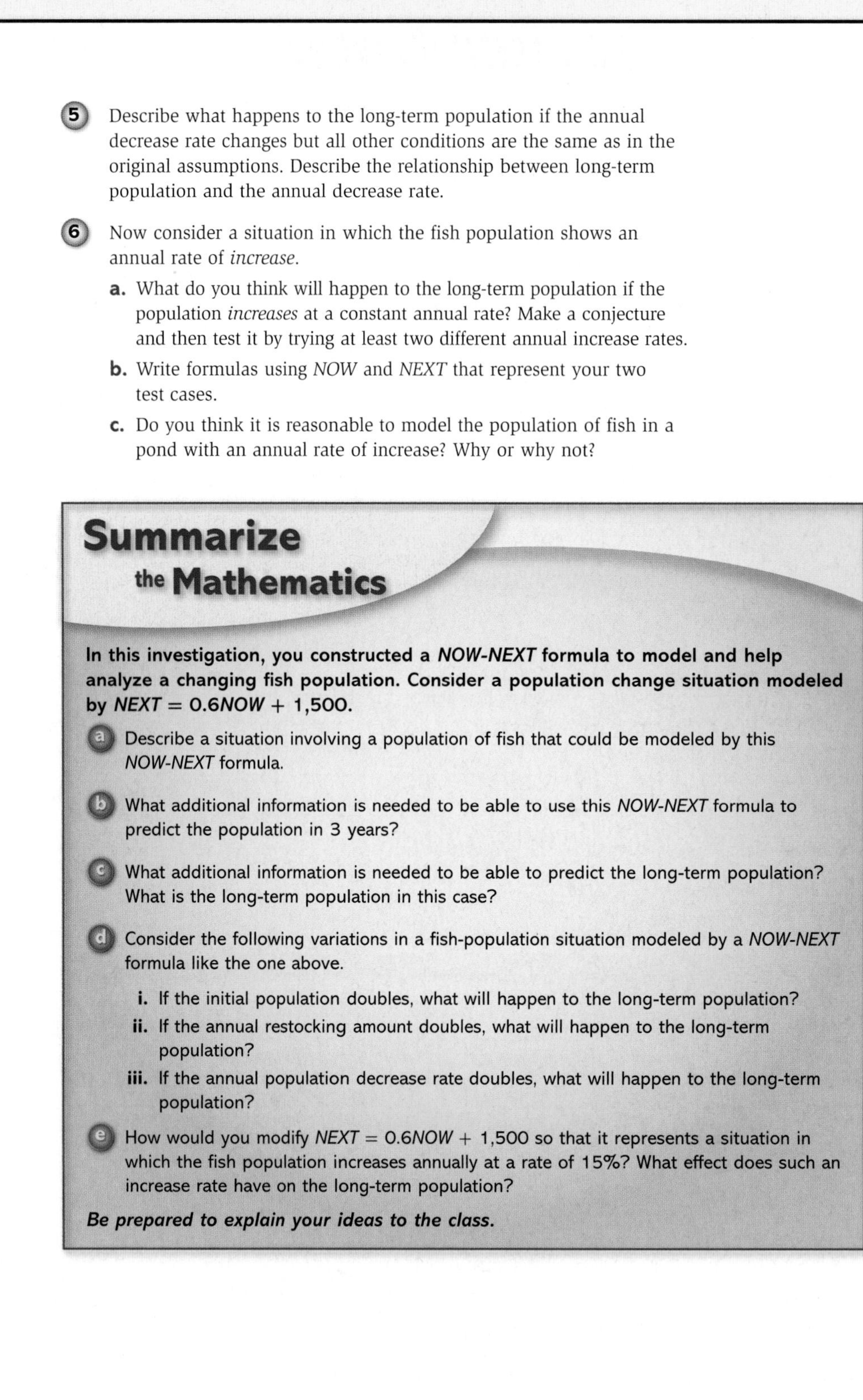

5. Describe what happens to the long-term population if the annual decrease rate changes but all other conditions are the same as in the original assumptions. Describe the relationship between long-term population and the annual decrease rate.

6. Now consider a situation in which the fish population shows an annual rate of *increase*.

   a. What do you think will happen to the long-term population if the population *increases* at a constant annual rate? Make a conjecture and then test it by trying at least two different annual increase rates.

   b. Write formulas using *NOW* and *NEXT* that represent your two test cases.

   c. Do you think it is reasonable to model the population of fish in a pond with an annual rate of increase? Why or why not?

Summarize the Mathematics

In this investigation, you constructed a *NOW-NEXT* formula to model and help analyze a changing fish population. Consider a population change situation modeled by *NEXT* = 0.6*NOW* + 1,500.

a. Describe a situation involving a population of fish that could be modeled by this *NOW-NEXT* formula.

b. What additional information is needed to be able to use this *NOW-NEXT* formula to predict the population in 3 years?

c. What additional information is needed to be able to predict the long-term population? What is the long-term population in this case?

d. Consider the following variations in a fish-population situation modeled by a *NOW-NEXT* formula like the one above.

   i. If the initial population doubles, what will happen to the long-term population?

   ii. If the annual restocking amount doubles, what will happen to the long-term population?

   iii. If the annual population decrease rate doubles, what will happen to the long-term population?

e. How would you modify *NEXT* = 0.6*NOW* + 1,500 so that it represents a situation in which the fish population increases annually at a rate of 15%? What effect does such an increase rate have on the long-term population?

Be prepared to explain your ideas to the class.

5 There is an inverse proportional relationship here; for example, if the decrease rate triples, then the long-term population goes down by a factor of $\frac{1}{3}$. Some students may determine that the restocking amount divided by the annual decrease rate will give the long-term population. (See the algebraic explanation in Problem 4.) Thus, with restocking held constant at 1,000, an annual decrease rate of D yields long-term population $L = \frac{1,000}{D}$.

6 **a.** An annual rate of increase, combined with the growth from restocking, will result in the population increasing without bound.

b. Responses will vary. The *NOW-NEXT* formulas should be of the form $NEXT = r \cdot NOW + 1,000$, starting at c, where r is any number larger than 1 and c is the initial value.

c. It does not seem reasonable to model the population of fish in a pond with an annual rate of increase and all other assumptions intact, because no fishing pond can have a fish population that grows without bound. The pond ecology (and the finite size of the pond) puts limits on the number of fish possible.

Summarize the Mathematics

a The population has an annual decrease rate of 40% and an annual restocking amount of 1,500 fish. No information is given about initial population.

b In order to use this formula to predict the population in 3 years, we must know the initial population.

c No additional information is needed to be able to use this formula to predict long-term population. Since initial population does not affect long-term population, any initial population can be assumed. Students might find the long-term population by choosing an initial population and computing, or they might generalize some of the reasoning they used in Problems 2–5. For example, they may state that, in general in situations like these, $D \cdot L = A$, where D is the decrease rate, L is the long-term population, and A is the restocking amount. Thus, for the formula given in this STM, the long-term population is $\frac{1,500}{0.4} = 3,750$. (Note that the initial population does not affect long-term population in formulas like those studied here because the coefficient of *NOW* is less than 1 in absolute value—see Lesson 3, Investigation 2, on iterating linear functions, for a detailed analysis.)

Teaching Resources

Transparency Master 2.

UNIT 7 *Recursion and Iteration*

Summarize the Mathematics

In this investigation, you constructed a *NOW-NEXT* formula to model and help analyze a changing fish population. Consider a population change situation modeled by $NEXT = 0.6NOW + 1,500$.

a Describe a situation involving a population of fish that could be modeled by this *NOW-NEXT* formula.

b What additional information is needed to be able to use this *NOW-NEXT* formula to predict the population in 3 years?

c What additional information is needed to be able to predict the long-term population? What is the long-term population in this case?

d Consider the following variations in a fish-population situation modeled by a *NOW-NEXT* formula like the one above.

i. If the initial population doubles, what will happen to the long-term population?

ii. If the annual restocking amount doubles, what will happen to the long-term population?

iii. If the annual population decrease rate doubles, what will happen to the long-term population?

e How would you modify $NEXT = 0.6NOW + 1,500$ so that it represents a situation in which the fish population increases annually at a rate of 15%? What effect does such an increase rate have on the long-term population?

Be prepared to explain your ideas to the class.

2 UNIT 7 • Recursion and Iteration Transparency Master

NOTE Solutions to Parts d and e of the Summarize the Mathematics are on page T462.

Check Your Understanding

A hospital patient is given an antibiotic to treat an infection. He is initially given a 30-mg dose and then receives another 10 mg at the end of every six-hour period thereafter. Through natural body metabolism, about 20% of the antibiotic is eliminated from his system every six hours.

a. Estimate the amount of antibiotic in his system after the first six hours and after the second six hours.

b. Write a formula using the words *NOW* and *NEXT* that models this situation.

c. Find the amount of antibiotic in the patient's system after 10 days.

d. Suppose his doctor decides to modify the prescription so that the long-term amount of antibiotic in his system will be about 25 mg. How should the prescription be modified?

Investigation 2 The Power of Notation and Technology

Situations involving sequential change, as in the fish-population problem, are sometimes called **discrete dynamical systems**. A discrete dynamical system is a situation (system) involving change (dynamical) in which the nature of the change is step-by-step (discrete). An important part of analyzing discrete dynamical systems is determining long-term behavior, as you did when you found the long-term fish population or the long-term amount of antibiotic in a patient's system.

Sequential change situations can often be analyzed using *recursion* and *iteration*. Sequential change is step-by-step change. **Recursion** is the method of describing a step in a sequential process in terms of previous steps. **Iteration** is the process of repeating the same procedure or computation over and over again.

Notation and technology can be very helpful when analyzing sequential change situations. As you work on the problems of this investigation, look for answers to these questions:

How can recursion and iteration be used to model and analyze sequential change situations?

How can subscript, function, and spreadsheet notation be used in the modeling process?

How can spreadsheets be used in the modeling process?

Think about how recursion and iteration were used in your analysis of the changing fish population in Investigation 1.

a. Describe an instance where you used recursion to model or analyze the fish-population problem.

b. Describe an instance where you used iteration in the fish population problem.

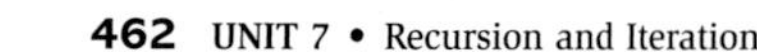

Unit 7

d Some students may need to create specific examples to help them answer these questions. After they do so, help them generalize their findings.

i. Doubling the initial population will not change the long-term population.
ii. Since this is a direct proportion relationship, doubling the restocking amount will double the long-term population.
iii. Since this is an inverse proportion relationship, doubling the decrease rate will cut the long-term population in half.

e The coefficient for *NOW* would become 1.15. This would have the effect of predicting a long-term population that grows without bound.

MATH TOOLKIT Give a specific example of a population situation whose growth can be represented by a *NOW-NEXT* formula. Then explain what happens to the long-term population under each of the three conditions described in Part d of the STM.

Check Your Understanding

a. There will be 34 mg after the first six hours and 37.2 mg after the second six hours. (Encourage students to consider why the decimal answers make sense here but did not make sense in the fish problem.)

b. $NEXT = 0.8NOW + 10$, or $NEXT = NOW - 0.2NOW + 10$, starting at 30.

c. Ten days is 40 six-hour periods, and the amount of antibiotic in the patient's system after this number of periods is approximately 50 mg.

d. The goal is to change the long-term amount by a factor of $\frac{1}{2}$. This could be done by changing the regular dosage amount by a factor of $\frac{1}{2}$ or changing the decrease rate by a factor of 2. Since the decrease rate is a function of body metabolism and not under direct control, it makes sense for the doctor to change the prescription by decreasing the dosage administered every 6 hours to 5 mg.

INSTRUCTIONAL NOTE
This problem is virtually identical to the fish-population problem, except the parameters are 30 and 10 instead of 3,000 and 1,000. Ask students to compare these two problems to help them recognize the mathematical commonalities that are not dependent on the specific context.

Investigation 2 The Power of Notation and Technology

The goals of this investigation are to introduce subscript and function notation for recursive formulas, use spreadsheet software as an analytical tool, analyze using equations, tables, and graphs, and continue to investigate formulas of the form $U_n = rU_{n-1} + b$. Based on previous work with *NOW-NEXT* rules and function notation, students generally do not have much difficulty making the transition to subscript and spreadsheet notation.

1 **a.** For example, recursion was used to represent the changing fish population by $NEXT = 0.8NOW + 1{,}000$, because this method of describing the sequential fish population change describes a given step (the *NEXT* step) in terms of the previous step (the *NOW* step).

b. For example, iteration was used when the last-answer key was repeatedly pressed on a graphing calculator in order to repeat the same computation over and over again to show the year-by-year changes in the fish population.

Unit 7

Subscript and Function Notation You can use subscripts and function notation to more compactly write formulas like those in Investigation 1 that use the words *NOW* and *NEXT*. These notations can help you analyze the formulas and the situations they model. Consider the context of a changing fish population from the last investigation. The subscript notation P_n can be used to represent the population after n years. (The notation P_n is read "P sub n.") Thus, P_0 ("P sub 0") is the population after 0 years, that is, the initial population. P_1 is the population after 1 year, P_2 is the population after 2 years, and so on.

Recall that the fish-population problem is based on these three assumptions:

- There are 3,000 fish currently in the pond.
- The population decreases by 20% each year due to natural causes and fish being caught.
- 1,000 fish are added at the end of each year.

2 Find P_0, P_1, and P_2. Compare to the population values from Investigation 1. Sketch a graph of P_n versus n. Include the three values you have just found, for $n = 0, 1,$ and 2. Also, indicate the shape of the graph based on all the population values from Investigation 1. A rough sketch by hand is fine.

3 The subscript notation relates closely to the way you have used the words *NOW* and *NEXT* to describe sequential change in many contexts.

a. In the context of a changing population, if P_1 is the population *NOW*, what subscript notation represents the population *NEXT* year?

b. If P_{24} is the population *NEXT* year, what subscript notation represents the population *NOW*?

c. If P_n is the population *NEXT* year, what subscript notation represents the population *NOW*?

d. If P_{n+1} is the population *NEXT* year, what subscript notation represents the population *NOW*?

e. A formula that models the annual change in fish population as described in Investigation 1 is

$$NEXT = 0.8NOW + 1{,}000, \text{ starting at } 3{,}000.$$

i. Rewrite this formula using P_n and P_{n-1} notation.

ii. Rewrite this formula using P_n and P_{n+1} notation.

4 Function notation can often be used interchangeably with subscript notation. For example, both P_0 and $P(0)$ can represent the initial population. The subscript notation is read "P sub 0" and the function notation is read "P of 0." Each notation can be used to represent the population at time 0.

a. Refer to Problem 2 above. In the context of the fish population problem, if $P(n)$ is the population after n years, what are the values of $P(0)$, $P(1)$, and $P(2)$? Calculate $P(3)$.

b. Rewrite the *NOW-NEXT* formula from Problem 3 Part e using function notation. Is there more than one way to do this? Explain.

2 $P_0 = 3{,}000$; $P_1 = 3{,}400$; $P_2 = 3{,}720$. These are the same values computed in the previous investigation, but now subscript notation is used. Students should sketch a graph like the one below of n versus P_n.

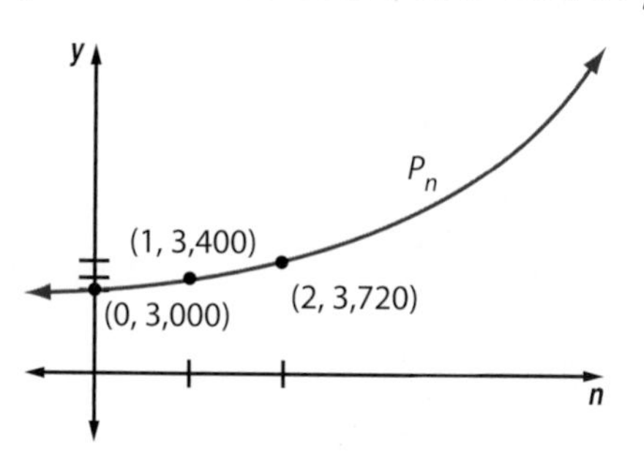

3 **a.** If P_1 is the population *NOW*, then P_2 represents the population *NEXT* year.

b. If P_{24} is the population *NEXT* year, then P_{23} represents the population *NOW*.

c. If P_n is the population *NEXT* year, then P_{n-1} represents the population *NOW*.

d. If P_{n+1} is the population *NEXT* year, then P_n represents the population *NOW*.

e. **i.** $P_n = 0.8P_{n-1} + 1{,}000$

ii. $P_{n+1} = 0.8P_n + 1{,}000$

4 **a.** For $P(0)$, $P(1)$, and $P(2)$, students can simply read off the corresponding values they computed in Problem 2 using subscript notation. So, $P(0) = 3{,}000$; $P(1) = 3{,}400$; $P(2) = 3{,}720$. Calculating $P(3)$ yields $P(3) = 3{,}976$.

b. The formula $NEXT = 0.8NOW + 1{,}000$, starting at 3,000, could be represented as $P(n) = 0.8 \cdot P(n-1) + 1{,}000$. Other representations are possible, such as $P(n+1) = 0.8 \cdot P(n) + 1{,}000$. (As with subscript notation, there are other ways to express the relationship between the population in sequential years, including $P(n) = P(n-1) - 0.2P(n-1) + 1{,}000$.)

Unit 7

Spreadsheet Analysis You can analyze situations that involve sequential change by using the iteration and recursion capability of a calculator or computer software. In particular, spreadsheet software can be used to analyze these situations.

5 Spreadsheets have their own notation, which is similar to subscript and function notations. Spreadsheets are organized into cells, typically labeled by letters across the top and numbers down the side. If cell A1 contains the fish population *NOW*, and A2 contains the population *NEXT* year, write a formula using A1 and A2 that shows the relationship between *NOW* and *NEXT*. (*Note*: When using formulas that reference spreadsheet cells, a * must be used for multiplication.)

6 Analyze the fish population situation using a spreadsheet, as follows.

a. A formula like that in Problem 5 does not tell you what the population is for any given year; it only shows how the population changes from year to year. To be able to compute the population for any year, you need to know the initial population. Using spreadsheet software available to you, enter the initial population of 3,000 into cell A1.

Spreadsheet

File Edit Insert Tools Examples Help

Cell A2: =0.8*A1+1000

Fish Population

	A	B	C	D	E	F	G
1	3,000						
2	=0.8*A1+1000						
3	3,720						
4	3,976						
5	4,181						
6	4,345						
7	4,476						
8	4,581						
9	4,664						
10	4,732						
11	4,785						
12	4,828						
13	4,863						
14	4,890						
15	4,912						
16	4,930						
17	4,944						
18	4,955						
19	4,964						
20	4,971						
21	4,977						
22	4,982						

b. You want A2 to show the population in the next year. So, enter "=" and your expression for A2 from Problem 5 into cell A2. Press Enter or Return. The population for the next year (3,400) should appear in cell A2. If it does not, check with other students and resolve the problem.

c. Now you want A3 to show the population in the next year. So, you need to enter an expression for A3 into the A3 cell. Then to get the next population, you would enter an expression for A4 into the A4 cell. And so on. Repeating this procedure is an example of iteration. The spreadsheet software will do this automatically, using the Fill Down command, as follows.

- Click and hold on cell A2, then drag down to cell A50.
- Then in the Edit menu, choose Fill Down.
- Cells A3 through A50 should now show the population from year to year. If not, check with other students and resolve the problem.

d. Describe the pattern of change you see in the spreadsheet list of population values. Compare to your analysis of the fish-population situation in Investigation 1.

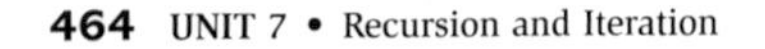

Unit 7

5 A2=0.8*A1+1000

6

a. Students should enter "3000" into cell A1 of a spreadsheet.

b. Students should enter "=0.8*A1+1000" into cell A2, press return, and 3400 should be displayed in cell A2.

c. Students should use the fill down command of a spreadsheet to display population values in cells A1 to A50.

d. The table produced by the spreadsheet will show the same values and patterns as those found in Investigation 1.

TECHNOLOGY NOTE
Students need to use spreadsheets for the rest of this investigation. They can use the spreadsheet in *CPMP-Tools* or spreadsheet software such as *Excel*.

Unit 7

e. You can use the graphing capability of a spreadsheet to help analyze the situation.

i. Use the spreadsheet software to create a scatterplot of the fish population over time. When there is only one column of data, some spreadsheet software has a default setting that will assign integers beginning with 1 as the independent variable for a scatterplot. If your spreadsheet software does not have this default setting, fill column B with the year numbers that correspond to the populations in column A.

ii. Describe any patterns of change you see in the population graph. Compare to your analysis of the fish-population situation in Investigation 1. Be sure to describe how the long-term population trend shows up in the graph.

Compound Interest You have been using recursion and iteration, along with appropriate notation and technology tools, to analyze a population problem. Another common application of recursion and iteration is compound interest. *Compound interest* is interest that is applied to previous interest as well as to the original amount of money borrowed or invested. The original amount of money is called the *principal*. The more often the interest is applied, that is, the more often it is *compounded*, the faster the total amount of money (principal plus interest) grows. Thus, the interest rate and compounding period are crucial factors in consumer loans, such as car loans and college loans.

In the U.S., the Truth in Lending Act requires that lenders must report interest rates in a standard way, using the Annual Percentage Rate (APR), so that consumers can more easily compare and understand loans. Unfortunately, the APR itself is sometimes interpreted and computed in different ways—see Extensions Task 18. In any case, even with some clarity provided by the APR, you still need to carefully analyze the interest rate on a loan.

For example, it is common to advertise car loans with a stated *annual* interest rate. However, the interest is usually compounded *monthly*, not annually, so careful analysis is required to make sure you know what the loan will really cost. Consider the following car loan ad.

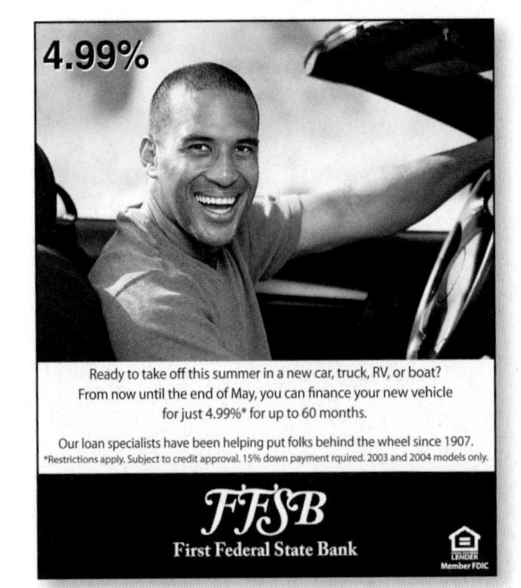

e. **i.** Students should create a graph using spreadsheet software.

ii. The graph clearly shows a rapid increase in the population (y values) during the early years and then a leveling off. This can also be seen in the table. This pattern matches the pattern seen in the last investigation.

Unit 7

7. The stated interest rate is 4.99%. Given the law about stating the APR, we will assume that this is an annual rate. The ad also implies that the loan will be computed monthly ("for up to 60 months"), so we will also assume that the interest will be compounded monthly. Finally, it is common to give the annual rate without adjusting for the effect of the monthly compounding. To carefully analyze this situation, we need to know the monthly interest rate. Under the assumptions just discussed, the monthly rate is $\frac{1}{12}$ of the annual rate. Explain why. For the annual rate shown in the ad, what is the monthly interest rate?

8. Suppose you borrow \$10,000 to buy a new compact car at the interest rate shown in the ad, with repayment due in 48 monthly payments. You are told that your monthly payment will be \$235. As a wise consumer, you should check to see if this payment amount is correct.

   a. Figure out a method for how you can determine the amount you still owe, called the *balance*, after a given month's payment. Then find the balance of the car loan after each of the first three payments. Assume that the first payment is made exactly one month after the contract is signed. Compare your balances to those of other groups, and resolve any differences.

   b. Write a formula using the words *NOW* and *NEXT* that models the month-by-month change in the balance of the loan. Write equivalent formulas using subscripts, function notation, and spreadsheet notation. Be sure to specify the initial balance.

   c. Now think about whether the payment amount is correct.

   - If the monthly payment of \$235 is correct, what should the balance be after the 48th payment? Use the formulas from Part b and your calculator or computer to see if \$235 is the correct payment for this loan.
   - If the payment is incorrect, is it too high or too low? How can you tell? Experiment to find the correct monthly payment.

9. Investigate further the loan situation from Problem 8.

   a. How much total interest was paid on the \$10,000 loan, using the correct monthly payment?

   b. Is the balance of the loan reduced faster at the beginning of the repayment period or at the end? Explain and give evidence to support your answer.

   c. Suppose someone offers you a "great deal," whereby you must pay only \$40 per month until the loan is paid off. Describe what happens to the repayment process in this situation. Is this such a great deal after all?

Unit 7

466 UNIT 7 • Recursion and Iteration

7 Divide the annual rate by 12 to get the monthly rate because there are 12 months in a year and our assumptions are that the stated rate is an annual rate that does not take into account the effect of monthly compounding. The annual rate of 4.99% shown in the ad will yield a monthly rate of about 0.416%, or 0.00416 expressed as a decimal.

INSTRUCTIONAL NOTE Different rounding will yield slightly different monthly interest rates. For consistency, after Problem 7, you might encourage all students to use 0.416%.

INSTRUCTIONAL NOTE Unfortunately, consumer loan interest rates are not consistently stated, computed, and applied. For example, sometimes the APR is computed simply as the monthly rate multiplied by 12, while at other times it is computed from the monthly rate by also taking into account the monthly compounding (which will yield a higher APR value). For more details, direct students to Connections Task 8 and Extensions Task 18. However, for the rest of this investigation, we will proceed with the assumptions stated in Problem 7.

TECHNOLOGY NOTE A spreadsheet is an effective tool to use to experiment with different payments. Alternatively, students might use the "last answer" feature on a graphing calculator, but this requires lots of button pushing. A payment calculator on the Internet could also be used (search for "auto loan calculator"), but one that shows the amortization table along with the payment is most useful. You could have a good discussion here about choosing the best technology tool for a given task.

8 **a.** The balance after a given month's payment is computed by first adding the interest for a month to the previous month's balance and then subtracting the payment.

Using an interest rate of $\frac{0.0499}{12}$, the balance after the first payment is \$9,806.58; after the second payment, the balance is \$9,612.36; and after the third payment, the balance is \$9,417.33.

b. Using an interest rate of approximately 0.00416 per month, $NEXT = 1.00416NOW - 235$. Some possible equivalent formulas are: $B_{n+1} = 1.00416B_n - 235$; $B(n) = 1.00416B(n - 1) - 235$; A2=1.00416*A1–235. In all cases, the initial balance is 10,000.

c.
- The balance should be \$0 after the 48th month, but it is –\$251.89.
- The payment is a little high since there is a negative balance. Using a spreadsheet, for example, students could quickly experiment with different payment amounts to find one that gives a final balance of \$0 (or very close to \$0). The correct payment is \$230.25.

DIFFERENTIATION In Problems 8 and 9, students investigate interest on loans. In Problem 8 Part a, they are asked to figure out how loans work month by month. You may need to provide guidance here for some students; but if possible, let the students figure it out themselves.

9 **a.** The loan will be paid off with 48 payments of \$230.25. (48)(230.25) = 11,052. The amount borrowed was \$10,000, so the interest paid is about \$1,052.

b. The balance is reduced faster at the end of the repayment period because there is more interest added on at the beginning. For example, 0.416% of \$10,000 is more than 0.416% of \$2,000. So at the beginning, more of the payment must go to pay the interest for that month, and less of the principal gets paid off. Near the end of the four years, most of the payment goes to pay off the principal.

c. Each month, the balance owed will increase and the loan will never be paid off. You will pay \$40/month forever. This is not a good deal, except maybe to the lender. Any payment less than \$41.60 will have this property because 0.416% of 10,000 is 41.6.

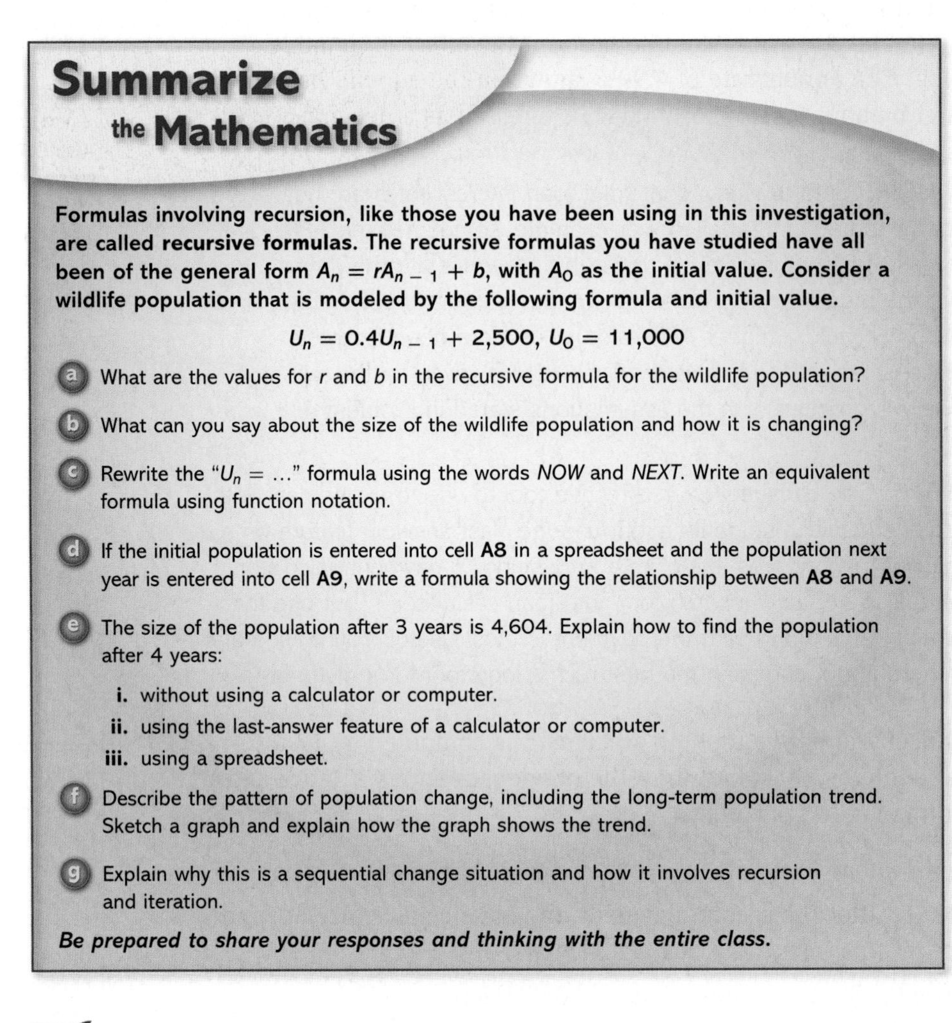

Summarize the Mathematics

Formulas involving recursion, like those you have been using in this investigation, are called recursive formulas. The recursive formulas you have studied have all been of the general form $A_n = rA_{n-1} + b$, with A_0 as the initial value. Consider a wildlife population that is modeled by the following formula and initial value.

$$U_n = 0.4U_{n-1} + 2{,}500,\ U_0 = 11{,}000$$

a. What are the values for r and b in the recursive formula for the wildlife population?

b. What can you say about the size of the wildlife population and how it is changing?

c. Rewrite the "$U_n = \ldots$" formula using the words *NOW* and *NEXT*. Write an equivalent formula using function notation.

d. If the initial population is entered into cell **A8** in a spreadsheet and the population next year is entered into cell **A9**, write a formula showing the relationship between **A8** and **A9**.

e. The size of the population after 3 years is 4,604. Explain how to find the population after 4 years:

   i. without using a calculator or computer.

   ii. using the last-answer feature of a calculator or computer.

   iii. using a spreadsheet.

f. Describe the pattern of population change, including the long-term population trend. Sketch a graph and explain how the graph shows the trend.

g. Explain why this is a sequential change situation and how it involves recursion and iteration.

Be prepared to share your responses and thinking with the entire class.

Check Your Understanding

Recall the situation (page 462) involving a hospital patient taking an antibiotic to treat an infection. He was initially given a 30-mg dose, and then he took another 10 mg at the end of every six hours. Through natural body metabolism, about 20% of the antibiotic was eliminated from his system every six hours.

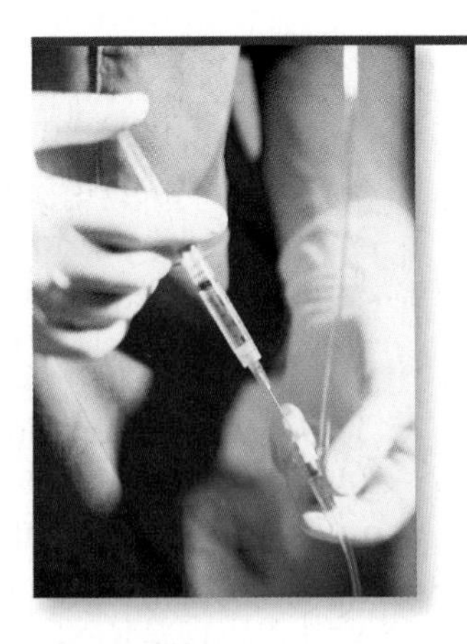

a. Write a recursive formula in the form "$U_n = \ldots$" that models this situation. Write an equivalent formula using function notation.

b. Using spreadsheet software, produce a table and graph of (n, U_n) pairs with n as the input variable.

c. Describe how the amount of antibiotic in the patient's system changes over time, including the long-term change.

Summarize the Mathematics

a For the recursive formula here, $r = 0.4$ and $b = 2{,}500$.

b The decrease rate is 60%, the restocking amount is 2,500, and the initial population is 11,000. Students may also state that the population decreases from 11,000 and levels off at about 4,167. (Also, see Part f below.)

c $NEXT = 0.4NOW + 2{,}500$; $U(n) = 0.4U(n - 1) + 2{,}500$; both have initial values of 11,000.

d A9=0.4*A8+2500

e $U_4 = 4{,}341.6$ (4,341 or 4,342 could be used to represent population.)

i. Without a calculator, find 40% of 4,604 and add 2,500.

ii. Using **ANS** for the last answer, enter **4604** and then calculate **0.4ANS+2500**.

iii. Using a spreadsheet, just find the number in the cell following 4604.

f The population will decrease, quickly at first and then level off. The long-term population will be approximately 4,166. This can be seen by the graph below, which decreases quickly at first and levels off at about 4,166.

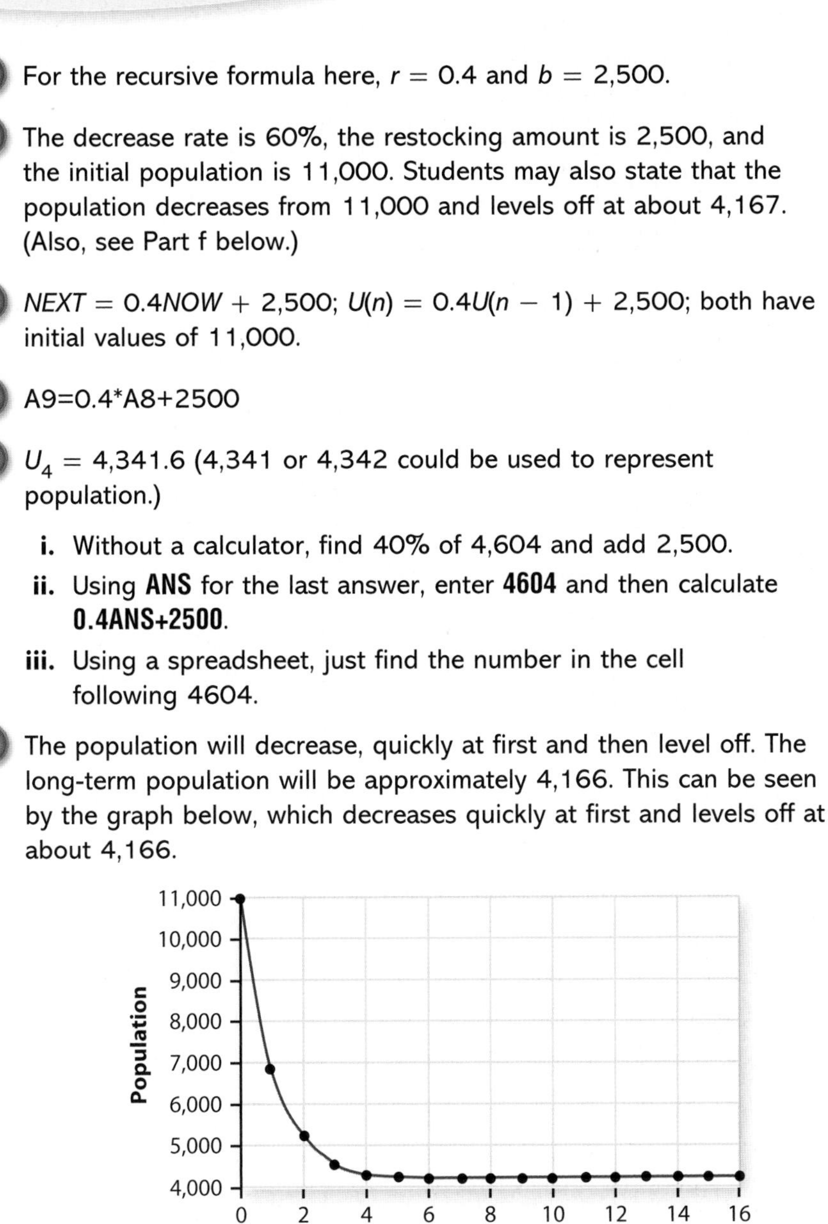

g It is sequential change since the population changes step-by-step, for example, year-by-year. Recursion is involved since the population in a given year is described in terms of the population in the previous year. Iteration is involved since the same calculation (multiply by 0.4 and add 2,500) is repeated again and again.

Teaching Resources

Transparency Masters 3–4.

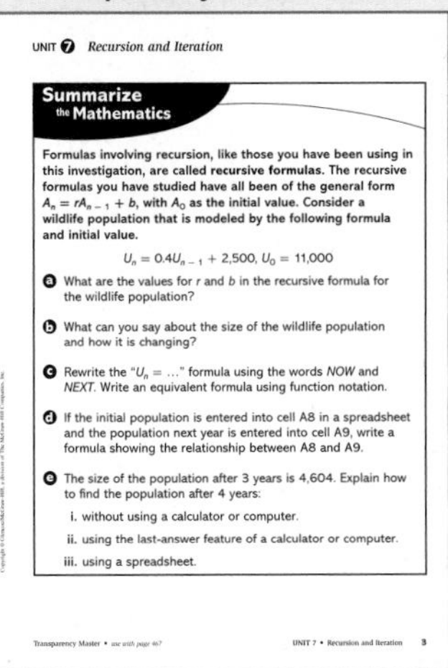
UNIT 7 Recursion and Iteration

Summarize the Mathematics

Formulas involving recursion, like those you have been using in this investigation, are called recursive formulas. The recursive formulas you have studied have all been of the general form $A_n = rA_{n-1} + b$, with A_0 as the initial value. Consider a wildlife population that is modeled by the following formula and initial value.

$U_n = 0.4U_{n-1} + 2{,}500$, $U_0 = 11{,}000$

a What are the values for r and b in the recursive formula for the wildlife population?

b What can you say about the size of the wildlife population and how it is changing?

c Rewrite the "$U_n = \ldots$" formula using the words NOW and NEXT. Write an equivalent formula using function notation.

d If the initial population is entered into cell A8 in a spreadsheet and the population next year is entered into cell A9, write a formula showing the relationship between A8 and A9.

e The size of the population after 3 years is 4,604. Explain how to find the population after 4 years:

i. without using a calculator or computer.

ii. using the last-answer feature of a calculator or computer.

iii. using a spreadsheet.

Transparency Master • use with page 467 UNIT 7 • Recursion and Iteration 3

ASSIGNMENT NOTE/ MATH TOOLKIT After completing A3 and A4 or A5, complete A6 and retain in Math Toolkits. (Alternatively, the chart in A6 could be completed in the Looking Back lesson.)

TERMINOLOGY NOTE Recursive formulas are also called *recurrence relations*, *recurrences*, or *difference equations*. In this unit, only the term recursive formula will be used, since it is most descriptive.

Unit 7

Check Your Understanding

a. $U_n = 0.8U_{n-1} + 10,\ U_0 = 30$
$A(n) = 0.8A(n - 1) + 10,\ A(0) = 30$

b.

Data Analysis

File Data Edit Graph Statistics Custom Tools Help

Antibiotic

	A: # 6-hr Time Periods	B: Mg in System	C	D	E
1	1	30			
2	2.0	34.0			
3	3.0	37.2			
4	4.0	39.760000000000...			
5	5.0	41.808000000000...			
6	6.0	43.446400000000...			
7	7.0	44.757120000000...			
8	8.0	45.805696000000...			
9	9.0	46.644556800000...			
10	10.0	47.315645440000...			
11	11.0	47.852516352			
12	12.0	48.282013081600...			
13	13.0	48.625610465280...			
14	14.0	48.900488372224...			
15	15.0	49.120390697779...			
16	16.0	49.296312558223...			
17	17.0	49.4370500465787			
18	18.0	49.549640037262...			

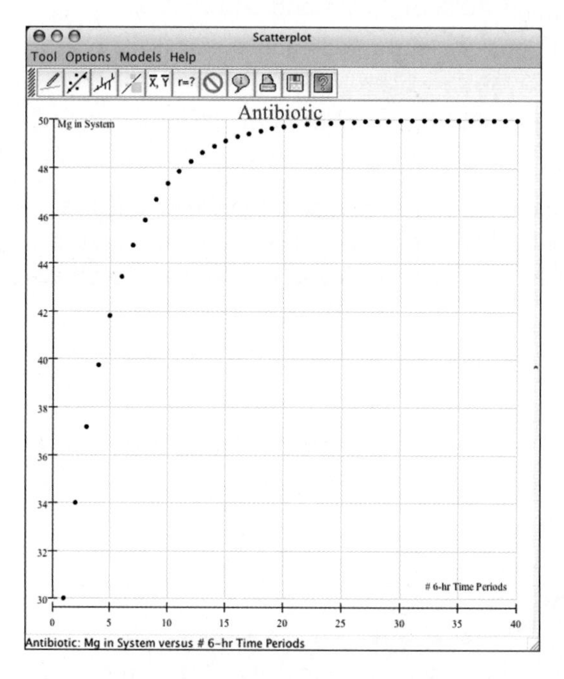

c. The amount of antibiotic in the patient's body increases over time, rapidly in the beginning, and then eventually levels off at about 50 mg.

Teacher Notes

On Your Own

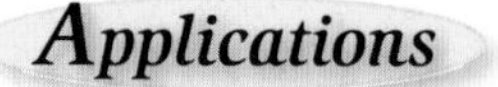

Applications

For the following tasks, use spreadsheet software, *CPMP-Tools*, or a graphing calculator as needed to help you solve the problems.

1 Chlorine is used to keep swimming pools safe by controlling certain harmful microorganisms. However, chlorine is a powerful chemical, so just the right amount must be used. Too much chlorine irritates swimmers' eyes and can be hazardous to their health; too little chlorine allows the growth of microorganisms to be uncontrolled, which can be harmful.

A pool manager must measure and add chlorine regularly to keep the level just right. The chlorine is measured in parts per million (ppm) by weight. That is, one ppm of chlorine means that there is one ounce of chlorine for every million ounces of water.

Chlorine dissipates in reaction to bacteria and to the sun at a rate of about 15% of the amount present per day. The optimal concentration of chlorine in a pool is from 1 to 2 ppm, although it is safe to swim when the concentration is as high as 3 ppm.

a. Suppose you have a summer job working at a swimming pool, and one of your responsibilities is to maintain a safe concentration of chlorine in the pool. You are required to add the same amount of chlorine to the pool every day. When you take the job, you find that the concentration is 3 ppm.

How much chlorine (in parts per million) do you need to add each day in order to maintain a long-term optimal concentration? Write a recursive formula that models your optimal chlorine maintenance plan. Describe any assumptions you have made in your analysis.

b. There are three key factors in this problem: the initial concentration, the daily increase in concentration due to the amount you add, and the dissipation rate. Systematically explore changes in each of these three factors and record the corresponding effects on the long-term chlorine concentration in the swimming pool.

c. Suppose the chlorinating pellets you use are 65% active chlorine, by weight. If the pool contains 50,000 gallons of water, and water weighs 8.337 pounds per gallon, how many pounds of chlorine pellets must you add to the pool each day?

Unit 7

468 UNIT 7 • Recursion and Iteration

On Your Own

Applications

1 **a.** A plausible recursive formula could be $C_n = 0.85C_{n-1} + (\textit{daily dosage})$, $C_0 = 3$. Students can experiment numerically with different daily dosages to find one that yields a long-term level between 1 and 2 ppm. Or, they might use other formulas from their work in Investigation 1, such as, $D \cdot L = A$, where D is the decrease rate, L is the long-term amount, and A is the regularly-added amount. If the daily dosage is between 0.15 and 0.30 ppm, the long-term chlorine concentration will be between 1 and 2 ppm. For example, a daily dosage of 0.2 ppm will yield a long-term concentration of $\frac{0.20}{0.15}$, or approximately 1.33 ppm. Students might discuss assumptions such as adding chlorine once per day and basing decisions about chlorine level by one measurement per day, even though of course the chlorine concentration is changing all the time.

b. Changing the initial concentration has no effect on the long-term concentration (except that it will change the time it takes to achieve the long-term concentration).

Changing the daily dosage by a factor of k will result in changing the long-term concentration by the same factor k.

Changing the dissipation rate by a factor of k will result in the long-term concentration changing by a factor of $\frac{1}{k}$. These patterns result when you change one factor at a time and leave the others as they were originally.

c. Students need to convert their ppm dosage from Part a to pounds.

In the previous example given, a daily dosage of 0.2 is used. The number of pounds of water in the pool is $50{,}000 \times 8.337$, or 416,850. Thus, the number of pounds of chlorine needed per day is $\frac{0.2}{1{,}000{,}000} \times 416{,}850$, or about 0.083. However, the pellets are only 65% active chlorine, so the amount of pellets needed is $0.083 \div 0.65$, or about 0.128 pounds.

TECHNOLOGY NOTE
Students should use spreadsheet software, *CPMP-Tools*, or graphing calculators for many of these tasks. Encourage them to consider which tool is best for particular tasks.

2. Retirement is probably not something you are currently concerned about. However, working adults, even very young working adults, should have a financial plan for retirement. If you start saving early and take advantage of compound interest, then you should be in great financial shape by the time you retire. Consider twin sisters with different retirement savings plans.

   Plan I: Cora begins a retirement account at age 20. She starts with \$2,000 and then saves \$2,000 per year at 7% interest, compounded annually, for 10 years. (*Compounded annually* means that the interest is compounded every year, once per year at the end of the year.) Then she stops contributing to the account but keeps her savings invested at the same rate.

   Plan II: Miranda does not save any money in her twenties. But when she turns 30, she starts with \$2,000 and then saves \$2,000 per year at 7% interest, compounded annually, for 35 years.

   Both sisters retire at age 65. Who do you think will have more retirement savings at age 65? Test your conjecture by determining the amount of money saved by each sister at age 65.

3. Every ten years, the United States Census Bureau conducts a complete census of the nation's population. In 2000, the census report stated that there were about 281 million residents in the United States and its territories. The population changes extensively between census reports, but it is too expensive to conduct the census more often. Annual changes can be determined using estimates like the following.

   - Births will equal about 1.5% of the total population each year.
   - Deaths will equal about 0.9% of the total population each year.
   - Immigrants from other countries will add about 0.8 million people each year. (Source: 2001 World Population Data Sheet, Population Reference Bureau, www.prb.org.)

   a. Using the statistics above, what population is estimated for the United States in 2001? In the year 2010?

   b. Write a formula using the words *NOW* and *NEXT* that represents this situation.

   c. Write a recursive formula that represents this situation. Specify the initial value.

   d. Produce a table and a graph that show the population estimates through the year 2020. Describe the expected long-term trend in population change over time.

   e. Describe some hypothetical birth and death rates that would result in a population that levels off over time. Represent this situation with a recursive formula, a table, and a graph.

Unit 7

2 **Plan I:** At the end of 10 years of adding to her savings, Cora has approximately \$31,567. Then she lets this money sit for 35 years at 7% interest, resulting in a total amount at age 65 of approximately \$337,027.

Plan II: Miranda saves \$2,000 per year at 7% interest for 35 years, resulting in a total amount at age 65 of approximately \$297,827.

The net result is that Cora, who saved \$2,000 per year for only 10 years (\$20,000), has about \$40,000 more saved than Miranda, who saved \$2,000 per year for 35 years (\$70,000), due to the effect of compound interest.

Students will probably determine these answers by using a recursive formula with a spreadsheet or the **ANS** functionality on a calculator. Some students may use an explicit formula derived from thinking about exponential functions. Such a formula can also be derived based on the work with geometric sequences in Lesson 2. For example, they may determine Cora's amount using the formula $C = 2{,}000\left(\frac{1.07^{11} - 1}{1.07 - 1}\right)1.07^{35}$.

They may determine Miranda's amount using the formula $M = 2{,}000\left(\frac{1.07^{36} - 1}{1.07 - 1}\right)$.

3 **a.** The estimated population for 2001 is about 283 million. $281(1.006) + 0.8 = 283.486$. For the year 2010, the estimated population is approximately 307 million people.

b. $NEXT = 1.006NOW + 0.8$, starting at 281

c. $U_n = 1.006U_{n-1} + 0.8$ or $P_{n+1} = 1.006P_n + 0.8$. The initial value is 281.

d. In the table and graphs that follow, year 0 represents 2000. In the long term, the population grows without bound, according to this model.

Year	Population
0	281
1	283.49
2	285.99
3	288.50
4	291.03
5	293.58
6	296.14

Year	Population
7	298.72
8	301.31
9	303.92
10	306.54
11	309.18
12	311.84
13	314.51

Year	Population
14	317.19
15	319.90
16	322.62
17	325.35
18	328.10
19	330.87
20	333.66

Students should recall that the plot is exponential but that it may appear linear if only a few points are plotted, since the coefficient on the *NOW-NEXT* formula is 1.006. See plots below.

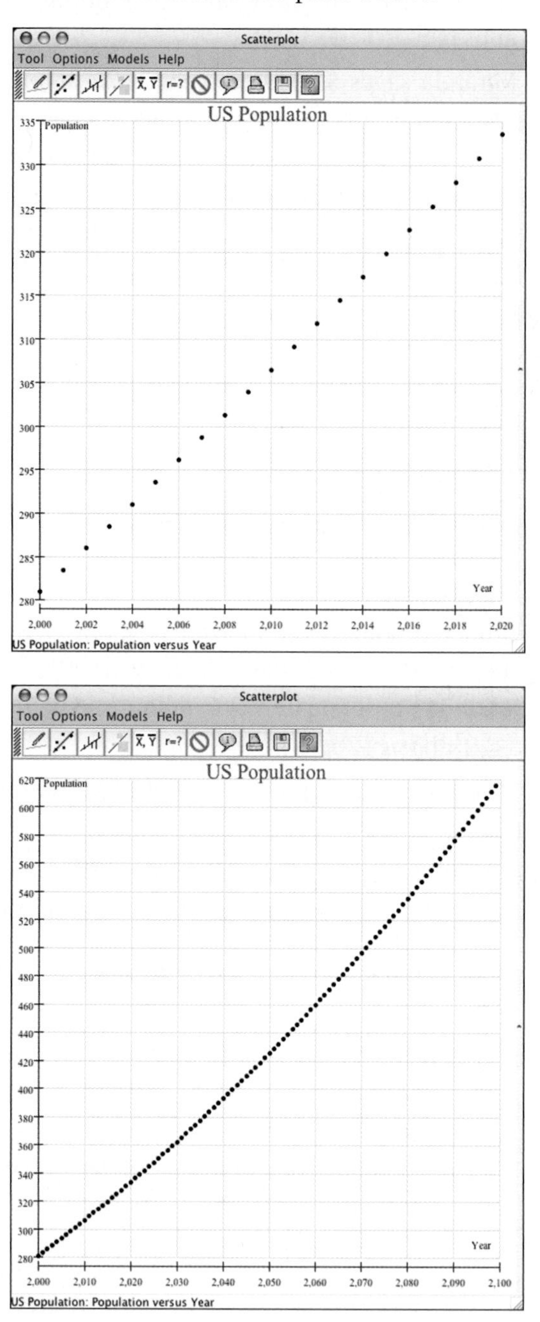

e. Any birthrate and death rate such that the death rate is greater than the birthrate will result in a population that levels off over time. For example, the birthrate could be 2.5% of the population, while the death rate could be 3.5% of the population. If immigrants still add 0.8 million people per year, then the population will level off at 80 million people. This relation is modeled by $U_n = 0.99U_{n-1} + 0.8$ or $P_{n+1} = 0.99P_n + 0.8$. Tables and graphs will depend on the specific values chosen but should reflect a leveling off of the population.

The population could increase or decrease as it levels off, depending on the birth and death rates chosen. In this task, suppose $x =$ (*death rate* – *birth rate*), then values of x that are solutions to $0.8 - x(281) > 0$ will result in a population that increases and levels off.

Unit 7

Teacher Notes

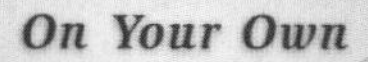
On Your Own

4. Commercial hunting of whales is controlled to prevent the extinction of some species. Because of the danger of extinction, scientists conduct counts of whales to monitor their population changes. A status report on the bowhead whales of Alaska estimated that the 1993 population of these whales was between 6,900 and 9,200 and that the difference between births and deaths yielded an annual growth rate of about 3.1%. No hunting of bowhead whales is allowed, except that Alaskan Inuit are allowed to take, or harvest, about 50 bowhead whales each year for their livelihood. (Source: nmml.afsc.noaa.gov/CetaceanAssessment/bowhead/bmsos.htm)

a. Use 1993 as the initial year. The initial population is a range of values, rather than a single value. That is, the range of initial population values is 6,900 to 9,200. Think about the *range* of population values for later years. Using the given information about annual growth rate and harvesting by Alaskan Inuit, what is the range of population values in 1994?

b. Let LOW(n) be the lower population value in the range of values in year n.

i. What is the initial value, that is, what is LOW(0)? What is LOW(1)? Write a recursive formula for the growth of the lower population values in the range of population values.

ii. Similarly, let HIGH(n) be the higher population value in the range of values in year n. Write a recursive formula for the growth of the higher population values in the range of population values, and state the initial value.

c. Put the formulas in Part b together to write a recursive formula for this situation, by completing the following work. Fill in the missing steps and provide the requested explanations.

Let $R(n)$ represent the population range in year n.

(1) So, $R(0) = 6{,}900$ to $9{,}200$.	Explain.
(2) $R(1) = 7{,}063.9$ to $9{,}435.2$.	Explain.
(3) $R(2) =$	Fill in the range for $R(2)$.
(4) $R(n) =$	Fill in the range for $R(n)$, using the formulas from Part b. Include the initial values for both the lower and higher population values.

d. Sketch a graphical representation for $R(n)$, by drawing vertical line segments for the range corresponding to each year n, with values of n on the horizontal axis and population values on the vertical axis. Use at least 4 years. Elaborate on this graphical representation by sketching graphs for n vs LOW(n) and n vs HIGH(n) on the same set of axes. Describe some patterns in the ranges $R(n)$. (See Lesson 2, Extensions Task 25 for further investigation of this situation.)

e. So far in this task, population values have been growing. Suppose that, because of some natural disaster, the initial bowhead whale population is reduced to 1,500, but growth rate and number harvested by the Inuit stay the same. Under these conditions, what happens to the long-term population?

Unit 7

470 UNIT 7 • Recursion and Iteration

4 **a.** Using 6,900 as the initial population yields a population of 7,063.9 for 1994. Using 9,200 as the initial population yields a population of 9,435.2 for 1994. Thus, the range of population values in 1994 is 7,063.9 to 9,435.2.

b. i. LOW(0) = 6,900; LOW(1) = 7,063.9
LOW(n) = 1.031 • LOW(n − 1) − 50

ii. HIGH(n) = 1.031 • HIGH(n − 1) − 50, with HIGH(0) = 9,200.

c. (1) $R(0)$ is the population range in year 0 (i.e., 1993), which is 6,900 to 9,200, as given in the statement of this task.

(2) $R(1)$ is the population range in 1994, which is 7,063.9 to 9,435.2, as calculated in Part a.

(3) $R(2)$ = 7,232.9 to 9,677.7

(4) $R(n)$ = LOW(n) to HIGH(n)
= 1.031 • LOW(n − 1) − 50 to 1.031 • HIGH(n − 1) − 50,
with LOW(0) = 6,900 and HIGH(0) = 9,200.

d. The graphic below is an example of what the students might produce. Some patterns that students might consider are the size of the ranges $R(n)$ (i.e., the difference HIGH − LOW), the ratio HIGH/LOW in the ranges, and the long-term pattern in both these cases. For example, the size of the range $R(n)$ gets bigger as n increases, as seen by the increasing vertical distance between the graphs of LOW(n) and HIGH(n). See Lesson 2 Extensions Task 26 for a more formal analysis and some other possible student responses, specifically as related to the size of the population ranges and the ratio of the higher value to the lower value of the ranges over time.

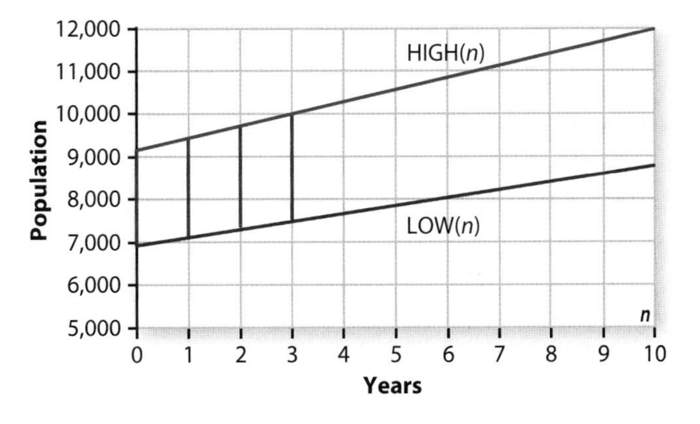

e. The population will slowly die off. (Since the multiplier in this formula is greater than 1, in contrast to the fish population problem in Investigation 1, the initial population will affect long-term population—see Lesson 3 for a more complete analysis.) In this case, each year there are more whales being harvested than are replaced due to the growth rate. (Note that the mathematical models, that is, the recursive formulas, for the high and low populations and the range are no longer applicable when the size of the population becomes less than 50 since then it is not possible for the Inuit to harvest 50 whales. At this point, the mathematical formulas can still be computed, including with negative number results, but the results no longer represent the size of the whale population.)

5 Money grows when it is kept in an interest-bearing savings account. Recursive formulas can be used to analyze how the money grows due to compound interest. For this task, assume that you deposit money into a savings account and make no withdrawals.

a. Suppose you deposit $100 in a savings account that pays 4% interest, compounded annually. (*Compounded annually* means that the interest is compounded every year, once per year at the end of the year.) Write a *NOW-NEXT* formula and a recursive formula that show how the amount of money in your account changes from year to year. Find the amount of money in the account after 10 years.

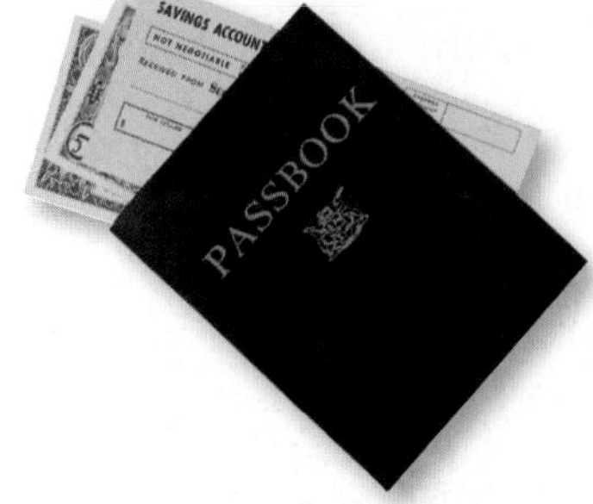

b. Most savings accounts pay interest that compounds more often than annually. Suppose that you make an initial deposit of $100 into an account that pays 4% annual interest, compounded monthly.

i. Write a recursive formula that models the month-by-month change in the amount of money in your account.

ii. How much money is in the account after 1 month? After 2 months? After 2 years?

iii. How much money is in the account after 10 years? Compare your answer to the answer you got in Part a. Which kind of interest is a better deal, compounding annually or compounding monthly?

c. Suppose that, in addition to the initial $100, you deposit another $50 at the end of every year, and the interest rate is 4% compounded annually.

i. Write a recursive formula that models this situation.

ii. How much money is in the account after 10 years?

iii. Describe the pattern of growth of the money in the savings account.

6 In this lesson, you have investigated recursive formulas of the form $A_n = rA_{n-1} + b$. Different values for r and b yield models for different situations. Consider some of the possibilities by completing a table like the one on the next page. For each cell in the table, do the following.

- Describe a situation that could be modeled by a recursive formula with the designated values of r and b. (You may use examples from the lesson if you wish.)
- Write the recursive formula.
- Describe the long-term trend.

5 **NOTE** The interpretation of stated interest rates taken here is common. However, there is another interpretation possible due to the APR law and the nature of compound interest. See the Instructional Note after Problem 7 on page T466; also see Connections Task 8 and Extensions Task 18. In the situation here, a 4% annual rate is interpreted to yield a monthly rate of $\frac{4}{12}\%$, or approximately 0.00333.

Under this interpretation (which is common), the stated 4% rate does not take into account the effect of monthly compounding. Alternatively, if we assume that the stated 4% annual rate *does* take into account the effect of monthly compounding, then the monthly rate would be $(1 + 0.04)^{\frac{1}{12}} - 1 \approx 0.00327$. Note that this is close to the monthly rate under the other interpretation, 0.00333.

Once the monthly interest rate is in hand, then the computation of compound interest is clear and consistent. The only issue is how to interpret the stated annual rate in order to determine the monthly rate.

a. $NEXT = 1.04NOW$, starting at 100
$U_n = 1.04U_{n-1}$ or $P_{n+1} = 1.04P_n$, $U_0 = P_0 = 100$
After 10 years (compounded annually), there will be \$148.02 in the account.

b. **i.** If the interest is compounded monthly and the annual interest rate is 4%, each month you get $\frac{1}{12}$ of the 4%. Therefore, $\frac{4}{12}\%$ interest is paid each month. $\frac{4}{12}\% \approx 0.0033$, so $U_n = 1.0033U_{n-1}$ or $P_{n+1} = 1.0033P_n$, $U_0 = P_0 = 100$.

ii. Using the formula in Part b after one month, there is \$100.33. After two months, there is \$100.66. After two years, there is \$108.23. (If students do not round the $\frac{4}{12}\%$, they will get \$100.67 after two months and \$108.31 after two years.)

iii. After ten years, the amount is \$148.49 (or \$149.08 if $\frac{4}{12}\%$ is not rounded). The interest that is compounded monthly is a better deal. In this situation, you have \$0.47 (or \$1.06 if $\frac{4}{12}\%$ is not rounded) more after ten years.

c. **i.** $U_n = 1.04U_{n-1} + 50$ or $P_{n+1} = 1.04P_n + 50$, $U_0 = P_0 = 100$

ii. After ten years, there is \$748.33 in the account.

iii. The money grows without bound. Once again, the pattern may look linear in the short term, but it is nonlinear. The amount of money is growing at an increasing rate.

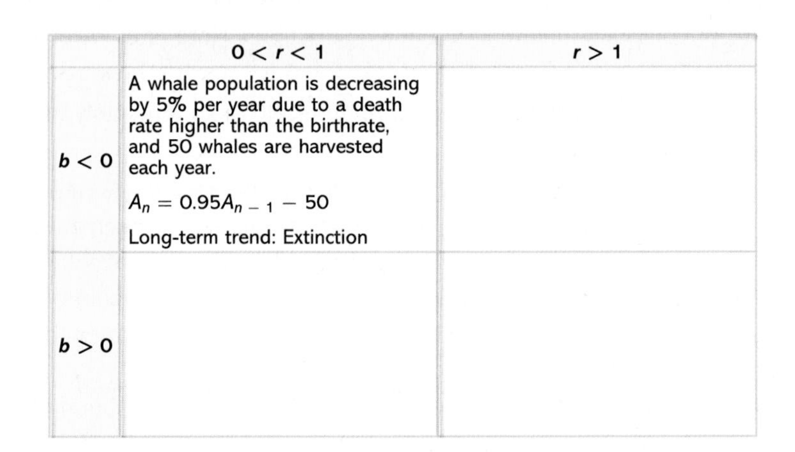

	$0 < r < 1$	$r > 1$
$b < 0$	A whale population is decreasing by 5% per year due to a death rate higher than the birthrate, and 50 whales are harvested each year. $A_n = 0.95A_{n-1} - 50$ Long-term trend: Extinction	
$b > 0$		

Connections

7 In Investigation 2, you found the following recursive formula to model a fish population.

Formula I $P_n = 0.8P_{n-1} + 1{,}000$, with $P_0 = 3{,}000$

Here is another formula that represents this situation.

Formula II $P_n = -2{,}000(0.8^n) + 5{,}000$

a. You can provide an algebraic argument for why the two formulas above are equivalent (see Connections Task 11 in Lesson 2 and Extensions Task 18 in Lesson 3). For now, give an informal argument using graphs, as follows.

i. Use geometric transformations to describe how the graph of the function indicated by Formula II is related to the graph of the exponential function $f(n) = 0.8^n$.

ii. Compare the graph of the function given by Formula II to the graph you generated in Investigation 2 using Formula I. Describe how the graphs are similar.

iii. Why do you think it makes sense that these two formulas could be equivalent models of the fish-population problem?

b. Verify that Formula II gives the same values for P_1 and P_5 as those found using the recursive formula.

c. Verify that Formula II yields an initial population of 3,000.

d. Use Formula II to verify the long-term population you found in Problem 2 of Investigation 1 (page 466). Explain your thinking. How is the long-term population revealed in the symbolic form of this formula?

472 UNIT 7 • Recursion and Iteration

6 **Recursive Formulas of the Form $A_n = rA_{n-1} + b$**

	$0 < r < 1$	$r > 1$
$b < 0$	A whale population is decreasing by 5% per year due to a death rate higher than the birthrate, and 50 whales are harvested each year. $A_n = 0.95A_{n-1} - 50$ Long-term trend: Extinction **Note:** This combination of parameters will always lead to extinction.	A whale population is increasing by 20% per year due to a birthrate higher than the death rate, and 50 whales are harvested each year. $A_n = 1.2A_{n-1} - 50$ Long-term trend: Unbounded population growth (if initial population is over 250) **Note:** In this situation, if $A_0 > \frac{b}{1-r}$, then the long-term trend will be unbounded growth. If $A_0 < \frac{b}{1-r}$, then the long-term trend will be extinction. If $A_0 = \frac{b}{1-r}$, then the population will remain constant at $A_0 = \frac{b}{1-r}$.
$b > 0$	A whale population is decreasing by 5% per year due to a death rate higher than the birthrate, and 50 whales are added to the stock each year. $A_n = 0.95A_{n-1} + 50$ Long-term trend: A fixed population of $\frac{50}{0.05}$, or 1,000 **Note:** This combination will always lead to a long-term population equal to $\frac{b}{1-r}$.	A whale population is increasing by 20% per year due to a birthrate higher than the death rate, and 50 whales are added to the stock each year. $A_n = 1.2A_{n-1} + 50$ Long-term trend: Unbounded growth **Note:** This combination will always produce unbounded growth.

Teaching Resources

Student Master 5.

UNIT 7 Recursion and Iteration

Recursive Formulas of the Form $A_n = rA_{n-1} + b$

Applications Task 6

	$0 < r < 1$	$r > 1$
$b < 0$	A whale population is decreasing by 5% per year due to a death rate higher than the birthrate, and 50 whales are harvested each year. $A_n = 0.95A_{n-1} - 50$ Long-term trend: Extinction	
$b > 0$		

Connections

7 **a.** **i.** $f(n) = (0.8^n)$ is an exponential function. Its graph is above the n-axis, comes down from left to right, and has the positive n-axis as a horizontal asymptote. Transform this graph: reflect the graph across the n-axis, stretch it vertically by a factor of 2,000, and then shift it up by 5,000.

ii. This yields a graph that looks like the graph generated in Investigation 2 using the recursive formula given in Formula I. Similarities in the graphs include the horizontal asymptote at 5,000, the y-intercept at 3,000, and rising from left to right.

iii. These transformations correspond algebraically to negating 0.8^n, multiplying by 2,000, and then adding 5,000, which yields the function corresponding to Formula II, $g(n) = -2{,}000(0.8^n) + 5{,}000$. Thus, we have a very informal graphical argument that the two formulas given in this task are equivalent. This makes sense since the population growth situation modeled by the recursive formula, where we multiply by 0.8 each year, has the features of an exponential growth situation, and Formula II in this task is in the exponential family. Also, we know from the analysis of Formula I in Investigations 1 and 2 that the fish population levels off at 5,000, which corresponds to the horizontal asymptote of the graph of $g(n) = -2{,}000(0.8^n) + 5{,}000$ at $y = 5{,}000$.

DIFFERENTIATION This On Your Own task and others address the explicit formula for the fish population problem. The recursive formula is the main focus of the lesson. You could have some students investigate explicit formulas by assigning them the following On Your Own tasks throughout this unit: Lesson 1 Connections Task 7 and Extensions Task 16, Lesson 2 Connections Task 11, and Lesson 3 Extensions Task 18.

NOTE Solutions to Connections Task 7 Parts b–d are on page T473.

8 In Investigation 2, there was a brief discussion of Annual Percentage Rate (APR). The APR is meant to be a standard way to state interest rates on loans so that different loans can be compared and understood more easily. A related method of stating interest rates is used for investments, like when you deposit money into a savings account.

The **Annual Percentage Yield** (**APY**) expresses an interest rate on an investment in a way that takes into account the effect of compounding the interest. The APY is different, and usually higher, than a "nominal" annual rate. For example, consider the table below showing interest rates for the Los Alamos National Bank in New Mexico.

Savings Account Interest Rates

as of April 3, 2008

TYPE	INTEREST RATE	APY*	MINIMUM BALANCE**	TIER BALANCE
Regular Savings Account	1.000%	1.010%	None	None
Campus Savings Account	1.000%	1.010%	None	None
Universal Savings Tier 1	1.000%	1.010%	None	$0.00 - $49,999.00
Universal Savings Tier 2	1.750%	1.770%	None	$50,000.00 - $99,999.00
Universal Savings Tier 3	2.500%	2.530%	None	$100,000.00 - $999,999.00
Universal Savings Tier 4	2.750%	2.790%	None	$1,000,000.00 and above
Money Market Tier 1	0.500%	0.500%	$1,000.00	$0.00 - $19,999.00
Money Market Tier 2	1.750%	1.770%	$1,000.00	$20,000.00 - $49,999.00
Money Market Tier 3	2.250%	2.280%	$1,000.00	$50,000.00 - $99,999.00
Money Market Tier 4	2.500%	2.530%	$1,000.00	$100,000.00 and above

The above Interest Rates are subject to change without prior notice.

*Annual Percentage Yield
**Minimum balance required to avoid periodic service charge.

Source: www.lanb.com/rates/savings.asp, retrieved April 3, 2008

This bank pays interest compounded monthly. The rates shown in the column labeled "INTEREST RATE" are sometimes called *nominal interest rates*. These rates are annual rates, and they do not take into account the effect of compounding. The APY is the nominal annual rate adjusted for the effect of monthly compounding. Here is how it works.

a. Let's think big and consider Universal Savings Tier 3. The stated nominal interest rate is 2.500%. This is an annual rate.

i. What is the corresponding monthly rate?

ii. Suppose you invest $1 at this monthly rate and you compound the interest for 12 months. How much will you have at the end of the year?

b. 2.500% is an annual interest rate that does *not* take into account the monthly compounding. Explain why the number you determined in Part a can be thought of as an *annual growth rate* that *does* take the monthly compounding into account.

c. Subtract 1 from the number you determined in Part a. Compare the result to the APY for Universal Savings Tier 3. Describe similarities and differences.

b. $P_1 = -2{,}000(0.8) + 5{,}000 = 3{,}400$
$P_5 = -2{,}000(0.8^5) + 5{,}000 = 4{,}344.64$
These values match P_1 and P_5 found earlier.

c. To get the initial population from the new formula, substitute $n = 0$. This gives $-2{,}000 + 5{,}000$, or 3,000.

d. To find the long-term population, substitute a very large number for n. This makes 0.8^n very small. Thus, $-2{,}000(0.8^n)$ is very small, and you can see that $-2{,}000(0.8^n) + 5{,}000$ is very close to 5,000. So, the long-term population is easily seen to be 5,000.

8 **a.** **i.** The monthly rate is 0.20833%.

ii. If you invest $1 at this rate compounded monthly, you will have $1.025288 at the end of a year.

ROUNDING NOTE Students should retain full values of answers and not round intermediate computations.

b. The number from Part a, 1.025288, was computed by using monthly compounding, so it clearly takes monthly compounding into account. It can be thought of as an annual growth rate since it is the multiplier by which you would multiply an initial deposit to determine the amount of money you would have after one year if you invested under the stated terms. (In fact, this growth rate yields the same year-by-year amounts as those obtained by using the monthly compounding process in Part a.)

c. Subtracting 1 from 1.025288 yields 0.025288, which converted to a percent is the same as the APY shown in the table, 2.530% corresponding to the nominal interest rate 2.500%. (Note that rounding may cause the answer here and the APY value in the table to be slightly different. The percentages shown in the table seem to be rounded to two significant digits after the decimal point. If you round the percentage derived from this task, 2.5288%, similarly you get 2.530%, which matches exactly with the APY percentage in the table.)

On Your Own

d. The formula for computing APY is

$$APY = \left(1 + \frac{r}{n}\right)^n - 1,$$

where r is the nominal annual rate, expressed as a decimal, and n is the number of compound periods in a year.

i. Explain how each part of this formula relates to the numbers and computations in Parts a–c.

ii. Use this formula to compute the APY for another type of savings account in the table on the previous page.

9 You can represent recursive formulas with subscript notation or function notation. For example, in the fish-population problem, you can think of the population P as a function of the number of years n and you can write P_n or $P(n)$ for the population after n years. In the case of the fish-population problem, what are the practical domain and practical range of the function P?

10 Think about how matrix multiplication can be used to calculate successive values generated by recursive formulas of the form $A_n = rA_{n-1} + b$. For example, consider the recursive formula for the original fish-population situation at the beginning of this lesson: $P_n = 0.8P_{n-1} + 1{,}000$, with $P_0 = 3{,}000$.

a. A first attempt at a matrix multiplication that would be equivalent to evaluating the recursive formula might use the following matrices.

$$A = \begin{bmatrix} 3{,}000 & 1 \end{bmatrix} \text{ and } B = \begin{bmatrix} 0.8 \\ 1{,}000 \end{bmatrix}$$

Compute AB and compare it to P_1.

b. AB is just a 1×1 matrix and so is not much good for repeated multiplication. Thus, you cannot use repeated multiplication of these matrices to successively evaluate the recursive formula. A better try might be to use the following matrices.

$$A = \begin{bmatrix} 3{,}000 & 1 \end{bmatrix} \text{ and } C = \begin{bmatrix} 0.8 & 0 \\ 1{,}000 & 1 \end{bmatrix}$$

Compute AC and compare it to P_1. What matrix multiplication would you use next to find P_2? To find P_3?

c. There is just one finishing touch needed. Modify the matrices so that the multiplication computes not only the successive values but also the number of the year. Consider the following matrices.

$$A = \begin{bmatrix} 0 & 3{,}000 & 1 \end{bmatrix} \text{ and } D = \begin{bmatrix} 1 & 0 & 0 \\ 0 & 0.8 & 0 \\ 1 & 1{,}000 & 1 \end{bmatrix}$$

Compute AD, AD^2, AD^3, AD^4, and AD^5. Compare the results to P_1 through P_5.

d. Use matrix multiplication to generate three successive values of the recursive formula $P_n = 1.04P_{n-1} - 350$, with $P_0 = 6{,}700$. Do so in a way that also generates the successive values of n.

e. Explain why this matrix multiplication method works to find successive values of a recursive formula.

Unit 7

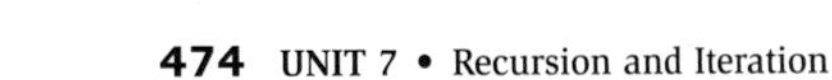
474 UNIT 7 • Recursion and Iteration

d. **i.** Since the interest is compounded monthly, the number of compound periods in a year is 12, so $n = 12$. In the APY formula, $\left(1 + \frac{r}{n}\right)^n$ is the computation used in Part a, then subtracting 1 is the computation from Part c. Thus, the formula can be understood as determining the annual interest rate that takes into account the monthly compounding.

ii. The computed APY value will depend upon the type of savings account a student examines but should match the APY given in the table, except possibly for rounding differences.

9 The practical domain is all non-negative integers, and the practical range is integers between 3,000 and 5,000. (The theoretical range does include nonintegers.)

10 **a.** $AB = [0.8(3{,}000) + 1{,}000] = [3{,}400]$. This is the value of P_1.

b. $AC = [3{,}400 \quad 1]$. Multiply this answer matrix by C to find P_2. This would be the same as AC^2. Similarly, AC^3 will produce P_3.

c. $P_1 = 3{,}400$; $P_2 = 3{,}720$; $P_3 = 3{,}976$; $P_4 = 4{,}180.8$; $P_5 = 4{,}344.64$
$AD = [1 \quad 3{,}400 \quad 1]$; $AD^2 = [2 \quad 3{,}720 \quad 1]$; $AD^3 = [3 \quad 3{,}976 \quad 1]$;
$AD^4 = [4 \quad 4{,}180.8 \quad 1]$; $AD^5 = [5 \quad 4{,}344.64 \quad 1]$

Note that the first entry in the matrix is the year and the second entry is the population for that year.

d. $A = [0 \quad 6{,}700 \quad 1]$ and $B = \begin{bmatrix} 1 & 0 & 0 \\ 0 & 1.04 & 0 \\ 1 & -350 & 1 \end{bmatrix}$

$AB = [1 \quad 6{,}618 \quad 1]$; $AB^2 = [2 \quad 6{,}532.72 \quad 1]$;
$AB^3 = [3 \quad 6{,}444.03 \quad 1]$

The second entries of these matrices are the first three successive values of the recursive formula (the successive values of P_n). The first entries give the term numbers (the successive values of n).

e. To explain why this matrix multiplication works and how someone might have thought of it in the first place, students might reason as follows. First of all, it seems reasonable to try to use repeated matrix multiplication, and particularly matrix powers, to mimic the iteration of a recursive formula, since computing a matrix power is an iterative process. A first attempt at matrix multiplication using $A = [3{,}000 \quad 1]$ and $B = \begin{bmatrix} 0.8 \\ 1{,}000 \end{bmatrix}$ is reasonable because you set up the simplest matrices which, when multiplied, will yield P_1. However, this result is just a 1×1 matrix and is, therefore, not much good for repeated multiplication. Add an extra column to B so that the multiplication will yield a 1×2 matrix, which can then be used for further multiplications. Then the last step is to modify the matrices so that the multiplication computes not only the successive values but also the number of the iteration. This is done by using the matrices as given in Part c.

Unit 7

Reflections

11 When using some graphing calculators, you have the option of graphing in "connected" mode or "dot" mode. Find out what the difference is between these two modes of graphing. Which do you think is more appropriate for the graphing you have been doing in this lesson? Why?

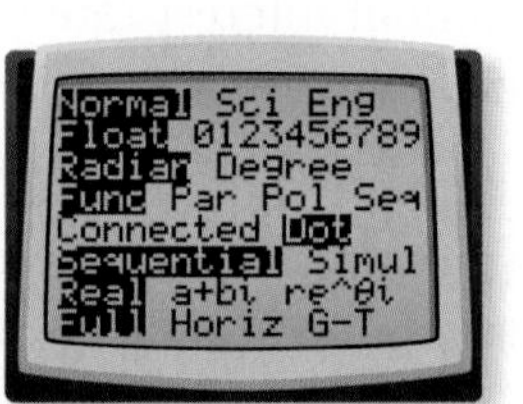

12 Consider again the fish population change modeled by $NEXT = 0.8NOW + 1{,}000$, from Investigation 1. You used several different formulas to represent this fish population, for example, a formula using the words *NOW* and *NEXT*, a formula with subscripts using P_n and P_{n-1}, a formula with subscripts using P_n and P_{n+1}, a formula with function notation using $A(n)$ and $A(n + 1)$, and a formula using spreadsheet notation.

Suppose that one of your classmates has not completed this task. Write a paragraph to the classmate explaining how all these formulas accurately represent the changing fish population.

13 In this lesson, you used recursive formulas to model sequential change in several situations, such as population growth, drug concentration, chlorine concentration, and money saved or owed. Describe one result of your investigations that was particularly interesting or surprising.

14 Recursive formulas are also sometimes called *difference equations*. What difference would be of interest in studying a recursive formula?

Extensions

15 These days, almost every state has a lottery, and the jackpots are often quite large. But are they really as large as they seem? Suppose you win $500,000 in a lottery (which you will, of course, donate to the mathematics department at your school). Typically, these large jackpots are not paid immediately as a lump sum. Instead, they are paid over time. For example, suppose you receive your $500,000 over 20 years at $25,000 per year. To accurately analyze how much you have *really* won in this situation, you need to include the effect of compound interest.

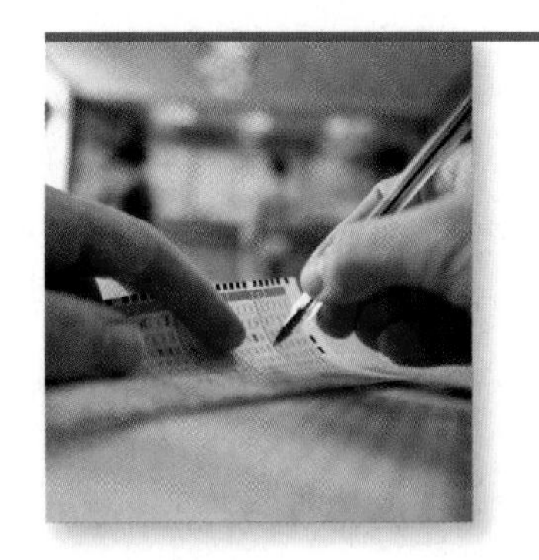

a. Suppose you deposit $500,000 in a bank account paying 3.5% annual interest, and you withdraw $25,000 at the end of every year. Write a recursive formula that models this situation, and calculate how much money will be in the account after 20 years.

b. Experiment to find an initial deposit that will yield a balance of $0 after 20 years.

Reflections

11 Connected mode will draw a continuous graph by connecting the computed values with line segments. Dot mode is discontinuous or discrete; it will show the graph as a series of dots. The dot mode is most appropriate in this lesson since the change is sequential (for example, from year to year) and there are no computed values between steps.

12 The fish population changes from one year to the next by a factor of 0.8, plus an added 1,000. This pattern of change is accurately described by all four formulas. One way to see that they are all accurate representations is to use each one to compute the changing fish population and see that you get the same values. The symbolic notation is different in the different forms; however, the formulas using *NOW* and *NEXT*, P_n and P_{n-1}, U_n and U_{n+1}, $A(n)$ and $A(n + 1)$, and A2=0.8A1+1,000 all compute the population of the following year given the current population in the same way.

13 Student responses may vary. For example, it is interesting that when $|r| < 1$ in $A_n = rA_{n-1} + b$, no matter what you pick for an initial value, the sequence will reach the same long-term value $\frac{b}{1-r}$ (as in the trout-population problem or the antibiotic problem).

14 The differences between any two successive terms are of interest in studying a recursive formula. By examining these differences, you can get valuable information about the sequence of numbers determined by the recursive formula. For example, in the next lesson, the pattern in these differences helps students determine if the associated sequence is arithmetic, geometric, or a sequence associated with a polynomial function. Also, it is possible to rewrite any recursive formula in terms of these differences. (This is formalized in the study of the difference operator Δ and the study of finite differences. For more about the difference operator Δ see, for example, *Discrete Algorithmic Mathematics*, Stephen B. Maurer and Anthony Ralston, A K Peters, Ltd., 2004. For a brief look at finite differences, see Investigation 3 of Lesson 2.)

Extensions

15 **a.** $U_n = 1.035U_{n-1} - 25{,}000$. After 20 years, there will be $287,902 in the account.

b. If you start with $355,310, you get −0.16 after 20 years.

c. A $500,000 jackpot is really worth about $355,310.

d. The actual cash value of a $1,000,000 jackpot, if there is 5% annual interest for 20 years, is $623,110.50. This can be found using the recursive formula $U_n = 1.05U_{n-1} - 50{,}000$.

e. Inflation can affect the actual present value even more.

c. The result from Part b is called the **present value** of your lottery winning. The present value is the lump sum amount that, if deposited now at 3.5% annual interest, would generate payments of $25,000 per year for 20 years. The present value is what your lottery winning is really worth, taking into account the reality of compound interest. So in this situation, how much is a $500,000 jackpot paid over 20 years really worth?

d. Find the actual value, that is, the present value, of a lottery winning of $1,000,000 that is paid at $50,000 per year for 20 years, if you can invest money at 5% annual interest.

e. What other factors besides compound interest do you think could affect the present value?

16 In this lesson, you modeled a fish population with the recursive formula $P_n = 0.8P_{n-1} + 1{,}000$, with $P_0 = 3{,}000$. You can get another modeling formula for this situation by fitting a curve to the population data and finding the equation for that curve. Use the following steps to carry out this plan.

a. Use the formula $P_n = 0.8P_{n-1} + 1{,}000$, with $P_0 = 3{,}000$, to generate the sequence of population figures for 20 years. Put these figures into a data list, say L2, on your calculator or computer. Generate another list, say L1, that contains the sequence of years 0 through 20. Produce a scatterplot of L1 and L2.

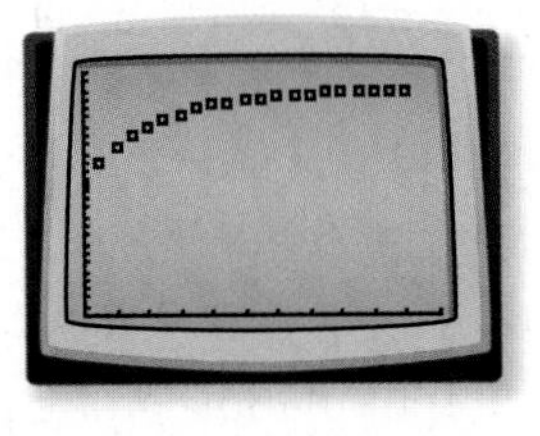

b. Modify your scatterplot by transforming the data in the lists so that the plot matches one of the standard regression models of your calculator or computer software. Find a regression equation that fits the transformed data.

c. Now, transform your regression equation so that it fits the original data.

d. Test your equation. Does the graph fit the original scatterplot? Compare the function value for $n = 20$ to what you get when you find P_{20} using the recursive formula $P_n = 0.8P_{n-1} + 1{,}000$, with $P_0 = 3{,}000$.

17 The Towers of Hanoi is a mathematical game featured in an old story about the end of the world. As the story goes, monks in a secluded temple are working on this game; and when they are finished, the world will end! The people of the world would like to know how long it will take the monks to finish the game.

476 UNIT 7 • Recursion and Iteration

Unit 7

NOTE Solutions to Task 15 Parts c–e are on page T475.

16 **DIFFERENTIATION** This On Your Own task and others address the explicit formula for the fish population problem. The recursive formula is the main focus of the lesson. You could have some students investigate the explicit formula by assigning them the following On Your Own tasks throughout this unit: Lesson 1 Connections Task 7 and Extensions Task 16, Lesson 2 Connections Task 11, and Lesson 3 Extensions Task 18.

a.

L1	L2	L1	L2	L1	L2
0	3,000	7	4,581	14	4,912
1	3,400	8	4,664	15	4,930
2	3,720	9	4,732	16	4,944
3	3,976	10	4,785	17	4,955
4	4,181	11	4,828	18	4,964
5	4,345	12	4,863	19	4,971
6	4,476	13	4,890	20	4,977

b. Students first need to realize that this graph has the general shape of a transformed exponential model. If the plot is transformed by first reflecting it across the x-axis and then translating it up 5,000 units, the graph looks like a standard exponential decay model of the form $y = a(b^x)$, $0 < b < 1$. The original and transformed data are shown.

This modification to the lists can be completed by letting L3 = −L2 + 5,000. Using a calculator to find the exponential regression equation for L1 and L3 gives $y = 2{,}000(0.8^x)$.

c. You can transform the modified data back into the original data by reflecting across the x-axis and then shifting up 5,000. This is accomplished by the equation $y = -2{,}000(0.8^x) + 5{,}000$.

d. The graph matches the scatterplot perfectly, as shown here. $-2{,}000(0.8^{20}) + 5{,}000 = 4{,}976.94$, which is the same as P_{20}.

The game is played with 3 pegs mounted on a board and 64 golden disks of successively larger sizes with holes in the center. (Commercial games such as the example on the previous page have many fewer disks.) The game begins with all 64 disks stacked on one peg, from largest to smallest. The goal of the game is to move all 64 disks onto another peg, subject to these rules: (1) Only one disk may be moved at a time. (2) You are not allowed to put a larger disk on top of a smaller disk. (3) Disks may be placed temporarily on any peg, including the one on which the disks were originally stacked. (4) Eventually, the disks must be stacked from largest to smallest on a new peg.

a. You may not have 64 golden disks to play this game. But to get an idea of how it works, you can play with some homemade disks and pegs. Cut out four successively larger squares of paper to use as disks (or use different size coins for the disks). Put three large dots on a piece of paper to use as pegs mounted on a board. Play the game several times, first with just one disk stacked on the starting peg, then with two disks, then three, and so on. As you play each game, keep track of the *fewest* number of moves it takes to finish the game. Make a table listing the number of disks in the game and the fewest number of moves it takes to finish the game.

b. By thinking about strategies for how to play the game with more and more disks and by looking for patterns in the table from Part a, find a recursive formula and any other formula you can for the fewest number of moves needed to finish the game with n disks.

c. What is the fewest number of moves needed to finish a game with 64 disks? If the monks in the story move one disk every second and work nonstop, should we worry about the world ending soon? Explain.

18 The Annual Percentage Rate (APR), which you considered in Investigation 1, is not interpreted consistently in all ads and descriptions on the Internet. This may be because the law on which the APR is based is long and complicated. The APR comes from the U.S. Federal Truth in Lending Act, which is contained in Title I of the Consumer Credit Protection Act from May 29, 1968. This Act is implemented by the Truth in Lending Act Regulation, known as Regulation Z, as amended on December 20, 2001. At one place in these laws, it is stated that:

> "The annual percentage rate [APR] ... shall be determined ... as that annual percentage rate which will yield a sum equal to the amount of the finance charge when it is applied to the unpaid balances of the amount financed ... ." Furthermore, "the amount of the finance charge shall be determined as the sum of all charges ... which include interest, [and other charges]." (Sections 106 and 107 of the Truth in Lending Act)

17 a.

Number of Disks	Fewest Number of Moves
1	1
2	3
3	7
4	15
5	31
6	63

b. $U_n = 2U_{n-1} + 1$ or $U_n = 2^n - 1$

c. It would take 18,446,744,073,709,551,615 moves. There are $365 \times 24 \times 60 \times 60 = 31{,}536{,}000$ seconds in a year. Therefore, it would take 584,942,417,355 years to complete the game, over 40 times the estimated age of the universe. Clearly, we do not need to worry about the end of the world because of monks finishing a game.

18 **a.** **i.** If the lender takes compounding into account, then the APR could be computed using a method similar to the method used to compute the APY, as in Connections Task 8, which computes an annual rate that takes into account the effect of monthly compounding. Thus, the APR could be computed as:
$APR = (1 + r)^{12} - 1 = (1 + 0.008)^{12} - 1 = 0.1003 \approx 10\%$.

ii. According to the method stated in Regulation Z, the APR might be reported as simply $12r = 12(0.008) = 0.096 = 9.6\%$.

b. In the first interpretation, as in part i above, the formula involves an exponential function, and so this is related to exponential growth. In the second interpretation, as in part ii, the computation involves a linear function and so this is related to linear growth.

Since exponential growth is much faster than linear growth, this is a very significant difference in these two interpretations.

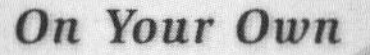

On Your Own

Elsewhere in the law it is stated that:

"The annual percentage rate [APR] shall be the nominal annual percentage rate determined by multiplying the unit-period rate by the number of unit-periods in a year." (Appendix J of Regulation Z)

a. Suppose a lender advertises a loan with an interest rate of 0.8% per month compounded monthly.

i. Using the first statement from the Truth in Lending Act, which implies that the APR must be stated as an annual rate that takes into account compounding interest, what annual interest rate might the lender state?

ii. Using the second statement above, from Regulation Z, what annual rate might the lender state?

b. Explain how the different interpretations of the APR that may be possible based on the two statements above can be described in terms of the difference between growth determined by an exponential function and growth determined by a linear function.

19 Suppose you have a recursive formula that can be used to compute the next term in a sequence from the current term. Think about how you could compute every second term or perhaps every tenth term. (For example, you might want to predict the population every decade instead of every year.)

a. Suppose *NEXT* = 3*NOW* and the starting value is 1. List the first 10 terms in the sequence generated by this recursive formula and initial value. Starting with 1, list every second term within this list. Write a recursive formula that describes the list of every second term.

b. Think about every tenth term in the original sequence in Part a, that is, the sequence determined by *NEXT* = 3*NOW*, starting at 1. Write a new recursive formula that would generate every tenth term in the sequence.

c. Consider the sequence of numbers generated by $A_n = 3A_{n-1} + 2$, with $A_0 = 1$. List the first 11 terms of this sequence. Think about new recursive formulas that will generate every second term or every tenth term of this sequence.

i. Let $\{S_n\}$ be the sequence of every second term, starting at 1. Explain each step in the following argument to find a recursive formula for S_n.

$$
\begin{aligned}
S_0 &= A_0 = 1 && (1)\\
S_1 &= A_2 = 17 && (2)\\
S_2 &= A_4 = 161 && (3)\\
&\ \vdots\\
S_n &= A_{2n} && (4)\\
&= 3A_{2n-1} + 2 && (5)\\
&= 3(3A_{2n-2} + 2) + 2 && (6)\\
&= 3^2A_{2n-2} + 3(2) + 2 && (7)\\
&= 3^2A_{2(n-1)} + 3(2) + 2 && (8)\\
&= 3^2S_{n-1} + 3(2) + 2 && (9)
\end{aligned}
$$

Thus, $S_n = 3^2S_{n-1} + 3(2) + 2$.

Unit 7

478 UNIT 7 • Recursion and Iteration

19 **a.** In the table below, every second term is in bold.

Term Number	0	1	2	3	4	5	6	7	8	9
Value	**1**	3	**9**	27	**81**	243	**729**	2,187	**6,561**	19,683

To get to every second term, you multiply by 9, so a recursive formula could be *NEXT* = 9*NOW*, starting at 1. Notice that $9 = 3^2$.

b. To move term-by-term, from a given term to the tenth term farther on in the sequence, you would need to multiply by 3 ten times. So, you could get to the tenth term farther on by multiplying the current term by 3^{10}. Thus, a recursive formula could be *NEXT* = 3^{10}*NOW*.

c. The first 11 terms are 1, 5, 17, 53, 161, 485, 1,457, 4,373, 13,121, 39,365, and 118,097.

i. $S_0 = A_0 = 1$ — (1) Both sequences start at the same number, 1.

$S_1 = A_2 = 17$ — (2) The next term of the sequence of every second term is two terms farther along in the original sequence, which is 17.

$S_2 = A_4 = 161$ — (3) The next term of the sequence of every second term is two terms farther along in the original sequence, which is 161.

$\vdots$

$S_n = A_{2n}$ — (4) The terms of S_n are every second term of the A_n sequence.

$= 3A_{2n-1} + 2$ — (5) You get a term in the A sequence by multiplying the previous term by 3 and adding 2.

$= 3(3A_{2n-2} + 2) + 2$ — (6) You get a term in the A sequence by multiplying the previous term by 3 and adding 2.

$= 3^2A_{2n-2} + 3(2) + 2$ — (7) Distributive property

$= 3^2A_{2(n-1)} + 3(2) + 2$ — (8) Distributive property

$= 3^2S_{n-1} + 3(2) + 2$ — (9) From Step 4, the terms of S_n are every second term of A_n, so $S_{n-1} = A_{2(n-1)}$.

Thus, $S_n = 3^2S_{n-1} + 3(2) + 2$.

NOTE Solutions to Task 18 are on page T477.

Teaching Resources

Student Master 6.

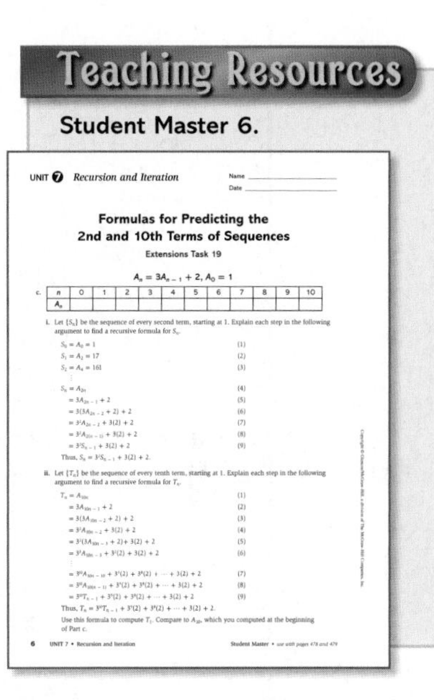

UNIT 7 *Recursion and Iteration* Name ________ Date ________

Formulas for Predicting the 2nd and 10th Terms of Sequences

Extensions Task 19

$A_n = 3A_{n-1} + 2, A_0 = 1$

c.

n	0	1	2	3	4	5	6	7	8	9	10
A_n											

i. Let $\{S_n\}$ be the sequence of every second term, starting at 1. Explain each step in the following argument to find a recursive formula for S_n.

$S_0 = A_0 = 1$ (1)
$S_1 = A_2 = 17$ (2)
$S_2 = A_4 = 161$ (3)
$\vdots$
$S_n = A_{2n}$ (4)
$= 3A_{2n-1} + 2$ (5)
$= 3(3A_{2n-2} + 2) + 2$ (6)
$= 3^2A_{2n-2} + 3(2) + 2$ (7)
$= 3^2A_{2(n-1)} + 3(2) + 2$ (8)
$= 3^2S_{n-1} + 3(2) + 2$ (9)
Thus, $S_n = 3^2S_{n-1} + 3(2) + 2$.

ii. Let $\{T_n\}$ be the sequence of every tenth term, starting at 1. Explain each step in the following argument to find a recursive formula for T_n.

$T_n = A_{10n}$ (1)
$= 3A_{10n-1} + 2$ (2)
$= 3(3A_{10n-2} + 2) + 2$ (3)
$= 3^2A_{10n-2} + 3(2) + 2$ (4)
$= 3^2(3A_{10n-3} + 2) + 3(2) + 2$ (5)
$= 3^3A_{10n-3} + 3^2(2) + 3(2) + 2$ (6)
$\vdots$
$= 3^{10}A_{10n-10} + 3^9(2) + 3^8(2) + \cdots + 3(2) + 2$ (7)
$= 3^{10}A_{10(n-1)} + 3^9(2) + 3^8(2) + \cdots + 3(2) + 2$ (8)
$= 3^{10}T_{n-1} + 3^9(2) + 3^8(2) + \cdots + 3(2) + 2$ (9)
Thus, $T_n = 3^{10}T_{n-1} + 3^9(2) + 3^8(2) + \cdots + 3(2) + 2$.

Use this formula to compute T_1. Compare to A_{10}, which you computed at the beginning of Part c.

6 UNIT 7 • Recursion and Iteration — Student Master • use with pages 478 and 479

Unit 7

ii. Let $\{T_n\}$ be the sequence of every tenth term, starting at 1. Explain each step in the following argument to find a recursive formula for T_n.

$$
\begin{aligned}
T_n &= A_{10n} && (1)\\
&= 3A_{10n-1} + 2 && (2)\\
&= 3(3A_{10n-2} + 2) + 2 && (3)\\
&= 3^2A_{10n-2} + 3(2) + 2 && (4)\\
&= 3^2(3A_{10n-3} + 2) + 3(2) + 2 && (5)\\
&= 3^3A_{10n-3} + 3^2(2) + 3(2) + 2 && (6)\\
&\ \vdots\\
&= 3^{10}A_{10n-10} + 3^9(2) + 3^8(2) + \cdots + 3(2) + 2 && (7)\\
&= 3^{10}A_{10(n-1)} + 3^9(2) + 3^8(2) + \cdots + 3(2) + 2 && (8)\\
&= 3^{10}T_{n-1} + 3^9(2) + 3^8(2) + \cdots + 3(2) + 2 && (9)
\end{aligned}
$$

Thus, $T_n = 3^{10}T_{n-1} + 3^9(2) + 3^8(2) + \cdots + 3(2) + 2$.
Use this formula to compute T_1. Compare to A_{10}, which you computed at the beginning of Part c on the previous page.

20 So far, you have used recursive formulas to predict future values in a sequential change situation. This is a natural use of recursive formulas since they typically show how to get from one term in a sequence to the next. Think about reversing the perspective and computing past terms.

a. Suppose *NEXT* = 2*NOW*, and one of the terms in the sequence is 460.8. What is the previous term? Describe how you found the previous term.

b. Suppose a changing population is modeled by this recursive formula.

$P_n = 0.8P_{n-1} + 500$, where P_n is the population at year n

If the population predicted by this formula in a given year is 1,460, what is the population the previous year?

c. The recursive formula in Part b can be used to compute the population in future years. Construct a new recursive formula that you could use to compute the population in past years. Use the new recursive formula to compute the population 10 years ago if the current population is 2,341.

Review

21 A study of milk samples from 167,460 Holstein cows measured the percent of fat in each milk sample. The data was normally distributed with mean milk fat of 3.59% and a standard deviation of 0.71%.

a. Approximately how many of the samples had milk fat between 2.17% and 5.01%?

b. Approximately how many of the samples had less than 4.3% milk fat?

c. Approximately what percentage of the samples had more than 5.01% milk fat?

ii. $T_n = A_{10n}$ (1) The terms of T_n are every tenth term of the A_n sequence.

$= 3A_{10n-1} + 2$ (2) You get a term in the A sequence by multiplying the previous term by 3 and adding 2.

$= 3(3A_{10n-2} + 2) + 2$ (3) You get a term in the A sequence by multiplying the previous term by 3 and adding 2.

$= 3^2A_{10n-2} + 3(2) + 2$ (4) Distributive property

$= 3^2(3A_{10n-3} + 2) + 3(2) + 2$

(5) You get a term in the A sequence by multiplying the previous term by 3 and adding 2.

$= 3^3A_{10n-3} + 3^2(2) + 3(2) + 2$

(6) Distributive property

$\vdots$

$= 3^{10}A_{10n-10} + 3^9(2) + 3^8(2) + \cdots + 3(2) + 2$

(7) This is a good conjecture based on the pattern exhibited above. You could carry out the missing steps to verify.

$= 3^{10}A_{10(n-1)} + 3^9(2) + 3^8(2) + \cdots + 3(2) + 2$

(8) Distributive property

$= 3^{10}T_{n-1} + 3^9(2) + 3^8(2) + \cdots + 3(2) + 2$

(9) From Step 1, the terms of T_n are every tenth term of A_n, so $T_{n-1} = A_{10(n-1)}$.

Thus, $T_n = 3^{10}T_{n-1} + 3^9(2) + 3^8(2) + \cdots + 3(2) + 2$.

Using this formula, $T_1 = 3^{10}T_0 + 3^9(2) + 3^8(2) + \cdots + 3(2) + 2 = 3^{10}(1) + 3^9(2) + 3^8(2) + \cdots + 3(2) + 2 = 118{,}097$.

This is the same as A_{10}, which was computed at the beginning of Part c above. (Note that A_{10} is the eleventh term in the sequence since the first term is A_0.)

20 **a.** If a given term is 460.8, then the previous term is 230.4. The recursive formula generates the next term by multiplying the current term by 2. Thus, to find the previous term from a given term you would reverse this process and divide by 2.

b. Just as in Part a, we need to reverse the process shown by the recursive formula to find the previous term. So, start with the current term, 1,460, then subtract 500 to get 960, then divide by 0.8 to get 1,200. Thus, the previous term is 1,200.

c. Students might use several methods to find a recursive formula to compute past populations. They might reason as in Part b to conclude that such a recursive formula would be $PREVIOUS = \frac{NOW - 500}{0.8}$. Or, equivalently, they might solve the given recursive formula for P_{n-1}, to get $P_{n-1} = 1.25(P_n - 500)$. The population 10 years ago is 1,019.

NOTE Solutions to Task 21 are on page T480.

Unit 7

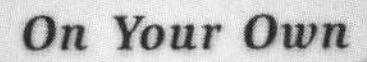

22 Perform each indicated operation. Write the polynomial in standard form.

a. $(3x^3 - 5x + 14) - (x^3 + 4x^2 - 6x)$

b. $(6 - x^3)^2(x + 1)$

c. $8(-x^2 + 7) + 5(x^4 - 5x^2 + 10)$

d. $(x^3 + 5x) - (7x^3 - 3x) + (4x^2 + 8x)$

23 Determine whether each data pattern is linear, exponential, or quadratic. Then find a function rule that matches each pattern.

a.

x	−3	−2	−1	0	1	2	3
y	3	9	27	81	243	729	2,187

b.

x	−4	−3	−2	0	2	4	7
y	1	5	9	17	25	33	45

c.

x	−2	−1	0	1	2	3	4
y	4,800	2,400	1,200	600	300	150	75

d.

x	−3	−2	−1	0	1	2	3
y	20	12	6	2	0	0	2

24 Simplify each algebraic fraction as much as possible. Then determine if the two expressions are undefined for the same values.

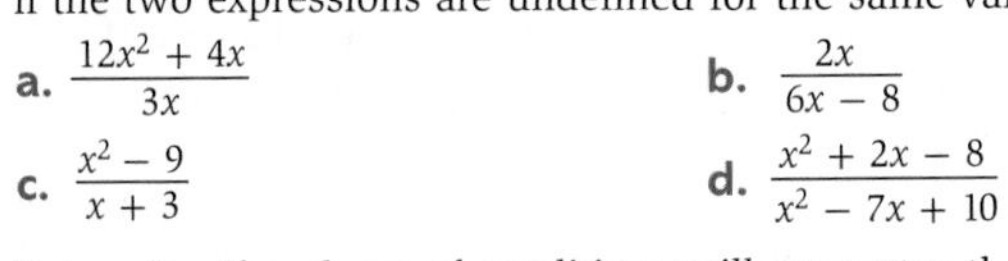

a. $\frac{12x^2 + 4x}{3x}$

b. $\frac{2x}{6x - 8}$

c. $\frac{x^2 - 9}{x + 3}$

d. $\frac{x^2 + 2x - 8}{x^2 - 7x + 10}$

25 Determine if each set of conditions will guarantee that quadrilateral *ABCD* is a parallelogram. If not, draw a counterexample. If so, provide a proof.

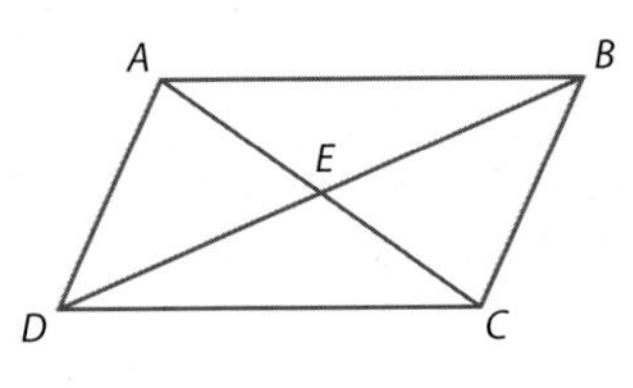

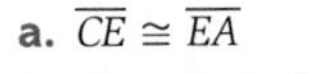

a. $\overline{CE} \cong \overline{EA}$

b. $\triangle AED \cong \triangle CEB$

c. $\overline{AC} \perp \overline{DB}$

26 Solve each exponential equation.

a. $10^x = 0.01$

b. $5(10^x) = 5{,}000$

c. $25(10^x) = 1{,}300$

d. $12(3^x) = 324$

Unit 7

480 UNIT 7 • Recursion and Iteration

Review

21 **a.** Since $2.17\% = \mu - 2\sigma$ and $5.01\% = \mu + 2\sigma$, 95% of the samples should be within 2 standard deviations of the mean. This is 159,087 samples.

b. $4.3 - 3.59 = 0.71$. So, 4.3% is one standard deviation above the mean. About 34% of the data are between the mean and one standard deviation of the mean. Thus, 84% of the samples should have milk fat percentages that are less than 4.3%. This is 140,666 samples.

c. Since $5.01\% = \mu + 2\sigma$, approximately 2.5% of the samples had more than 5.01% milk fat.

22 **a.** $2x^3 - 4x^2 + x + 14$

b. $(6 - x^3)^2(x + 1) = (36 - 12x^3 + x^6)(x + 1)$
$= x^7 + x^6 - 12x^4 - 12x^3 + 36x + 36$

c. $8(-x^2 + 7) + 5(x^4 - 5x^2 + 10) = -8x^2 + 56 + 5x^4 - 25x^2 + 50$
$= 5x^4 - 33x^2 + 106$

d. $(x^3 + 5x) - (7x^3 - 3x) + (4x^2 + 8x) = -6x^3 + 4x^2 + 16x$

23 **a.** Exponential; $y = 81(3^x)$

b. Linear; $y = 4x + 17$

c. Exponential; $y = 1{,}200\left(\frac{1}{2}\right)^x$

d. Quadratic; $y = (x - 1)(x - 2) = x^2 - 3x + 2$

24 **a.** $\frac{12x^2 + 4x}{3x} = \frac{4x(3x + 1)}{3x} = \frac{4(3x + 1)}{3}$

The original fraction is undefined when $x = 0$, but the simplified fraction is not.

b. $\frac{2x}{6x - 8} = \frac{2x}{2(3x - 4)} = \frac{x}{3x - 4}$

The original and simplified fractions are both undefined when $x = \frac{4}{3}$.

c. $\frac{x^2 - 9}{x + 3} = \frac{(x + 3)(x - 3)}{x + 3} = x - 3$

The original fraction is undefined when $x = -3$, but the simplified fraction is not.

d. $\frac{x^2 + 2x - 8}{x^2 - 7x + 10} = \frac{(x + 4)(x - 2)}{(x - 2)(x - 5)} = \frac{x + 4}{x - 5}$

The original fraction is undefined when $x = 2$ and when $x = 5$. The simplified fraction is undefined only when $x = 5$.

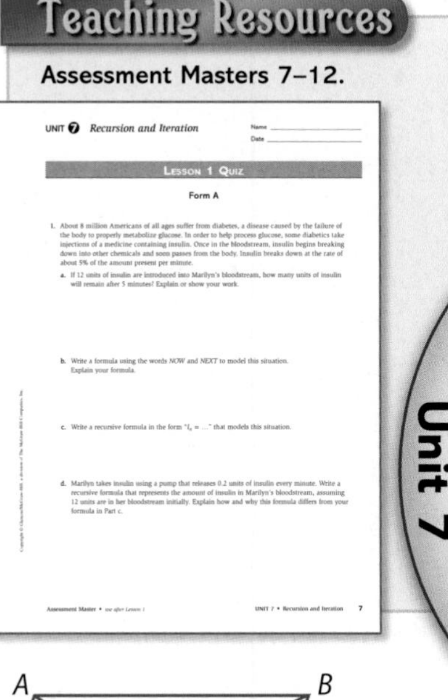

Teaching Resources

Assessment Masters 7–12.

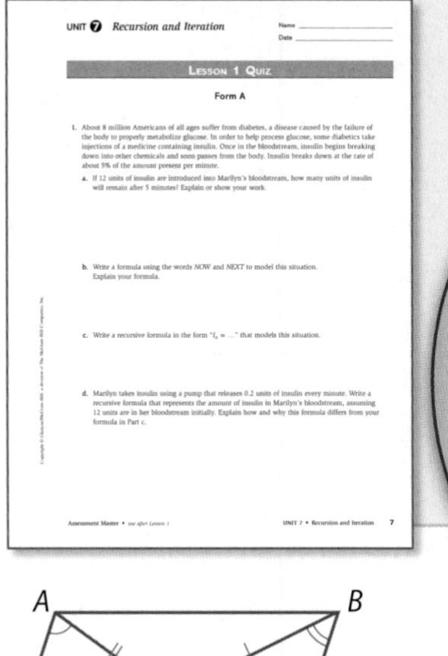

UNIT 7 *Recursion and Iteration* Name ______ Date ______

LESSON 1 QUIZ

Form A

1. About 8 million Americans of all ages suffer from diabetes, a disease caused by the failure of the body to properly metabolize glucose. In order to help process glucose, some diabetics take injections of a medicine containing insulin. Once in the bloodstream, insulin begins breaking down into other chemicals and soon passes from the body. Insulin breaks down at the rate of about 5% of the amount present per minute.
   a. If 12 units of insulin are introduced into Marilyn's bloodstream, how many units of insulin will remain after 5 minutes? Explain or show your work.
   b. Write a formula using the words *NOW* and *NEXT* to model this situation. Explain your formula.
   c. Write a recursive formula in the form "$I_n = \ldots$" that models this situation.
   d. Marilyn takes insulin using a pump that releases 0.2 units of insulin every minute. Write a recursive formula that represents the amount of insulin in Marilyn's bloodstream, assuming 12 units are in her bloodstream initially. Explain how and why this formula differs from your formula in Part c.

Assessment Master • *use after Lesson 1* UNIT 7 • Recursion and Iteration 7

25 **a.** No. Consider the kite at the right.

b. The most direct way to prove that $ABCD$ is a parallelogram is to reason that the diagonals bisect each other (CPCTC). Other proofs are possible.

c. No. Consider the kite with Part a.

A B C D E

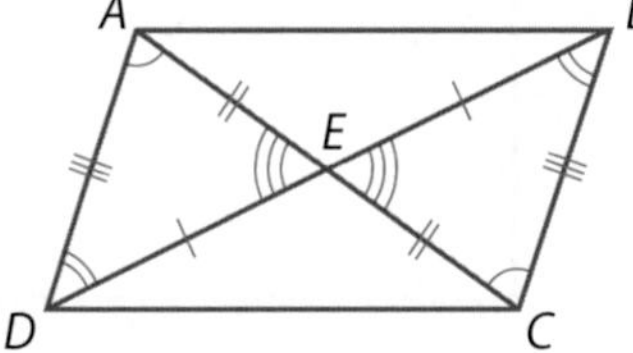

26 **a.** $x = -2$ **b.** $x = 3$

c. $x = \log 52 \approx 1.716$ **d.** $x = 3$

LESSON 2

A Recursive View of Functions

In the previous lesson, you investigated a variety of situations that were modeled by recursive formulas, including population growth, consumer loans, and medicine dosage. In each of these situations, you examined a sequence of numbers and looked for patterns and formulas to represent the situation. In this lesson, you will take a closer look at sequences of numbers. As you do so, you will extend your understanding of recursion and iteration. In the process, you will revisit three important function families: linear, exponential, and polynomial. To begin, consider the exciting but dangerous sport of sky diving.

A Recursive View of Functions

The main topics of study in this lesson are arithmetic and geometric sequences and series, and the connections to linear and exponential functions. In addition, sequences generated by polynomial functions are investigated using finite differences tables.

NOTE There are many examples of sequences in this lesson. Each is represented by the first several terms in the sequence. In general, this would not be enough information to establish for certain the overall pattern or formula for the sequence. However, within the instructional context of this lesson, you should assume that the entire sequence follows the regular pattern indicated by the terms shown.

Lesson Objectives

- Understand arithmetic sequences and their connections to linear functions, using recursive formulas, function formulas, and applications
- Understand geometric sequences and their connections to exponential functions, using recursive formulas, function formulas, and applications
- Understand and apply arithmetic and geometric series (sums of sequences)
- Use finite differences tables to find function formulas for certain recursive formulas and to describe the connection between such tables and polynomial functions
- Use linear, exponential, and polynomial functions to model discrete situations

Lesson Launch

This lesson launch is perhaps more detailed than many others. You might have students work in groups for a few minutes and then report out as you lead them through this launch. Be sure everyone is clear on the difference between the distance fallen *during* each second and the *total* distance fallen *after* a given number of seconds.

Think About This Situation

Imagine a sky diver jumping from a plane at a height of about 5,000 feet. Because of Earth's gravity and ignoring wind resistance, the sky diver will fall 16 feet in the first second. Thereafter, until the parachute opens, the distance fallen during each second will be 32 feet more than the distance fallen during the previous second.

a Think about the pattern of change in the distance the sky diver falls *during* each second. How would you describe the number of feet fallen during each second:

- **i.** using a recursive formula?
- **ii.** as a function of the number of seconds n?

b Now consider the pattern of change in the *total* distance fallen *after* a given number of seconds.

- **i.** How far has the sky diver fallen after each of the first four seconds?
- **ii.** Describe any patterns you see in this sequence of numbers. Compare this sequence to the sequence of distances fallen during each second.

c Think about a possible formula for the total distance fallen.

- **i.** How could the total distance fallen be computed from the sequence of numbers in Part a?
- **ii.** If you found a function formula for the total distance fallen after n seconds, what type of function do you think it will be?
- **iii.** How might a sky diver use a formula for total distance fallen in planning a jump?

In this lesson, you will learn about arithmetic and geometric sequences and series, and finite differences tables. In the process, you will use recursion and iteration to revisit linear, exponential, and polynomial functions.

Arithmetic and Geometric Sequences

Sequences of numbers occur in many situations. Certain sequences are particularly common and important, such as *arithmetic* and *geometric* sequences. You will learn about these sequences in this investigation. As you work on the problems of this investigation, look for answers to these questions:

What are formulas for arithmetic and geometric sequences?

What functions correspond to arithmetic and geometric sequences?

Unit 7

482 UNIT 7 • Recursion and Iteration

Think About This Situation

a Students should be able to find recursive and function formulas for the distance D fallen each second using their past knowledge of recursion and linear functions. They may find the linear equation using algebraic methods such as those learned in Course 1, *Linear Functions*, or by linear regression. Students should recognize that for this data it is quicker to use algebraic reasoning than linear regression to determine the equation. In this lesson, students will learn how to find this equation by finding the function formula for an arithmetic sequence.

i. $D_n = D_{n-1} + 32$, starting at 16

ii. $D(n) = 32n - 16$

b **i.**

Seconds, n	1	2	3	4	5
Total Distance Fallen after n Seconds, T_n	16	64	144	256	400

ii. The total distance fallen is increasing very rapidly. The pattern is not linear as in Part a.

c Although some students may be able to find a formula for total distance fallen as a result of the work they previously did with falling objects, it is *not* the goal to come up with a specific formula at this time. This situation will be revisited later using sums of sequences and finite differences. For now, students should think about characteristics of a formula for the total distance fallen. For reference, a function rule for the total distance fallen after n seconds is $T(n) = 16n^2$. A recursive formula is $T_n = T_{n-1} + D_n$ or $T_n = T_{n-1} + 32n - 16$. Do not strive for all these formulas at this time; they all come later in the lesson.

i. The total distance fallen after, say, 2 seconds is the sum of the distances fallen during seconds 1 and 2. Thus, the total distance fallen can be computed from the sequence of numbers in Part a by summing those numbers up to the second under consideration.

ii. Students should make conjectures. They should know from the pattern of numbers in Part b that a function formula for the total distance fallen cannot be a linear function. They might correctly conjecture quadratic, or perhaps some other nonlinear function.

iii. A sky diver could use a formula for total distance fallen to figure out the falling distance and thus help decide how many seconds into the dive to open the chute.

Teaching Resources

Transparency Master 13.

UNIT 7 *Recursion and Iteration*

Think About This Situation

Imagine a sky diver jumping from a plane at a height of about 5,000 feet. Because of Earth's gravity and ignoring wind resistance, the sky diver will fall 16 feet in the first second. Thereafter, until the parachute opens, the distance fallen during each second will be 32 feet more than the distance fallen during the previous second.

a Think about the pattern of change in the distance the sky diver falls *during* each second. How would you describe the number of feet fallen during each second:

i. using a recursive formula?

ii. as a function of the number of seconds n?

b Now consider the pattern of change in the *total* distance fallen *after* a given number of seconds.

i. How far has the sky diver fallen after each of the first four seconds?

ii. Describe any patterns you see in this sequence of numbers. Compare this sequence to the sequence of distances fallen during each second.

c Think about a possible formula for the total distance fallen.

i. How could the total distance fallen be computed from the sequence of numbers in Part a?

ii. If you found a function formula for the total distance fallen after n seconds, what type of function do you think it will be?

iii. How might a sky diver use a formula for total distance fallen in planning a jump?

Unit 7

Arithmetic Sequences As you can imagine, sky diving requires considerable training and careful advance preparation. Although the sport of bungee jumping may require little or no training, it also requires careful preparation to ensure the safety of the jumper. In Course 1, you may have explored the relationship between jumper weight and bungee cord length by conducting an experiment with rubber bands and weights.

 In one such experiment, for each ounce of weight added to a 3-inch rubber band, the rubber band stretched about $\frac{1}{2}$ inch.

a. Describe the relationship between weight added and stretched rubber band length. What type of function represents this relationship?

b. Complete a copy of the table below.

Bungee Experiment

Weight (in ounces)	0	1	2	3	4	5	...	50	...	99	...	n
Length (in inches)							...		...		...	

c. The sequence of numbers that you get for the lengths is called an *arithmetic sequence*. An **arithmetic sequence** of numbers is one in which you add the same constant to each number in the sequence to get the next number. An arithmetic sequence models **arithmetic growth**. Explain why the sequence of stretched rubber band lengths is an arithmetic sequence.

d. Which, if any, of the sequences in the Think About This Situation is an arithmetic sequence? Why?

2 There are several different formulas that can be used to represent the weight-length relationship.

a. Write a formula using the words *NOW* and *NEXT* that shows how the length changes as weight is added.

b. Write a formula for this situation that looks like

$$L_n = (\text{expression involving } L_{n-1}).$$

This is called a *recursive formula for the sequence.*

c. Use the recursive formula to predict the rubber band length when 15 ounces of weight are attached.

Investigation 1 Arithmetic and Geometric Sequences

Although many of the ideas in this investigation are so familiar to your students that much of this may seem like a review, you may want to ask them probing questions as they work on the following problems, to keep them from overgeneralizing these ideas to sequences for which the ideas do not apply.

For example, you might ask if the entries in the table produced in the fish-population problem of Lesson 1 are also an arithmetic or geometric sequence and if these entries can be obtained using a function formula. (They are neither arithmetic nor geometric, and, while they can be obtained through a function formula, it is not immediately obvious what that formula should be.)

The goal is for your students to realize that arithmetic sequences are connected to linear functions and that, in those cases, U_n can be expressed using both function and recursive formulas. Also, geometric sequences are related to exponential functions. In Investigation 2, the sums of arithmetic and geometric series are developed, and in Investigation 3, more complicated recursive formulas are related to polynomial functions.

COMMON DIFFICULTY An unavoidable complication when working with formulas for arithmetic and geometric sequences and series is whether the starting subscript is 0 or 1 (or another integer). This lesson addresses these complications in context and by making sense of the algebraic reasoning involved. Students should stay focused on the key ideas and patterns and not attempt to memorize a multitude of formulas.

INSTRUCTIONAL NOTE Note that this bungee jumping activity was done on page 4 of Course 1 Unit 1, *Patterns of Change*. It is not necessary that students remember the activity to proceed here, but it is expected that they retain some familiarity with the analysis of such a situation using a function in the form "$y = \ldots$."

1 **a.** The rubber band length will increase by 0.5 inches for each ounce of weight added. Thus, this is a situation of a constant rate of change of length with respect to weight. Formulas that students might use to model the situation include $NEXT = NOW + 0.5$, starting at 3, and $y = 0.5x + 3$. The table will show constant rate of change and will be similar to the table in Part b. This relationship is modeled by a linear function. (Note, of course, that the rubber band will eventually break, ending the sequence.)

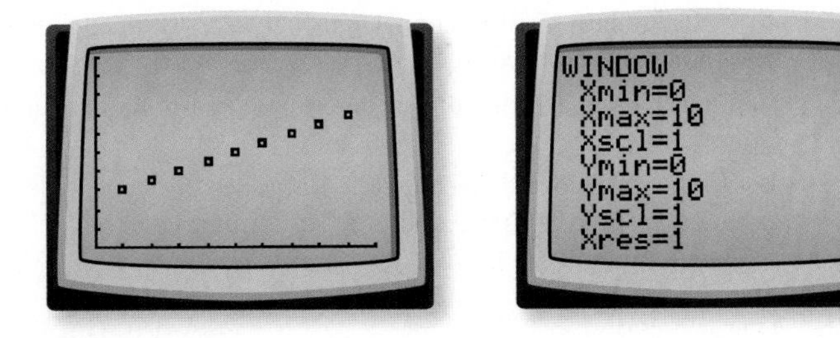

b. **Bungee Experiment**

Weight (in ounces)	0	1	2	3	4	5	...	50	...	99	...	n
Length (in inches)	3	3.5	4	4.5	5	5.5	...	28	...	52.5	...	$3 + 0.5n$

c. 0.5 is added to each term of the sequence to produce the next term of the sequence.

d. The sequence of distances fallen during each second is an arithmetic sequence. Each second the distance fallen during that second increases by 32.

NOTE Solutions to Problem 2 are on page T484.

Unit 7

d. Write a formula for the weight-length situation that looks like

$$L_n = (\text{expression involving } n, \text{ but not } L_{n-1}).$$

This form can be called a *function formula for the sequence* of lengths.

i. Explain why it makes sense to call this form a function formula.

ii. Rewrite the formula using function notation.

e. Use the function formula in Part d to predict the rubber band length when 15 ounces of weight are attached.

f. Describe the difference between the processes of using the recursive formula and using the function formula to compute the rubber band length when 15 ounces of weight are attached.

3 Cell phones, pagers, and telephone calling cards are convenient ways to stay in contact with friends and family. The details of phone cards can be quite complicated, even though the prices and plans may look simple. For example, there might be connection fees, payphone surcharges, and different schemes for rounding the number of minutes used. Suppose you have a phone card with a rate of 2¢ per minute and no other fees or charges, except for a payphone charge of 89¢ per call. When the minutes used are not an integer, the value is rounded to the next minute.

a. Suppose you make a call from a payphone using this phone card. Determine recursive and function formulas for the minute-by-minute sequence of phone card charges for this call.

b. Compare these formulas to those you found for the rubber band experiment in Problem 2. How are they similar? How are they different?

4 Now think about possible connections between arithmetic sequences and functions you have studied.

a. In each case, describe the shape of the graph of the function formula.

b. What is the slope of each graph? How does the slope appear in each of the recursive and function formulas you have been examining?

Unit 7

484 UNIT 7 • Recursion and Iteration

INSTRUCTIONAL NOTE
Be sure students include the starting value with each recursive formula.

2 **TERMINOLOGY NOTES** (1) There are several other terms that are often used instead of "function formula," such as "explicit formula" or "closed-form formula." Since students have previously studied formulas such as $L(n) = 3 + 0.5n$ and have called them function formulas, we use the phrase "function formula" here. The terms "explicit" and "closed-form" are highlighted in the Summarize the Mathematics section at the end of this investigation. (2) Note that the recursive formula in Part b can also be considered in terms of functions, where L_n is a function of L_{n-1}. However, this is a more complicated function and to keep the recursive aspect of the formula clear, *recursive formula* is a more apt description.

a. $NEXT = NOW + 0.5$, starting at 3

b. $L_n = L_{n-1} + 0.5$, $L_0 = 3$

c. Students should determine that the length of the rubber band, with 15 ounces of weight, is 10.5 inches. They might compute by hand, using the last answer feature of a graphing calculator, or using a spreadsheet.

d. $L_n = 3 + 0.5n$

i. It makes sense to call this a function formula because it is a formula that gives one length for each value of n; n is the input (independent variable), and L is the output (dependent variable). That is, L (or length) is a function of n (or weight).

ii. $L(n) = 3 + 0.5n$

e. $L_{15} = 3 + 0.5(15) = 3 + 7.5 = 10.5$ inches

f. When using the recursive formula, you must use the formula 15 times, adding 0.5 to the previous result each time. When using the function formula, only one evaluation of the formula, by substituting 15 for n, is needed.

3 **a.** The recursive formula is $P_n = P_{n-1} + 0.02$, $P_0 = 0.89$. The function formula is $P(n) = 0.89 + 0.02n$.

b. Recursive formulas: Both have a coefficient of 1 on the P_n or L_n term; the constants 0.5 and 0.02 are the differences between consecutive terms.

Function formulas: Both are linear relationships; 0.5 and 0.02 are the coefficient of n (slopes), and the initial value associated with the recursive formula is the constant (y-intercept) in the function formula. The initial values were different: 3 for the rubber band experiment and 0.89 for the cell phone situation.

4 **a.** The graph of each function formula is a line with y-intercept equal to the initial value and slope equal to the difference between consecutive terms.

b. The slope of the graph associated with Problem 2 is 0.5. The slope of the graph associated with Problem 3 is 0.02. The slope is what you add to *NOW* or L_{n-1} or P_{n-1} in the recursive formulas, and it is the coefficient of n in the function formulas.

Unit 7

5. Suppose t_0 is the initial term of a *general* arithmetic sequence for which you add d to each term of the sequence to get the next term of the sequence.

   a. Write the first five terms of this sequence. Then find recursive and function formulas for the sequence. Compare your formulas to those of other students. Resolve any differences.

   b. LaToya explained her function formula as follows.

   > This sequence starts with t_0, and then to get to t_n you add d, n times. Thus, the general formula is $t_n = t_0 + dn$.

   Explain how LaToya's explanation matches her formula.

   c. How would you interpret t_0, d, and n in the context of the rubber band experiment?

   d. The constant d is sometimes called the **common difference** between terms. Explain why it makes sense to call d the common difference.

   e. Suppose an arithmetic sequence $t_0, t_1, t_2, \ldots$ begins with $t_0 = 84$ and has a common difference of -6. Find function and recursive formulas for this sequence and then find the term t_{87}.

Geometric Sequences Now consider a different type of sequence. As you investigate this new type of sequence, think about similarities to and differences from arithmetic sequences.

6. Consider the growth sequence of bacteria cells if a cut by a rusty nail puts 25 bacteria cells into a wound and then the number of bacteria doubles every quarter-hour.

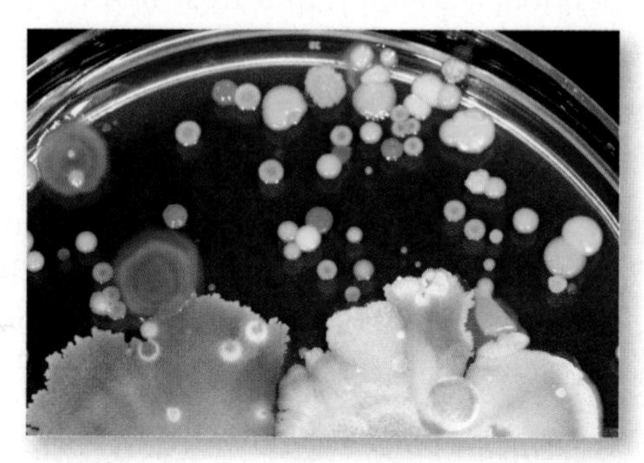

   a. Use words, graphs, tables, and algebraic rules to describe the relationship between the number of quarter-hours and the number of bacteria. What type of function represents this relationship?

   b. Complete a copy of the table below for this situation.

Bacterial Growth

Number of Quarter-Hours	0	1	2	3	4	5	...	50	...	99	...	n
Bacteria Count							...		...		...	

   c. The sequence of numbers that you get for the bacteria count is called a *geometric sequence*. A **geometric sequence** of numbers is one in which each number in the sequence is multiplied by a constant to get the next number. Explain why the sequence of bacteria counts is a geometric sequence.

   d. Which, if any, of the sequences in the Think About This Situation (page 482) is a geometric sequence? Why?

5 a. $t_0, t_0 + d, t_0 + 2d, t_0 + 3d, t_0 + 4d$
Recursive formula: $t_n = t_{n-1} + d$, starting at t_0
Function formula: $t_n = t_0 + nd$

b. Analyzing LaToya's explanation will help students add more meaning to the formulas they are developing. LaToya's explanation fits well (and is a good way for students to remember the formula) since t_0 is the first term and then you add d over and over to get the subsequent terms. Adding d n times is equivalent to multiplying d times n. Thus, $t_n = t_0 + nd$.

c. In the context of the rubber-band experiment, t_0 is the initial length of the rubber band (3 inches), d is the constant amount of stretch (0.5 inches) for each ounce of weight added, and n is the number of one-ounce weights added.

d. It makes sense to call d the common difference because the difference (subtraction) of any two successive terms, $t_n - t_{n-1}$, is d.

e. Recursive formula: $t_n = t_{n-1} - 6$, $t_0 = 84$
Function formula: $t_n = 84 - 6n$
$t_{87} = -438$

6 a. The number of bacteria doubles each quarter-hour. Thus, this is not a constant rate of change. The pattern of change is exponential since 2 is a common multiplier between all successive time periods. A graph of this relationship is shown below. Formulas that students might use to describe this relationship include $NEXT = 2NOW$, starting at 25; $B_n = 2B_{n-1}$, where $B_0 = 25$; and $y = 25(2^x)$. A table for this situation will show nonconstant rate of change and will be similar to the table in Part b. This relationship can be modeled by an exponential function.

INSTRUCTIONAL NOTE
This bacterial growth activity was done on page 295 of Course 1 in Unit 5, *Exponential Functions*. It is not necessary that students remember the activity to proceed here, but it is expected that they retain some familiarity with the analysis of such a situation using a function in the form "$y = \ldots$."

b. **Bacterial Growth**

Number of Quarter-Hours	0	1	2	3	4	5	...	50	...	99	...	n
Bacteria Count	25	50	100	200	400	800	...	25×2^{50}	...	25×2^{99}	...	25×2^n

c. The constant multiplier is 2. That is, you multiply each term by 2 to get the next term.

d. None of the sequences in the Think About This Situation section is a geometric sequence since none of them has a constant multiplier.

Unit 7

7 If B_n represents the bacteria count after n quarter-hours, then there are several different formulas that can be used to model this situation.

a. Write a formula using the words *NOW* and *NEXT* that shows how the bacteria count increases as time passes.

b. Write a recursive formula beginning "$B_n = \ldots$" for the sequence of bacteria counts. Use the recursive formula to predict the bacteria count after 18 quarter-hours.

c. Write a function formula beginning "$B_n = \ldots$" for the sequence of bacteria counts. Use the function formula to predict the bacteria count after 18 quarter-hours.

d. Describe the difference between the processes of using the recursive formula and using the function formula to compute the bacteria count after 18 quarter-hours.

8 One of the simplest fractal patterns is the Sierpinski carpet. Starting with a solid square "carpet" one meter on a side, smaller and smaller squares are cut out of the carpet. The first two stages in forming the carpet are shown below.

U07-009A-877261

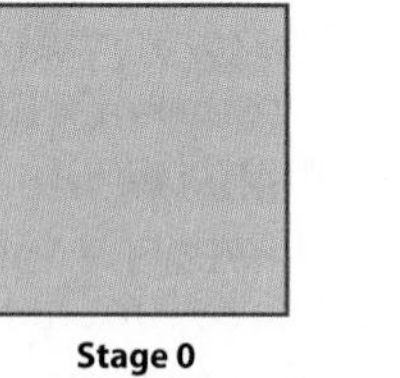

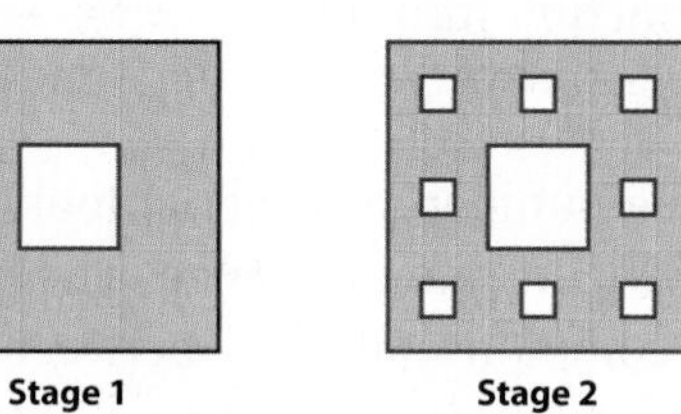

Stage 0 **Stage 1** **Stage 2**

a. Find recursive and function formulas for the sequence of carpet area that remains at each stage.

b. Compare your formulas to those you found for the bacteria present after a cut by a rusty nail, in Problem 7. How are they similar? How are they different?

9 Think about connections between geometric sequences and functions you have studied.

a. What type of function is represented by each of the function formulas in Problems 7 and 8?

b. The growth (or decay) modeled by a geometric sequence is called **geometric growth**. It is also called **exponential growth**. Explain why *exponential growth* is a reasonable way to describe geometric sequences and geometric growth.

10 Suppose t_0 is the initial term of a *general* geometric sequence for which each term of the sequence is multiplied by r ($r \neq 1$) to get the next term of the sequence.

a. Write the first five terms of this sequence and then find recursive and function formulas for the sequence. Compare your formulas to those of other students. Resolve any differences.

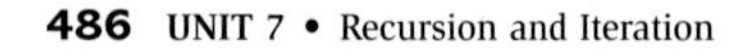

7 **a.** $NEXT = 2NOW$, starting at 25

b. $B_n = 2B_{n-1}$, $B_0 = 25$
$B_{18} = 6{,}553{,}600$ bacteria

c. $B_n = 25(2^n)$
$B_{18} = 25(2^{18}) = 6{,}553{,}600$ bacteria

d. Using the recursive formula requires multiplying the previous result by 2 eighteen times, while using the function formula requires only one step, substituting 18 for n and computing the result.

8 **a.** The area of the carpet at each stage is $\frac{8}{9}$ of the area of the carpet at the preceding stage.
Recursive formula: $A_n = \frac{8}{9} A_{n-1}$, $A_0 = 1$
Function formula: $A_n = \left(\frac{8}{9}\right)^n$

b. In each of the recursive formulas, there is a constant multiplier that takes you from one term to the next. That is, the coefficient of the term numbered $(n - 1)$, P_{n-1}, is a constant.

Each of the function formulas is an exponential function of the form $y = a(b^x)$. (Also, see Problem 9.) The value of a is the initial value of the sequence and the y-intercept of the graph of the function, and b is the common multiplier.

9 **a.** Each of the function formulas in Problems 7 and 8 is an exponential function.

b. Geometric sequences are constructed by multiplying each term by a constant to get the next term, which is the same sort of process that describes an exponential function. Additionally, the function formula for a geometric sequence is an exponential function. Thus, exponential growth is a reasonable way to describe geometric sequences and geometric growth.

10 **a.** $t_0, rt_0, r^2t_0, r^3t_0, r^4t_0$
Recursive formula: $t_n = rt_{n-1}$, starting at t_0
Function formula: $t_n = t_0r^n$

Unit 7

b. Eva explained her function formula as follows.

I started the sequence with t_0, then I multiplied by r each time to get the next terms. To get to t_n, I multiplied by r, n times. Thus, $t_n = t_0 r^n$.

Explain how Eva's explanation matches her formula.

c. What are t_0, r, and n in the situation involving bacterial growth?

d. The constant r is sometimes called the **common ratio** of terms. Explain why it makes sense to call r the common ratio.

e. Suppose a geometric sequence $t_0, t_1, t_2, \ldots$ begins with $t_0 = -4$ and has a common ratio of 3. Find function and recursive formulas for this sequence and then find the term t_{17}.

Different Starting Points The sequences you have studied in this investigation have started with $n = 0$. For example, the initial term for the sequence of rubber band lengths was L_0, and the initial term for the sequence of bacteria counts was B_0. It is possible to have different starting subscripts. Consider what happens to the recursive and function formulas when the starting subscript is 1 instead of 0.

11 In the Think About This Situation, you considered the distance fallen by a sky diver. The table below shows the distance fallen in a free fall by a sky diver, assuming no wind resistance, during each of the first nine seconds of a jump.

Sky Diving Free Fall

Time n (in seconds)	1	2	3	4	5	6	7	8	9
Distance Fallen during Second n, D_n (in feet)	16	48	80	112	144	176	208	240	272

a. Is D_n an arithmetic sequence, geometric sequence, or neither? Explain.

b. What is the starting value of n for this sequence?

c. What is a recursive formula for this sequence?

d. In the Think About This Situation, you may have figured out that a function formula for this sequence is

$$D_n = 16 + 32(n - 1).$$

Check this formula for a few values of n. Explain this formula by modifying LaToya's explanation in Problem 5 on page 485, so that the explanation fits this formula.

12 In Problem 5, you found that a function formula for an arithmetic sequence with initial term t_0 and common difference d is

$$t_n = t_0 + dn.$$

Using the form "$t_n = \ldots$," write a similar function formula if the initial term is t_1, instead of t_0.

b. Sam's explanation fits well (and is a good way for students to remember the formula) since t_0 is the first term and then you multiply by r over and over to get the subsequent terms. Multiplying by r, n times, is equivalent to r^n. Thus, $t_n = t_0 r^n$.

c. In the context of bacterial growth, t_0 is the initial size of the bacteria population (25), r is the constant multiplier (2), and n is the number of quarter-hours.

d. The term *common ratio* is a sensible term to use because r is the ratio of *any* two successive terms in the sequence (common to all successive pairs) $r = \frac{t_n}{t_{n-1}}$.

e. Recursive formula: $t_n = 3t_{n-1}$, $t_0 = -4$

Function formula: $t_n = -4(3^n)$

$t_{17} = -516,560,652$

> **INSTRUCTIONAL NOTE**
> Analyzing Sam's explanation in Problem 10 Part b will help students add more meaning to the formulas.

11 **a.** Arithmetic sequence

b. The starting value for n is $n = 1$.

c. $D_n = D_{n-1} + 32$, $D_1 = 16$

d. Students may have found this formula during the Think About This Situation discussion, or perhaps they found a different form of the formula. In any case, they should now reason about this formula in a manner similar to LaToya's reasoning. They might say that, "You start with 16, then you add 32 over and over to get the other terms. The trick is to figure out how many times you must add 32 in order to get to the nth second. By looking at the table, you can see it is $(n - 1)$ times, which means that you multiply 32 times $(n - 1)$."

> **INSTRUCTIONAL NOTE**
> In Problem 11, students revisit sky diving from the Think About This Situation. This provides a familiar context within which to begin the potentially confusing study of different starting points in sequences.

12 $t_n = t_1 + (n - 1)d$; the initial term is t_1.

13 **a.** The common ratio is $r = 2$.

b. Recursive formula: $A_n = 2A_{n-1}$, $A_0 = 3$
Function formula: $A_n = 3(2)^n$

c. Recursive formula: $A_n = 2A_{n-1}$, $A_1 = 3$
Function formula: $A_n = 3(2)^{n-1}$

d. The recursive formulas are the same. (The initial term 3 is associated with the recursive formulas but they have different subscripts.) The function formulas are similar, but the exponent differs, n or $n - 1$ depending on whether the initial subscript is 0 or 1.

14 **a.** Students should compare and discuss sequences with other students.

b. Students should note that an arithmetic sequence is characterized by adding a constant to get from term to term and that a geometric sequence is characterized by multiplying by a constant to get from term to term. There are many examples of sequences that exhibit neither pattern, such as 2, 3, 5, 8, 12, 17, 23, ... (add 1, then add 2, then add 3, then add 4, and so on).

c. Answers will vary depending on the sequences the students construct. Be sure they start one sequence with subscript 0 and the other with subscript 1.

> **INSTRUCTIONAL NOTE**
> In Problem 14, students should generate and compare a variety of sequences.

13 Consider this geometric sequence: 3, 6, 12, 24, 48, … .

a. What is the common ratio r?

b. Call the general term of this sequence A_n. Suppose that the starting subscript for the sequence is 0. Thus, the initial term is $A_0 = 3$. What is a recursive formula for this sequence? What is a function formula for this sequence? (Write both formulas in the form "$A_n = \dots$.")

c. Suppose the starting subscript is 1. Thus, $A_1 = 3$. What is a recursive formula for the sequence in this case? What is a function formula? (Write both formulas in the form "$A_n = \dots$.")

d. Compare the formulas in Parts b and c. Explain similarities and differences.

14 Working individually, write the first five terms for three different sequences. One sequence should be arithmetic, one should be geometric, and the third should be neither.

a. Challenge a classmate to correctly identify your sequence type.

b. Describe how you can tell by inspection whether a sequence is arithmetic, geometric, or neither.

c. For the two sequences you constructed that are arithmetic or geometric, find a recursive and a function formula. For one sequence, choose the starting subscript to be 0. For the other, choose the starting subscript to be 1.

Summarize the Mathematics

In this investigation, you studied two important patterns of growth: arithmetic growth, modeled by arithmetic sequences, and geometric growth, modeled by geometric sequences. You also investigated recursive and function formulas for sequences and made connections to linear and exponential functions.

a Consider arithmetic and geometric sequences.

i. How are arithmetic and geometric sequences different? How are they similar?

ii. Describe one real-world situation different from those you studied in this investigation that could be modeled by an arithmetic sequence. Do the same for a geometric sequence.

iii. What is the connection between arithmetic and geometric sequences and linear and exponential functions?

b Consider recursive and function formulas for sequences.

i. Describe the difference between a recursive formula and a function formula for a sequence. What information do you need to know to find each type of formula?

ii. What is one advantage and one disadvantage of a recursive formula for a sequence? What is one advantage and one disadvantage of a function formula?

Summarize the Mathematics

a **i.** They are different in that arithmetic sequences are generated by adding a constant to each term to get the next term and geometric sequences are generated by multiplying each term by a constant to get the next term. They are similar in that in each case, you use a constant to generate the terms.

ii. Students' situations may vary. For example, a taxi fare that begins with a flat rate and then increases by a fixed amount each tenth of a mile can be modeled by an arithmetic sequence. The growth of an initial deposit of money in an interest-bearing savings account can be modeled by a geometric sequence.

iii. The function formula for an arithmetic sequence is a linear function. The function formula for a geometric sequence is an exponential function.

b **i.** The recursive formula tells you how to get from one term to the next, but it does not directly tell you what the nth term is. The function formula gives you a formula for directly computing the nth term.

Students may say that the same information is needed to find the two types of formulas, namely, the initial term and the constant that is added or multiplied. However, strictly speaking, for the recursive formula, you need to know just the constant that is multiplied or added to get from one term to the next. The initial value does not show up in the recursive formula directly, although, it is an additional piece of important information.

ii. One advantage of a recursive formula is that you can easily see the pattern of change. One disadvantage is that it may be time-consuming to find a term far into the sequence. One advantage of a function formula is that finding any desired term is straightforward. One disadvantage is that the relationship between successive terms is not as clear.

NOTE Solutions to Problems 13 and 14 are on page T487.

Teaching Resources

Transparency Masters 14–15.

UNIT 7 *Recursion and Iteration*

Summarize the Mathematics

In this investigation, you studied two important patterns of growth: arithmetic growth, modeled by arithmetic sequences, and geometric growth, modeled by geometric sequences. You also investigated recursive and function formulas for sequences and made connections to linear and exponential functions.

a Consider arithmetic and geometric sequences.

i. How are arithmetic and geometric sequences different? How are they similar?

ii. Describe one real-world situation different from those you studied in this investigation that could be modeled by an arithmetic sequence. Do the same for a geometric sequence.

iii. What is the connection between arithmetic and geometric sequences and linear and exponential functions?

b Consider recursive and function formulas for sequences.

i. Describe the difference between a recursive formula and a function formula for a sequence. What information do you need to know to find each type of formula?

ii. What is one advantage and one disadvantage of a recursive formula for a sequence? What is one advantage and one disadvantage of a function formula?

c Explain why changing the starting subscript for a sequence has no effect on a recursive formula. Explain why this will cause a change in a function formula.

14 UNIT 7 • Recursion and Iteration   Transparency Master • *use with pages 488 and 489*

Unit 7

c Explain why changing the starting subscript for a sequence has no effect on a recursive formula. Explain why this will cause a change in a function formula.

d In the first lesson of this unit, you investigated situations that could be modeled by recursive formulas of the form $A_n = rA_{n-1} + b$. You can think of these formulas as *combined recursive formulas*. What is the connection between such combined recursive formulas and recursive formulas for arithmetic and geometric sequences? Why does it make sense to call these formulas "combined recursive formulas?"

e You have represented sequences using recursive and function formulas. A function formula for a sequence is also called an **explicit formula** or a **closed-form formula**. Why do you think the terms "explicit" or "closed-form" are used?

Be prepared to explain your ideas to the class.

Check Your Understanding

For each of the sequences below, do the following.

- Complete a copy of the table.
- State whether the sequence is arithmetic, geometric, or neither.
- For those sequences that are arithmetic or geometric, find a recursive formula and a function formula.
- If a sequence is neither arithmetic nor geometric, find whatever formula you can that describes the sequence.

a.

n	0	1	2	3	4	5	6	...	10	...	100	...
A_n	2	6	18	54	162							

b.

n	0	1	2	3	4	5	6	...	10	...	100	...
B_n	1	2	5	10	17							

c.

n	0	1	2	3	4	5	6	...	10	...	100	...
C_n	3	7	11	15	19							

Investigation 2 Some Sums

Sometimes it is useful to sum the numbers in a sequence, which is the focus of this investigation. As you work on the problems of this investigation, look for answers to the following questions:

What are strategies for summing the terms of arithmetic and geometric sequences?

What are formulas for these sums?

c Changing the starting subscript does not change the relationship between successive terms, and thus it does not change the recursive formula. However, the starting subscript does change the function formula because the starting subscript determines how many steps are needed to get to the *n*th term.

d Recursive formulas for geometric and arithmetic sequences are special cases of combined recursive formulas of the form $A_n = rA_{n-1} + b$. If $b = 0$, you get a recursive formula for geometric sequences; if $r = 1$ you get a recursive formula for arithmetic sequences.

e Responses will vary. The function formula may be thought of as "explicit" because it explicitly states how to compute a given term of the sequence, as opposed to the recursive form. In some sense, the recursive form is "implicit" in that you cannot compute a given term directly but rather must first find the previous terms.

"Closed-form" seems to capture the idea that to find any term in the sequence, you just substitute and calculate; it is closed because you do not need any information other than the formula and one input. For example, to find A_{100}, you just substitute 100 for *n* in the formula for A_n and compute. This is in contrast to the more "open-ended" recursive form, in which to find A_{100} you must know A_{99}, which requires knowing A_{98}, and so on.

Check Your Understanding

a.
-

n	0	1	2	3	4	5	6	...	10	...	100	...
A_n	2	6	18	54	162	486	1,458	...	118,098	...	$(2)3^{100}$	...

- The sequence is geometric since you multiply each term by 3 to get the next term.
- $A_n = 3A_{n-1}$, $A_0 = 2$
  $A_n = 2(3^n)$

b.
-

n	0	1	2	3	4	5	6	...	10	...	100	...
B_n	1	2	5	10	17	26	37	...	101	...	10,001	...

- The sequence is neither arithmetic nor geometric since getting from one term to the next does not involve adding a constant or multiplying by a constant.
- $B_n = n^2 + 1$
  $B_n = B_{n-1} + (2n - 1)$

c.
-

n	0	1	2	3	4	5	6	...	10	...	100	...
C_n	3	7	11	15	19	23	27	...	43	...	403	...

- The sequence is arithmetic since you add 4 to each term to get the next term.
- $C_n = C_{n-1} + 4$, $C_0 = 3$
  $C_n = 3 + 4n$

Teaching Resources

Student Master 16.

Sequences, Recursive Formulas, and Function Formulas
Check Your Understanding

INSTRUCTIONAL NOTE
Students may not be able to identify the second formula in Part b until they study Investigation 2.

Unit 7

Arithmetic Sums Consider the sky diving situation once again. The table showing the distance fallen during each second is reproduced below.

Sky Diving Free Fall

Time n (in seconds)	1	2	3	4	5	6	7	8	9
Distance Fallen during Second n, D_n (in feet)	16	48	80	112	144	176	208	240	272

1 From the previous investigation, you know that a function formula for this sequence is

$$D_n = 16 + 32(n - 1).$$

This formula gives the distance fallen *during the nth second*. Use the function formula for D_n to:

a. verify the entries in the table for D_1 and D_5.

b. compute D_{18}, D_{19}, and D_{20}.

2 A sky diver would be very interested in knowing the *total distance* fallen *after n seconds*.

a. What is the total distance fallen after 3 seconds? After 5 seconds?

b. How could you determine the total distance fallen after 20 seconds? Do not actually find this total distance yet. Just explain how you could find it.

c. One approach to finding the sum of the first 20 terms of the sequence D_n is based on a method reportedly discovered by Carl Friedrich Gauss (1777–1855) when he was only 10 years old. Gauss, considered to be one of the greatest mathematicians of all time, noticed that the sum of the terms of an arithmetic sequence, such as $16 + 48 + 80 + \cdots + 560 + 592 + 624$, could be quickly calculated by writing the sum again in reverse order and then adding pairs of corresponding terms, as follows.

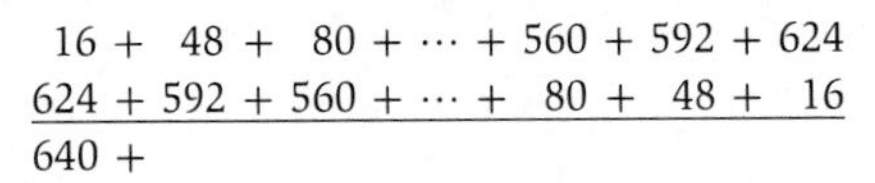

$$\begin{array}{l} 16 + 48 + 80 + \cdots + 560 + 592 + 624 \\ \underline{624 + 592 + 560 + \cdots + 80 + 48 + 16} \\ 640 + \end{array}$$

i. What is the sum of each pair of terms? How many pairs are there?

ii. What is the total distance fallen after 20 seconds?

d. Use Gauss' method, and the function formula for D_n given in Problem 1, to determine the total distance the sky diver would fall in 30 seconds.

e. An expert sky diver typically free-falls to about 2,000 feet above Earth's surface before pulling the rip cord on the parachute. If the altitude of the airplane was about 5,000 feet when the sky diver began the jump, how much time can the sky diver safely allow for the free-fall portion of the flight?

490 UNIT 7 • Recursion and Iteration

Investigation 2 Some Sums

In this investigation, students study finite sums of arithmetic and geometric sequences, also known as *series*.

1. **a.** Students use the formula to verify the entries.

   b. These terms can be computed by plugging into the function formula.
   $D_{18} = 16 + (17)32 = 560$
   $D_{19} = 16 + (18)32 = 592$
   $D_{20} = 16 + (19)32 = 624$

2. **a.** After 3 seconds, the sky diver has fallen 144 feet.
   After 5 seconds, the sky diver has fallen 400 feet.

   b. The most obvious response here is to calculate all 20 distances and then add them together. That is, compute $D_1 + \cdots + D_{20}$.

   c. **i.** The sum of each pair is 640. There are 20 pairs. (Note that students computed $D_{20} = 624$ in Problem 1, so they know that 624 is the twentieth term.)

   ii. Since each distance has been used twice, the total distance fallen after 20 seconds is $\frac{1}{2}(20)(640) = 6{,}400$ feet.

   d. Using the function formula from Problem 1, we get $D_{30} = 16 + 32(29) = 944$. Now using Gauss' method, each pair sums to $D_1 + D_{30}$, which is $16 + 944 = 960$. There will be 30 pairs, so the total distance fallen will be $\frac{1}{2}(30)(960) = 14{,}400$ feet.

   e. Students can estimate to find the correct time. The sky diver can free-fall about 3,000 feet. From Part c, students know that the time available for free fall is less than 20 seconds, since the total distance fallen after 20 seconds is 6,400 ft. Try 13 seconds: Since $D_{13} = 16 + 12(32) = 400$, the total distance fallen in the first 13 seconds is $\frac{1}{2}(13)(400 + 16) = 2{,}704$ feet. After 14 seconds, the sky diver will have fallen a total of 3,136 feet. Thus, the sky diver can free-fall for approximately 13 seconds.

INSTRUCTIONAL NOTE
Students will learn how to find a sum of an arithmetic sequence in the next several problems. For Problem 2 Part b, some students might use what they know about gravity and falling objects and write the formula $S(n) = 16n^2$, and then evaluate when $n = 20$. But the goal here is not to compute this specific value but to see the need for summing an arithmetic sequence.

3 You can use Gauss' idea in Problem 2 and algebraic reasoning to derive a general formula for the sum of the terms of an arithmetic sequence with common difference d.

a. If $a_1, a_2, \ldots, a_n$ is an arithmetic sequence with common difference d, explain why the sum S_n of the terms a_1 through a_n can be expressed by the formula

$$S_n = a_1 + (a_1 + d) + (a_1 + 2d) + \cdots + (a_n - 2d) + (a_n - d) + a_n.$$

b. If you rewrite S_n in reverse order and then add pairs of corresponding terms as in Problem 2, what is the sum of each pair of terms? How many pairs are there?

c. Use your answers in Part b to write a formula for S_n in terms of a_1, a_n, and n. Compare your formula to those of others. Resolve any differences.

d. Sondra developed the following formula-in-words for the sum of the terms of an arithmetic sequence.

$$S = \frac{(\textit{initial term} + \textit{final term})(\textit{number of terms})}{2}$$

Explain why this formula makes sense.

4 As you discovered in the last investigation, the starting subscript used in a sequence can affect the formulas for the sequence. An important feature of the formula-in-words in Part d of Problem 3 is that it does not depend on the subscript notation used for the sequence. In contrast, the formula in Part c of Problem 3 only works if the starting subscript is 1. Consider what happens when the starting subscript is 0.

a. Suppose $a_0, a_1, \ldots, a_n$ is an arithmetic sequence. Find a formula for the sum S_n of the terms a_0 through a_n. Your formula should use a_0, a_n and n.

b. Find the sum of the terms of this sequence: 7, 12, 17, 22, … , 52.

Accumulated versus Additional Amount In modeling a situation involving sequential change, it is important to decide whether the situation involves a pattern of change in *additional* amount or in *accumulated* amount.

5 It may happen that in two different situations, you get the same sequence of numbers, but it makes sense to add the terms of the sequence in only one of the situations. Consider an epidemic that begins at Day 1 with one infected person and spreads rapidly through two counties.

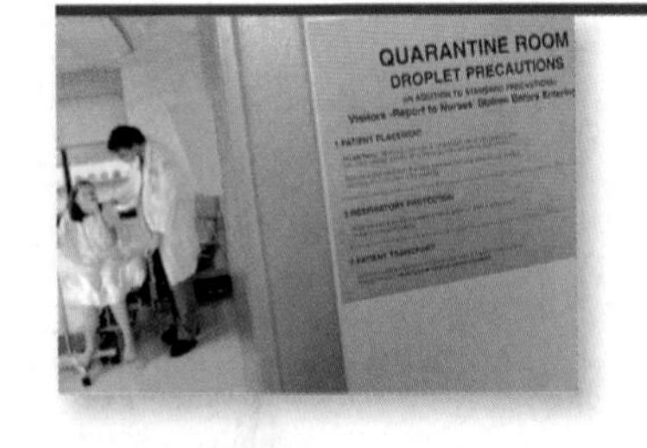

a. In Adair County, a health official states, "The population of sick people triples every day." The table below can be used to represent this situation.

Day	1	2	3	4	5	6	7	8	9
Number of Sick People	1	3	9						

What is the total number of sick people at the end of Day 6?

3 **a.** Since the sequence is arithmetic, the terms of the sequence can be expressed as the first term a_1 plus multiples of the common difference (or the last term a_n minus multiples of the common difference). So the right-hand side of the given formula is the sum of the terms a_1 through a_n.

b. The sum of each pair is $a_1 + a_n$. There are n such pairs.

c. $S_n = \dfrac{n(a_1 + a_n)}{2}$

d. This formula makes sense because, using Gauss' idea, the terms of the sequence are paired up in such a way that (*sum of each pair*) = (*initial term*) + (*final term*), and the number of pairs is the number of terms. Since each term is added twice in this method, you must divide by 2.

INSTRUCTIONAL NOTE
In Problem 3, students derive a formula for the sum of an arithmetic sequence when the starting subscript is 1. They also consider a formula expressed in words in Part d. In Problem 4, students find a formula when the starting subscript is 0.

4 **a.** $S_n = \dfrac{(n + 1)(a_0 + a_n)}{2}$

b. The sum is 295. In order to use the formulas developed above, students will need to choose whether they will start the sequence with subscript 0 or subscript 1, and then they must figure out what value of n corresponds to 52. Try to encourage them to find a method other than writing out all of the terms between 22 and 52. For example, if the starting subscript is taken to be 0, then the function formula for the terms of this sequence is $t_n = 7 + 5n$. In particular, $52 = 7 + 5n$. Solving gives $n = 9$, so $52 = t_9$. Since the starting subscript is 0, they should use the formula for S_n obtained in Problem 4 Part a. Thus, $S_9 = \dfrac{(9 + 1)(7 + 52)}{2} = 5(59) = 295$. Alternatively, once students figure out that there are 10 terms, they can use the formula-in-words to compute $\dfrac{(\textit{initial term} + \textit{final term})(\textit{number of terms})}{2} = \dfrac{(10)(7 + 52)}{2} = 295$.

INSTRUCTIONAL NOTE
When considering S_n with a starting subscript of 0 (i.e., the sum of the terms in any sequence from a_0 to a_n), be prepared to ask appropriate questions to make sure students understand that S_n has $n + 1$ terms.

5 **INSTRUCTIONAL NOTE** This problem addresses an important point about how the same numbers in the same table can be interpreted differently. The difference between *additional* amount and *accumulated* amount relates to the difference between derivatives and definite integrals in calculus. Under the interpretation of additional amounts, the terms would need to be summed to give a total amount, whereas accumulated amounts are already totals.

a. The first six terms are 1, 3, 9, 27, 81, and 243. The total number of sick people at the end of day 6 is 243, which is the last of the six terms. It is not necessary to sum the terms of the sequence since, according to the health official's statement, the population triples each day, which implies that each number in the sequence is the total number of sick people through the corresponding day.

DIFFERENTIATION For some students, for challenge or to connect to their geometry knowledge, you might give them the geometric drawing at the right and ask them to explain how the drawing illustrates Sondra's formula-in-words for the sum of the terms of an arithmetic sequence.

t_0
$t_0 + d$
$t_0 + 2d$
$t_0 + 3d$
$t_0 + 4d$
t_0

Unit 7

b. In Benton County, a different health official states, "The number of new sick people triples every day." Given this statement, you could construct the same table as in Part a. In this case, what is the total number of sick people at the end of Day 6 (assuming no sick person gets well in that time)?

c. Look back at Parts a and b. In which situation do the terms in the sequence represent an *additional* amount? In which situation do the terms represent an *accumulated* amount? Explain why it makes sense to sum the terms of the sequence in one situation but not in the other.

Geometric Sums In the epidemic example from Problem 5, assume that the epidemic begins at Day 1 with one sick person and the *additional* number of sick people triples every day. Then the total number of sick people at the end of Day n is found by summing the terms in the sequence.

6 Using algebraic reasoning, you can derive a formula for quickly calculating this geometric sum, as outlined below.

a. The total number of sick people at the end of day n can be represented as

$$S_n = 1 + 3 + 3^2 + 3^3 + \cdots + 3^{n-1}.$$

Explain why the exponent on the final term is $n - 1$ and not n.

b. The formula in Part a can be used to compute the sum, but it would take many steps for a large value of n. Derive a shorter formula by carrying out the following plan.

Create a new formula by multiplying both sides of the formula in Part a by 3. Subtract the formula in Part a from your new formula. Then solve the resulting formula for S_n.

c. Compare your work in Part b to the derivation below. Provide reasons for each step in the derivation below.

$$\begin{aligned} S_n &= 1 + 3 + 3^2 + 3^3 + 3^4 + \cdots + 3^{n-1} && (1)\\ 3(S_n) &= 3(1 + 3 + 3^2 + 3^3 + 3^4 + \cdots + 3^{n-1}) && (2)\\ &= 3 + 3^2 + 3^3 + 3^4 + \cdots + 3^{n-1} + 3^n && (3)\\ 3S_n - S_n &= 3^n - 1 && (4)\\ (3 - 1)S_n &= 3^n - 1 && (5)\\ S_n &= \frac{3^n - 1}{3 - 1} && (6) \end{aligned}$$

d. Explain why the strategy in Part c works to create a short formula.

e. Use this formula to calculate the total number of sick people at the end of Day 6. Compare your answer to your response to Problem 5 Part b.

f. Using similar reasoning, prove that the *sum of the terms of the geometric sequence* $1, r, r^2, r^3, r^4, \ldots, r^{n-1}$, where $r \neq 1$, is

$$1 + r + r^2 + r^3 + r^4 + \cdots + r^{n-1} = \frac{r^n - 1}{r - 1}.$$

Unit 7

492 UNIT 7 • Recursion and Iteration

b. The total number of sick people at the end of day 6 is $1 + 3 + 9 + 27 + 81 + 243 = 364$, which is the sum of the six terms in the table in Part a. In this case, the terms must be summed to yield a total number since, according to the health official's statement, each number in the sequence is the number of new additional sick people for that corresponding day.

c. In Part a, the terms are *accumulated* amounts. In Part b, the terms are *additional* amounts. You sum the terms in Part b because each term is the additional number of sick people each day. In Part a, each term already represents the total number of sick people through that day; thus, a given term gives the total directly, and there is no need to sum the terms.

6 **INSTRUCTIONAL NOTE** If students are not seeing the reason for the exponent of $n - 1$, ask, "On what day does the epidemic begin?"

a. S_n is the sum up through the term corresponding to day n. Since this sequence starts with day 1, S_n has n terms, starting at 3^0 for day 1, then 3^1 for day 2, and so on. So, the pattern is that the exponent on 3 is one less than the day number. So, day n corresponds to 3^{n-1}.

b. Students carry out the given strategy to derive a succinct formula for a geometric sum.

c.

$S_n = 1 + 3 + 3^2 + 3^3 + 3^4 + \cdots + 3^{n-1}$	(1) From Part a
$3(S_n) = 3(1 + 3 + 3^2 + 3^3 + 3^4 + \cdots + 3^{n-1})$	(2) Multiply both sides by 3
$= 3 + 3^2 + 3^3 + 3^4 + \cdots + 3^n$	(3) Distribute the 3
$3S_n - S_n = 3^n - 1$	(4) Subtract the first equation from the third equation
$(3 - 1)S_n = 3^n - 1$	(5) Factor out S_n
$S_n = \frac{3^n - 1}{3 - 1}$	(6) Divide by $(3 - 1)$

d. Students' explanations might be similar to the following one. The terms of the original sum are all powers of 3 (note that $1 = 3^0$), so multiplying by 3 will create new terms that also are powers of 3, with the exponents being one larger. So when you subtract, almost all the powers of 3 "cancel" and you are left only with $3^n - 1$.

e. At the end of day 6, the number of sick people is S_6, which is $\frac{3^6 - 1}{3 - 1} = 364$. This is the same value as the one in Part b of Problem 5.

f.

$$S_n = 1 + r + r^2 + r^3 + \cdots + r^{n-1}$$
$$rS_n = r + r^2 + r^3 + r^4 + \cdots + r^n$$
$$rS_n - S_n = r^n - 1$$
$$(r - 1)S_n = r^n - 1$$
$$S_n = \frac{r^n - 1}{r - 1}$$

DIFFERENTIATION
For Problem 6 Part b, if some students have undue difficulty carrying out the algebraic derivation you can direct them to Part c where they are given a derivation and asked to explain each step.

7 When summing terms in a geometric sequence, the exponent of the last term could be any positive integer. In Part f of Problem 6, the exponent of r in the last term is $n - 1$; and then the exponent of r in the numerator on the right side of the sum formula is n. Consider other possibilities.

a. Complete the formula for this sum.
$1 + r + r^2 + r^3 + r^4 + \cdots + r^n = \ldots$

b. Complete the formula for this sum.
$1 + r + r^2 + r^3 + r^4 + \cdots + r^{n+1} = \ldots$

c. It can get very confusing keeping track of when the formula should use n, $n - 1$, $n + 1$, and so on. But the pattern is always the same. State in words the relationship between the ending exponent on r in the sum in the left side of the formulas above and the exponent on r in the numerator of the right side.

8 The sums and formulas you have worked with so far apply to sequences with initial term 1. Consider sums of geometric sequences when the initial term is not 1.

a. Suppose an epidemic begins with two infected people on Day 1 and the additional number of infected people triples every day. What is the total number of sick people at the end of Day 4?

b. Suppose an ice cream store sold 22,000 ice cream cones in 2008. Based on sales data from other stores in similar locations, the manager predicts that the number of ice cream cones sold each year will increase by 5% each year. Using the formulas for the sum of a geometric sequence that you developed in Problems 6 and 7, find the total predicted number of ice cream cones sold during the period from 2008 to 2014. (*Hint*: You may find it helpful to write the sum term-by-term and then factor out 22,000.)

c. Consider a general geometric sequence with common ratio r, where $r \neq 1$, and initial term b. Find a formula for the sum, $S_n = b + br + br^2 + \cdots + br^n$. Provide an argument for why your formula is correct.

9 An expression showing the terms of a sequence added together is called a **series**. For example, $a_0 + a_1 + a_2 + \cdots + a_n$ and $B_1 + B_2 + \cdots + B_n$ are both examples of a series. A series is called an **arithmetic series** or a **geometric series**, depending on whether the sequence that generates the terms is arithmetic or geometric, respectively. (Note that the terms "sequence" and "series" have very specific meanings in mathematics, which may be different than their English meanings.)

i. Write a formula for an arithmetic series $B_1 + B_2 + \cdots + B_n$.

ii. Write a formula for a geometric series $B_1 + B_2 + \cdots + B_n$, with common ratio r.

7 **a.** $1 + r + r^2 + r^3 + r^4 + \cdots + r^n = \dfrac{r^{n+1} - 1}{r - 1}$

b. $1 + r + r^2 + r^3 + r^4 + \cdots + r^{n+1} = \dfrac{r^{n+2} - 1}{r - 1}$

c. A key pattern for students to notice and describe is that the exponent on r in the numerator of the right side is always one greater than the exponent on r in the last term of the sum on the left side. This relationship makes sense when you think about the strategy used to derive the formula in Problem 6, whereby S_n is multiplied by r and then you subtract $rS_n - S_n$.

INSTRUCTIONAL NOTE
Students need to see patterns and make sense of the sum formulas, not just try to memorize all the different possibilities.

8 **a.** If the epidemic begins with two people, the sequence of numbers of additional sick people is $2, 2 \cdot 3, 2 \cdot 3^2, 2 \cdot 3^3, \ldots$. Thus, the total number of sick people at the end of day 4 will be $S_4 = 2 + 2 \cdot 3 + 2 \cdot 3^2 + 2 \cdot 3^3 = 2(1 + 3 + 3^2 + 3^3) = 2(40) = 80$. Students may notice that the total number of sick people will be twice the total number when the epidemic begins with only one person.

b. For the period from 2008 to 2014, the predicted sales are approximately 179,124 ice cream cones. This period of time comprises 7 years. If we use the formula from Problem 6, then we are assuming that the initial subscript is 1 and $n = 7$. Thus, the total predicted number of ice cream cones sold is

$$22{,}000 + 1.05(22{,}000) + 1.05^2(22{,}000) + \cdots + 1.05^6(22{,}000) =$$
$$22{,}000(1 + 1.05 + 1.05^2 + 1.05^3 + 1.05^4 + 1.05^5 + 1.05^6) =$$
$$22{,}000\left(\frac{1.05^n - 1}{1.05 - 1}\right) \text{ (where } n = 7) = 22{,}000\left(\frac{1.05^7 - 1}{1.05 - 1}\right) \approx 179{,}124.$$

c. $S_n = \dfrac{b(r^{n+1} - 1)}{r - 1}$. Students might provide an algebraic argument similar to the derivations in Parts b and c of Problem 6, or they might first factor b out of the sum. Students might also use the pattern they found in Problem 7 to help explain this formula.

9 **i.** $B_1 + B_2 + \cdots + B_n = \dfrac{n(B_1 + B_n)}{2}$

ii. $B_1 + B_2 + \cdots + B_n = \dfrac{B_1(r^n - 1)}{r - 1}$

Unit 7

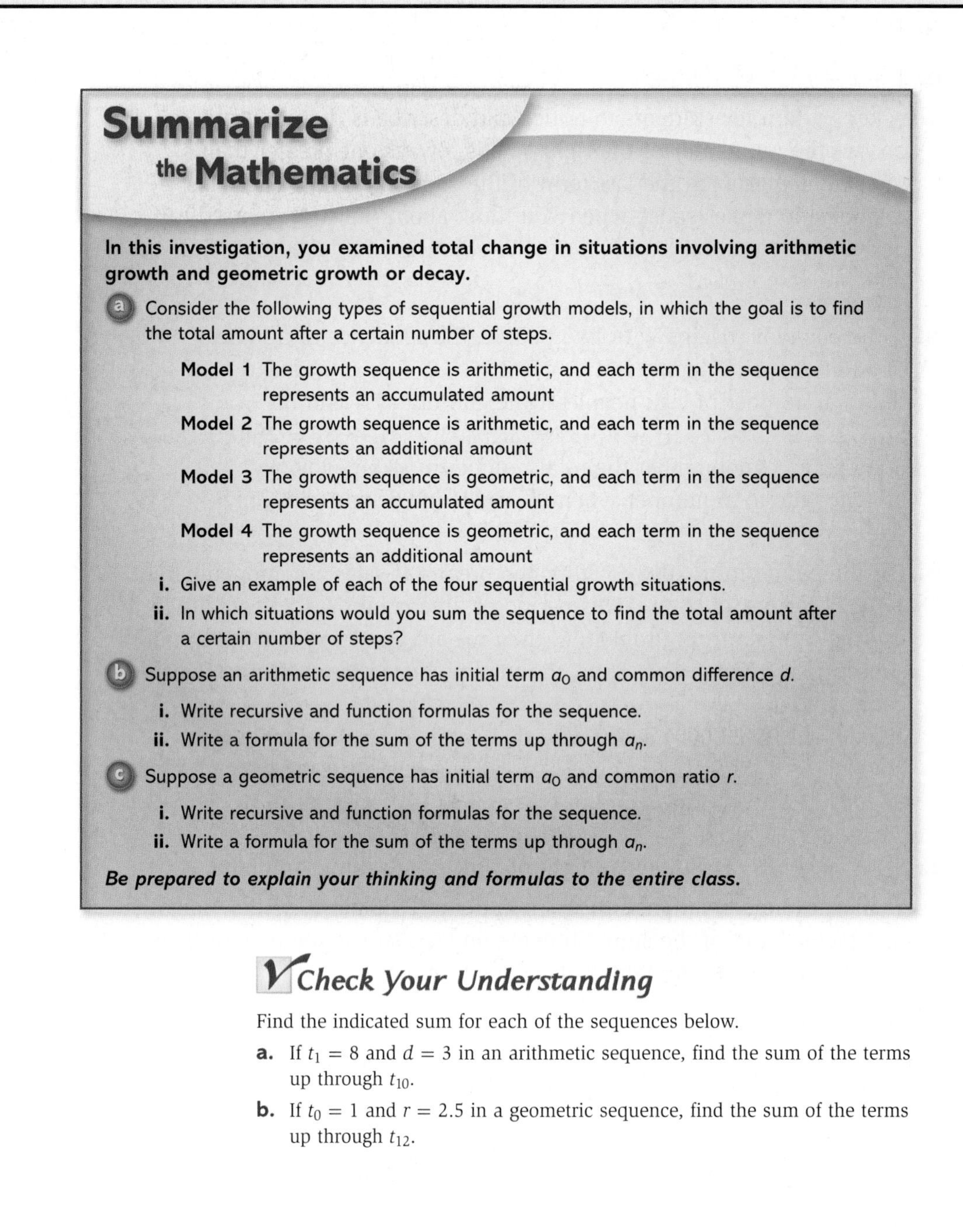

Summarize the Mathematics

In this investigation, you examined total change in situations involving arithmetic growth and geometric growth or decay.

a Consider the following types of sequential growth models, in which the goal is to find the total amount after a certain number of steps.

Model 1 The growth sequence is arithmetic, and each term in the sequence represents an accumulated amount

Model 2 The growth sequence is arithmetic, and each term in the sequence represents an additional amount

Model 3 The growth sequence is geometric, and each term in the sequence represents an accumulated amount

Model 4 The growth sequence is geometric, and each term in the sequence represents an additional amount

i. Give an example of each of the four sequential growth situations.

ii. In which situations would you sum the sequence to find the total amount after a certain number of steps?

b Suppose an arithmetic sequence has initial term a_0 and common difference d.

i. Write recursive and function formulas for the sequence.

ii. Write a formula for the sum of the terms up through a_n.

c Suppose a geometric sequence has initial term a_0 and common ratio r.

i. Write recursive and function formulas for the sequence.

ii. Write a formula for the sum of the terms up through a_n.

Be prepared to explain your thinking and formulas to the entire class.

✓ *Check Your Understanding*

Find the indicated sum for each of the sequences below.

a. If $t_1 = 8$ and $d = 3$ in an arithmetic sequence, find the sum of the terms up through t_{10}.

b. If $t_0 = 1$ and $r = 2.5$ in a geometric sequence, find the sum of the terms up through t_{12}.

Unit 7

494 UNIT 7 • Recursion and Iteration

Summary

Have students discuss and make notes on their ideas for this STM. Then after a class discussion, students should write complete solutions for their toolkits. When thinking about S_n for either arithmetic or geometric series, it may be helpful to focus students' attention on the number of terms when summing from a_0 to a_n, $n + 1$ terms.

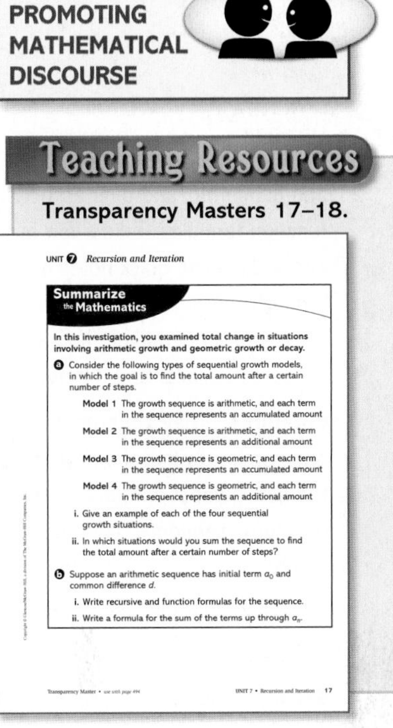
PROMOTING MATHEMATICAL DISCOURSE

Teaching Resources

Transparency Masters 17–18.

UNIT 7 *Recursion and Iteration*

Summarize the Mathematics

In this investigation, you examined total change in situations involving arithmetic growth and geometric growth or decay.

a Consider the following types of sequential growth models, in which the goal is to find the total amount after a certain number of steps.

Model 1 The growth sequence is arithmetic, and each term in the sequence represents an accumulated amount

Model 2 The growth sequence is arithmetic, and each term in the sequence represents an additional amount

Model 3 The growth sequence is geometric, and each term in the sequence represents an accumulated amount

Model 4 The growth sequence is geometric, and each term in the sequence represents an additional amount

i. Give an example of each of the four sequential growth situations.

ii. In which situations would you sum the sequence to find the total amount after a certain number of steps?

b Suppose an arithmetic sequence has initial term a_0 and common difference d.

i. Write recursive and function formulas for the sequence.

ii. Write a formula for the sum of the terms up through a_n.

Transparency Master • use with page 494 UNIT 7 • Recursion and Iteration 17

Summarize the Mathematics

a **Model 1** An example of an arithmetic sequence in which each term represents an *accumulated* amount is the amount of money in a young child's piggy bank if a dollar is placed into the piggy bank each week. (For another accumulated amount example, see the bungee experiment sequence in Investigation 1 on page 483).

Model 2 An example of an arithmetic sequence in which each term represents an *additional* amount is the number of times a grandfather clock chimes each hour from 1:00 P.M. to 12:00 A.M. You would sum an arithmetic sequence to find the total number of times the clock chimes from 1:00 P.M. to midnight. (For another additional amount example, see the auditorium seat example in Task 3 of Lesson 4 on page 535.)

Model 3 An example of a geometric sequence in which each term represents an *accumulated* amount is population growth. (For another accumulated amount example, see the Sierpinski carpet sequence in Investigation 1 on page 486.)

Model 4 An example of a geometric sequence in which each term represents an *additional* amount is a situation in which the number of hamburgers served each year increases by a constant factor each year. You would sum the geometric sequence to find the total number of hamburgers served in 10 years. (For another additional amount example, see the fractal tree sequence in Task 2 of Lesson 4 on page 534.)

b **i.** Recursive formula: $a_n = a_{n-1} + d$, starting at a_0
Function formula: $a_n = a_0 + nd$

ii. Sum of the terms: $S_n = \dfrac{(n+1)(a_0 + a_n)}{2}$

c **i.** Recursive formula: $a_n = ra_{n-1}$, starting at a_0
Function formula: $a_n = a_0 r^n$

ii. Sum of the terms: $S_n = \dfrac{a_0(r^{n+1} - 1)}{r - 1}$

MATH TOOLKIT See the Summary note above.

Unit 7

Check Your Understanding

a. $t_{10} = 8 + 3(9) = 35$; $t_1 + t_2 + \cdots + t_{10} = \dfrac{(10)(8+35)}{2} = 215$

b. Since $t_{12} = (2.5)^{12}$, the sum is $\dfrac{1(2.5^{13} - 1)}{2.5 - 1}$, or approximately 99,340.41.

Promoting Mathematical Discourse

Summarize the Mathematics, *page 494*

Teacher: We have been studying two patterns of growth, arithmetic and geometric, and their associated sequences and recursive and function formulas. Take a few minutes with your group to discuss and make some quick notes on your thinking to the STM Parts a through c. *(The teacher gives students a few minutes to discuss these parts.)* Geraldine, how are arithmetic and geometric sequences similar and different?

Geraldine: They are both lists of numbers that are found by using one number to find the next number. For an arithmetic sequence, the next number is found by *adding* a constant each time. For a geometric sequence, you *multiply* by a constant to find the next number.

Teacher: Who has an example of an arithmetic sequence to share with us?

Kacie: I thought about when I run. I usually try to run at the same speed, for each minute more that I run, I cover about 750 feet. That is an arithmetic sequence since I add 750 feet to get to each term in the sequence of distance-per-minute values: 0, 750, 1,500, and so on.

Rabar: I thought of a geometric sequence. It was the pay it forward idea from that movie. The idea was to do three deeds of kindness and that each person who was treated kindly would then also do three kind deeds for others. Each next term in the sequence would be multiplied by 3, making a geometric sequence.

Teacher: *(The teacher collects one addition example of each sequence and then asks about Part ai in a slightly different form.)* So, which of those sequences can be modeled by a linear function and which by a geometric function? Tristen?

Tristen: Any sequence made by adding a constant can be written as a linear function and any sequence made by multiplying by a constant can be written as an exponential function.

Teacher: Does this jibe with what you have previously learned about the table values and *NOW-NEXT* rules? *(Students indicate it does.)* Then let's hear what you discussed for Part bi. Lin, please read Part bi for us and then share what your group discussed.

Lin: Describe the difference between a recursive formula and a function formula for a sequence. What information do you need to know to find each type of formula? We decided that the recursive formula tells you how to get from one term to the next and the function formula gives a rule to find *any* term in the sequence. The information you need for both types is the starting value and the constant that is added or multiplied.

Teacher: Does everyone agree?

Demarco: The function type of formulas we have been using for a long time now. The recursive types are really like the *NOW-NEXT* rules we used before, but now we are using subscripts too.

Teacher: Good connection Demarco. It helps to tie new mathematical notation back to notation that you are comfortable using. What is one advantage and disadvantage of a recursive formula for a sequence? Emma.

Emma: Well, the recursive formula lets you easily see the pattern of adding or multiplying by a constant. These formulas are: $L_n = L_{n-1} + c$ or $L_n = cL_{n-1}$. But they do not help you find a term that is way out from where you currently are, like term 100. When you want to find way-out terms, it is best to have a function formula. Then you can just plug in the term number to find the value of that term. For example, well, Chloe, you tell your example.

Chloe: We talked about the bacteria example in Problem 7. To find the number of bacteria after 18 hours, it was easier to use the function formula $B_n = 25(2^n)$ and use 18 for n than to take the recursive formula out 18 times.

Teacher: Well, you seem to have discussed the advantages and disadvantages of each type of formula. Does anyone have questions or things to add to this discussion? No, well just for the record, the initial value for a recursive formula does not show up directly in the formula. But it is an additional piece of important information needed to compute subsequent values. Note that the recursive formulas given by Emma did not state the initial value. Now remember when you changed the starting subscript from 0 to 1 in Problems 11–14. Why did this have no effect on the recursive formula but has an effect on the function formula?

James: The relationship stays the same, so the recursive formula just tells you how to get to the next term. We did change subscript numbers, but that is all. But it is more complicated with the function rule. There, the starting subscript determines how many times the adding or multiplying needs to happen to get to the nth term. If you start with $n = 0$, you need n additions or multiplications to get to the nth term. If you start with $n = 1$, then you only need $(n - 1)$ additions or multiplications to get to the nth term—one less than before. That is how I think about it.

Teacher: Thanks, James. This idea about starting subscripts is a little tricky. Think about it as you do the Check Your Understanding task on page 495. We will continue to think about it when we do more work with sequences in Investigation 2. We seem to be running out of class time, so please think about Parts d and e of the STM tonight and do the CYU task so we can discuss them first thing tomorrow.

Unit 7

Teacher Notes

c. Find the sum of the first 15 terms of each sequence below.

n	1	2	3	4	5	6	7	...	15	...
A_n	2	6	18	54	162					

n	0	1	2	3	4	5	6	...	14	...
B_n	95	90	85	80	75					

d. A popular shoe store sold 5,700 pairs of athletic shoes in 2008. Projections are for a 3% increase in sales each year for several years after 2008. What is the projected total sales (number of athletic shoes sold) during the period from 2008 to 2013?

Investigation 3 Finite Differences

So far, you have been able to find a function formula for a sequence by detecting and generalizing a pattern. Sometimes that is not so easily done. In this investigation, you will learn how to use *finite differences tables* to find a function formula for certain sequences. As you work on the problems of this investigation, look for answers to these questions:

How do you construct a finite differences table for a sequence?

How can you use such a table to find a function formula for a sequence?

What kind of function formulas can be found using finite differences tables?

1 To learn how to use finite differences tables, start with a sample function formula. Suppose you toss a rock straight down from a high bridge. If the rock is thrown from a bridge 300 feet above the river with an initial velocity of 10 feet per second, then the distance D_n of the rock from the river after n seconds is given by the function formula

$$D_n = -16n^2 - 10n + 300.$$

An analysis of the pattern of change in the distance between the rock and the river is shown in the following table.

Number of Seconds, n	D_n	1st Difference	2nd Difference
0	300		
		−26	
1	274		−32
		−58	
2	216		___
		___	
3	___		___
		___	
4	___		

a. On a copy of the table, complete the D_n column.

c. The 15th term A_{15} is $2(3)^{14}$. So, the sum of A_1 through A_{15} is $\frac{2(3^{15} - 1)}{3 - 1} = 14{,}348{,}906$.

The 15th term B_{14} is $95 + (14)(-5) = 25$. So, the sum of B_0 through B_{14} is $\frac{(15)(95 + 25)}{2} = 900$.

d. The term for year 2013 will be $5{,}700(1.05)^5$. It is the 6th term in the sequence that begins with $5{,}700(1.05)^0$. The projected total number of shoes sold is $\frac{5{,}700(1.03^6 - 1)}{1.03 - 1}$, or approximately 36,870.

Investigation 3 Finite Differences

In this investigation, students use finite differences tables to help them determine the polynomial function that generates a sequence. This method works only for polynomial functions. As a result of the three investigations in this lesson, students will have studied a recursive view of linear, exponential, and polynomial functions, in terms of related sequences and their sums.

INSTRUCTIONAL NOTE In this finite differences table, you should subtract the upper number D_{n-1} from the lower number D_n, rather than subtracting in the other order. In general, either order of subtraction is acceptable, as long as it is done consistently, but it is more common to subtract D_{n-1} from D_n. Subtracting in this manner models the real-world situation better. Think about time passing and computing the average velocity for each one-second interval. Such a computation requires that you subtract D_{n-1} from D_n. Velocity should be negative because the distance is decreasing over time.

a.

Number of Seconds, n	D_n	1st Difference	2nd Difference
0	300		
		−26	
1	274		−32
		−58	
2	216		−32
		−90	
3	126		−32
		−122	
4	4		

Teaching Resources

Student Master 19.

Unit 7

b. The third column contains differences between consecutive terms of the sequence D_n. How was the "−58" calculated? Find the remaining entries in the "1st Difference" column.

c. The fourth column contains differences between consecutive terms of the "1st Difference" column. Verify the entry "−32" and find the remaining entries in the "2nd Difference" column.

d. A table like this is called a **finite differences table**. Describe any patterns you see in your completed table.

Fact 1 about Finite Differences It is a fact that for any function formula that is a quadratic, such as the one in Problem 1, the 2nd differences in a finite differences table will be a constant.

Conversely, if the 2nd differences are a constant, then the function formula is a quadratic. (See Extensions Task 24.) For example, consider the following counting problem involving vertex-edge graphs.

2 A complete graph is a graph in which there is exactly one edge between every pair of vertices. The diagram at the right shows a complete graph with 4 vertices. In this problem, you will investigate the number of edges E_n in a complete graph with n vertices.

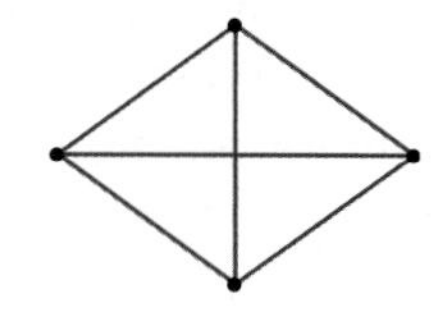

a. On a copy of a table like the one below, enter the number of edges for complete graphs with 0 to 5 vertices. Then compute the 1st and 2nd differences. Describe any patterns you see in the table.

Number of Vertices, n	E_n	1st Difference	2nd Difference
0	—		
		—	
1	—		—
		—	
2	—		—
		—	
3	—		—
		—	
4	—		—
		—	
5	—		

b. What pattern in the finite differences table tells you that the function formula for the sequence of edge counts must look like $E_n = an^2 + bn + c$?

c. How could you find the coefficients a, b, and c? With some classmates, brainstorm some ideas and try them out. When you find a, b, and c, or if you are having trouble finding them, go on to Problem 3.

Unit 7

496 UNIT 7 • Recursion and Iteration

b. The "−58" was calculated 216 − 274. In general, the entries in the "1st Difference" column are found by evaluating $D_n - D_{n-1}$. See the table in Part a for the remaining entries in the "1st Difference" column.

c. $-58 - (-26) = -32$. See Part a for the completed table.

d. The most obvious pattern is that the 2nd differences are all −32. Students might also notice that the distances are decreasing in the D_n column, which makes the 1st differences negative; likewise, the 1st differences are decreasing (becoming more negative), which makes the 2nd differences negative. Some students may notice that −32 ft/sec/sec is the acceleration due to the force of gravity.

2 **DIFFERENTIATION** For some students, Problem 2 Part c may be too open ended, and you may decide to suggest finding a regression equation or direct them to Problem 3 rather quickly. Other students may use the method in Problem 3 as part of their work on Problem 2 Part c, so they can skip Problem 3. All students should in one way or another work through the matrix method in Problem 3 since it is powerful and a good review of matrices and systems of equations.

a.

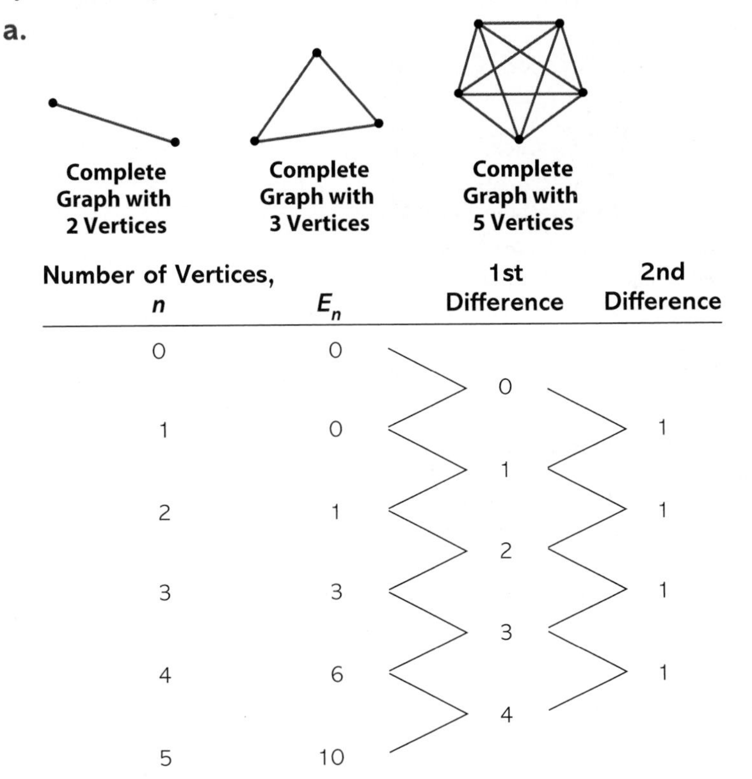

Number of Vertices, n	E_n	1st Difference	2nd Difference
0	0		
		0	
1	0		1
		1	
2	1		1
		2	
3	3		1
		3	
4	6		1
		4	
5	10		

Patterns in the table include all 1s in the "2nd Difference" column and the sequence of counting numbers in the "1st Difference" column.

b. Given the fact stated in the paragraph before Problem 2, the constant entries in the "2nd Difference" column indicate that the formula for edge counts must be a quadratic. That is, $E_n = an^2 + bn + c$.

c. Students should be encouraged to develop and try methods for finding the coefficients a, b, and c. For example, they may use some values for n and E_n from the table and solve some equations, or they may use quadratic regression.

Teaching Resources

Student Master 20.

Unit 7

3 One way to find a, b, and c is to set up and solve a system of three linear equations. If you already did that in Part c of Problem 2, then read through this problem, compare it to your method, and discuss any differences. If you did not set up and solve a system of three linear equations, then do so now, as follows. You can get a system of equations by letting n equal any three values, for example, 1, 2, and 3.

a. To get the first equation, suppose $n = 1$. If you substitute $n = 1$ in the equation $E_n = an^2 + bn + c$, you get $E_1 = a(1)^2 + b(1) + c = a + b + c$. Explain why one equation is $a + b + c = 0$.

b. Use similar reasoning with $n = 2$ and $n = 3$ to get the second and third equations.

c. Compare the system of three linear equations you found to the systems found by others. Resolve any differences.

d. You can solve systems of three equations like these using matrices, as you did for the case of systems of two linear equations in Course 2 Unit 2, *Matrix Methods*. Written in matrix form, the system looks like the partially completed matrix equation below. Fill in the missing entries and solve this matrix equation.

$$\begin{bmatrix} 1 & 1 & \_ \\ \_ & 2 & 1 \\ 9 & \_ & 1 \end{bmatrix}\begin{bmatrix} a \\ b \\ c \end{bmatrix} = \begin{bmatrix} 0 \\ 1 \\ \_ \end{bmatrix}$$

$$A \cdot X = C$$

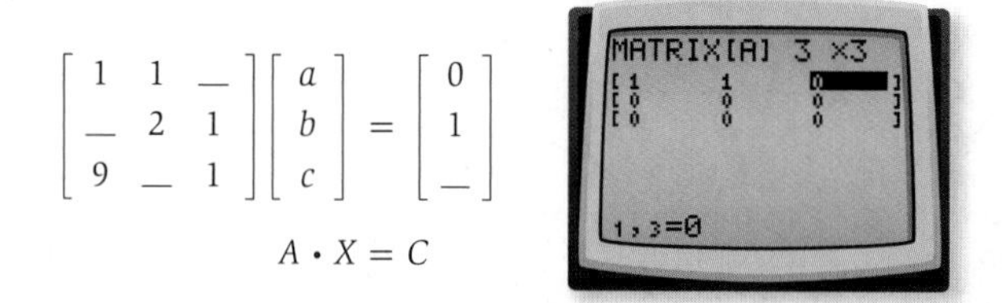

e. Use the results of Part d to write the function formula for the number of edges in a complete graph with n vertices. Use this formula to check the entries in the table from Problem 2.

f. Now that you have a function formula, find a recursive formula for the sequence of edge counts. Do so by examining the table in Problem 2.

4 So far in this investigation, you have examined situations in which the function formula is a quadratic. Now consider the case of a higher-degree function formula. Suppose $A_n = 4n^3 + 2n^2 - 5n - 8$. Make a prediction about which column in the finite differences table for this sequence will be constant. Construct the finite differences table to check your conjecture.

Unit 7

3 **INSTRUCTIONAL NOTE** If students already used this matrix method in Problem 2 Part c, then they can skip this problem. If not, they should now use this method. In the Check Your Understanding, students are asked to again use matrices as outlined in this problem. In the On Your Own tasks, students will have opportunities to use this matrix method, a different matrix method, and statistical regression to find function formulas.

a. From the table, $E_1 = 0$. A complete graph with 1 vertex has 0 edges.

b. From the table, $E_2 = 1$. So, $1 = a(2)^2 + b(2) + c = 4a + 2b + c$.
$9a + 3b + c = 3$

c. All students in the class should have the same system of equations. Having students talk to each other about the equations will help them really understand where the equations originate.

d. $$\begin{bmatrix} 1 & 1 & 1 \\ 4 & 2 & 1 \\ 9 & 3 & 1 \end{bmatrix} \begin{bmatrix} a \\ b \\ c \end{bmatrix} = \begin{bmatrix} 0 \\ 1 \\ 3 \end{bmatrix}$$

This matrix equation looks like $AX = C$. The solution is

$$X = (A^{-1})(C) = \begin{bmatrix} 0.5 \\ -0.5 \\ 0 \end{bmatrix}.$$

Thus, $a = 0.5$, $b = -0.5$, and $c = 0$. Note that the calculator may give c as a very small number. Students must interpret this number in terms of round-off error and conclude that $c = 0$.

e. Substituting these values into $E_n = an^2 + bn + c$ gives $E_n = 0.5n^2 - 0.5n$. Using this formula to check the entries in the table from Problem 2 gives the following:

$E_0 = (0.5)0^2 - (0.5)0 = 0$ $\quad$ $E_1 = (0.5)1^2 - (0.5)1 = 0$
$E_2 = (0.5)2^2 - (0.5)2 = 1$ $\quad$ $E_3 = (0.5)3^2 - (0.5)3 = 3$
$E_4 = (0.5)4^2 - (0.5)4 = 6$ $\quad$ $E_5 = (0.5)5^2 - (0.5)5 = 10$

f. A recursive formula is $E_n = E_{n-1} + (n - 1)$. Note that you cannot use a *NOW-NEXT* rule in this situation because of the $(n - 1)$ term.

4 Since A_n is a polynomial of degree 3, the 3rd differences should be constant. The finite differences table is shown below, and the 3rd differences are indeed constant.

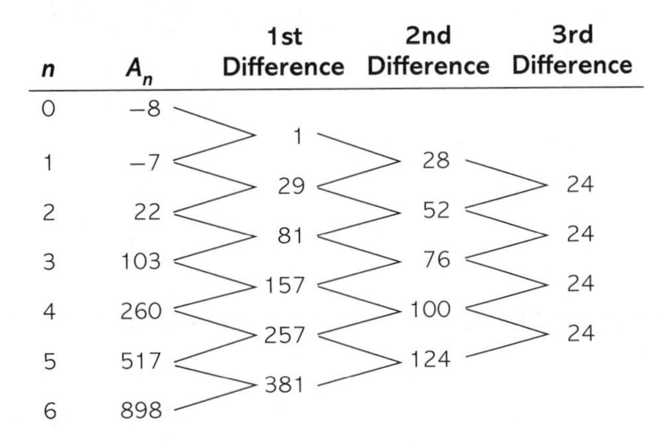

n	A_n	1st Difference	2nd Difference	3rd Difference
0	−8			
		1		
1	−7		28	
		29		24
2	22		52	
		81		24
3	103		76	
		157		24
4	260		100	
		257		24
5	517		124	
		381		
6	898			

Unit 7

Fact 2 about Finite Differences In general, it is possible to compute more than just 2nd or 3rd differences. If the function formula is an rth degree polynomial, then the rth differences will be constant. The converse is also true. These facts can be used to help find function formulas for certain sequences.

Summarize the Mathematics

In this investigation, you learned about finite differences tables.

a. Describe how to construct a finite differences table for a sequence of numbers.

b. If the 4th differences in the finite differences table for a sequence are constant, what do you think the function formula for the sequence will look like? How would you go about finding the function formula?

c. In general, what kind of function formulas can be found using finite differences tables?

d. The title of this lesson is "A Recursive View of Functions." Explain how this title describes the mathematics you have been studying in all three investigations of the lesson.

Be prepared to share your descriptions and thinking with the entire class.

Check Your Understanding

Use a finite differences table and matrices to find a function formula for the sequence below.

n	0	1	2	3	4	5	6	7	8	9	10	11
A_n	3	12	25	42	63	88	117	150	187	228	273	322

Unit 7

498 UNIT 7 • Recursion and Iteration

Summarize the Mathematics

a Make a table in which the first column consists of the subscripts, that is, 0, 1, 2, 3, ... , which might represent numbers of seconds or numbers of vertices or just subscripts for the terms of the sequence. In the second column, list the actual terms of the sequence. The third column is the 1st differences, that is, the differences between successive terms (($n + 1$)st term $-$ nth term) in the sequence; the fourth column is the 2nd differences, that is, the differences between successive terms in the previous column; and so on.

b If the 4th differences in the finite differences table for a sequence are constant, then the function formula for the sequence must be quartic (degree 4). The function formula will be of the form $A_n = an^4 + bn^3 + cn^2 + dn + e$. (To find the specific formula, students can use a calculator or computer software to solve the matrix equation

$$\begin{bmatrix} 1 & 1 & 1 & 1 & 1 \\ 16 & 8 & 4 & 2 & 1 \\ 81 & 27 & 9 & 3 & 1 \\ 256 & 64 & 16 & 4 & 1 \\ 625 & 125 & 25 & 5 & 1 \end{bmatrix} \begin{bmatrix} a \\ b \\ c \\ d \\ e \end{bmatrix} = \begin{bmatrix} a_1 \\ a_2 \\ a_3 \\ a_4 \\ a_5 \end{bmatrix}$$

where a_1, a_2, a_3, a_4, and a_5 are the output values for terms 2–6 of the sequence.)

c The only use of finite differences tables investigated in this investigation produced polynomial functions. This occurs when a column of differences becomes constant. When the rth differences are constant, the function formula is a polynomial of degree r. (It is possible to use finite differences tables in creative ways to find function formulas for a variety of sequences.)

d This lesson can be described as a "recursive view of functions" since sequences are studied particularly from a recursive perspective (recursive formulas and the recursive nature of a finite differences table), and the resulting function formulas are linear, exponential, and polynomial functions.

Teaching Resources

Transparency Master 21.

UNIT 7 *Recursion and Iteration*

Summarize the Mathematics

In this investigation, you learned about finite differences tables.

a Describe how to construct a finite differences table for a sequence of numbers.

b If the 4th differences in the finite differences table for a sequence are constant, what do you think the function formula for the sequence will look like? How would you go about finding the function formula?

c In general, what kind of function formulas can be found using finite differences tables?

d The title of this lesson is "A Recursive View of Functions." Explain how this title describes the mathematics you have been studying in all three investigations of the lesson.

Be prepared to share your descriptions and thinking with the entire class.

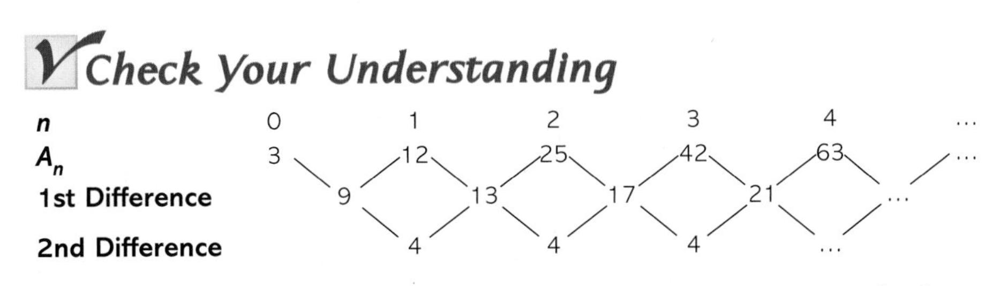

Check Your Understanding
n 0 1 2 3 4 ...
A_n 3 12 25 42 63 ...
1st Difference 9 13 17 21 ...
2nd Difference 4 4 4 ...

The 2nd differences are constant, so the function formula is a quadratic function of the form $A_n = an^2 + bn + c$.

Teaching Resources

Student Master 22.

UNIT 7 *Recursion and Iteration*

Check Your Understanding

Finite Differences Table

n	A_n
0	3
1	12
2	25
3	42
4	63
5	88
6	117
7	150
8	187
9	228
10	273
11	322

Unit 7

Find the coefficients by solving the following system of three equations.

$$\begin{aligned} a + b + c &= 12 \\ 4a + 2b + c &= 25 \\ 9a + 3b + c &= 42 \end{aligned} \qquad \begin{bmatrix} 1 & 1 & 1 \\ 4 & 2 & 1 \\ 9 & 3 & 1 \end{bmatrix} \begin{bmatrix} a \\ b \\ c \end{bmatrix} = \begin{bmatrix} 12 \\ 25 \\ 42 \end{bmatrix}$$

$a = 2$, $b = 7$, and $c = 3$. Thus, the function formula is $A_n = 2n^2 + 7n + 3$.

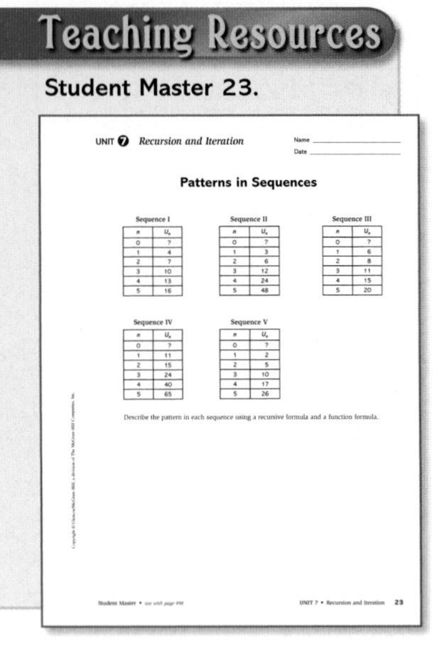

Teaching Resources

Student Master 23.

UNIT 7 *Recursion and Iteration*

Name ______

Date ______

Patterns in Sequences

Sequence I

n	U_n
0	?
1	4
2	7
3	10
4	13
5	16

Sequence II

n	U_n
0	?
1	3
2	6
3	12
4	24
5	48

Sequence III

n	U_n
0	?
1	6
2	8
3	11
4	15
5	20

Sequence IV

n	U_n
0	?
1	11
2	15
3	24
4	40
5	65

Sequence V

n	U_n
0	?
1	2
2	5
3	10
4	17
5	26

Describe the pattern in each sequence using a recursive formula and a function formula.

Student Master • use with page 498 UNIT 7 • Recursion and Iteration 23

DIFFERENTIATION You may decide that some students need more practice with sequences. If so, you might consider writing several sequences on the board and asking your students to describe the sequences using a recursive formula or a function formula. Your sequences should include an arithmetic sequence, a geometric sequence, and some others.

It is not important that your students find both formulas for each, but they should realize that there are patterns other than arithmetic and geometric and that sometimes the same pattern can be generated in two ways. A student master is provided containing the sequences below.

n	U_n
0	?
1	4
2	7
3	10
4	13
5	16

n	U_n
0	?
1	3
2	6
3	12
4	24
5	48

n	U_n
0	?
1	6
2	8
3	11
4	15
5	20

n	U_n
0	?
1	11
2	15
3	24
4	40
5	65

n	U_n
0	?
1	2
2	5
3	10
4	17
5	26

- The first sequence is arithmetic, $U_n = U_{n-1} + 3$, $U_0 = 1$, or $U_n = 1 + 3n$.
- The second sequence is geometric, $U_n = 2U_{n-1}$, $U_0 = 1.5$, or $U_n = 1.5(2^n)$.
- The third is generated by $U_n = U_{n-1} + n$, $U_0 = 5$, or $U_n = 0.5n^2 + 0.5n + 5$.
- The fourth is $U_n = U_{n-1} + n^2$, $U_0 = 10$, or $U_n = \frac{1}{3}n^3 + \frac{1}{2}n^2 + \frac{1}{6}n + 10$.
- The last is $U_n = U_{n-1} + 2n - 1$, $U_0 = 1$, or $U_n = n^2 + 1$.
- Finally, you might have students generate their own sequences with "mystery" polynomial or exponential functions and challenge other students to find the function formula.

Unit 7

Teacher Notes

On Your Own

Applications

1. For many people, a college education is a desirable and worthwhile goal. But the cost of a college education is growing every year. For the 2006–07 school year, the average cost for four-year public colleges (tuition and fees) was $5,836, which was up 6.3% from the previous year. (Source: College Board; www.collegeboard.com/student/pay/add-it-up/4494.html)

   a. Assume an annual increase rate in college costs of 6% per year. Make a table showing the average cost of a year of college education (tuition and fees) at a four-year public college for the next 5 years following 2006–07.

   b. Is the sequence of increasing costs arithmetic, geometric, or neither?

   c. Determine recursive and function formulas for the sequence of costs.

   d. Use your formulas to predict the average cost of the first year of your college education if you go to a four-year public college right after you graduate from high school.

   e. Predict the average cost of four years of college at a four-year public college for a child born this year.

2. Animal behavior often changes as the outside temperature changes. One curious example of this is the fact that the frequency of cricket chirps varies with the outside temperature in a very predictable way. Consider the data below for one species of cricket.

Cricket Chirps

Temperature (in °F)	45	47	50	52	54	55	60
Frequency (in chirps/min)	20	28	41	50	57	61	80

   a. If you were to choose an arithmetic sequence or a geometric sequence as a model for the frequency sequence, which type of sequence would you choose? Why?

   b. As is often the case in mathematical modeling, the model you chose in Part a does not fit the data exactly. Nevertheless, it may be quite useful for analysis of the situation.

      i. Find a recursive formula for the frequency sequence, based on the type of sequence you chose in Part a.

      ii. Use the formula to predict the frequency of cricket chirps for a temperature of 75°F.

   c. At what temperature would you expect crickets to stop chirping?

On Your Own

Applications

1. a. **College Education Cost (Tuition and Fees), One Year**

Year	Cost (in $)
0	5,836
1	6,186.16
2	6,557.33
3	6,950.77
4	7,367.82
5	7,809.89

b. The sequence is geometric. The constant multiplier is 1.06.

c. Recursive formula: $C_n = C_{n-1}(1.06)$, $C_0 = 5{,}836$

Function formula: $C_n = 5{,}836(1.06^n)$, where n is the number of years after 2006–07.

d. Responses will vary depending on your students. As an example, for students who are juniors in 2008–09, the average cost for the first year will be $C_n = 5{,}836(1.06)^4$, or approximately $7,367.82.

e. Responses will vary depending on the current year. For example, if the child is born in 2008–09, starts college 18 years later, and spends four years in college, then the cost is represented by $C_{20} + C_{21} + C_{22} + C_{23}$. This is approximately 18,717 + 19,840 + 21,030 + 22,292, or $81,879. (If students have completed Investigation 2, they might choose to find this value by evaluating $S_{23} - S_{19}$.)

2. **a.** It appears that the data would be better modeled by an arithmetic sequence. The added constant seems to be approximately 4. (Note that the table is not set up with one degree increments in temperature.) Also, if you plot the data, the graph appears to be linear, which indicates an arithmetic sequence.

b. **i.** $C_n = C_{n-1} + 4$

ii. Using $C_{45} = 20$ or $C_{60} = 80$, the recursive formula predicts $C_{75} = 140$ chirps per minute when the temperature is 75°F.

c. The crickets would stop chirping at about 40°F. The recursive formula can be interpreted to mean that for each 1°F decrease in temperature, the number of chirps per minute will decrease by 4. From 45°F, we need a decrease of 5°F to get to 0 chirps per minute.

Unit 7

d. You can use the relationship between the frequency of cricket chirps and the temperature as a kind of thermometer. What would you estimate the temperature to be if a cricket is chirping at 100 chirps per minute?

e. Based on your recursive formula in Part b, find a function formula for the sequence of cricket chirps. Use your function formula to find the frequency of cricket chirps for a temperature of 75°F. Compare to your answer in Part b.

f. Rewrite your function formula to express temperature as a function of frequency of cricket chirps. Use this new formula to answer the question in Part d.

3 The square Sierpinski carpet you examined in Investigation 1 is an example of a *fractal* in that small pieces of the design are similar to the design as a whole. Other fractal shapes can also be constructed using recursive procedures.

a. A *Sierpinski triangle* is constructed through a sequence of steps illustrated by the figures below.

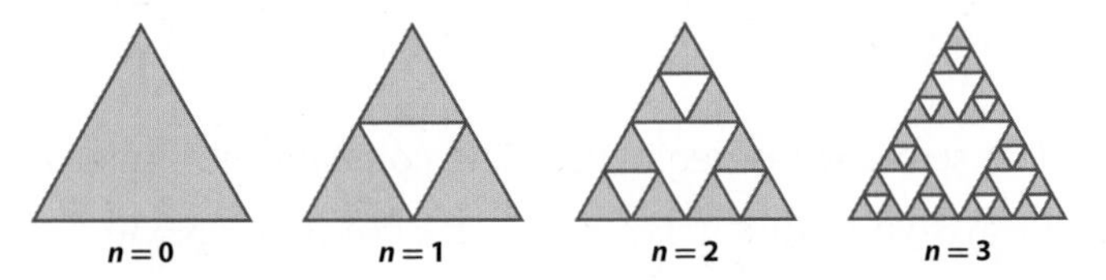

At stage $n = 0$, you construct an equilateral triangle whose sides are all of length 1 unit. In succeeding stages, you remove the "middle triangles," as shown in stages $n = 1$, 2, and 3. This process continues indefinitely. Consider the sequence of areas of the figures at each stage. Find recursive and function formulas for the sequence of areas.

b. Another interesting fractal is the *Koch snowflake*. The procedure for constructing the Koch snowflake also begins with an equilateral triangle whose sides are of length 1 unit.

At each stage, you remove the segment that is the middle third of each side and replace it with two outward-extending segments of the same length, creating new equilateral triangles on each side as shown in the diagrams below. The process continues indefinitely.

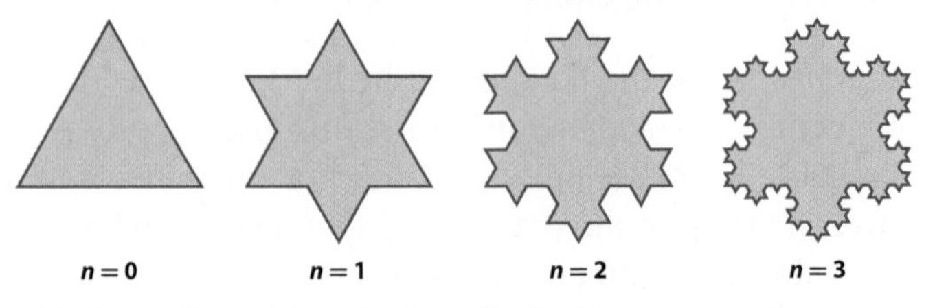

Find recursive and function formulas for the sequence of perimeters of the snowflake.

Unit 7

d. The temperature would be about 65°F, based on an increase of 4 chirps per minute for a 1°F increase in temperature and 80 chirps per minute at 60°F.

e. Using the recursive formula in Part b, $C_n = C_{n-1} + 4$, and a starting value of $n = 45$, corresponding to the beginning temperature value shown in the table, yields the following function formula: $C_n = 20 + 4(n - 45) = 4n - 160$. Substituting $n = 75$ gives $C_{75} = 140$, which is the same answer as in Part b.

f. Solving for n gives $n = \frac{C_n + 160}{4}$. So if $C_n = 100$, then $n = 65$, which is the same answer as in Part d.

3 **a.** The area of the initial triangle ($n = 0$) is $\frac{\sqrt{3}}{4}$. Each successive figure has area that is $\frac{3}{4}$ of the area of the previous figure. Thus, the formulas for the geometric sequence of areas are as follows.

Recursive formula: $A_n = \frac{3}{4}A_{n-1}$, $A_0 = \frac{\sqrt{3}}{4}$

Function formula: $A_n = \frac{\sqrt{3}}{4}\left(\frac{3}{4}\right)^n = \frac{3^n\sqrt{3}}{4^{n+1}}$

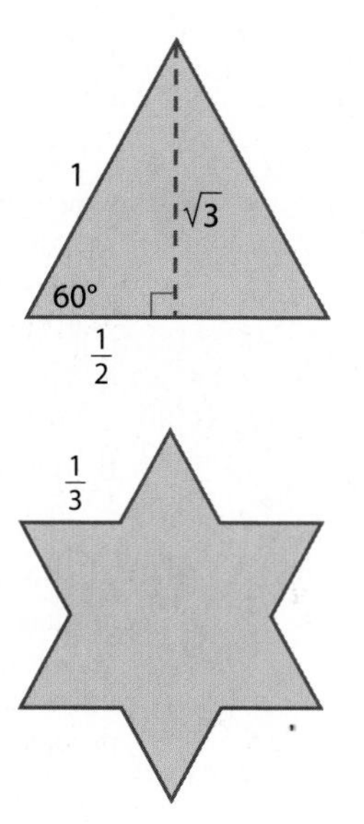

b. The perimeter of the initial "snowflake" is 3. The perimeter at $n = 1$ is $12\left(\frac{1}{3}\right) = 3\left(\frac{4}{3}\right)$. So, the perimeter of each succeeding figure is $\frac{4}{3}$ times the perimeter of the previous figure. Thus, the formulas for the geometric sequence of perimeters are as follows.

Recursive formula: $P_n = \frac{4}{3}P_{n-1}$, $P_0 = 3$

Function formula: $P_n = 3\left(\frac{4}{3}\right)^n$

4 *Glottochronology* is the study of changes in languages. Over time, certain words in a language are no longer used. In effect, they disappear from the language. Suppose a linguist examines a list of 500 words used in a language 1,000 years ago. Let $W(n)$ be the percentage of the words in this list that are still in use n years later, given as a decimal.

It is commonly assumed that $W(n)$ is proportional to $W(n - 1)$. Glottochronologists have determined that the constant of proportionality can be estimated to be about 0.99978. (Problem adapted from Sandefur, James T. *Discrete Dynamical Modeling*. Oxford, 1993, page 63.)

a. Find recursive and function formulas for this sequence.

b. According to this model, about how many of the 500 words are still in use today?

5 Irene has a sales job which pays her a monthly commission. She made $250 in her first month. Her supervisor tells her that she should be able to increase her commission income by 10% each month for the next year. For this task, assume that the supervisor's prediction is correct.

a. Find recursive and function formulas for the sequence of monthly commission income.

b. How much total commission income will Irene earn in her first ten months on the job?

6 As you complete this task, think about the defining characteristics of arithmetic and geometric sequences and how those characteristics are related to the sum of their terms. For each sequence below, determine if the sequence is arithmetic, geometric, or neither. Then find the sum of the indicated terms.

a. 13, 26, 52, 104, … , 6,656

b. 13, 12.25, 11.5, 10.75, … , 1

c. 1, 4, 9, 16, … , 225

d. 5, 4, 3.2, 2.56, … , 0.8388608

7 In this task, you will use the idea of sequential change to investigate the number of diagonals that can be drawn in a regular n-sided polygon.

a. Draw the first few regular n-gons and make a table showing the number of diagonals that can be drawn in each of them.

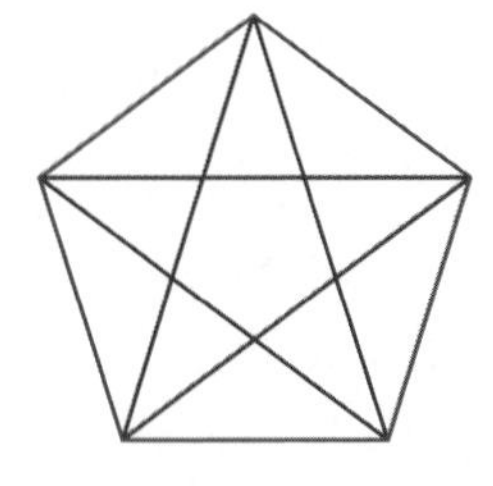

b. Determine a recursive formula for the number of diagonals that can be drawn in a regular n-gon.

4 a. This is a geometric sequence. The percentage of words in the list that are still in use n years later, expressed as a decimal, is given by the formulas below.
Recursive formula: $W(n) = (0.99978)W(n-1)$, $W(0) = 1$
Function formula: $W(n) = 1(0.99978^n)$

b. The number of words still in use is about $500(0.99978)^{1{,}000} = 401$.

5 a. Recursive formula: $I_n = 1.1I_{n-1}$, $I_1 = 250$
Function formula: $I_n = 250(1.1)^{n-1}$, where n is the number of months

b. $$\begin{aligned}\text{Total income} &= 250 + 250(1.1) + 250(1.1)^2 + \cdots + 250(1.1)^9 \\ &= 250(1 + 1.1 + 1.1^2 + \cdots + 1.1^9) \\ &= 250\left(\frac{1.1^{10} - 1}{1.1 - 1}\right) \\ &\approx \$3{,}984.36\end{aligned}$$

6 In order to use the formulas developed in this lesson for the sum of a sequence, students will first have to determine how long each sequence is. They may do this by solving equations, as shown below, or by computing and counting terms.

a. This sequence is a geometric sequence with $r = 2$ and initial value 13.

$$6{,}656 = 13(2^n)$$
$$512 = 2^n$$
$$9 = n$$
$$S_9 = 13\left(\frac{2^{10} - 1}{2 - 1}\right) = 13{,}299$$

b. This is an arithmetic sequence with $d = -0.75$ and initial value 13. Solving, $1 = 13 - 0.75n$, $n = 16$.

$$S_{16} = \frac{17(13 + 1)}{2} = 119$$

c. The sequence is neither arithmetic nor geometric, but it is described by $a_n = n^2$ if the subscripts start with 1 or by $a_n = (n - 1)^2$ if the subscripts start with 0. The sum of the indicated terms is 1,240.

d. The sequence is geometric with $r = 0.8$ and initial value 5.

$$0.8388608 = 5(0.8^n)$$
$$0.16777216 = 0.8^n$$
$$8 = n$$
$$S_8 = 5\left(\frac{0.8^9 - 1}{0.8 - 1}\right) = 21.6445568$$

TECHNOLOGY NOTE
In Task 6 Part d, students should individually decide whether to use calculations to find the sum of squares from 1 to 225 or calculator or spreadsheet lists. You might wish to have students share their methods with classmates.

7 a. **Regular n-gons**

Number of Sides	Number of Diagonals
3	0
4	2
5	5
6	9
7	14
8	20

b. $D_n = D_{n-1} + (n - 2)$

c. Use a finite differences table to find a function formula for the number of diagonals that can be drawn in a regular n-gon.

d. Find the number of diagonals in a regular 20-gon.

e. What other methods might you use to find a function formula for the sequence in Part a?

8 Use a finite differences table and matrices to find the function formula for the sequence given by $B_n = B_{n-1} + 3n$, with $B_0 = 2$.

Connections

9 In Applications Task 2, you may have established that the sequence of chirping frequencies for one species of cricket is approximately an arithmetic sequence with recursive formula

$$C_n = C_{n-1} + 4.$$

a. Plot the (*temperature, frequency*) data from the table on page 499. Find a regression equation that fits the data.

b. Using the equation from Part a, write a function formula for the sequence. Check that your formula generates the values given in the table for the chirping frequencies at temperatures of 47°F and 60°F.

10 In Course 2 Unit 8, *Probability Distributions*, you investigated the waiting-time distribution in the context of a modified Monopoly® game in which 36 students are in jail and a student must roll doubles to get out of jail.

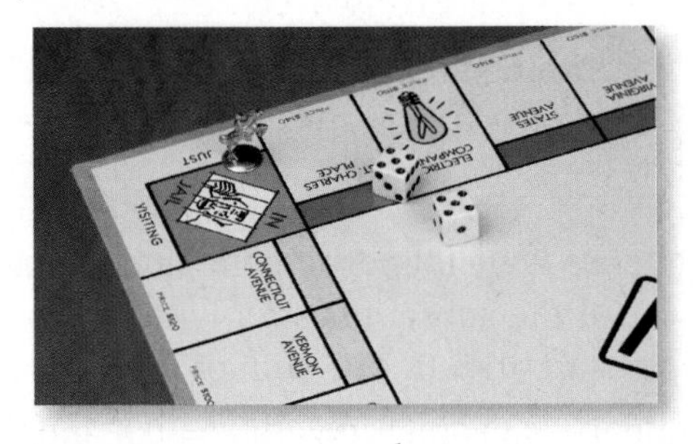

a. The probability of rolling doubles is $\frac{1}{6}$. Thus, the probability of getting out of jail on any given roll of the dice is $\frac{1}{6}$. What is the probability of remaining in jail on any given roll of the dice?

502 UNIT 7 • Recursion and Iteration

c. 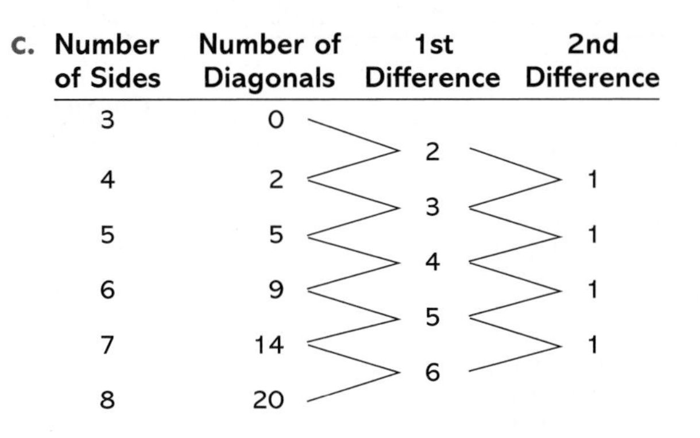

Number of Sides	Number of Diagonals	1st Difference	2nd Difference
3	0		
		2	
4	2		1
		3	
5	5		1
		4	
6	9		1
		5	
7	14		1
		6	
8	20		

The 2nd differences are constant, so the function formula is a quadratic function. Students might use quadratic regression or solve a matrix equation to find the function formula.

One matrix equation is $\begin{bmatrix} 9 & 3 & 1 \\ 16 & 4 & 1 \\ 25 & 5 & 1 \end{bmatrix}\begin{bmatrix} a \\ b \\ c \end{bmatrix} = \begin{bmatrix} 0 \\ 2 \\ 5 \end{bmatrix}$.

Solving gives $D_n = 0.5n^2 - 1.5n$.

d. The number of diagonals is D_{20}, which is $0.5(20)^2 - 1.5(20) = 170$.

e. Responses will depend on the method used in Part c. One could look for a pattern in the table and try to find a formula that describes the pattern. In fact, another (equivalent) formula is $D_n = \frac{n(n-3)}{2}$. One could also use quadratic regression or solve a system of linear equations.

8 The 2nd differences are constant (3), so the function formula is a quadratic function with the form $B_n = an^2 + bn + c$. Solve the system:

$$a + b + c = 5$$
$$4a + 2b + c = 11$$
$$9a + 3b + c = 20$$

The matrix equation is $\begin{bmatrix} 1 & 1 & 1 \\ 4 & 2 & 1 \\ 9 & 3 & 1 \end{bmatrix}\begin{bmatrix} a \\ b \\ c \end{bmatrix} = \begin{bmatrix} 5 \\ 11 \\ 20 \end{bmatrix}$.

The function formula is $B_n = an^2 + bn + c = 1.5n^2 + 1.5n + 2$.

Connections

9 **a.**

Linear regression equation: $y = -160.53 + 4.024x$

NOTE Solutions to Task 9 Part b and Task 10 Part a are on page T503.

b. Complete a copy of the following table. The waiting-time distribution refers to the first two columns, since you want to know how long a student has to wait to get out of jail. The last column provides important related information about the number of students still in jail.

Rolling Dice to Get Doubles

Number of Rolls to Get Doubles	Expected Number of Students Released on the Given Number of Rolls	Expected Number of Students Still in Jail
1	6	30
2	5	
3		
4		
5		

c. Consider the sequence of numbers in the last column.

i. Is the sequence an arithmetic or geometric sequence? Why?

ii. Determine the recursive and function formulas for the sequence. (Use 36 as the initial term of the sequence since that is the initial number of students in jail.)

iii. Use the formulas to find the expected number of students left in jail after 20 rolls.

d. Sketch a histogram for the waiting-time distribution shown in the first two columns.

i. Write a recursive formula that shows how the height of any given bar compares to the height of the previous bar.

ii. What kind of sequence is the sequence of bar heights?

e. A waiting-time distribution is also called a *geometric distribution*. Explain why the use of the word "geometric" for this type of distribution seems appropriate in terms of sequences.

11 In this lesson, you found function formulas for arithmetic and geometric sequences. In Lesson 1, you studied combined recursive formulas of the form $A_n = rA_{n-1} + b$. You can now use what you know about geometric sequences and their sums to find a function formula for such combined recursive formulas.

a. Complete the following list of terms for the combined recursive formula $A_n = rA_{n-1} + b$. Examine the list for patterns so that you can write a function formula for A_n.

$A_0 = A_0$
$A_1 = rA_0 + b$
$A_2 = rA_1 + b = r(rA_0 + b) + b = r^2A_0 + rb + b$
$A_3 = r(r^2A_0 + rb + b) + b = r^3A_0 + r^2b + rb + b$
$A_4 = ?$
$A_5 = ?$
$\vdots$
$A_n = ?$

Unit 7

b. Given this problem situation, it seems reasonable to round the coefficients of the equation in Part a to whole numbers. Thus, a function formula would be $C_n = -160 + 4n$. Evaluating this formula for 47°F and 60°F gives $C_{47} = -160 + 4(47) = 28$ and $C_{60} = -160 + 4(60) = 80$. These values match the values in the table. Students may also find a function formula for the sequence based on the recursive formula and using the methods in this unit to get $C_n = 4(n - 45) + 20$, which is equivalent to the rounded linear regression equation.

10 **a.** $P(\text{left in jail}) = \frac{5}{6}$

b. **Rolling Dice to Get Doubles**

Number of Rolls to Get Doubles	Expected Number of Students Released on the Given Number of Rolls	Expected Number of Students Still in Jail
1	6	30
2	5	25
3	4.17	20.83
4	3.47	17.36
5	2.89	14.47

c. **i.** It is a geometric sequence, since each entry is $\frac{5}{6}$ of the previous entry.

ii. Recursive formula: $J_n = \left(\frac{5}{6}\right)J_{n-1}$; $J_0 = 36$

Function formula: $J_n = 36\left(\frac{5}{6}\right)^n$

iii. $J_{20} = 0.94$ students left in jail

d.

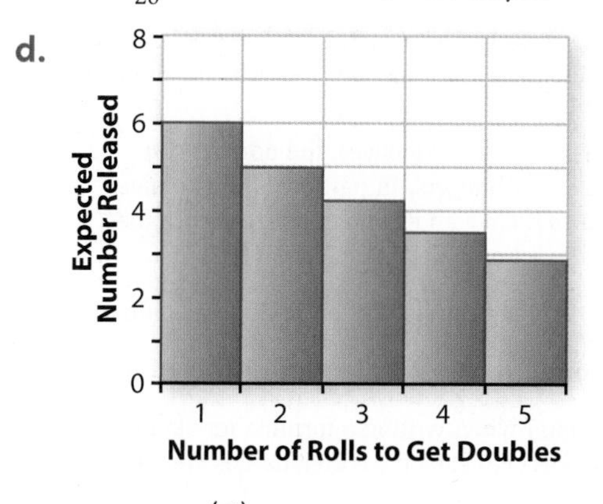

i. $H_n = \left(\frac{5}{6}\right)H_{n-1}$, $H_1 = 6$

ii. It is a geometric sequence with a constant multiplier of $\frac{5}{6}$, starting at 6.

e. "Geometric" seems appropriate to describe a waiting-time distribution, at least with reference to sequences, since the sequences that emerge from a waiting-time distribution are geometric sequences.

11 **a.** $A_4 = r(r^3A_0 + r^2b + rb + b) + b = r^4A_0 + r^3b + r^2b + rb + b$
$A_5 = r(r^4A_0 + r^3b + r^2b + rb + b) + b = r^5A_0 + r^4b + r^3b + r^2b + rb + b$
$A_n = r^nA_0 + r^{n-1}b + r^{n-2}b + \cdots + rb + b$

DIFFERENTIATION
This On Your Own task and others address the explicit formula for the fish population problem. See the Lesson 2 introduction for a list of relevant tasks.

b. The expression you have for A_n at the end of Part a is a function formula, but it can be simplified. To simplify, use what you know about the sum of the terms of a geometric sequence.

c. Now reconsider the combined recursive formula that modeled the fish-population problem in Lesson 1: $A_n = 0.8A_{n-1} + 1{,}000$, with $A_0 = 3{,}000$.

   i. Use the general function formula from Part b to write a function formula that models the fish population.

   ii. Now use this formula to find A_2 and A_{10}. Choose a year far in the future, and find the long-term population. Compare your results to those you found in Lesson 1, using other methods.

d. Suppose the combined recursive formula $A_n = rA_{n-1} + b$ represents year-to-year population change. Assume that r is a positive number less than 1. Use the function formula from Part b to explain why the long-term population in this situation is $\frac{b}{1-r}$. Use this fact to find the long-term population in the fish-population problem, and compare it to what you had previously found.

e. Compare the function formula you obtained in Part c to the one given in Connections Task 7 of Lesson 1, page 472. Explain and resolve any differences.

12 You have seen that a sequence can be represented with function notation. There is an even stronger connection between sequences and functions. In fact, a finite sequence can be defined as a function whose domain is the set $\{1, 2, \ldots, n\}$ and whose range is a set containing the terms of the sequence. For example, the sequence $7, 10, 13, \ldots, 7 + 3(n-1)$ can be defined as a function, s, from the set $\{1, 2, \ldots, n\}$ to the set $\{7, 10, 13, \ldots, 7 + 3(n-1)\}$, where $s(1) = 7$, $s(2) = 10$, ..., and $s(n) = 7 + 3(n-1)$.

a. Consider the sequence $3, 6, 12, 24, \ldots, 3(2)^{n-1}$. Describe how this sequence can be defined as a function. Describe the domain and range as sets.

b. When using functions to define sequences, the domain can actually be any finite set of integers. In particular, the domain might be $\{0, 1, 2, \ldots, n\}$. Give an example of a sequence that could be defined as a function whose domain is $\{0, 1, 2, \ldots, n\}$.

13 A series $a_0 + a_1 + a_2 + \cdots + a_n$ can be written in a more compact form using sigma notation as $\sum_{i=0}^{n} a_i$. You have previously used sigma notation (without subscripts) when writing a formula for standard deviation and when considering Pearson's correlation as well as other occasions.

a. Suppose $x_1, x_2, x_3, \ldots, x_n$ are sample data values. Use sigma notation with subscripts to write an expression for:

   i. the mean of this distribution.

   ii. the standard deviation of this distribution.

Unit 7

b. $r^{n-1}b + r^{n-2}b + \cdots + rb + b$ is the sum of a geometric sequence of n terms with initial term b and constant factor r. So, this part of A_n sums to $b\left(\frac{r^n - 1}{r - 1}\right)$. Thus, $A_n = r^n A_0 + b\left(\frac{r^n - 1}{r - 1}\right)$.

c. **i.** $A_n = 0.8^n(3{,}000) + (1{,}000)\left(\frac{0.8^n - 1}{0.8 - 1}\right)$

ii. $A_2 = (0.8^2)(3{,}000) + (1{,}000)\left(\frac{0.8^2 - 1}{0.8 - 1}\right) = 3{,}720$

$A_{10} = (0.8^{10})(3{,}000) + (1{,}000)\left(\frac{0.8^{10} - 1}{0.8 - 1}\right) = 4{,}785.25$

To find the long-term population, let n be a large number, such as 1,000. (When rounding to the hundredths place, n can be as low as 58 to round to the long-term population.)

$A_{1{,}000} = (0.8^{1{,}000})(3{,}000) + (1{,}000)\left(\frac{0.8^{1{,}000} - 1}{0.8 - 1}\right) = 5{,}000$

These values should match those obtained earlier.

d. Because $|r| < 1$, if you choose a very large value for n (corresponding to the long-term population), r^n will be very close to zero. Thus, $A_n = r^n A_0 + b\left(\frac{r^n - 1}{r - 1}\right) \approx 0 + b\left(\frac{0 - 1}{r - 1}\right) = \frac{-b}{r - 1} = \frac{b}{1 - r}$. If we apply this formula to the fish-population problem, we get $\frac{1{,}000}{1 - 0.8} = 5{,}000$. This is the same long-term population that we obtained in Part c.

e. These two formulas look different, but they are equivalent, as shown below.

$$\begin{aligned}
A_n &= 0.8^n(3{,}000) + (1{,}000)\left(\frac{0.8^n - 1}{0.8 - 1}\right) \\
&= 0.8^n(3{,}000) + \frac{1{,}000(0.8^n - 1)}{-0.2} \\
&= 0.8^n(3{,}000) - 5{,}000(0.8^n - 1) \\
&= 0.8^n(3{,}000) - 5{,}000(0.8^n) + 5{,}000 \\
&= -2{,}000(0.8^n) + 5{,}000
\end{aligned}$$

12 **a.** The sequence can be defined as a function t with domain $\{1, 2, \ldots, n\}$ and range $\{3, 6, \ldots, 3(2)^{n-1}\}$ such that $t(1) = 3$, $t(2) = 6, \ldots,$ and $t(n) = 3(2)^{n-1}$.

b. An example is the sequence 5, 9, 13, 17, ..., $5 + 4n$. This sequence can be defined as a function v with domain $\{0, 1, 2, \ldots, n\}$ and range $\{5, 9, 13, 17, \ldots, 5 + 4n\}$, where $v(0) = 5$, $v(1) = 9, \ldots,$ and $v(n) = 5 + 4n$. This case, where the domain has 0 as its least element instead of 1, corresponds to the situation where the initial subscript is 0 instead of 1.

13 **a.** **i.** $\dfrac{\sum_{i=1}^{n} x_i}{n}$

ii. $\sqrt{\dfrac{\sum_{i=1}^{n} (x_i - \bar{x})^2}{n}}$, where $\bar{x}$ is the mean of $x_1, x_2, \ldots, x_n$.

Unit 7

b. Write $\sum_{k=0}^{12} 3k$ in expanded form and then find the sum.

c. Write $\sum_{i=3}^{10} 2^i$ in expanded form and then find the sum.

d. Complete the formula below by determining the subscripts.

$$3 + 5 + 7 + 9 + 11 + 13 + 15 = \sum_{n=?}^{?} (2n + 1)$$

14 Below is the sequence from the Check Your Understanding task on page 504.

n	0	1	2	3	4	5	6	7	8	9	10	11
A_n	3	12	25	42	63	88	117	150	187	228	273	322

a. Produce a scatterplot of n versus A_n using a graphing calculator or computer software. Describe the shape of the graph. Which function family would best model this data pattern?

b. Find a regression equation that seems to best fit the scatterplot. Compare this equation to the function formula you derived in the Check Your Understanding task using a finite differences table. Describe and resolve any differences in the two solutions.

c. Do you think statistical regression methods will work to find a function formula for any sequence? Explain.

15 In Investigation 2, you considered two sequences related to the free fall of a sky diver: the sequence D_n of distance fallen *during* each second and the sequence T_n of total distance fallen *after* n seconds. Continue analyzing these sequences.

a. Use the information given in the Think About this Situation on page 482 to verify that the two sequences below, D_n and T_n, are accurate models if you assume Earth's gravity and no air resistance.

Distance Fallen (in feet)

n	D_n	T_n
1	16	16
2	48	64
3	80	144
4	112	256
5	144	400
6	176	576
7	208	784
8	240	1,024
9	272	1,296
10	304	1,600

b. Use a finite differences table to find a function formula that describes the sequence of total distance fallen.

b. $\sum_{k=0}^{12} 3k = 0 + 3 + 6 + 9 + 12 + 15 + 18 + 21 + 24 + 27 + 30 + 33 + 36$

$= \frac{13(36 + 0)}{2}$

$= 234$

c. $\sum_{i=3}^{10} 2^i = 2^3 + 2^4 + 2^5 + 2^6 + 2^7 + 2^8 + 2^9 + 2^{10} = \frac{8(2^8 - 1)}{2 - 1} = 2{,}040$

d. $3 + 5 + 7 + 9 + 11 + 13 + 15 = \sum_{n=1}^{7} (2n + 1)$

14 **a.** The rate of change is not constant, so a linear model is not a good choice. There is not a constant multiplier, so an exponential model is not a good choice. The graph could be a parabola, so a quadratic model would be appropriate to try.

A power model will fit well if the A_n data are shifted down by 3 so that the data go through the origin. (However, because many calculators compute a power model by using logarithms, students will get an undefined error unless they remove the (0, 0) point before trying to fit a power model.)

Then the 3 must again be added to the equation. Doing this yields a function that is a little too high at first and a little too low for the last few points. So, the best type of function in this situation is the quadratic function.

b. Using quadratic regression, the equation is $A_n = 2n^2 + 7n + 3$. This is the same formula found using finite differences.

c. Sequences can have many different patterns, but they also may be random. Many sequences do not have a function formula. So, statistical regression will clearly not work to find the function formula for any sequence. However, it can be a useful tool in many cases.

It is most useful when you already have a good idea about the pattern of the sequence, and that pattern is one that is included in the statistical regression options on calculators or computers. Then regression can be used to find the "best-fitting" model of a certain type (based on the criterion of least squares).

For example, in this task, after students suspect that the scatterplot is a parabola, they can use quadratic regression to find the best-fitting quadratic model. (Students continuing on to Course 4 will take a more technical look at how to use statistics to fit functions to data.)

15 **a.** To verify D_n, students can use the fact given in the Think About This Situation on page 482 that the sky diver will fall 32 feet farther each second. To verify T_n, they can find the total distance fallen up to that point by finding the sum $D_1 + D_2 + \cdots + D_n$.

NOTE The Solution to Task 15 Part b is on page T506.

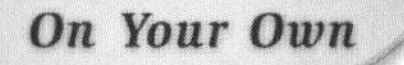

On Your Own

c. Use calculator- or computer-based regression methods to find a function formula relating total distance fallen to the number of seconds fallen.

d. For the Think About This Situation questions, you wrote recursive and function formulas for the sequence D_n. Note that each term (after the first) of T_n is the result of adding the corresponding term of D_n to the previous term of T_n. Use this fact to help you find a recursive formula for T_n.

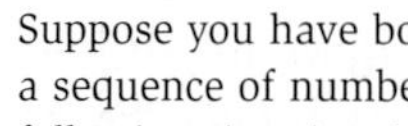

Reflections

16 Suppose you have both a recursive formula and a function formula for a sequence of numbers. Which formula would you use in each of the following situations? Why?

a. Suppose you want to find the 100th term of the sequence of numbers.

b. Suppose you want to find all of the first 100 terms of the sequence.

17 Describe one situation in your daily life or in the daily newspaper that could be modeled by a geometric sequence. Describe another situation that could be modeled by an arithmetic sequence.

18 The English economist Thomas Malthus (1766–1834) is best remembered for his assertion that *food supply grows arithmetically while population grows geometrically*. Do some research, and write a brief paper about this idea. Your essay should address the following questions.

- What is the meaning of Malthus' statement in terms of sequences you have studied?
- Do you think it is a reasonable statement?
- What are its consequences?
- Why has this statement been called "apocalyptic"?
- Have the events of the last 200 years borne out the statement?
- What can we learn from Malthus' statement even if it is not completely accurate?

19 In Problem 3 on page 497, you solved the matrix equation $AX = C$ to find the coefficients of a quadratic equation.

$$\text{You found that } A = \begin{bmatrix} 1 & 1 & 1 \\ 4 & 2 & 1 \\ 9 & 3 & 1 \end{bmatrix}.$$

Do you think this matrix will change if you work a similar problem that involves different data? Explain.

506 UNIT 7 • Recursion and Iteration

b.

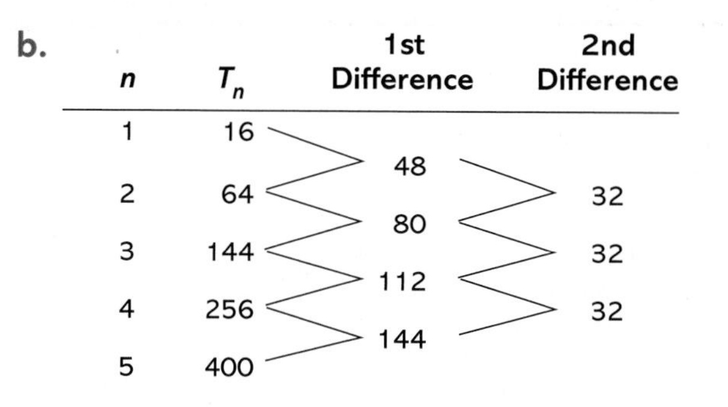

n	T_n	1st Difference	2nd Difference
1	16		
		48	
2	64		32
		80	
3	144		32
		112	
4	256		32
		144	
5	400		

$$\begin{bmatrix} 1 & 1 & 1 \\ 4 & 2 & 1 \\ 9 & 3 & 1 \end{bmatrix} \begin{bmatrix} a \\ b \\ c \end{bmatrix} = \begin{bmatrix} 16 \\ 64 \\ 144 \end{bmatrix}$$

Since the 2nd differences are the same, the function formula is quadratic. Solving the matrix equation at the right gives $a = 16$, $b = 0$, and $c = 0$. Thus, the function formula is $T_n = 16n^2$.

c. Using quadratic regression will also give $T_n = 16n^2$.

d. A recursive formula for T_n is $T_n = T_{n-1} + D_n = T_{n-1} + (32n - 16)$. (See the notes for the Think About This Situation on page 482 for further discussion of this formula.)

Reflections

16 **a.** The function formula is a more efficient way to find the 100th term of the sequence. It involves only one application of a formula rather than 100 applications of the recursive formula.

b. The recursive formula is more suitable for finding all of the first 100 terms since it is designed to compute terms one after the other and is easily implemented with technology such as a calculator or spreadsheet.

17 Responses will vary. The height of a bouncing ball dropped from a certain height could be modeled by a geometric sequence. An exercise program for which you add 10 minutes per week to an exercise routine until you reach 6 hours per week would be modeled by an arithmetic sequence.

18 Responses will vary. Arithmetic sequences grow slowly and steadily, while geometric sequences grow very quickly once they get started. Thus, if food supply growth is arithmetic and population growth is geometric, there will come a time when population growth far outpaces the food supply available to support the population. This would be an "apocalyptic" situation, with mass starvation due to lack of food.

Although there are countries that experience famine and severe starvation, this situation of mass starvation due to global lack of food has not happened. Nevertheless, the comparison of arithmetic growth to geometric growth, particularly where population growth or even compound interest is concerned, is an important perspective that is useful for understanding the changing world in which we live.

19 The matrix A will always be the same in quadratic situations when using 1, 2, and 3 as values for n. This observation allows us to solve similar problems by immediately using matrix A, without going through the derivation each time.

Extensions

20 In this unit, you have investigated recursive formulas and sequences that can be modeled by *NOW-NEXT* formulas. This means that to find *NEXT*, you need to use only *NOW*, one step before *NEXT*. However, there are sequences for which finding *NEXT* requires using more than one step before *NEXT*. One of the most famous sequences of this type is called the *Fibonacci sequence*, named after the mathematician who first studied the sequence, Leonardo Fibonacci (c. 1175–c. 1250).

a. Here is the Fibonacci sequence: 1, 1, 2, 3, 5, 8, 13, 21, 34, 55, 89, 144, … . Using the words *NEXT*, *NOW*, and *PREVIOUS*, describe the pattern of the sequence.

b. Let F_{n+1} represent *NEXT*. Use F_{n+1}, F_n, and F_{n-1} to write a recursive formula for the Fibonacci sequence.

c. A recursive formula for a sequence similar to the Fibonacci sequence is $A_n = 2A_{n-1} - A_{n-2}$.

i. Why can't you list the terms of this sequence?

ii. Choose two initial values, and list the first six terms of the sequence. Then choose different initial values, and list the first six terms of the sequence. Compare the two sequences. Describe any patterns you see.

iii. Write a recursive formula for this sequence that uses only A_n, A_{n-1}, A_1, and A_0.

d. Consider the sequence given by $A_n = A_{n-1} + A_{n-2} + 7A_{n-3}$. Choose some initial values. List the first six terms of this sequence.

e. The Fibonacci sequence has many interesting patterns and shows up in the most amazing places. In the photo at the right, the flower has 34 spirals in the counterclockwise direction and 21 in the clockwise direction. These two numbers are successive terms in the Fibonacci sequence. Sunflowers and pine cones also have spirals with numbers from the Fibonacci sequence, as do many other things in nature.

In fact, entire books and journals have been written about this sequence. Find an article or book about the Fibonacci sequence. Write a brief report on one of its patterns or applications.

Extensions

20 **a.** *NEXT* = *NOW* + *PREVIOUS*

b. $F_{n+1} = F_n + F_{n-1}$

c. **i.** You cannot list the terms with the information given because you do not have the initial terms.

ii. Two initial values are needed. Students' choices of initial values will vary.

For initial values 2 and 4, the sequence is 2, 4, 6, 8, 10, 12, … .
For initial values 1 and 5, the sequence is 1, 5, 9, 13, 17, 21, … .

Both of the sequences are arithmetic, and the common difference is the difference between the two initial values.

iii. An equivalent recursive form is $A_n = A_{n-1} + (A_1 - A_0)$.

d. Three initial values are needed. For example, if the first three terms are 1, 3, and 8, then the first six terms are 1, 3, 8, 18, 47, and 121.

e. The following are good resources on the Fibonacci sequence.

Barnard, Jane. "Those fascinating fibonaccis!" Student Math Notes in the *NCTM News Bulletin*, January 1996.

Garland, Trudi Hammel. *Fascinating Fibonaccis: Mystery and Magic in Numbers*. Palo Alto, CA: Dale Seymour Publications, 1987.

Hoggatt, Verner E., Jr. *Fibonacci and Lucas Numbers.* Boston: Houghton-Mifflin Publishing Co., 1969.

On Your Own

21 In Investigation 2, you found formulas for the sum of a finite number of terms of a geometric sequence. A sequence can also have an infinite number of terms. It is possible to mathematically analyze the sum of an infinite number of terms. Consider this sequence.

$$\frac{1}{2}, \frac{1}{4}, \frac{1}{8}, \frac{1}{16}, \ldots, \frac{1}{2^n}, \ldots$$

a. Explain why this is a geometric sequence. Find recursive and function formulas for this sequence.

b. Find a formula for the sum of the terms up through $\frac{1}{2^n}$.

c. This sequence has infinitely many terms. Does the geometric model of this sequence shown below suggest what the infinite sum of all the terms of the sequence might be?

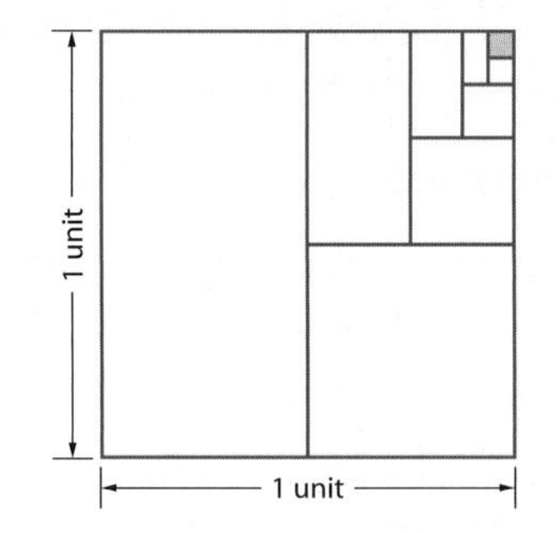

d. A mathematical analysis of infinite sums involves thinking about what happens to the sum of n terms as n gets very large. Examine the formula for the sum of terms up through $\frac{1}{2^n}$ from Part b. What happens to this formula as n gets very large? Your answer should give you the infinite sum.

e. Consider a general geometric sequence with terms t_n and common multiplier r. Suppose that $0 < r < 1$. Determine a general formula for the infinite sum by considering what happens to the finite sum formula if n is very large.

f. Use the general infinite sum formula for $0 < r < 1$ from Part e to find the infinite sum of the sequence $\frac{1}{2}, \frac{1}{4}, \frac{1}{8}, \frac{1}{16}, \ldots, \frac{1}{2^n}, \ldots$. Compare the sum to your answer for Part d.

g. Construct a geometric sequence of your choice with $0 < r < 1$. Use the general infinite sum formula from Part e to find the infinite sum.

508 UNIT 7 • Recursion and Iteration

21 **a.** This is a geometric sequence because there is a common ratio of $\frac{1}{2}$.

Recursive formula: $a_n = \frac{1}{2}a_{n-1}$, $a_1 = \frac{1}{2}$

Function formula: $a_n = \left(\frac{1}{2}\right)^n$

b. A formula for the sum of the terms of the finite geometric sequence up through $\frac{1}{2}n$ is $\frac{1}{2} + \frac{1}{4} + \frac{1}{8} + \cdots + \frac{1}{2^n} = \frac{1}{2}\left[1 + \frac{1}{2} + \frac{1}{4} + \cdots + \left(\frac{1}{2}\right)^{n-1}\right]$

$$= \frac{1}{2}\left(\frac{1 - \left(\frac{1}{2}\right)^n}{1 - \frac{1}{2}}\right)$$

$$= 1 - \left(\frac{1}{2}\right)^n$$

c. It requires some delicate mathematics to make sense of adding infinitely many terms. The theory of infinite limits provides the necessary mathematical machinery. In this task, students will get just a taste of that theory. Intuition can be misleading when it comes to thinking about infinity, so the conjectures that students make may vary considerably. Some may think that the sum must be infinite since infinitely many terms are added. Others may think that there is some finite sum. However, by looking at the square, they should be able to reason that the sum will be 1.

d. Let $S_n = \frac{1}{2} + \frac{1}{4} + \frac{1}{8} + \cdots + \frac{1}{2^n}$. Then, from Part b, $S_n = 1 - \left(\frac{1}{2}\right)^n$.

If n is very large in the formula $S_n = 1 - \left(\frac{1}{2}\right)^n$, then $\left(\frac{1}{2}\right)^n$ becomes almost 0 and S_n becomes very close to 1. Thus, we take 1 to be the sum of all the (infinitely many) terms of the sequence.

e. Let $S_n = t_1 + t_2 + t_3 + \cdots + t_n$. Then, $S_n = t_1 + rt_1 + r^2t_1 + \cdots + r^{n-1}t_1$

$$= t_1(1 + r + r^2 + \cdots + r^{n-1})$$

$$= t_1\left(\frac{1 - r^n}{1 - r}\right).$$

If n is very large and $0 < r < 1$, then r^n gets very close to 0, and S_n becomes very close to $\frac{t_1}{1 - r}$. Thus, $S = \frac{t_1}{1 - r}$ is a formula for the sum of the terms in an infinite geometric sequence $\{t_n\}$ when $0 < r < 1$.

In words, the sum of the terms in an infinite geometric sequence is $\frac{\textit{initial term}}{1 - \textit{common ratio}}$ if the common ratio is between 0 and 1.

f. Using the formula in Part e, the sum of the terms in the infinite geometric sequence given at the beginning of this task is $\frac{\frac{1}{2}}{1 - \frac{1}{2}} = 1$.

This is the same answer as that found in Part d.

g. Responses will vary, depending on sequences. Consider the sequence $4, \frac{8}{3}, \frac{16}{9}, \frac{32}{27}, \ldots$, where the common ratio is $\frac{2}{3}$. The sum of the infinitely many terms is $\frac{4}{1 - \frac{2}{3}} = 12$.

Unit 7

22 Extensions Task 21 involved infinite geometric sums. Infinite sums lead to some surprising results. Consider a figure that consists of the rectangles of width 1 and height $\frac{1}{2^n}$ arranged as shown below.

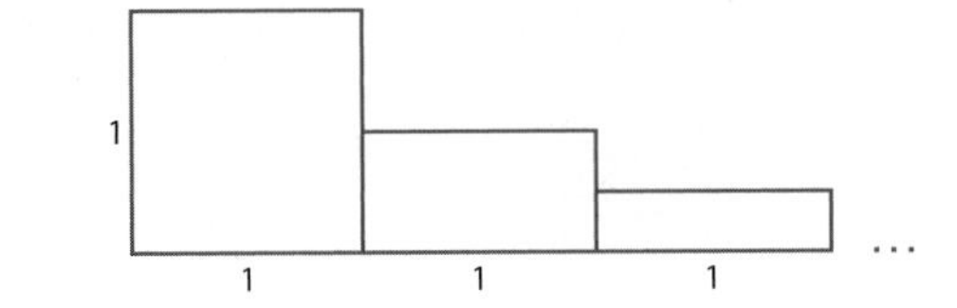

There are infinitely many rectangles that comprise this figure. Do you think it is possible for a figure to have finite area but infinite perimeter? Explain using this particular figure.

23 Oranges are one of the most popular foods during Chinese New Year. During the New Year celebration, you may find them in many homes stacked on a platter in the shape of a pyramid with a square base. The number of oranges in such a stack depends on the number of layers in the stack.

a. Complete a table like the one below.

Pyramid of Oranges

Number of Layers in a Stack	0	1	2	3	4	5	6
Number of Oranges in a Stack	0	1	5				

b. Find a recursive formula for the sequence of number of oranges in a stack.

c. Use a finite differences table to find a function formula for the sequence of number of oranges in a stack. How many oranges are in a stack with 15 layers?

24 In Investigation 3, you used a finite differences table to find a function formula for certain sequences. You used the fact that the function formula for a sequence is a quadratic if and only if the 2nd differences in a finite differences table are constant. In this task, you will prove that fact.

a. Suppose a sequence has a quadratic function formula: $A_n = an^2 + bn + c$. Construct a finite differences table. Verify that the 2nd differences are constant. Describe any relationship you see between the constant 2nd differences and the function formula.

b. Now, conversely, suppose the 2nd differences are constant. Provide an argument for why the function formula is a quadratic.

22 The area of the figure can be represented by the infinite sum $1 + \frac{1}{2} + \cdots + \frac{1}{2^n} + \cdots$. From Extensions Task 21 Part e, we know that this sum is $\frac{1}{1 - \frac{1}{2}} = 2$.

An expression for the perimeter can be derived in several ways. One way is to think of the figure already completely drawn. In this case, the perimeter can be represented by the length of the vertical side on the left, 1, then, for each rectangle, add 1 + 1 for the parallel horizontal sides of unit length, plus the right side length, which is one-half of the full side length. Thus, the perimeter can be represented by the sum $1 + 2 + \frac{1}{2} + 2 + \frac{1}{4} + 2 + \frac{1}{8} + \cdots$.

Or, the perimeter can be represented by thinking about adding rectangles one by one. The first rectangle all by itself has perimeter 4. With the next rectangle added, the perimeter of the new figure is 4 + 2, since you have added two unit-length horizontal sides, lost one-half of the left side and regained that length on the right side. Similarly, when the next rectangle is added, the perimeter of the new figure is 4 + 2 + 2. In general, if $P(n)$ is the perimeter of the figure with n rectangles, then $P(n) = P(n - 1) + 2$, with $P(1) = 4$. The explicit formula is $P(n) = 2(n + 1)$.

Using either representation of the perimeter, it is clear that the perimeter of the figure with infinitely many rectangles is infinite. The area is finite since the sum representing the area is 2. Thus, the area is finite, but the perimeter is infinite. Students may have a hard time believing that this can be the case, and, in any case, they should be amazed.

23 **a. Pyramid of Oranges**

Number of Layers in a Stack	0	1	2	3	4	5	6
Number of Oranges in a Stack	0	1	5	14	30	55	91

b. $U_n = U_{n-1} + n^2$

c.

Number of Layers	Number of Oranges	1st Difference	2nd Difference	3rd Difference
0	0			
		1		
1	1		3	
		4		2
2	5		5	
		9		2
3	14		7	
		16		2
4	30		9	
		25		2
5	55		11	
		36		
6	91			

Since the 3rd differences are constant, the general form of the function formula for the number t_n of oranges in a stack will be:

$$t_n = an^3 + bn^2 + cn + d$$
$$t_0 = 0 = d$$
$$t_1 = 1 = a + b + c + d = a + b + c$$
$$t_2 = 5 = 8a + 4b + 2c + d = 8a + 4b + 2c$$
$$t_3 = 14 = 27a + 9b + 3c + d = 27a + 9b + 3c$$

So, one matrix equation is $\begin{bmatrix} 1 & 1 & 1 \\ 8 & 4 & 2 \\ 27 & 9 & 3 \end{bmatrix}\begin{bmatrix} a \\ b \\ c \end{bmatrix} = \begin{bmatrix} 1 \\ 5 \\ 14 \end{bmatrix}$. Solving this equation gives $a = \frac{1}{3}$, $b = \frac{1}{2}$, and $c = \frac{1}{6}$. So, the function formula is $t_n = \frac{1}{3}n^3 + \frac{1}{2}n^2 + \frac{1}{6}n$. There are 1,240 oranges in a stack with 15 layers.

INSTRUCTIONAL NOTE
The arguments in Parts a and b of Task 24 are not complete proofs. Students could be encouraged to complete the proof in Part a by extending the finite differences table to include n, $n + 1$, and $n + 2$. The argument in Part b is not a complete proof since we have not proven that the pattern generalizations are correct. Completing this proof by using mathematical induction, for example, is beyond the scope of this book.

24 **a.**

n	A_n	1st Difference	2nd Difference
0	c		
		$a + b$	
1	$a + b + c$		$2a$
		$3a + b$	
2	$4a + 2b + c$		$2a$
		$5a + b$	
3	$9a + 3b + c$		$2a$
		$7a + b$	
4	$16a + 4b + c$		

Note that the 2nd differences are constant. Also note that the 2nd difference is twice the leading coefficient of the polynomial.

b. Suppose the 2nd differences are a constant k. Thus, $(A_{n+2} - A_{n+1}) - (A_{n+1} - A_n) = k$. So, $A_{n+2} = 2A_{n+1} - A_n + k$.

Now we will use this fact to find a function formula for A_n and see if it is quadratic. To do this, we will list the terms of the sequence and look for a pattern.

A_0
A_1
$A_2 = 2A_1 - A_0 + k$ (using the equation above)
$A_3 = 2(2A_1 - A_0 + k) - A_1 + k = 3A_1 - 2A_0 + 3k$
$A_4 = \cdots = 4A_1 - 3A_0 + 6k$
$A_5 = \cdots = 5A_1 - 4A_0 + 10k$
$\vdots$
$A_n = nA_1 - (n - 1)A_0 + \frac{n(n-1)}{2}k$
(by generalizing the patterns seen in A_2 through A_5; the pattern for the coefficient of k looks like 3, 6, 10, … , which appears to generalize to $\frac{n(n-1)}{2}$ in the A_n term)
$A_n = \frac{k}{2}n^2 + \left(A_1 - A_0 - \frac{k}{2}\right)n + A_0$
This last equation is a function formula for A_n, and it is quadratic. Thus, we have argued that if the 2nd differences are constant, then the function formula is quadratic.

Teacher Notes

On Your Own

25 Recall the bowhead whale situation from Applications Task 4 in Lesson 1. A status report on the bowhead whales of Alaska estimated that the 1993 population of these whales was between 6,900 and 9,200 and that the difference between births and deaths yielded an annual growth rate of about 3.1%. No hunting of bowhead whales is allowed, except that Alaskan Inuit are allowed to take, or harvest, about 50 bowhead whales each year for their livelihood. (Source: nmml.afsc.noaa.gov/CetaceanAssessment/ bowhead/bmsos.htm)

a. Use 1993 as the initial year, Year 0. The initial population is a range of values, rather than a single value. Specifically, the range of initial population values is 6,900 to 9,200. Let $L(n)$ be the lower population value in the range of values in year n. Similarly, let $H(n)$ be the higher population value in the range of values in year n. Find recursive formulas for $L(n)$ and $H(n)$.

b. Find a recursive formula and a function formula for $S(n) = H(n) - L(n)$. Describe how the size of the population range changes over time.

c. The recursive formulas for $H(n)$ and $L(n)$ that you found in Part a are combined recursive formulas of the form $A_n = rA_{n-1} + b$. Thus, as in Connections Task 11 (page 503), it is possible to find a function formula for $H(n)$ and $L(n)$ by listing the terms and summing a geometric series. This yields the following formulas.

$$L(n) = 1.031^n(6{,}900) - 50\left(\frac{1.031^n - 1}{1.031 - 1}\right)$$

$$H(n) = 1.031^n(9{,}200) - 50\left(\frac{1.031^n - 1}{1.031 - 1}\right)$$

Verify that the above two formulas can be transformed to the two equivalent formulas below.

$$L(n) = 1.031^n\left(6{,}900 - \frac{50}{0.031}\right) + \left(\frac{50}{0.031}\right)$$

$$H(n) = 1.031^n\left(9{,}200 - \frac{50}{0.031}\right) + \left(\frac{50}{0.031}\right)$$

d. In Part b, you considered the difference between the higher and lower values of the population range. Now consider the ratio of the higher value to the lower value.

i. Use the recursive formulas in Part a, along with a spreadsheet or other technology tool, to create a table of values for the ratio of higher value to lower value. Describe any patterns that you see in the table, particularly the long-term trend.

ii. Use the formulas in Part c to construct a function formula for the ratio of higher values to lower values. Estimate the formula if n is very, very large. Use the formula to predict the long-term trend in the ratios. Compare it to the trend that you observed above in part i. Explain any similarities and differences.

Unit 7

510 UNIT 7 • Recursion and Iteration

25 **a.** Recursive formulas for the lower and higher population range values:

$L(n) = 1.031L(n - 1) - 50$, with $L(0) = 6{,}900$
$H(n) = 1.031H(n - 1) - 50$, with $H(0) = 9{,}200$

b. Recursive formula:

$$\begin{aligned} S(n) &= H(n) - L(n) \\ &= [1.031 \cdot H(n-1) - 50] - [1.031 \cdot L(n-1) - 50] \\ &= 1.031[H(n-1) - L(n-1)] \\ &= 1.031 \cdot S(n-1), \text{ with } S(0) = 2{,}300 \end{aligned}$$

Function formula: $S(n) = 1.031^n(2{,}300)$

The size of the population range increases over time (as n increases without bound, $S(n)$ increases without bound).

c. $$\begin{aligned} L(n) &= 1.031^n(6{,}900) - 50\left(\frac{1.031^n - 1}{1.031 - 1}\right) \\ &= 1.031^n(6{,}900) - \frac{50}{0.031}(1.031^n - 1) \\ &= 1.031^n\left(6{,}900 - \frac{50}{0.031}\right) + \left(\frac{50}{0.031}\right) \end{aligned}$$

d. **i.** A spreadsheet would be a good tool to use. Use a large number of significant digits so that round-off error does not spoil the results. The initial ratio is $\frac{4}{3}$. The ratios get larger over time. After a very large number of years, the ratio is about 1.43502135.

ii. A function formula for the ratio is:

$$\frac{H(n)}{L(n)} = \frac{1.031^n\left(9{,}200 - \frac{50}{0.031}\right) + \left(\frac{50}{0.031}\right)}{1.031^n\left(6{,}900 - \frac{50}{0.031}\right) + \left(\frac{50}{0.031}\right)}$$

For very large values of n this becomes (in the limit)

$$\frac{\left(9{,}200 - \frac{50}{0.031}\right)}{\left(6{,}900 - \frac{50}{0.031}\right)} \approx 1.43502135.$$

Alternatively, students might just evaluate the ratio using a very large value of n without trying to take a limit. In either case, the long-term trend shown in this computation may not be exactly the same as the trend seen in the spreadsheet computation using recursive formulas in part i because of round-off errors.

ASSIGNMENT NOTE
It would be helpful to review the solutions to Applications Task 4 in Lesson 1 on page 470 prior to assigning Extensions Task 25.

INSTRUCTIONAL NOTE
Help students cultivate the symbolic sense to recognize that showing the two forms of $H(n)$ are equivalent is simply the same process they just used with 6,900 replaced by 9,200. You could value this by providing extra credit when students recognize it.

Review

26 Rewrite each quadratic expression in vertex form.

a. $x^2 + 8x + 10$

b. $x^2 - 18x - 6$

c. $x^2 + 3x - 9$

27 In 2005, approximately 31% of people 65 or older in the United States used the Internet. Suppose that in 2005, Nate randomly selected 150 people in the United States who were 65 or older.

a. How many of these people do you expect to say that they used the Internet?

b. Is the binomial distribution approximately normal?

c. What is the standard deviation of this distribution? What does it tell you?

d. Would you be surprised to find that 60 of the people in Nate's survey said that they used the Internet? Explain your reasoning.

e. Use a standardized value to estimate the probability that only 40 of the people in Nate's study used the Internet.

28 Consider the statement: If quadrilateral *ABCD* is a parallelogram, then $\overline{BD}$ divides the quadrilateral into two congruent triangles.

a. Is this a true statement? If yes, prove the statement. If not, provide a counterexample.

b. Write the converse of this statement.

c. Is the converse true? If yes, provide a proof. If not, provide a counterexample.

29 Write each product or quotient of rational expressions in equivalent form as a single algebraic fraction. Then simplify the result as much as possible.

a. $\frac{5x}{x+4} \cdot \frac{3x+12}{x^3}$

b. $\frac{x-4}{2} \cdot \frac{6}{4-x}$

c. $\frac{x^2+x}{5} \div \frac{2x+2}{15}$

d. $\frac{12x-6}{x+1} \div \frac{6x-3}{x}$

Review

26 a. $(x + 4)^2 - 6$

b. $(x - 9)^2 - 87$

c. $\left(x + \frac{3}{2}\right)^2 - \frac{45}{4}$

27 a. $(0.31)(150) = 46.5 \approx 47$ people

b. Since $(0.31)(150)$ and $(0.69)(150)$ are both greater than 10, the binomial distribution will be approximately normal.

c. $\sigma = \sqrt{np(1 - p)} = \sqrt{150(0.31)(0.69)} \approx 5.66$. This tells us that in a random 2005 sample of 150 people in the United States who were 65 or older, about 68% of the time you will find that between $46.5 - 5.66 = 40.84$ and $46.5 + 5.66 = 52.16$ of the people will have used the Internet. Students might also indicate that about 95% of the time, between $46.5 - 2(5.66) = 35.18$ and $46.5 + 2(5.66) = 57.82$ people will have used the Internet.

d. Yes because 60 is more than two standard deviations above the mean.

e. $z = \frac{40 - 46.5}{5.66} = \frac{-6.5}{5.66} \approx -1.148$

Using the table of standardized values (in Unit 4 on page 245), the probability is about 0.1357.

28 a. This is a true statement. $\overline{DA} \cong \overline{BC}$ and $\overline{AB} \cong \overline{CD}$ because they are opposite sides of the parallelogram. Also, $\overline{DB}$ is a side of each triangle. So, the triangles are congruent by the SSS Triangle Congruence condition.

b. If $\overline{BD}$ divides quadrilateral *ABCD* into two congruent triangles, then *ABCD* is a parallelogram.

c. The converse is false. Consider a kite as shown below.

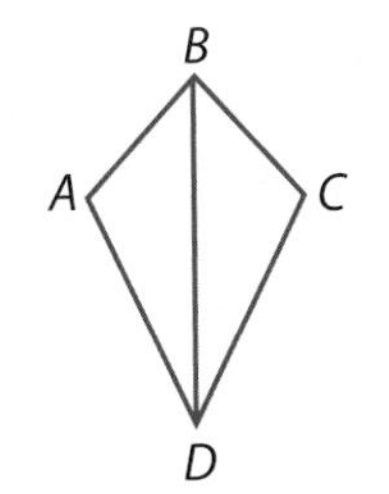

29 a. $\frac{5x}{x + 4} \cdot \frac{3x + 12}{x^3} = \frac{5x(3x + 12)}{x^3(x + 4)} = \frac{15x(x + 4)}{x^3(x + 4)} = \frac{15}{x^2}$

b. $\frac{x - 4}{2} \cdot \frac{6}{4 - x} = \frac{6(x - 4)}{2(4 - x)} = -3$

c. $\frac{x^2 + x}{5} \div \frac{2x + 2}{15} = \frac{15(x^2 + x)}{5(2x + 2)} = \frac{15x(x + 1)}{10(x + 1)} = \frac{3x}{2}$

d. $\frac{12x - 6}{x + 1} \div \frac{6x - 3}{x} = \frac{x(12x - 6)}{(x + 1)(6x - 3)} = \frac{6x(2x - 1)}{3(x + 1)(2x - 1)} = \frac{2x}{x + 1}$

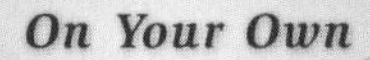

30 Find the solution set for each inequality. Represent the solution set using a number line, symbols, and interval notation.

a. $x^2 - 5x > x + 7$ **b.** $\frac{4}{x} > 3 - x$

31 The spinner below is used at the community fair in Lennox each year. The spinner is divided into eight equal sections. Suppose Sonia buys two spins of the spinner.

a. What is the probability that she will not win a prize?

b. What is the probability that she will win two cookies?

c. What is the probability that she will win a cookie and a drink?

d. What is the probability that she will win two drinks?

32 In the triangle below, $\overline{DE} \parallel \overline{BC}$.

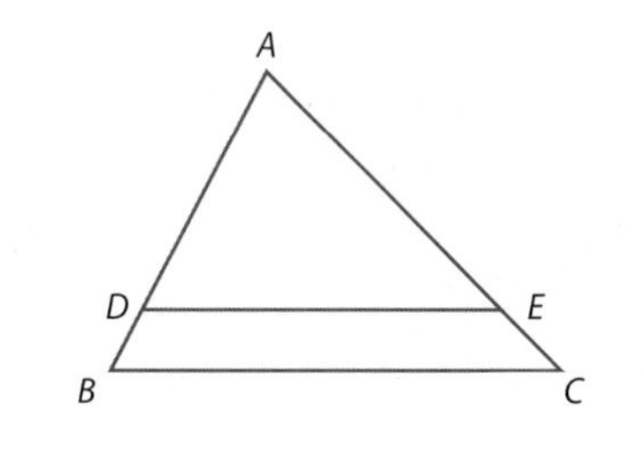

a. Explain why $\frac{AB}{AD} = \frac{AC}{AE}$.

b. Suppose that $AD = 10$ cm, $AB = 12$ cm, and $AE = 15$ cm. Find AC and EC.

c. For the lengths in Part b, is it the case that $\frac{DB}{AD} = \frac{EC}{AE}$?

d. Provide reasons for each step in the proof below that Jamal wrote to show that $\frac{DB}{AD} = \frac{EC}{AE}$ is always true given $\overline{DE} \parallel \overline{BC}$. His proof begins with the result from Part a.

$$\frac{AB}{AD} = \frac{AC}{AE}$$

$$\frac{AD + DB}{AD} = \frac{AE + EC}{AE}$$

$$1 + \frac{DB}{AD} = 1 + \frac{EC}{AE}$$

$$\frac{DB}{AD} = \frac{EC}{AE}$$

e. Suppose that $AD = 8$ ft, $DB = 2$ ft, and $AE = 18$ ft. How long is $\overline{EC}$?

Unit 7

512 UNIT 7 • Recursion and Iteration

a. $x^2 - 5x = x + 7$
$x^2 - 6x - 7 = 0$
$(x - 7)(x + 1) = 0$
$x = -1$ or $x = 7$

Thus, the solution for
$x^2 - 5x > x + 7$ is $(-\infty, -1) \cup (7, \infty)$.

b. $\frac{4}{x} = 3 - x$
$4 = 3x - x^2$
$x^2 - 3x + 4 = 0$
$x = \frac{3}{2} \pm \frac{\sqrt{9 - 4(1)(4)}}{2}$
$x = \frac{3}{2} \pm \frac{\sqrt{-7}}{2}$
No real solutions

This indicates that the graphs of $y = \frac{4}{x}$ and $y = 3 - x$ do not intersect.

But by considering the graphs, we can see that for $x > 0$, $\frac{4}{x} > 3 - x$.

So, the solution set is $x > 0$. $(0, \infty)$.

31 **a.** $P(\textit{no prize at all}) = P(\textit{no prize 1st spin}) \cdot P(\textit{no prize 2nd spin})$
$= \frac{3}{8} \cdot \frac{3}{8}$
$= \frac{9}{64}$

b. $P(\textit{2 cookies}) = P(\textit{cookie 1st spin}) \cdot P(\textit{cookie 2nd spin})$
$= \frac{1}{4} \cdot \frac{1}{4}$
$= \frac{1}{16}$

c. $P(\textit{cookie and drink}) = P(\textit{cookie 1st spin}) \cdot P(\textit{drink 2nd spin}) + P(\textit{drink 1st spin}) \cdot P(\textit{cookie 2nd spin})$
$= \frac{1}{4} \cdot \frac{3}{8} + \frac{3}{8} \cdot \frac{1}{4}$
$= \frac{6}{32}$

d. $P(\textit{2 drinks}) = P(\textit{drink 1st spin}) \cdot P(\textit{drink 2nd spin})$
$= \frac{3}{8} \cdot \frac{3}{8}$
$= \frac{9}{64}$

Unit 7

NOTE Solutions to Task 32 are on page T513.

33 The arch above the portion of a door shown at the right is part of a circular region bounded by a chord and part of a circle. The chord is 40 inches long and the height of the arch is 8 inches. The radius of the circle that forms $\widehat{AB}$ is 29 inches. What is the measure of $\widehat{AB}$?

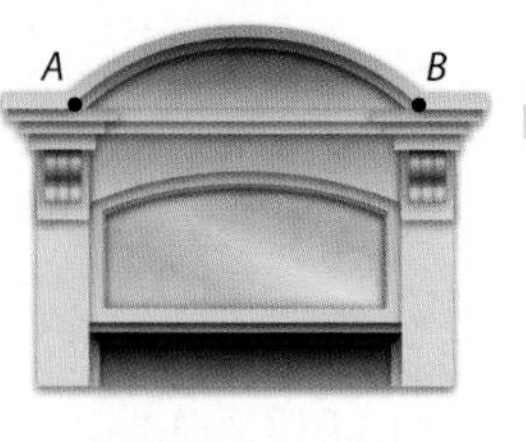

U07-004A-877261

34 Determine the number and type (integer, noninteger rational, irrational, or nonreal complex) of solutions for each quadratic equation.

a. $3x^2 - 5x + 2 = 0$

b. $4x^2 + 25 = 20x$

c. $x^2 + 6x = 10$

35 As part of the preparation for the 2008 Beijing Olympics, a great observation wheel with a diameter of 198 meters was built. The wheel has 48 capsules which are evenly spaced around the outside of the wheel.

a. What is the distance from one capsule to the next along the outside of the wheel?

b. What is the shortest distance between two adjacent capsules?

c. If the wheel completes one revolution every 30 minutes, what is the linear velocity of the wheel in kilometers per hour?

32 **a.** $\triangle ADE \sim \triangle ABC$ (AA), so the corresponding sides are proportional.

b. $\frac{12}{10} = \frac{AC}{15}$, so $AC = 18$ cm and $EC = 3$.

c. Yes, because $\frac{2}{10} = \frac{3}{15}$.

d.

$\frac{AB}{AD} = \frac{AC}{AE}$	(1) Part a
$\frac{AD + DB}{AD} = \frac{AE + EC}{AE}$	(2) Segment Addition Postulate and substitution
$1 + \frac{DB}{AD} = 1 + \frac{EC}{AE}$	(3) Simplifying the expression (for example, an intermediate step would be $\frac{AD + DB}{AD} = \frac{AD}{AD} + \frac{DB}{AD} = 1 + \frac{DB}{AD}$)
$\frac{DB}{AD} = \frac{EC}{AE}$	(4) Subtract 1 from both sides

e. $\frac{2}{8} = \frac{EC}{18}$, so $EC = 4.5$ ft.

33 $\sin \theta = \frac{20}{29}$

$\theta \approx 43.6°$

$m\overset{\frown}{AB} \approx 87.2°$

34 **a.** $\frac{5 \pm \sqrt{1}}{6}$; one integer and one noninteger rational solution

b. $\frac{20 \pm \sqrt{0}}{8}$; one noninteger rational solution

c. $\frac{-6 \pm \sqrt{76}}{2}$; two irrational solutions

35 **a.** The distance along the wheel between capsules is $\frac{1}{48}(\textit{circumference}) = \frac{\pi(198)}{48} \approx 13$ m.

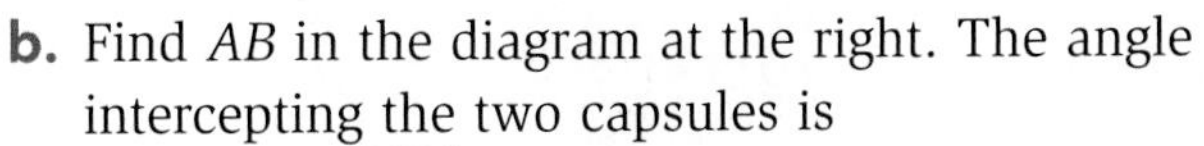

b. Find AB in the diagram at the right. The angle intercepting the two capsules is $m\angle AOB = \frac{360°}{48} = 7.5°$.

$\sin 3.75° = \frac{AC}{99}$

$AC \approx 6.4749$ m

$AB \approx 12.95$ m

(*Note*: Art not to scale.)

c. Circumference: $198\pi = 622$ m

In one hour, the wheel travels approximately 1,244 m. So, the velocity is 1.244 km/hr.

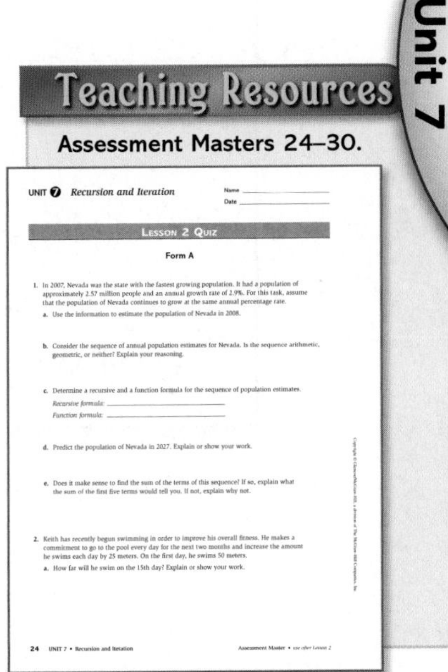

LESSON 3

Iterating Functions

Function iteration is a relatively new field of mathematical study, with many unanswered questions and connections to contemporary mathematical topics such as fractal geometry and chaos theory. Applications of function iteration are being discovered every day, in areas like electronic transmission of large blocks of data, computer graphics, and modeling population growth.

A function can be thought of as a machine that accepts inputs and produces outputs. For example, for the function $f(x) = x^2$, an input of 2 produces an output of 4. To begin understanding function iteration, imagine starting with a specific input, such as 2, and then sequentially feeding the outputs back into the function as new inputs.

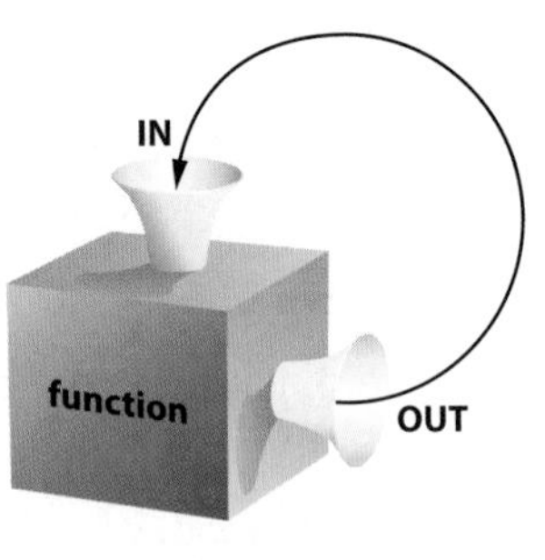

Unit 7

514 UNIT 7 • Recursion and Iteration

Iterating Functions

LESSON 3

Although some real-world contexts are investigated, this lesson deals primarily with "pure" mathematics, albeit in an exploratory, hands-on manner. The mathematical topic explored, function iteration, is a fascinating and growing area of current mathematical development, with many applications. It leads to such contemporary topics as fractals and chaos. Although the term function composition is never used or explicitly discussed, function iteration consists of composing a function with itself. Thus, this lesson also implicitly addresses function composition, which is formalized in Course 4 Unit 1, *Families of Functions*.

Lesson Objectives

- Iterate functions and describe the resulting patterns, the long-term behavior in particular
- Describe the connection between function iteration and recursive formulas
- Analyze long-term behavior when iterating linear functions, using graphical iteration, numerical iteration, and algebraic methods, including fixed point analysis and connections to slope

SCOPE AND SEQUENCE
The content in this lesson is not prerequisite for Unit 8 nor for Course 4 and may be viewed as optional.

Lesson Launch

You might have students work briefly on the problems in the Think About This Situation and then have a whole group discussion. This will give students an informal feel for function iteration before they begin the formal analysis.

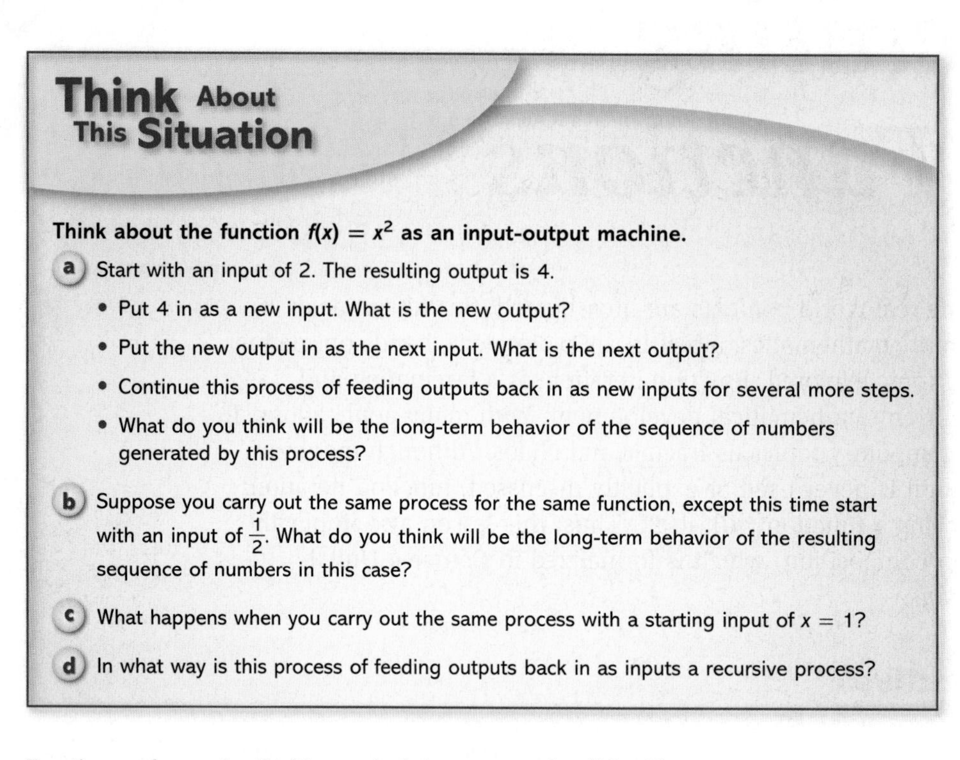

Think About This Situation

Think about the function $f(x) = x^2$ as an input-output machine.

a Start with an input of 2. The resulting output is 4.

- Put 4 in as a new input. What is the new output?
- Put the new output in as the next input. What is the next output?
- Continue this process of feeding outputs back in as new inputs for several more steps.
- What do you think will be the long-term behavior of the sequence of numbers generated by this process?

b Suppose you carry out the same process for the same function, except this time start with an input of $\frac{1}{2}$. What do you think will be the long-term behavior of the resulting sequence of numbers in this case?

c What happens when you carry out the same process with a starting input of $x = 1$?

d In what way is this process of feeding outputs back in as inputs a recursive process?

Functions and recursive thinking are both important and unifying ideas in *Core-Plus Mathematics*. In this lesson, you will explore a connection between recursive formulas and function iteration. You will use this connection to further analyze processes of sequential change.

Investigation 1 Play It Again ... and Again

The process of feeding the outputs of a function back into itself as inputs is called **iterating a function**. Imagine making a reduced copy of an image, then making a reduced copy of your copy, then making a reduced copy of that copy, and so on.

Think About This Situation

a
- 16
- 256
- The following terms in the sequence will be 65,536 and 4,294,967,296.
- The long-term behavior is that the sequence grows without bound.

b Starting with $\frac{1}{2}$, the sequence of numbers is $\frac{1}{2}, \frac{1}{4}, \frac{1}{16}, \frac{1}{256}, \frac{1}{65{,}536}, \ldots$. The long-term behavior of this sequence is that the numbers get smaller and smaller, tending toward 0.

c Starting with 1, the sequence is 1, 1, 1, 1, ... The long-term behavior is that the terms of the sequence will be 1.

d This is a recursive process because you use the current output to get the next output. It is also an example of sequential change (outputs are generated step by step), and iteration (doing the same process over and over again). As usual with such processes, it is often useful and interesting to examine the long-term behavior.

Teaching Resources

Transparency Master 31.

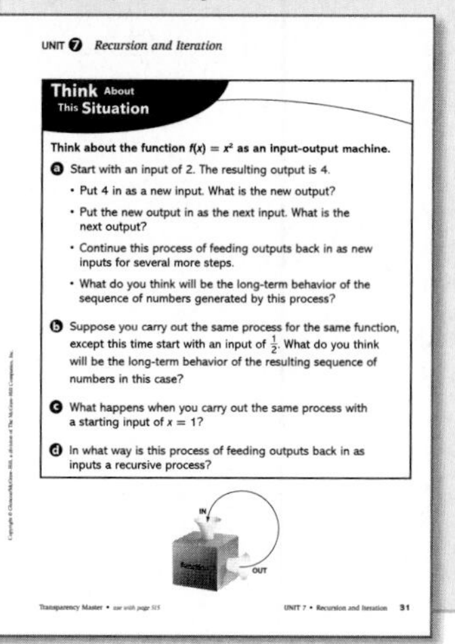
UNIT 7 *Recursion and Iteration*

Think About This Situation

Think about the function $f(x) = x^2$ as an input-output machine.

a Start with an input of 2. The resulting output is 4.
- Put 4 in as a new input. What is the new output?
- Put the new output in as the next input. What is the next output?
- Continue this process of feeding outputs back in as new inputs for several more steps.
- What do you think will be the long-term behavior of the sequence of numbers generated by this process?

b Suppose you carry out the same process for the same function, except this time start with an input of $\frac{1}{2}$. What do you think will be the long-term behavior of the resulting sequence of numbers in this case?

c What happens when you carry out the same process with a starting input of $x = 1$?

d In what way is this process of feeding outputs back in as inputs a recursive process?

Transparency Master • *use with page 515* UNIT 7 • Recursion and Iteration 31

Investigation 1 Play It Again ... and Again

This investigation is designed to establish the connection between evaluating recursive formulas and iterating functions and to give students an experience of the richness of long-term behavior that is possible when you iterate even simple functions. Iterating a function is fundamentally the same idea as sequentially evaluating a recursive formula. But the *notation* is different. The problems in this investigation will help students see connections among evaluating a function, iterating a function, and evaluating a recursive formula.

In Lesson 1, students investigated the recursive formula $U_n = rU_{n-1} + b$ and found that the long-term behavior could be influenced by the parameters r and b and also by the initial value. In this investigation, they find that iterating different functions can create an amazing diversity of outcomes, including oscillations that eventually converge to a single value, oscillations that do not converge, and chaotic behavior. Small changes in parameters can cause surprising results.

In this investigation, many questions are raised without attempting to reach closure on them, since the mathematics required for such closure is beyond the scope of high school mathematics. However, the details of iterating *linear* functions are investigated more closely in Investigation 2 of this lesson.

Unit 7

As you work on the problems of this investigation, look for answers to the following questions:

How do you iterate a function, and how can technology help?

What are connections between recursive formulas and function iteration?

What are some possibilities for long-term behavior in function iteration sequences?

Connection between Recursive Formulas and Function Iteration As you might expect, there is a close connection between iterating a function and evaluating a recursive formula.

1 Consider the rule $NEXT = 2(NOW)^2 - 5$.

a. Use an initial value of 1 and find the next three values.

b. Rewrite the rule as a recursive formula using U_n and U_{n-1}. Let $U_0 = 1$ and then find U_1, U_2, and U_3.

c. Now think about iterating a function, as illustrated in the "function machine" diagram on page 514. Iterate $f(x) = 2x^2 - 5$ three times, starting with $x = 1$.

d. Compare the sequences of numbers you got in Parts a, b, and c. Explain why the three sequences are the same, even though the representations used to generate the sequences are different—using *NOW-NEXT* in Part a, using U_n and U_{n-1} in Part b, and iterating a function in Part c. (If the three sequences you generated in Parts a, b, and c are not the same, go back and examine your work, compare to other students, and resolve any problems.)

2 Think about iterating the function $f(x) = 3x + 1$. A table that shows the iteration process is similar to function tables that you have previously used but with a new twist.

a. Complete a table like the one below, starting with $x = 2$.

Iterating $f(x) = 3x + 1$

	x IN	$f(x)$ OUT
Start →	2	7
	7	22
	?	?
	?	?
	?	?
	?	?

b. How would the table be different if you started with $x = 0$?

c. What recursive formula yields the same sequence of numbers as that generated by iterating $f(x)$?

516 UNIT 7 • Recursion and Iteration

1. **a.** Using the *NOW-NEXT* rule with an initial value of 1 yields the sequence 1, −3, 13, 333.

   b. $U_n = 2(U_{n-1})^2 - 5$; $U_0 = 1$; $U_1 = -3$; $U_2 = 13$; $U_3 = 333$

   c. Iterating $f(x)$ three times starting with $x = 1$ yields the sequence 1, −3, 13, 333.

   d. The sequences in Parts a, b, and c are the same. Iterating the function $f(x) = 2x^2 - 5$ is the same as evaluating the recursive formula $U_n = 2(U_{n-1})^2 - 5$, which is the same as finding successive values of the *NOW-NEXT* rule. All three processes produce identical sequences. It is just the notation that is different.

2. **a.** For their tables, students may include arrows as shown in the student text.

Iterating $f(x) = 3x + 1$

x IN	$f(x)$ OUT
2	7
7	22
22	67
67	202
202	607

   b. The table with initial value 0 is shown below. Although the numbers are different from those in Part a, the table values are still growing quickly.

Iterating $f(x) = 3x + 1$

x IN	$f(x)$ OUT
0	1
1	4
4	13
13	40
40	121

   c. $U_n = 3(U_{n-1}) + 1$. Note that letters different than U could be used and the subscripts might be $n + 1$ and n, rather than n and $n - 1$.

Unit 7

3 Consider the recursive formula $U_n = (U_{n-1})^2 + 3U_{n-1} + 4$, with $U_0 = 1$.

a. Compute U_1, U_2, and U_3.

b. Rewrite the recursive formula as a rule using the words *NOW* and *NEXT*.

c. What function can be iterated to yield the same sequence of numbers as that generated by the recursive formula? Check your answer by iterating your function, starting with an input of 1, and comparing to your answers for Part a.

Using Technology to Iterate Functions Use of technology such as calculators and spreadsheets can be very helpful when iterating functions.

4 Consider the function $g(x) = -0.7x + 6$.

a. Complete a table like the one in Problem 2 showing the first few steps of iterating $g(x)$, starting with $x = 14$.

b. Use a spreadsheet to iterate $g(x)$ at least 30 times, starting with 14. Describe any patterns you see in the iteration sequence.

Iterate Function.xls

◇	A	B	C	D
1	14			
2	−3.8			
3	=−0.7*A2+6			
4				
5				
6				
7				

c. Use the last-answer feature of a calculator to iterate $g(x)$ at least 30 times, starting with 14. Make sure you get the same sequence of numbers as in Part b.

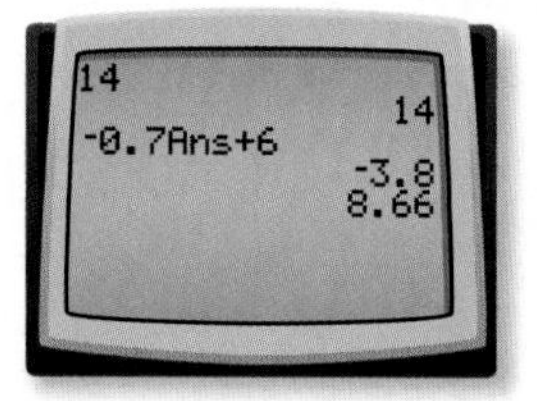

d. In Parts a, b, and c, you used three methods for iterating $g(x)$: completing a table by hand, using a spreadsheet, and using the last-answer feature on a calculator. What are some advantages and disadvantages of each method for iterating a function?

e. Use the recursion mode on your calculator or use spreadsheet software to produce a graph illustrating the iteration of $g(x)$, starting with $x = 14$. Describe how the numerical patterns that you found in Part b are illustrated in the graph.

3 a. $U_1 = 8$; $U_2 = 92$; $U_3 = 8{,}744$

b. $NEXT = NOW^2 + 3NOW + 4$

c. $f(x) = x^2 + 3x + 4$. The sequence generated starting at 1 is 1, 8, 92, 8,744, 76,483,772. This is the same sequence (and same process) as that in Part a.

4 a. **Iterating $g(x) = -0.7x + 6$**

x IN	$g(x)$ OUT
14	−3.8
−3.8	8.66
8.66	−0.062
−0.062	−6.0434

DIFFERENTIATION You may wish to encourage some students to include arrows as shown in the student text.

b. Patterns that students may notice include an oscillation between positive and negative numbers at the beginning, but then they are all positive and eventually seem to approach a number near 3.529. If you iterate even further, you get convergence (to 9 decimal places) to 3.529411765. Students may also notice that as the numbers approach 3.529411765, they are alternately above and below that limit. (The convergence point will be carefully explored in the next investigation, so you should not expect students to explain it now. The exact number to which the sequence tends in the long term is $\frac{6}{1.7}$, which is the solution to the equation $x = -0.7x + 6$. This value is sometimes called a "fixed point" since, if you ever get to it, you never move from it. See Problem 3 of Investigation 2, on page 520.)

TECHNOLOGY NOTE When students are using the last-answer feature of a calculator for Part b, you could display spreadsheet results for comparison.

c. Students should use the last-answer feature of a calculator to iterate $g(x)$.

d. Completing the table by hand shows the function iteration process clearly, in which an output becomes the next input. The last-answer feature on a calculator is convenient and quick, but it does not show the entire iteration sequence. Using a spreadsheet is similar to using the last-answer feature on a calculator with the added advantage that you can see the entire iteration sequence (and also easily change the function to see the result of iterating different functions or the result starting with a different initial value.)

e. The graph gives a compelling visual picture of the initial oscillating behavior and the long-term limiting value or "fixed point." Below are shown the screens for creating a graph using the recursion mode of a calculator and a time series plot using the *CPMP-Tools* "Function Iteration" custom tool.

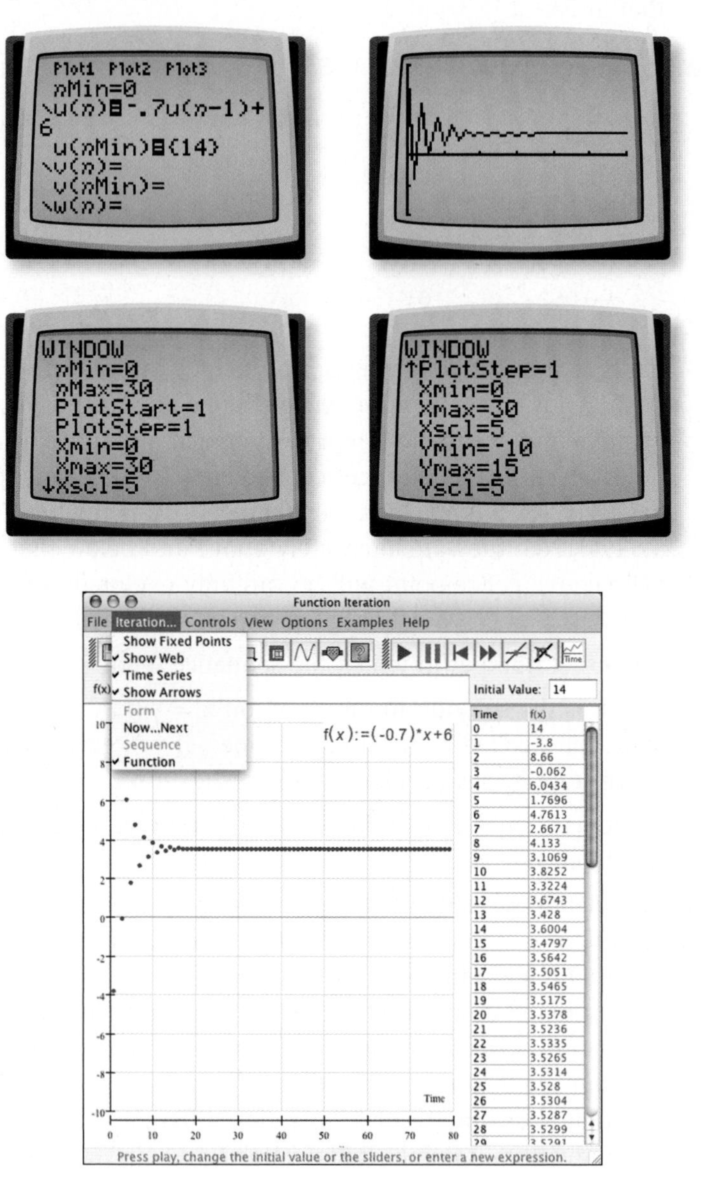

5 The iteration sequence is 256, 16, 4, 2, 1.414, 1.189, 1.091, … . The long-term behavior tends to 1. Students could iterate the function in several ways. Using a calculator, they could enter **256**, type in 2nd x^2 2nd (–)), and press ENTER repeatedly. Or, they might put their calculator in "recursion mode," enter $U_n = \sqrt{U_{n-1}}$, and then look at a table of values. Or, they could use a spreadsheet.

6 **a.** 5, −4, 5, −4, 5, …
The long-term behavior is that the sequence oscillates between 5 and −4.

b. −28, 29, −28, 29, …
The long-term behavior is that the sequence oscillates between −28 and 29.

c. 0.5, 0.5, 0.5, 0.5, …
This sequence is fixed at 0.5.

7 **MATHEMATICAL NOTE** In this problem, students investigate a famous recurrence relation: $U_{n+1} = rU_n(1 - U_n)$, which corresponds to iterating the function $f(x) = rx(1 - x)$. There is also a related differential equation: $\frac{dx}{dt} = rx(1 - x)$. The differential equation is usually called the *logistic equation*, while the recurrence relation is usually called the *logistic map*. Much has been studied and written about this equation. For example, see *Chaos* by James Gleick (Viking, 1987) or *Chaos, Fractals, and Dynamics* by Robert Devaney (Addison-Wesley, 1990). Here, students try a few experiments to see the richness of iterative behavior. Note that the experiments show "convergence" to one number, a two-cycle, a four-cycle, a three-cycle, and "chaos." By varying the parameter *r*, it is possible to get cycles of all possible lengths, although they become difficult to find by computer experimentation. One of the fundamental results in this field of mathematics is that if there is a three-cycle, as in Part d, then there will be a cycle of every other length, as well as completely chaotic cycles, as in Part e.

a. Converges to a single value $\frac{1.7}{2.7}$, or approximately 0.6296296.

b. Converges to a "two-cycle"; that is, it oscillates between approximately 0.5130445 and 0.7994555.

c. Converges to a "four-cycle"; that is, it oscillates among approximately 0.8749973, 0.3828197, 0.8269407, and 0.5008842.

d. Converges to a "three-cycle"; that is, it oscillates among approximately 0.9574166, 0.1561493, and 0.5046665.

e. There is no discernible pattern ("chaos"). Note that not all calculator and computer outputs will agree for this iteration, not only because of round-off errors but also, and more importantly, because of the nature of chaotic behavior, in particular, the property of chaos to have "sensitive dependence on initial conditions." This means even a very small difference in initial conditions can result in wildly different long-term behavior. Thus, if at any given point in the iteration two calculators disagree slightly (due to round-off), then they are liable to vary considerably later.

Long-Term Behavior As with any process of sequential change, it is important to study the long-term behavior of function iteration.

5 Suppose $f(x) = \sqrt{x}$. Iterate this function, starting with $x = 256$. Describe the long-term behavior of the resulting sequence of numbers.

6 Suppose $h(x) = 1 - x$. Iterate this function. Describe the long-term behavior of the iteration sequence for each of the following starting values.

a. Start with $x = 5$.

b. Start with $x = -28$.

c. Start with $x = \frac{1}{2}$.

In the next problem, you will iterate functions of the form $f(x) = rx(1 - x)$. This is a broadly useful equation in mathematics called the **logistic equation** (or **logistic map**). For different values of r, you get different functions, each of which may have a different behavior when iterated. Iterating these functions has proven to be a very useful method of modeling certain population growth situations. Also, the study of the iterated behavior of these functions has contributed to many important developments in modern mathematics over the last several decades.

7 For each of the function iterations below, use $x = 0.02$ as the starting value. Describe any patterns you see, including the long-term behavior.

a. Iterate $f(x) = 2.7x(1 - x)$.

b. Iterate $g(x) = 3.2x(1 - x)$.

c. Iterate $h(x) = 3.5x(1 - x)$.

d. Iterate $j(x) = 3.83x(1 - x)$.

e. Iterate $k(x) = 4x(1 - x)$.

Summarize the Mathematics

In this investigation, you explored iteration of linear and nonlinear functions.

a Explain the connection between function iteration and recursive formulas.

b Consider evaluating the rule $NEXT = (NOW)^3 + 5$, starting with 2.

i. What recursive formula (using subscript notation), when evaluated, will produce the same sequence?

ii. What function, when iterated, will generate the same sequence?

c Describe some of the possible long-term behaviors that can occur when a function is iterated.

Be prepared to share your descriptions and thinking with the entire class.

Unit 7

Summarize the Mathematics

a If the function and the recursive formula express the same pattern of change, then function iteration and sequential evaluation of recursive formulas produce the same output values for the same starting values. More specifically, to iterate a function, you start with some value as the initial input. Using that input, you perform the computations indicated by the function rule, and that gives you the first output. Then you use that output as the next input, perform the computations, and get the next output. That output becomes the next input, which generates the next output, and so on. In this way, a sequence of outputs is generated.

Similarly, to sequentially evaluate a recursive formula, you start with some initial value. Using that value, you perform the computations indicated by the recursive rule, and that gives you the next value, and so on. In this way, a sequence of values is generated.

Thus, if the function rule and the recursive rule have the same computations, then you get the same sequence when you iterate the function or sequentially evaluate the recursive formula.

b

i. If U_n corresponds to *NEXT*, then U_{n-1} corresponds to *NOW* and $NEXT = (NOW)^3 + 5$ becomes $U_n = (U_{n-1})^3 + 5$ (with $U_0 = 2$).

ii. A function having the same computations, which will thus generate the same sequence when iterated, is $f(x) = x^3 + 5$ (with 2 as the initial input, or rather the initial value of x).

c Possible long-term behaviors seen in this investigation are no change at all, eventual convergence to a single value, oscillation among several values, and "chaos."

NOTE Solutions to Problems 5–7 are on page T517B.

Teaching Resources

Transparency Master 32.

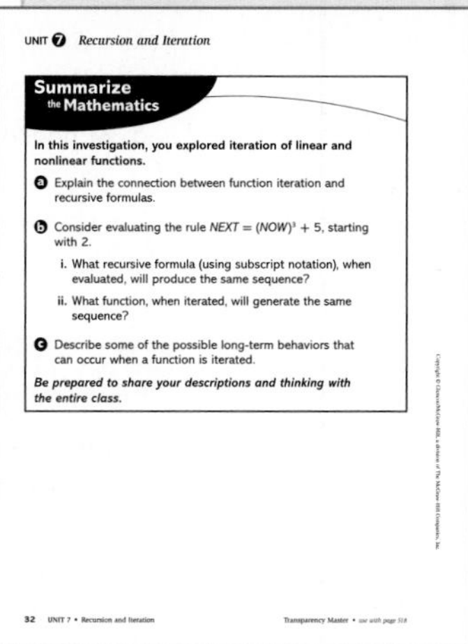
UNIT 7 *Recursion and Iteration*

Summarize the Mathematics

In this investigation, you explored iteration of linear and nonlinear functions.

a Explain the connection between function iteration and recursive formulas.

b Consider evaluating the rule $NEXT = (NOW)^3 + 5$, starting with 2.

i. What recursive formula (using subscript notation), when evaluated, will produce the same sequence?

ii. What function, when iterated, will generate the same sequence?

c Describe some of the possible long-term behaviors that can occur when a function is iterated.

Be prepared to share your descriptions and thinking with the entire class.

32 UNIT 7 • Recursion and Iteration   Transparency Master • *use with page 518*

Unit 7

Check Your Understanding

Function iteration can be applied to any function.

a. Iterate $g(x) = \cos x$, starting with $x = 10$. (Use radians, not degrees.) Describe the long-term behavior of the iteration sequence.

  i. What recursive formula yields the same sequence as iterating $g(x)$?

  ii. Rewrite your recursive formula using the words *NOW* and *NEXT*.

b. Choose any function not used in this investigation and several different starting points. Iterate your function using each of your starting points. Describe the long-term behavior of the iteration sequences.

Investigation 2 Iterating Linear Functions

In Investigation 1, you iterated a variety of functions, both linear and nonlinear. The iterative behavior of nonlinear functions is not yet completely understood and is currently a lively area of mathematical research. On the other hand, iteration of linear functions, which is the focus of this investigation, is well understood. As you work on the problems of this investigation, look for answers to the following questions:

How can you graphically iterate a function?

What are all the possible long-term behaviors when iterating linear functions?

How can you use slope to predict these behaviors?

Graphical Iteration Just as with many other ideas in mathematics, the process of function iteration can be represented visually.

To see how graphical iteration works, consider the function $f(x) = 0.5x + 2$. The graphs of $y = x$ and $y = 0.5x + 2$ are shown below on the same set of axes. Think graphically about how an input becomes an output, which then becomes the next input, which produces the next output, and so on.

Graphical Function Iteration

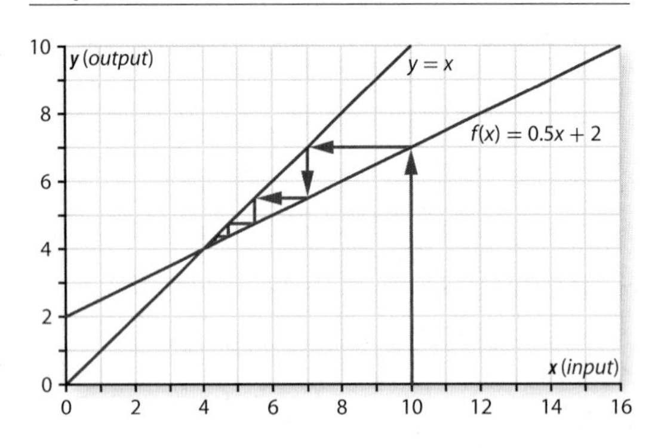

Check Your Understanding

a. The iteration sequence converges to approximately 0.739085. (This is the x value of the intersection point of the graphs of $y = x$ and $y = \cos x$.)

i. $A_n = \cos(A_{n-1}), A_0 = 10$

ii. $NEXT = \cos(NOW)$, starting at 10

b. You may wish to have students share their results with others in the class.

Investigation 2 Iterating Linear Functions

In this investigation, students are challenged to determine the influence of a and b when the linear function $f(x) = ax + b$ is iterated. A new graphical technique is introduced: graphical iteration. This process is sometimes called creating a web graph. This technique is difficult for some students, since they are already working with functions in two ways: evaluating $y = f(x)$ to get outputs for any x in the domain and iterating $f(x)$ to generate a sequence of outputs, each of which is the next input. In a sense, the web graph selects points on the complete graph of a function to mirror the way that iterating a function selects input/output pairs from the "complete" table of a function. As it does this, the long-term behavior of the iterated function becomes apparent.

Iteration of nonlinear functions is not investigated here, but students have an opportunity to experiment with these in Applications Tasks 2 and 3.

Fixed Points When we talk here about "reaching" a fixed point, we are technically referring to attracting fixed points and infinite limits. Attracting fixed points will be investigated explicitly in Problem 7. Infinite limits are not dealt with in this investigation except in an intuitive and implicit manner. This is not something you need to stress with students, but it may come up. It is always the case that if you start at a fixed point, then you will never leave it. But "reaching a fixed point" happens only with attracting fixed points, and then only at the limit. That is, $f^n(x_0) \to$ (*fixed point*) as $n \to \infty$. The rounding done on a calculator or computer makes it seem that a fixed point is actually reached after finitely many iterations.

Concerning attracting fixed points, a subtle point to be aware of (in case it comes up) is that, in general, only iteration sequences that start "close" to an attracting fixed point will converge to the fixed point. However, in the case of linear functions, all iteration sequences converge to an attracting fixed point, if there is one.

Concerning repelling fixed points, a subtle point is that iteration sequences might not be steadily repelled away from the fixed point, although they will be in the case of linear functions. See Applications Tasks 4–7 for more detailed exploration of attracting and repelling fixed points.

In the diagram on the previous page, 10 has been chosen as the original input. To find an input's (x value's) resulting output (y value), you go up to the graph of the function you are iterating. Next, according to the process of function iteration, the output gets put back into the function as an input. This is accomplished graphically by moving horizontally to the $y = x$ graph, since on this line the y value (the current output) is identical to the x value (the new input).

Now go vertically again to find the output associated with the new input. The process continues in this way until, in this example, you are drawn into the intersection point of the two graphs. This is the process of **graphical iteration**.

1 From this graphical perspective, what is the long-term behavior of the function $f(x) = 0.5x + 2$ when iterated? Use your calculator or a spreadsheet to iterate $f(x)$, starting with $x = 10$, and see if the numerical result matches the graphical result.

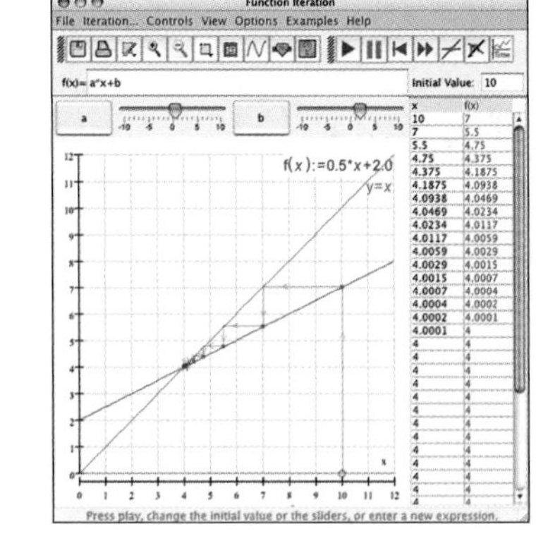

2 Analyze the process of graphical iteration as illustrated in the diagram on the previous page. If available, use a technology tool such as the "Function Iteration" custom tool in *CPMP-Tools* to illustrate the process.

a. Explain, in your own words, why you can graphically find the output of a function for a given input by moving vertically to the graph of the function.

b. Explain, in your own words, why you can graphically turn an output into the next input by moving horizontally from the graph of the function to the graph of $y = x$.

c. Complete a table like the one in Investigation 1 Problem 2 on page 516 that shows the first few steps of the graphical iteration illustrated above. Explain how the entries in the table correspond to the steps of the graphical iteration process.

d. Illustrate the process of graphical iteration for this function using $x = 1$ as the original input. Describe the pattern of graphical iteration.

3 Sketch graphs and illustrate the process of graphical function iteration for the function $g(x) = -0.5x + 8$. Choose your own starting value. Compare the overall pattern of the graphical iteration to the patterns you saw for the function in Problems 1 and 2. Make a conjecture about what kinds of linear rules yield graphical iteration patterns like the one you found in this problem. You will test your conjecture later in this lesson.

Fixed Points As you have seen, sometimes when you iterate a function, you are drawn to a particular value; and if you reach that value, you never leave it. Such a value is called a *fixed point*.

4 Consider fixed points in the case of linear functions.

a. Look back at Problem 1. What is the fixed point when iterating the function $f(x) = 0.5x + 2$?

b. What is the fixed point when iterating the function $f(x) = -0.7x + 6$?

520 UNIT 7 • Recursion and Iteration

Differentiation Some students may need additional practice and discussion to become comfortable with graphical iteration and fixed points and to make connections among the different representations. You may decide to pause after Problem 2 and have a class discussion to be sure that students understand graphical iteration and how it relates to a recursive formula and to iterating a function.

After Problem 3, you may want to provide additional practice by having students examine the long-term behavior of $U_n = 0.5U_{n-1} + 2$ in multiple ways. They can numerically iterate with a spreadsheet or last-answer feature of a calculator, carry out function iteration with $f(x) = 0.5x + 2$ in a handmade table, and use graphical iteration. Ask what $y = 0.5x + 2$ would mean in the fish-population context and what the fixed point means in that context.

Use small integer values for the parameters at this point to facilitate graphing. But in each case, you can ask what the relation would mean in the fish-population context. Some students may benefit from this additional discussion and practice before moving on to Problem 4 and continuing their investigation of fixed points.

Technology It is helpful for students to work through at least one example of graphical iteration by sketching graphs by hand on graph paper. Depending on your students' needs and performance, you may encourage more or less use of the "Function Iteration" custom tool in *CPMP-Tools* or similar technology tools, especially in Problem 3 and later in Problem 6. In any case, all students should analyze and explain the process of graphical iteration, as prompted in Parts a–c of Problem 2.

Launch

A teaching master is provided to help facilitate a launch of this investigation.

Teaching Resources

Transparency Master 33.

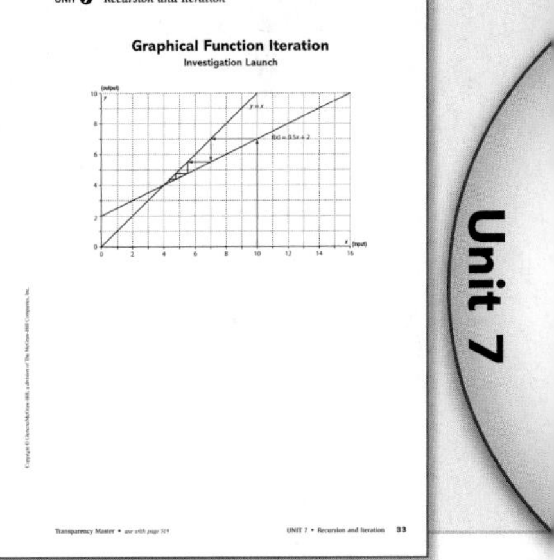

Unit 7

1. The graph seems to indicate that the long-term iterative behavior of $f(x)$ is that it will converge at 4. Iterating the function shows that the long-term behavior is steady at 4, just as in the graphical iteration.

2. Student responses may vary. Examples follow.

   a. For a function $y = f(x)$, x is the input and y is the output. You get y (the output) by substituting for x (the input). This substitution gives an ordered pair (x, y) on the graph of $f(x)$. But the conventional rule for graphing is that (x, y) means to go horizontally to x and then vertically to y. Thus, to find the output using the graph, you first find x on the horizontal (input) axis, and then you go vertically to the graph to find the y (output) that goes with it.

   b. Roughly, to turn an output into an input means to turn y into x, and that is what the $y = x$ line does. Graphically, you want to reflect the y (output) value onto the x (input) axis.

   A more detailed explanation might be the following. An output is on the vertical axis. If you want to use it as the next input, then you need to get it onto the horizontal (input) axis. However, you want to keep the same distance from the origin along the axis because you want the same numerical value. Moving over to the line $y = x$ and looking down to the x-axis will accomplish this.

DIFFERENTIATION You may wish to encourage some students to include arrows as shown in the student book.

c. Student explanations should include discussion of how moving from IN to OUT in a row of the table corresponds to moving vertically to the function graph in the graphical iteration process, and moving from a value in the OUT column to the same value in the IN column in the table corresponds to moving horizontally to the $y = x$ line in the graphical iteration process.

Iterating $f(x) = 0.5x + 2$

x IN	$f(x)$ OUT
10	7
7	5.5
5.5	4.75
4.75	4.375

d. The graphical iteration starting with $x = 1$ also converges to 4.

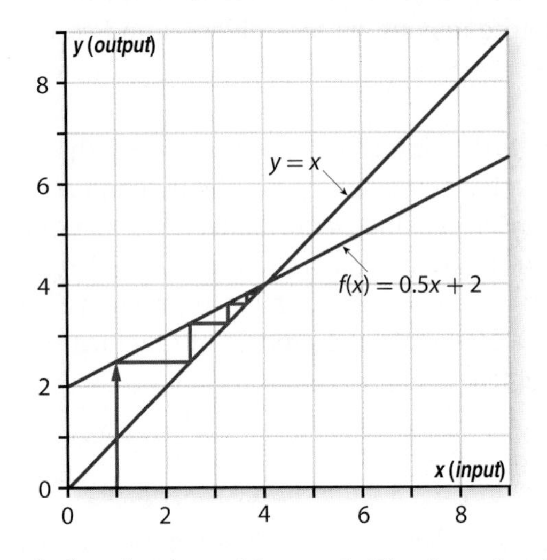

3 The iteration shown below begins with $x = 1$. The iteration is converging to $\frac{8}{1.5}$, or approximately 5.33. In Problem 1, the pattern was a "stair step," while here the pattern is more of a spiral or a "cobweb." Similar patterns occur whenever the slope of the iterated function is negative. (Accept any reasonable conjecture about types of linear rules that yield the iteration patterns at this point.) Students will study iteration patterns more as the lesson progresses.

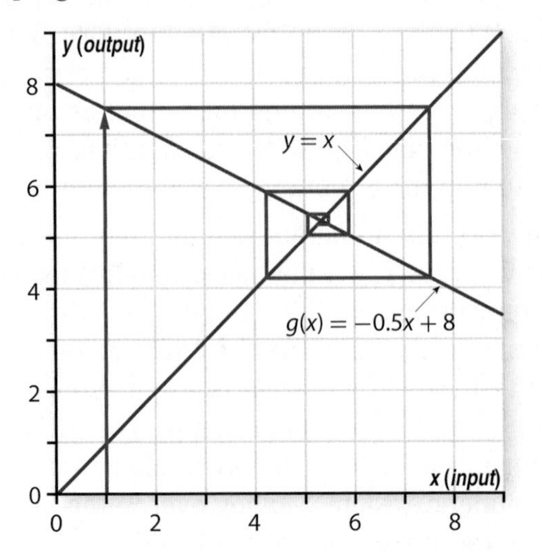

Unit 7

4 **a.** The fixed point is $x = 4$. Note that the fixed point is a limiting value; it is only the round-off of the calculator or computer making it seem that you actually get to the fixed point.

b. By iterating, you can estimate that the fixed point is approximately 3.529. Students will probably find the fixed point by iterating since that is the only technique discussed so far. (The exact value is $\frac{6}{1.7}$.)

c. You might think of the equation $x = f(x)$ as saying *input* = *output*. Thus, if $x = f(x)$, then the outputs and inputs never change as you iterate $f(x)$ starting from x. So, in the iteration process, once you get to x you will never get anything different. That is, "if you reach that value, you never leave it."

Unit 7

c. The precise definition of a **fixed point** is a value x such that $f(x) = x$. Explain why this definition fits the previous description of a fixed point: "If you reach that value, you never leave it."

5 One method that sometimes works to find a fixed point is iterating the function, either numerically or graphically, and seeing what happens. Another method for finding a fixed point is to use the definition of a fixed point. Since the definition says that a fixed point is a value x such that $f(x) = x$, set the rule for the function equal to x and solve. Use this symbolic method to find the fixed point when iterating the function $f(x) = 0.5x + 2$. Compare your answer to your response in Problem 4 for Part a.

6 For each of the following functions, in Parts a–h, try to find a fixed point using each of these three methods.

Method I Iterate by using the last-answer feature of your calculator or spreadsheet software (numeric method).

Method II Iterate graphically (graphic method).

Method III Solve the equation $f(x) = x$ (symbolic method).

Organize your work as follows.

- Try a variety of starting values for each function.
- Keep a record of what you try, the results, and any patterns that you notice.
- Prepare a display of the graphical iteration.

Each student should use all three of the methods listed above for the functions in Parts a and b. For Parts c through h, share the workload among classmates.

a. $s(x) = 0.6x + 3$

b. $u(x) = 4.3x + 1$

c. $t(x) = 0.2x - 5$

d. $v(x) = 3x - 4$

e. $w(x) = x + 2$

f. $f(x) = -0.8x + 4$

g. $h(x) = -x + 2$

h. $k(x) = -2x + 5$

Slope and Long-Term Behavior Fixed points are examples of the long-term behavior of iterated functions. The different types of fixed points for linear functions can be completely characterized and predicted.

7 Three important characteristics to look for when iterating functions are *attracting fixed points*, *repelling fixed points*, and *cycles*. An **attracting fixed point** is a fixed point such that iteration sequences that start close to it get pulled into it. In contrast, iteration sequences move away from a **repelling fixed point**, except of course, for the sequence that begins at the fixed point. A **cycle** is a set of numbers in an iteration sequence that repeats over and over.

a. For each of the linear functions you iterated in Problem 6, decide with some classmates whether it has an attracting fixed point, a repelling fixed point, a cycle, or none of these.

b. Is there a connection between the slope of the graph of a linear function and the function's behavior when iterated? If so, explain how you could complete Part a of this problem simply by knowing the slope of each linear function's graph.

5 Setting $x = f(x)$ yields $x = 0.5x + 2$. Solving this gives $x = 4$ for the fixed point. This is the same result you get if you numerically or graphically iterate to find the fixed point.

NOTE The solution to Task 4 Part c is on page T520B.

6 **a.** $s(x) = 0.6x + 3$: The fixed point is 7.5. You are pulled into the fixed point no matter where you start; the graphical pattern as you approach the fixed point is a stair step.

b. $u(x) = 4.3x + 1$: The fixed point is $-\frac{10}{33}$. With numerical and graphical iteration, you will never find this fixed point unless you start right at it; all numerical and graphical iterations from starting values that are not the fixed point itself are pushed away from the fixed point; the graphical iteration pattern is a stair step.

c. $t(x) = 0.2x - 5$: The fixed point is -6.25. Same analysis as in Part a.

d. $v(x) = 3x - 4$: The fixed point is 2. Same analysis as in Part b.

e. $w(x) = x + 2$: There is no fixed point. Graphical iteration will produce a stair-step pattern; all numerical and graphical iteration sequences tend to positive infinity.

f. $f(x) = -0.8x + 4$: The fixed point is $\frac{20}{9}$. Graphical iteration produces a spiral pattern; all numerical and graphical iteration sequences are pulled into the fixed point.

g. $h(x) = -x + 2$: The fixed point is 1. The graphical iteration pattern is a "cycle." Each starting value (except the fixed point) is part of its own two-cycle, and the other value is the reflection of the starting point across the line $x = 1$. Using numerical iteration, you will never see the fixed point unless you start there, because all starting values not equal to the fixed point are caught in their own two-cycle.

h. $k(x) = -2x + 5$: The fixed point is $\frac{5}{3}$. The graphical iteration pattern is a cobweb that spirals out. All starting values, except the fixed point itself, are pushed away from the fixed point.

INSTRUCTIONAL NOTE
Since Parts c–h will not be completed by all students, these functions should be discussed as a class. As part of their work on Problem 6, encourage groups to prepare a display illustrating the graphical iteration using graph paper, chart paper, features of a graphing calculator, or with the "Function Iteration" custom tool in *CPMP-Tools*.

7 **a.** Problem 6 Parts a, c, and f each have an attracting fixed point. Parts b, d, and h each have a repelling fixed point. In Part h, every iteration sequence (other than the one starting at the fixed point) eventually alternates between large positive and negative numbers; while in Parts b and d, starting values greater than the fixed point are repelled to positive infinity and starting values less than the fixed point are repelled to negative infinity. Part g has two-cycle behavior with a different two-cycle for each starting value (except for the fixed point), and the fixed point is not considered repelling or attracting since iteration sequences do not get further or closer to the fixed point. Part e is the only one that does not have a fixed point at all.

b. If $|slope| > 1$, then the linear function has a repelling fixed point.

If $|slope| < 1$, then the linear function has an attracting fixed point.

If the slope is equal to 1 (and the y-intercept is not 0), then the linear function has no fixed point.

If the slope is equal to -1, then the linear function has two-cycles and the fixed point is neither attracting nor repelling.

A function with a positive slope will have a stair-step pattern, and one with a negative slope will have a cobweb or spiral pattern.

TERMINOLOGY
The definitions of attracting and repelling fixed points stated here are accurate but intuitive. The formal definitions require infinite limits. (See the introduction to Investigation 2.) Infinite limits should not be stressed with students at this time; additional work with infinite limits is undertaken in Course 4 Unit 7, *Concepts of Calculus*.

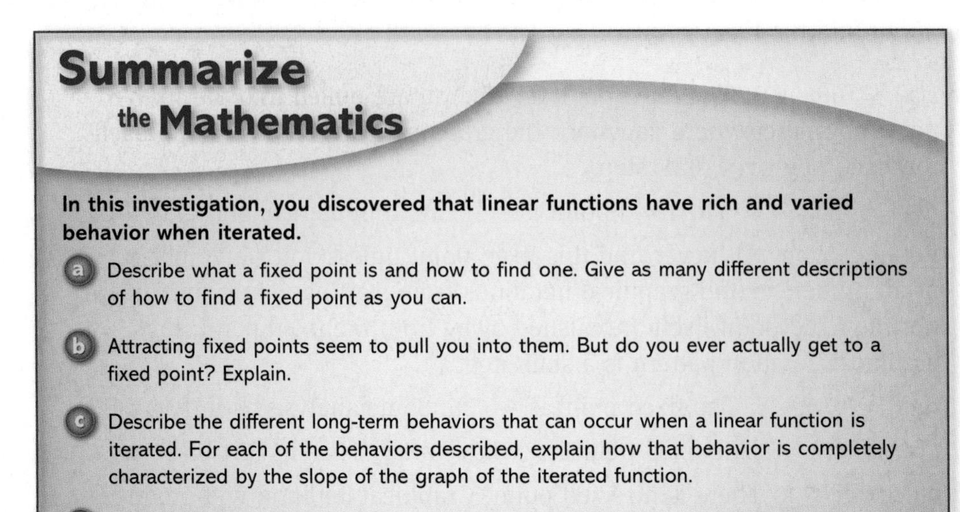

Summarize the Mathematics

In this investigation, you discovered that linear functions have rich and varied behavior when iterated.

a Describe what a fixed point is and how to find one. Give as many different descriptions of how to find a fixed point as you can.

b Attracting fixed points seem to pull you into them. But do you ever actually get to a fixed point? Explain.

c Describe the different long-term behaviors that can occur when a linear function is iterated. For each of the behaviors described, explain how that behavior is completely characterized by the slope of the graph of the iterated function.

d In the first lesson of this unit, you investigated situations that could be modeled by combined recursive formulas of the form $A_n = rA_{n-1} + b$. What is the connection between these combined recursive formulas and iterating linear functions?

Be prepared to share your descriptions and thinking with the entire class.

Check Your Understanding

At the beginning of this unit, you analyzed the changing fish population in a pond. The pond has an initial population of 3,000 fish. The population decreases by 20% each year due to natural causes and fish being caught. At the end of each year, 1,000 fish are added. A rule that models this situation is

$$NEXT = 0.8NOW + 1{,}000, \text{ starting at } 3{,}000.$$

a. Rewrite this rule as a recursive formula, using subscript notation.

b. What function can be iterated to produce the same sequence of population numbers generated by the recursive formula? With what value should you start the function iteration?

c. Iterate the function in Part b and describe the long-term behavior of the iteration sequence. Compare this behavior to the long-term behavior of the fish population that you discovered in Investigation 1 of Lesson 1.

d. Graphically iterate this function, starting with $x = 3{,}000$.

e. Find the fixed point by solving an equation. Is the fixed point attracting or repelling? How can you tell by examining the slope of the function's graph?

f. Explain what the fixed point and its attracting or repelling property tell you about the changing fish population.

Unit 7

522 UNIT 7 • Recursion and Iteration

Summary

This summary overlaps somewhat with Problem 7, but there are more behaviors to be described in the summary, and those in Problem 7 are important enough to warrant a second systematic look. To prepare for this discussion, you may wish to review the investigation overview explanation of fixed points.

Summarize the Mathematics

a By definition, a fixed point is a number x such that $x = f(x)$. In terms of graphs, one important way to think about fixed points that has not been explicitly mentioned so far is that a fixed point is the point of intersection of the graphs for $y = x$ and $y = f(x)$. (Students should have recognized this fact by now, and they should be encouraged to articulate it.) In terms of iteration sequences, a fixed point is a number in a function iteration sequence such that if you ever get to it, it will be repeated forever. This interpretation arises since the equation $x = f(x)$ in effect says that *input* = *output*, so feeding outputs back in as inputs will result in generating the same number over and over again.

A fixed point can be attracting, repelling, or neither. An attracting fixed point has the property that iteration sequences converge to it. (In general, only iteration sequences that start "close" to an attracting fixed point will converge to the fixed point, but in the case of linear functions, all iteration sequences converge to an attracting fixed point, if one exists.) In contrast, iteration sequences move away from a repelling fixed point. A fixed point might be neither attracting nor repelling, as when there are two-cycles with linear functions.

Methods for finding fixed points include numerical or graphical iteration, if the fixed point is attracting; solving the equation $x = f(x)$; or finding the point of intersection of the graphs for $y = x$ and $y = f(x)$.

b It is always the case that if you start at a fixed point, then you will never leave it. But "reaching a fixed point" happens only with attracting fixed points, and then only in the limit. That is,

$$f^n(x_0) \rightarrow (\textit{fixed point}) \text{ as } n \rightarrow \infty.$$

POSSIBLE MISCONCEPTION
Some students may persist in thinking that fixed points exist only when the iterated function sequence is convergent. If it seems that they equate "attracting" and "fixed," ask probing questions to help resolve this misconception. Make sure students can correctly explain this as part of the Summarize the Mathematics discussion.

Teaching Resources

Transparency Master 34.

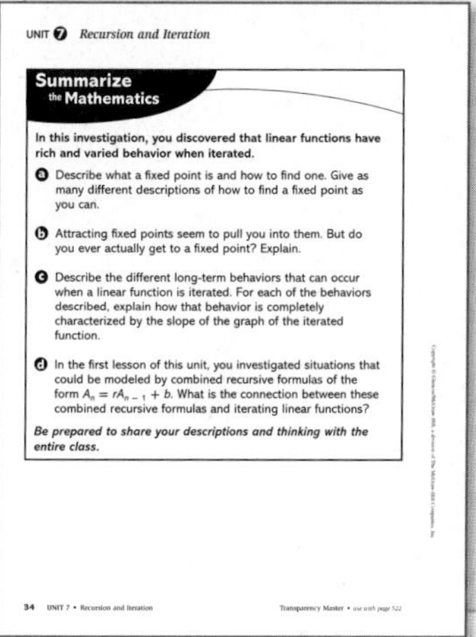
UNIT 7 *Recursion and Iteration*

Summarize the Mathematics

In this investigation, you discovered that linear functions have rich and varied behavior when iterated.

a Describe what a fixed point is and how to find one. Give as many different descriptions of how to find a fixed point as you can.

b Attracting fixed points seem to pull you into them. But do you ever actually get to a fixed point? Explain.

c Describe the different long-term behaviors that can occur when a linear function is iterated. For each of the behaviors described, explain how that behavior is completely characterized by the slope of the graph of the iterated function.

d In the first lesson of this unit, you investigated situations that could be modeled by combined recursive formulas of the form $A_n = rA_{n-1} + b$. What is the connection between these combined recursive formulas and iterating linear functions?

Be prepared to share your descriptions and thinking with the entire class.

34 UNIT 7 • Recursion and Iteration — Transparency Master • *use with page 522*

Unit 7

c Some of the behaviors that students might describe and characterize follow.

- Sequence approaches an attracting fixed point. ($|slope| < 1$)
- Sequence moves away from a repelling fixed point. ($|slope| > 1$)
- There is no fixed point ($slope = 1$ and the y-intercept is not 0).
- Sequence is a two-cycle. Fixed point is not attracting or repelling. ($slope = -1$)
- Stair step pattern of iteration (positive slope)
- Cobweb/spiral pattern of iteration (negative slope)
- Sequence tends to positive infinity. ($slope = 1$ with positive y-intercept, or $slope > 1$ and starting value greater than fixed point)
- Sequence tends to negative infinity. ($slope = 1$ and negative y-intercept, or $slope > 1$ and starting value less than fixed point)
- Sequence oscillates. (negative slope)

d Successively evaluating recursive formulas of the form $A_n = rA_{n-1} + b$ is the same as iterating linear functions, as long as the starting point for each process is the same.

Unit 7

Check Your Understanding

a. $P_n = 0.8P_{n-1} + 1{,}000$, $P_0 = 3{,}000$

b. Iterate $f(x) = 0.8x + 1{,}000$, starting with $x = 3{,}000$.

c. The long-term behavior of the iteration sequence is that it levels off at 5,000. This is the same as the long-term behavior of the trout population.

d.

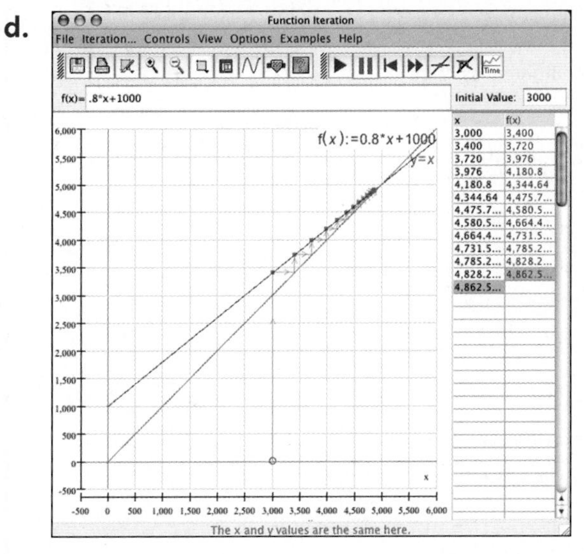

e. Solving $x = 0.8x + 1{,}000$ yields $x = 5{,}000$ as the fixed point. The fixed point is attracting. The slope of the line is 0.8, and $|0.8| < 1$.

f. The fact that the iterated function modeling the fish-population problem has an attracting fixed point at 5,000 tells us that the population will level off over time at 5,000, regardless of where it starts.

INSTRUCTIONAL NOTE
This CYU task is a powerful connection and synthesis with the earlier work in Lesson 1. Be sure students can explain this connection, particularly in Parts c and f.

Unit 7

On Your Own

Applications

1. Consider the three tables below. Describe similarities, differences, and connections among the three tables.

x	$f(x) = 2x + 1$
0	1
1	3
2	5
3	7
⋮	⋮

n	$U_n = 2U_{n-1} + 1$, $U_0 = 1$
0	1
1	3
2	7
3	15
⋮	⋮

x	Iterate $f(x) = 2x + 1$
0	1
1	3
3	7
7	15
⋮	⋮

2. Iterate $f(x) = \frac{1}{x}$, using several different starting values. Describe the iterated behavior. Explain why the iterated behavior makes sense because of the nature of the function f.

3. **a.** Give an example of a function and a starting value such that the iterated sequence increases without bound.

   b. Give an example of a function and a starting value such that the iterated sequence oscillates between positive and negative values.

4. Experiment with iterating the function $f(x) = x^3 - x^2 + 1$.

   a. Describe the behavior of the iteration sequence when you iterate $f(x)$ with the following beginning values.

   i. Begin with $x = 1$.

   ii. Begin with $x = 0.8$.

   iii. Begin with $x = 1.2$.

   b. Find a fixed point for $f(x)$. Is this fixed point repelling, attracting, some combination of repelling and attracting, or none of these? Explain.

5. Experiment with iterating $g(x) = 3.7x - 3.7x^2$.

   a. Find the fixed points of $g(x)$ by writing and solving an appropriate equation.

   b. Iterate $g(x)$ starting with $x = 0.74$, which is close to a fixed point. Carefully examine the iteration sequence by listing these iterations.

   - List iterations 1 through 6.
   - List iterations 16 through 20.
   - List iterations 50 through 55.
   - List iterations 64 through 68.

Unit 7

On Your Own

Applications

1. Students may describe several connections among these three tables. The third table, iterating a function, contains a selection of inputs and outputs from the first table, evaluating a function. The second and third tables have identical output entries, but the input entries are different.

2. For all starting values except 0, the iterated behavior is to oscillate between the starting value and the reciprocal of the starting value. This makes sense since the reciprocal of the reciprocal of a number is the number.

3. **a.** For example, $f(x) = 2^x$, with starting value $x = 3$.

   b. For example, $f(x) = -\frac{1}{x^3}$, with starting value $x = 2$.

4. **a.** **i.** The iterated values are always 1.

   ii. The iterated values are attracted to 1.

   iii. The iterated values are repelled to positive infinity.

   b. A fixed point for $f(x)$ is 1. It is a combination of attracting and repelling. It is attracting when you start with x slightly less than 1 and repelling when you start with x slightly greater than 1.

NOTE The point of Tasks 5 and 6 is to illustrate the variety of behavior that is possible for repelling fixed points. An attracting fixed point always behaves in the same way in that iteration sequences that start close to it converge to it. In contrast, there are many ways that repelling behavior can occur. For example, iteration sequences may "blow up" and tend to positive or negative infinity. They may oscillate and become unbounded, or they may get pushed away from a repelling fixed point and toward an attracting fixed point. Task 5 illustrates another type of behavior, in which iteration sequences get pushed away, then bounce back close, get pushed away again, bounce back, and so on. In Task 6, students will see an example of how iteration sequences can be pushed away to a two-cycle.

5. **a.** Solving $x = 3.7x - 3.7x^2$ produces $x = 0$ or $x = \frac{27}{37} = 0.\overline{729}$.

   b. Student responses may vary. The following uses the suggested initial value, 0.74.

   - Iterations 1–6:
     0.71188, 0.75890, 0.67700, 0.80908, 0.57153, 0.90607
   - Iterations 16–20:
     0.72825, 0.73224, 0.72544, 0.73695, 0.71725
   - Iterations 50–55:
     0.87707, 0.39892, 0.88719, 0.37030, 0.86276, 0.43810
   - Iterations 64–68:
     0.73218, 0.72555, 0.73677, 0.71757, 0.74985

Unit 7

c. Describe any patterns you see in the iteration sequence. Does the iteration sequence get attracted to the fixed point? Does it get steadily repelled?

A fixed point is called repelling if iteration sequences that begin near it get pushed away from the fixed point at some time, even if such sequences occasionally come back close to the fixed point. Is the fixed point at about 0.73 repelling?

6 Consider iterating $h(x) = 3.2x - 0.8x^2$.

a. The fixed points of $h(x)$ are repelling. Do you think you will find them by numerical iteration? Explain your reasoning.

b. Find the fixed points of $h(x)$ using symbolic reasoning.

c. Experiment with iterating $h(x)$, starting with initial values just above and below each fixed point. Carefully describe the characteristics of each fixed point.

7 Function iteration can be used to model population change. Consider, for example, the bowhead whale population described in Applications Task 4 of Lesson 1. A status report on the bowhead whales of Alaska estimated that the 1993 population of this stock was between 6,900 and 9,200 and that the difference between births and deaths yielded an annual growth rate of about 3.1%. No hunting of bowhead whales is allowed, except that Alaskan Inuit are allowed to take, or harvest, about 50 bowhead whales each year for their livelihood. (Source: nmml.afsc.noaa.gov/CetaceanAssessment/bowhead/bmsos.htm)

a. Write a recursive formula and a corresponding function that can be iterated to model this situation.

b. Using the low population estimate as the initial value, iterate and describe the long-term behavior of the population. Do you think this model is a good one to use for predicting the bowhead whale population hundreds of years from now? Why or why not?

c. Find the fixed point. By examining the slope of the graph of the iterated function, decide if the fixed point is attracting or repelling. Illustrate your conclusions by graphically iterating the function.

d. Write a brief analysis of the changing bowhead whale population, as described by your model. As part of your analysis, describe the role played by the fixed point. Make some long-term predictions based on different initial whale populations.

c. The iterated values seem to oscillate above and below 0.73. More interesting, they seem to move away from 0.73, then come back close, then move away, and then come back close, and it seems that this pattern continues. The iterated values do not get attracted to the fixed point, and they are not steadily repelled. But since the iterated values do get repelled at times, we classify the fixed point as repelling.

(A more detailed analysis of this iterated function behavior is the following. There are two fixed points, $x = 0$ and $x = 0.\overline{729} \approx 0.73$. Below 0, iteration sequences are repelled toward negative infinity. Above 1, iteration sequences also tend toward negative infinity. Between 0 and 1 (except at $x = 0.\overline{729}$), there is the pattern seen above: Iteration sequences are pushed away and then at some time jump back toward $0.\overline{729}$. Iteration sequences that begin in this range are not attracted to $0.\overline{729}$. Whenever a sequence gets close to $0.\overline{729}$, either slightly larger or slightly smaller, it is then pushed away. Thus, $x = 0.\overline{729}$ is a repelling fixed point.)

6 **a.** Since the fixed points are repelling, iteration sequences are pushed away from them. Thus, it would be virtually impossible to find them by trial-and-error iteration, since you would not be pulled into them by the iteration.

b. Solving $x = 3.2x - 0.8x^2$ produces $x = 0$ or $x = 2.75$.

c. Initial values below 0 repel to negative infinity; initial values just above 0 are repelled from 0 and then attracted to a two-cycle oscillating between about 2.05 and 3.20. Initial values just above and just below 2.75 are repelled from 2.75 and attracted to the same two-cycle. So, the fixed points are both repelling (and the two-cycle is attracting).

ASSIGNMENT NOTE
This task provides another example of repelling fixed point behavior. See also Applications Task 5.

7 **a.** $U_n = 1.031U_{n-1} - 50$
$f(x) = 1.031x - 50$

b. The long-term behavior is that the iterated values are always increasing. This is not a good model for predicting the population hundreds of years from now. It is not realistic to predict that the whale population will increase without bound. There would be too many possible outside interferences that could cause changes in the population.

c. The fixed point is $\frac{50}{0.031} \approx 1{,}612.9$.
The fixed point is repelling since the slope of the iterated function is 1.031, which is greater than 1.

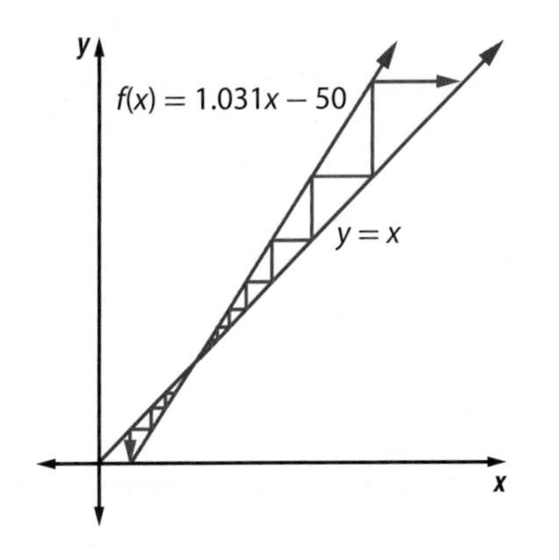

d. If the initial population is greater than the fixed point (1,613 whales), then the population will continue to grow without bound. If the population gets below the fixed point, the population will die out. The further you get beyond the fixed point, the faster the population grows (dies).

Connections

8 Consider iteration of an arbitrary function, $y = f(x)$.

a. Represent the process of iterating $f(x)$ by a rule using the words *NOW* and *NEXT*.

b. Represent the process of iterating $f(x)$ by a recursive formula with subscript notation.

9 In Problem 7 of Investigation 1, you investigated the logistic equation, $f(x) = rx(1 - x)$. You found that different values of r produce different long-term iteration behavior. You can program a computer to play music that corresponds to the long-term behavior. For example, consider the BASIC program below.

```
10  volume = 50
20  duration = 0.5
30  input "r = "; r
40  x = 0.02
50  print x
60  pitch = 220*4^x
70  sound pitch,duration,volume
80  x = r*x*(1-x)
90  go to 50
```

a. Explain the purpose of each step of this program.

b. Enter this program, or an equivalent program, into a computer. Run the program using the values 2.7, 3.2, 3.5, 3.83, and 4.0 for r. Describe the results. Explain how the patterns in sound generated by the computer program compare to the numerical patterns that you found in Problem 7 of Investigation 1.

10 It is possible to use function iteration to solve equations. Consider the equation $x - 3 = 0.5x$.

a. Before solving the equation by using function iteration, solve it using at least two other methods. In each case, explain your method.

b. To solve $x - 3 = 0.5x$ by function iteration, you will make use of fixed points. Consider this equation written in an equivalent form: $x = 0.5x + 3$.

i. Explain why this form is equivalent to the original form.

ii. For what function does this equation define a fixed point?

Connections

8 **a.** $NEXT = f(NOW)$

b. $U_n = f(U_{n-1})$

9 **a.** **10** Set the volume level for the tones.

20 Play a tone for a duration corresponding to 0.5.

30 Ask the user to input a number that will be the value for r.

40 Set the initial value of the sequence to be $x = 0.02$.

50 Print the current value of x (the current term of the iteration sequence).

60 Set a pitch for the tone corresponding to the current value of x. You can see from the formula that higher values of x will have higher tones. Moreover, x values vary between 0 and 1, so the pitch varies between 220Hz and 880Hz, which is between the notes A3 and A5.

70 Play the tone for the current value of x for the defined duration at the defined volume.

80 Generate the next term in the iteration sequence for this function.

90 Repeat the process of printing the current term in the sequence and playing a tone corresponding to the term.

b. How to run the program depends on your system. The program will ask the user to input a value for r. Then it will play tones for each term in the iteration sequence corresponding to that value of r. The tones will indicate the different patterns seen in Problem 7 of Investigation 1. That is, you will hear an attracting fixed point, two-cycle, four-cycle, three-cycle, and "chaos," for $r = 2.7, 3.2, 3.5, 3.83$, and 4.0, respectively. Note that to stop one iteration sequence and start another using a different value of r, you must interrupt the program. How to interrupt depends on your system.

10 **a.** One method is to graph $y = x - 3$ and $y = 0.5x$. Then find the point of intersection; the x value is the solution. A second method is to solve the equation algebraically. The solution is 6.

b. **i.** We can add 3 to both sides of the original equation and get the equivalent equation $x = 0.5x + 3$.

ii. $f(x) = 0.5x + 3$

On Your Own

c. Iterate the function you identified in Part b for some initial value. Describe the long-term behavior. Explain why the observed long-term behavior gives you a solution to the original equation. Compare the solution you obtained to what you found in Part a.

d. Use the method of function iteration to solve $2x + 5 = 6x - 7$. (If at first you do not succeed, try rewriting the equation in an equivalent form.)

e. Summarize the method of function iteration to solve linear equations.

f. When you know several methods for solving a given problem, you should always think about which one is "best." In the case of solving linear equations, would you rather use one of the solution methods from Part a or use function iteration?

11 In this task, you will find and use a general formula for the fixed point of a linear function.

a. Use the algebraic method for finding fixed points to derive a general formula for the fixed point of the linear function $f(x) = rx + b$.

b. Use the general formula to find the fixed point for $h(x) = 0.75x - 4$.

c. If the fixed point is attracting, then you can find it by iteration.

i. How can you tell from the formula for $h(x)$ that this function has an attracting fixed point?

ii. Iterate $h(x)$ to find the fixed point. Compare it to what you found using the general formula in Part b.

12 In Lesson 1, you investigated recursive formulas of the form $A_n = rA_{n-1} + b$. Suppose such a recursive formula represents year-to-year change in some population. Assume that r is a positive number less than 1.

a. Explain why the long-term population in this situation can be found by finding the fixed point of the function $f(x) = rx + b$.

b. Use the general fixed point formula from Part a of Connections Task 11 to explain the following patterns that you previously discovered about the fish population problem in Lesson 1.

- Changing the initial population does not change the long-term population.
- Doubling the restocking amount doubles the long-term population.
- Doubling the population-decrease rate cuts the long-term population in half.

Unit 7

526 UNIT 7 • Recursion and Iteration

c. Regardless of the starting value, the iterated values are attracted to 6, which is the solution to the original equation. This long-term behavior provides a solution to the equation because the fixed point is attracting, and, by definition, the fixed point is the value of x such that $x = f(x)$. So, in this case, the iteration method will generate the solution to the equation.

d. Rewrite the equation as $x = \frac{1}{3}x + 2$ and iterate. The long-term behavior of the sequence will be attracted to the fixed point, 3, which is the solution. Note that this iteration does approach the fixed point because the slope has absolute value less than 1, so the fixed point is attracting. If the equation is reformulated in a way such that the slope is greater than 1 (for example, $x = 3x - 6$), then the fixed point is repelling and cannot be found by iteration.

e. First, rewrite the equation in the form $x = rx + b$, where $|r| < 1$. Then iterate the function $f(x) = rx + b$. Rewriting the equation in this form forces the iterated function to have an attracting fixed point, which is the solution to the original equation.

f. Using function iteration to solve linear equations is a good way to learn this solution method and see a connection to past mathematics. However, function iteration is a cumbersome method compared to other possible solution methods, a fact which students will likely notice.

11 **a.** Setting $x = f(x)$ and solving for x gives $x = \frac{b}{1 - r}$.

b. The fixed point is $\frac{b}{1 - r}$, in this case, $\frac{-4}{1 - 0.75}$, or -16.

c. **i.** The function will have an attracting fixed point if and only if $|slope| < 1$.

ii. The fixed point found by iterating is -16. This is the same point found using the formula.

12 **a.** To find the long-term population, you must find A_n for very large values of n. In terms of the sequence of values of A_n, you can think of successively evaluating A_n and looking for a pattern after many evaluations. This is the same process as looking for the long-term behavior when iterating $f(x) = rx + b$. Since $|r| < 1$, the fixed point of $f(x)$ is attracting. Thus, the fixed point of $f(x)$ will give the long-term population.

b. From Connections Task 11, we know that the fixed point, and thus the long-term population in this case, is $\frac{b}{1 - r}$.

- The initial population is not part of this formula, so changing the initial population will not affect the long-term population.
- Doubling the restocking amount means doubling b, which will double the numerator in the formula for the long-term population. Thus, the long-term population is doubled.
- r is the population growth rate, so $1 - r$ is the population decrease rate. Thus, doubling the population decrease rate will double $1 - r$, which doubles the denominator in the formula for long-term population. So, the long-term population is cut in half.

Unit 7

Reflections

13 In this unit, you have studied recursion in several contexts, for example, recursive formulas and function iteration. Recursion is sometimes described as a "self-referral" process. Explain why this is a reasonable description of recursion.

14 In this lesson, you briefly explored a famous equation in mathematics and science called the logistic equation (also called the logistic map), $f(x) = rx(1 - x)$. This equation was first studied extensively in the 1970s. Some of the first discoveries about the behavior of the iterated function came from trying to apply it as a model in biology and ecology. Its behavior turned out to be surprisingly complex and profound, giving rise to what is sometimes called *chaos theory*.

a. Review what you found out about the iterated behavior of the logistic equation in Problem 7 of Investigation 1, page 518. Why do you think the term "chaos" has been used to describe certain long-term behavior of the logistic equation?

b. One of the first investigators of the logistic equation was an Australian physicist and biologist named Robert May. May argued that the world would be a better place if every student was given a pocket calculator and encouraged to play with the logistic equation. What do you think May meant?

c. *Optional:* Obtain a copy of the book *Chaos: Making a New Science* by James Gleick (New York: Viking, 1987). Read Chapter 3, entitled "Life's Ups and Downs." This chapter is an entertaining account of some of the history of the logistic equation. Write a two-page report summarizing the chapter.

15 The idea of "chaos" in mathematics comes from a new area of mathematics that is sometimes called *chaos theory*. Chaos theory is related to certain long-term behavior of the logistic equation, which you examined in Problem 7 of Investigation 1, page 518. Read the article on the next page, which attempts to apply chaos theory to politics. Summarize the description of chaos given in the article.

How does this description relate to the long-term behavior of the logistic equation? Do you think the conclusions in the article are valid? Why or why not?

Reflections

13 Recursion seems like a self-referral process because, for example, an iterated function must refer back to itself in order to produce the next values. With population, you need to know the population now before you can know the next population; thus, population refers back to population. Likewise, amount of money saved now refers back to amount of money saved previously.

14 **a.** With minor changes in the value of r, different things happen. The iterated values get attracted, cycle, get repelled, or follow no observable pattern at all. It is difficult to predict what will happen with different values of r. More to the point, the long-term behavior for $r = 4$ showed no discernible pattern, that is, chaos. In this case, with $r = 4$, not all calculator and computer outputs will agree on the iteration, not only because of round-off errors but also, and more importantly, because of the nature of the chaotic behavior, in particular, the property of chaos to have "sensitive dependence on initial conditions." This means even a very small difference in initial conditions can result in wildly different long-term behavior. Thus, if at any given point in the iteration two calculators disagree slightly (due to round-off), then they are liable to disagree considerably later.

b. Responses will vary. Robert May was probably referring to the incredibly rich and complex behavior of this simple equation when it is iterated. Experimenting with this equation and seeing the rich tapestry of patterns that emerge might, at least it seemed to May, create a sense of wonder about and appreciation for the complexity that resides in even mundane-looking mathematical equations. Perhaps people gaining this perspective would, in May's mind, contribute to a better world.

c. Reports will vary.

15 **INSTRUCTIONAL NOTE** You may want to suggest that students read the chapter mentioned in Part c of Reflections Task 14 in preparation for doing this task. Chaos is characterized in the newspaper article in several ways. Each is mentioned below and related to the behavior of the logistic equation that students studied in the lesson.

- ... "butterfly fluttering its wings in Argentina which ultimately leads to a thunderstorm in New Jersey." This relates to the idea that a small change in initial conditions (butterfly wing flutterings) can cause big changes in the long-term behavior (thunderstorm in New Jersey). The author of the article is probably referring to a property of chaos called "sensitive dependence on initial conditions."
- ... "you will not be able to predict, with any degree of precision, when lightning will form and strike ... ." This relates to the fact that the chaotic behavior seen when iterating the logistic equation when $r = 4$ is completely deterministic in that there is a specific formula (the logistic equation) that determines what the iteration values will be. Yet, it is unpredictable in that you cannot predict what the exact pattern of the iteration sequence will be.

NOTE The remainder of the solution to Task 15 is on page T528.

Counting on Chaos to Save Day for Dole

by Al Kamen

It's come to this. Robert J. Dole's poll numbers are so bad that Rich Galen, director of political communications for House Speaker Newt Gingrich (R-Ga.), is touting "Chaos Theory" to inspire the GOP faithful.

"Stay with me, here," Galen began in a memo written last week "For Distribution to Talk Show Hosts," a regular salvo he sends out to about 100 or so conservative radio folks.

"There is a relatively new branch of science which is called Chaos Theory," he explained. It talks about a "butterfly fluttering its wings in Argentina which ultimately leads to a thunderstorm in New Jersey."

But "you will not be able to predict, with any degree of precision, when lightning will form and strike ... One second there is no lightning, and the next second the sky is bright. Chaos."

He went on: "Take another example. Suppose you take a wineglass and begin to squeeze it at its upper rim. If you continue to apply pressure, at some point the glass will break. The system will collapse entirely and instantaneously. Until the moment it breaks, it will be a perfectly usable glass. After the glass breaks, it will be nothing but a pile of shards."

"What does this have to do with the presidential campaign?" Galen asked, which seems like a pretty good question.

"My strong impression is there will come a time ... when the Clinton campaign, like the glass, will entirely and instantaneously collapse. One moment it will be a campaign, the next moment it will be unrecognizable."

"That's why we don't have to be frightened by the current Dole-Clinton polling numbers," he said. Chaos theory will save the day, or at least win New Jersey.

"What we must do, however, is to continue to keep the pressure on. If we get discouraged [and] stop squeezing the rim of the glass, then the glass will never break."

Now we know why the Republicans are infinitely more interesting than the Democrats. The Republicans look to science. All the Democrats can say is: "It's the economy, stupid."

Source: *The Washington Post*, September 16, 1996.

16 Explain why the fixed points for a function $f(x)$ correspond to the points of intersection of the graphs of $y = f(x)$ and $y = x$.

17 Why do you think it is sometimes said that you can never "see" a repelling fixed point?

528 UNIT 7 • Recursion and Iteration

- The article talks about gradually squeezing a wineglass until, suddenly, it breaks. The author may be referring here to the sudden onset of chaos that is evident when iterating the logistic equation with different values of r. As you gradually increase r, the long-term behavior changes, but it is stable in the sense that it is characterized by attraction toward fixed points or cycles. Then, suddenly, somewhere between $r = 3.83$ and $r = 4$, chaos sets in, and there is no discernible pattern in the long-term behavior.

It is interesting that this new branch of mathematical analysis has attracted so much attention that it appears even in articles such as this. However, the analogy made in the article is nothing more than an analogy; the points made are rather superficial. To really apply chaos theory to politics would require a much more careful analysis.

16. By definition, a fixed point for a function $f(x)$ is a number x such that $x = f(x)$. To graphically find a number such that $x = f(x)$, you must look for the points of intersection of the graphs of $y = x$ and $y = f(x)$.

17. Iteration sequences will not converge to a repelling fixed point, so you will never see them by experimental iteration unless you get unbelievably lucky and choose the fixed point itself to begin your iteration.

Extensions

18 The recursive formula for a geometric sequence looks like a combined recursive formula of the form $A_n = rA_{n-1} + b$ without the added b. This connection can be used to find a function formula for such combined recursive formulas. The strategy involves building from a function formula for a geometric sequence.

a. What is the function formula for a geometric sequence with recursive formula $A_n = rA_{n-1}$ and initial value A_0?

b. As the next step, think about the long-term behavior of $A_n = r^n A_0$. Compare it to the long-term behavior of $A_n = rA_{n-1} + b$. Consider the situation when $|r| < 1$.

- **i.** Explain why $A_n = rA_{n-1} + b$ has an attractive fixed point for its long-term behavior.
- **ii.** What is the long-term behavior of $A_n = r^n A_0$?

c. Now modify the formula $A_n = r^n A_0$ so that it has the same long-term behavior as $A_n = rA_{n-1} + b$, as follows. Begin by adding the fixed point, denoted *FIX*, to the function formula $A_n = r^n A_0$ so that the new function will have the same long-term behavior as $A_n = rA_{n-1} + b$. Explain why $A_n = r^n A_0 + FIX$ has long-term behavior converging to *FIX*, if $|r| < 1$.

d. Finally, modify the formula $A_n = r^n A_0 + FIX$ so that it has the same initial value A_0 as $A_n = rA_{n-1} + b$.

- **i.** Explain why the initial value of $A_n = r^n A_0 + FIX$ is equal to $A_0 + FIX$.
- **ii.** Explain why the initial value of $A_n = r^n(A_0 - FIX) + FIX$ is equal to A_0.

e. As you explained in Part d, the function formula $A_n = r^n(A_0 - FIX) + FIX$ has the same long-term behavior and the same initial value as the combined recursive formula $A_n = rA_{n-1} + b$. Use this new type of formula to find A_5 for $A_n = 2A_{n-1} + 1$, with $A_0 = 3$. Then compute A_5 by successively evaluating $A_n = 2A_{n-1} + 1$, and compare your two results.

f. Compare the function formula in Part e to the function formula you derived in Connections Task 11 of Lesson 2 (page 503). Resolve any apparent differences.

19 In Connections Task 10, you investigated the method of function iteration to solve linear equations. Investigate if this method will work for quadratic equations. Consider the quadratic equation $2x^2 + 5x = 3$.

a. Find a function that you could iterate in order to use the method of function iteration to solve this equation. Iterate with several different initial values. Describe the results in each case.

b. Solve this equation using another method. How many solutions are there?

Extensions

18 **a.** $A_n = r^n A_0$

b. **i.** The long-term behavior of $A_n = rA_{n-1} + b$ is the same as the long-term behavior when iterating $f(x) = rx + b$. We know that since $|r| < 1$, the fixed point of this iterated function is attracting.

ii. When the absolute value of r is less than one and you raise r to bigger values of n, the result gets closer and closer to zero. Thus, the product $r^n A_0$ is getting closer and closer to zero. That is, it has long-term behavior of convergence to zero.

c. If $|r| < 1$, then r^n will converge to 0 as n gets very large (long-term behavior). Thus, $r^n A_0$ will converge to 0, so $r^n A_0 + FIX$ will converge to FIX.

d. **i.** When looking for the initial value, set $n = 0$. This will give you $r^0 A_0 + FIX$. Since $r^0 = 1$ $(r \neq 0)$, the initial value is $A_0 + FIX$.

ii. Substituting $n = 0$ gives $A_0 = r^0(A_0 - FIX) + FIX = 1(A_0 - FIX) + FIX = A_0$.

e. The fixed point of $y = 2x + 1$ is -1, so $A_n = 2^n(3 + 1) - 1 = 4(2^n) - 1$.
$A_5 = 4(2^5) - 1 = 127$
Using the recursive formula:
$A_0 = 3; A_1 = 7; A_2 = 15; A_3 = 31; A_4 = 63; A_5 = 127.$
They are the same value.

f. The function formula derived in Connections Task 11 of Lesson 2, on page 503, is $A_n = r^n A_0 + b\left(\frac{r^n - 1}{r - 1}\right)$. The fixed point of $A_n = rA_{n-1} + b$ can be found by solving $x = rx + b$. This yields $\frac{b}{1 - r}$. Substituting $\frac{b}{1 - r}$ for FIX in the formula $A_n = r^n(A_0 - FIX) + FIX$ produces the following:

$$\begin{aligned} A_n &= r^n\left(A_0 - \frac{b}{1 - r}\right) + \frac{b}{1 - r} \\ &= r^n A_0 - r^n\left(\frac{b}{1 - r}\right) + \frac{b}{1 - r} \\ &= r^n A_0 - b\left(\frac{r^n - 1}{1 - r}\right) \\ &= r^n A_0 + b\left(\frac{r^n - 1}{r - 1}\right) \end{aligned}$$

This algebraic reformulating shows that the two formulas are equivalent.

19 **a.** To find a function to iterate, you need to solve the given equation for x so that it is in the form $x = f(x)$. There are several ways to do this. One way will be illustrated here. By factoring the left-hand side of the given equation and dividing by $(2x + 5)$, we get $x = \frac{3}{2x + 5}$. Iterating $f(x) = \frac{3}{2x + 5}$ starting anywhere except $x = -3$ or $x = -2.5$ will go to the fixed point of $x = 0.5$.

b. Algebraic or graphical methods can be used to obtain the two solutions $x = 0.5$ and $x = -3$.

DIFFERENTIATION This On Your Own task and others address the explicit formula for the fish population problem. See the Lesson 2 introduction for a list of relevant tasks.

NOTE Other ways to find a function to iterate may be more or less complicated. The reasoning will be similar, although the repelling or attracting behavior of the fixed points may vary depending on the iterated function. See Part d.

c. What properties of fixed points allow you to either find or not find a solution when using the method of function iteration?

d. Use your calculator or computer software to help you sketch graphs of the iterated function and $y = x$ on the same set of axes. (Your graph may look different than the one shown here, depending on which function you found to iterate in Part a.) Locate the fixed points on this graph. At each of the fixed points, visualize a line drawn tangent to the graph of the iterated function at the fixed point.

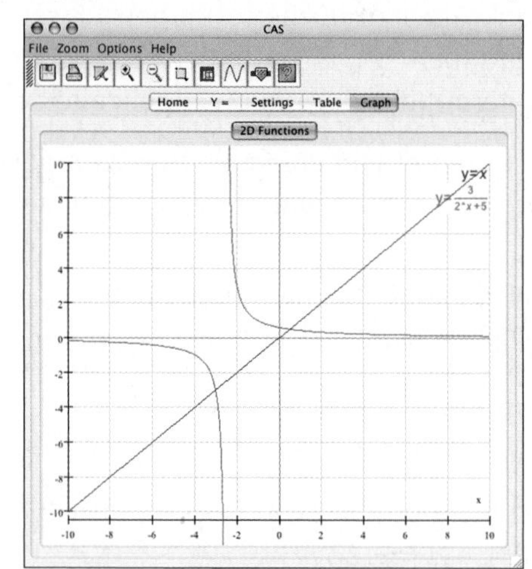

Estimate the slope of each of these tangent lines. For which fixed point is the absolute value of the slope of the tangent line greater than 1? For which tangent line is the absolute value of the slope less than 1?

e. Recall the connection between iterating linear functions and slope. Explain how the slope of the tangent line at a fixed point tells you if the fixed point is attracting or repelling. Explain what attracting or repelling fixed points have to do with solving nonlinear equations using the method of function iteration.

20 Although it is relatively easy to iterate linear functions graphically by hand with a fair degree of accuracy, it is quite difficult to iterate nonlinear functions graphically. This is because, as you have seen, the shape of a graphical iteration is determined by the slope of the graph of the iterated function. And while lines have constant slopes, graphs of nonlinear functions have changing slopes. Thus, it is usually necessary to use a computer or graphing calculator to accurately iterate nonlinear functions graphically. Graphical iteration capability is built into many calculators and computer graphing packages.

a. Consult a manual, if necessary, to find how to use your calculator or computer software to iterate graphically. Practice by graphically iterating $f(x) = -0.8x + 6$. You should get a graph that looks like the one at the right.

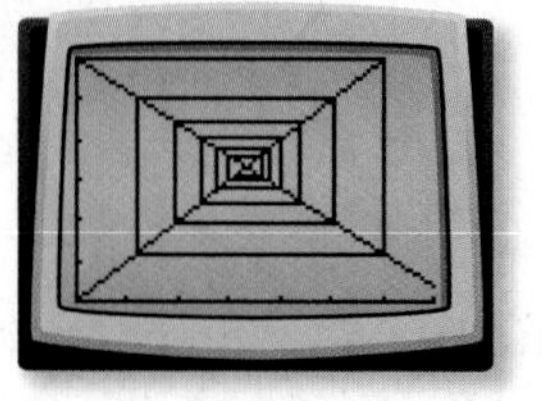

c. The fixed points in the context of function iteration are the solutions to the equation. You will probably find a fixed point by iteration if it is attracting. You will probably not find it by iteration if it is repelling.

d. The fixed points are shown by the intersection of the graphs of $y = x$ and $y = \frac{3}{2x + 5}$.

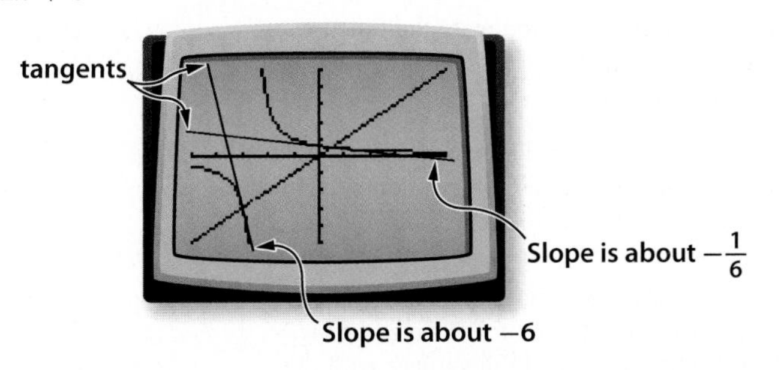

At the fixed point −3, the absolute value of the slope of the tangent is 6, which is greater than 1. The absolute value of the slope of the tangent at 0.5 is $\frac{1}{6}$, which is less than 1.

(If a different function is found in Part a such that $x = f(x)$, then you will get the same fixed points, but they may not have the same repelling or attracting behavior. For example, if in Part a you solve for x such that $x = 3 - 2x^2 - 4x$, then you will iterate the function $f(x) = 3 - 2x^2 - 4x$ to try to find the solutions of the original equation. The solutions are still the fixed points, $x = 0.5$ and $x = -3$, but now the graph looks very different than what is shown in the text. The slopes of the tangent lines at the fixed points are both greater than 1 in absolute value, and thus both fixed points are repelling.)

e. If the absolute value of the slope of the tangent at the fixed point is less than 1, then it will be an attracting fixed point. If the absolute value of the slope of the tangent at the fixed point is greater than 1, then it will be a repelling fixed point.

If there is an attracting fixed point when solving a nonlinear equation by function iteration, then that fixed point, which is a solution to the equation, will probably be found; if the fixed point is repelling, then it is highly unlikely that you will find it by iteration.

20 **a.** Since this is an Extensions task, it is reasonable to expect students to read a manual, if necessary, to determine how to graphically iterate a function using a calculator or computer. On the TI-83, TI-84, and TI-89, the mode must be set to **Seq**, and the graphing format must be set to **Web**.

After entering the function and setting the starting point and the window, using the trace command and arrow buttons will draw the graphical iteration. Alternatively, students might use *CPMP-Tools* to do graphical iteration.

b. In Applications Task 6, you were asked to iterate the function $h(x) = 3.2x - 0.8x^2$. Use a graphing calculator or computer software to iterate $h(x)$ graphically, starting with $x = 2.6$. Compare the graphical iteration pattern to the numerical iteration results.

c. In Applications Task 4, you were asked to iterate the function $f(x) = x^3 - x^2 + 1$. Graphically iterate $f(x)$ to illustrate each of your results in Applications Task 4.

21 In this lesson, you iterated algebraic functions. It is also possible to iterate geometric transformations. As an example, play the following "Chaos Game." (Algorithm originally described in Barnsley, M., *Fractals Everywhere*, Academic Press, 1988.)

a. On a clean sheet of paper, draw the vertices of a large triangle. Any type of triangle will work; but for your first time playing the game, use an isosceles triangle. Label the vertices with the numbers 1, 2, and 3.

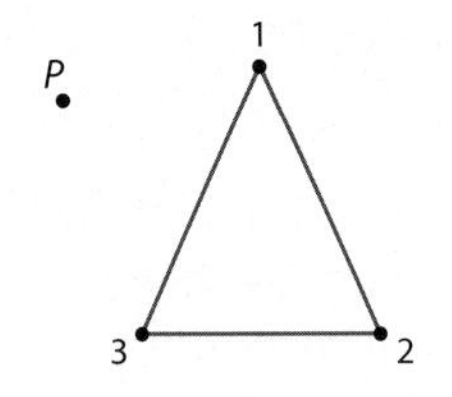

b. Start with a point anywhere on the sheet of paper. This is your initial input. Randomly choose one of the vertices (for example, use a random number generator to choose one of the numbers 1, 2, or 3). Mark a new point one-half of the distance between your input and that vertex. This is your first output and also your new input. Then randomly choose another vertex. Mark the next point, half the distance from the new input to that vertex. Repeat this process until you have plotted six points.

c. The goal of the Chaos Game is to see what happens in the long term. What do you think the pattern of plotted points will look like if you plot 300 points? Make a conjecture.

d. Program a calculator or computer to play the Chaos Game, or find such a program on the Internet, and then carry out several hundred iterations. Since you are interested only in the long-term behavior, you might carry out the first ten iterations without plotting the resulting points and then plot all points thereafter.

e. Repeat the game for several other initial points. Do you think you will always get the same resulting figure? Try it.

f. The figure that results from the Chaos Game is an example of a familiar *fractal*. One of the most important characteristics of fractals is that they are *self-similar*, which means that if you zoom in, you keep seeing figures just like the original figure. What is the scale factor of successively smaller triangles in the fractal that you produced?

g. Give a geometrical explanation for why the Chaos Game will always generate a Sierpinski triangle. (For more about Sierpinski triangles, see Applications Task 3 from Lesson 2 on page 500.)

b. Student graphs should look like the one at the right. After several iterations, the cobweb graph "cycles" over and over in the same rectangle. The values that it cycles between are the same values found by numerical iteration in Applications Task 6 on page 524, that is, about 3.20 and 2.05.

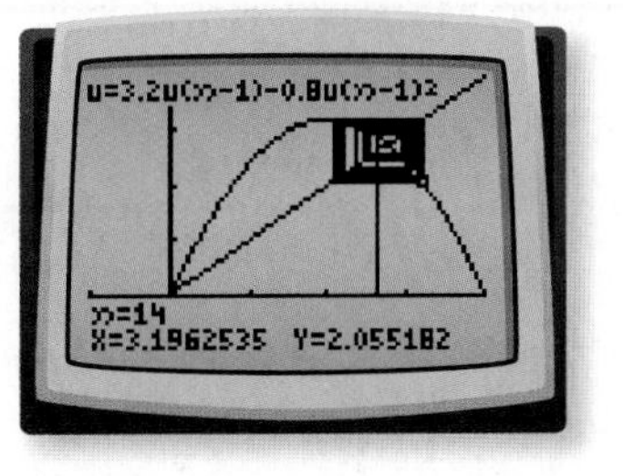

c. When the initial value is 1, the fixed point stays at 1.

When the initial value is 0.8, the fixed point is attracted to 1.

When the initial value is 1.2, the fixed point is repelled.

21 **a–b.** See students' work. Students should have six points plotted from their Chaos Game.

c. It is unlikely that students will conjecture the correct pattern.

d. For example, see the sample program in the manual for the TI-83 calculator (page 17-7).

This is an example created using a TI-84.

e. For the same starting triangle, you will always get the same general pattern, no matter what initial point is used.

f. The scale factor is $\frac{1}{2}$. Each triangle has sides $\frac{1}{2}$ the length of the next larger triangle.

NOTE The solution to Task 21 Part g is on page T532.

Unit 7

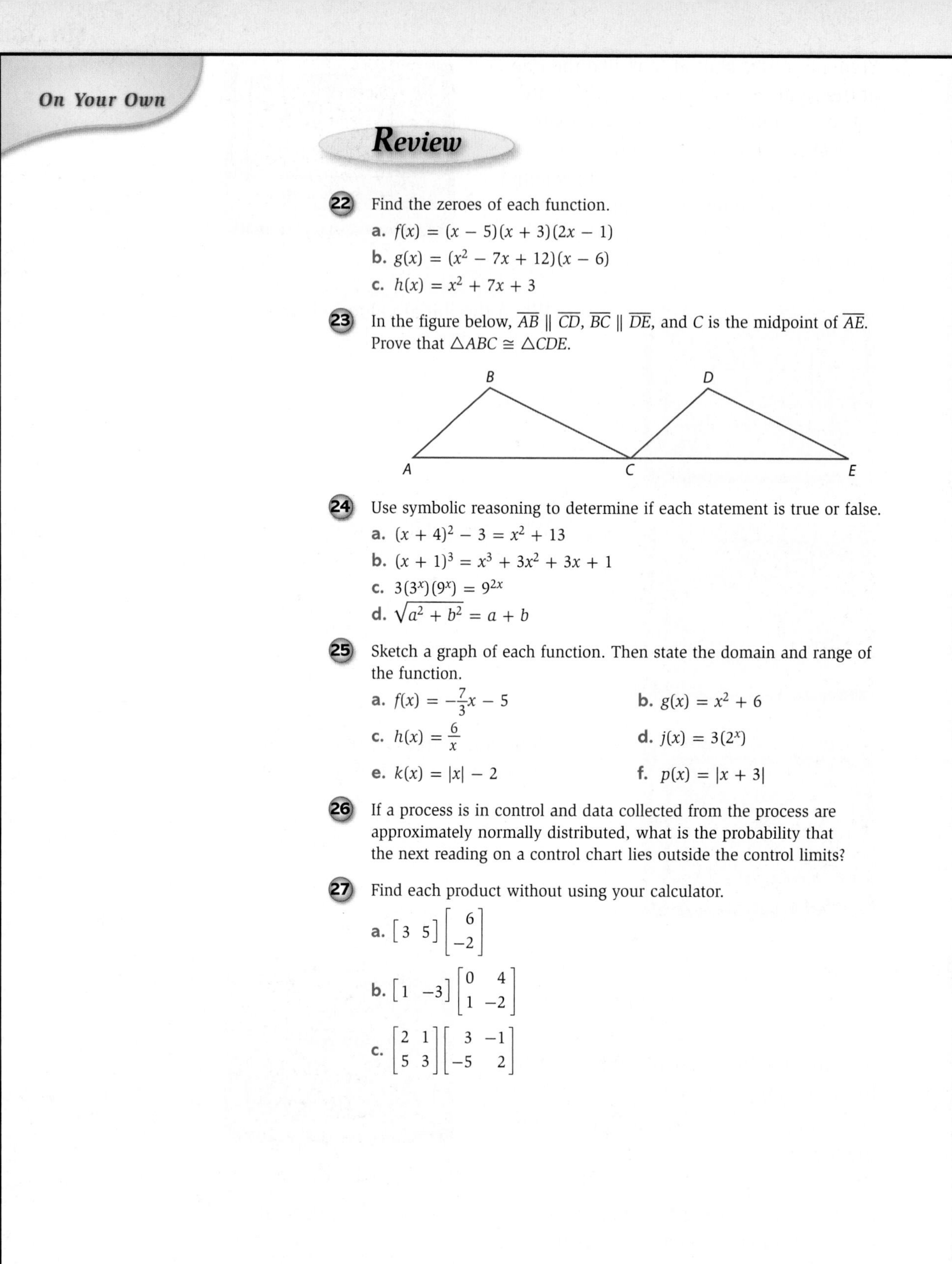

On Your Own

Review

22 Find the zeroes of each function.

a. $f(x) = (x - 5)(x + 3)(2x - 1)$

b. $g(x) = (x^2 - 7x + 12)(x - 6)$

c. $h(x) = x^2 + 7x + 3$

23 In the figure below, $\overline{AB} \parallel \overline{CD}$, $\overline{BC} \parallel \overline{DE}$, and C is the midpoint of $\overline{AE}$. Prove that $\triangle ABC \cong \triangle CDE$.

24 Use symbolic reasoning to determine if each statement is true or false.

a. $(x + 4)^2 - 3 = x^2 + 13$

b. $(x + 1)^3 = x^3 + 3x^2 + 3x + 1$

c. $3(3^x)(9^x) = 9^{2x}$

d. $\sqrt{a^2 + b^2} = a + b$

25 Sketch a graph of each function. Then state the domain and range of the function.

a. $f(x) = -\frac{7}{3}x - 5$

b. $g(x) = x^2 + 6$

c. $h(x) = \frac{6}{x}$

d. $j(x) = 3(2^x)$

e. $k(x) = |x| - 2$

f. $p(x) = |x + 3|$

26 If a process is in control and data collected from the process are approximately normally distributed, what is the probability that the next reading on a control chart lies outside the control limits?

27 Find each product without using your calculator.

a. $\begin{bmatrix} 3 & 5 \end{bmatrix} \begin{bmatrix} 6 \\ -2 \end{bmatrix}$

b. $\begin{bmatrix} 1 & -3 \end{bmatrix} \begin{bmatrix} 0 & 4 \\ 1 & -2 \end{bmatrix}$

c. $\begin{bmatrix} 2 & 1 \\ 5 & 3 \end{bmatrix} \begin{bmatrix} 3 & -1 \\ -5 & 2 \end{bmatrix}$

532 UNIT 7 • Recursion and Iteration

g. An alternative way to get a Sierpinski triangle is to successively remove triangles formed by joining the midpoints of sides of existing triangles. Suppose one of the early iteration points is in one of the removed triangles. In the next iteration, it will move half the distance to some vertex. This will put the next point in one of the removed triangles at the next level, since the removed triangles at a given level consist of all the points that are half the distance to the three vertices from points in the previous level (larger) removed triangle.

Thus, as the iteration continues, points will move from a removed triangle at one level to a removed triangle at the next (smaller) level. After a few iterations, the point will be in a removed triangle that is too small to see, so it will appear to be in one of the infinitely chopped-up regions that make up the Sierpinski triangle.

Note that the resulting figure is a Sierpinski triangle because we started with a triangle. Starting with 5 points at the vertices of a pentagon or 6 points at the vertices of a hexagon will result in a Sierpinski pentagon or hexagon, respectively. However, starting with a square will not yield a "Sierpinski square." Instead, the entire square will be filled.

Review

22 **a.** $x = 5$, $x = -3$, $x = \frac{1}{2}$

b. $x = 6$, $x = 3$, $x = 4$

c. $x = -\frac{7}{2} \pm \frac{\sqrt{37}}{2}$

23 One possible proof is provided.
Since $\overline{AB} \parallel \overline{CD}$ and $\angle 1$ and $\angle 2$ are corresponding angles, we know that $\angle 1 \cong \angle 2$. Similarly, since $\overline{BC} \parallel \overline{DE}$ and $\angle 3$ and $\angle 4$ are corresponding angles, we know that $\angle 3 \cong \angle 4$. Since C is the midpoint of $\overline{AE}$, $\overline{AC} \cong \overline{CE}$. Thus, $\triangle ABC \cong \triangle CDE$ (ASA).

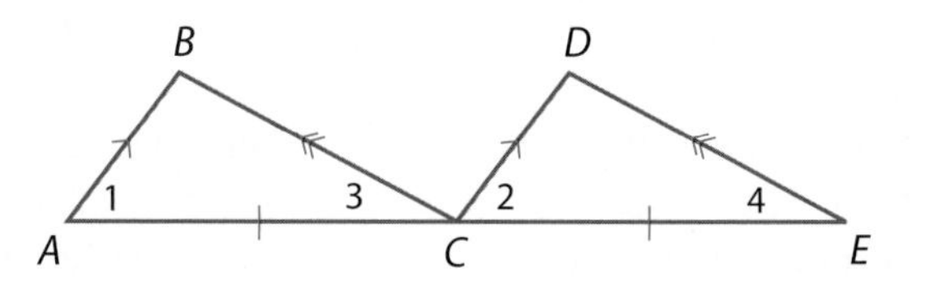

24 **a.** False
$(x + 4)^2 - 3 = x^2 + 8x + 16 - 3 = x^2 + 8x + 13 \neq x^2 + 13$

b. True

$$\begin{aligned}(x + 1)^3 &= (x + 1)^2(x + 1)\\ &= (x^2 + 2x + 1)(x + 1)\\ &= x^3 + x^2 + 2x^2 + 2x + x + 1\\ &= x^3 + 3x^2 + 3x + 1\end{aligned}$$

c. False
$3(3^x)(9^x) \neq (9^x)(9^x) = (9^x)^2 = 9^{2x}$

d. False
A counterexample is $\sqrt{3^2 + 4^2} \neq 7$. Symbolically, if $\sqrt{a^2 + b^2} = a + b$, then $a^2 + b^2 = (a + b)^2$, but $(a + b)^2 = a^2 + 2ab + b^2 \neq a^2 + b^2$.

25 **a.**

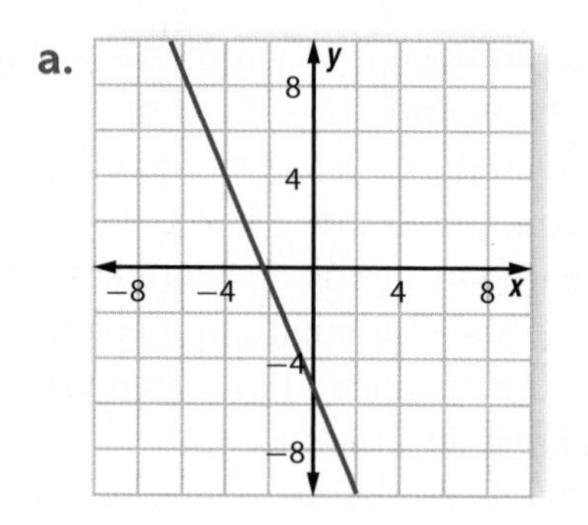

The domain and range are all real numbers.

b.

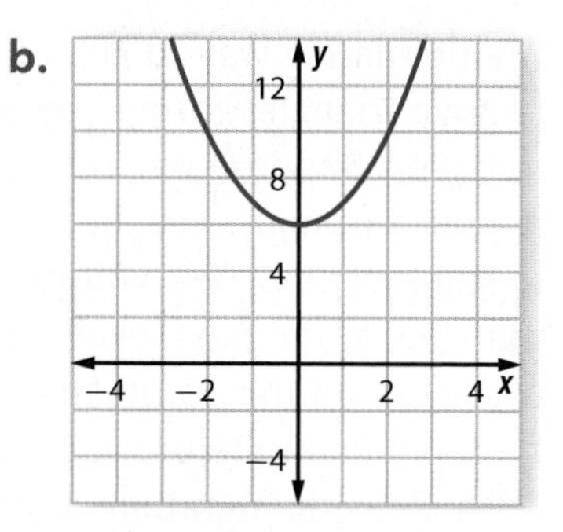

The domain is all real numbers. The range is all real numbers greater than or equal to 6.

c.

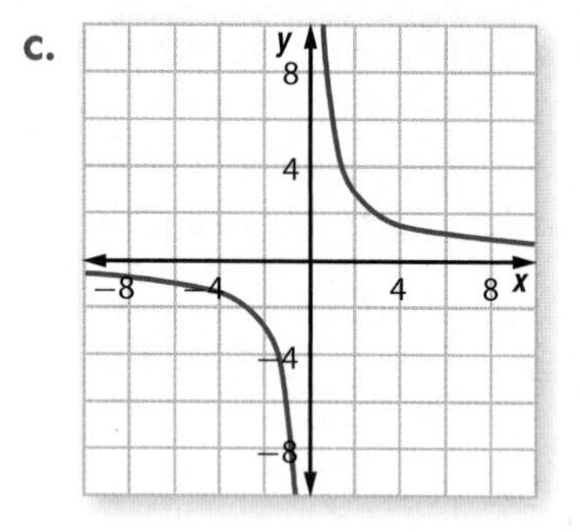

The domain and range are all real numbers except zero.

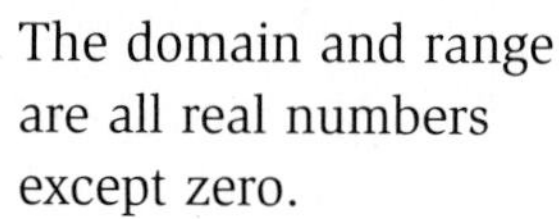

d.

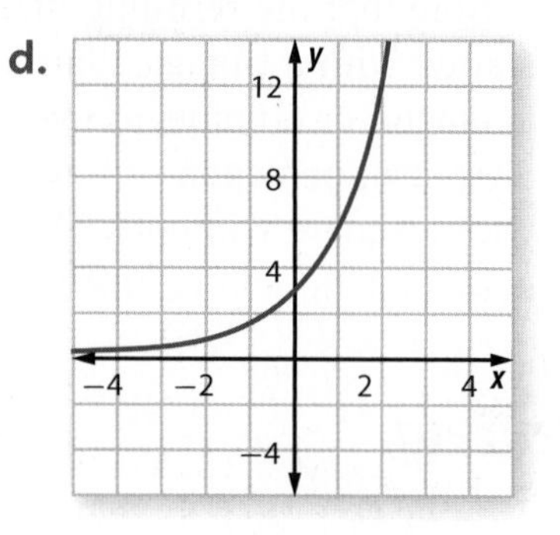

The domain is all real numbers. The range is all positive real numbers.

e.

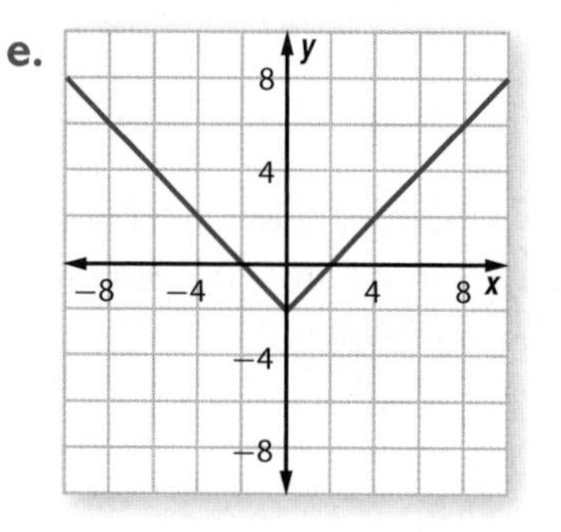

The domain is all real numbers. The range is all real numbers greater than or equal to −2.

f.

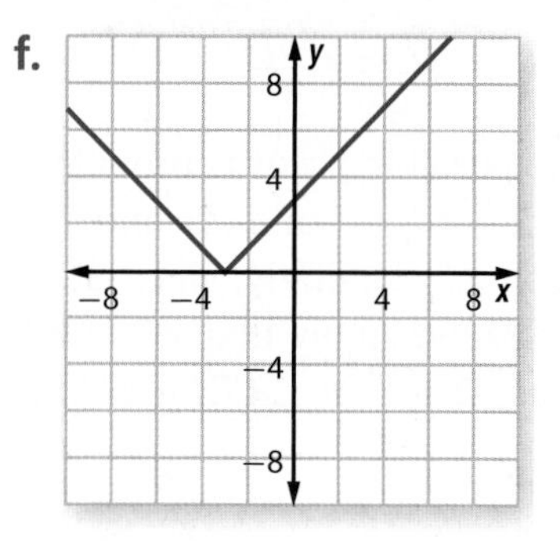

The domain is all real numbers. The range is all non-negative real numbers.

26 Assume that the control limits are at ±3 standard deviations from the mean. Since 99.7% of the values are within three standard deviations of the mean, approximately 0.3% of the values are more than three standard deviations from the mean. Thus, the probability of the next reading on the control chart lying outside the control limits is 0.003.

27
a. $[8]$

b. $[-3 \quad 10]$

c. $\begin{bmatrix} 1 & 0 \\ 0 & 1 \end{bmatrix}$

Teaching Resources

Assessment Masters 35–40.

UNIT 7 Recursion and Iteration

Name
Date

LESSON 3 QUIZ

Form A

1. Consider the recursive formula $U_n = 0.7U_{n-1} + 1$.

a. What function can be iterated to yield the same sequence of numbers generated by the recursive formula?

b. Iterate the function, starting with $x = 10$. Write the first five terms of the sequence.

c. Describe the long-term behavior of the function iteration.

d. Does the long-term behavior of an iteration of this function depend on the starting value? Explain your reasoning.

Assessment Master • use after Lesson 3 UNIT 7 • Recursion and Iteration 35

Looking Back

In this unit, you have investigated sequential change in a variety of contexts using the tools of recursion and iteration. You have extended the idea of using *NOW-NEXT* formulas to model sequential change; you have studied recursive formulas, function iteration, and sequences; and you have made connections to previous work with linear, exponential, and polynomial functions. In this final lesson, you will pull together and review the key ideas in the unit.

1 In Lesson 1, you modeled a variety of situations with combined recursive formulas of the form $A_n = rA_{n-1} + b$. In Lesson 3, you iterated linear functions. These two topics are closely connected. In this task, you will summarize key features of that connection.

By using different values for r and b in the combined recursive formula $A_n = rA_{n-1} + b$, you can build models for different situations. Four different possibilities are indicated by the table below. One recursive formula has already been entered into the table. If you completed Applications Task 6 on page 471, you already have a start on this task.

Four Different Versions of the Recursive Formula $A_n = rA_{n-1} + b$

	$0 < r < 1$	$r > 1$
$b < 0$		
$b > 0$	$A_n = 0.8A_{n-1} + 1{,}000$	

Choose *one* of the empty table cells. In a copy of the table, write an appropriate recursive formula in the cell and then analyze the recursive formula and its use as a mathematical model. Title your work with the particular recursive formula on which you are reporting. Organize your analysis of the recursive formula as follows.

a. Briefly describe a real-world situation that can be modeled by the recursive formula along with a chosen initial value.

b. Rewrite the recursive formula as a *NOW-NEXT* formula.

Unit 7

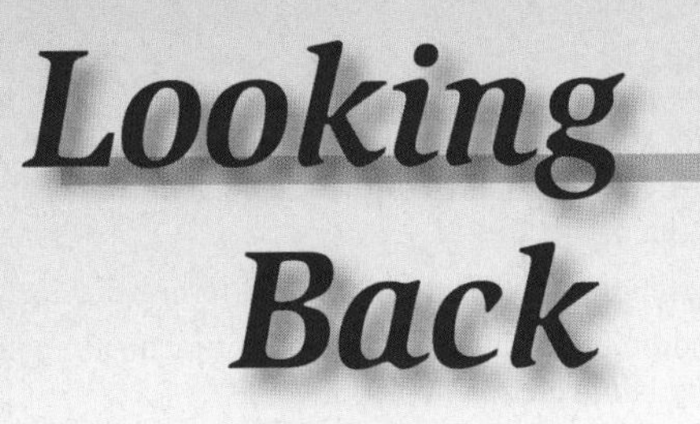

LESSON 4

In this lesson, students will pull together what they have learned about using iteration and recursion to model and solve problems related to sequential change, including the study of arithmetic and geometric sequences, the method of finite differences, a recursive view of linear, exponential, and polynomial functions, function iteration, and specific study of recursive formulas of the form $U_n = rU_{n-1} + b$.

1 Two possible recursive formulas and appropriate responses are given below.

Four Different Versions of the Recursive Formula $A_n = rA_{n-1} + b$

	$r < 1$	$r > 1$
$b < 0$	$A_n = 0.8A_{n-1} - 200$	$A_n = 1.06A_{n-1} - 350$
$b > 0$	$A_n = 0.8A_{n-1} + 1{,}000$	$A_n = 1.01A_{n-1} + 35$

Sample 1: $A_n = 0.8A_{n-1} - 200$

a. Whale population has a death rate higher than birthrate with a net result of 20% decrease in population each year. In addition, 200 whales are harvested each year. Suppose the initial population is 2,000 whales.

b. *NEXT* = 0.8*NOW* − 200, starting at 2,000

Unit 7

c. Write a linear function that can be iterated to yield the same sequence as the successive values of the recursive formula. Choose an initial value.

i. Iterate the function, and describe the long-term behavior.

ii. Find the fixed point. Decide whether it is attracting, repelling, or neither. Explain in terms of slope.

iii. Sketch a graph showing graphical iteration of the function for the initial value previously chosen.

d. Sketch a graph of A_n versus n, using the same initial value that you chose in Part c.

e. Describe the long-term behavior of the real-world situation being modeled, for different initial values. Refer to the fixed point and its properties, but keep your description in the context of the particular situation being modeled.

2 Many irregular shapes found in the natural world can be modeled by fractals. Study the first few stages of the fractal tree shown below.

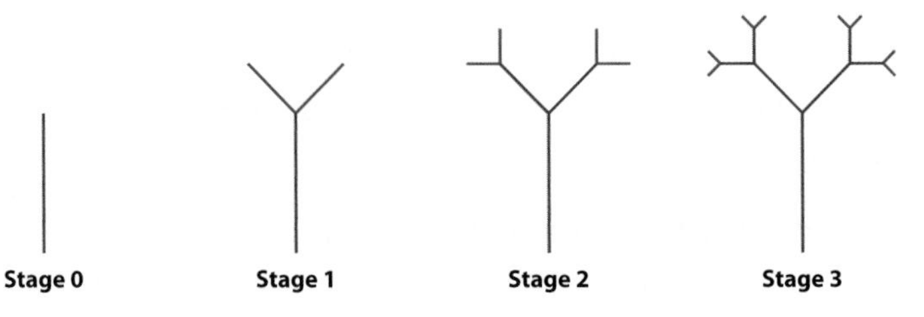

a. Write the number of new branches at each stage for the first several stages. Then write recursive and function formulas that describe this sequence. Use one of the formulas to predict the number of *new* branches at Stage 12. Check your prediction using the other formula.

b. Find the *total* number of branches at Stage 12.

c. Suppose that the length of the initial branch is 1 unit and that the branches at each successive stage of the fractal tree are half the length of the branches at the previous stage.

i. Write the total length of all the branches at each stage for the first several stages.

ii. Find the total length of all the branches at Stage 15.

Unit 7

534 UNIT 7 • Recursion and Iteration

c. $f(x) = 0.8x - 200$

i. Long-term behavior is convergence to $-1,000$ (whales die out at 0) since $x = -1,000$ when you solve $x = 0.8x - 200$.

ii. The fixed point is $-1,000$. It is attracting because $|slope| = 0.8 < 1$.

iii.

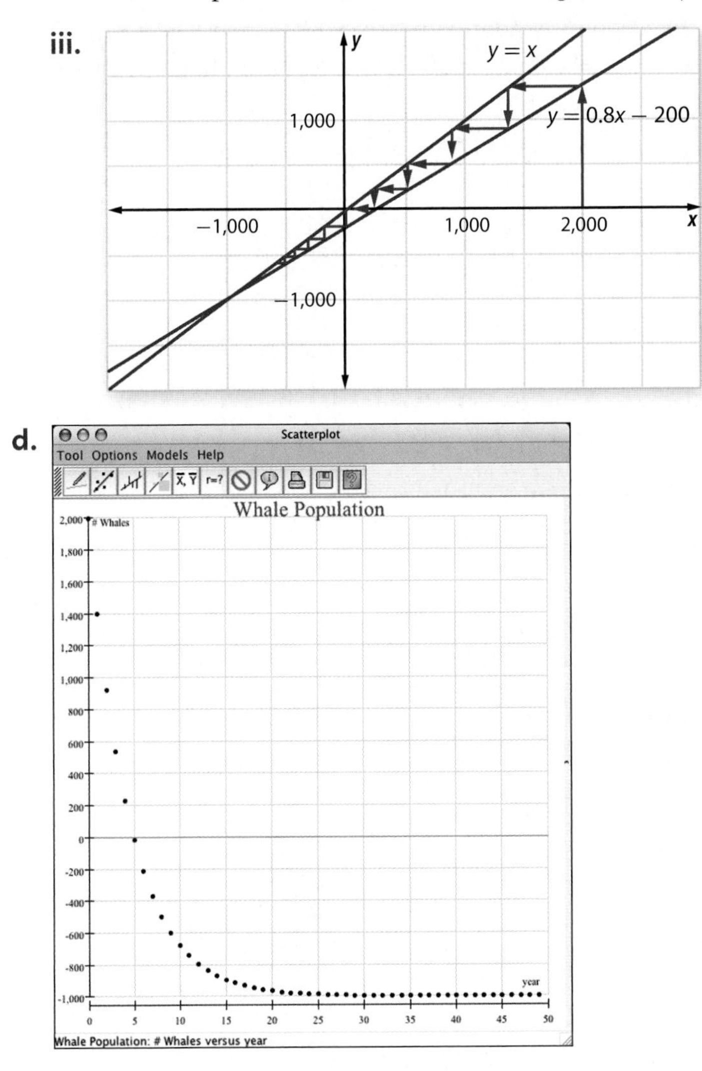

d. (see scatterplot above)

e. All initial values yield iteration sequences that converge to the fixed point at $x = -1,000$. For the whale population, the sequence will steadily decrease toward the fixed point of $x = -1,000$. But since population cannot be negative, the population will die out, corresponding to $f(x) = 0$. This will happen after about 5 years. Even if the initial count was incorrect and there are more or fewer whales initially, the population will still converge toward the fixed point of $-1,000$. The population will still die out, although it may take a greater or lesser amount of time for that to happen.

Sample 2: $A_n = 1.06A_{n-1} - 350$

a. Money is invested in a savings account at 6% interest compounded annually, but every year \$350 is withdrawn. Suppose the initial deposit is \$6,000. (For this problem, the fixed point is approximately 5,833.33, and it is repelling. Thus, behavior will be quite different depending on whether the initial value is greater than, less than, or equal to 5,833.33.)

Unit 7

b. $NEXT = 1.06NOW - 350$, starting at 6,000

c. $f(x) = 1.06x - 350$

i. Long-term behavior is for the money to grow without bound but rather slowly.

ii. The fixed point is approximately 5,833 since $x \approx 5{,}833$ when you solve $x = 1.06x - 350$. It is a repelling fixed point since $|slope| = 1.06 > 1$.

iii.

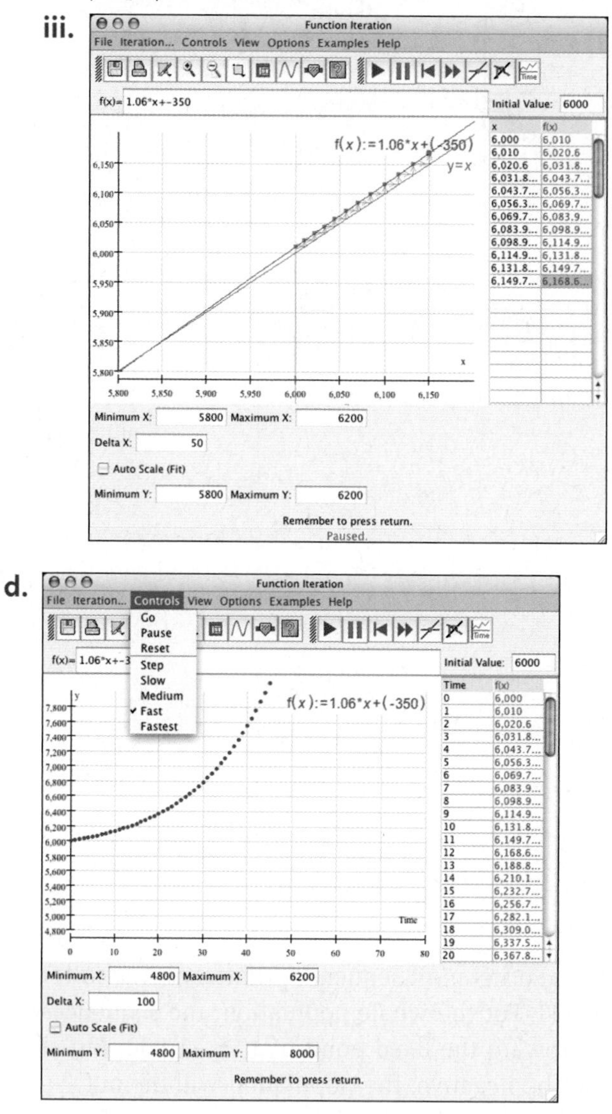

e. The fixed point is about \$5,833.33, and it is repelling. If the starting value is above \$5,833.33, the long-term behavior is unbounded, tending to positive infinity. If the starting value is below \$5,833.33, the long-term behavior is also unbounded, but this time tending to negative infinity. Thus, it makes a big difference what the initial deposit is. If the initial deposit is \$5,833.33, then \$350 can be withdrawn each year and the principal will stay fixed at \$5,833.33. If the starting balance is more than \$5,833.33, then \$350 can be withdrawn each year and the principal will grow forever. If the starting balance is less than \$5,833.33, then withdrawing \$350 each year will eventually deplete the account.

2 **a.** The first several terms of the sequence are 1, 2, 4, 8, … .
Recursive formula: $a_n = 2a_{n-1}$, $a_0 = 1$
Function formula: $a_n = 2^n$
There are 2^{12}, or 4,096 new branches at Stage 12.

b. The total number of branches at Stage 12 is S_{12}, the sum of the terms a_0 through a_{12} of the geometric sequence in Part a.

c. **i.** The first several terms of the sequence of the total length of all branches at each stage are 1, 2, 3, 4, … .

ii. This is an arithmetic sequence with $a_n = 1 + n$ and $a_0 = 1$. So, $a_{15} = 16$. The total length of all the branches at Stage 15 is 16 units.

Unit 7

3. When you attend a movie, concert, or theater production, you may notice that the number of seats in a row increases as you move from the front of the theater to the back. This permits the seats in consecutive rows to be offset from one another so that you have a less-obstructed view of the stage.

The center section of the orchestra level of Shaw Auditorium is arranged so that there are 42 seats in the first row, 44 seats in the second row, 46 seats in the third row, and so on for a total of 25 rows.

a. Determine the number of seats in the last row in two different ways. Compare your result and your methods to those of other students. Resolve any differences.

b. Determine the total number of seats in the center section of the orchestra level in at least two different ways. One method should involve using a rule showing the total number of seats as a function of number of rows n.

4. Amy was investigating the maximum number of regions into which a plane is separated by n lines, no two of which are parallel and no three of which intersect at a common point. For example, the diagram below shows the maximum number of regions for 3 lines.

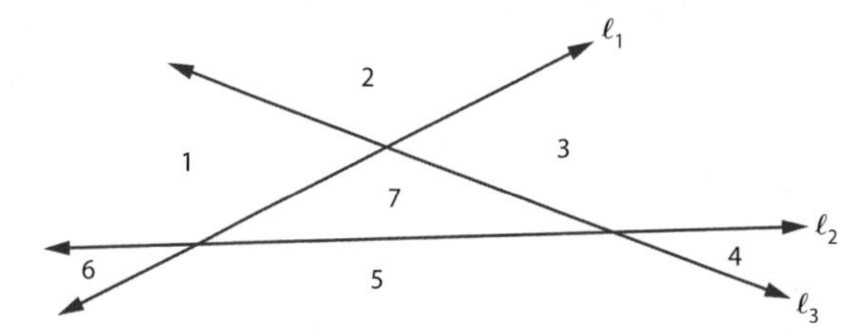

Amy gathered the data shown in the table below.

Number of Lines	0	1	2	3	4
Number of Regions	1	2	4	7	11

a. Verify the entries in the table.

b. Find a function formula for the maximum number of regions formed by n lines, using the method of finite differences.

c. Write a recursive formula for this relationship.

Unit 7

3 **a.** The 25th row will have 90 seats in it.

Students might represent this situation using *NEXT* = *NOW* + 2, starting at 42, and then use a calculator or mental arithmetic to compute step by step to find the number of seats in the 25th row. However, encourage students to use the notation and formulas from the unit. For example, students can represent this recursively as $r_n = r_{n-1} + 2$, with $r_0 = 42$, in which case r_{24} represents the 25th row and $r_{24} = r_0 + 24(2) = 42 + 48 = 90$. Or, if students let $r_1 = 42$, then r_{25} represents the 25th row and $r_{25} = r_1 + (25 - 1)(2) = 42 + 48 = 90$.

b. Students may use the formula-in-words from Lesson 2.

$$S = \frac{(\textit{initial term} + \textit{final term})(\textit{number of terms})}{2},$$

which yields $\frac{(42 + 90)(25)}{2} = 1{,}650$ seats. Or, they might use the formula for the sum of an arithmetic sequence that corresponds to an initial subscript of 0 or 1. If they choose to represent the initial term as a_0, then they should use the formula $S_n = \frac{(n + 1)(a_0 + a_n)}{2}$ to find the sum of the terms. In this case, they must find S_{24}, which is the sum from a_0 up to and including a_{24}. $S_{24} = \frac{(24 + 1)(42 + 90)}{2} = 1{,}650$ seats. If students choose a_1 as the initial term, then they should use $S_n = \frac{n(a_1 + a_n)}{2}$ and $S_{25} = \frac{25(42 + 90)}{2} = 1{,}650$ seats. Students could also use a data list to produce the first 25 terms of the sequence and then find the sum of the list.

4 **a.** Students should verify the entries in the table. The diagram at the right shows eleven regions that can be formed using four lines.

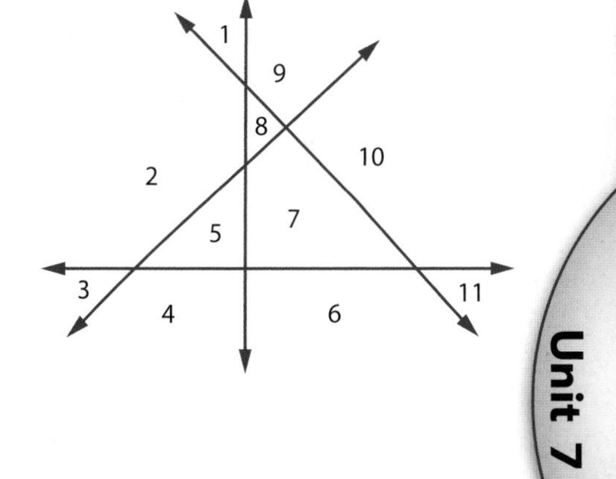

b.

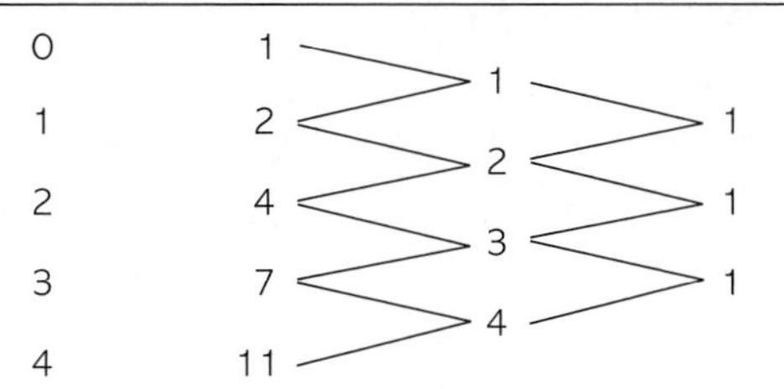

Number of Lines	Number of Regions	1st Difference	2nd Difference
0	1		
		1	
1	2		1
		2	
2	4		1
		3	
3	7		1
		4	
4	11		

Since the second differences are constant the function formula will be of the form $A_n = an^2 + bn + c$. Solving the matrix equation

$$\begin{bmatrix} 1 & 1 & 1 \\ 4 & 2 & 1 \\ 9 & 3 & 1 \end{bmatrix} \begin{bmatrix} a \\ b \\ c \end{bmatrix} = \begin{bmatrix} 2 \\ 4 \\ 7 \end{bmatrix}$$

gives $a = 0.5$, $b = 0.5$, and $c = 1$. So, the function formula is

$$A_n = 0.5n^2 + 0.5n + 1.$$

c. $A_n = A_{n-1} + n$

Unit 7

5 Find recursive and function formulas for each of the sequences below. Then find the sum of the terms up through the term with subscript 15.

a.

n	0	1	2	3	4	5	6	…	15	…
L_n	600	300	150	75	37.5			…		…

b.

n	1	2	3	4	5	6	7	…	15	…
P_n	−3	2	7	12	17			…		…

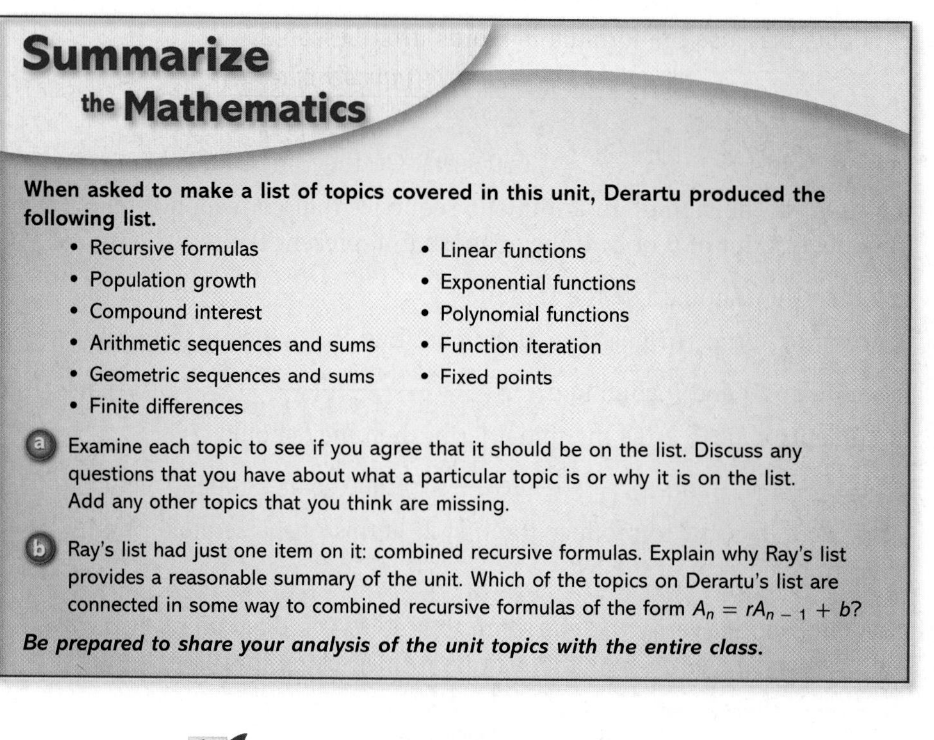

Summarize the Mathematics

When asked to make a list of topics covered in this unit, Derartu produced the following list.

- Recursive formulas
- Population growth
- Compound interest
- Arithmetic sequences and sums
- Geometric sequences and sums
- Finite differences
- Linear functions
- Exponential functions
- Polynomial functions
- Function iteration
- Fixed points

a Examine each topic to see if you agree that it should be on the list. Discuss any questions that you have about what a particular topic is or why it is on the list. Add any other topics that you think are missing.

b Ray's list had just one item on it: combined recursive formulas. Explain why Ray's list provides a reasonable summary of the unit. Which of the topics on Derartu's list are connected in some way to combined recursive formulas of the form $A_n = rA_{n-1} + b$?

Be prepared to share your analysis of the unit topics with the entire class.

Check Your Understanding

Write, in outline form, a summary of the important mathematical concepts and methods developed in this unit. Organize your summary so that it can be used as a quick reference in future units and courses.

Unit 7

536 UNIT 7 • Recursion and Iteration

a. This is a geometric sequence with common multiplier $r = 0.5$. Note that the starting subscript is $n = 0$.

$L_n = (0.5)L_{n-1}$
$L_n = (600)(0.5^n)$
$L_{15} = 600(0.5)^{15} \approx 0.0183$
$S_{15} = \dfrac{600(1 - 0.5^{16})}{1 - 0.5} \approx 1{,}199.98$

b. This is an arithmetic sequence with common difference $d = 5$. Note that the starting subscript is $n = 1$.

$P_n = P_{n-1} + 5$
$P_n = -3 + 5(n - 1)$
$P_{15} = -3 + 5(14) = 67$
$S_{15} = \dfrac{(-3 + 67)15}{2} = 480$

Summarize the Mathematics

a Other topics that could be added to the list include subscript notation, recursion, sequential change, long-term behavior, repelling, attracting, and cycles. Students may think of others as well.

b It is reasonably accurate to say that this unit is about combined recursive formulas, that is, recursive formulas of the form $A_n = rA_{n-1} - b$. In Lesson 1, combined recursive formulas are used as models for real-world situations (like population growth, medicine absorption, and compound interest), and subscript notation is used to help analyze them. In Lesson 2, the recursive formulas for arithmetic and geometric sequences are special cases of combined recursive formulas. In Lesson 3, iterating linear functions is just another way of thinking about successively evaluating combined recursive formulas.

The only major topics in the unit that are not directly connected to combined recursive formulas are finite differences in Lesson 2 and some of the more general function iteration in Lesson 3. All of the items on Derartu's list are connected in some way to combined recursive formulas. (The connections to finite differences and polynomial functions are weak, but a possible connection can be made if one thinks of a linear function as a special case of a polynomial function.)

Teaching Resources

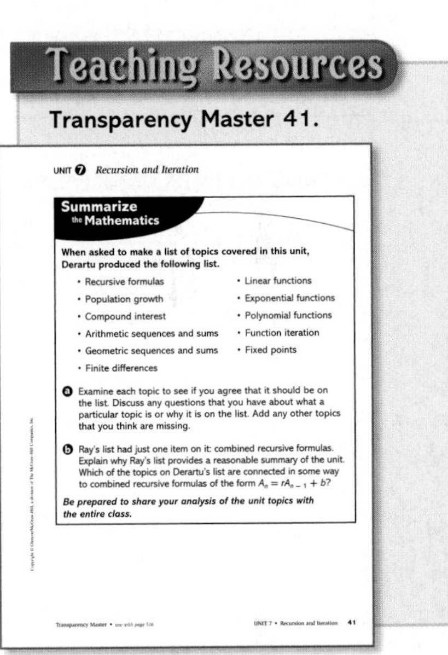

Transparency Master 41.

UNIT 7 *Recursion and Iteration*

Summarize the Mathematics

When asked to make a list of topics covered in this unit, Derartu produced the following list.

- Recursive formulas
- Population growth
- Compound interest
- Arithmetic sequences and sums
- Geometric sequences and sums
- Finite differences
- Linear functions
- Exponential functions
- Polynomial functions
- Function iteration
- Fixed points

a Examine each topic to see if you agree that it should be on the list. Discuss any questions that you have about what a particular topic is or why it is on the list. Add any other topics that you think are missing.

b Ray's list had just one item on it: combined recursive formulas. Explain why Ray's list provides a reasonable summary of the unit. Which of the topics on Derartu's list are connected in some way to combined recursive formulas of the form $A_n = rA_{n-1} + b$?

Be prepared to share your analysis of the unit topics with the entire class.

Unit 7

Teaching Resources

Student Masters 42–44.

UNIT 7 *Recursion and Iteration* Name Date

UNIT SUMMARY

Arithmetic and Geometric Sequences

	Arithmetic Sequence	Geometric Sequence
Example		
Recursive formula for example		
Function formula for example		
Definition		
General recursive formula		
General function formula		
Formula for sum of first *n* terms		
Formula in words for sum of the terms of an arithmetic sequence		

Assessment Masters 45–67.

UNIT 7 *Recursion and Iteration* Name Date

UNIT TEST

Form A

Year	Amount Owed (in dollars)
2009	12,000
2010	
2011	
2012	

Student Masters 68–69.

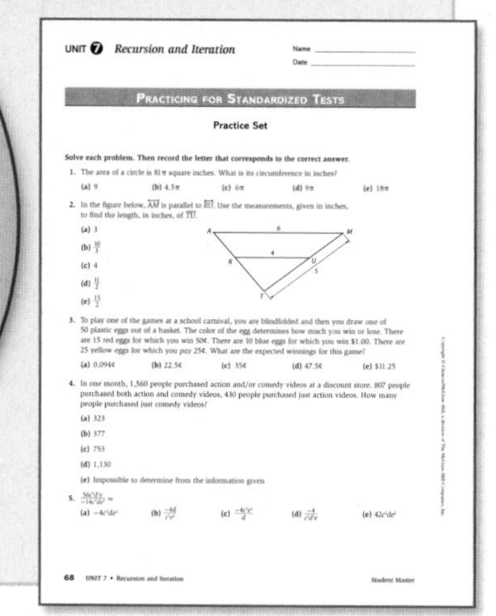
UNIT 7 *Recursion and Iteration* Name Date

PRACTICING FOR STANDARDIZED TESTS

Practice Set

Check Your Understanding

You may wish to have students use the Teaching Master, *Recursion and Iteration* Unit Summary, to help them organize the information. Above all, this should be something that is useful to the individual student.

Practicing for Standardized Tests

Each Practicing for Standardized Tests master presents 10 questions in the multiple-choice format of test items similar to how they often appear in standardized tests. Answers are provided below.

Answers to Practice Set 7

1. (e)	**2.** (b)	**3.** (d)	**4.** (a)	**5.** (b)
6. (d)	**7.** (c)	**8.** (e)	**9.** (e)	**10.** (c)

Unit 7

Teacher Notes

INVERSE FUNCTIONS

In earlier units, you learned how polynomial, rational, exponential, and trigonometric functions can be useful tools for modeling the relationships between dependent and independent variables in a wide variety of problem situations. In many of those problems, the key challenge is finding values of the independent variable that lead to required values of the dependent variable.

For example, if you know the rate at which an endangered animal population is recovering, you certainly want to find the time when that population is likely to reach a specified safe level. Solution of problems like that is helped by calculation of the inverse for the function relating population to time.

Work on the investigations of this unit will develop your understanding and skill in use of inverse functions, especially the square root, logarithm, and inverse trigonometric functions. Key ideas are encountered in three lessons.

Lessons

1 *What Is An Inverse Function?*

Discover conditions that guarantee existence of inverse functions, develop strategies for finding rules of inverse functions, and use inverse functions to solve problems of coding and decoding information.

2 *Common Logarithms and Their Properties*

Develop the definition and important properties of inverses for exponential functions and use those logarithmic functions to solve exponential equations.

3 *Inverse Trigonometric Functions*

Develop definitions and important properties for inverses of sine, cosine, and tangent functions and use those inverse functions to solve trigonometric equations.

UNIT 8

INVERSE FUNCTIONS

Unit Overview

This final algebra and functions unit of Course 3 builds on the units of Courses 1 and 2 that developed student understanding of functions in general and exponential functions, common logarithms, and trigonometric functions in particular. It draws on many prior examples to develop the concept of inverse function, reviews the definition of logarithms, and develops the standard properties of logarithms and their uses in solving exponential equations. It also develops definitions of inverse trigonometric functions and their use in solving trigonometric equations.

In work with any function $f(x)$ that relates dependent and independent variables, there are important problems that require solving an equation in the form $f(x) = k$. That is, find the value(s) of the independent variable x that lead to specified values of the dependent variable. When the problem situation requires solving many such equations, it turns out to be efficient to devise a second function $f^{-1}(x)$ that shows how to reverse the ordered pairs defining $f(x)$ to directly calculate the required solutions. The functions $f^{-1}(x)$ that accomplish this inverse task are called inverse functions.

Many, but not all, of the functions that students have studied have inverses. For example, the inverse of $f(x) = 3x$ is $f^{-1}(x) = \frac{x}{3}$; the inverse of $f(x) = x + 3$ is $f^{-1}(x) = x - 3$; the inverse of $f(x) = 3^x$ is $f^{-1}(x) = \log_3 x$; and for restricted domains, the functions $f(x) = x^2$, $f(x) = \sin x$, and $f(x) = \cos x$ have useful inverse functions as well. The goal of this unit is to develop student understanding and skill in work with inverse functions and, in particular, the use of the common logarithm function and the inverse trigonometric functions.

The following material gives overviews of the three main lessons in *Inverse Functions*.

Lesson 1 *What Is An Inverse Function?* The initial goal of this lesson is to draw on students' many prior experiences with functions and the natural undoing questions that occur in applications of those functions to develop and articulate the concept of an inverse function. Then the lesson develops techniques for finding inverses of important function families.

Lesson 2 *Common Logarithms and Their Properties* The goal of this lesson is to develop understanding of common logarithms and how they relate to and can help in solving exponential equations. The first investigation provides a quick review of the concept of logarithm and basic properties that were developed in Course 2 Unit 5, *Nonlinear Functions and Equations*. Investigation 2 extends use of logarithms to solution of exponential equations in situations where 10 is not the natural base. The third investigation develops the standard properties of logarithms that are used in algebraic manipulations with exponential and logarithmic functions.

Lesson 3 *Inverse Trigonometric Functions* The goal of this lesson is to develop understanding of inverse sine, cosine, and tangent functions and their applications to solution of trigonometric equations. The first investigation motivates and develops the definition and applications of the inverse sine function. Investigation 2 develops definitions and applications of the inverse cosine and tangent functions.

Unit Objectives

- Discover conditions that guarantee existence of inverse functions
- Develop strategies for finding rules for inverse functions
- Use inverse functions to solve problems of coding and decoding information
- Develop the definition and important properties of inverses for exponential functions
- Use logarithms to solve exponential equations
- Develop the definition and important properties of the inverse sine, cosine, and tangent functions
- Use inverse trigonometric functions to solve trigonometric equations and inequalities and the problems in which those equations and inequalities arise

CPMP-Tools

The CAS available in the Algebra software can be used to solve some of the more difficult trigonometric equations and graph functions.

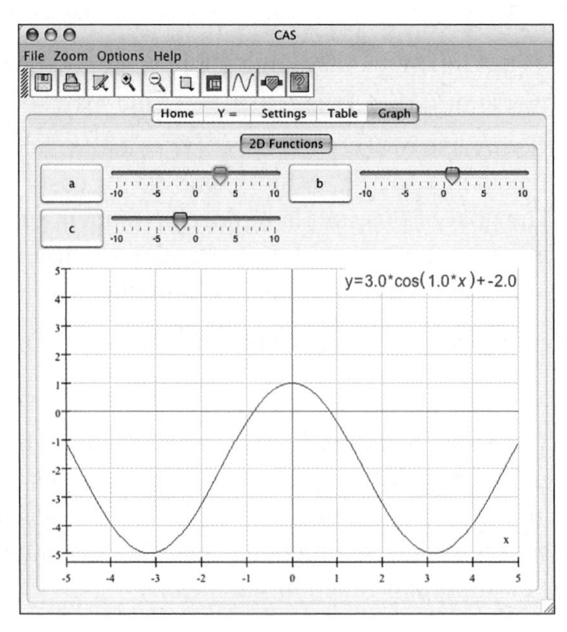

Unit 8 Planning Guide

Lesson Objectives	On Your Own Assignments*	Suggested Pacing	Materials
Lesson 1 ***What Is An Inverse Function?*** • Solve problems involving direct and inverse variation • Discover conditions that guarantee existence of an inverse for a given function • Develop and use strategies for recognizing invertible functions from study of tables of values and/or graphs of those functions • Develop and use strategies for finding rules of inverses for linear and power functions	**After Investigation 1:** Choose two of A1–A4, A5, C9 or C10, R17 or R18, E23, E24, Rv30–Rv33 **After Investigation 2:** A6–A8, choose one of C11–C13, C14, C15 or C16, R19, R20 or R21, R22, E26 or E27, E28 or E29, Rv34–Rv38	4 days (including assessment)	• *CPMP-Tools* CAS or other CAS technology • Unit Resources
Lesson 2 ***Common Logarithms and Their Properties*** • Express a positive number as a power of 10 • Define and evaluate common logarithms • Use logarithms to solve exponential equations • Develop and use basic properties of the logarithmic function	**After Investigation 1:** A1–A5, C14, R23, R24, Rv34–Rv38 **After Investigation 2:** A6–A8, A9 or A10, C15, C16, E30, Rv39 **After Investigation 3:** A11–A13, C17, C18 or C19, C20, C21 or C22, R25, R26, choose one of R27–R29, choose one of E31–E33, Rv41–Rv43	6 days (including assessment)	• *CPMP-Tools* CAS or other CAS technology • Unit Resources
Lesson 3 ***Inverse Trigonometric Functions*** • Know and be able to use the definition of the inverse sine, inverse cosine, and inverse tangent functions • Know and be able to use properties of the inverse sine, inverse cosine, and inverse tangent functions • Use the inverse functions, to find one solution (when one exists) of $a \cdot f(bx) + c = d$, where $f(x)$ is the sine, cosine, or tangent • Express the general solutions of a trigonometric equation in forms such as $x = k + 2\pi n$ or $x = k + 360°n$ for any integer n • Use trigonometric equations and their solutions to model and answer questions about periodic phenomena	**After Investigation 1:** A1–A5, choose two of C15–C17, R24, R25, E28, Rv36–Rv39 **After Investigation 2:** A6–A14, choose two of C18–C23, R26 or R27, choose one of E29–E35, Rv40–Rv42	7 days (including assessment)	• *CPMP-Tools* CAS or other CAS technology • Unit Resources
Lesson 4 ***Looking Back*** • Review and synthesize the major objectives of the unit		2 days (including assessment)	• Unit Resources

* *When choice is indicated, it is important to leave the choice to the student.*

Note: *It is best if Connections tasks are discussed as a whole class after they have been assigned as homework.*

LESSON 1

What Is An Inverse Function?

We live in a world of instant information. Numbers, text, and graphic images stream around the globe at every hour of the day on every day of the year. For most data transmission media, information must be translated into numerical form and then into electronic signals. When the signal reaches its destination, it must be translated back into the intended text, graphic, or numerical information format.

Cell phones are one of the most popular communication devices of the electronic information era. Like standard landline telephones, they permit spoken conversations across great distances. They can also be used to send *text messages*. A study in the fall of 2007 found that about 1 billion text messages were sent each day.

Sending text via cell phones takes advantage of the fact that the standard telephone dial has letters associated with numbered buttons. When your cell phone is set in text message mode, pressing number buttons sends letters to the intended receiver.

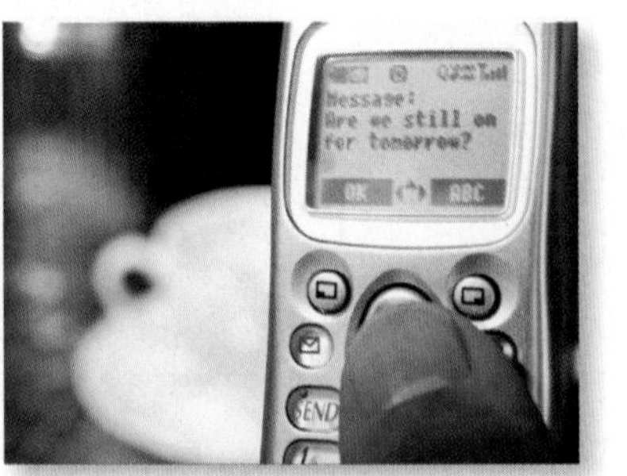

538 UNIT 8 • Inverse Functions

What Is An Inverse Function?

LESSON 1

This first lesson develops the general notion of an inverse function, criteria for existence of inverses, and strategies for developing and using inverse function rules. The first investigation asks students to consider the general inverse problem in the context of coding information. The second investigation provides a precise definition of inverse function and strategies for finding rules of inverses when they exist.

Lesson Objectives

- Solve problems involving direct and inverse variation
- Discover conditions that guarantee existence of an inverse for a given function
- Develop and use strategies for recognizing invertible functions from study of tables of values and/or graphs of those functions
- Develop and use strategies for finding rules of inverses for linear and power functions

Lesson Launch

The launch for this lesson and the first investigation in the lesson pose questions about how cellular telephones transmit text messages. Because each button on the cell phone keypad corresponds to a number or special symbol (* and #), text messages are sent by pressing number buttons. However, since there are several letters corresponding to each numbered button, the intended message is not coded and sent in a way that can be decoded by the receiver without ambiguity.

There are algorithms designed to make good guesses about the intended letter sequences, but they are not foolproof. That is the point of the introductory situation—to focus student attention on the importance of inverse problems like decoding messages and the conditions required to make such decoding accurate. The TATS is designed to get students thinking about those issues. Complete and accurate answers to the questions are not essential. See the notes prior to Problem 1 also as you plan this launch. If you plan to allow students time to consider the TATS Part b, you might direct them to Problem 1 for small-group or pair discussions and then have a class discussion.

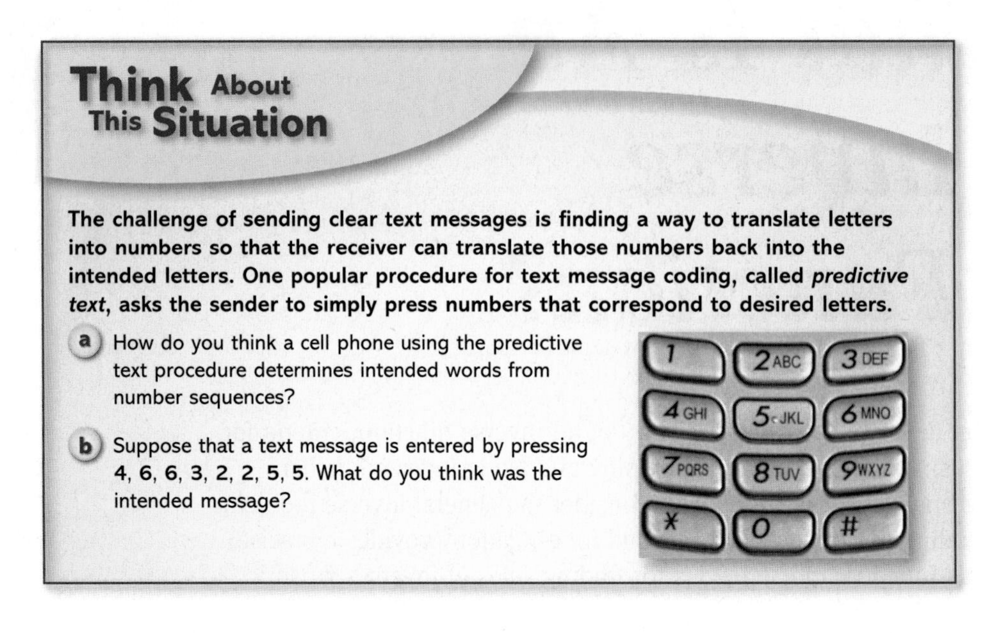

Think About This Situation

The challenge of sending clear text messages is finding a way to translate letters into numbers so that the receiver can translate those numbers back into the intended letters. One popular procedure for text message coding, called *predictive text*, asks the sender to simply press numbers that correspond to desired letters.

a How do you think a cell phone using the predictive text procedure determines intended words from number sequences?

b Suppose that a text message is entered by pressing 4, 6, 6, 3, 2, 2, 5, 5. What do you think was the intended message?

In this lesson, you will learn how mathematical functions and their inverses are used to make accurate coding and decoding of information possible and how function inverses are used to solve other important mathematical problems.

Investigation 1 Coding and Decoding Messages

Using the predictive text procedure, the keypad of a cell phone assigns each letter a numerical code. However, this coding function cannot be reversed reliably to find the intended letters from the numbers that were transmitted. As you work on the problems of this investigation, look for an answer to the following question:

What properties of a mathematical function f make it possible to find a related function that reverses the domain, range, and individual assignments of f?

1. Suppose that f is the function that uses a standard cell phone keypad to assign number codes to letters of a text message using the predictive text procedure.

   a. What number sequence would be used to send the message GOOD CALL?

   b. What different messages could result from attempts to decode the number sequence produced in Part a?

   c. What is the problem with predictive text coding that can lead to unclear message transmission?

   d. What changes in the coding process could avoid the problems revealed in your answers to Parts b and c?

Think About This Situation

a Most cell phone text messaging systems have built-in decoding programs that scan number sequences to identify patterns associated with familiar words that are then reported to the receiver as if they were the intended message. You can learn more about one particular algorithm for doing predictive text coding and decoding by visiting the Web site www.t9.com.

Even there, you will discover that coding/decoding is not foolproof. For instance, if you want to send BIKING and press the corresponding keys, the cell phone screen is likely to guess that you want to send AILING, with a second guess BIKINI.

Students may be more familiar with a second kind of coding called "multi-tapping." This procedure requires the sender to press keys several times to get the second or third or fourth letter on a key. In the Part b question, we want students to assume that a predictive text algorithm is in use, not multi-tapping.

b If a text message is coded in numbers as 4, 6, 6, 3, 2, 2, 5, 5, there are many different possible intended messages: GOOD CALL is one, but HOME CALL, GOOD BALL, GOOFBALL, and HONDA ALL are others. You can go to www.phonespell.org to get all possibilities.

Teaching Resources

Transparency Master 1.

UNIT 8 *Inverse Functions*

Think About This Situation

The challenge of sending clear text messages is finding a way to translate letters into numbers so that the receiver can translate those numbers back into the intended letters. One popular procedure for text message coding, called *predictive text*, asks the sender to simply press numbers that correspond to desired letters.

a How do you think a cell phone using the predictive text procedure determines intended words from number sequences?

b Suppose that a text message is entered by pressing 4, 6, 6, 3, 2, 2, 5, 5. What do you think was the intended message?

Transparency Master • use with page 539 UNIT 8 • Inverse Functions 1

Investigation 1 Coding and Decoding Messages

In many situations, it is absolutely essential to send messages without any ambiguity in their content as received by the addressee. Since computers and other information transmission media translate letters and other symbols into numbers and then into electronic signals, there are conventions for this sort of coding process.

The first requirement is that each symbol to be sent must have a unique numeric code. The problems of this investigation highlight that point, but they also show ways of making the coding algorithms difficult to crack so that information is secure as sent. Most coding schemes that require very secure and highly accurate data transmission (e.g., credit card charge transmissions) will always send extra electronic signals (called check bits) to separate each intended signal from any others that might result from slips and be misinterpreted.

SCOPE AND SEQUENCE Coding and decoding concepts will be extended in Course 4 Unit 10, *Mathematics of Information Processing and the Internet.*

Launch

It should be easy to make a transition from the TATS situation to the problems of Investigation 1 with just that motivation. You do not need to define inverse function formally at this point. It is enough to simply mention that the decoding functions are called inverses and that students should "keep an eye out" for critical properties of those inverses as they work on the coding problems of the investigation. The first problem might be used as simply a continuation of the TATS discussion.

NOTE Solutions to Problem 1 are on page T540.

2. To avoid the problems that can occur when several letters are assigned the same numerical code on a cell phone keypad, information systems, like those used by computers, employ more than ten numbers to code the letters of the alphabet and important symbols. For example, a coding scheme might make the assignments in the next table.

Symbol	0	1	⋯	9	A	B	C	⋯	X	Y	Z	.	—
Code	0	1	⋯	9	10	11	12	⋯	33	34	35	36	37

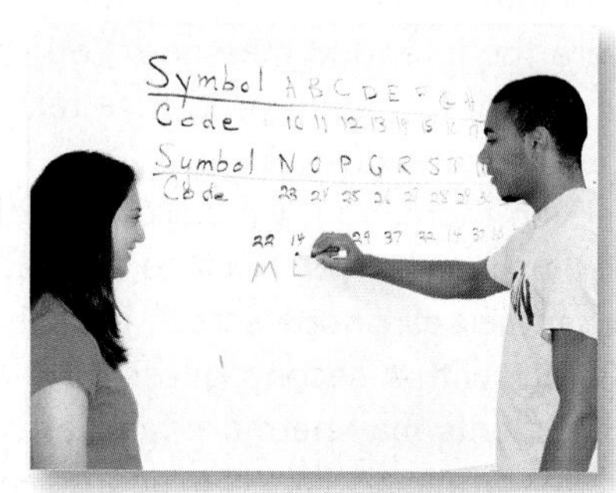

a. Using this coding scheme, what message is implied by the sequence of code numbers 22, 14, 14, 29, 37, 22, 14, 37, 10, 29, 37, 9?

b. Why does this coding scheme involve very low risk of incorrect message transmission?

c. If you want a message to be sent so that only the intended recipient can read it, why will a simple code like that shown in the table *not* be effective?

To make messages difficult for data spies to decode, the first step of letter-to-number coding is often followed by use of further *encryption* algorithms. The aim is to disguise decoding clues like known letter frequencies and patterns of repeated letters in the English language. For example, the letter "E" has been found to occur roughly 13% of the time in English text.

3. Using the basic coding scheme from Problem 2, the message I WILL BE THERE is translated into the number sequence 18, 37, 32, 18, 21, 21, 37, 11, 14, 37, 29, 17, 14, 27, 14. Suppose that the basic symbols-to-numbers coding is followed by application of the linear function $f(x) = x + 16$ to each code number.

a. What number sequence gives the encrypted message now?

b. What decoding formula would you give to the recipient of your messages?

c. Why does this encryption method still fail to disguise decoding clues like known letter frequencies?

540 UNIT 8 • Inverse Functions

1. a. The number sequence is 4, 6, 6, 3, 2, 2, 5, 5.

   b. There are the same code numbers, such as GOOD CALL, HOME CALL, GOOD BALL, GOOFBALL, and HONDA ALL. See www.phonespell.org for all possibilities.

   c. The problem of predictive text coding is that several letters get the same number code, so it may not be clear to the receiver which letter was intended to be sent.

   d. One change in the coding process that is sometimes used is to press buttons several times if the second, third, or fourth letter on a button is what the sender wants to transmit. That is, to send the letter B, one would press the 2 button twice; to send the letter C, one would press the 2 button three times. (Some students may know that cell phone companies have text recognition algorithms built into their text messaging systems to scan signals and identify numeric patterns in order to guess the intended messages.)

2. a. The intended message is MEET ME AT 9.

   b. This coding scheme uses a correspondence between numbers, letters, and spaces of a message and numeric code numbers that assigns every number and every letter exactly one code and assigns each code to exactly one letter or number. The risk of errors is reduced to possible typing errors by the sender or electronic glitches in the signal that is sent or received.

   c. Simple direct assignment codes are easy to crack. Inspecting the frequency with which certain code numbers occur and correlating that information with known letter frequencies in English is one way that such codes can be cracked. The direct letters-to-numbers coding scheme is also probably the first idea that a code breaker would try.

3. a. 34, 53, 48, 34, 37, 37, 53, 27, 30, 53, 45, 33, 30, 43, 30

   b. Subtract 16 from each received number. That is, the recipient should apply $g(x) = x - 16$ to each element of the received message.

   c. The relative frequency of various letters is still not disguised (e.g., the number $14 + 16 = 30$ will occur often and be a clue that 30 represents the letter E). One would probably guess the shift code $f(x) = x + 16$ and easily set up a decoding function.

   One can also observe spots where the same number appears twice in a row and guess that such numbers must be one of the fairly small number of commonly appearing double letter patterns like TT, SS, EE, OO, DD, LL, etc.

Teaching Resources

Student Master 2.

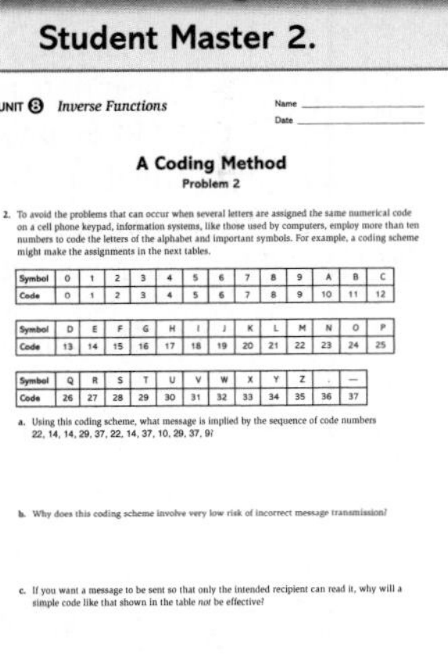

UNIT 8 *Inverse Functions* Name ______ Date ______

A Coding Method
Problem 2

2. To avoid the problems that can occur when several letters are assigned the same numerical code on a cell phone keypad, information systems, like those used by computers, employ more than ten numbers to code the letters of the alphabet and important symbols. For example, a coding scheme might make the assignments in the next tables.

Symbol	0	1	2	3	4	5	6	7	8	9	A	B	C
Code	0	1	2	3	4	5	6	7	8	9	10	11	12

Symbol	D	E	F	G	H	I	J	K	L	M	N	O	P
Code	13	14	15	16	17	18	19	20	21	22	23	24	25

Symbol	Q	R	S	T	U	V	W	X	Y	Z	.	—
Code	26	27	28	29	30	31	32	33	34	35	36	37

a. Using this coding scheme, what message is implied by the sequence of code numbers 22, 14, 14, 29, 37, 22, 14, 37, 10, 29, 37, 9?

b. Why does this coding scheme involve very low risk of incorrect message transmission?

c. If you want a message to be sent so that only the intended recipient can read it, why will a simple code like that shown in the table *not* be effective?

2 UNIT 8 • Inverse Functions Student Master • use with page 540

INSTRUCTIONAL NOTE
Students will use this coding and decoding scheme in Applications Tasks 2–4. Thus, they may want to keep the table that they create.

Unit 8

4 Because *shift encryption* algorithms like $f(x) = x + 16$ are easy to decode, it is tempting to try more complex encryption functions.

a. Study the patterns of code assignments made by the following functions, and explain why they also have weaknesses as encryption algorithms.

i. $g(x) = 2x + 1$

ii. $h(x) = x^2$

iii. $k(x) = 38x - x^2$

b. See if you can devise an encryption algorithm of your own that does not have the flaws of the examples in Part a.

5 Where possible, describe in words and find algebraic expressions for strategies that could be used to *decode* messages that have been encrypted by the following functions.

a. $f(x) = x + 7$

b. $g(x) = 2x + 1$

c. $h(x) = x^2$

d. $k(x) = 38x - x^2$

If an encryption algorithm assigns the same code number to every occurrence of a symbol, it can be broken easily. For example, if the letter "E" is always assigned the code number 29, code breakers will use the fact that "E" is the most common letter in English to guess that 29 stands for that letter. An encryption scheme that uses matrices avoids this problem of simpler coding algorithms.

6 One simple matrix coding scheme begins by arranging the message number codes in the form of 1×2 matrix blocks. For example, the sequence 2, 0, 11, 11, 7, 14, 12, 4 becomes:

$M_1 = \begin{bmatrix} 2 & 0 \end{bmatrix}$ $M_2 = \begin{bmatrix} 11 & 11 \end{bmatrix}$ $M_3 = \begin{bmatrix} 7 & 14 \end{bmatrix}$ $M_4 = \begin{bmatrix} 12 & 4 \end{bmatrix}$

Next, each of those message blocks is multiplied by a coding matrix, like $C = \begin{bmatrix} 2 & 1 \\ 5 & 3 \end{bmatrix}$.

a. Find the encrypted form of each message block: M_1C, M_2C, M_3C, M_4C. Then rewrite the message number sequence in its newly encrypted form.

b. What do you notice about the resulting pattern of numbers in the encrypted message sequence? How does this strategy appear to solve the problem of coding clues given by known letter frequencies?

c. What decoding directions would you give to the message recipient?

4 **a.** **i.** $g(x) = 2x + 1$ does assign unique encrypted codes to each number from 0 to 37. Unfortunately, this sort of linear encryption function has the disadvantage that it does not disguise letter frequencies, so inspecting any fairly long message will give clues to which encrypted number stands for the letter E and so on.

ii. $h(x) = x^2$ does not assign unique encrypted codes to each number, although students may suggest that it does when using integers from 0 to 37. This squaring function has other weaknesses. If one inspects the encrypted form of a message, it will quickly be apparent that those numbers are all perfect squares. And as a result, anyone could quickly guess the decrypting scheme. Furthermore, squaring leads to very large encrypted numbers that complicate calculations.

iii. $k(x) = 38x - x^2$ does not assign unique encrypted codes to all numbers between 0 and 37. Every number (except 19) will be assigned the same encrypted code as one other number, making decoding ambiguous.

b. Students may try and reject several algorithms. This should confirm for them that effective codes require a method other than a straightforward function rule.

5 **INSTRUCTIONAL NOTE** The notational issue with inverse functions is a bit problematic. For example, if we think of $y = f(x)$, then the goal of an inverse function is to use values of y to find values of x. Thus, students might feel that the natural notation might seem to be $f^{-1}(y) = y - 7$. However, the convention in mathematics is to use x as the standard independent variable; so once the "undoing" rule is discovered, the inverse function is generally expressed as a function of x. In this case, we would be expected to write the inverse of $f(x)$ as $f^{-1}(x) = x - 7$.

It is our recommendation that the standard inverse function notation not be introduced at this point (it is not mentioned in the text until the beginning of Investigation 2). Instead, we suggest that students simply write the expression that undoes the coding function calculations. Thus, in the case of the $f(x)$ given in this example, students could say, "Use the expression $x - 7$ or even $y - 7$ (or some equivalent form) to guide decoding calculations."

Students should recognize, whichever form they use, that the input value is the original coding result and the output is the original input.

a. $f(x) = x + 7$ has inverse rule that can be described in words as "subtract seven" or in symbols by $y - 7$ or $x - 7$.

b. $g(x) = 2x + 1$ has inverse or decoding rule "subtract 1 and divide by 2" or $\frac{y-1}{2}$ or $\frac{x-1}{2}$.

c. $h(x) = x^2$ has decoding rule "take the square root," $\sqrt{y}$, or $\sqrt{x}$.

d. $k(x) = 38x - x^2$ does not have a decoding rule.

INSTRUCTIONAL NOTE Some students may expect that all rules in Parts a–d have a decoding rule. Direct their attention to the words in the introduction to Problem 5: "Where possible."

6 **a.** $M_1C = [4 \quad 2]$, $M_2C = [77 \quad 44]$, $M_3C = [84 \quad 49]$, $M_4C = [44 \quad 24]$. This implies that the new message code number sequence is: 4, 2, 77, 44, 84, 49, 44, 24.

b. Students should notice that the number 11 has been encrypted to 77 and 44 when it appears in different positions in the original message. This is especially effective coding, since simply dividing those encrypted numbers by the obvious factor of 11 does not retrieve the numbers from which they were derived.

NOTE The solution to Problem 6 Part c is on page T542.

Summarize the Mathematics

In this investigation, you compared several encryption procedures to reveal properties of schemes that provide accurate and difficult-to-break message-coding methods. The methods you examined were:

(1) the assignment of number codes to letters by cell phone buttons.

(2) the assignment of number codes to digits, letters, periods, and spaces as in $0 \rightarrow 0$, $1 \rightarrow 1$, ... , $A \rightarrow 10$, $B \rightarrow 11$, ... , $Z \rightarrow 35$, $. \rightarrow 36$, $\text{—} \rightarrow 37$.

(3) the algorithm that encrypted numbers with the function $f(x) = x + 16$.

(4) the algorithm that encrypted numbers with the function $g(x) = 2x + 1$.

(5) the algorithm that encrypted numbers with the function $h(x) = x^2$.

(6) the algorithm that encrypted numbers with the function $k(x) = 38x - x^2$.

(7) the algorithm that encrypted number blocks by multiplication with $C = \begin{bmatrix} 2 & 1 \\ 5 & 3 \end{bmatrix}$.

a Which of the coding and encryption functions assigns code numbers to message letters and numbers in ways that can always be decoded to accurately retrieve the intended message? For the methods that do *not* decode accurately, explain why not.

b What properties of a coding function f will guarantee that messages encrypted by that function can always be decoded accurately?

Be prepared to explain your ideas to the class.

Check Your Understanding

The mathematical challenge of decoding messages is similar to the problem that occurs in many other situations. For example, the student government at Rosa Parks High School was planning a fundraising project that involved selling pizza at girls' and boys' basketball games. Market research among students and parents revealed two functions relating *sales* and *profit* to *price*:

Sales: $n(x) = 250 - 80x$, where x is price in dollars per slice and $n(x)$ is number of slices sold.

Profit: $P(x) = -80x^2 + 290x - 125$, where x is price in dollars per slice and $P(x)$ is profit.

Study tables and graphs of these two functions to explain the answer to each question below.

a. Is it possible to find the number of slices sold if you know the price per slice?

b. Is it possible to find the price per slice if you know the number of slices sold?

c. Is it possible to find the profit from the project if you know the price per slice?

d. Is it possible to find the price per slice if you know the profit from the project?

542 UNIT 8 • Inverse Functions

c. To decode the encrypted message, one would direct the recipient to rewrite the transmitted sequence again in 1×2 matrix blocks and multiply those blocks by the inverse of the encryption matrix.

In this case, that inverse matrix is $C^{-1} = \begin{bmatrix} 3 & -1 \\ -5 & 2 \end{bmatrix}$.

Summary

Have students spend some time summarizing their conclusions about the answers to Parts a and b before sharing ideas and negotiating differences with the whole class.

Summarize the Mathematics

a The methods that accurately decode are Methods 2, 3, 4, and 7. Every code number for these methods can be tracked back to exactly one input value.

The methods that do not accurately decode are Methods 1, 5, and 6. For the cell phone method, the code number can be tracked back to one of three options (or four options for the number 9). The squaring function $h(x) = x^2$ cannot be decoded accurately unless the domain is restricted to non-negative numbers. The rule $k(x) = 38x - x^2$ uniquely codes only 19.

b At this point, students will probably settle for an informal condition something like this: "You can always decode when each letter has its own private code number" or "No two different letters have the same code number."

Teaching Resources

Student Masters 3–4.

UNIT 8 *Inverse Functions*

Summarize the Mathematics

In this investigation, you compared several encryption procedures to reveal properties of schemes that provide accurate and difficult-to-break message-coding methods. The methods you examined were:

(1) the assignment of number codes to letters by cell phone buttons.

(2) the assignment of number codes to digits, letters, periods, and spaces as in $0 \to 0$, $1 \to 1$, …, $A \to 10$, $B \to 11$, …, $Z \to 35$, $. \to 36$, $— \to 37$.

(3) the algorithm that encrypted numbers with the function $f(x) = x + 16$.

(4) the algorithm that encrypted numbers with the function $g(x) = 2x + 1$.

(5) the algorithm that encrypted numbers with the function $h(x) = x^2$.

(6) the algorithm that encrypted numbers with the function $k(x) = 38x - x^2$.

(7) the algorithm that encrypted number blocks by multiplication with $C = \begin{bmatrix} 2 & 1 \\ 5 & 3 \end{bmatrix}$.

Transparency Master • use with page 542 UNIT 8 • Inverse Functions 3

Check Your Understanding

a. The function $n(x)$ does allow you to determine the number of slices sold when the price is given because for each value of x, there is only one value of $n(x)$.

b. It is always possible to solve an equation in the form $250 - 80x = n$ for x in terms of n, so it is possible to find the price if you know the number of slices.

c. The function $P(x)$ does tell the profit for any given price per slice because it produces an output value for all input values.

d. It is not possible to find the price per slice if you know the profit earned because the graph of the profit function is a parabola with maximum point at $x = 1.8125$. Each price between 0 and 3.63 produces a profit that is matched by some other price located at a point symmetric about $x = 1.8125$. For example, $f(1.125) = f(2.5) = 100$ but $1.125 \neq 2.5$.

INSTRUCTIONAL NOTE
Do not introduce the formal derivation of inverse rules at this point. This is the subject of Investigation 2.

Investigation 2 Finding and Using Inverse Functions

A mathematical function f sets up a correspondence between two sets so that each element of the domain D is assigned exactly one image in the range R. If another function g makes assignments in the opposite direction so that when $f(x) = y$ then $g(y) = x$, we say that g is the **inverse** of f.

The inverse relationship between two functions is usually indicated with the notation $g = f^{-1}$ or $g(x) = f^{-1}(x)$. The notation $f^{-1}(x)$ is read "f inverse of x." In this context, the exponent "-1" *does not mean* the reciprocal "one over $f(x)$." Inverses are often useful in solving problems, but there are many functions that do not have inverses. You have seen examples in your work on the coding problems of Investigation 1.

For functions with numeric domains and ranges, it is usually very helpful to describe the rule of assignment with an algebraic expression. It is also useful to find such rules for inverse functions. As you work on the problems of this investigation, look for answers to the following questions:

Which familiar types of functions have inverses?

How can rules for inverse functions be derived?

Which Functions Have Inverses? It is often helpful to think about inverse functions by using *arrow diagrams* and *coordinate graphs*.

For example, the next arrow diagrams show the patterns of assignments by two familiar functions.

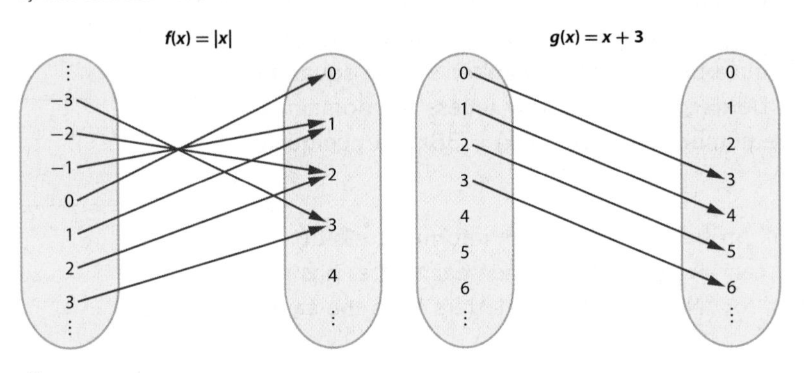

1. Consider the two functions and the given (incomplete) arrow diagrams.
   a. Does $f(x) = |x|$ have an inverse? How does the diagram show reasons for your answer?
   b. Does $g(x) = x + 3$ have an inverse? How does the diagram show reasons for your answer?
   c. How can you use an arrow diagram like those shown to decide whether a function does or does not have an inverse?

Investigation 2 Finding Inverse Functions

This investigation is a follow-up to the exploratory work of Investigation 1. It leads to articulation of general conditions for existence of inverse functions and algebraic techniques for finding the rules of those inverses in tractable cases. The concept of inverse function is represented in a variety of useful forms—tables (reversing ordered pairs), graphs (reflecting across $y = x$), arrow diagrams, and symbolic notation.

The basic condition required for a function to have an inverse is that it assign unique images to each number or point in its domain. That is, no two domain elements can have the same image (except for Extensions Task 27 on page 556). This condition is commonly expressed in mathematics by the phrase, "the function has an inverse only if it is one-to-one," or in symbolic form, $f(a) = f(b)$ implies $a = b$." We will not use the term "one-to-one" in the student text (except for E27 on p. 556), because we want students to focus on the core idea, not the language. However, periodically, we will use the term "one-to-one" in the solutions assuming that you will understand that language.

Launch

You might launch the investigation by asking students to read the definition of inverse function that starts the text of the investigation. In discussing that definition, it might be useful to anticipate Reflections Task 20 and ask students to compare the notion of inverse function to that of inverse operation (subtraction and division usually) and inverse variation $\left(y = \frac{k}{x} \text{ or } yx = k\right)$. There are similarities (in both, the inverses "cancel each other out"), but an "inverse function" is an object.

Then consider the two arrow diagrams shown to illustrate some sample assignments made by the absolute value function and the simple "add three" linear function and the questions in Problem 1.

Then segue into the rest of the investigation by indicating that the rest of the problems ask students to develop their ideas about how graphs, tables, and rules for functions can be studied to determine whether given functions have inverses and then to develop some algebraic techniques for finding rules of those inverses.

1 **a.** $f(x) = |x|$ does not have an inverse. The diagram shows two arrows ending at each range element (except 0), so "decoding" cannot be done without ambiguity.

b. $g(x) = x + 3$ does have an inverse. The diagram shows that each range element is the ending point for only one arrow so that the "decoding" can be done without ambiguity in every case by simply reversing the direction of the arrows.

c. The key to deciding whether a function does or does not have an inverse is whether each domain element is mapped to its own "private" range element. If a function has an inverse, there will never be two domain elements mapped to the same range element. (In more formal mathematical symbolism and language: A function f has an inverse if and only if $a \neq b$ implies $f(a) \neq f(b)$ or $f(a) = f(b)$ implies $a = b$. See Extensions Task 27 on page 556.)

COMMON DIFFICULTY
Students might have some difficulty with the transition from inverse questions about finite arrow diagrams in Problem 1 to the continuous Cartesian graphs of Problem 2.
You might want to have a short class discussion after Problem 1. During that discussion, give students a "heads-up" about the change in representation for Problem 2.

2 Since functions are often represented by coordinate graphs, it helps to be able to inspect such graphs to see if inverses exist. Consider the graphs of functions given below.

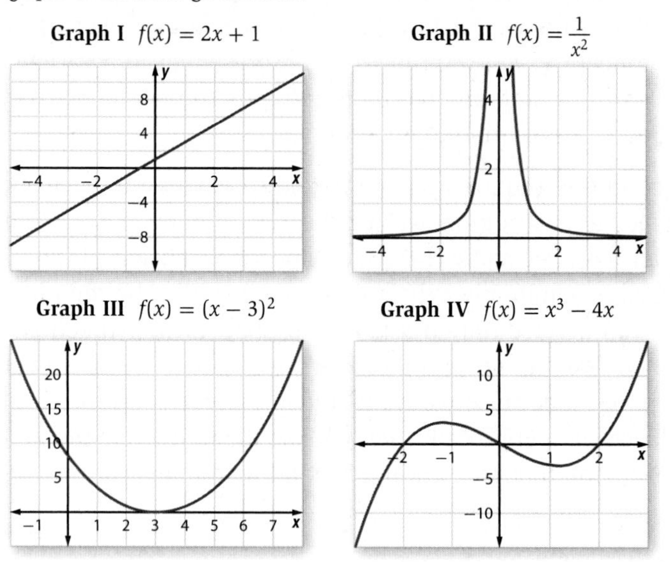

a. Which of the graphs show functions that have inverses?

b. For each function that does not have an inverse, see if you can describe a restricted (reduced) domain for the given algebraic rule so that the resulting function does have an inverse.

c. Based on your work with the four graphs, describe what you think are the key differences between graphs of functions that have inverses and graphs of those that do not.

Applications of Inverse Functions The information provided by an inverse function is often very helpful for solving practical problems in science or in business.

Hot air balloon flying is a popular recreation in several southwestern states. At some gatherings of balloonists, there is a competition to hit targets on the ground with bags dropped from balloons at various altitudes.

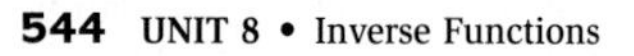

Unit 8

INVERSES OF EACH OTHER Notice that what we have given is a criterion for existence of an inverse. If the slightly different question "Under what conditions are functions f and g inverses of each other?" was asked, then one must worry about the fit of domains and ranges of each. The answer to this question could be stated as "Functions f and g are inverses of each other if and only if the domain of g is the range of f and vice versa; and for every a in the domain of f, $f(a) = b$ implies that $g(b) = a$ and vice versa." It really is not important to worry about these issues with such precision in this first encounter with the inverse function idea. More formal work with composition and inverses of functions occurs in Course 4, Unit 1.

2 **a.** Only the graph of $f(x) = 2x + 1$ shows a function that has an inverse because each y value can be tracked back to a unique x value. For each of the others, there are values of y that are connected with more than one x value.

b. The function $f(x) = \frac{1}{x^2}$ has an inverse on either of two restricted domains ($x < 0$ or $x > 0$).

The given quadratic function has an inverse on either of two restricted domains ($x \leq 3$ or $x \geq 3$).

The given cubic function has an inverse on any domain for which the function is always increasing or always decreasing. For example, $x \leq -1.1547$ (the approximate local maximum there) or $-1.1547 \leq x \leq 1.1547$ (between the local maximum and the local minimum) or $1.1547 \leq x$.

c. Graphs of (continuous) functions that have inverses are always increasing or always decreasing. Therefore, every x value and every y value is the result of a unique x value. Students might suggest something equivalent to the "horizontal line test" for existence of inverses, observing that if every horizontal line cuts the graph in at most one point, then the function will have an inverse.

HORIZONTAL LINE TEST
If students do not suggest using a horizontal line test, do not introduce that strategy here. If students focus too quickly or exclusively on the horizontal line test, it can become mechanical and obscure the fundamental concept. See the Promoting Mathematical Discourse scenario on pages T547A–B.

The balloons drift toward and over the target at various speeds. To have the best chance that their drop bags will hit the target, balloonists need to know how fast the bags will fall toward the ground. Principles of physics predict that the velocity in feet per second will be a function of time in seconds with rule $v(t) = 32t$. The distance fallen in feet will also be a function of time in seconds with rule $d(t) = 16t^2$.

a. How long will it take the drop bag to reach velocity of:

- **i.** 48 feet per second?
- **ii.** 100 feet per second?
- **iii.** 150 feet per second?

b. What rule can be used to calculate values for the inverse of the velocity function—to find the time when any given velocity is reached?

c. How long will it take the drop bag to reach the ground from altitudes of:

- **i.** 144 feet?
- **ii.** 400 feet?
- **iii.** 500 feet?

d. What rule can be used to calculate values of the inverse of the distance function—to find the time it takes for the drop bag to fall any given distance?

4 The daily profit of the Texas Theatre movie house is a function of the number of paying customers with rule $P(n) = 5n - 750$.

a. What numbers of paying customers will be required for the theater to have:

- **i.** a profit of \$100?
- **ii.** a profit of \$1,250?
- **iii.** a loss of \$175?

b. What rule can be used to calculate values for the inverse of the profit function—to find the number of paying customers required to reach any particular profit target?

Finding Rules for Inverse Functions The situations in Problems 3 and 4 illustrate the main reason for being concerned about inverse functions: We often know a function that shows how to calculate values of one variable y from known values of another variable x. But problems in such situations often require discovering the value(s) of x that will produce specific target values of y.

If the function f shows how to use values of x to calculate values of y, then f^{-1} shows how to use values of y to calculate corresponding values of x. The challenge is using the rule for f to find the rule for f^{-1}.

POSSIBLE MISCONCEPTION "Always increasing" is not the same as "non-decreasing" or "just increasing." Other ways to express "always increasing" are "strictly increasing" and "monotone increasing." If students do create a criterion for existence of inverse functions that focuses on "always increasing" or "always decreasing," you might want to pose the following discrete discontinuous graph as a counterexample to focus their attention on the criterion that no distinct x values can have the same assigned y value.

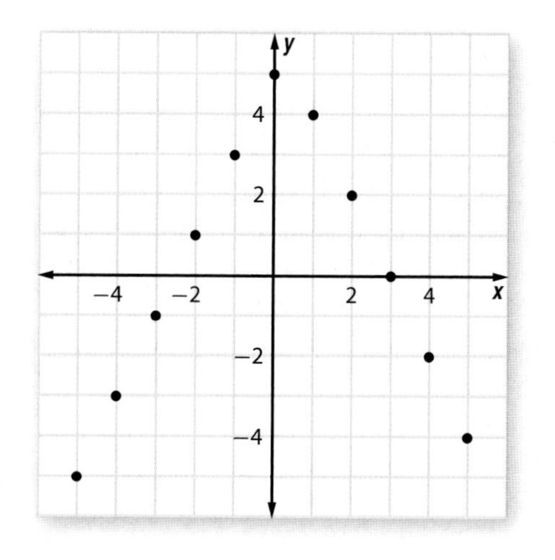

3 **a.** **i.** 1.5 seconds

ii. 3.125 seconds

iii. 4.6875 seconds

b. Divide the velocity by 32, or $t = \frac{v(t)}{32}$.

c. **i.** 3 seconds

ii. 5 seconds

iii. Approximately 5.59 seconds

d. Divide the distance by 16 and take the square root of the result, or $t = \sqrt{\frac{d(t)}{16}}$.

4 **a.** **i.** 170 customers

ii. 400 customers

iii. 115 customers

b. Add 750 to the profit target and divide by 5, or $n = (P(n) + 750) \div 5$.

INSTRUCTIONAL NOTE
Since $d(t) = 16t^2$ is a function of elapsed time, $t \geq 0$, the quadratic distance function has an inverse on the domain $t \geq 0$. Restricted domains will be discussed in Lesson 3 with inverses of the trigonometric functions. It does not need to be addressed here.

5 For each of the following linear relationships between y and x, describe in words the calculations required to find the value of x corresponding to any given value of y.

a. $y = g(x)$ and $g(x) = 3x$

b. $y = h(x)$ and $h(x) = 3x + 5$

c. $y = j(x)$ and $j(x) = 3x - 7$

d. $y = k(x)$ and $k(x) = \frac{3}{5}x + 4$

e. $y = s(x)$ and $s(x) = mx + b$ $(m \neq 0)$

When analysis of the relationship between two variables begins with the equation $y = f(x)$, it probably seems natural to express the inverse relationship with the equation $x = f^{-1}(y)$ and to write the rule for the inverse function using y as the independent variable.

However, the convention in mathematical practice is to write the rule for f^{-1} in terms of x as well—with the understanding that the letter x stands for the independent variable in the rules for both f and f^{-1}.

6 Use this notational convention to write algebraic rules for each inverse function in Problem 5.

a. If $g(x) = 3x$, then $g^{-1}(x) = \ldots$.

b. If $h(x) = 3x + 5$, then $h^{-1}(x) = \ldots$.

c. If $j(x) = 3x - 7$, then $j^{-1}(x) = \ldots$.

d. If $k(x) = \frac{3}{5}x + 4$, then $k^{-1}(x) = \ldots$.

e. If $s(x) = mx + b$ $(m \neq 0)$, then $s^{-1}(x) = \ldots$.

7 Finding inverses (when they exist) for nonlinear functions is generally more challenging than for linear functions. Study the following strategies for finding the inverse of $f(x) = \frac{5}{x - 2}$ to see if you agree that they are both correct.

Strategy I

If $y = \frac{5}{x - 2}$

Then $y(x - 2) = 5$

Then $x - 2 = \frac{5}{y}$

Then $x = \frac{5}{y} + 2$

So, $f^{-1}(x) = \frac{5}{x} + 2.$

Strategy II

If $y = \frac{5}{x - 2}$

Swap the roles of y and x to get $x = \frac{5}{y - 2}$

Then $y - 2 = \frac{5}{x}$

Then $f^{-1}(x) = \frac{5}{x} + 2.$

Adapt one strategy or the other to find rules for inverses of the following functions.

a. If $g(x) = \frac{7}{x} + 4$, then $g^{-1}(x) = \ldots$.

b. If $h(x) = \frac{7}{x + 4}$, then $h^{-1}(x) = \ldots$.

c. If $j(x) = \frac{7}{x}$, then $j^{-1}(x) = \ldots$.

d. If $k(x) = x^2$ $(x \geq 0)$, then $k^{-1}(x) = \ldots$.

Unit 8

546 UNIT 8 • Inverse Functions

5 **a.** Divide the value of y by 3.

b. Subtract 5 from the value of y and then divide that result by 3, or divide the value of y by 3 and then subtract $\frac{5}{3}$ from that result.

c. Add 7 to the value of y and then divide that result by 3, or divide the value of y by 3 and then add $\frac{7}{3}$ to that result.

d. Subtract 4 from the value of y and then divide that result by $\frac{3}{5}$ $\left(\text{or multiply the value of } y \text{ by } \frac{5}{3}\right)$, or divide the value of y by $\frac{3}{5}$ $\left(\text{multiply by } \frac{5}{3}\right)$ and then subtract $\frac{20}{3}$ from that result (or other possible sequences of operations).

e. Subtract b from the value of y and then divide that result by m, or divide the value of y by m and then subtract $\frac{b}{m}$ from that result.

6 **a.** If $g(x) = 3x$, then $g^{-1}(x) = \frac{x}{3}$.

b. If $h(x) = 3x + 5$, then $h^{-1}(x) = \frac{x - 5}{3}$.

c. If $j(x) = 3x - 7$, then $j^{-1}(x) = \frac{x + 7}{3}$.

d. If $k(x) = \frac{3}{5}x + 4$, then $k^{-1}(x) = \frac{x - 4}{\frac{3}{5}} = \frac{5(x - 4)}{3} = \frac{5}{3}x - \frac{20}{3}$.

e. If $s(x) = mx + b$ $(m \neq 0)$, then $s^{-1}(x) = \frac{x - b}{m}$.

INSTRUCTIONAL NOTE The strategy illustrated by the left example (Strategy I) in Problem 7 operates from the premise that the goal is to find a rule that "recovers" the value of x from y, thus the algebraic manipulations to solve the equation for x in terms of y. Then the translation of the rule into a general function of x form is done at the end.

The strategy illustrated by the right example operates from the premise that y and x are eventually going to interchange roles, when the inverse rule is expressed with x as the generic independent variable, so the swapping of x and y is done right away, with the understanding that the goal is then to solve for y in terms of x.

The rules for inverse functions can be expressed in several possible ways. One for each case is provided below.

a. If $g(x) = \frac{7}{x} + 4$, then $g^{-1}(x) = \frac{7}{x - 4}$.

b. If $h(x) = \frac{7}{x + 4}$, then $h^{-1}(x) = \frac{7}{x} - 4$.

c. If $j(x) = \frac{7}{x}$, then $j^{-1}(x) = \frac{7}{x}$.

d. If $k(x) = x^2$ $(x \geq 0)$, then $k^{-1}(x) = \sqrt{x}$.

8 **a.**

x	−6	−5	−4	−3	−2	−1	0	1	2
$f^{-1}(x)$	4	3	2	1	0	−1	−2	−3	−4

The domain of $f(x)$ is the integers from −4 to 4. The range is the integers from −6 to 2.

The domain of $f^{-1}(x)$ is the integers from −6 to 2. The range is the integers from −4 to 4.

INSTRUCTIONAL NOTE
You may wish to read and discuss the paragraph before Problem 5 in the student text as a whole class.

Teaching Resources

Student Master 5.

UNIT 8 *Inverse Functions*

Strategies for Finding Inverses

Problem 7

INSTRUCTIONAL NOTE
When students find in Problem 7 Part c that the function and its inverse are the same, they often think that they made a mistake. Encourage them to check some values to verify their inverse function.

INSTRUCTIONAL NOTE
Problem 8 highlights considerations of domain and range for inverse function pairs and the symmetric relationship of graphs for such pairs about the line $y = x$.

8 In some situations, you will need to find the inverse of a function that is defined only by a table of values or a graph.

a. Suppose that assignments of the function $f(x)$ are as shown in the following table. Make a similar table that shows the assignments made by $f^{-1}(x)$. Then describe the domain and range of $f(x)$ and $f^{-1}(x)$.

x	−4	−3	−2	−1	0	1	2	3	4
***f*(*x*)**	2	1	0	−1	−2	−3	−4	−5	−6

b. Suppose that the assignments of the function $g(x)$ are as shown on the graph below.

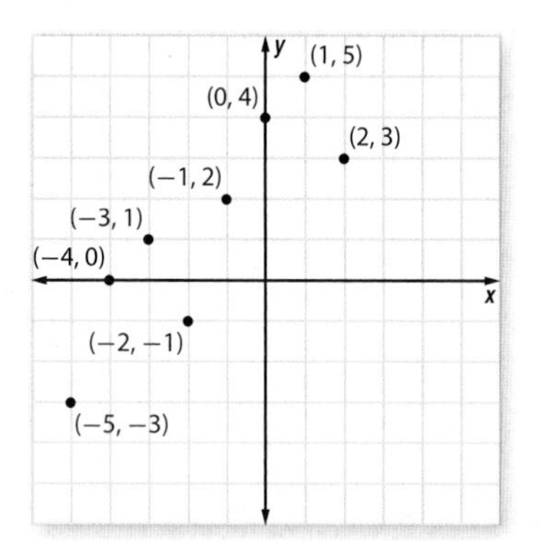

i. On a copy of that graph, plot points that represent assignments made by $g^{-1}(x)$. Then describe the domain and range of $g(x)$ and $g^{-1}(x)$.

ii. Draw line segments connecting each point (a, b) on the graph of $g(x)$ to the corresponding point (b, a) on the graph of $g^{-1}(x)$. Then describe the pattern that seems to relate corresponding points on the graphs of $g(x)$ and $g^{-1}(x)$.

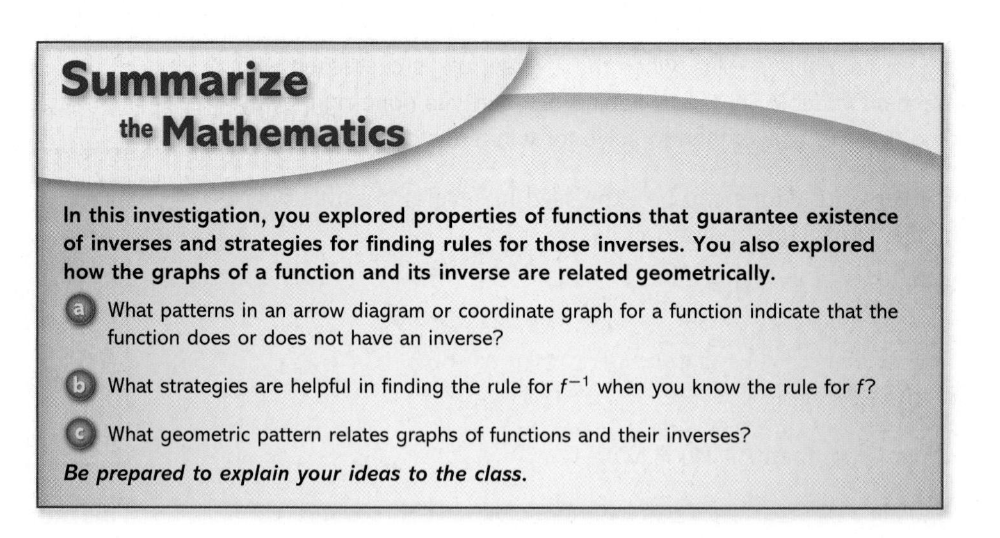

Summarize the Mathematics

In this investigation, you explored properties of functions that guarantee existence of inverses and strategies for finding rules for those inverses. You also explored how the graphs of a function and its inverse are related geometrically.

a What patterns in an arrow diagram or coordinate graph for a function indicate that the function does or does not have an inverse?

b What strategies are helpful in finding the rule for f^{-1} when you know the rule for f?

c What geometric pattern relates graphs of functions and their inverses?

Be prepared to explain your ideas to the class.

b. **i.** The graph at the right of $g(x)$ is red dots and the graph of $g^{-1}(x)$ is blue dots.

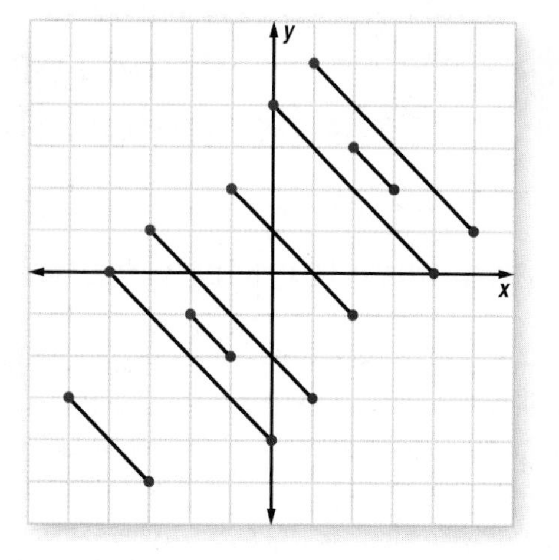

The domain of $g(x)$ is the integers from -5 to 2. The range is the integers from -3 to 5 except -2.

The domain of $g^{-1}(x)$ is the integers from -3 to 5 except -2. The range is the integers from -5 to 2.

ii. Line segments connecting each point (a, b) on the graph of $g(x)$ to the corresponding point (b, a) on the graph of $g^{-1}(x)$ will be perpendicular to and bisected by the line $y = x$. This indicates that the graphs of $g(x)$ and $g^{-1}(x)$ are reflections of each other across the line $y = x$.

NOTE The solution to Problem 8 Part a is on page T546.

Teaching Resources

Student Master 6.

UNIT 8 *Inverse Functions*

Name

Date

Finding Inverse Functions
Problem 8

Summary

Problems of this investigation should have given students ideas about how to recognize properties of functions that guarantee existence of inverses and strategies for finding rules of those inverses. Be sure that students can explain how to determine whether or not a function has an inverse in a variety of ways.

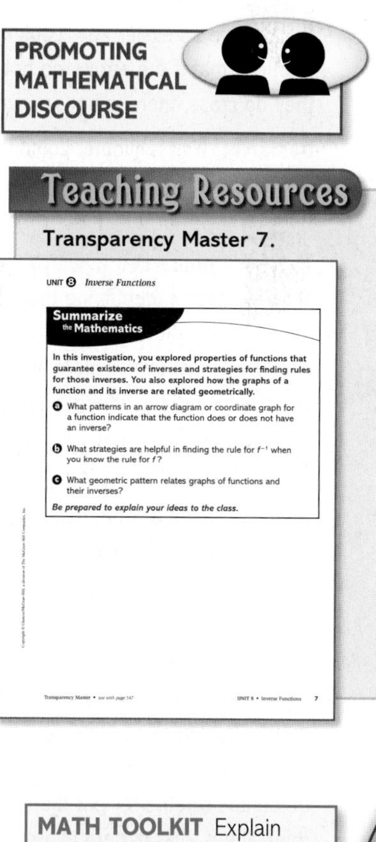
PROMOTING MATHEMATICAL DISCOURSE

Teaching Resources

Transparency Master 7.

UNIT 8 *Inverse Functions*

Summarize the Mathematics

In this investigation, you explored properties of functions that guarantee existence of inverses and strategies for finding rules for those inverses. You also explored how the graphs of a function and its inverse are related geometrically.

a. What patterns in an arrow diagram or coordinate graph for a function indicate that the function does or does not have an inverse?

b. What strategies are helpful in finding the rule for f^{-1} when you know the rule for f?

c. What geometric pattern relates graphs of functions and their inverses?

Be prepared to explain your ideas to the class.

Summarize the Mathematics

a Arrow diagrams for functions that do not have inverses will show more than one arrow ending at a single value in the range; diagrams for functions with inverses will have only one arrow ending at each range value.

Coordinate graphs for functions that have inverses will have no points with the same *y* value. Coordinate graphs for functions that do not have inverses will have two or more points with the same *y*-coordinate. (A horizontal line with that *y*-coordinate will cross the graph more than once. Graphs of functions that do have inverses will not have that "multiple crossing" property.)

b There are two standard strategies for finding the rule of f^{-1} when you know the rule for *f*. The first states to solve the equation $y = f(x)$ for *x* in terms of *y* and then interchange *x* and *y*. The second states to interchange *y* and *x* and then solve the resulting equation for *y* in terms of *x*.

c The graphs of a function and its inverse are reflections of each other across the line $y = x$.

MATH TOOLKIT Explain how you can tell from a table, a graph, or an arrow diagram whether or not a function has an inverse. Give an example using a specific function rule of how to find its inverse rule.

Unit 8

Promoting Mathematical Discourse

Summarize the Mathematics, *page 547*

Teacher: In this investigation, you explored properties of functions that guarantee existence of inverses. Think individually for a minute about this question, "What patterns in an arrow diagram for a function indicate that the function does or does not have an inverse?" Juleen, please explain your ideas to us.

Juleen: I look at the end of the arrows to make sure that no number has two arrows pointing at it.

(The teacher waits to see if Juleen will complete her answer and include an explanation. Classroom norms have been developed that expect students' replies to include their thinking, not just answers.)

Juleen: If there are two or more arrows pointing at an output number, then there is not an inverse. This is because you cannot know which input number to go back to.

Ike: I have an easier way. Look at the arrow diagrams on page 543. I noticed that if the arrows do not cross, there is an inverse and if they do cross, there is not an inverse.

Demarco: Wait a minute. Couldn't arrows cross in a diagram without pointing at the same output value more than one time? Here let me draw one. *(He draws an example on the board.)*

Teacher: Notice that Demarco has provided a counterexample for Ike's method of identifying that an inverse does not exist. What are the characteristics of the two methods—looking for crossing arrows and looking for two or more arrows at the same output—that make one helpful and the other not helpful for identifying inverses? Isabelle.

Isabelle: We need to have only one arrow at the output value to have an inverse. Just because arrows are crossing doesn't mean that they must point at one than one output, so crossing arrows doesn't help us decide anything.

Teacher: Are we all agreed on this? *(Students indicate they are in agreement.)* This is a good reminder that we must be careful when looking at examples. Ike's criteria of no crossing edges works for the example on page 543, but does not hold up for the example that Demarco provided. In addition, looking for crossing edges really does not identify the pattern of the arrows that allows you to determine whether or not the function has an inverse. Now let's think about what pattern in a coordinate graph for a function indicates that the function does or does not have an inverse. Rene?

Rene: Well, it is somewhat the same. We need to look at the graph to make sure that no y values (this is like the output values) are used more than one time. Then there will be an inverse; otherwise not. For the graphs on page 544, I scanned from left to right to see if any y values are used twice.

Teacher: Other comments? *(None are offered.)* What Rene was describing is sometimes formalized in mathematics books as "the horizontal line test." Drawing horizontal lines on paper or in your mind through the range values of a function is a way to find output values that occur more than one time. We agreed that finding these repeating values was the key to deciding on whether or not an inverse for a specific function exists. Now let's discuss the strategies we can use to find a rule for inverse functions once we have identified that one exists. Discuss with a partner the two strategies we used so that you are ready to explain them to the class. Robyn, how would you summarize these strategies?

Robyn: The function rule is usually written as $f(x) = \dots$ or $k(x) = \dots$ or some other function letter with an expression in terms of x on the other side of the equal to sign. We can change the function letter to y and have an equation with xs and ys. You can then solve for x and then switch the xs and ys. Or you can switch xs and ys first and then solve for y to get a $y = \dots$ equation again. Then you use the function inverse notation to describe the rule.

Teacher: What seems to be the reason for switching the xs and ys in this method?

Kaya: To me, it seems that the inverses kinda go back to the original values. So, you are finding a rule that goes from the outputs to the inputs. This is switching which values, xs or ys, are outputs.

Teacher: What geometric pattern relates the graphs of functions and their inverses? Think back to what you did in Problem 8. Damien.

Damien: We saw that the x- and y-coordinates for the inverse function were switched from the original function, like we just talked about.

Teacher: That's true, but how could you describe this relationship geometrically?

Marcie: The domain and range were switched. The domain of the original function is the range of the inverse function.

Bill: When we drew the segments connecting the points and inverse points, we noticed that they were all parallel.

Teacher: That is a geometric pattern. Did anyone notice anything else that could be characterized as a geometric pattern?

Karina: Yeah, we did. We noticed that you could describe the inverse points as being reflected across the line $y = x$. I drew the line $y = x$ on my plot. Here, see. *(She holds up her paper for display.)*

Scott: We did that too. I wonder if that would be true of the other functions and inverses we looked at in this lesson.

Teacher: What do you think?

Scott: Probably, since we were switching *x*s and *y*s.

Teacher: Let's check that out real quickly. Let's graph the two functions from the strategies in Problem 7. She graphs $f(x) = \frac{5}{x - 2}$ and its inverse $f^{-1}(x) = \frac{5}{x} + 2$. *(She graphs them in CPMP Tools so the functions display as different colors.)* What do you notice?

Karina: Graph $y = x$ too. Look, the red one seems to be the blue one reflected across the $y = x$ line. Cool.

Teacher: Good discussion, class. I think we are gaining a good understanding of how to determine whether or not a function has an inverse, how to find the inverses, and patterns in graphs of these functions. We will continue to consider inverse functions in the next two lessons where we will study exponential functions and trigonometric functions and their inverses.

Check Your Understanding

Use your understanding of functions and their inverses to complete the following tasks.

a. Draw arrows on a copy of the next diagram to illustrate image variable assignments made by the function $f(x) = -x$. Then explain how the pattern of those arrows suggests that the function does or does not have an inverse.

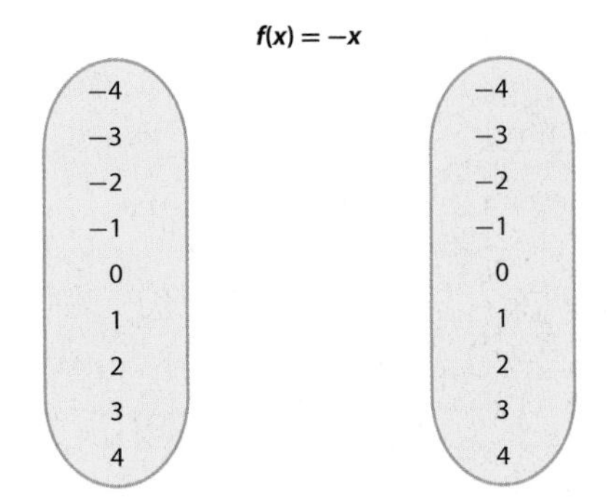

b. Which of the graphs below show functions that have inverses? Justify your response.

Graph I $f(x) = 0.5^x - 4$

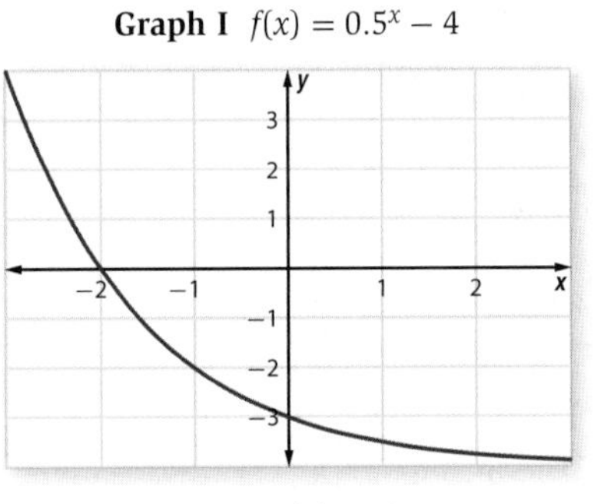

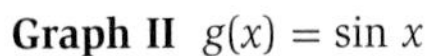
Graph II $g(x) = \sin x$

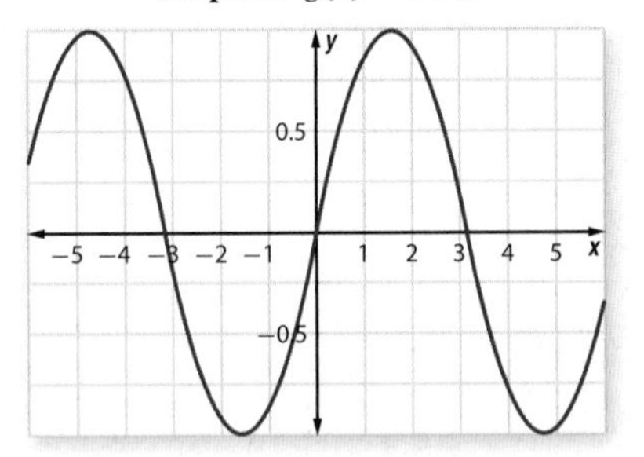

c. Find algebraic rules for the inverses of the following functions.

i. $f(x) = 0.5x - 2$

ii. $g(x) = \frac{0.5}{x} - 2$

548 UNIT 8 • Inverse Functions

Check Your Understanding

a.

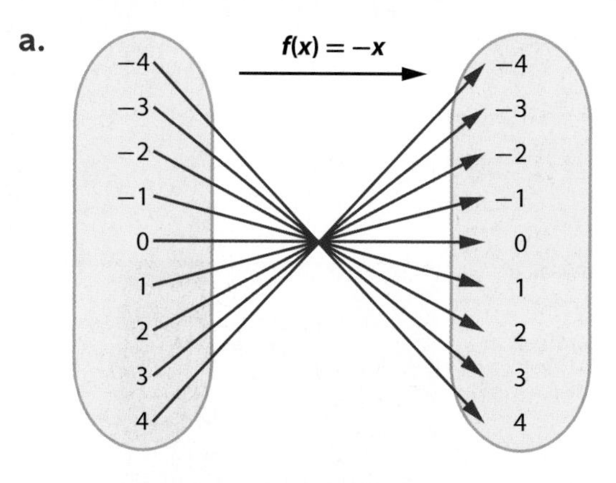

The pattern of the arrows suggests that the function does have an inverse because each number in the range is at the tip of only one arrow.

b. $f(x) = 0.5^x - 4$ has an inverse because every y value is paired with exactly one x value.

$g(x) = \sin x$ does not have an inverse since y values in the range $(-1 \leq y \leq 1)$ are paired with more than one x value.

c. **i.** $f^{-1}(x) = \dfrac{x + 2}{0.5} = 2x + 4$

ii. $g^{-1}(x) = \dfrac{0.5}{x + 2}$

Teaching Resources

Student Master 8.

INSTRUCTIONAL NOTE

In Lesson 3, students will consider restricted domains for the sine and cosine functions to allow for inverse functions.

On Your Own

Applications

1. Suppose that you want to send the message MATH QUIZ TODAY as a cell phone text message using the predictive text procedure.
   a. What sequence of numbers would you press on the standard cell phone keypad?
   b. What different message might actually be received?

2. Suppose that a message was first coded by assigning 0, 1, … , 37 to numbers, letters, periods, and spaces as in Investigation 1 and then encrypted by the function $f(x) = x + 9$.
   a. If the received message is given in encrypted form by 37, 23, 23, 46, 43, 33, 39, 46, 11, 46, 32, 27, 38, 23, what was the message that was sent?
   b. What algebraic expression would decode any message that had been encrypted by $f(x) = x + 9$?

3. Suppose that a message was first coded by assigning 0, 1, … , 37 to numbers, letters, periods, and spaces as in Investigation 1 and then encrypted by the function $f(x) = 2x$.
   a. If the received message is given in encrypted form by 38, 48, 36, 46, 74, 58, 34, 28, 74, 22, 20, 46, 26, what was the message that was sent?
   b. What algebraic expression would decode any message that had been encrypted by $f(x) = 2x$?
   c. Why do the encrypted message numbers make the decoding rule easy to guess?

4. Suppose that a message was first coded by assigning 0, 1, … , 37 to numbers, letters, periods, and spaces as in Investigation 1 and then encrypted by the function $f(x) = 3x + 2$.
   a. If the received message is given in encrypted form by 86, 44, 71, 41, 113, 32, 113, 77, 56, 38, 89, 92, 83, 44, what was the message that was sent?
   b. What algebraic expression would decode any message that had been encrypted by $f(x) = 3x + 2$?

On Your Own

Applications

1. a. MATH QUIZ TODAY would be coded (ignoring spaces) as 6, 2, 8, 4, 7, 8, 4, 9, 8, 6, 3, 2, 9.

   b. There are a number of different messages that might be received. One possibility is MATH QUIZ TO FAX. Another is MATH STIX TO FAX. Another that might seem like nonsense but consists of real English words could be MATH RUG YUM DAY. (By seeing the difficulty of creating sensible messages, students might begin to sense how decoding algorithms could be designed to check "all" sensible translations of the received number sequences.)

2. a. Subtracting 9 from each number produces the numbers 28, 14, 14, 37, 34, 24, 30, 37, 2, 37, 23, 18, 29, 14. Then decoding using the table gives the message SEE YOU 2 NITE.

   b. Decode the encrypted code using minus 9. This could be expressed as $y - 9$ or $x - 9$. In each case, x and y represent the encrypted code.

3. a. Dividing each number by 2 produces the numbers 19, 24, 18, 23, 37, 29, 17, 14, 37, 11, 10, 23, 13. Then using the table gives the message JOIN THE BAND.

   b. Decode using $\frac{x}{2}$, or $0.5x$.

   c. The fact that every encrypted number is even, strongly suggests multiplication by 2 is involved. (Other even values can be checked and rejected since they would not be multiples of all the encrypted values. In fact 22, the smallest value, has only factors of 2 and 11.)

4. a. Subtracting 2 from each number and then dividing by 3 produces the numbers 28, 14, 23, 13, 37, 10, 37, 25, 18, 12, 29, 30, 27, 14. Then using the table gives the message SEND A PICTURE.

   b. Decode using $\frac{x - 2}{3}$, or $\frac{x}{3} - \frac{2}{3}$, (or some equivalent rule).

Unit 8

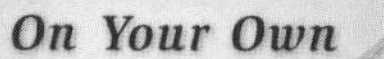

On Your Own

5 Suppose that a message was first coded by assigning 0, 1, ... , 37 to numbers, letters, periods, and spaces as in Investigation 1. Study patterns in code numbers assigned by the following encryption functions to see which would allow decoding of any message without confusion.

For those that are suitable, give a rule for decoding. For those that are not, explain why not.

a. $f(x) = 37 - x$

b. $g(x) = x^2 - 38x + 361$

c. $h(x) = |x - 37|$

d. $k(x) = 1.5x + 0.5$

6 Which of these graphs represent functions that have inverses? Be prepared to justify each answer.

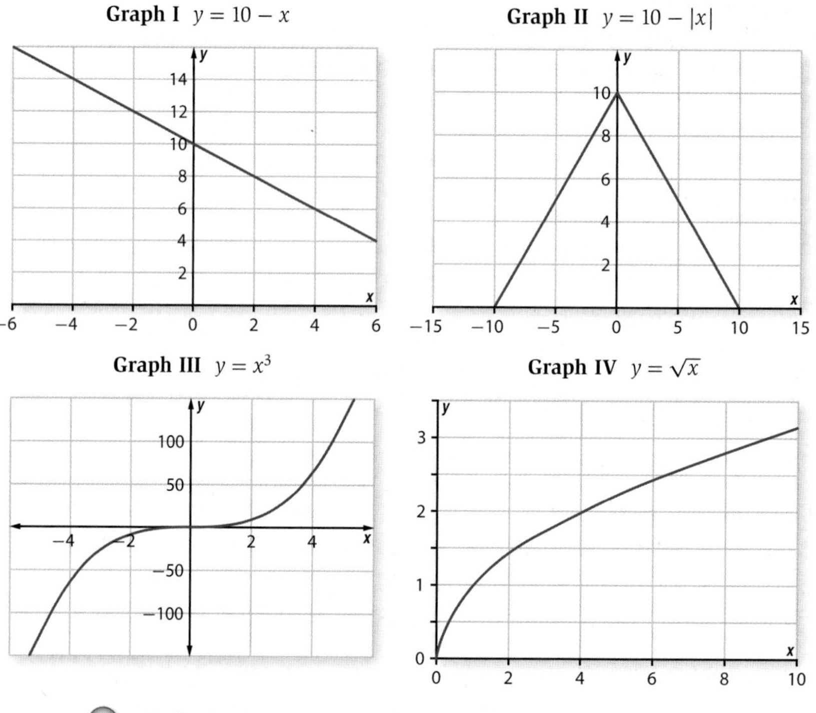

7 Find rules for the inverses of the following functions.

a. $f(x) = 4x - 5$

b. $g(x) = 8x^2$ (domain $x \geq 0$)

c. $h(x) = \frac{5}{x}$ (domain $x \neq 0$)

d. $k(x) = -5x + 7$

Unit 8

550 UNIT 8 • Inverse Functions

5 **a.** Yes, decode using $37 - x$.

b. No, because any pairs of x values that are symmetric about the point $x = 19$ will have the same code numbers assigned. The given quadratic function has axis of symmetry $x = 19$.

c. Yes, decode using $37 - x$. Although the given encryption function is not a one-to-one function, for the domain $0 \leq x \leq 37$, it is one-to-one. On that domain, its rule is equivalent to that of Part a, so the decoding function has the same rule.

d. Yes, decode using $\frac{x - 0.5}{1.5}$, or $\frac{2}{3}x - \frac{1}{3}$.

6 **a–d.** The graphs of $y = 10 - x$, $y = x^3$, and $y = \sqrt{x}$ have inverses because each domain value has its own private range value. No distinct domain values have the same range value.

7 **a.** $f^{-1}(x) = \frac{x + 5}{4}$, or $f^{-1}(x) = 0.25x + 1.25$

b. $g^{-1}(x) = \sqrt{\frac{x}{8}}$

c. $h^{-1}(x) = \frac{5}{x}$

d. $k^{-1}(x) = \frac{x - 7}{-5}$, or $k^{-1}(x) = -0.2x + 1.4$

8 The following statements describe situations where functions relate two quantitative variables. For each situation:

- if possible, give a rule for the function that is described.
- determine whether the given function has an inverse.
- if an inverse exists, give a rule for that inverse function (if possible) and explain what it tells about the variables of the situation.

a. If regular gasoline is selling for $3.95 per gallon, the price of any particular purchase p is a function of the number of gallons of gasoline g in that purchase.

b. If a school assigns 20 students to each mathematics class, the number of mathematics classes M is a function of the number of mathematics students s in that school.

c. The area of a square A is a function of the length of each side s.

d. The number of hours of daylight d at any spot on Earth is a function of the time of year t.

Connections

9 The U.S. Postal Service uses two kinds of zip codes. One short form uses five digits, like 20906. The longer form uses nine digits, like 20742-3053.

a. How many five-digit zip codes are possible?

b. How many nine-digit zip codes are possible?

c. How do your answers to Parts a and b explain the fact that every possible U.S. mail address has a unique nine-digit zip code but not a unique five-digit code?

10 U.S. Social Security numbers all use nine-digits, generally written in three groups like 987-65-4321.

a. How many U.S. citizens can be assigned social security numbers with the current system so that each person has a unique code?

b. No social security numbers begin with the three digits 666. By how much does that restriction reduce the number of available unique social security code numbers?

c. When social security numbers were first issued, the beginning three digits of each number indicated the area office (one of eight across the U.S.) from which it was issued. How many distinct social security numbers could be issued from one such area?

8 **a.** $p = 3.95g$; This function has an inverse. Ignoring the inevitable rounding of prices to nearest penny, the price function does have an inverse. If the total cost of a purchase is known, then the number of gallons in the purchase can be determined by $g = \frac{p}{3.95}$.

b. $M = \frac{s}{20}$. This function has an inverse. If the school manages to exactly meet the prescribed student-to-math-class ratio, then it will be possible to calculate the number of mathematics students in the school from the number of teachers by $s = 20M$.

c. $A = s^2$. This function has an inverse. If one knows the area of a square, it is always possible to calculate the length of each side by $s = \sqrt{A}$. The domain is restricted to $s > 0$.

d. The given information does not really allow construction of a function rule because it depends on the latitude of the particular spot. An inverse for this function does not exist. The number of hours of daylight at any spot on Earth is a periodic function for which times that are at symmetric points on either side of the summer or winter solstice will have the same number of hours of daylight.

Thus, the function that gives hours of daylight at any time of the year cannot be inverted to find time of year from hours of daylight. In general, there will always be two times of the year that have each possible number of daylight hours.

Connections

9 **a.** $10^5 = 100{,}000$, though there are some restrictions on the forms of five-digit numbers that are actually used.

b. $10^9 = 1{,}000{,}000{,}000$, though there are some restrictions on the forms of nine-digit numbers that are actually used.

c. There are clearly more than 100,000 mailing addresses in the U.S. but not more than one billion.

10 **a.** $10^9 = 1{,}000{,}000{,}000$, though there are some restrictions on the forms of nine-digit numbers that are actually used.

b. This restriction removes all numbers in the form 666 ab cdef, or a total of $10^6 = 1{,}000{,}000$ possible social security numbers.

c. $10^6 = 1{,}000{,}000$, though there are some restrictions on the forms of five-digit numbers that are actually used.

ADDITIONAL RESOURCES
For the explanation of the restriction in Part b and much other information about how Social Security numbers have been and are now assigned, you might direct students to the Wikipedia article on the subject.

On Your Own

11 Consider the geometric transformation with coordinate rule $(x, y) \rightarrow (x + 3, y + 2)$.

a. What kind of transformation is defined by that rule?

b. What is the rule for the inverse of that transformation?

12 The arithmetic mean is a statistical function that assigns a single number to any set of numbers $x_1, x_2, \ldots, x_n$ by the general rule $\frac{\Sigma x_i}{n}$. Does this function have an inverse? Explain.

13 The formula $P = 2L + 2W$ assigns a numerical perimeter to every rectangle with length L and width W. Does this function have an inverse? Explain.

14 The following graphs show pairs of functions that are inverses of each other and the line $y = x$. For each pair of functions:

- find two points (a, b) and (c, d) on one graph and show that the points (b, a) and (d, c) are on the other graph.
- explain why the transformation $(x, y) \rightarrow (y, x)$ maps every point of one graph onto a point of the other graph.

a. $f(x) = x^2$ and $f^{-1}(x) = \sqrt{x}, x \geq 0$

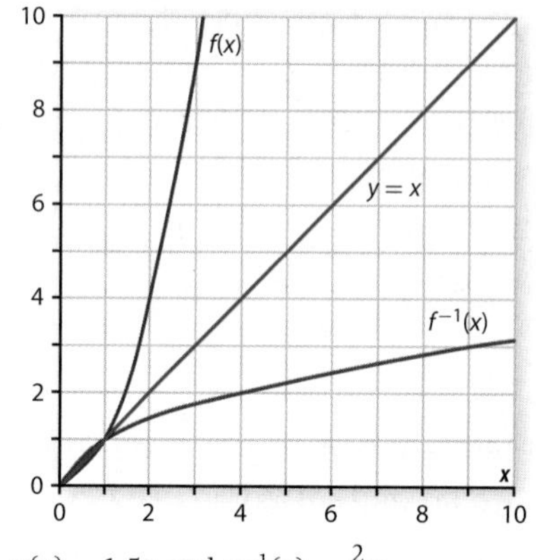

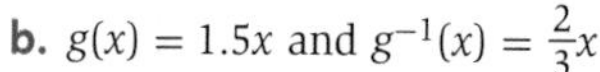

b. $g(x) = 1.5x$ and $g^{-1}(x) = \frac{2}{3}x$

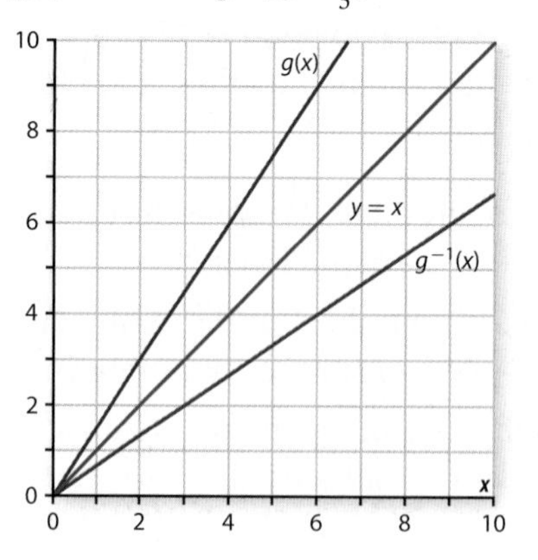

552 UNIT 8 • Inverse Functions

11 **a.** The given rule defines a translation that maps every point of the plane to a point that is 3 units to the right and up 2 units.

b. $(x, y) \rightarrow (x - 3, y - 2)$

12 No, it is not possible to recover the data from the mean, so that function does not have an inverse. For example 3, 2, 1 and 4, 2, 0 both have mean of 2.

13 No, the perimeter function assigns exactly one number to every rectangle, but many different rectangles have the same perimeter. For example, both 3×5 and 6×2 rectangles have perimeter of 16.

14 **a.** For example, the points (0, 0) and (2, 4) are on the graph of $f(x)$ and (0, 0) and (4, 2) are on the graph of $f^{-1}(x)$.

Proof:

If (x, x^2) is on the graph of $f(x) = x^2$, then $f^{-1}(x^2) = \sqrt{x^2} = x$, so $(x^2, \sqrt{x^2}) = (x^2, x)$ is on the graph of $f^{-1}(x)$.

b. For example, the points (0, 0) and (4, 6) are on the graph of $g(x)$ and the points (0, 0) and (6, 4) are on the graph of $g^{-1}(x)$.

Proof:

If $(x, 1.5x)$ is on the graph of $g(x) = 1.5x$, then $(1.5x, x) = \left(1.5x, \frac{2}{3}(1.5x)\right)$ is on the graph of $g^{-1}(x)$.

Unit 8

15 Calculators and computers use the *floor* and *ceiling* functions in work with data. The functions are defined as follows.

- The floor function $f(x) = \lfloor x \rfloor$ assigns to any number x the greatest integer less than or equal to x. For example, $\lfloor 3.1415 \rfloor = 3$.
- The ceiling function $c(x) = \lceil x \rceil$ assigns to any number x the smallest integer greater than or equal to x. For example, $\lceil 2.71828 \rceil = 3$.

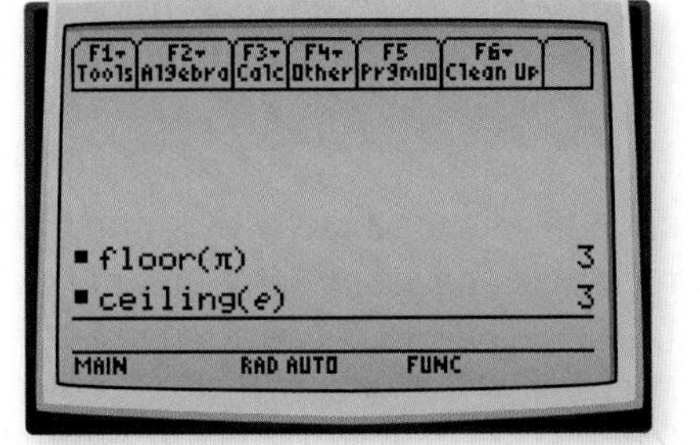

a. Explain why it is or is not possible to find the value of x when you know the value of $f(x)$.

b. Explain why it is or is not possible to find the value of x when you know the value of $c(x)$.

16 Rounding is a function used often in calculator or computer work with numeric data.

a. If $r_2(x)$ rounds every number to two decimal places, find these results from using that function.

i. $r_2(3.141)$ **ii.** $r_2(2.718)$ **iii.** $r_2(2.435)$

b. Explain why it is or is not possible to find the value of x when you know the value of $r_2(x)$.

Reflections

17 In what kinds of everyday situations do you use systems that code and decode information? Explain why that coding is required and the properties that useful coding schemes must have.

18 Many computer systems require entry of passwords before allowing users to access sites like email servers and other private sources of information. What are some criteria that make sense when assigning passwords?

19 When Brianna looked up "inverse function" on the Internet, she found a sentence that stated, "A function has an inverse if and only if it is a one-to-one function." She wondered what the phrase "one-to-one" means.

Does it mean that for each value of x there is exactly one paired value of y?
Or does it mean that for each value of y there is exactly one paired value of x?

Based on your investigation of inverse functions, what do you think the one-to-one condition tells about a function?

15 **a.** There are many different numbers that have the same floor value. For example, for $1 \leq x < 2$, $f(x) = 1$.

b. There are many different numbers that have the same ceiling value. For example, for $1 < x \leq 2$, $c(x) = 2$.

16 **a.** **i.** 3.14 (This is a rounded value of π.)

ii. 2.72 (This is a rounded value of e, which will be introduced in Course 4.)

iii. 2.44 (This rounding uses the convention that for any number that is at least half-way to the next higher digit, you round up.)

b. There are many numbers that round to the same number. For example, 3.414 and 3.413 both round to 3.41. So after rounding has occurred, we cannot recover the original number.

Reflections

17 Students might mention Web transactions where payments are involved and it is important to keep things like credit card numbers secure from prying hackers. Bar codes identify all possible products for sale and connect to prices at each local store that sells the products. ISBN numbers identify all books. Good coding schemes should assign unique codes to objects so that there is no confusion about what object is intended by a particular code.

Also, good coding schemes are those in which one single slip/error in transmission can be caught and corrected by the receiver. For instance, if the code number for a product is 123456 but through human or electronic error what is sent is 123457, one wants the receiver to recognize that an error has been made and to figure out what really was intended. This attribute of codes called "error correcting" is accomplished in a variety of ways, usually by sending some redundancy.

18 It would be desirable to have a password system where each distinct user has a personal unique password. This means that the password allows access to only one user. For most individuals, a password that has some personal meaning is usually easier to remember; but it cannot be too obviously personal or an identity thief might easily guess it.

19 The phrase "one-to-one" means that for each value of y, there is exactly one paired value of x. In other words, no y value is the image of two or more values of x. The other meaning that Arrillio was considering is actually a defining condition for a correspondence of values to be a function. That is, each x value in the domain is assigned exactly one image in the range. In the visual language of function arrow diagrams, a correspondence is not a function if there are two arrows starting at a domain point. A function is not one-to-one if there are two arrows ending at a range point.

20 The word "inverse" is used in several different ways in algebra. For example, we say that -7 is the *additive inverse* of 7 because $-7 + 7 = 0$. Similarly, we say that $\frac{7}{2}$ is the *multiplicative inverse* of $\frac{2}{7}$ because $\left(\frac{7}{2}\right)\left(\frac{2}{7}\right) = 1$.
How is the use of the word "inverse" in the phrase "inverse function" similar to its use in the phrases "additive inverse" and "multiplicative inverse"?

21 Look back at your work on Problem 8 of Investigation 1 and Connections Task 14. Given the graph of a function that has an inverse, how could you quickly sketch the graph of the inverse function? Give an example illustrating your ideas.

22 Here are two ways to think about finding the rule for an inverse function.

Brandon's Strategy: If I know the rule for $f(x)$ as an equation relating y and x, I simply swap the symbols y and x and then solve the resulting equation for y. For example, if $f(x) = 3x + 5$ or $y = 3x + 5$, then I swap y and x to get $x = 3y + 5$ and solve for y to get the rule $y = \frac{x - 5}{3}$ for the inverse.

Luisa's Strategy: If I know the rule for $f(x)$ as an equation relating y and x, I solve that equation for x in terms of y and then use that equation to write the rule for the inverse of f. For example, if $f(x) = 3x + 5$ or $y = 3x + 5$, I solve for x to get $x = \frac{y - 5}{3}$, that tells me the inverse function has rule $f^{-1}(x) = \frac{x - 5}{3}$ or $y = \frac{x - 5}{3}$.

a. Will either or both of these strategies always give the correct inverse function rule?

b. Which of the two strategies (or some other strategy of your own) makes most sense to you as a way of thinking about inverse functions and their rules?

Extensions

As you used the linear function and matrix encryption algorithms for coding, you probably noticed that the code numbers get quite large quickly. Mathematicians have devised a kind of remainder arithmetic that solves that problem. The idea is to apply the sort of counting involved in calculating with time—hours in a day or days in a week.

If you want to find the day of the week 23 days from today, you notice that 23 days is really just 2 days more than 3 weeks and count on 2 days from today. To apply this idea to simplifying code numbers, you take any number calculated with an encryption algorithm and reduce it by taking out multiples of 38. That is, you count from 0 to 37 and then start over from 0 again.

Unit 8

554 UNIT 8 • Inverse Functions

20 The additive inverse of 7 is -7 because $7 + -7 = 0$. Essentially adding the inverse -7 has the effect of undoing the addition of 7. You can think of this property as retrieving the original number. For example, $(n + 7) + (-7) = n$. Similarly, multiplying by 7 and then by $\frac{1}{7}$ $\left(\text{because } 7 \times \frac{1}{7} = 1\right)$ has the effect of undoing the multiplication by 7 and retrieving the original number. That is $(n \times 7) \times \left(\frac{1}{7}\right) = n$.

21 You could sketch a reflection of the graph over the line $y = x$. Student examples will vary.

22 **a.** The two strategies both work. In fact, the "swap x and y and then solve for y in terms of x" method seems to be the standard strategy.

b. Students will have their own preference of a strategy that makes the most sense to them.

INSTRUCTIONAL NOTE
Students will probably struggle with the process of finding inverse functions, so some opportunity for them to share their thinking with each other is likely to be productive, even if they say that listening to an approach different from their own is simply confusing!

For example, suppose that you are using the encryption function $f(x) = 2x + 1$.

Step 1. The letter T is assigned the code number 29 and then $f(29) = 59$.

Step 2. If we start counting at 0 when reaching 38, the code number 59 is reduced to 21.

This method using a function and remainder arithmetic results in code numbers no larger than 37, but it must be used with some care as you will see in Extensions Tasks 23–25.

23 Simplify the result of the arithmetic of the following calculations based on the idea above.

a. $23 + 34$

b. $2(23) + 15$

c. $5(23) + 4$

d. $9(4) + 3$

e. $9(8) + 3$

f. 13^2

24 Consider the message I WILL BE THERE AT 1 that translates first into the following number sequence.

18, 37, 32, 18, 21, 21, 37, 11, 14, 37, 29, 17, 14, 27, 14, 37, 10, 29, 37, 1

a. Use the coding function $f(x) = 2x + 1$ and remainder arithmetic that starts over at 38 to find the encrypted number sequence carrying this message.

b. What problem with this encryption algorithm is revealed by coding the given message?

25 Now explore encryption by remainder arithmetic that starts over at 38 with the function $g(x) = 5x + 1$.

a. Encrypt the following message number sequence.

18, 37, 32, 18, 21, 21, 37, 11, 14, 37, 29, 17, 14, 27, 14, 37, 10, 29, 37, 1

b. Compare the result of Part a to the encryption result using $f(x) = 2x + 1$. Show that the problem encountered with that function does not occur with $g(x) = 5x + 1$, at least for this message.

c. Complete a copy of the following table to show the encrypted form of each number from 0 to 37. Explain how the pattern of those results shows that $g(x)$ does not assign the same code number to any pair of distinct letters.

Symbol	0	1	...	9	A	B	...	Z	.	—
Code Number	0	1	...	9	10	11	...	35	36	37
Encrypted	1	6	...	8	13	18	...	24	29	34

d. Apply the function $d(x) = 23x + 15$ with remainder arithmetic to each number that results from encryption by $g(x)$ in Part c. What does the pattern of results in that table suggest about the relationship of $g(x)$ and $d(x)$?

Extensions

> **NOTE** Tasks 23–25 all require the introductory paragraph before Task 23 in the student text.

23

a. 19, since $23 + 34 = 57 = 38 + 19$

b. 23, since $2(23) + 15 = 46 + 15 = 61 = 38 + 23$

c. 5, since $5(23) + 4 = 119 = 3(38) + 5$

d. 1, since $9(4) + 3 = 39 = 38 + 1$

e. 37, since $9(8) + 3 = 75 = 38 + 37$

f. 17, since $13^2 = 4(38) + 17$

24

a. 37, 37, 27, 37, 5, 5, 37, 23, 29, 37, 21, 35, 29, 17, 29, 37, 21, 21, 37, 3

b. The problem is that two different starting numbers can end up at the same coded number and thus not be decodable without ambiguity. For example, 18 encrypts to 37 and 37 also encrypts to 37. (This occurs because 2 is a factor of 38, which students might notice after they do Task 23.)

CHOOSING TECHNOLOGY TOOLS A student master is purposely *not* provided for Extensions Task 25. Providing a copy might divert student thinking about choosing a technology tool that would be helpful to expedite the computation. In particular, developing a spreadsheet of this task eliminates tedious computation and copying of results in a table. We advise letting students make decisions about which (if any) technology tools to use and how to use it.

25

a. The message I WILL BE THERE AT 1 becomes 15, 34, 9, 15, 30, 30, 34, 18, 33, 34, 32, 10, 33, 22, 33, 34, 13, 32, 34, 6.

b. Using $5x + 1$, every starting number has its own encrypted number.

c. The full list of encrypted numbers using $2x + 1$, $5x + 1$, and the proposed decoding function $23x + 15$ applied to the codes created by $5x + 1$ is shown on the following page. The entries in the column under $5x + 1$ are all distinct, indicating that this encryption algorithm assigns unique codes to every number and letter.

Unit 8

Symbol	Code Number	Encrypted $f(x) = 2x + 1$	Encrypted $g(x) = 5x + 1$	$d(x) = 23(5x + 1) + 15$
0	0	1	1	0
1	1	3	6	1
2	2	5	11	2
3	3	7	16	3
4	4	9	21	4
5	5	11	26	5
6	6	13	31	6
7	7	15	36	7
8	8	17	3	8
9	9	19	8	9
A	10	21	13	10
B	11	23	18	11
C	12	25	23	12
D	13	27	28	13
E	14	29	33	14
F	15	31	0	15
G	16	33	5	16
H	17	35	10	17
I	18	37	15	18
J	19	1	20	19
K	20	3	25	20
L	21	5	30	21
M	22	7	35	22
N	23	9	2	23
O	24	11	7	24
P	25	13	12	25
Q	26	15	17	26
R	27	17	22	27
S	28	19	27	28
T	29	21	32	29
U	30	23	37	30
V	31	25	4	31
W	32	27	9	32
X	33	29	14	33
Y	34	31	19	34
Z	35	33	24	35
.	36	35	29	36
—	37	37	34	37

d. The results in column 5, produced by applying $23x + 15$ to the numbers that have been encrypted by $5x + 1$, show that this second function $d(x)$ is the inverse of $g(x)$.

a. The graph below shows that for any value of x, there is a unique value of y assigned by the cube function. Thus, it is always possible to work back from the y value to the cube root.

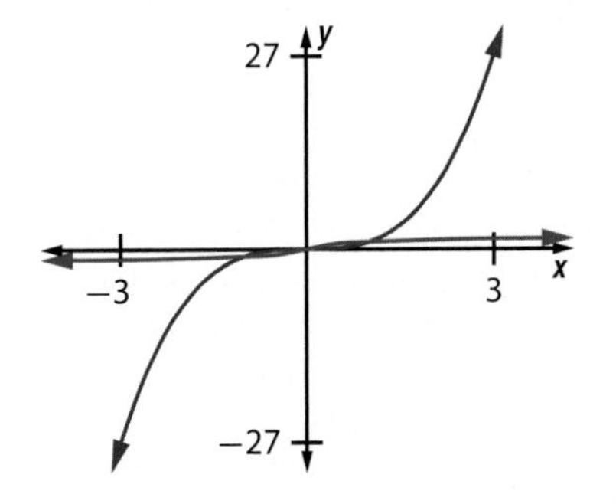

b. Any cubic with rule in the form $y = a(x \pm b)^3 \pm c$ is invertible because it will be a stretch and/or translation of the basic cubic $y = x^3$ and thus each x value has a unique image (based on the answer to Part a). This way of expressing the answer actually foreshadows work on transformation of function graphs and rules that comes at the beginning of Course 4. At this point, you should probably only expect students to come up with shifts up and down for $y = x^3$ or rules in the form $y = x^3 \pm a$. Cubics that have graphs with hills and valleys will not be invertible. For example, the cubic with rule $y = x^3 - 12x$ has a hilltop at $(-2, 16)$ and a valley bottom at $(2, -16)$.

On Your Own

26 You have seen that without domain restrictions, quadratic functions never have inverses. Explore that same question for the case of cubic polynomials.

a. Show by analysis of the graph of $y = x^3$, that this simplest possible cubic has an inverse, the cube root function. Then sketch a graph of both the cube and cube root functions on the same coordinate diagram for $-5 \le x \le 5$ and $-5 \le y \le 5$.

b. Give other examples (where possible) of cubic polynomials that do have inverses and some that do not.

c. The general form of a cubic polynomial is $a_3x^3 + a_2x^2 + a_1x + a_0$. Use algebraic reasoning and a graphing tool to search for patterns of coefficients in cubic functions that have inverses and patterns of coefficients in cubic functions that do not have inverses.

27 A function $f(x)$ is said to be **one-to-one** or **injective** if whenever $f(a) = f(b)$, we can conclude that $a = b$.

a. Provide justifications for each step in the following proof that the function $g(x) = 3x + 5$ is one-to-one.

Step 1. Whenever $g(a) = g(b)$, we can conclude that $3a + 5 = 3b + 5$.

Step 2. The equation in Step 1 implies that $3a = 3b$.

Step 3. The equation in Step 2 implies that $a = b$.

Step 4. Therefore, $g(x)$ is one-to-one.

b. Adapt the argument in Part a to prove that any linear function $h(x) = mx + n$ is one-to-one.

c. Prove that $q(x) = x^2$ (and in fact, any quadratic polynomial function) is not one-to-one.

d. Explain why any exponential function is one-to-one.

e. Explain why the sine and cosine functions are not one-to-one.

f. Explain why a function that is *not* one-to-one does not have an inverse.

g. Explain why a function that is one-to-one does have an inverse.

28 Any 2×2 matrix defines a transformation of points in the coordinate plane that maps points in the following general form.

$$\begin{bmatrix} a & b \\ c & d \end{bmatrix}\begin{bmatrix} x \\ y \end{bmatrix} = \begin{bmatrix} ax + by \\ cx + dy \end{bmatrix}$$

a. Show that the matrices $\begin{bmatrix} 1 & 2 \\ 3 & 5 \end{bmatrix}$ and $\begin{bmatrix} -5 & 2 \\ 3 & -1 \end{bmatrix}$ are inverses of each other.

b. Evaluate $\begin{bmatrix} -5 & 2 \\ 3 & -1 \end{bmatrix}\begin{bmatrix} x \\ y \end{bmatrix}$.

c. Multiply the result from Part b by $\begin{bmatrix} 1 & 2 \\ 3 & 5 \end{bmatrix}$.

556 UNIT 8 • Inverse Functions

c. A full answer with proof is beyond what can be expected from CPMP students. At this point, they might observe that there are basically three kinds of cubic graphs—those that look like the basic $y = x^3$ form (perhaps stretched and/or translated around the coordinate grid), those that have one hill and one valley, and some others that look like the basic cubic but do not have the locally horizontal inflection point that one associates with the basic cubic at (0, 0). When a hill or valley occurs in a graph, this means that some pairs of x values have the same assigned y value, so the function will not have an inverse. The connection between coefficients and types of cubic graphs is rather hard to identify and articulate at this point. Students should be able to come up with some beginning pattern types and realize that once they have found one example, stretches and translations of that example will be in the same class with respect to inverse existence.

NOTE Solutions to Task 26 Parts a and b are on page T555B.

27 a. **Step 1.** Substitution in the rule for $g(x)$.

Step 2. Subtract 5 from both sides of the equation.

Step 3. Divide both sides of the equation by 3.

Step 4. Argument in Steps 1–3 fit the definition of one-to-one.

b. Suppose that $h(x) = mx + n$.

Step 1. Whenever $h(a) = h(b)$, we can conclude that $ma + n = mb + n$.

Step 2. The equation in Step 1 implies that $ma = mb$.

Step 3. The equation in Step 2 implies that $a = b$.

Step 4. Therefore, $h(x)$ is one-to-one.

c. To prove that a function is *not* one-to-one, you need only to provide a counterexample that $f(a) = f(b)$ does not always imply that $a = b$. One such example is $f(-3) = f(3)$, but $-3 \neq 3$.

d. Give the shape of the graph of any exponential growth or decay function, each positive y value occurs exactly once, so if $E(a) = E(b)$, we can conclude that $a = b$.

e. The values of these periodic functions repeat in periods of 2π, 2π, and π respectively, so many different values of x have the same assigned y values. For example, $\sin 0 = \sin 2\pi = 0$ and $\cos 0 = \cos 2\pi = 1$.

f. If a function is not one-to-one, then two distinct inputs have the same output, meaning that it is not possible to infer the input from the output. Thus, the function will not have an inverse.

g. If each distinct input value has a unique output value, it is always possible to "recover" the input value if you know the output value. That is the criterion for an inverse function to exist.

28 a. The product in either order will be the identity matrix $\begin{bmatrix} 1 & 0 \\ 0 & 1 \end{bmatrix}$.

b. $\begin{bmatrix} -5x + 2y \\ 3x - y \end{bmatrix}$

c. $\begin{bmatrix} x \\ y \end{bmatrix}$ when results are simplified as far as possible

29 The simplest 2 × 2 coding matrices are those in the form $A = \begin{bmatrix} a & b \\ c & d \end{bmatrix}$ for which $ad - bc = 1$. In those cases, the inverse of A can be found using the formula: $\begin{bmatrix} a & b \\ c & d \end{bmatrix}^{-1} = \begin{bmatrix} d & -b \\ -c & a \end{bmatrix}$

a. Use the given formula to find the inverse of $\begin{bmatrix} 4 & 1 \\ 7 & 2 \end{bmatrix}$.

b. Prove that the given formula will always produce the inverse of such a matrix by showing that $\begin{bmatrix} a & b \\ c & d \end{bmatrix} \cdot \begin{bmatrix} a & b \\ c & d \end{bmatrix}^{-1} = \begin{bmatrix} 1 & 0 \\ 0 & 1 \end{bmatrix}$, the 2 × 2 identity matrix.

Review

30 Use properties of exponents to write each of these expressions in a different equivalent form.

a. $(x^5)(x^2)$

b. $(x^5) \div (x^2)$

c. $(x^5)^2$

d. x^{-5}

31 In the figure at the right, $\overline{AB} \parallel \overline{CD}$.

a. Prove that $\triangle ABE \sim \triangle DCE$.

b. If $BC = 6$ cm, $CE = 9$ cm, $CD = 8$ cm, and $DE = 12$ cm, find AB, AE, and AD.

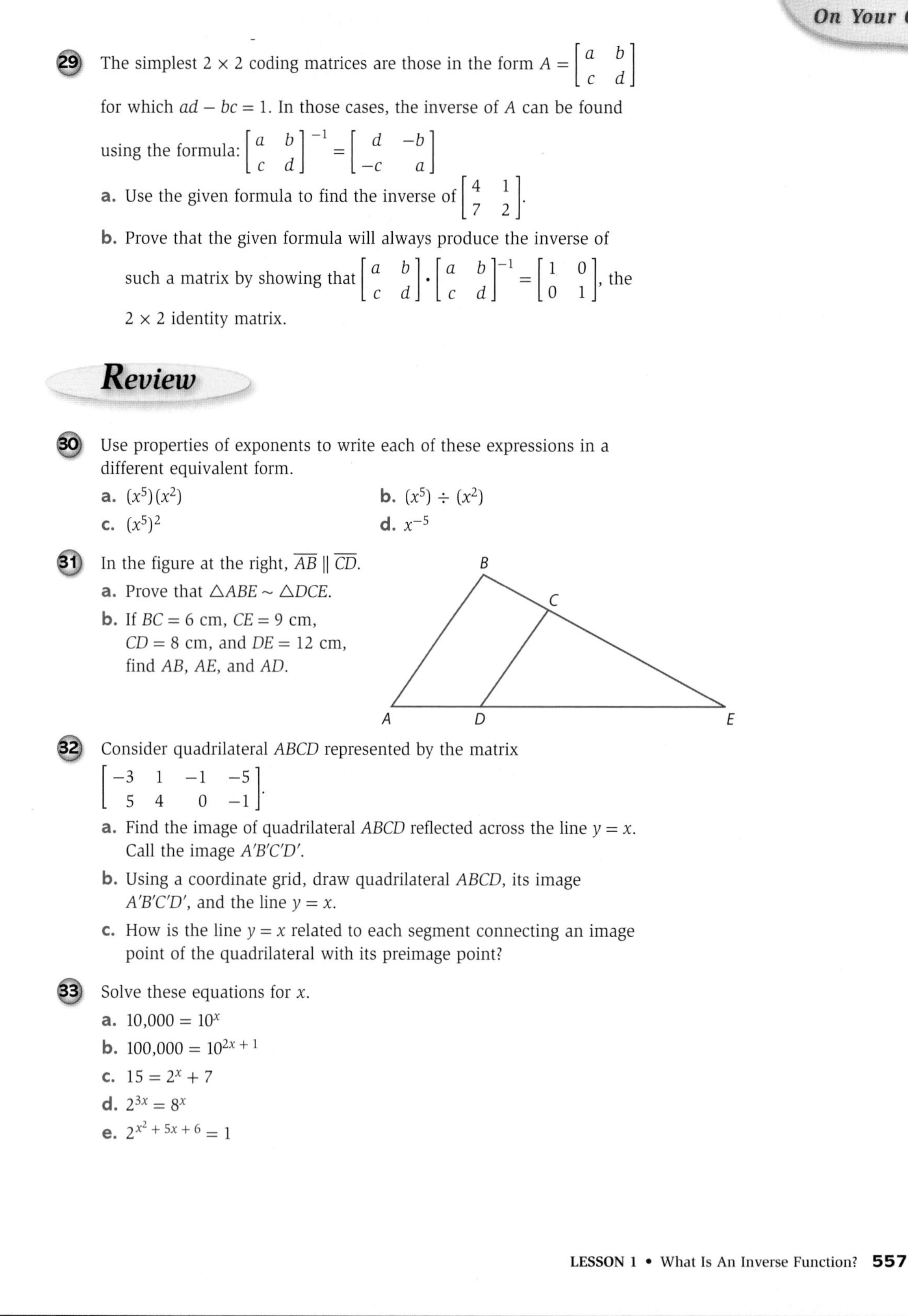

32 Consider quadrilateral $ABCD$ represented by the matrix $\begin{bmatrix} -3 & 1 & -1 & -5 \\ 5 & 4 & 0 & -1 \end{bmatrix}$.

a. Find the image of quadrilateral $ABCD$ reflected across the line $y = x$. Call the image $A'B'C'D'$.

b. Using a coordinate grid, draw quadrilateral $ABCD$, its image $A'B'C'D'$, and the line $y = x$.

c. How is the line $y = x$ related to each segment connecting an image point of the quadrilateral with its preimage point?

33 Solve these equations for x.

a. $10{,}000 = 10^x$

b. $100{,}000 = 10^{2x+1}$

c. $15 = 2^x + 7$

d. $2^{3x} = 8^x$

e. $2^{x^2+5x+6} = 1$

29 **a.** $\begin{bmatrix} 4 & 1 \\ 7 & 2 \end{bmatrix}^{-1} = \begin{bmatrix} 2 & -1 \\ -7 & 4 \end{bmatrix}$

b. $\begin{bmatrix} a & b \\ c & d \end{bmatrix} \cdot \begin{bmatrix} d & -b \\ -c & a \end{bmatrix} = \begin{bmatrix} ad - bc & a(-b) + ba \\ cd + d(-c) & c(-b) + da \end{bmatrix}$

$ad - bc = 1$ (given criteria on a, b, c, and d)

$a(-b) + ba = 0$

$cd + d(-c) = 0$

$c(-b) + da = ad - bc = 1$

So, the product of the original matrix and the inverse predicted by the formula is equal to the identity matrix $\begin{bmatrix} 1 & 0 \\ 0 & 1 \end{bmatrix}$.

Review

30 There are, of course, many possible equivalent forms. We give only the most common responses to the four tasks.

a. x^7 **b.** x^3 **c.** x^{10} **d.** $\frac{1}{x^5}$

31 **a.** $\angle ECB \cong \angle ECB$, $\angle EDC \cong \angle EAB$ (parallel lines cut by a transversal, corresponding angles are congruent)

Therefore, $\triangle ABE \sim \triangle DCE$ (AA similarity condition).

Some students might recognize that $\angle E$ is common to both triangles and use that fact and one of the pairs of corresponding angles to get the required similarity. It might be worth a reminder to ask students why only 2 pairs of congruent angles is sufficient to guarantee similarity.

b. The scale factor from $\triangle DCE$ to $\triangle ABE$ is $\frac{5}{3}$.

$AB = 8 \cdot \frac{5}{3} = \frac{40}{3} = 13\frac{1}{3}$

$AE = 12 \cdot \frac{5}{3} = 20$

$AD = 20 - 12 = 8$

Just in Time

32 **a.** $A'B'C'D' = \begin{bmatrix} 5 & 4 & 0 & -1 \\ -3 & 1 & -1 & -5 \end{bmatrix}$

b.

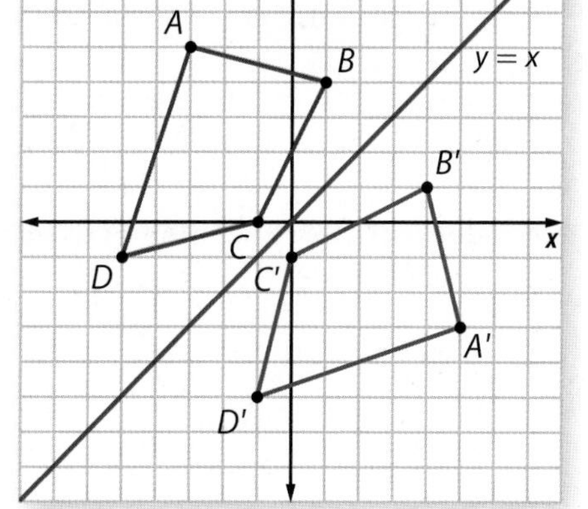

c. The line $y = x$ is the perpendicular bisector of each segment joining an image point with its preimage.

NOTE The solution to Task 33 is on page T558.

Unit 8

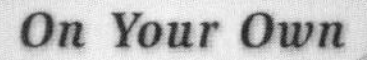

On Your Own

34 Suppose that Alvin and Tia are each starting a new walking program. On the first day, they will each walk 1,000 yards. Alvin will increase his distance by 100 yards each day. Tia will increase her distance by 6% each day.

a. Is the sequence of each person's daily walking distance arithmetic, geometric, or neither? Explain your reasoning.

b. Who will walk further on the 20th day? By how much?

c. Who will have walked further over the entire 20-day period? By how much?

d. Write a function rule that will give the distance each person walked on day n.

35 Write these expressions in equivalent form as products of linear factors.

a. $x^2 + 7x$ **b.** $x^2 + 7x + 12$

c. $x^2 + 7x - 8$ **d.** $x^2 - 49$

e. $x^2 - 6x + 9$ **f.** $3x^2 - 2x - 8$

36 Matthew is riding a bike with wheels that have a 24-centimeter radius. Suppose that he is able to pedal at a steady rate so that the wheels make 120 rotations per minute.

a. Find his angular velocity in both degrees per minute and radians per minute.

b. How many meters will he travel in 5 minutes of riding at this speed?

37 Describe the largest possible domains for functions with these rules.

a. $f(x) = \sqrt{5 - x}$ **b.** $g(x) = \frac{3x}{x - 5}$

c. $h(x) = \frac{3x + 5}{x^2 + 5x + 6}$ **d.** $k(x) = 10^x$

38 Solutions of the following equations are not integers. For each equation, find the two consecutive integers between which the solution lies.

a. $2^x = 36$ **b.** $5^x = 100$

c. $7^x = \frac{1}{50}$ **d.** $10^x = 0.0035$

e. $10^{2x} = 3,000$ **f.** $11^{x-2} = \frac{1}{2}$

558 UNIT 8 • Inverse Functions

Just in Time

33 Students should be able to solve the equations in Parts a–e using symbolic reasoning without using technology.

a. $x = 4$

b. $x = 2$

c. $x = 3$

d. x can be any real number.

e. $x = -3$ or $x = -2$

34 **a.** The sequence of Alvin's daily walking distance is arithmetic since the difference between any two consecutive days is 100.

The sequence of Tia's daily walking distance is geometric since the ratio between any two consecutive days is 1.06.

b. Tia will walk 125.6 yards farther than Alvin on the 20th day.

$1{,}000(1.06)^{19} - (1{,}000 + 100(19)) \approx 125.6$

c. Alvin will walk approximately 2,214 yards farther than Tia over the 20-day period.

Alvin's total distance is $A_{20} = \frac{20}{2}(1{,}000 + 2{,}900) = 39{,}000$ yards

Tia's total distance is $T_{20} = 1{,}000\left(\frac{1 - 1.06^{20}}{1 - 1.06}\right) \approx 36{,}785.59$ yards

$A_{20} - T_{20} = 39{,}000 - 36{,}785.59 \approx 2{,}214$ yards

d. Alvin: $d_A = 1{,}000 + 100(n - 1)$

Tia: $d_T = 1{,}000(1.06^{n-1})$

35 **a.** $x(x + 7)$ **b.** $(x + 3)(x + 4)$

c. $(x + 8)(x - 1)$ **d.** $(x + 7)(x - 7)$

e. $(x - 3)(x - 3) = (x - 3)^2$ **f.** $(3x + 4)(x - 2)$

36 **a.** 43,200 degrees per minute, 240π radians per minute

b. 120 rotations per minute implies 600 rotations in 5 minutes. Matthew rides $48\pi \cdot 600$ cm in 5 minutes, or approximately 90,477.87 cm, or 904.78 m.

37 **a.** $x \leq 5$

b. $x \neq 5$, or all real numbers except 5

c. $x \neq -3$ or -2, or all real numbers except -2 and -3

d. All real numbers

Just in Time

38 **a.** $5 < x < 6$ **b.** $2 < x < 3$

c. $-3 < x < -2$ **d.** $-3 < x < -2$

e. $1 < x < 2$ **f.** $1 < x < 2$

Teaching Resources

Assessment Masters 9–14.

UNIT 8 *Inverse Functions* Name Date

Lesson 1 Quiz

Form A

1. In this lesson, you learned that not all functions have inverses.

a. Provide an equation for a function that does not have an inverse. Explain why the function does not have an inverse.

b. How can you use the graph of a function to determine whether or not the function has an inverse?

2. The area of a circle is a function of the radius of the circle.

a. Does this function have an inverse? Explain your reasoning.

b. Explain what the inverse function will tell you about the variables in the situation.

Unit 8

LESSON 2

Common Logarithms and Their Properties

At several points in your study of algebra and functions, you have discovered relationships between variables that are well-modeled by exponential functions. The rules of those functions have the form $f(x) = a(b^x)$, where a and b are positive numbers ($b \neq 1$). Answering questions about these functions often requires solving equations in which the unknown quantity is the exponent. For example:

- If a count shows 50 bacteria in a lab dish at the start of an experiment and that number is predicted to double every hour, then to estimate the time when there will be 10,000 bacteria in the dish, you need to solve the equation $50(2^t) = 10{,}000$.
- The Washington Nationals baseball team was purchased in 2006 for 450 million dollars. To find how long it will take for the value of this investment to reach $1 billion, if it increases at the fairly conservative rate of 5% per year, you need to solve the equation $450(1.05^t) = 1{,}000$.

Common Logarithms and Their Properties

The goal of this lesson is to extend student understanding of common logarithms and how they relate to and can help in solving exponential equations. The first investigation reviews ideas that appear in Unit 5 of Course 2.

There are two additional investigations on using logs to solve exponential equations and on properties of logarithms. There will be further work with logarithms in Course 4, where natural logarithms will be developed. Here, we limit our attention to base 10 or common logarithms.

Lesson Objectives

- Express a positive number as a power of 10
- Define and evaluate common logarithms
- Use logarithms to solve exponential equations
- Develop and use basic properties of the logarithmic function

Lesson Launch

The three problems posed here should look quite familiar to students from their work with exponential functions. The aim of the Think About This Situation is to give you a chance to check on their recall of the key ideas and the approximation strategies using tables and graphs for solving equations. We suspect that few students will have figured out how to use logarithms to solve exponential equations, so they will not have much in the way of algebraic solution strategies. The purpose of this lesson is to develop those strategies.

- If 500 mg of a medicine enters a hospital patient's bloodstream at noon and decays exponentially at a rate of 15% per hour, the amount remaining active in the patient's blood t hours later will be given by $d(t) = 500(0.85^t)$. To find the time when only 25 mg of the original amount remains active, you need to solve $25 = 500(0.85^t)$.

Think About This Situation

Solving equations like those in the three exponential growth and decay situations is a kind of inverse problem. In each case, you know the output of a function but need to find the corresponding input.

a How could you estimate solutions for the given equations by exploring patterns in tables and graphs of function values?

b How would you approach solution of each equation by algebraic reasoning?

In this lesson, you will extend your understanding and skill in using *logarithms*—a mathematical idea that helps in solving equations like those in the given examples and in many similar problems involving exponential functions.

Investigation 1 Common Logarithms Revisited

In the *Nonlinear Functions and Equations* unit of Course 2, you learned how to use common logarithms to answer questions very similar to those in the preceding Think About This Situation. The key difference is that all problems in your earlier work involved only exponential functions with base 10 like $B(t) = 50(10^{0.3t})$, $V(t) = 450(10^{0.02t})$, and $s(t) = 200(10^{-0.046t})$.

To deal with those kinds of problems, you learned that mathematicians have developed procedures for finding exponents.

If $10^x = y$, then x is called the **base 10 logarithm** of y.

This definition of base 10 or *common* logarithms is usually expressed in function notation as:

$\log_{10} y$ or simply $\log y$, read "log base 10 of y" or "log of y"

Graphing calculators have a LOG key that automatically finds the required exponent values.

Work on the problems of this investigation will review and extend your understanding of logarithms to consider this question:

How can logarithms be used to solve equations involving exponential functions with base 10?

Unit 8

560 UNIT 8 • Inverse Functions

Think About This Situation

a Students will have solved exponential equations by approximation using scans of function graphs and tables of function values. For example, in the first problem, good approximate solutions can be obtained by scanning graphs and/or tables of $f(t) = 50(2^t)$ in search of values of t that make $f(t) = 10{,}000$. The goal here is simply to recall strategy, not to find exact solutions. In this case, $t \approx 7.65$. For the other problems, approximate solutions will be $t \approx 16.5$ and $t \approx 50$.

b Algebraic reasoning might begin with operations on the given equations to try to isolate the unknown. However, in each case, the closest one can come is an equation in the form $b^t = constant$. (Students might be tempted to try some illegal exponent maneuvers to uncover the unknown, but the point of the question is to focus attention on the need for some new concepts and techniques for finding exact solutions.)

Investigation 1 Common Logarithms Revisited

In this investigation, students will review the definition of common logarithms and how they can be used to solve exponential equations when the base is 10. Although this is a topic that has been treated in Course 2, it is quite likely that students will be unsure about their method. Thus, it probably makes sense to introduce the investigation by posing some questions like this: "Suppose you encountered an equation like $10^x = 53$. How could you find the solution(s) by tabular or graphic estimation? By algebraic reasoning?"

If no one recalls the fact that $x = \log 53$, it probably makes sense for you to gently remind them that they have seen that idea in earlier work. Also, review the notation and "pronunciation" of the basic logarithm definition. It might be useful to actually start as a class on the first few parts of Problem 1 before launching the students into the investigation tasks on their own or in groups.

INSTRUCTIONAL NOTE The standard mathematical notation for logarithms—writing simply log 5 to indicate the value of the logarithm function when $x = 5$, and 7 log 5 to indicate 7 times that value—is fraught with potential for misinterpretation and misuse by students who have grown accustomed to function notation that would suggest at least log(5) and 7log(5). The same sort of notational convention occurs in trigonometry where sin 45° means the value of the sine function when $x = 45°$. You might find it useful to employ function notation log(5) for a while before adopting the shorthand log 5. In fact, in most computer languages, it is necessary to use the function notation form. In any event, be alert to the possible confusions that students will have with the standard logarithm notation.

Teaching Resources

Transparency Master 15.

UNIT 8 *Inverse Functions*

Think About This Situation

Solving equations like those in the three exponential growth and decay situations below is a kind of inverse problem. In each case, you know the output of a function but need to find the corresponding input.

a How could you estimate solutions for the given equations by exploring patterns in tables and graphs of function values?

b How would you approach solution of each equation by algebraic reasoning?

- If a count shows 50 bacteria in a lab dish at the start of an experiment and that number is predicted to double every hour, then to estimate the time when there will be 10,000 bacteria in the dish, you need to solve the equation $50(2^t) = 10{,}000$.
- The Washington Nationals baseball team was purchased in 2006 for 450 million dollars. To find how long it will take for the value of this investment to reach $1 billion, if it increases at the fairly conservative rate of 5% per year, you need to solve the equation $450(1.05^t) = 1{,}000$.
- If 500 mg of a medicine enters a hospital patient's bloodstream at noon and decays exponentially at a rate of 15% per hour, the amount remaining active in the patient's blood t hours later will be given by $d(t) = 500(0.85^t)$. To find the time when only 25 mg of the original amount remains active, you need to solve $25 = 500(0.85^t)$.

Transparency Master • use with page 560 UNIT 8 • Inverse Functions 15

MATH TOOLKIT If students are not carrying over their Math Toolkit from Courses 1 and 2, you may wish to have them include the definition of a logarithm in this year's toolkit.

Unit 8

1. Without use of a calculator or computer **log** function, find each of the following logarithms. Be prepared to explain how you know that your answers are correct.

   a. $\log 10^{2.5}$
   b. $\log 100$
   c. $\log 10{,}000$
   d. $\log 0.01$
   e. $\log (-0.001)$
   f. $\log (10^2 \cdot 10^5)$

2. Without use of a calculator or computer **log** function, find the consecutive integers just below and just above the exact values of these logarithms. Be prepared to explain how you know that your answers are correct.

   a. $\log 25$
   b. $\log 314$
   c. $\log 3.14$
   d. $\log 0.005$

3. Use what you know about logarithms as necessary to find exact solutions for these equations.

   a. $10^x = 100$
   b. $10^{x+2} = 100$
   c. $10^{3x+1} = 100$
   d. $3(10)^{x+3} = 300$
   e. $2(10)^x = 600$
   f. $10^{2x} = 500$
   g. $10^{3x+1} = 43$
   h. $42(10)^{3x+2} = 840$
   i. $5(10)^{x+3} + 9 = 44$

4. Answer these questions related to the Think About This Situation on the previous page by using the helpful translation of the functions into exponential form with base 10.

   a. Suppose that the number of bacteria in a lab dish at any time t hours after the start of an experiment is given by the function $B(t) = 50(10^{0.3t})$. Show how to use logarithms to find the time when there will be 10,000 bacteria in the lab dish.

   b. Suppose that the value (in millions of dollars) of the Washington Nationals baseball team at any time t years after 2006 is given by the function $V(t) = 450(10^{0.02t})$. Show how to use logarithms to find the time when that investment will be worth \$1 billion.

   c. Suppose that the amount of medicine (in mg) active in a patient's blood at any time t hours after an injection is given by $m(t) = 500(10^{-0.071t})$. Show how to use logarithms to find the time when only 25 mg of the medicine remain active.

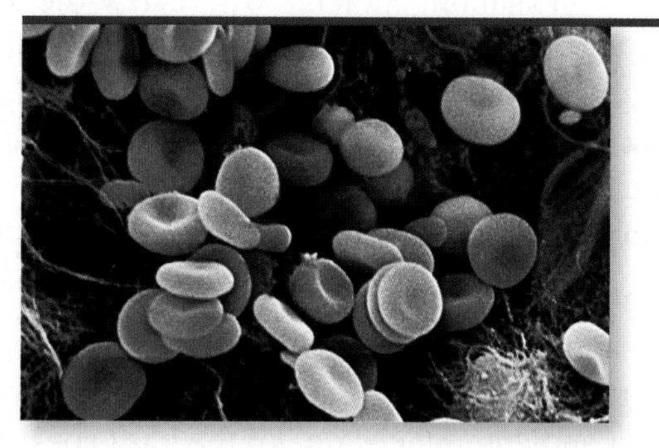

1. a. 2.5 b. 2 c. 4
   d. −2 e. not possible f. 7

2. a. $1 < \log 25 < 2$ since $10^1 = 10$ and $10^2 = 100$.
   b. $2 < \log 314 < 3$ since $10^2 = 100$ and $10^3 = 1{,}000$.
   c. $0 < \log 3.14 < 1$ since $10^0 = 0$ and $10^1 = 10$.
   d. $-3 < \log 0.005 < -2$ since, $10^{-3} = 0.001$ and $10^{-2} = 0.01$.

3. a. $x = 2$ b. $x = 0$
   c. $x = \frac{1}{3}$ d. $x = -1$
   e. $x = \log 300$ f. $x = \frac{\log 500}{2}$
   g. $x = \frac{\log 43 - 1}{3}$ h. $x = \frac{\log 20 - 2}{3}$
   i. $x = \log 7 - 3$

4. a. $t = \log\left(\frac{10{,}000}{50}\right) \div 0.3$, so $t \approx 7.67$ days.
   b. $t = \log\left(\frac{1{,}000}{450}\right) \div 0.02$, so $t \approx 17.3$ years.
   c. $t = \log\left(\frac{25}{500}\right) \div (-0.071)$, so $t \approx 18.3$ days.

Summarize the Mathematics

In this investigation, you reviewed the definition of the base 10 or common logarithm function. You then considered the ways that this function can be used to solve inverse problems involving exponential functions with base 10.

a How would you explain to someone who did not know about logarithms what the expression $\log b = a$ tells about the numbers a and b?

b What can be said about the value of $\log y$ in each case below? Give brief justifications of your answers.

i. $0 < y < 1$ **ii.** $10 < y < 100$
iii. $0.1 < y < 1$ **iv.** $1 < y < 10$
v. $100 < y < 1{,}000$ **vi.** $0.01 < y < 0.1$

c Describe the main steps in solving equations in these forms for x.

i. $10^{ax+b} = c$
ii. $k(10^{ax+b}) = c$

Be prepared to explain your ideas to the class.

Check Your Understanding

Use your understanding of common logarithms to help complete the following tasks.

a. Find these common (base 10) logarithms without using technology.

i. $\log 1{,}000{,}000$ **ii.** $\log 0.001$ **iii.** $\log 10^{3.2}$

b. Use the function $y = 10^x$, but not the **log** function of technology, to estimate each of these logarithms to the nearest integer. Explain how you arrived at your answers.

i. $\log 85$ **ii.** $\log 850$ **iii.** $\log 8.5$

c. In 2007, the U.S. Department of Interior removed grizzly bears from the endangered species list in Yellowstone National Park. The population of grizzly bears in the park at any time t years after 2007 can be estimated by the function $P(t) = 500(10^{0.02t})$. Use logarithms to find the time when this model predicts a grizzly population of 750.

Unit 8

562 UNIT 8 • Inverse Functions

Summarize the Mathematics

a The most common explanation of a logarithm is something like, "the number a is the power that 10 is raised to to get the number b." $\log b = a$ tells that $10^a = b$. For example, 3 is the $\log_{10} 1{,}000$ because $10^3 = 1{,}000$.

b
- **i.** When $0 < y < 1$, $\log y < 0$ because numbers between 0 and 1 can be represented by negative powers of 10.
- **ii.** When $10 < y < 100$, $1 < \log y < 2$ because $10^1 = 10$ and $10^2 = 100$.
- **iii.** When $0.1 < y < 1$, $-1 < \log y < 0$ because $10^{-1} = 0.1$ and $10^0 = 1$.
- **iv.** When $1 < y < 10$, $0 < \log y < 1$ because $10^0 = 1$ and $10^1 = 10$.
- **v.** When $100 < y < 1{,}000$, $2 < \log y < 3$ because $10^2 = 100$ and $10^3 = 1{,}000$.
- **vi.** When $0.01 < y < 0.1$, $-2 < \log y < -1$ because $10^{-2} = 0.01$ and $10^{-1} = 0.1$.

c
- **i.** To solve an equation in the form $10^{ax+b} = c$ for x, you rewrite the equation in logarithmic form as $ax + b = \log c$. Since $\log c$ is a number, you need now only solve a linear equation. So, $x = \frac{\log c - b}{a}$. (Note this method uses only the definition of a logarithm. See the introduction to Investigation 2 for the reasoning underlying this approach.)
- **ii.** The steps for solving $k(10^{ax+b}) = c$ for x are the same as above once both sides are divided by k. Students should recognize that $10^{ax+b} = \frac{c}{k}$ is the same form as the equation in part i. So, $x = \frac{\log\left(\frac{c}{k}\right) - b}{a}$.

Teaching Resources

Transparency Master 16.

UNIT 8 *Inverse Functions*

Summarize the Mathematics

In this investigation, you reviewed the definition of the base 10 or common logarithm function. You then considered the ways that this function can be used to solve inverse problems involving exponential functions with base 10.

a How would you explain to someone who did not know about logarithms what the expression $\log b = a$ tells about the numbers a and b?

b What can be said about the value of $\log y$ in each case below? Give brief justifications of your answers.
- i. $0 < y < 1$
- ii. $10 < y < 100$
- iii. $0.1 < y < 1$
- iv. $1 < y < 10$
- v. $100 < y < 1{,}000$
- vi. $0.01 < y < 0.1$

c Describe the main steps in solving equations in these forms for x.
- i. $10^{ax+b} = c$
- ii. $k(10^{ax+b}) = c$

Be prepared to explain your ideas to the class.

16 UNIT 8 • Inverse Functions — Transparency Master • use with page 562

POSSIBLE MISCONCEPTION Some students may still be trying to connect the sign of the exponent with the sign of the expression.

INSTRUCTIONAL NOTE The intervals and corresponding values in Part b can be considered as benchmarks for logarithms.

MATH TOOLKIT Record the definition of the base 10 logarithm, some examples, and the method of solving the equations in Part c using the definition.

Check Your Understanding

a.
- **i.** $\log 1{,}000{,}000 = 6$ because $10^6 = 1{,}000{,}000$.
- **ii.** $\log 0.001 = -3$ because $10^{-3} = 0.001$.
- **iii.** $\log 10^{3.2} = 3.2$ because $10^{3.2} = 10^{3.2}$.

b.
- **i.** $\log 85 \approx 1.93$ can be found by scanning table of $y = 10^x$ to find x that gives y close to 85.
- **ii.** $\log 850 = 2.93$ can be found by scanning table of $y = 10^x$ to find x that gives y close to 850. (Note the pattern that hints at the future property of logarithms $\log 850 = \log (85 \times 10) = \log 85 + \log 10$.)
- **iii.** $\log 8.5 = 0.93$ can be found by scanning table of $y = 10^x$ to find x that gives y close to 8.5. (Note again the pattern that hints at the future property of logarithms $\log 8.5 = \log (85 \times 0.1) = \log 85 + \log 0.1$.)

c. $t = \log\left(\frac{750}{500}\right) \div 0.02$, so $t \approx 8.8$ years.

Unit 8

Investigation 2 Covering All the Bases

Logarithms are useful for solving equations in the form $k(10^{ax+b}) = c$. However, many of the functions that you have used to model exponential growth and decay have not used 10 as the base. On the other hand, it is not too hard to transform any exponential expression in the form b^x into an equivalent expression with base 10. As you work on the problems of this investigation, look for an answer to the following question:

How can common logarithms help in finding solutions of all exponential equations?

1 Use common logarithms to express each of the following numbers as a power of 10. For example, $15 = 10^k$ when $k \approx 1.176$.

a. $2 = 10^k$ when $k = \ldots$ **b.** $5 = 10^k$ when $k = \ldots$
c. $1.0114 = 10^k$ when $k = \ldots$ **d.** $25 = 10^k$ when $k = \ldots$
e. $250 = 10^k$ when $k = \ldots$ **f.** $0.003 = 10^k$ when $k = \ldots$

2 Use your results from Problem 1 and what you know about properties of exponents to show how each of these exponential expressions can be written in equivalent form like $(10^k)^x$ and then 10^{kx}.

a. 2^x **b.** 5^x **c.** 1.0114^x

3 Use your results from Problems 1 and 2 to solve these exponential equations. Check each solution. Be prepared to explain your solution strategy.

a. $2^x = 3.5$ **b.** $5(2^n) = 35$ **c.** $5(2^t) + 20 = 125$
d. $5^p = 48$ **e.** $3(5^r) + 12 = 60$ **f.** $300(0.9^v) = 60$

4 Use the strategies you have developed from work on Problems 1–3 to solve these problems about exponential growth and decay. In each case, it will probably be helpful to write an exponential growth or decay function with the base suggested by problem conditions. Next, transform the rule for that function into an equivalent form with exponential base 10. Then solve the related equation.

a. If the world population at the beginning of 2008 was 6.7 billion and growing exponentially at a rate of 1.16% per year, in what year will the population be double what it was in 2008?

b. If 500 mg of a medicine enters a hospital patient's bloodstream at noon and decays exponentially at a rate of 15% per hour, when will only 10% of the original amount be active in the patient's body?

c. If the average rent for a two-bedroom apartment in Kalamazoo, Michigan is currently \$750 per month and increasing at a rate of 8% per year, in how many years will average rent for such apartments reach \$1,000 per month?

Investigation 2 Covering All the Bases

In this investigation, students will use what they learned about logarithms in Investigation 1 to solve exponential equations in which the natural base is not 10. The only required logarithmic knowledge needed to solve these equations was gained in Investigation 1. It is *not* necessary to supplement with the traditional logarithm rules (e.g., $\log x^m = m \log x$). Those rules will be developed in the next investigation, and we will revisit solving exponential equations using the approach "take the log of both sides."

Our reasoning for developing things as we do here is to avoid a highly formal and abstract approach that emphasizes the general rules for operating with logarithms. This approach is typically very difficult for students, and they revert to memorization without understanding. A second rationale is that when the formulation of exponential growth and decay settles on the mathematically powerful base-e exponentiation, it is standard to enter a parameter k in the expression to give e^{kx} that accounts for various exponential growth and decay rates.

Launch

You might refer back to the TATS at the beginning of this lesson to motivate attention to solving exponential equations and point out that the goal of this investigation is to discover ways of dealing with such equations. Alert students that Problems 1–3 build on each other.

1 **a.** $2 = 10^{\log 2}$, or $2 \approx 10^{0.3}$

b. $5 = 10^{\log 5}$, or $5 \approx 10^{0.7}$

c. $1.0114 = 10^{\log 1.0114}$, or $1.0114 \approx 10^{0.0049}$

d. $25 = 10^{\log 25}$, or $25 \approx 10^{1.4}$

e. $250 = 10^{\log 250}$, or $250 \approx 10^{2.4}$

f. $0.003 = 10^{\log 0.003}$, or $0.003 \approx 10^{-2.52}$

INSTRUCTIONAL NOTE
It is important for students to express answers exactly as well as approximately, as shown at the left.

2 **a.** $2^x = (10^{\log 2})^x = 10^{(\log 2)x} \approx 10^{0.3x}$

b. $5^x = (10^{\log 5})^x = 10^{(\log 5)x} \approx 10^{0.7x}$

c. $1.0114^x = (10^{\log 1.0114})^x = 10^{(\log 1.0114)x} \approx 10^{0.0049x}$

3 **a.** Since $2^x = 10^{(\log 2)x}$, $2^x = 3.5$ is equivalent to $10^{(\log 2)x} = 3.5$. Thus, by the definition of a logarithm, $(\log 2)x = \log 3.5$.
So, $x = \dfrac{\log 3.5}{\log 2} \approx 1.8$.

b. $5(2^n) = 35$
$2^n = 7$
$10^{(\log 2)n} = 7$
$(\log 2)n = \log 7$
$n = \dfrac{\log 7}{\log 2}$, or $n \approx 2.8$

c. $2^t = 21$
$10^{(\log 2)t} = 21$
$(\log 2)t = \log 21$
$t = \dfrac{\log 21}{\log 2}$, or $t \approx 4.39$

d. $p = \dfrac{\log 48}{\log 5}$, or $p \approx 2.41$

e. $r = \dfrac{\log 16}{\log 5}$, or $r \approx 1.72$

f. $v = \dfrac{\log 0.2}{\log 0.9}$, or $v \approx 15.28$

NOTE Solutions to Problem 4 are on page T564.

Unit 8

In this investigation, you learned how to use logarithms to solve equations related to exponential functions with any base, $b > 0$.

a How can any exponential function with rule in the form $f(x) = b^x$ $(b > 0)$ be written in an equivalent form using 10 as the base for the exponential expression?

b How can logarithms be used to solve any equation like $a(b^x) = c$ $(b > 0)$?

Be prepared to explain your ideas to the class.

Check Your Understanding

Use logarithms and other algebraic reasoning as needed to complete these tasks.

a. Solve each equation.

i. $3^x = 243$ **ii.** $8(1.5^x) = 200$ **iii.** $8x^2 + 3 = 35$

b. The population of Nigeria at the beginning of 2008 was about 140 million and growing exponentially at a rate of about 2.4% per year. (Source: www.cia.gov/library/publications/the-world-factbook/geos/ni.html)

i. What function $P(t)$ will give the population of Nigeria in millions in year $2008 + t$, assuming that the growth rate stays at 2.4% per year?

ii. According to current trends, when is the Nigerian population predicted to reach 200 million? Explain how to estimate the answer to this question with a table or a graph of $P(t)$. Show how to find an "exact" answer using logarithms and other algebraic reasoning.

Investigation 3 Properties of Logarithms

To use logarithms in reasoning about problems involving exponential functions, it helps to understand key features and properties of the function $f(x) = \log_{10} x$. As you work on the problems of this investigation, look for answers to these questions:

What are the important patterns in tables and graphs for the logarithm function?

How can properties of logarithms be used to write algebraic expressions in useful equivalent forms?

Remember the relationship between logarithms and exponents:

$$10^r = s \text{ if and only if } r = \log s.$$

564 UNIT 8 • Inverse Functions

4. **a.** $13.4 = 6.7(1.0116)^x$ can be rewritten as $2 = 10^{(\log 1.0116)x}$.

   Then $\log 2 = (\log 1.0116)x$; so, $x = \dfrac{\log 2}{\log 1.0116} \approx 60$ years after 2008.

   The population will double in the year 2068.

   b. $50 = 500(0.85)^x$ can be rewritten as $0.1 = 10^{(\log 0.85)x}$.

   $\log 0.1 = (\log 0.85)x$, or $-1 = (\log 0.85)x$

   $x = \dfrac{-1}{\log 0.85} \approx 14.17$ hours later

   c. $1{,}000 = 750(1.08)^x$ can be rewritten as $\frac{4}{3} = 10^{(\log 1.08)x}$.

   By the definition of a logarithm, $(\log 1.08)x = \log \frac{4}{3}$, so

   $x = \left(\log \frac{4}{3}\right) \div \log 1.08 \approx 3.7$ years later.

Summarize the Mathematics

a $f(x)$ can be rewritten in the form $f(x) = 10^{(\log b)x}$.

b First, both sides of the equation can be divided by a. Then the equation can be changed to an equivalent form involving a power of 10. Finally, use the definition of logarithms to convert the equation again and divide both sides by $\log b$. The process is shown symbolically below.

$$a(b)^x = c$$
$$b^x = \frac{c}{a}$$
$$10^{(\log b)x} = \frac{c}{a}$$
$$(\log b)x = \log \frac{c}{a}$$
$$x = \frac{\log \frac{c}{a}}{\log b}$$

Teaching Resources

Transparency Master 17.

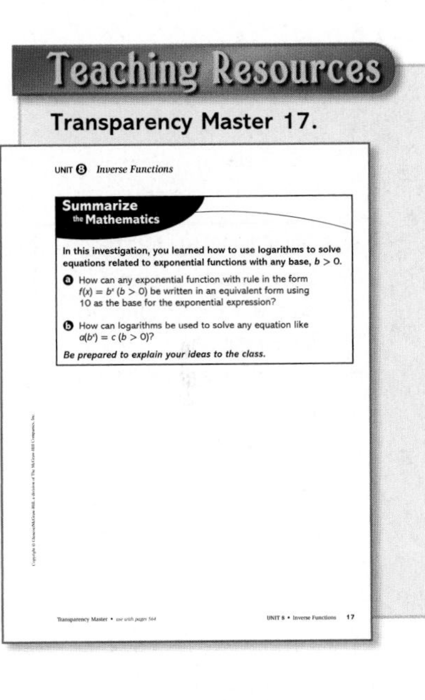

UNIT 8 *Inverse Functions*

Summarize the Mathematics

In this investigation, you learned how to use logarithms to solve equations related to exponential functions with any base, $b > 0$.

a How can any exponential function with rule in the form $f(x) = b^x$ $(b > 0)$ be written in an equivalent form using 10 as the base for the exponential expression?

b How can logarithms be used to solve any equation like $a(b^x) = c$ $(b > 0)$?

Be prepared to explain your ideas to the class.

Transparency Master • *use with pages 564* UNIT 8 • Inverse Functions 17

MATH TOOLKIT Explain why $b^x = 10^{(\log b)x}$. Then use logarithms to solve the equation $5(4)^x = 300$ for x.

Check Your Understanding

a. **i.** $10^{(\log 3)x} = 243$

$(\log 3)x = \log 243$

$x = \dfrac{\log 243}{\log 3} = 5$

Check: $3^5 = 243$

ii. $1.5x = 25$

$10^{(\log 1.5)x} = 25$

$(\log 1.5)x = \log 25$

$x = \dfrac{\log 25}{\log 1.5} \approx 7.94$

Check: $8(1.5)^{7.94} \approx 200.1$

iii. $x^2 = 4$

$x = \pm 2$

Check: $8(2)^2 + 3 = 35$

Unit 8

b. **i.** $P(t) = 140(1.024)^t$, where t is the number of years after 2008.

ii. The population will reach 200 million about 15 years after 2008, or 2023. An approximation to the answer can be determined by scanning a table or graph for the population function, looking for time t when $P(t) = 200$. Then add t to 2008 to get the calendar year.

$$200 = 140(1.024)^x$$
$$\frac{10}{7} = 10^{(\log 1.024)x}$$
$$\log\left(\frac{10}{7}\right) = (\log 1.024)x$$
$$x = \frac{\log\left(\frac{10}{7}\right)}{\log 1.024} \approx 15 \text{ years}$$

The population will reach 200 million in 2023.

Investigation 3 Properties of Logarithms

INSTRUCTIONAL NOTE
You may wish to assign Reflections Task 24 prior to this investigation.

The goal of this investigation is to develop student understanding and skill in use of the basic properties of the logarithmic function. This is a notoriously difficult part of the algebra/functions curriculum. There will be another pass at logarithms in Course 4 where natural logarithms (base e) will be introduced. So, do not despair if students do not seem to master things in this investigation. Many students will find it useful to be continually reminded about the meaning of logarithms with the simple phrase "logarithms are really just exponents."

Launch

You might consider launching students on this investigation by displaying a partial graph of the log function (say, in a window that shows values for $0 < x < 100$). Ask students what is striking about the pattern in that graph and what they think might happen outside the limited window shown. Then ask how $\log x$ seems to change as x increases (rapidly increasing until $x = 1$ and very slowly thereafter) and why that is a reasonable pattern.

After students consider Problems 1 and 2, have a class discussion of their ideas before going ahead to the rest of the investigation. Students should be able to explain the reasonableness of the pattern of change in the logarithm function by reference to the related exponential function with which they are much more familiar and comfortable. See the Instructional Note with Problem 2.

1. **a.** The domain is all real numbers.

   b. The range is all positive numbers.

2. **Domain:** The domain is all positive numbers. This will be shown in a table of values by the fact that when you request log values for negative numbers most table programs will report "error" or something comparable.

The domain is shown on a graph by the fact that no points at or to the left of $x = 0$ are plotted.

The domain is logically determined by the fact that the base 10 exponential function takes on all possible positive numbers (and only positive numbers) as values; so for any positive number, there must be an exponent that gives that value when 10 is used as a base. (This is a difficult idea for students to articulate. Many will find it useful to be continually reminded with the simple phrase "logarithms are really just exponents.")

INSTRUCTIONAL NOTE Students will need to look at a wide range of values for x between 0 and 1 to see that smaller positive numbers have negative log values of larger magnitude. Further, because the log function increases very slowly for positive values of x, students might imagine that there is some upper limit to its values. To disabuse them of this notion, you might have them try large step sizes (like 1,000,000). However, even this will not work because log 1,000,000 is only 6, and it will not increase very rapidly even with the large step size. That is one of the major reasons why logarithms are so useful. They allow calculation with very large numbers by substituting their much smaller logarithms. You will probably need to rely on a logical argument (see below) to prove no upper limit for logarithms.

Range: The range is all real numbers. This will be shown in a table of values by the fact that when you request log values for numbers close to 0, the outputs will begin as negative numbers and then increase until becoming positive when $x = 1$ and increasingly positive thereafter.

The negative part of the range is shown on a graph by the fact that most graph programs will show a rapidly decreasing graph moving left of $x = 1$. The slow increase of the graph to the right of $x = 1$ might lead students to believe that there has to be an upper bound for logarithm values.

The range is logically determined by the fact that starting from $x = 1$ ($\log 1 = 0$) each increase in x by a factor of 10 leads to an increase in the logarithm value of 1, and each decrease in x by a factor of 10 leads to a decrease in the logarithm value of 1. For example, $\log 10 = 1$, $\log 100 = 2$, $\log 1{,}000 = 3$, etc. Similarly, $\log 0.1 = -1$, $\log 0.01 = -2$, $\log 0.001 = -3$, etc. Thus, logically, there is no upper or lower limit to the logarithm values, though they grow very slowly. For example, it takes a googol (10^{100}) to yield a logarithm of only 100 (or $\frac{1}{10^{100}}$ to yield a logarithm of only -100)!

TECHNOLOGY NOTE
The graphing window is critical in this problem. The behavior of the function between $x = 0$ and $x = 1$ can go unnoticed with some windows.

Unit 8

1 Consider the domain and range of the function $g(x) = 10^x$.

a. What is the domain of $g(x) = 10^x$; that is, for what values of x can you calculate 10^x?

b. What is the range of $g(x) = 10^x$; that is, what are the possible values of 10^x?

2 What are the domain and range of $f(x) = \log x$?

For both the domain and range, explain:

- how your answer is shown by patterns in tables of values for $f(x) = \log x$.
- how your answer is shown by patterns in the graph of $f(x) = \log x$.
- how your answer can be explained logically, using the relationship of the logarithmic function $f(x) = \log x$ and the exponential function $g(x) = 10^x$.

3 The logarithmic function $f(x) = \log x$ is the *inverse* of the exponential function $g(x) = 10^x$. Complete the following sentences to illustrate that relationship between the two functions. Be prepared to justify your claims.

a. $10^3 = 1{,}000$, so $\log 1{,}000 =$ ___.

b. $10^{1.5} \approx 31.6$, so $\log 31.6 \approx$ ___.

c. $\log 0.01 = -2$, so $10^{-2} =$ ___.

d. $\log 125 \approx 2.097$, so $10^{2.097} \approx$ ___.

4 Sketch graphs of the logarithmic function $f(x) = \log x$ and the exponential function $g(x) = 10^x$. Explain how the shape and relationship of those graphs illustrates the fact that the two functions are inverses of each other.

5 Use what you know about logarithms to evaluate these expressions.

a. $\log 10^6$ **b.** $10^{\log 100}$ **c.** $\log 10^{0.0124}$

d. $10^{\log 8.5}$ **e.** $\log 10^w$ **f.** $10^{\log z}$

6 The close connection between logarithmic and exponential functions can be used to derive some useful rules for working with algebraic expressions involving logarithms. Use what you know about exponents to write each of these expressions in a different but equivalent form.

a. $10^m 10^n$ **b.** $10^m \div 10^n$ **c.** 10^0

d. $(10^m)^n$ **e.** $1 \div 10^m$ **f.** $10^{(m-n)}$

7 Which of the following claims are true? Explain each response.

a. $\log (10^m 10^n) = m + n$ **b.** $\log (10^m \div 10^n) = m - n$

c. $\log (10^m + 10^n) = m + n$ **d.** $\log ((10^m)^n) = mn$

e. $\log (1 \div 10^m) = -m$ **f.** $\log 1 = 0$

3 **a.** 3 **b.** 1.5
c. 0.01 **d.** 125

NOTE Solutions to Problems 1 and 2 are on page T564B.

4 The graph of $f(x) = \log_{10} x$ is the reflection of $g(x) = 10^x$ across the line $y = x$, indicating that for every point (x, y) on the graph of $f(x) = \log_{10} x$, there is a corresponding point with coordinates (y, x) on the graph of $g(x) = 10^x$. Thus, the list of ordered pairs defining the logarithmic function can be constructed by reversing entries in all pairs defining the exponential function. That is what it means for two functions to be inverses of each other.

INSTRUCTIONAL NOTE While the symmetric relationship of graphs for the logarithmic and exponential functions is a mathematically elegant way to illustrate the inverse relationship of those two functions, it tends to be seen by many students as quite an abstract argument. It might help to sketch a graph showing both functions for $-2 < x < 2$ and $-2 < y < 2$ (scaling issues make it hard to produce a useful graph on a calculator or computer graphing program), to locate several key inverse pair points on the two graphs (e.g., $(-1, 0.1)$ and $(0.1, -1)$; $(0, 1)$ and $(1, 0)$; and $(1, 10)$ and $(10, 1)$) and to show how the line $y = x$ is the perpendicular bisector of the line segments connecting matching points. Even with this visual confirmation of the inverse relation, do not expect immediate or universal confident understanding of the idea. Students may be comfortable with more informal reasoning like, "The exponential function uses numbers as exponents and the logarithmic function finds the exponents to be used."

MATH TOOLKIT Drawing on their work in Lesson 1, have students explain how the inverse relationship of an exponential and logarithmic function can be seen in a table of values, graph, and arrow diagram. They might use $f(x) = \log_{10} x$ and $g(x) = 10^x$.

5 **a.** 6 **b.** 100 **c.** 0.0124
d. 8.5 **e.** w **f.** z

6 There are many different possible equivalent forms. The most natural and useful forms are given here, but you should be careful not to suggest that they are the only ways to respond accurately to the task.

a. 10^{m+n} **b.** 10^{m-n} **c.** 1
d. 10^{mn} **e.** 10^{-m} **f.** $10^m \div 10^n$, or $\frac{10^m}{10^n}$

7 **COMMON ERROR** The pattern shown in Part c is the most tempting error in work with logarithms. Students should be able to find counterexamples easily, but the familiarity of a kind of distributive pattern will induce many subsequent mistakes like that shown. Like the non-pattern $\sqrt{a+b} \neq \sqrt{a} + \sqrt{b}$, this mistake in use of the logarithmic function illustrates the most common source of such errors: overgeneralization of a pattern. It reminds us that if we rely too heavily on inductive reasoning and numerical patterns as justification or convincing evidence of mathematical principles, that habit of reasoning can come back to cause trouble.

These items can be explained by reference to the answers in Problem 6. It will probably be helpful to ask students to produce specific numerical illustrative examples also (and a counterexample in Part c).

a. true **b.** true **c.** false
d. true **e.** true **f.** true

8 You have seen that every positive number can be written as a power of 10. For example,

$$5 = 10^{\log 5}, \text{ or } 5 \approx 10^{0.7}$$
$$\text{and } 0.2 = 10^{\log 0.2}, \text{ or } 0.2 \approx 10^{-0.7}.$$

There are several other properties of the logarithmic function that are useful in transforming expressions to equivalent forms. Complete the sentences that describe each property below. For Part a, provide a reason for each step in the justification. Then adapt the reasoning in Part a to justify the reasoning in Parts b–e.

a. For any positive numbers s and t, $\log st = \log s + \log t$.

This property states that the ***logarithm of a product*** *of two numbers is equal to ...*

This is true because:

$$st = 10^{\log s} \cdot 10^{\log t} \quad (1)$$
$$st = 10^{\log s + \log t} \quad (2)$$
$$\log st = \log s + \log t \quad (3)$$

b. For any positive numbers s and t, $\log \frac{s}{t} = \log s - \log t$.

This property states that the ***logarithm of a quotient*** *of two numbers is equal to ...*

This is true because ...

c. For any positive number s and any number t, $\log s^t = t \log s$.

This property states that the ***logarithm of a power*** *of a number is equal to ...*

This is true because ...

d. Another way to see why the property in Part c holds is to look at an example like $\log 5^3 = \log (5 \cdot 5 \cdot 5)$, which by the ____________________ property is equal to ...

e. For any positive number t, $\log \frac{1}{t} = -\log t$.

This property states that the ***logarithm of the reciprocal*** *of a number is equal to ...*

This is true because ... (*Hint:* Recall that $\frac{1}{t} = t^{-1}$.)

9 Use the facts that $\log 2 \approx 0.3$ and $\log 5 \approx 0.7$ and the properties of logarithms that you proved in Problem 8 to estimate the values of these expressions without the use of technology.

a. $\log 4$ **b.** $\log 20$ **c.** $\log 8$

d. $\log 25$ **e.** $\log \frac{5}{4}$ **f.** $\log 625$

10 As with properties of exponents, there are some common errors when people use the properties of logarithms. Find the errors in the following calculations. Explain why you think the error occurs and how you would help someone see the error of his or her thinking.

a. $\log (12 + 17) = \log 12 + \log 17$ **b.** $\log 0 = 0$

c. $\log 5^3 = \log 15$ **d.** $\log (7 \times 5) = (\log 7)(\log 5)$

e. $\frac{\log 20}{\log 2} = \log 10$

Unit 8

566 UNIT 8 • Inverse Functions

8 **DIFFERENTIATION** The questions in this problem call for derivation of logarithm properties that have been suggested in Problem 7 by reference to corresponding properties of exponents. Depending on the ability of students in your class, you might find it necessary to work through these items in a more guided, whole-class format. There are also several levels of mathematical precision and formality with which each of these properties can be addressed. Pick one that seems to fit the sophistication of your class. Several suggestions are offered in the solutions below. As a general rhetorical suggestion, continue reminding students that "logarithms are really just exponents."

a. This property states that the **logarithm of a product** of two numbers is equal to the sum of the logarithms of the factors. It can be explained informally by restating it in terms of exponents, "The exponent of a product of two numbers is the sum of the exponents of the factors."

The reasons for each step in the justification are as follows:

(1) $s = 10^{\log s}$ and $t = 10^{\log t}$; substitute for s and t.

(2) Product of Powers Property of Exponents: $10^m 10^n = 10^{m+n}$.

(3) Definition of Logarithm: If $y = 10^x$, then $\log y = x$.

This property can be illustrated in a special case by noticing that:

$$100 \times 10{,}000 = 10^2 \times 10^4 = 10^6,$$
$$\text{so } \log (100 \times 10{,}000) = \log 100 + \log 10{,}000.$$

b. This property states that the **logarithm of a quotient** of two numbers is the difference of the logarithm of the numerator minus the logarithm of the denominator. It can be explained informally by restating it in terms of exponents, "The exponent of a quotient of two numbers is the difference of the exponents of the numerator (dividend) and the denominator (divisor) in that order."

We can reason as follows:

$$\frac{s}{t} = \frac{10^{\log s}}{10^{\log t}}, \text{ so } \frac{s}{t} = 10^{\log s - \log t}.$$

(Division of Powers Property of Exponents)

This implies that $\log \frac{s}{t} = \log s - \log t$.

This property can be illustrated in a special case by noticing that:

$$100 \div 10{,}000 = 10^2 \div 10^4 = 10^{-2},$$
$$\text{so } \log (100 \div 10{,}000) = \log 100 - \log 10{,}000.$$

c. This property states that the **logarithm of a power** of a number is equal to the product of the power and the logarithm of the number.

We can reason as follows:

$$s^t = (10^{\log s})^t, \text{ so } s^t = 10^{t \log s}.$$

(Power of a Power Property of Exponents)

This implies that $\log s^t = t \log s$.

d. $\log 5^3 = \log (5 \cdot 5 \cdot 5)$ which, by the Logarithm of a Product Property, is equal to $\log 5 + \log 5 + \log 5$ which is equal to $3 \log 5$.

MATH TOOLKIT This is an appropriate time for students to record the logarithm properties in their toolkits.

INSTRUCTIONAL NOTE
There are several different accurate paths to these answers. One is provided for each part. This problem offers an opportunity to share alternative solutions.

COMMON ERROR
$\log 0 = 0$ illustrates a common informal rule that students use based on their informal concept of 0 as "nothing."

COMMON ERROR
$\log 5^3 = \log 15$ illustrates a common error in work with exponents.

e. This property states that the **logarithm of the reciprocal** of a number is the additive inverse or opposite of the logarithm of the number (Students will almost always say, "the log of one over a number is the negative of the log of the number." This informal language is generally not too much of a problem and seems ineradicable anyway.)

The property is a direct consequence of the property about logarithms of quotients in Part b, which tells us that

$$\log \frac{1}{t} = \log 1 - \log t.$$

Because $\log 1 = 0$, $\log \frac{1}{t} = 0 - \log t$, or $-\log t$. Another way to prove this property is to recognize that $\frac{1}{t} = t^{-1}$ and apply the rule in Part c about logs of powers. Thus, $\log \left(\frac{1}{t}\right) = \log (t^{-1}) = -1 \log t$.

9 **a.** $\log 4 = \log (2 \times 2) = \log 2 + \log 2 \approx 0.3 + 0.3 = 0.6$

b. $\log 20 = \log (4 \times 5) = \log 4 + \log 5 \approx 0.6 + 0.7 = 1.3$

c. $\log 8 = \log 2^3 = 3 \log 2 \approx 3(0.3) = 0.9$

d. $\log 25 = \log (5 \times 5) = \log 5 + \log 5 \approx 0.7 + 0.7 = 1.4$

e. $\log \frac{5}{4} = \log 5 - \log 4 \approx 0.7 - 0.6 = 0.1$

f. $\log 625 = \log 5^4 = 4 \log 5 \approx 4(0.7) = 2.8$

10 **a.** They incorrectly assumed that the distributive property could be used here. They need to recall that the log of a sum is not the sum of the logs. For example, $\log (100 + 100) \neq \log 100 + \log 100$.

b. There is no logarithm of 0 because there is no exponent n for which $10^n = 0$; $10^0 \neq 0$. They might have reasoned that the logarithm of nothing has to be nothing.

c. They probably presumed (incorrectly); because exponentiation involves multiplication, you simply multiply the base and the exponent. A reminder could be that 5^3 means three factors of 5, or 125.

d. $\log (7 \times 5) = (\log 7)(\log 5)$ is a sort of symmetric form of the addition error in Part a. The interesting thing about both exponential and logarithmic functions is that their key properties show relationships between multiplication and addition. The correct conclusion here would be $\log (7 \times 5) = \log 7 + \log 5$.

e. They did not treat log 20 and log 2 as the numbers forming the quotient. Reducing $\frac{20}{2}$ is not correct unless the expression is $\log \left(\frac{20}{2}\right)$.

11 **a.** (1) Apply the log function to both sides of the equation.

(2) Logarithm of a power

(3) Division by log 5

(4) Subtraction of 3

(5) Division by 2

b. $x = \frac{\log 25}{\log 3}$, or $x \approx 2.93$

c. $x = \frac{\log 35}{\log 5} - 4$, or $x \approx -1.79$

d. $x = \left(\frac{\log 12}{\log 1.5} - 1\right) \div 2$, or $x \approx 2.56$

e. $x = \frac{\frac{\log 6}{\log 3}}{0.5}$, or $x \approx 3.26$

Unit 8

11 Properties of logarithms can be used to solve exponential equations in a different way than what you developed in Investigation 2.

a. Explain how properties of logarithms are used in this sample equation solution. Then adapt the reasoning to solve the equations in Parts b–e.

$$\text{If } 5^{2x+3} = 48, \text{ then } \log 5^{2x+3} = \log 48. \quad (1)$$

$$(2x + 3) \log 5 = \log 48 \quad (2)$$

$$2x + 3 = \frac{\log 48}{\log 5} \quad (3)$$

$$2x = \frac{\log 48}{\log 5} - 3 \quad (4)$$

$$x = \left(\frac{\log 48}{\log 5} - 3\right) \div 2 \quad (5)$$

b. $3^x = 25$

c. $5^{x+4} = 35$

d. $1.5^{2x+1} = 12$

e. $7(3^{0.5x}) = 42$

Summarize the Mathematics

In this investigation, you learned properties of logarithms that can be used to write logarithmic and exponential expressions in useful equivalent forms.

a Why are the functions $f(x) = 10^x$ and $g(x) = \log x$ inverses of each other?

b Rewrite each of these expressions in an equivalent form.

i. $\log (pn)$ **ii.** $\log (p \div n)$ **iii.** $\log (n^p)$

c Explain how properties of logarithms can be used to solve equations like $a(b^{kx}) = c$.

Be prepared to explain your ideas to the class.

Check Your Understanding

Use your understanding of properties of logarithms to help complete these tasks.

a. Use properties of logarithms to write simpler expressions that are equivalent to these forms.

i. $\log (10^5 10^3)$ **ii.** $\log (10^5 \div 10^3)$ **iii.** $\log (10^5)^3$

b. Use properties of logarithms to write expressions equivalent to these in what seem to you to be simplest possible forms.

i. $\log x^5 x^3$ **ii.** $\log (x^5 \div x^3)$ **iii.** $\log m - \log n$

iv. $\log m + \log n$ **v.** $m \log p + n \log p$ **vi.** $\log 10^3 + \log m^3$

c. Use properties of logarithms to solve $25(1.5^{3x}) = 1{,}000$.

Summarize the Mathematics

 The functions $f(x) = \log x$ and $g(x) = 10^x$ are inverses of each other because for any x, $\log 10^x = x$ and $10^{\log x} = x$, meaning that the exponential and logarithmic functions reverse the assignments that each make.

b The given expressions can be written in a variety of equivalent forms. Only the most common and useful alternative form is given here.

i. $\log p + \log n$ **ii.** $\log p - \log n$ **iii.** $p \log n$

c Properties of logarithms can be used to solve equations like $a(b^{kx}) = c$ roughly as follows.

$$a(b^{kx}) = c \text{ implies } b^{kx} = \frac{c}{a}$$
$$\text{so, } \log b^{kx} = \log\left(\frac{c}{a}\right)$$
$$\text{so, } kx \log b = \log\left(\frac{c}{a}\right)$$
$$\text{so, } x = \frac{\log\left(\frac{c}{a}\right)}{k \log b} = \frac{\log c - \log a}{k \log b}$$

NOTE Solutions to Problem 11 are on page T566B.

Teaching Resources

Transparency Master 18.

UNIT 8 *Inverse Functions*

Summarize the Mathematics

In this investigation, you learned properties of logarithms that can be used to write logarithmic and exponential expressions in useful equivalent forms.

a. Why are the functions $f(x) = 10^x$ and $g(x) = \log x$ inverses of each other?

b. Rewrite each of these expressions in an equivalent form.
i. $\log (pn)$
ii. $\log (p \div n)$
iii. $\log (n^p)$

c. Explain how properties of logarithms can be used to solve equations like $a(b^{kx}) = c$.

Be prepared to explain your ideas to the class.

MATH TOOLKIT If not previously done, ask students to summarize the properties of logarithms for products, quotients, and powers.

Check Your Understanding

a. **i.** $\log (10^5 10^3) = \log 10^8 = 8$

ii. $\log (10^5 \div 10^3) = \log 10^2 = 2$

iii. $\log (10^5)^3 = 3 \log 10^5 = 15$

b. Answers may vary but should be equivalent to the following ones.

i. $\log x^5 x^3 = \log x^8 = 8 \log x$

ii. $\log (x^5 \div x^3) = \log x^2 = 2 \log x$

iii. $\log m - \log n = \log \frac{m}{n}$

iv. $\log m + \log n = \log mn$

v. $m \log p + n \log p = (m + n) \log p = \log p^{m+n}$

vi. $\log 10^3 + \log m^3 = 3 + 3 \log m = 3 \log 10m$

c. $25(1.5^{3x}) = 1{,}000$

$1.5^{3x} = 40$

$3x \log 1.5 = \log 40$

$x = \frac{\log 40}{3 \log 1.5}$

$x \approx 3.03$

INSTRUCTIONAL NOTE You may wish to have students present alternative methods for the CYU tasks.

Unit 8

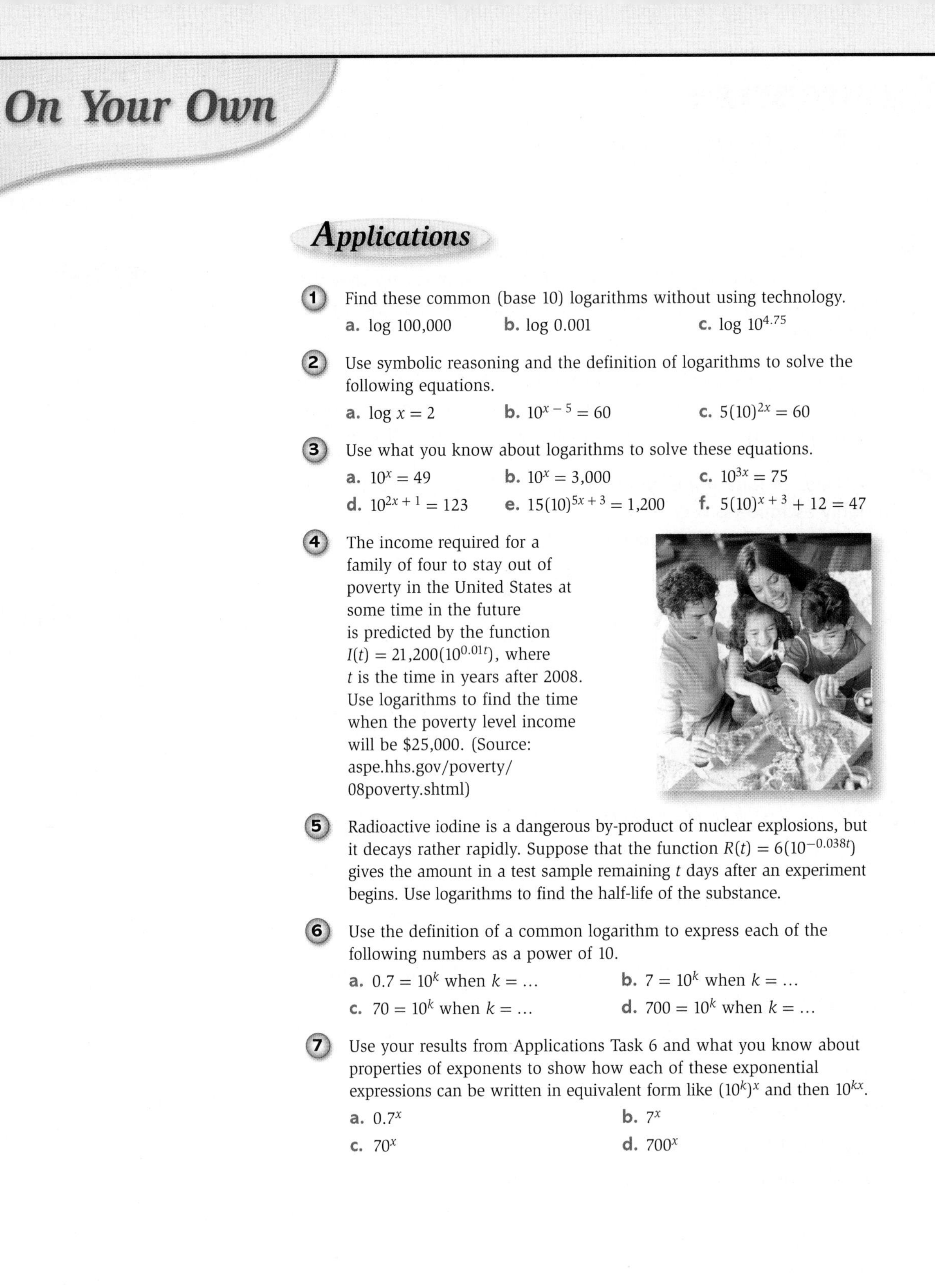

On Your Own

Applications

1. Find these common (base 10) logarithms without using technology.

   a. $\log 100{,}000$ b. $\log 0.001$ c. $\log 10^{4.75}$

2. Use symbolic reasoning and the definition of logarithms to solve the following equations.

   a. $\log x = 2$ b. $10^{x-5} = 60$ c. $5(10)^{2x} = 60$

3. Use what you know about logarithms to solve these equations.

   a. $10^x = 49$ b. $10^x = 3{,}000$ c. $10^{3x} = 75$

   d. $10^{2x+1} = 123$ e. $15(10)^{5x+3} = 1{,}200$ f. $5(10)^{x+3} + 12 = 47$

4. The income required for a family of four to stay out of poverty in the United States at some time in the future is predicted by the function $I(t) = 21{,}200(10^{0.01t})$, where t is the time in years after 2008. Use logarithms to find the time when the poverty level income will be $25,000. (Source: aspe.hhs.gov/poverty/08poverty.shtml)

5. Radioactive iodine is a dangerous by-product of nuclear explosions, but it decays rather rapidly. Suppose that the function $R(t) = 6(10^{-0.038t})$ gives the amount in a test sample remaining t days after an experiment begins. Use logarithms to find the half-life of the substance.

6. Use the definition of a common logarithm to express each of the following numbers as a power of 10.

   a. $0.7 = 10^k$ when $k = \ldots$ b. $7 = 10^k$ when $k = \ldots$

   c. $70 = 10^k$ when $k = \ldots$ d. $700 = 10^k$ when $k = \ldots$

7. Use your results from Applications Task 6 and what you know about properties of exponents to show how each of these exponential expressions can be written in equivalent form like $(10^k)^x$ and then 10^{kx}.

   a. 0.7^x b. 7^x

   c. 70^x d. 700^x

Unit 8

568 UNIT 8 • Inverse Functions

On Your Own

Applications

1 a. 5 b. -3 c. 4.75

2 a. 100 b. $\log 60 + 5 \approx 6.78$ c. $\log 12 \div 2 \approx 0.54$

3 a. $\log 49 \approx 1.69$

b. $\log 3{,}000 \approx 3.48$

c. $\frac{\log 75}{3} \approx 0.63$

d. $(\log 123 - 1) \div 2 \approx 0.54$

e. $\left(\log\left(\frac{1{,}200}{15}\right) - 3\right) \div 5 \approx -0.22$

f. $\log 7 - 3 \approx -2.15$

4 $21{,}200(10^{0.01t}) = 25{,}000$

$0.01t = \log \frac{25{,}000}{21{,}200}$

$t \approx 7.16$

The poverty level will be \$25,000 when $t \approx 7.16$, or during 2015.

5 $6(10^{-0.038t}) = 3$

$-0.038t = \log 0.5$

$t = \frac{\log 0.5}{-0.038} \approx 7.9$

The half-life of radioactive iodine is about 7.9 days.

6 a. $0.7 = 10^k$ when $k = \log 0.7 \approx -0.155$.

b. $7 = 10^k$ when $k = \log 7 \approx 0.845$.

c. $70 = 10^k$ when $k = \log 70 \approx 1.845$.

d. $700 = 10^k$ when $k = \log 700 \approx 2.845$.

7 a. $0.7^x = 10^{(\log 0.7)x} \approx 10^{-0.155x}$

b. $7^x = 10^{(\log 7)x} \approx 10^{0.845x}$

c. $70^x = 10^{(\log 70)x} \approx 10^{1.845x}$

d. $700^x = 10^{(\log 700)x} \approx 10^{2.845x}$

8. Use your results from Applications Tasks 6 and 7 to solve these exponential equations. Check each solution. Be prepared to explain your solution strategy.

   a. $7^x = 3.5$
   b. $5(7^n) = 35$
   c. $5(7^t) + 20 = 125$
   d. $70^p = 48$
   e. $3(7^r) + 120 = 600$
   f. $300(0.7^v) = 60$

9. A vacuum pump attached to a chamber removes 5% of the gas in the chamber with each pump cycle.

   a. What function shows the percent of gas remaining in the chamber after n pump cycles?
   b. How many full cycles are needed before at least 99% of the gas is removed?

10. A light filter lets 40% of the light that hits it pass through to the other side.

   a. What function shows the fraction of light intensity allowed through by n filters?
   b. How many filters are needed to reduce the light intensity to:
      i. 16% of the original intensity?
      ii. less than 5% of the original intensity?
      iii. less than 1% of the original intensity?

11. Use the facts that $\log 20 \approx 1.3$ and $\log 16 \approx 1.2$ and the properties of logarithms to find approximate decimal values for each of these calculations—without the use of technology.

   a. $\log 320$
   b. $\log 1.25$
   c. $\log 400$

12. Use properties of logarithms to write the following expressions in different equivalent forms.

   a. $\log 3x$
   b. $\log 5x^3$
   c. $\log \left(\frac{7x}{5y}\right)$
   d. $\log \left(\frac{1}{3x}\right)$
   e. $\log 7 + \log x$
   f. $3 \log y$
   g. $\log x - \log 3y$
   h. $\log 7x^3y^2$
   i. $\log \left(\frac{7 + x}{49 - x^2}\right)$

13. Use what you know about logarithms to solve these equations without rewriting the exponential expressions in equivalent base 10 form.

   a. $2^x = 10{,}000$
   b. $3^{x+3} = 10{,}000$
   c. $4^{2x+3} = 100{,}000$
   d. $5(2)^x + 7 = 42$
   e. $5(3)^{x+1} = 2{,}500$
   f. $1.8^{3x} = 75$

8 **a.** $\frac{\log 3.5}{\log 7} \approx 0.64$ **b.** 1 **c.** $\frac{\log 21}{\log 7} \approx 1.56$

d. $\frac{\log 48}{\log 70} \approx 0.91$ **e.** $\frac{\log 160}{\log 7} \approx 2.61$ **f.** $\frac{\log 0.2}{\log 0.7} \approx 4.51$

9 **a.** $g(n) = 100(0.95^n)$, or $g(n) = 0.95^n$ if representing the percent of gas removed as a decimal.

b. Using the equation $1 = 100(0.95)^n$:

$1 = 100(10^{(\log 0.95)n})$

$0.01 = 10^{-0.02228n}$

$-0.02228n = \log 0.01$

$n = \frac{-2}{-0.02228} \approx 89.8$

It will take 90 pump cycles to remove at least 99% of the gas.

10 **a.** The exponential decay function is $I(n) = 0.4^n$.

b. **i.** To reach 16% of entering light intensity, 2 filters are needed since 40% of 40% is 16%. $(0.4)(0.4) = 0.16$ Alternatively, students might solve $(0.4)^n = 0.16$ and get $n = \frac{\log 0.16}{\log 0.4} = 2$.

ii. To reach 5% of entering light intensity, at least 4 filters are needed because $0.05 = (0.4)^n$ when:

$10^{(\log 0.4)n} = 0.05$

$n \log 0.4 = \log 0.05$

$n = \frac{\log 0.05}{\log 0.4} \approx 3.3$

iii. At least 6 filters are needed, since $0.4^{5.026} \approx 0.01$.

11 **a.** $\log 320 = \log 20 + \log 16 \approx 2.5$

b. $\log 1.25 = \log 20 - \log 16 \approx 0.1$

c. $\log 400 = \log 20^2 = 2 \log 20 \approx 2.6$

12 Each of the given expressions can be written in a variety of equivalent forms.

a. $\log 3 + \log x$ **b.** $\log 5 + 3 \log x$

c. $\log 7x - \log 5y$, or $\log 7 + \log x - \log 5 - \log y$

d. $-\log 3x$, or $-\log 3 - \log x$ **e.** $\log 7x$

f. $\log y^3$ **g.** $\log \left(\frac{x}{3y}\right)$

h. $\log 7 + 3 \log x + 2 \log y$

i. $\log (7 + x) - \log (49 - x^2)$
(Note that if you simplify the algebraic fraction first, this reduces to $-\log (7 - x)$. You can also discover this by noting that $\log (49 - x^2) = \log ((7 - x)(7 + x))$, which equals $\log (7 - x) + \log (7 + x)$.)

13 **a.** $x = \frac{4}{\log 2} \approx 13.29$ **b.** $x = \frac{4}{\log 3} - 3 \approx 5.38$

c. $x = \frac{\frac{5}{\log 4} - 3}{2} \approx 2.65$ **d.** $x = \frac{\log 7}{\log 2} \approx 2.81$

e. $x = \frac{\log 500}{\log 3} - 1 \approx 4.66$ **f.** $x = \frac{\frac{\log 75}{\log 1.8}}{3} \approx 2.45$

Connections

14 The time it takes a computer program to run increases as the number of inputs increases. Three different companies wrote three different programs, A, B, and C, to perform the same calculation. The time, in milliseconds, it takes to run each of the programs when given n inputs is given by the three functions below.

$$A(n) = 10{,}000 + 2 \log n$$
$$B(n) = 100 + 4n^2$$
$$C(n) = (0.00003)(10^n)$$

a. Which program, A, B, or C, takes the least amount of time for 1 input?

b. Which program is most efficient for 300 inputs?

c. Which program is most efficient for 100,000 inputs?

15 Suppose a house was purchased five years ago for \$200,000. It just sold for \$265,000. Assume that this pattern of growth has been exponential at a constant annual percent rate of change.

a. What function will give the price at any time t years from now? (*Hints:* What equation relates the two house values, the five-year time interval of appreciation in value, and the percent rate of increase in value? You can estimate solutions to equations like $R^5 = k$ by studying tables or graphs of $y = x^5$.)

b. What will be the price of the house next year?

c. When will the price of the house be \$1 million?

16 By measuring the decay of radioactive carbon-14, scientists can estimate the age of the remains of living things. Carbon-14 decays at a rate of 0.0121% per year (or retains 99.9879% of its radioactivity).

a. Write a rule for the function that gives the amount of a 5-mg lab sample remaining t years after its mass is first measured.

b. Find the half-life of carbon-14.

17 If $y = 5(3^x)$, then a table of sample (x, y) values for this function will look like the one below.

x	−2	−1	0	1	2	3	4	5	6	7
y	$\frac{5}{9}$	$\frac{5}{3}$	5	15	45	135	405	1,215	3,645	10,935

a. Add a row to a copy of this table with values $z = \log y$. For example, if $x = 2$, then $y = 45$ and $z \approx 1.65$.

Unit 8

570 UNIT 8 • Inverse Functions

Connections

14 **a.** Program C would take the least amount of time.
$A(1) = 10{,}000$, $B(1) = 104$, $C(1) = 0.0003$

b. Program A would take the least amount of time.
$A(300) \approx 10{,}004.95$, $B(300) = 360{,}100$, $C(300) = 3 \times 10^{295}$

c. Program A would take the least amount of time.
$A(100{,}000) = 10{,}010$, $B(100{,}000) = 40{,}000{,}000{,}100$,
$C(100{,}000) = 3 \times 10^{99{,}995}$

15 **a.** $265{,}000 = 200{,}000(R)^5$ is true when $R \approx 1.058$, so the predictive model should be $v(t) = 265{,}000(1.058^t)$.

b. Therefore, the price next year will be $265{,}000(1.058) \approx \$280{,}370$.

c. $1{,}000{,}000 = 265{,}000(1.058^t)$ when $t \approx 23.6$ years from now.

16 **a.** $c(t) = 5(0.999879^t)$

b. $2.5 = 5(0.999879^t)$ is true when $t \approx 5{,}730$. Therefore, the half-life of carbon-14 is approximately 5,730 years.

17 **a.**

x	−2	−1	0	1	2	3	4	5	6	7
y	$\frac{5}{9}$	$\frac{5}{3}$	5	15	45	135	405	1,215	3,645	10,935
z	−0.26	0.22	0.70	1.18	1.65	2.13	2.61	3.08	3.56	4.04

SCOPE AND SEQUENCE
While Connections Task 17 might appear to simply be an exercise in use of logarithm properties, it actually foreshadows coming work in data analysis, where linearizing transformations of data patterns are used along with linear regression to find models for exponential data patterns.

b. Explain how the table pattern shows that z is a linear function of x.

c. Use properties of logarithms to write $\log 5(3^x)$ in an equivalent form that allows you to write a rule relating z to x in the form $z = mx + b$. Then compare the values produced by this linear function to those in row three of your table. Explain why the similarity occurs.

18 A large number like 2,364,700 is written in scientific notation as 2.3647×10^6 and a small number like 0.000045382 as 4.5382×10^{-5}.

a. Write each of the following numbers in scientific notation with five significant digits (rounding appropriately where necessary to meet this condition).

i. 47,265

ii. 584.73

iii. 97,485,302

iv. 0.00235148

b. Suppose the only calculator that you had was one that could multiply and divide numbers between 1 and 10 but no others. Explain how you could still use this calculator to find these products.

i. $584.73 \times 97{,}485{,}302$

ii. $47{,}265 \times 0.002351$

iii. $47{,}265 \div 584.73$

19 Logarithms were invented, in part, to help with multiplication and division of very large and very small numbers in the time long before electronic calculators. When combined with use of scientific notation, they provided a powerful tool for the sort of arithmetic required by calculations in astronomy, chemistry, and physics.

Mathematicians in the early seventeenth century produced tables of logarithms with great precision. Use what you know about scientific notation, logarithms, and the given logarithm values to do the following indicated calculations.

a. Show how the facts that $\log 1.2345 \approx 0.09149$, $\log 6.7890 \approx 0.83181$, and $\log 8.3810 \approx 0.92330$ imply that $12{,}345 \times 67{,}890 \approx 838{,}100{,}000$.

b. Show how the facts given in Part a imply that $1{,}234{,}500 \times 67{,}890{,}000 \approx 83{,}810{,}000{,}000{,}000$.

b. As x values increase by 1, z values increase by approximately 0.48.

c. $\log 5(3^x) = \log 5 + \log 3^x = \log 5 + x \log 3$. So, $z = (\log 3)x + \log 5$. Since $\log 3 \approx 0.48$ and $\log 5 \approx 0.7$, this equation is $z \approx 0.48x + 0.7$ which is a near perfect match for the table in Part a.

18 **a.** **i.** 4.7265×10^4

ii. 5.8473×10^2

iii. 9.7485×10^7

iv. 2.351×10^{-3}

b. For each calculation, you would use the calculator for the first product and then use mental arithmetic to multiply the result by the power of ten using mental arithmetic.

i. $5.8473 \times 9.7485302 \times 10^9$

ii. $4.7265 \times 2.351 \times 10$

iii. $4.7265 \div 5.8473 \times 10^2$

19 **a.** $12{,}345 = 1.2345 \times 10^4$ and $67{,}890 = 6.789 \times 10^4$.
So, $\log (12{,}345 \times 67{,}890) = \log (1.2345 \times 10^4) + \log (6.789 \times 10^4)$.
This equals $\log 1.2345 + \log 10^4 + \log 6.789 + \log 10^4$.
Since $\log 10^n = n$, the preceding sum is equal to:

$$\log 1.2345 + \log 6.789 + 8, \text{ or } 0.09149 + 0.83181 + 8,$$

which is equal to $0.92330 + 8$.
Now $\log 838{,}100{,}000 = \log (8.3810 \times 10^8)$, which is equal to $\log 8.3810 + \log 10^8$, or $0.92330 + 8$.

b. The facts given in Part a imply that $1{,}234{,}500 \times 67{,}890{,}000 \approx 83{,}810{,}000{,}000{,}000$ by similar reasoning with the powers of 10 increased in each factor from 4 to 6 and 4 to 7 and in the product from 8 to 13.

Unit 8

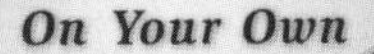

c. Use a graphing calculator to check the calculations in Parts a and b, and record the calculator outputs. Explain how the forms of those outputs tell the same story as your work with logarithms and scientific notation.

20 The common logarithm function has the very useful special property that for any positive numbers a and b, $\log ab = \log a + \log b$. Mathematicians say that the logarithm function satisfies the general functional equation $f(ab) = f(a) + f(b)$. Which, if any, of the following familiar functions satisfy that functional equation? Give proofs of those that do and counterexamples for those that do not.

a. $f(x) = 3x$ (To begin, consider: Does $3(ab) = 3a + 3b$ for all pairs (a, b)?)

b. $f(x) = x + 5$

c. $f(x) = x^2$

21 Another interesting type of functional equation asks whether $f(ab) = f(a)f(b)$ for all pairs (a, b). Which, if any, of the following functions satisfy that multiplicative functional equation? Give proofs of those that do and counterexamples for those that do not.

a. $f(x) = 3x$

b. $f(x) = x + 5$

c. $f(x) = x^2$

d. $f(x) = \frac{1}{x}$, $x \neq 0$

22 Another interesting type of functional equation asks if $f(a + b) = f(a) + f(b)$ for all pairs (a, b). Which, if any, of the functions in Task 21 satisfy that additive functional equation?

Reflections

23 Suppose that n is a positive number.

a. If $0 < \log n < 1$, what can you say about n?

b. If $5 < \log n < 6$, what can you say about n?

c. If $p < \log n < p + 1$, where p is a positive integer, what can you say about n?

24 Students learning about logarithms often find it helpful to deal with the new idea by frequent reminders that *logarithms are really just exponents*.

a. Why is it correct to say that $\log 20 \approx 1.3010$ is an exponent?

b. How does the phrase "logarithms are really just exponents" help in finding:

i. $\log 1{,}000$

ii. $\log 0.001$

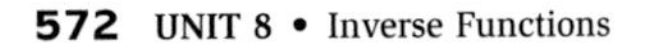

572 UNIT 8 • Inverse Functions

c. When the calculations are done by calculator, the first result is exactly 838,102,050. The second calculation will generally go past the exact answer capability of common calculators and produce a result that looks like 8.3810205 E 13.

20 **INSTRUCTIONAL NOTE** The following results highlight the very special property of logarithmic (and exponential) functions in the way they connect multiplication and addition. In abstract algebra, this correspondence of additive and multiplicative relationships is called an *isomorphism*.

a. $f(x) = 3x$ Does not hold:
Counterexample $3(7 \cdot 11) \neq 3(7) + 3(11)$

b. $f(x) = x + 5$ Does not hold:
Counterexample $(7 \cdot 11) + 5 \neq (7 + 5) + (11 + 5)$

c. $f(x) = x^2$ Does not hold:
Counterexample $(7 \cdot 11)^2 \neq 7^2 + 11^2$

21 a. $f(x) = 3x$ Does not hold:
Counterexample $3(7 \cdot 11) \neq (3 \cdot 7)(3 \cdot 11)$

b. $f(x) = x + 5$ Does not hold:
Counterexample $7 \cdot 11 + 5 \neq (7 + 5)(11 + 5)$

c. $f(x) = x^2$ Does hold:
$f(a \cdot b) = (ab)^2 = a^2b^2 = f(a) \cdot f(b)$ for all a, b

d. $f(x) = \frac{1}{x}$ Does hold:
$f(a \cdot b) = \frac{1}{ab} = \left(\frac{1}{a}\right)\left(\frac{1}{b}\right) = f(a) \cdot f(b)$ for all nonzero a, b

22 a. $f(x) = 3x$ Does hold:
$f(a + b) = 3(a + b) = 3a + 3b = f(a) + f(b)$ for all a, b

b. $f(x) = x + 5$ Does not hold:
Counterexample $(7 + 11) + 5 \neq (7 + 5) + (11 + 5)$

c. $f(x) = x^2$ Does not hold:
Counterexample $(7 + 11)^2 \neq 7^2 + 11^2$

d. $f(x) = \frac{1}{x}$ Does not hold:
Counterexample $\frac{1}{2 + 3} \neq \frac{1}{2} + \frac{1}{3}$

Reflections

23 a. $1 < n < 10$

b. $100{,}000 < n < 1{,}000{,}000$, or equivalently $10^5 < n < 10^6$

c. $10^p < n < 10^{p+1}$

24 a. $\log 20 \approx 1.3010$ is an exponent because $10^{1.3010} \approx 20$.

b. You can ask, "What exponents on the base 10 give 1,000 and 0.001?"

i. $\log 1{,}000 = \log 10^3 = 3$

ii. $\log 0.001 = \log 10^{-3} = -3$

25 The logarithmic function $f(x) = \log x$ is the inverse of the exponential function $g(x) = 10^x$. How can you use this fact and a graph of $g(x) = 10^x$ to quickly sketch the graph of $f(x) = \log x$ for $0 < x < 10{,}000$?

26 For $x > 1$, values of the logarithmic function $f(x) = \log x$ increase very slowly while values of the exponential function $g(x) = 10^x$ increase very rapidly. What is it about the definitions of those two functions that causes this contrasting behavior?

27 How do the properties of exponents and the phrase "logarithms are really just exponents" help in explaining these properties of the logarithm function?

a. $\log ab = \log a + \log b$

b. $\log (a \div b) = \log a - \log b$

c. $\log 1 = 0$

d. $\log a^n = n \log a$

28 With the introduction of logarithmic functions, you are now able to solve exponential equations using algebraic reasoning. Solve the equations below using each of the listed strategies. Then compare your solutions and the ease with which each method produces solutions or accurate estimates of solutions.

- Algebraic reasoning
- Approximation using function graphs
- Approximation using tables of function values

a. $100 = 4.5x - 885$

b. $3x^2 + x + 12 = 14$

c. $3(1.2^t) = 14$

29 What are the advantages of finding solutions to exponential equations by estimation using tables and graphs of exponential functions versus using algebraic reasoning with logarithms?

Extensions

30 Use properties of exponents and logarithms to solve the following equations.

a. $\log 10^x = 4$

b. $2^{2x+2} = 8^{x+2}$

31 Recall that a prime number n is an integer greater than 1 that has only 1 and n as divisors. The first eight primes are 2, 3, 5, 7, 11, 13, 17, and 19. Mathematicians have proven that the number of primes less than or equal to n is approximated by $\frac{0.4343n}{\log n}$. This formula is an amazing discovery since the primes appear irregularly among the natural numbers.

a. Count the actual number of primes less than or equal to n to complete a copy of the table below. Plot the resulting (n, *number of primes* $\leq n$) data.

n	10	25	40	55	70	85	100	115	130	145
Number of Primes $\leq n$	4				19	23	25	30	31	34

25 You can reflect the graph of $g(x)$ across $y = x$ to sketch the graph of $f(x)$.

26 For the function $f(x) = 10^x$, increasing the value of x by 1 increases the function output by a factor of 10, so the exponential function will grow very rapidly as x increases. The function $g(x) = \log_{10} x$, on the other hand, asks, "What exponent, when used with base 10, will give output of x?" Small increases in the exponent produce large increases in the exponential expression, so the logarithms increase very slowly.

27 **a.** The exponent of a product is the sum of exponents of the factors. For example, $10^a 10^b = 10^{a+b}$.

b. The exponent of a quotient is the difference of the exponents of the dividend and the divisor. For example, $\frac{10^a}{10^b} = 10^{a-b}$.

c. $10^0 = 1$

d. To find the power of a power, multiply the exponents. For example, $(10^a)^b = 10^{ab}$.

28 **a.** Algebraic reasoning:

$$4.5x - 885 = 100$$
$$4.5x = 985$$
$$x = \frac{985}{4.5} \approx 218.89$$

Graphically:

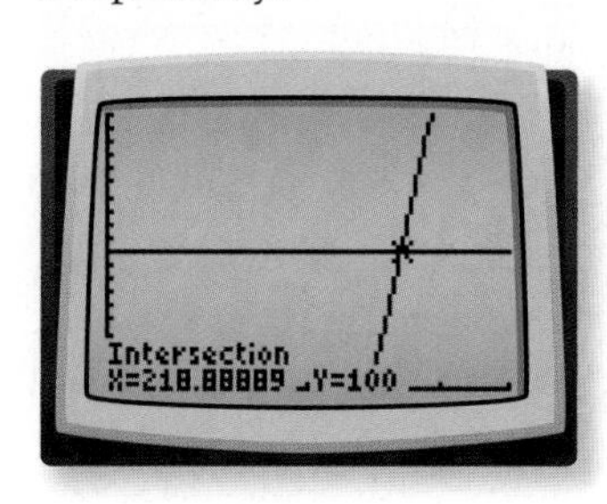

With tables of function values:

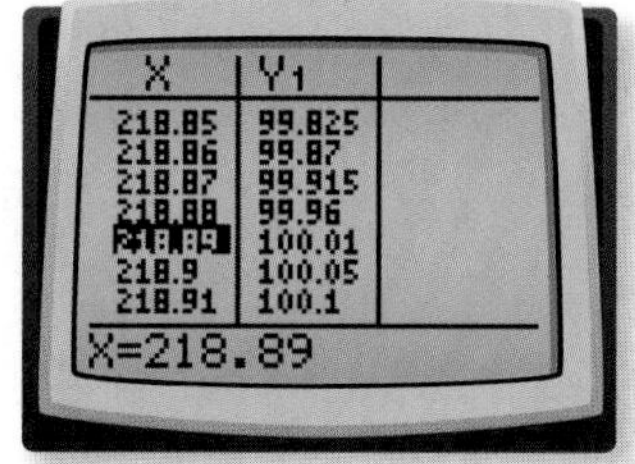

b. Algebraic reasoning:

$$3x^2 + x + 12 = 14$$
$$3x^2 + x - 2 = 0$$
$$(3x - 2)(x + 1) = 0$$
$$x = \frac{2}{3} \text{ or } -1$$

Graphically:

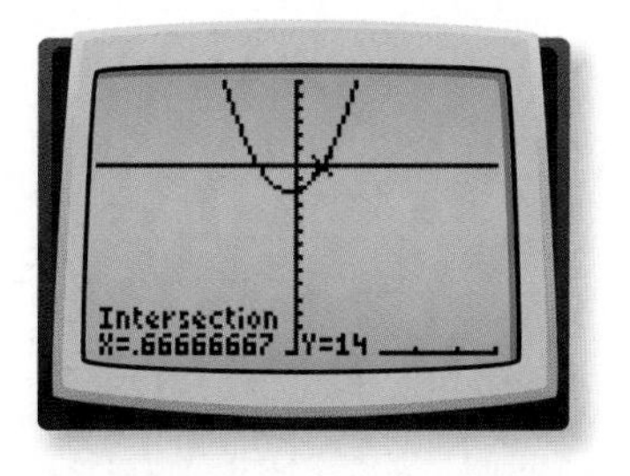

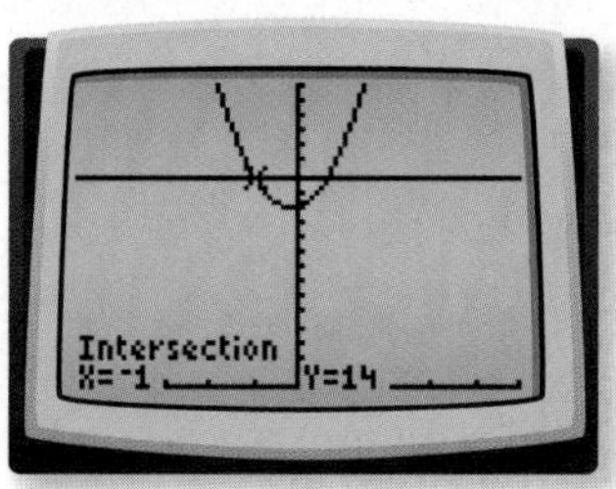

With tables of function values:

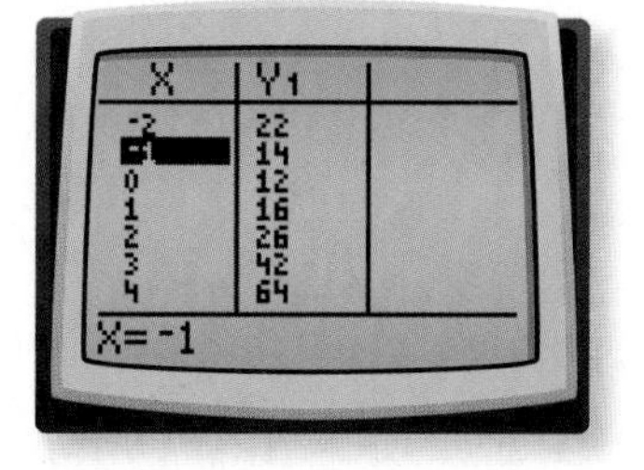

c. Algebraic reasoning:

$$3(1.2^t) = 14$$
$$1.2^t = \frac{14}{3}$$
$$10^{(\log 1.2)t} = \frac{14}{3}$$
$$(\log 1.2)t = \log \frac{14}{3}$$
$$t = \frac{\log \frac{14}{3}}{\log 1.2} \approx 8.449$$

Graphically:

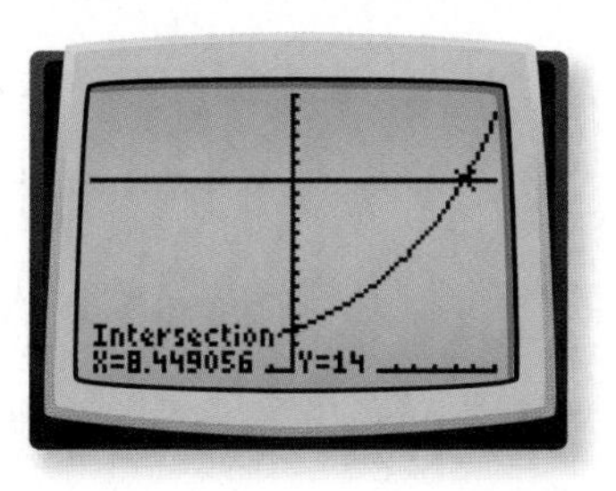

With tables of function values:

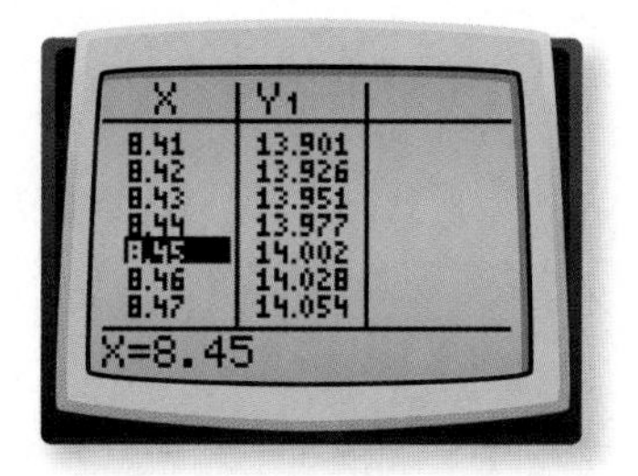

Unit 8

29 Tables and graphs are quite useful and efficient when an estimate of the solution will suffice. However, for an exact solution, algebraic reasoning is often required. In many simple equations, algebraic reasoning is probably more efficient than the steps required to enter a function and scan a table or graph for solutions. When one is looking for a general principle about a function, algebraic reasoning will generally provide the most useful tool.

Extensions

30 **a.** $\log 10^x = 4$ can be rewritten as $10^x = 10^4$, which means $x = 4$.

b. $2^{2x+2} = 8^{x+2}$ can be rewritten as $2^{2x+2} = (2^3)^{x+2}$. Therefore, $2x + 2 = 3x + 6$; $x = -4$.

31 **a.**

n	10	25	40	55	70	85	100	115	130	145
Number of Primes ≤ *n*	4	9	12	16	19	23	25	30	31	34

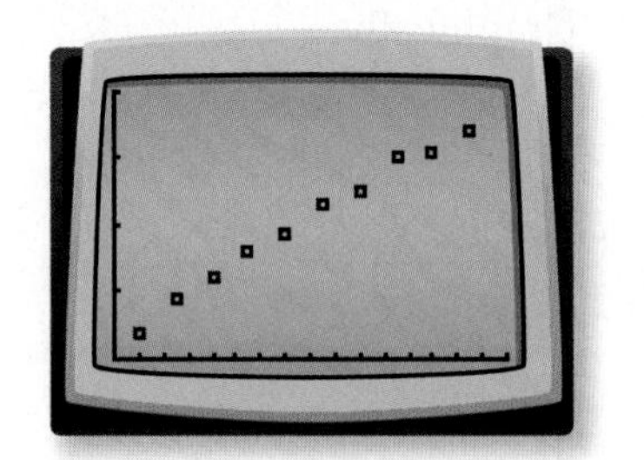

Teacher Notes

b. Graph $P(n) = \dfrac{0.4343n}{\log n}$, $0 < n \leq 150$. How well does this function model the counts in Part a?

c. Use the function $P(n)$ to estimate the number of primes less than or equal to 1,000. Less than or equal to 1,000,000. Less than or equal to 10^{18}.

d. According to this $P(n)$, about what percent of the numbers up to 10^6 are prime? Up to 10^{18}?

32 When you go to the movies, the number of frames that are displayed per second affects the "smoothness" of the perceived motion on the screen. If the frames are displayed slowly, our minds perceive the images as separate pictures rather than fluid motion.

However, as the frequency of the images increases, the perceived gap between the images decreases and the motion appears fluid. The frequency f at which we stop seeing a flickering image and start perceiving motion is given by the equation $f = K \log S$, where K is a constant and S is the brightness of the image being projected.

a. S is inversely proportional to the square of the observer's distance from the screen. What would be the effect on f if the distance to the screen is cut in half? What if the distance to the screen is doubled?

b. If the image is being projected at a slow frequency and you perceive a flicker, where should you move in the theater: closer to the screen or farther from the screen?

c. Suppose the show is sold out and you cannot move your seat. What could you do to reduce the flickering of the image on-screen?

33 It is possible to define logarithms for any positive base b as follows.

$$\log_b m = n \text{ if and only if } m = b^n$$

Justify each step in the following proof that $\log_b m = \dfrac{\log_{10} m}{\log_{10} b}$.

Suppose that $m = b^n$.

Then $\log_{10} m = n \log_{10} b$. (1)

$\log_{10} m = (\log_b m)(\log_{10} b)$ (2)

$\log_b m = \dfrac{\log_{10} m}{\log_{10} b}$ (3)

574 UNIT 8 • Inverse Functions

b. The graph of the function with the data points is at the right. It seems to give a low estimate for most of the data points.

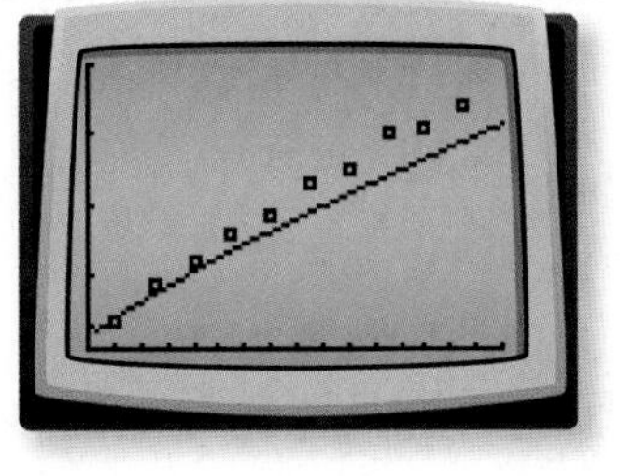

c. $P(1{,}000) \approx 145$
$P(1{,}000{,}000) \approx 72{,}383$
$P(10^{18}) \approx 2.4 \times 10^{16}$

d. Approximately 7.2% of the numbers less than 10^6 are prime, and approximately 2.4% of the numbers less than 10^{18} are prime.

32 **a.** If the distance is cut in half, the brightness will increase by a factor of 4, and f will increase but not by a factor of 2 or 4.

$f = K_1 \log S$ and $S = \frac{K_2}{d^2}$.

So, $f = K_1 \log \left(\frac{K_2}{d^2}\right)$.

If distance is halved,

$f = K_1 \log \left(\frac{K_2}{(0.5d)^2}\right)$.

So, $f = K_1 \log \left(\frac{4K_2}{d^2}\right)$.

So, $f = K_1 \log 4 + K_1 \log \left(\frac{K_2}{d^2}\right)$.

If the distance is doubled, the brightness will decrease by a factor of one-fourth, and f will decrease but not by a factor of one-half or one-fourth. If distance is doubled,

$f = K_1 \log \left(\frac{K_2}{(2d)^2}\right)$.

So, $f = K_1 \log \left(\frac{K_2}{4d^2}\right)$.

So, $f = K_1 \log \frac{1}{4} + K_1 \log \left(\frac{K_2}{d^2}\right)$.

So, $f = -K_1 \log 4 + K_1 \log \left(\frac{K_2}{d^2}\right)$.

b. Since you cannot change the frequency at which the movie is displayed, you want to change your value of f to a lower number. This can be accomplished by decreasing the brightness through increasing the distance to the image. This can be accomplished by moving away from the screen.

c. If you cannot move your seat, you should decrease the brightness of the image. This could be accomplished by wearing sunglasses.

33 (1) Logarithms of equal quantities are equal and then the property of logarithms $\log s^t = t \log s$.

(2) Substitution of $\log_b m$ for n

(3) Division of both sides of the preceding equation by $\log_{10} b$

Review

34 Consider the function $f(x) = (x^2 - 4x)(x + 3)$.

a. Determine the value of $f(-2)$.

b. Solve $f(x) = 0$.

c. Rewrite $f(x)$ in standard polynomial form. Identify the degree of $f(x)$.

d. For what values of x is $f(x) < 0$?

e. Estimate the coordinates of all local maximum and minimum points of $f(x)$.

35 In the diagram at the right, the circle with center O is inscribed in $\triangle ABC$, the radius of the circle is 6, and $m\angle DAE = 52°$. Determine each of the following measures.

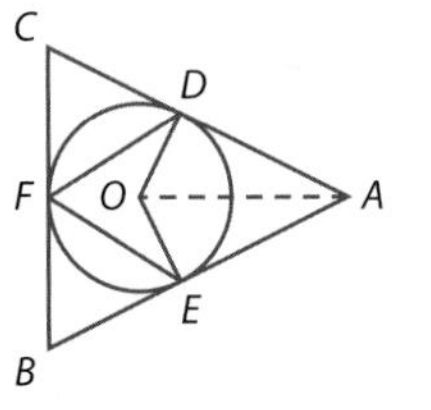

a. $m\angle DOE$

b. $m\widehat{DE}$

c. $m\angle DFE$

d. AD

36 Write each product or sum of rational expressions in equivalent form as a single algebraic fraction. Then simplify the result as much as possible.

a. $\frac{x^3}{x+2} \cdot \frac{x+4}{x}$

b. $\frac{3x}{x+4} \cdot \frac{x^2-16}{x^2}$

c. $\frac{6}{x+3} + \frac{4x+6}{x+3}$

d. $\frac{x}{5} + \frac{x+1}{10}$

37 Complete the following for each recursive definition of a sequence.

- Write the first five terms of the sequence.
- Determine if the sequence is arithmetic, geometric, or neither.
- If it is arithmetic or geometric, write a function formula for a_n.
- If it is arithmetic or geometric, find S_{12}.

a. $a_n = a_{n-1} - 3$, $a_0 = 50$

b. $a_n = 2a_{n-1} + 6$, $a_0 = 12$

c. $a_n = \frac{a_{n-1}}{2}$, $a_0 = 256$

38 How is the shape of an exponential function graph related to the base of the exponent?

39 Plans for the installation of a communication tower call for attaching a 200 feet long support wire to a point that is 125 feet above the ground. What is the degree measure of the angle formed by the support wire and the ground?

Review

34 **a.** 12

b. $x = -3$, $x = 0$, $x = 4$

c. $f(x) = x^3 - x^2 - 12x$; degree 3

d. Since the lead coefficient on the cubic function $f(x)$ is positive and the zeroes are at -3, 0, and 4, a sketch of the graph as shown at the right reveals the intervals where $f(x) < 0$ as $x < -3$ and $0 < x < 4$.

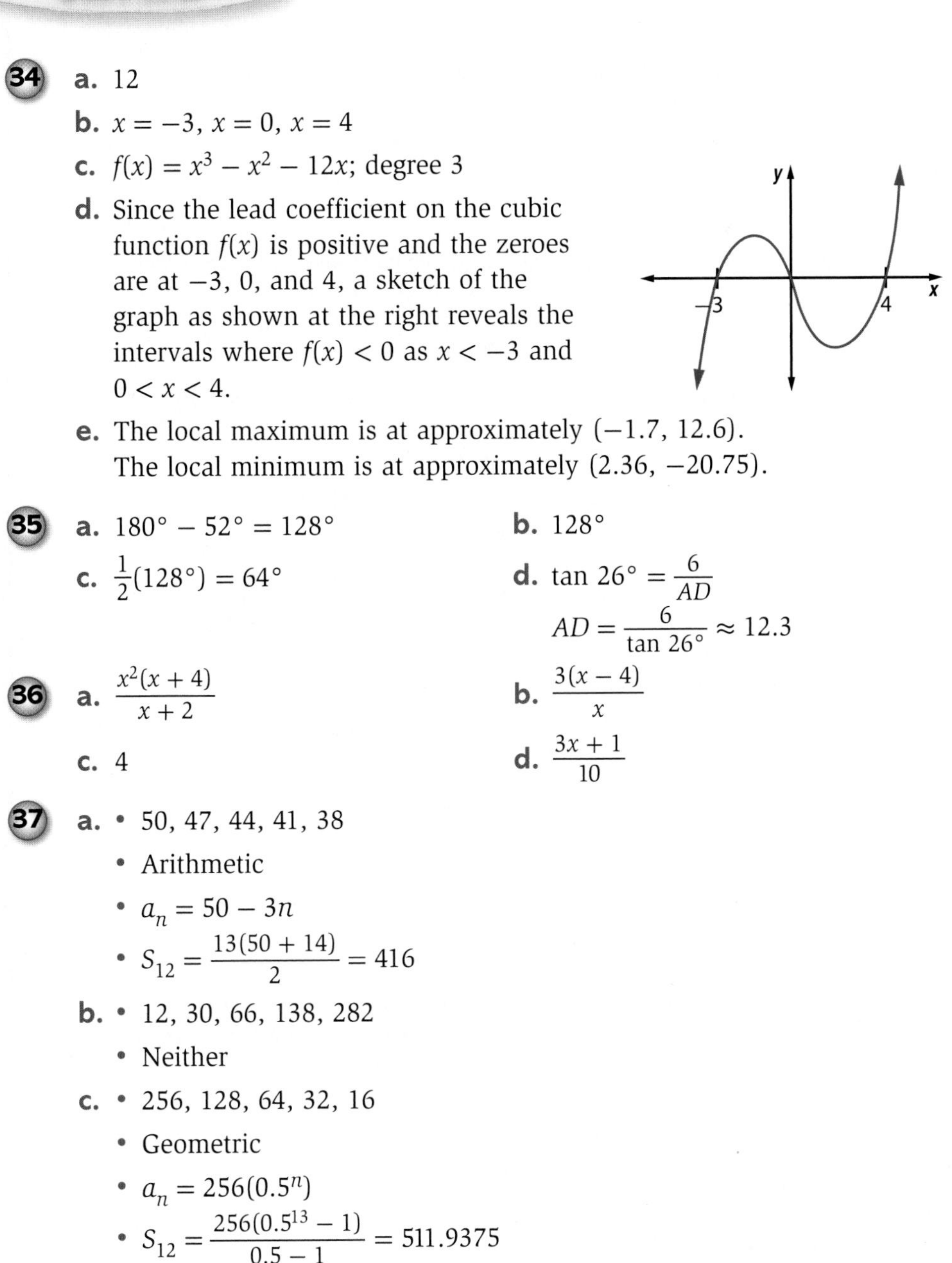

e. The local maximum is at approximately $(-1.7, 12.6)$. The local minimum is at approximately $(2.36, -20.75)$.

35 **a.** $180° - 52° = 128°$

b. $128°$

c. $\frac{1}{2}(128°) = 64°$

d. $\tan 26° = \frac{6}{AD}$

$AD = \frac{6}{\tan 26°} \approx 12.3$

36 **a.** $\frac{x^2(x + 4)}{x + 2}$

b. $\frac{3(x - 4)}{x}$

c. 4

d. $\frac{3x + 1}{10}$

37 **a.**
- 50, 47, 44, 41, 38
- Arithmetic
- $a_n = 50 - 3n$
- $S_{12} = \frac{13(50 + 14)}{2} = 416$

b.
- 12, 30, 66, 138, 282
- Neither

c.
- 256, 128, 64, 32, 16
- Geometric
- $a_n = 256(0.5^n)$
- $S_{12} = \frac{256(0.5^{13} - 1)}{0.5 - 1} = 511.9375$

Just in Time

38 When the base of the exponent is between 0 and 1, the function decreases at a decreasing rate. When the base is greater than 1, the function increases at an increasing rate.

39 $\sin x = \frac{125}{200}$

$x = \sin^{-1}\left(\frac{125}{200}\right)$

$x \approx 38.7°$

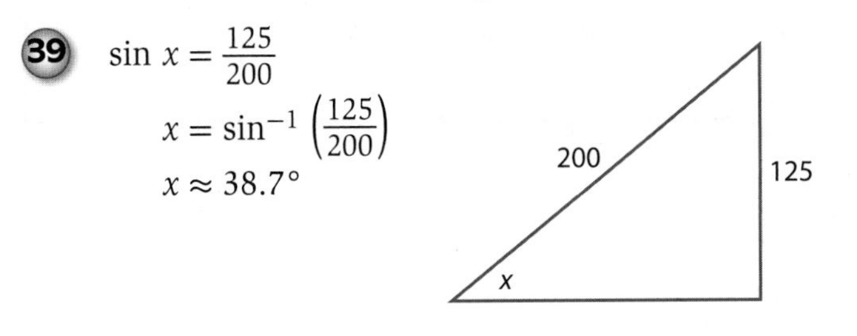

40 Write each of the following radicals in equivalent form with smallest possible numbers and simplest possible expressions under the radical sign.

a. $\sqrt{121}$

b. $\sqrt{48}$

c. $\sqrt{25x^2}$, $x > 0$

d. $\sqrt{5s^2}$, $s > 0$

e. $\sqrt{4w^3}$, $w > 0$

f. $\sqrt{\frac{9}{4}x^2}$, $x > 0$

41 Recall that angles can be measured in both degrees and radians, with the two measurement scales related by the fact that $180° = \pi$ radians or $360° = 2\pi$ radians. Complete a copy of the following table showing degree and radian equivalents for some important angles.

Degrees	0		45	60		120		150	180
Radians		$\frac{\pi}{6}$			$\frac{\pi}{2}$		$\frac{3\pi}{4}$		

42 The sketch at the right shows how the cosine and sine of 30° (or $\frac{\pi}{6}$ radians) determine coordinates of a point on the circle of radius 1 centered at the origin.

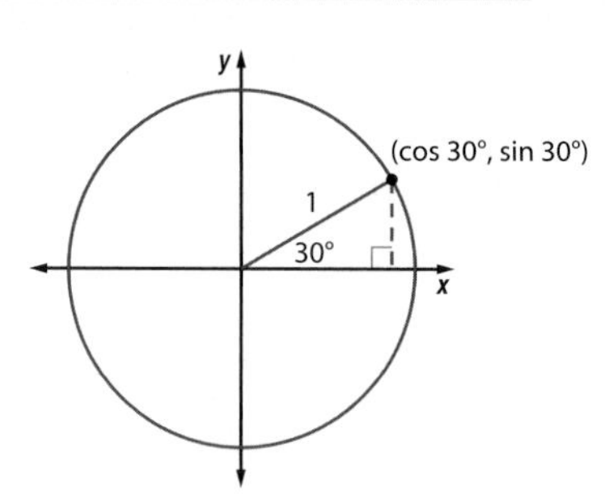

a. Give exact values of the coordinates.

b. Make a similar sketch showing the location and numerical coordinates of these points on the unit circle.

i. $\left(\cos \frac{3\pi}{4}, \sin \frac{3\pi}{4}\right)$

ii. $\left(\cos \frac{\pi}{3}, \sin \frac{\pi}{3}\right)$

iii. $\left(\cos \frac{3\pi}{2}, \sin \frac{3\pi}{2}\right)$

iv. $\left(\cos \frac{7\pi}{4}, \sin \frac{7\pi}{4}\right)$

v. $\left(\cos \frac{7\pi}{6}, \sin \frac{7\pi}{6}\right)$

43 Without using technology, sketch a graph of each function over the interval $[-2\pi, 2\pi]$. Then give the period and the amplitude of each function. Use technology to check your work.

a. $y = \sin x$

b. $y = 2 \sin x$

c. $y = \sin 2x$

Unit 8

576 UNIT 8 • Inverse Functions

40 **a.** 11 **b.** $4\sqrt{3}$ **c.** $5x$

d. $s\sqrt{5}$ **e.** $2w\sqrt{w}$ **f.** $\frac{3x}{2}$

Just in Time

41

Degrees	0	30	45	60	90	120	135	150	180
Radians	0	$\frac{\pi}{6}$	$\frac{\pi}{4}$	$\frac{\pi}{3}$	$\frac{\pi}{2}$	$\frac{2\pi}{3}$	$\frac{3\pi}{4}$	$\frac{5\pi}{6}$	π

Just in Time

42 **a.** $\left(\frac{\sqrt{3}}{2}, \frac{1}{2}\right)$

b. **i.** $\left(\cos \frac{3\pi}{4}, \sin \frac{3\pi}{4}\right)$
$= (\cos 135°, \sin 135°)$
$= \left(-\frac{\sqrt{2}}{2}, \frac{\sqrt{2}}{2}\right)$

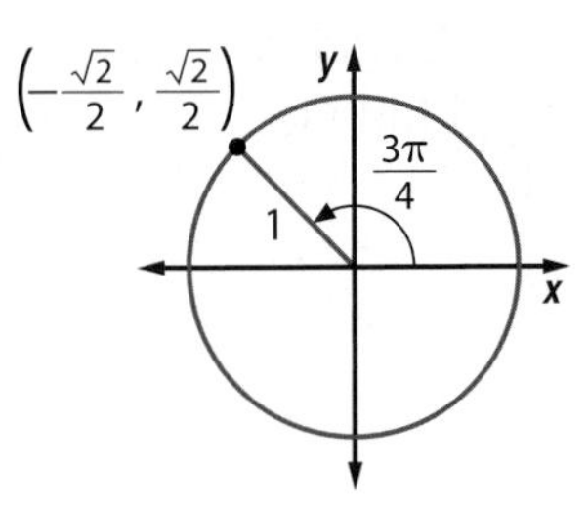

ii. $\left(\cos \frac{\pi}{3}, \sin \frac{\pi}{3}\right)$
$= (\cos 60°, \sin 60°)$
$= \left(\frac{1}{2}, \frac{\sqrt{3}}{2}\right)$

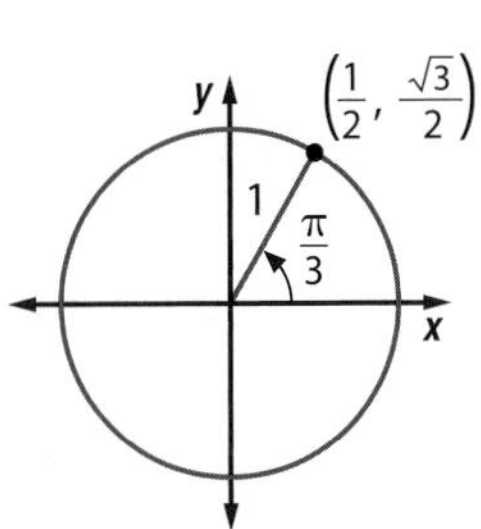

iii. $\left(\cos \frac{3\pi}{2}, \sin \frac{3\pi}{2}\right)$
$= (\cos 270°, \sin 270°)$
$= (0, -1)$

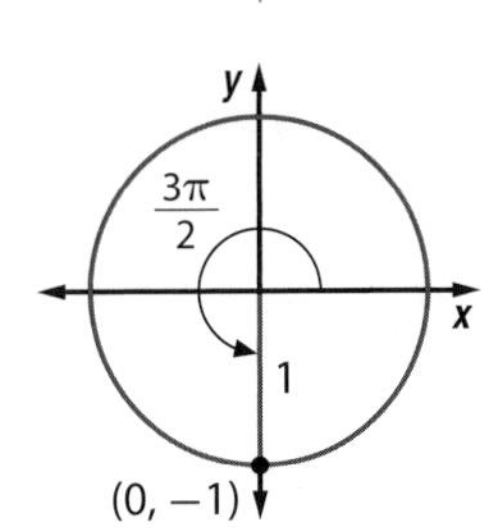

iv. $\left(\cos \frac{7\pi}{4}, \sin \frac{7\pi}{4}\right)$
$= (\cos 225°, \sin 225°)$
$= \left(\frac{\sqrt{2}}{2}, -\frac{\sqrt{2}}{2}\right)$

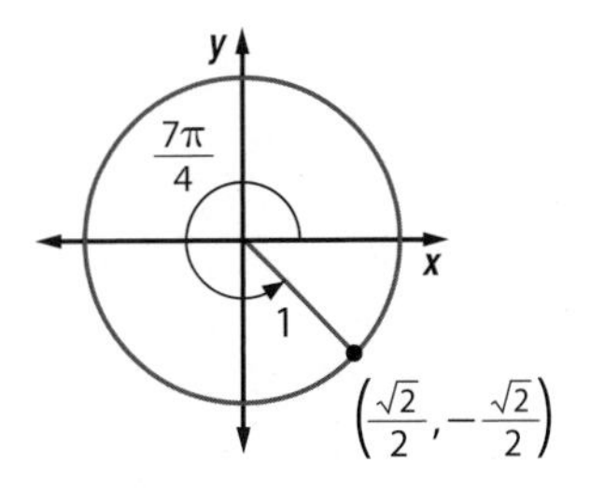

v. $\left(\cos \frac{7\pi}{6}, \sin \frac{7\pi}{6}\right)$
$= (\cos 210°, \sin 210°)$
$= \left(-\frac{\sqrt{3}}{2}, -\frac{1}{2}\right)$

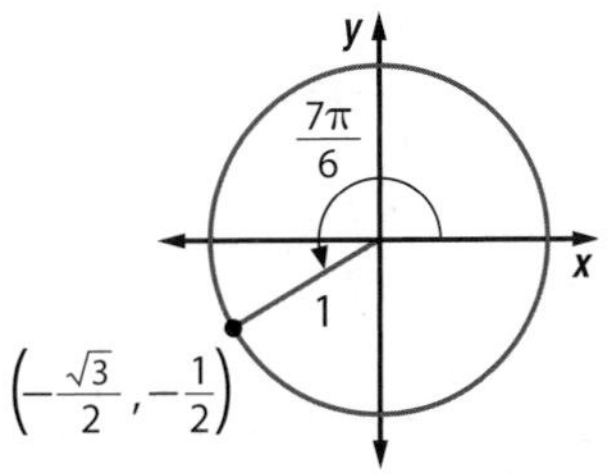

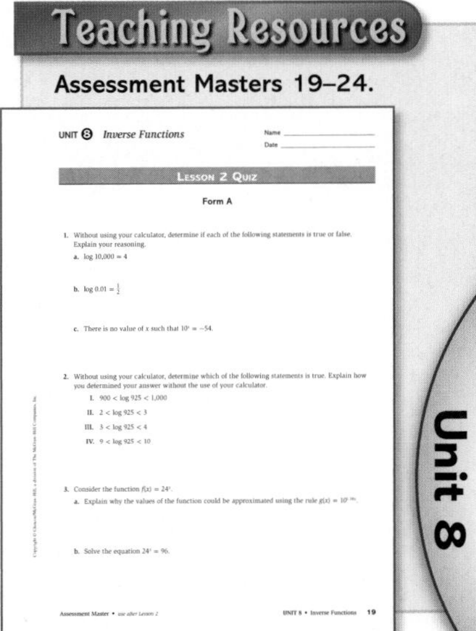

Teaching Resources

Assessment Masters 19–24.

UNIT 8 *Inverse Functions* Name ______ Date ______

Lesson 2 Quiz

Form A

1. Without using your calculator, determine if each of the following statements is true or false. Explain your reasoning.
   a. $\log 10{,}000 = 4$
   b. $\log 0.01 = \frac{1}{2}$
   c. There is no value of x such that $10^x = -54$.

2. Without using your calculator, determine which of the following statements is true. Explain how you determined your answer without the use of your calculator.
   I. $900 < \log 925 < 1{,}000$
   II. $2 < \log 925 < 3$
   III. $3 < \log 925 < 4$
   IV. $9 < \log 925 < 10$

3. Consider the function $f(x) = 24^x$.
   a. Explain why the values of the function could be approximated using the rule $g(x) = 10^{[illegible]}$.
   b. Solve the equation $24^x = 96$.

Assessment Master • *use after Lesson 2* UNIT 8 • Inverse Functions 19

Just in Time

43 **a.** The period is 2π, and the amplitude is 1.

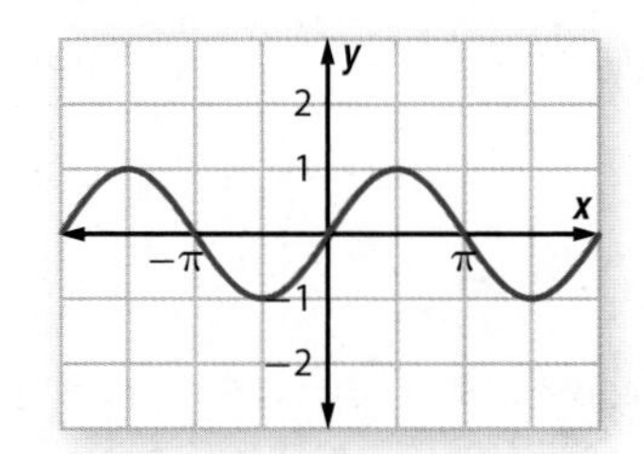

b. The period is 2π, and the amplitude is 2.

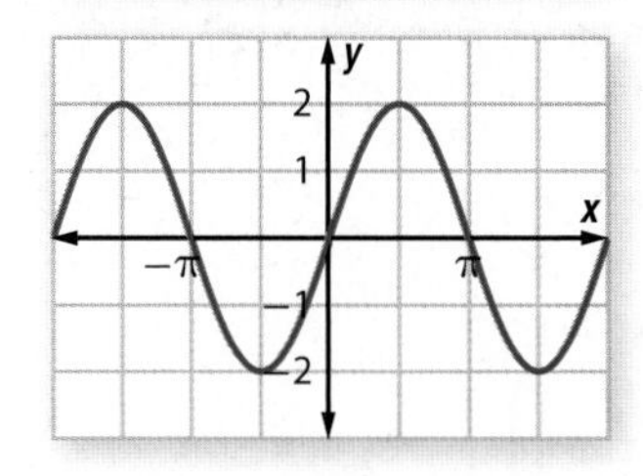

c. The period is π, and the amplitude is 1.

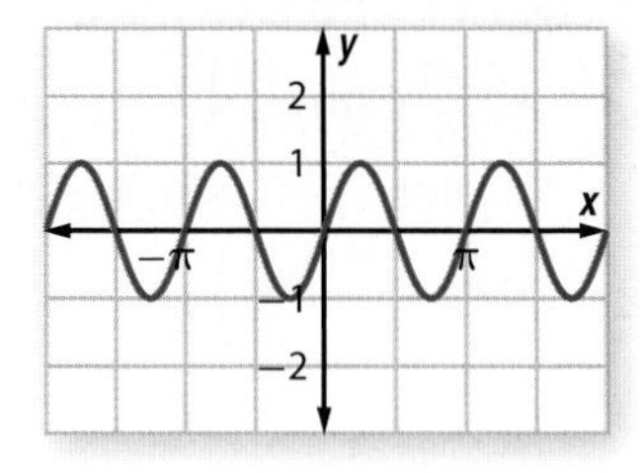

Teacher Notes

LESSON 3

Inverse Trigonometric Functions

In your previous study, you explored properties of trigonometric functions and used them to model patterns of change in periodic real-world phenomena. For example, the picture above shows Durdle Door in Dorset, England. Because of ocean tides, the water's depth d in feet under the cliff arch is a periodic function of time t in hours after noon.

- On one particular day, the depth function is

$$d(t) = 11 + 3 \sin 0.5t.$$

To find the time(s) between noon and midnight when the depth of the water is 13 feet, you need to solve $11 + 3 \sin 0.5t = 13$.

- On a later date, the depth function is

$$d(t) = 11 - 3 \cos 0.5t$$

To find the time(s) between noon and midnight when the depth of the water is 10 feet, you need to solve $11 - 3 \cos 0.5t = 10$.

Unit 8

LESSON 3

Inverse Trigonometric Functions

In previous lessons, students were introduced to the idea of an inverse of a function as an "undoing" operation or function. The sine, cosine, and tangent functions defined over their entire domains have no inverses because they are not one-to-one functions. In this lesson, the trigonometric functions and their possible inverses are revisited from a new perspective. Inverse functions are defined by limiting the domains of the sine, cosine, and tangent function to appropriate intervals over which they are one-to-one. The properties of these inverses and their graphs are one focus of this lesson.

A second focus is on the use of the inverses to solve equations in one variable that is linear in a trigonometric function, such as a function of the form $a \sin x + b = c$. The strategy for finding one solution is analogous to using logarithms to solve exponential functions. There is a new challenge, however. If a trigonometric equation has a solution, it will have infinitely many solutions. Students will investigate strategies for finding all solutions by using the solution generated by the inverse function and the symmetry and periodic properties of the trigonometric functions.

In the launch of the lesson, variation of water depth due to tides serves as a vehicle for motivating the definition of the inverse sine and cosine. The first investigation focuses on the sine function. After exploring the properties of the inverse sine and its graph, students consider methods of solving linear sine equations. In Investigation 2, the development of the inverse sine is used as a model to develop the inverses of the cosine and tangent. These inverses are then used to solve linear equations of the cosine and tangent, again drawing on the strategies already developed for linear equations of the sine.

Lesson Objectives

- Know and be able to use the definition of the inverse sine, inverse cosine, and inverse tangent functions
- Know and be able to use properties of the inverse sine, inverse cosine, and inverse tangent functions
- Use the inverse functions, to find one solution (when one exists) of $a \cdot f(bx) + c = d$, where $f(x)$ is the sine, cosine, or tangent
- Express the general solutions of a trigonometric equation in forms such as $x = k + 2\pi n$ or $x = k + 360°n$ for any integer n
- Use trigonometric equations and their solutions to model and answer questions about periodic phenomena

Solving equations like those that ask for times when tidal water has a specified depth is an inverse problem. You know the output of the function, and you need to find the corresponding input.

a What is the minimum depth of the water on the two particular days? The maximum depth?

b How could you estimate solutions for the given equations by exploring patterns in tables and graphs of function values?

c How would you approach solution of each equation by using algebraic reasoning and properties of the sine and cosine functions?

d What role could the **sin**$^{-1}$ or **cos**$^{-1}$ calculator commands have in solving these equations?

In this lesson, you will extend your study of trigonometry to consider inverses of the sine, cosine, and tangent functions. The inverse trigonometric functions will allow you to find complete solutions of trigonometric equations like those involved in predicting water depth under the cliff arch at Durdle Door.

Investigation 1 The Ups and Downs of the Sine

There are many situations exhibiting periodic change that are modeled well by variations of the sine function. Answering questions about those situations often requires solving equations involving that function. As you work on the problems of this investigation, look for answers to these questions:

How is the inverse of the sine function defined?

How can the inverse sine function be used to solve trigonometric equations?

Defining the Inverse Sine Function The next diagram shows a partial graph of the sine function, with scale on the x-axis in radians from -2π to 4π or from about -6.3 to 12.6.

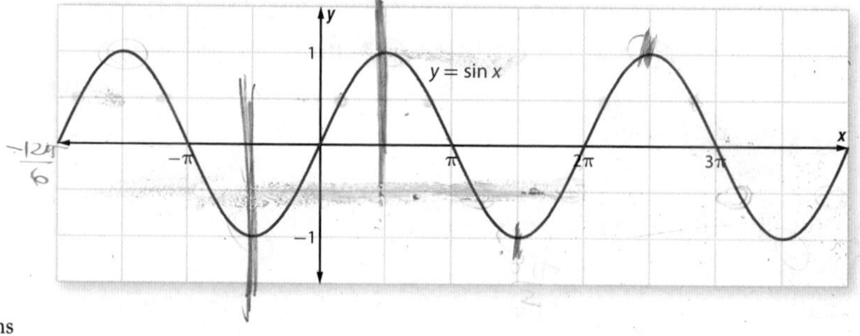

Unit 8

578 UNIT 8 • Inverse Functions

Lesson Launch

The Think About This Situation should focus student attention on the need for solving equations involving trigonometric functions. The idea to stress is that much of what is already known can be used in the solution of equations involving trigonometric functions.

Think About This Situation

a Since $-1 \leq \sin 0.5t \leq 1$, it follows that $-3 \leq 3 \sin 0.5t \leq 3$ and $8 \leq 11 + 3 \sin 0.5t \leq 14$. The maximum depth is 14 feet (this occurs when $t = \pi$). The minimum depth is 8 feet (this occurs when $t = 3\pi$).

Similarly, $-1 \leq \cos 0.5t \leq 1$; so, $-3 \leq -3 \cos 0.5t \leq 3$ and $8 \leq 11 - 3 \cos 0.5t \leq 14$. The minimum depth is 8 feet (this occurs when $t = 0$). The maximum depth is 14 feet (this occurs when $t = 0$ and $t = 2\pi$).

b To estimate the solutions to the first equation, graph or produce tables for $y = 11 + 3 \sin 0.5t$. The solutions are the t values when $y = 13$. There are two solutions in the interval [0, 12]. They are $t \approx 1.46$ (about 1:30 P.M.) and $t \approx 4.82$ (about 4:50 P.M.).

Similarly, to estimate solutions to the second equation, graph or produce tables for $y = 11 - 3 \cos 0.5t$. The solutions are the t values when $y = 10$. Again, there are two solutions in the interval [0, 12]. They are $t \approx 2.47$ (about 2:30 P.M.) and $t \approx 10.10$ (about 10:06 P.M.).

Accuracy of these answers is less important than clarity about a strategic approach that would yield the answers.

c – d Answers will vary, but students may suggest solving the equation for sin x or cos x by adding or multiplying both sides of the equations by appropriate numbers, as when solving linear equations.

Once the equation is in the form $\sin x = k$ or $\cos x = k$, the **sin**$^{-1}$ or **cos**$^{-1}$ functions can be used to find one solution. (This idea was introduced in Course 2 Unit 7, *Trigonometric Methods*, to solve for angle measures of right triangles. Subsequently, the inverse trig technology feature has been used in Course 3 Units 1 and 2. The inverse functions are developed in the investigations of this lesson.)

DIFFERENTIATION Some students will find the material of this lesson quite challenging. However, by making appropriate and timely use of calculator- or computer-generated tables and graphs or computer algebra system solve commands, even students with limited skill in trigonometry should be able to make meaningful progress on most questions of the lesson.

Teaching Resources

Transparency Master 25.

UNIT 8 *Inverse Functions*

Think About This Situation

Solving equations like those below that ask for times when tidal water has a specified depth is an inverse problem. You know the output of the function, and you need to find the corresponding input.

a What is the minimum depth of the water on the two particular days? The maximum depth?

b How could you estimate solutions for the given equations by exploring patterns in tables and graphs of function values?

c How would you approach solution of each equation by using algebraic reasoning and properties of the sine and cosine functions?

d What role could the **sin**$^{-1}$ or **cos**$^{-1}$ calculator commands have in solving these equations?

- On one particular day, the depth function is

$$d(t) = 11 + 3 \sin 0.5t.$$

To find the time(s) between noon and midnight when the depth of the water is 13 feet, you need to solve $11 + 3 \sin 0.5t = 13$.

- On a later date, the depth function is

$$d(t) = 11 - 3 \cos 0.5t.$$

To find the time(s) between noon and midnight when the depth of the water is 10 feet, you need to solve $11 - 3 \cos 0.5t = 10$.

1 Find coordinates of points on the given graph that represent solutions for the following equations. Use what you know about the sine function to find exact values for the coordinates, where possible.

Scan the given graph, a technology-generated table of $y = \sin x$, or a technology-produced graph of $y = \sin x$ to get good estimates of the coordinates as a check on your trigonometric reasoning.

a. $\sin x = 0.5$

b. $\sin x = -1$

c. $\sin x = 1$

d. $\sin x = -0.5$

2 Suppose that you were able to inspect a complete graph of $y = \sin x$.

a. What are the domain and range of $y = \sin x$?

b. For what values of k will the graph show solutions to the equation $\sin x = k$?

c. How many solutions will there be to the equation $\sin x = k$ for each value of k?

d. What do your answers to Parts a–c say about the possibility of defining an inverse for the sine function?

3 Examine the portion of the graph of $y = \sin x$ where $-\frac{\pi}{2} \leq x \leq \frac{\pi}{2}$.

a. How many solutions does $\sin x = 0.5$ have on the interval $\left[-\frac{\pi}{2}, \frac{\pi}{2}\right]$?

b. How many solutions in the interval $\left[-\frac{\pi}{2}, \frac{\pi}{2}\right]$ does $\sin x = k$ have for other values of $-1 \leq k \leq 1$?

c. Explain why $y = \sin x$ has an inverse, when x is restricted to the interval $\left[-\frac{\pi}{2}, \frac{\pi}{2}\right]$?

d. The width of the interval $\left[-\frac{\pi}{2}, \frac{\pi}{2}\right]$ is π units. Give two other intervals of width π on which $y = \sin x$ has an inverse.

4 Mathematical convention defines the **inverse sine** function as follows.

$$\sin^{-1} k = x \text{ if } \sin x = k \text{ and } -\frac{\pi}{2} \leq x \leq \frac{\pi}{2}$$

The inverse sine function is also called the *arcsine* function and written arcsin x.

a. Why do you think the definition focuses on the interval $-\frac{\pi}{2} \leq x \leq \frac{\pi}{2}$ to define values of the inverse sine function, rather than another interval of length π such as one of those you described in Part d of Problem 3?

b. What are the domain and the range of the inverse sine function?

Investigation 1 The Ups and Downs of the Sine

Many periodic phenomena are modeled by sine functions, and questions about the maxima, minima, zeroes, and arguments that correspond to specified y values give rise to sine equations. To solve such equations using symbolic reasoning, the inverse sine function is needed. Students will find a particular solution using the inverse sine and then generate all solutions using their knowledge of the symmetry and periodicity of the graph of the sine function.

The problems of this investigation help students notice that the sine function defined over all real numbers has no inverse. To define the inverse sine, the domain of $y = \sin x$ needs to be restricted to values of x for which $y = \sin x$ is one-to-one. Students should think about what intervals could work and why the standard restriction is preferable to others before settling on the standard interval $-\frac{\pi}{2} \leq x \leq \frac{\pi}{2}$.

Problems 9 and 10 develop and apply strategies for determining all solutions of equations of the form $a \sin x + b = c$. These and more complex trigonometric equations will be revisited in Course 4, so it is not necessary that all students reach complete mastery at this time.

For most of the development of inverse sine and cosine functions, we focus on real number domains and ranges—radian rather than degree measures—because that is the standard way of treating models for periodic phenomena. Investigation 1 closes with a short reprise of angle measures and trigonometric functions defined on angles. Then the work with the inverse tangent function makes further use of angle measurement in degrees.

1 **INSTRUCTIONAL NOTE** The goals of this problem are to solidify student understanding of the connection between equation solutions and graphs of related functions, to highlight some key points on the sine graph, and to plant the seed of the idea that trigonometric equations generally have multiple solutions that are related by their periods and by the symmetry of their graphs.

It is not important to have students work for many minutes to get very precise answers to these equations. Some students will not recall the special radian measures that give $\sin x = 0.5$, so scanning tables and graphs of $y = \sin x$ is quite an acceptable solution procedure at this point. Just reading approximate coordinates from the given graph is also acceptable, but it will require recognizing that scale marks π and $\frac{\pi}{2}$ are approximately 3.14 and 1.57 and estimating values between the scale marks from this.

Nonetheless, to make progress on subsequent problems more efficient, it will be useful to have a review of the solutions to the equations in this problem before moving ahead to Problem 2 and beyond. If students do not come up with the exact solutions themselves, it would be a good idea to point them out.

You could have pairs of students do two parts and then share results with a pair that completed the other two parts.

a. $\sin x = 0.5$ when $x = -\frac{11\pi}{6}, -\frac{7\pi}{6}, \frac{\pi}{6}, \frac{5\pi}{6}, \frac{13\pi}{6}$, and $\frac{17\pi}{6}$, or when $x \approx -5.76, -3.67, 0.52, 2.62, 6.81$, and 8.90.

b. $\sin x = -0.5$ when $x = -\frac{5\pi}{6}, -\frac{\pi}{6}, \frac{7\pi}{6}, \frac{11\pi}{6}, \frac{19\pi}{6}$, and $\frac{23\pi}{6}$, or when $x \approx -2.62, -0.52, 3.67, 5.76, 9.95$, and 12.04.

Teaching Resources

Student Master 26.

Defining the Inverse Sine Function
Problem 1

Unit 8

c. $\sin x = 1$ when $x = -\frac{3\pi}{2}, \frac{\pi}{2}$, and $\frac{5\pi}{2}$, or when $x \approx -4.71$, 1.57, and 7.85.

d. $\sin x = -1$ when $x = -\frac{\pi}{2}, \frac{3\pi}{2}$, and $\frac{7\pi}{2}$, or when $x \approx -1.57$, 4.71, and 11.0.

a. The domain of $y = \sin x$ is all real numbers and the range is $-1 \leq y \leq 1$.

b. The equation $\sin x = k$ has solutions for all k in $[-1, 1]$ (and only those values of k).

c. For any feasible k, there are infinitely many solutions to $\sin x = k$.

d. The sine function defined on its entire domain has no inverse, because it is clearly not one-to-one. For example, in the part of the sine graph shown in Problem 1, there are six values of x that correspond to $y = 0.5$.

3

a. The equation $\sin x = 0.5$ has one and only one solution in $\left[-\frac{\pi}{2}, \frac{\pi}{2}\right]$.

b. The equation $\sin x = k$ has one and only one solution in $\left[-\frac{\pi}{2}, \frac{\pi}{2}\right]$ for $-1 \leq k \leq 1$.

c. When x is restricted to the interval $-\frac{\pi}{2} \leq x \leq \frac{\pi}{2}$, each value of x has a unique image. The function is one-to-one on that interval. Thus, each image value (between -1 and 1) has exactly one well-defined preimage.

d. $\frac{\pi}{2} \leq x \leq \frac{3\pi}{2}$ and $-\frac{3\pi}{2} \leq x \leq -\frac{\pi}{2}$ are two other intervals of width π, lying on either side of $-\frac{\pi}{2} \leq x \leq \frac{\pi}{2}$ on which $y = \sin x$ has an inverse.

4

INSTRUCTIONAL NOTE Students will probably find the use of x and k in the development and definition of the inverse sine function a bit confusing. We have tried to use k when focusing on solvability of equations that are the motivation for an inverse function. But we have then reverted to the notational convention discussed earlier in this unit to use x as the independent variable when stating a function rule. This seems an unavoidable notational challenge in work with inverse functions. It was discussed in the notes about Lesson 1, and it also comes up when one deals with the exponential and logarithmic functions as inverse pairs.

a. Answers will vary. Any of an infinite number of intervals could be used. One good reason for using $-\frac{\pi}{2} \leq x \leq \frac{\pi}{2}$ is that it contains 0. Numbers close to zero are easier to work with than larger numbers.

b. The domain of the inverse sine function is $-1 \leq x \leq 1$ and the range is $-\frac{\pi}{2} \leq x \leq \frac{\pi}{2}$.

Teaching Resources

Student Master 27.

UNIT 8 *Inverse Functions*

The Sine and Inverse Sine Functions
Problem 4

Unit 8

Teacher Notes

c. The graph below shows the function $y = \sin x$ on a square window of $-1.57 \leq x \leq 1.57$ and $-1.57 \leq y \leq 1.57$. On a copy of this graph, sketch the graph of $y = \sin^{-1} x$. Check your sketch using technology that displays both functions on a square window.

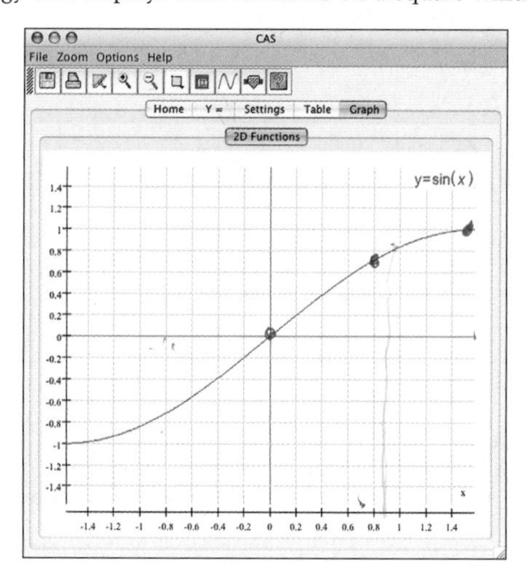

5 Use algebraic reasoning and **sin⁻¹** on a graphing calculator (2nd SIN) or the inverse sine function of a computer algebra system to find one solution for each of these trigonometric equations.

a. $\sin x = 0.9$

b. $\sin x = -0.8$

c. $5 \sin x + 9 = 12$

d. $11 + 3 \sin 0.5t = 13$

6 The introduction to this lesson proposed two models for predicting the water depth under the cliff arch at Durdle Door in Dorset, England between noon and midnight. One model was

$$d(t) = 11 + 3 \sin 0.5t,$$

where water depth is in feet and time t is in hours after noon. Use that model to analyze the pattern of change in water depth over time. Check your solutions graphically and numerically.

a. What is the depth of the water at 7:00 P.M. on the day that depth tracking begins?

b. What is the maximum depth of the water and at what time will it first occur?

c. At approximately what time(s) between noon and midnight will the water depth be 13 feet?

d. Write an inequality for the time period that the depth is more than 13 feet. Use your solution in Part c to find the solutions of this inequality.

580 UNIT 8 • Inverse Functions

c. The screen below displays the graph of $y = x$ along with the graphs of $y = \sin x$ and $y = \sin^{-1} x$. The window settings used are $-1.6 \leq x \leq 1.6$ and $-1.6 \leq y \leq 1.6$ with a scale of 0.2.

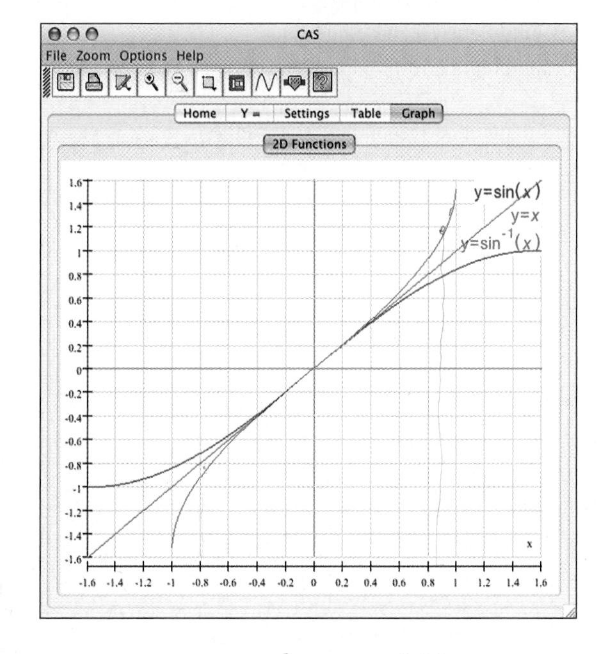

5 **a.** $x \approx 1.12$ **b.** $x \approx -0.93$

c. $x \approx 0.64$ **d.** $x \approx 1.46$

6 **a.** At 7:00 P.M., the water's depth is $d(7) = 11 + 3 \sin 0.5(7) \approx 9.9$ feet.

b. The maximum value of $\sin 0.5t$ is 1, so the maximum value of $11 + 3 \sin 0.5t$ is 14.

To find the time when the depth is maximum, solve the equation $11 + 3 \sin 0.5t = 14$, or $\sin 0.5t = 1$. The solution given by use of the inverse sine function is $0.5t = \sin^{-1} 1$; so, $0.5t = \frac{\pi}{2}$, or $t \approx 3.14$, which is about 3:08 P.M.

c. To find the time when the water depth is 13 feet, solve $11 + 3 \sin 0.5t = 13$, or $\sin 0.5t = 0.67$. The smallest positive solution is $0.5t = \sin^{-1} 0.67$, or $t \approx 1.47$, which is about 1:28 P.M.

The next positive solution can be located on the graph. It is $t \approx 4.82$, which is about 4:49 P.M.

d. The inequality is $11 + 3 \sin 0.5t \geq 13$. The solution (within the noon to midnight time period) is $1.47 \leq t \leq 4.82$, or time 1:28 P.M. to 4:49 P.M.

INSTRUCTIONAL NOTE
Although we will shortly point out that these equations have infinitely many solutions, at this point, we will be satisfied with the solution that is generated by use of the **sin^{-1}** function on a calculator or computer.

Unit 8

7 Graph $y = \sin^{-1} x$ in a window that shows the full domain and range of the function. Then use the graph to answer these questions.

a. What are the coordinates of the point corresponding to a solution of $\sin x = 0.5$?

b. What are the coordinates of the point corresponding to a solution of $\sin x = -0.8$?

c. What are the x- and y-intercepts of the graph of $y = \sin^{-1} x$?

d. Where is the function $y = \sin^{-1} x$ increasing? Where is it decreasing?

e. Where are the values of $y = \sin^{-1} x$ changing most rapidly? Where are the values changing most slowly?

8 Some consequences of the definition of the inverse sine function are important to emphasize.

a. Consider the expression $\sin (\sin^{-1} k)$.

- **i.** What are the values of the expression for $-1 \leq k \leq 1$?
- **ii.** What can you say about the expression if $k > 1$ or if $k < -1$?

b. Consider next the expression $\sin^{-1} (\sin x)$.

- **i.** What are the values of the expression for $-\frac{\pi}{2} \leq x \leq \frac{\pi}{2}$?
- **ii.** What can you say about the expression if $x > \frac{\pi}{2}$ or $x < -\frac{\pi}{2}$?

Finding All Solutions of Trigonometric Equations Your work on Problems 1 and 2 showed that trigonometric equations like $\sin x = k$ have infinitely many solutions as long as $-1 \leq k \leq 1$. The inverse sine function identifies one primary solution for each such equation, but there are certainly times when the other solutions are of interest.

For example, if the depth of water under the cliff arch at Durdle Door on one day is given by the function $d(t) = 11 + 3 \sin 0.5t$, the maximum depth of 14 feet occurs at about 3 P.M. But high tides occur at different times on the following days. It would be helpful to be able to use $d(t)$ to predict those other times of maximum water depth.

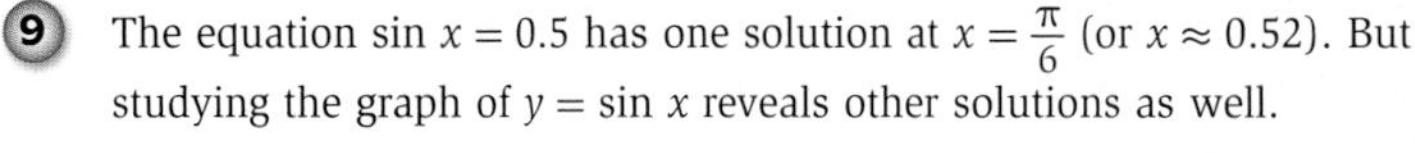

9 The equation $\sin x = 0.5$ has one solution at $x = \frac{\pi}{6}$ (or $x \approx 0.52$). But studying the graph of $y = \sin x$ reveals other solutions as well.

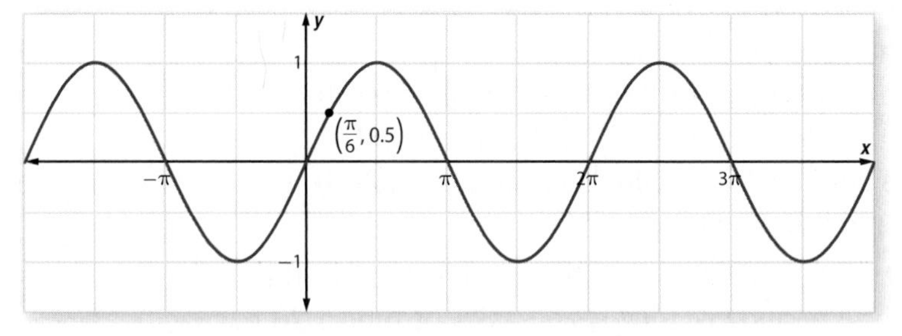

a. How does the fact that the period of $\sin x$ is 2π make it possible to identify infinitely many solutions of $\sin x = 0.5$ other than $x = \frac{\pi}{6}$? Which of those other solutions are shown on the given graph?

7

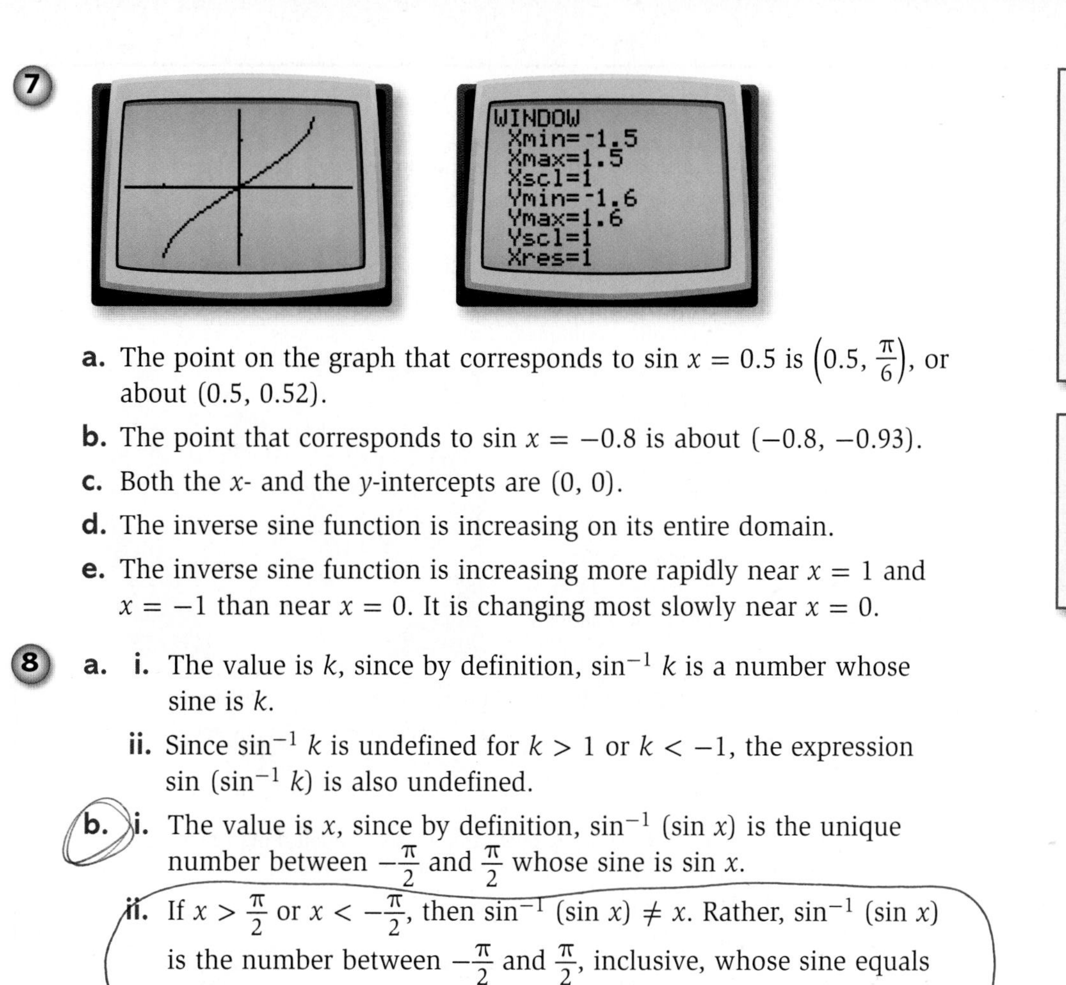

a. The point on the graph that corresponds to $\sin x = 0.5$ is $\left(0.5, \frac{\pi}{6}\right)$, or about $(0.5, 0.52)$.

b. The point that corresponds to $\sin x = -0.8$ is about $(-0.8, -0.93)$.

c. Both the x- and the y-intercepts are $(0, 0)$.

d. The inverse sine function is increasing on its entire domain.

e. The inverse sine function is increasing more rapidly near $x = 1$ and $x = -1$ than near $x = 0$. It is changing most slowly near $x = 0$.

NOTE In some books, $\sin^{-1} x$ or arcsin x, all lowercase, means the inverse sine relation. The function names are capitalized, $\text{Sin}^{-1} x$ or Arcsin x, to represent the inverse sine function. In this course, the lowercase terms always represent the inverse sine function.

INSTRUCTIONAL NOTE
You may want to emphasize that $\sin^{-1} x \neq (\sin x)^{-1}$. This is in contrast to the general rule, $\sin^n x = (\sin x)^n$, for any positive integer n.

8 **a.** **i.** The value is k, since by definition, $\sin^{-1} k$ is a number whose sine is k.

ii. Since $\sin^{-1} k$ is undefined for $k > 1$ or $k < -1$, the expression $\sin(\sin^{-1} k)$ is also undefined.

b. **i.** The value is x, since by definition, $\sin^{-1}(\sin x)$ is the unique number between $-\frac{\pi}{2}$ and $\frac{\pi}{2}$ whose sine is $\sin x$.

ii. If $x > \frac{\pi}{2}$ or $x < -\frac{\pi}{2}$, then $\sin^{-1}(\sin x) \neq x$. Rather, $\sin^{-1}(\sin x)$ is the number between $-\frac{\pi}{2}$ and $\frac{\pi}{2}$, inclusive, whose sine equals $\sin x$. For example, $\sin^{-1}\left(\sin \frac{3\pi}{2}\right) = \sin^{-1}(-1) = -\frac{\pi}{2}$.

9 **a.** The periodicity of $y = \sin x$ implies that $\sin x = \sin(x + 2\pi n)$ for all integer values of n. Thus, if $\sin x = 0.5$, then $\sin(x + 2\pi n) = 0.5$. On the given graph, you see points that represent solutions $x = \frac{\pi}{6}$, $\frac{\pi}{6} - 2\pi = -\frac{11\pi}{6}$, and $\frac{\pi}{6} + 2\pi = \frac{13\pi}{6}$.

Unit 8

b. The graph of $y = \sin x$ suggests that there are other solutions to the equation $\sin x = 0.5$ that *do not* differ from $x = \frac{\pi}{6}$ by a multiple of 2π.

   i. What is the exact radian value of the solution nearest to $x = \frac{\pi}{6}$?

   ii. What other solutions shown on the graph differ from that in part i by a multiple of 2π?

c. To find solutions to the equation $\sin x = 0.5$, other than $\frac{\pi}{6}$, students at Providence High School reasoned as follows.

Since the graph of $y = \sin x$ is symmetric about the line $x = \frac{\pi}{2}$, another solution is $\frac{\pi}{3}$ units to the right of $\frac{\pi}{2}$.

Why is the second solution $\frac{\pi}{3}$ units to the right of $\frac{\pi}{2}$? What is that solution?

d. Explain why $\frac{\pi}{6} + 2\pi n$, for any integer n, describes one set of solutions. Write a similar expression representing the remaining solutions.

10 Give formulas that describe *all* solutions to the following equations from Problem 5.

a. $\sin x = 0.9$

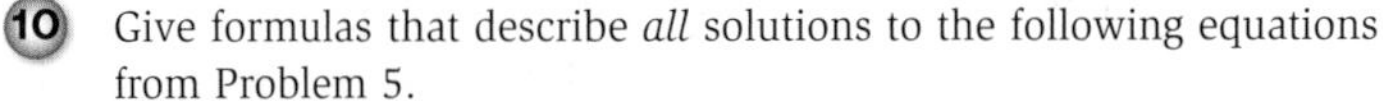

b. $\sin x = -0.8$

Inverse Sine of Degrees and Radians In situations where trigonometric functions are used to analyze properties of triangles, the angles are often measured in degrees, not radians. The inverse trigonometric functions can be applied to degree measures as well as radians.

For example, $30° = \frac{\pi}{6}$; so, $\sin 30° = \sin \frac{\pi}{6} = 0.5$. It follows that $\sin^{-1} 0.5 = 30°$, or $\frac{\pi}{6}$ radians.

11 In previous units, you learned the values of the sine function for some special angles. Use what you know about the sine of special angles and the inverse sine function to complete the following table. Use radian measures between $-\frac{\pi}{2}$ and $\frac{\pi}{2}$ and degree measures between $-90°$ and $90°$.

u	-1	$-\frac{\sqrt{3}}{2}$		$-\frac{1}{2}$	0	$\frac{1}{2}$			1
$\sin^{-1} u$ (in radians)			$-\frac{\pi}{4}$			$\frac{\pi}{6}$		$\frac{\pi}{3}$	
$\sin^{-1} u$ (in degrees)	-90					30	45		

Unit 8

582 UNIT 8 • Inverse Functions

b. **i.** The solution nearest to $\frac{\pi}{6}$ is $\frac{5\pi}{6}$. The symmetry of the graph reveals this. The symmetry line $y = \frac{\pi}{2}$ means that $\sin x = 0.5$ when $x = \frac{\pi}{2} + \left(\frac{\pi}{2} - \frac{\pi}{6}\right) = \frac{5\pi}{6}$. Alternatively, students may use the symmetry of the sine function to find that $\sin x = 0.5$ when $x = \pi - \frac{\pi}{6} = \frac{5\pi}{6}$. (This is $\frac{\pi}{6}$ units to the left of π.)

ii. The other related solutions shown on the graph are $x = \frac{5\pi}{6} - 2\pi = -\frac{7\pi}{6}$ and $\frac{5\pi}{6} + 2\pi = \frac{17\pi}{6}$.

c. **i.** Yes, the graph (if extended without bound to the left and right) has reflection symmetry about the line $x = \frac{\pi}{2}$.

ii. The graph of $y = \sin x$ is symmetric about the line $x = \frac{\pi}{2}$. Under this symmetry, $\frac{\pi}{6}$, which is $\frac{\pi}{3}$ units to the left of the line $x = \frac{\pi}{2}$, corresponds to $\frac{5\pi}{6}$ $\left(\text{which is } \frac{\pi}{3} \text{ units to the right of } x = \frac{\pi}{2}\right)$.

d. **i.** The period of the sine function is 2π, so the graph repeats itself over intervals of length 2π. Since $\sin\left(\frac{\pi}{6}\right) = 0.5$, the sine of $\frac{\pi}{6}$ plus any multiple of 2π will also equal 0.5.

ii. The remaining solutions will be of the form $\frac{5\pi}{6} + 2\pi n$ for any integer n.

10 **a.** $\sin x = 0.9$ has one solution $x \approx 1.12$ and thus infinitely many solutions in the form $1.12 + 2\pi n$ for any integer n. Using the symmetry of the graph of $y = \sin x$, you can see that there is a related solution at about $\frac{\pi}{2} + \left(\frac{\pi}{2} - 1.12\right)$ or $\pi - 1.12$, which is approximately 2.02. This implies that there are infinitely many solutions in the form $2.02 + 2\pi n$ for any integer n.

b. $\sin x = -0.8$ has one solution $x \approx -0.93$ and thus infinitely many solutions in the form $-0.93 + 2\pi n$ for any integer n. Using the symmetry of the graph of $y = \sin x$, you can see that there is a related solution at about $-\pi + 0.93$ (0.93 units to the right of $-\pi$) or $-\frac{\pi}{2} - \left(-0.93 - \left(-\frac{\pi}{2}\right)\right)$. This is about -2.21. This implies that there are infinitely many solutions in the form $-2.21 + 2\pi n$ for any integer n.

11

u	-1	$-\frac{\sqrt{3}}{2}$	$-\frac{\sqrt{2}}{2}$	$-\frac{1}{2}$	0	$\frac{1}{2}$	$\frac{\sqrt{2}}{2}$	$\frac{\sqrt{3}}{3}$	1
$\sin^{-1} u$ (in radians)	$-\frac{\pi}{2}$	$-\frac{\pi}{3}$	$-\frac{\pi}{4}$	$-\frac{\pi}{6}$	0	$\frac{\pi}{6}$	$\frac{\pi}{4}$	$\frac{\pi}{3}$	$\frac{\pi}{2}$
$\sin^{-1} u$ (in degrees)	-90	-60	-45	-30	0	30	45	60	90

Teaching Resources

Student Master 28.

UNIT 8 Inverse Functions

Inverse Sine of Degrees and Radians

Problems 11 and 12

Unit 8

12 Use algebra and trigonometry to find all solutions of the following equations in both degrees and radians. Give exact solutions, if possible.

a. $2 \sin x = -\sqrt{3}$

b. $2 \sin x - 3 = 1$

c. $3 \sin x + 2 = 4$

d. $5 - 3 \sin x = 2$

Summarize the Mathematics

In this investigation, you learned about the inverse sine function and some of its properties. You also used the inverse sine function to solve linear equations involving the sine.

a The sine function defined over the set of real numbers has no inverse function. Why not?

b Explain how the inverse sine function was defined in this lesson in order to overcome the difficulties you noted in Part a.

c Describe the conditions under which $\sin^{-1} (\sin x) = x$. Explain your reasoning.

d Consider an equation of the form $a \sin x + b = c$ which is linear in $\sin x$.

- **i.** How is solving this equation similar to and different from solving $ax + b = c$ which is linear in x?
- **ii.** Under what conditions on a, b, and c does $a \sin x + b = c$ have solutions?
- **iii.** If you know one solution, how many solutions will there be? Describe how to find all solutions.

Be prepared to share your thinking and procedures with the class.

Check Your Understanding

Use your understanding of the inverse sine function to help complete these tasks.

a. Determine whether the following statements are true or false. Explain how you know without use of a calculator or computer inverse sine function.

i. $\sin^{-1} 1 = \frac{\pi}{2}$

ii. $\sin^{-1} 0 = 0$

iii. $\sin^{-1} (-1) = -\frac{\pi}{2}$

iv. $\sin^{-1} \left(\frac{1}{\sqrt{2}}\right) = 45°$

v. $\sin^{-1} \left(\frac{\sqrt{3}}{2}\right) = \frac{2\pi}{3}$

vi. $\sin^{-1} \left(\frac{1}{2}\right) = 150°$

b. Use algebra and trigonometry to determine whether each equation has a solution for x. If so, find all solutions in radians. Give exact solutions, if possible.

i. $2 \sin x = \sqrt{2}$

ii. $2 \sin x - 2 = 1$

iii. $3 \sin x + 2 = 0$

iv. $2 - 3 \sin x = 2$

Unit 8

12 **a.** Primary solution: $x = -\frac{\pi}{3}$, or $-60°$, leading to other solutions $x = -\frac{\pi}{3} + 2\pi n$, or $x = -60° + 360°n$ for any integer n.

The solution related to $-\frac{\pi}{3}$, or $-60°$, by symmetry in the graph of $y = \sin x$ is $x = -\frac{2\pi}{3}$, or $-120°$, leading to other solutions $x = -\frac{2\pi}{3} + 2\pi n$, or $x = -120° + 360°n$.

b. No solutions; the given equation is equivalent to $\sin x = 2$ and there are no values of x that give $\sin x = 2$.

c. Primary solution comes from $x = \sin^{-1}\left(\frac{2}{3}\right) \approx 0.73$, or $42°$, leading to other solutions $0.73 + 2\pi n$, or $42° + 360°n$ for any integer n.

The solution related to 0.73, or 42°, by symmetry in the graph of $y = \sin x$ is $x \approx 2.41$, or $138°$, leading to other solutions $x \approx 2.41 + 2\pi n$, or $x \approx 138° + 360°n$.

d. No solutions; the given equation is equivalent to $\sin x = \frac{4}{3}$ and the sine function is never greater than 1.

Summarize the Mathematics

a The sine function defined over the set of real numbers is not a one-to-one function, so it has no inverse. Since the sine function assigns the same output to all inputs that differ by a multiple of 2π (and many others related by symmetry), it is impossible to find the single value of x that leads to any particular given value of $\sin x$.

b To avoid the problem described in Part a, the domain of the sine function is restricted to $-\frac{\pi}{2} \leq x \leq \frac{\pi}{2}$. On this interval, the sine function is one-to-one and its inverse is defined to be the inverse sine function.

c $\sin^{-1}(\sin x) = x$ provided $-\frac{\pi}{2} \leq x \leq \frac{\pi}{2}$. In other cases, $\sin^{-1}(\sin x) = x_0$, where x_0 is the number in $\left[-\frac{\pi}{2}, \frac{\pi}{2}\right]$ for which $\sin x_0 = \sin x$.

d **i.** In the case of $ax + b = c$, you transform the equation to an equivalent form $x = k$ and you are done. Similarly, to solve $a \sin x + b = c$, you begin by transforming the equation to the form $\sin x = k$, but you are not done. You must still write a general expression or expressions for the solutions to $\sin x = k$. There will only be one solution for $ax + b = c$ provided $a \neq 0$, but $a \sin x + b = c$ has either no solutions or an infinite number of solutions.

ii. The equation $a \sin x + b = c$ has solutions provided $\left|\frac{c - b}{a}\right| \leq 1$.

Teaching Resources

Transparency Master 29.

UNIT 8 *Inverse Functions*

Summarize the Mathematics

In this investigation, you learned about the inverse sine function and some of its properties. You also used the inverse sine function to solve linear equations involving the sine.

a The sine function defined over the set of real numbers has no inverse function. Why not?

b Explain how the inverse sine function was defined in this lesson in order to overcome the difficulties you noted in Part a.

c Describe the conditions under which $\sin^{-1}(\sin x) = x$. Explain your reasoning.

d Consider an equation of the form $a \sin x + b = c$ which is linear in $\sin x$.

i. How is solving this equation similar to and different from solving $ax + b = c$ which is linear in x?

ii. Under what conditions on a, b, and c does $a \sin x + b = c$ have solutions?

iii. If you know one solution, how many solutions will there be? Describe how to find all solutions.

Be prepared to share your thinking and procedures with the class.

Transparency Master • use with pages 583 UNIT 8 • Inverse Functions 29

INSTRUCTIONAL NOTE
Focus student thinking so they recognize that the form of the equation $a \sin x + b = c$ is linear in $\sin x$.

Unit 8

MATH TOOLKIT Students should record the definition of the inverse sine function, a process for solving sine equations, and an explanation of why sine equations may either have no solutions or an infinite number of solutions.

iii. If there is a solution, there are infinitely many because of the periodicity and symmetry of the sine function. One solution is $\sin^{-1}\left(\frac{c-b}{a}\right)$ on the interval $[0, \pi]$ or $[0°, 180°]$. Additional solutions are found by adding multiples of 2π to the solution on $[0, \pi]$. If $\left|\frac{c-b}{a}\right| \neq 1$, a second solution (that does not differ from the first by a multiple of 2π) can be found by using the symmetry of the sine curve. All solutions are again found by adding multiples of 2π to this second solution.

Check Your Understanding

a. **i.** True: $\sin^{-1} 1 = \frac{\pi}{2}$ because 1 is the maximum value of $y = \sin x$, which occurs when x is $\frac{\pi}{2}$.

ii. True: $\sin^{-1} 0 = 0$ because $\sin 0 = 0$.

iii. True: $\sin^{-1}(-1) = -\frac{\pi}{2}$ because -1 is the minimum value of $\sin x$ and $\sin\left(-\frac{\pi}{2}\right) = -1$.

iv. True: $\sin^{-1}\left(\frac{1}{\sqrt{2}}\right) = 45°$ because $\sin 45° = \frac{1}{\sqrt{2}}$.

b. **i.** $2 \sin x = \sqrt{2}$

$\sin x = \frac{\sqrt{2}}{2}$

One solution is $\sin^{-1}\left(\frac{\sqrt{2}}{2}\right) = \frac{\pi}{4}$; by symmetry of the sine curve, a second solution is $\frac{\pi}{2} + \frac{\pi}{4} = \frac{3\pi}{4}$. All solutions are of one of two forms: $\frac{\pi}{4} + 2\pi n$ or $\frac{3\pi}{4} + 2\pi n$ for any integer n.

ii. $2 \sin x - 2 = 1$

$\sin x = 1.5$

Since 1.5 is outside the range of the sine function, there is no solution.

iii. $3 \sin x + 2 = 0$

$\sin x = -\frac{2}{3}$

One solution is $\sin^{-1}\left(-\frac{2}{3}\right) \approx -0.7297$. By symmetry, a second solution is $-\pi + 0.7297 \approx -2.4119$. All solutions will have one of two forms: $-0.7297 + 2\pi n$ or $-2.4119 + 2\pi n$ for any integer n.

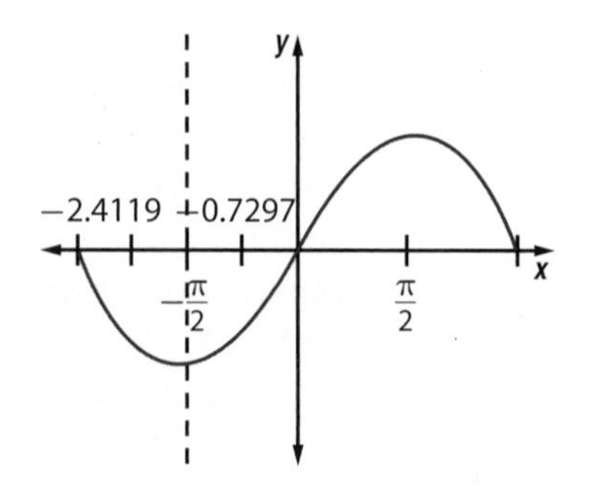

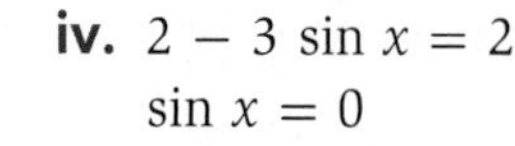

iv. $2 - 3 \sin x = 2$

$\sin x = 0$

One solution is $\sin^{-1} 0 = 0$. A second solution is $\frac{\pi}{2} + \left(\frac{\pi}{2} - 0\right) = \pi$. All solutions will be multiples of π, that is, they will have the form πn for any integer n.

INSTRUCTIONAL NOTE
For part iv, some students might not recognize that $0 + 2n\pi$ and $\pi + 2n\pi$ (even and odd multiples of π respectively) together represent all integer multiples of π.

Teacher Notes

Investigation 2 Inverses of the Cosine and Tangent

In Investigation 1, you developed the inverse sine function and used it to find solutions of equations involving the sine. Inverses of the cosine and tangent functions can be used in the same way to answer questions about phenomena that have been modeled with those functions.

As you work on the problems of this investigation, look for answers to these questions:

How are the inverses of the cosine and tangent functions defined?

How can the inverse cosine and inverse tangent functions be used to solve equations involving the cosine or tangent?

Defining and Using the Inverse Cosine Function

Suppose that an amusement park is planning a new roller coaster with part of its track shaped like the graph of $y = 12 \cos 0.1x + 6$, where x and y are in meters and $0 \leq x \leq 100$.

For positive values of y, the roller coaster track is above ground. For negative values of y, it is below ground in a tunnel. In order to find the horizontal distance to the point where the roller coaster enters the tunnel, you need to solve $12 \cos 0.1x + 6 = 0$ or its equivalent $\cos 0.1x = -0.5$. An inverse cosine function would help to find the required value of x.

1 Examine the following graph of $y = \cos x$.

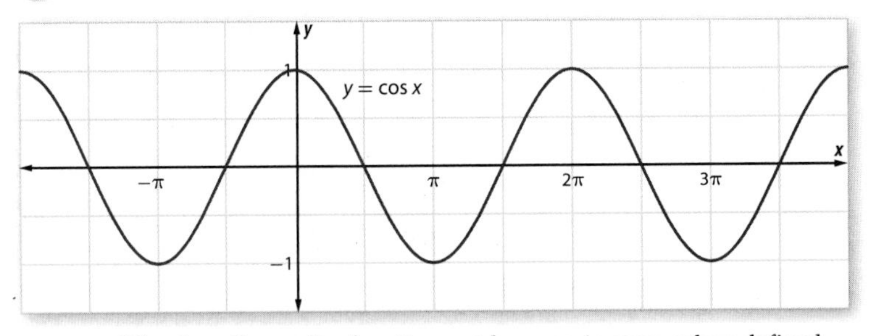

a. Why does the cosine function not have an inverse, when defined on its entire domain?

b. Would the cosine function have an inverse if it was defined on these restricted domains?

i. $-\frac{\pi}{2} \leq x \leq \frac{\pi}{2}$ **ii.** $0 \leq x \leq \pi$

iii. $-\pi \leq x \leq 0$ **iv.** $\frac{\pi}{2} \leq x \leq \frac{3\pi}{2}$

c. Of the feasible restricted domains for $y = \cos x$, which seems most useful for defining $\cos^{-1} x$?

Unit 8

584 UNIT 8 • Inverse Functions

Investigation 2 Inverses of the Cosine and Tangent

This investigation develops the inverse cosine and inverse tangent functions in much the same way that the inverse sine was treated in Investigation 1. The types of applications and equations that students solve are similar to those in the first investigation.

1. **a.** The cosine function is not a one-to-one function—no image points have unique preimages, making it impossible to define an inverse cosine function.

   b. **i.** The cosine does not have an inverse if restricted to the interval $-\frac{\pi}{2} \leq x \leq \frac{\pi}{2}$ because it is not one-to-one there.

   ii. The cosine does have an inverse if restricted to the interval $0 \leq x \leq \pi$ because it is one-to-one there.

   iii. The cosine does have an inverse if restricted to the interval $-\pi \leq x \leq 0$ because it is one-to-one there.

   iv. The cosine does not have an inverse if restricted to the interval $\frac{\pi}{2} \leq x \leq \frac{3\pi}{2}$ because it is not one-to-one there.

The standard mathematical definition of the **inverse cosine** function is

$$\cos^{-1} k = x \text{ if } \cos x = k \text{ and } 0 \leq x \leq \pi.$$

The inverse cosine function is also called the *arccosine* function and written arccos x.

2 Analyze the properties of the inverse cosine function.

a. What are the domain and range of $y = \cos^{-1} x$?

b. What window will show a complete graph of $y = \cos^{-1} x$?

c. Sketch a graph of $y = \cos^{-1} x$. Label the x- and y-intercepts.

d. Label the point on the graph of $y = \cos^{-1} x$ that corresponds to a solution of $\cos x = 0.5$.

e. Label the point on the graph of $y = \cos^{-1} x$ that shows a solution of $\cos x = -0.3$.

3 Use the inverse cosine function, a graph of $\cos x$, and reasoning like what you applied in studying the sine and inverse sine functions to find *all solutions* for these equations.

a. $\cos x = \frac{1}{\sqrt{2}}$

b. $6 \cos x = 3$

c. $2 \cos x + \sqrt{3} = 0$

d. $5 \cos 0.3x = 4$

4 The roller coaster described at the start of this investigation had a track matching the graph of $y = 12 \cos 0.1x + 6$, where x and y are in meters and $0 \leq x \leq 100$. For positive values of y, the roller coaster track is above ground. For negative values of y, it is below ground in a tunnel.

a. Graph the function that represents this portion of the track.

b. At what point does the track reach its maximum height?

c. Write and solve an equation that gives the horizontal distance traveled when the roller coaster first enters the tunnel.

d. What are the lowest point(s) of the track? At what value(s) of x does it occur?

e. Write and solve an inequality to find where the roller coaster is in the tunnel.

c. It seems most reasonable to restrict the domain of cos x to the positive interval $0 \leq x \leq \pi$ so that inverse cosines give outputs that are small positive numbers and 0 is included. This is especially appropriate when one wants to deal with triangles that have angle measures between 0 and π radians, or between 0 and 180°.

2 **a.** Domain: $[-1, 1]$
Range: $[0, \pi]$

b. The window Xmin = −1, Xmax = 1, Ymin = 0, Ymax = π will show the full graph.

c.

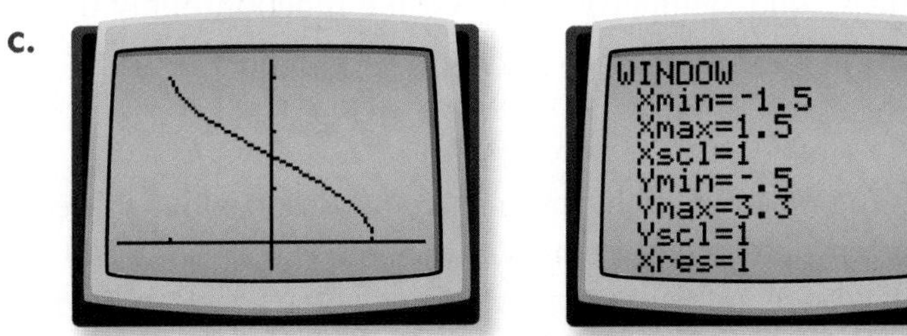

d. The point on the graph that corresponds to the solution of cos $x = 0.5$ is $\left(0.5, \frac{\pi}{3}\right)$, or approximately (0.5, 1.05).

e. The point on the graph that corresponds to the solution of cos $x = -0.3$ is approximately (−0.3, 1.9).

TECHNOLOGY NOTE Your students may have noticed using technology that the graph of the inverse cosine does not quite reach its endpoints, (1, 0) and $\left(-1, \frac{\pi}{2}\right)$. This is due to pixel limitations of the screen as the graph approaches ±1.

3 **INSTRUCTIONAL NOTE** The text does not give much scaffolding for students to generalize their approach to solution of equations involving the sine function to equations involving the cosine function. Depending on your judgment about the strength of your class, you might choose to provide some guidance by reviewing how one finds all solutions for an equation like $3 + 5 \sin x = 7$. In particular, review the way that one uses symmetry of the graph of $y = \sin x$ to find the solution paired with that produced by the inverse sine function. You might choose to remind students what the graph of $y = \cos x$ looks like and the kind of symmetry (about $x = 0$) it has. In fact, the symmetry about the y-axis makes finding the paired solutions easier with cosine than with the sine.

Once again, it probably makes sense to divide the work on these four equations among different pairs or groups of students and then have them discuss their results.

a. The primary solution is $x = \cos^{-1}\left(\frac{1}{\sqrt{2}}\right)$ which means $x = \frac{\pi}{4}$, or 45°. The periodicity of the cosine function implies other solutions in the general form $x = \frac{\pi}{4} + 2\pi n$ for any integer n.

Symmetry of the graph for $y = \cos x$ locates a solution $-\frac{\pi}{4}$ which implies other solutions in the form $x = -\frac{\pi}{4} + 2\pi n$ for any integer n.

b. The primary solution is $x = \cos^{-1} 0.5$ which means $x = \frac{\pi}{3}$, or 60°. The periodicity of the cosine function implies other solutions in the general form $x = \frac{\pi}{3} + 2\pi n$ for any integer n.

Symmetry of the graph for $y = \cos x$ locates a solution $-\frac{\pi}{3}$ which implies other solutions in the form $x = -\frac{\pi}{3} + 2\pi n$.

Unit 8

c. The primary solution is $x = \cos^{-1}\left(-\frac{\sqrt{3}}{2}\right)$ which means $x = -\frac{5\pi}{6}$, or $-150°$ (if one reasons only about angles). If you use the **cos⁻¹** function on a calculator, you will get $\cos^{-1}\left(-\frac{\sqrt{3}}{2}\right) \approx 2.618$ which is an approximate value for $\frac{5\pi}{6}$.

The periodicity and symmetry of the cosine function implies other solutions in the general form $x = -\frac{5\pi}{6} + 2\pi n$ and $x = \frac{5\pi}{6} + 2\pi n$ for any integer n.

d. The primary solution is when $0.3x = \cos^{-1} 0.8$, or when $x \approx 2.15$. The periodicity and symmetry of the cosine function imply other solutions in the general form $x \approx 2.15 + \frac{20}{3}\pi n$ and $x \approx -2.15 + \frac{20}{3}\pi n$ for any integer n.

DIFFERENTIATION The next two problems are nice applications but challenging! You might choose to complete one or both as a whole class activity so that you can provide appropriate guidance in the solution processes. Alternatively, a Student Master is provided with the graph over the specified domain. Encourage students to use a combination of algebraic reasoning and reasoning using the symmetry of the cosine function to determine solutions as outlined below.

4 **a. Roller Coaster Profile**

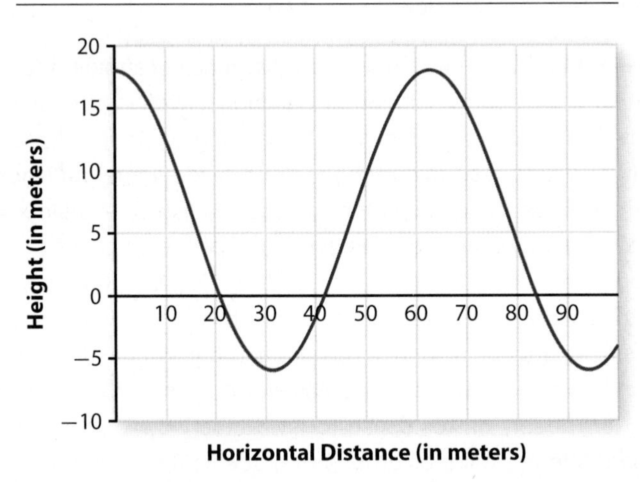

b. The coaster reaches its maximum height of 18 meters when $\cos 0.1x = 1$. In the given domain, this occurs when $0.1x$ is a multiple of 2π or when $x = 0$ and about $\frac{2\pi}{0.1}$, or 62.8. (Finding the maximum points also provides the period, the absolute value of the difference between the x-coordinates of these points. In this case, $|62.8 - 0| = 62.8$.)

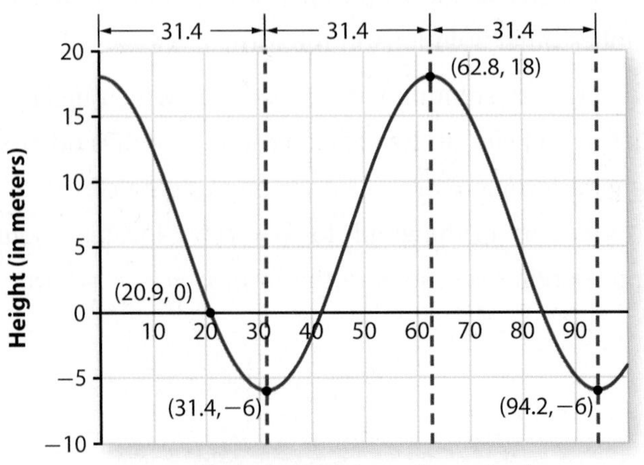

c. The solution for $12 \cos 0.1x + 6 = 0$ is when $0.1x = \cos^{-1}(-0.5)$, or $x \approx 20.9$ meters.

d. The minimum height is -6 meters. Sketching the symmetry lines as shown in the graph above, you can conclude that the x-coordinates of the minimum parts are $\frac{62.8}{2} = 31.4$ and $62.8 + 31.4 = 94.2$. $f(31.4) = -6$ and $f(94.2) = -6$.

Algebraically, the minimum occurs when $\cos 0.1x = -1$ or when $0.1x$ is an odd multiple of π. In the given domain, the minimum height is -6 meters when $x = \frac{\pi}{0.1} = 10\pi$ and $\frac{3\pi}{0.1} = 30\pi$, or about 31.4 meters and 94.2 meters.

e. To find the horizontal distance when the coaster is in the tunnel, one needs to solve $12 \cos 0.1x + 6 < 0$. The solution intervals are approximately (20.9, 41.9) and (83.7, 100).

To get a complete solution, one needs to find the points where the coaster enters and emerges from the tunnel and where it re-enters farther along for the remainder of these domain values. Using the symmetry of the graph about the vertical lines through minimum and maximum points on the graph, you can deduce that the coaster emerges from underground first at $x = 31.4 + (31.4 - 20.9) = 41.9$ meters. You can use the period of 62.8 to find where the roller coaster re-enters, at $x = 20.9 + 62.8 = 83.7$ meters.

So, the roller coaster is in the tunnel for $20.9 \leq x < 41.9$ and $83.7 < x \leq 100$.

5 At the start of this lesson, the function $d(t) = 11 - 3 \cos 0.5t$ was proposed as a model of change in tidal water depth at Durdle Door.

a. If $t = 0$ indicates noon on one day, what is the water depth at that time?

b. Use the inverse cosine to find the first time after noon when the water depth is 10 feet.

c. Use a graph of $d(t) = 11 - 3 \cos 0.5t$ and the inverse cosine function to find *all times* after noon when the water depth is 10 feet.

Defining and Using the Inverse Tangent Function If you have ever traveled on a highway with steep hills, you have probably seen signs like the one on the right. It is quite likely that the 9% grade figure was not found by sighting from top to bottom of the hill with a protractor. Instead, road engineers probably used other instruments to measure the horizontal and vertical distances involved.

If the 9% figure represents the slope of the road, it is also the tangent of $\angle A$ in the following diagram.

B
slope = 0.09
C
A

To find the measure of that angle, you need to solve the equation $\tan x = 0.09$. An inverse tangent function would provide the solution.

6 Examine the following graph of $y = \tan x$.

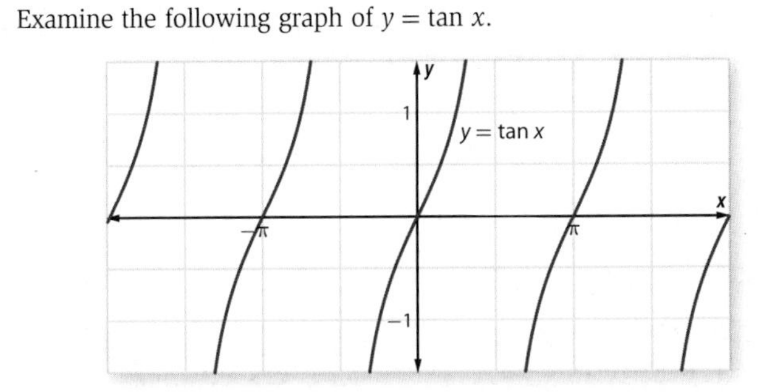

The graph of $y = \tan x$ is different from the sine and cosine functions in several ways.

a. What are the domain and range of $y = \tan x$?

b. Does $y = \tan x$ have any asymptotes? Explain.

c. What is the period of $y = \tan x$?

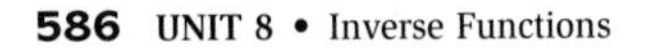

586 UNIT 8 • Inverse Functions

5 **a.** $d(0) = 8$

b. **Solve:** $11 - 3 \cos 0.5t = 10$

$0.5t = \cos^{-1}\left(\frac{1}{3}\right)$

$0.5t \approx 1.23$

$t \approx 2.46$ hours

So, the water depth is 10 feet at approximately 2:28 P.M.

c. The inverse cosine function used in Part b provides the solution $t \approx 2.46$. Use the symmetry of a graph to help find all solutions as follows.

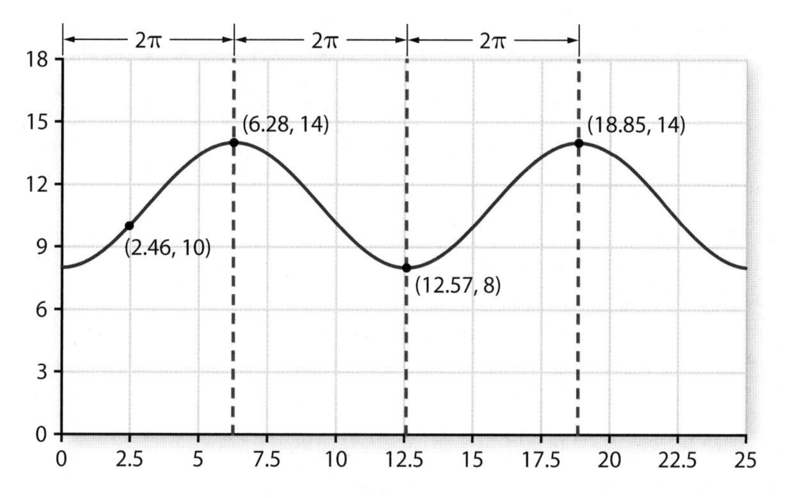

The period of $11 - 3 \cos 0.5t$ is 4π, not 2π. So, one set of times is given by $2.46 + 4\pi n$ for any integer n.

To find the second set of times, use symmetry of the graph about the maximum point ($t = 2\pi$) to find the y-coordinate that is paired with $t = 2.46$. That point is $6.28 + (6.28 - 2.46) \approx 10.10$, or about 10:06 P.M. This implies other times given by $10.1 + 4\pi n$.

6 **a.** The domain of $\tan x$ is all real numbers except odd multiples of $\frac{\pi}{2}$, or 90°. The range is all real numbers.

b. The graph appears to show vertical asymptotes at $k \cdot \frac{\pi}{2}$, where k is an integer. The tangent values are defined on the unit circle as the ratio of the y-coordinate to the x-coordinate of a point on the terminal side of the angle. This means that $\tan \theta$ will be undefined when the x-coordinate is zero. This occurs for an angle of $\frac{\pi}{2}$ and integer multiples of $\frac{\pi}{2}$.

Unit 8

d. Why does the tangent function not have an inverse, when defined on its entire domain?

e. Would the tangent function have an inverse if it was defined on these restricted domains? Why or why not?

i. $-\frac{\pi}{2} < x < \frac{\pi}{2}$

ii. $-\pi < x < \pi$

iii. $-\frac{3}{2}\pi < x < 0$

iv. $\frac{\pi}{2} < x < \frac{3\pi}{2}$

f. Of the feasible restricted domains in Part d for $y = \tan x$, which seems most useful for defining $\tan^{-1} x$?

The standard mathematical definition of the **inverse tangent** function is

$$\tan^{-1} k = x \text{ if } \tan x = k \text{ and } -\frac{\pi}{2} < x < \frac{\pi}{2}.$$

The inverse tangent function is also called the *arctangent* function and written arctan x.

7 Analyze properties of the inverse tangent function.

a. What are the domain and range of $y = \tan^{-1} x$.

b. Use a calculator or computer function graphing tool in radian mode to help make a sketch of $y = \tan^{-1} x$ in a window like $-5 \leq x \leq 5$ and $-2 \leq y \leq 2$. Then add the following features to your sketch.

i. Sketch the asymptotes.

ii. Label the point on the graph that represents a solution of $\tan x = 1$?

iii. Label the point on the graph that represents a solution of $\tan x = 3.5$.

iv. Label the x- and y-intercepts.

8 With slight adjustments, the strategies that you used to solve equations involving the sine and cosine will work to solve equations involving the tangent. Find all solutions of the following equations in both radians and degrees. Give exact solutions, if possible.

After you find one solution, remember the pattern in the graph of $y = \tan x$ and its period to find all others.

a. $\tan x = 1$

b. $\sqrt{3} \tan x = 1$

c. $-2 \tan x - 3 = 5$

d. $\sqrt{3} \tan x + 4 = -1$

9 To find the angle of depression of a road with 9% grade, you need to solve the equation $\tan x = 0.09$. Find the solution to this equation that makes sense in the problem situation. Give your answer in degrees and in radians.

c. The tangent function has period π.

d. Every real number (range value) is the image of infinitely many different preimage (domain) values, so it is impossible to identify *the* preimage when given an image value.

e. **i.** Yes, there is exactly one domain value for each range value.

ii. No, because one does not get a one-to-one function on this interval.

iii. No, because one does not get a one-to-one function on this interval.

iv. Yes, there is exactly one domain value for each range value.

f. $-\frac{\pi}{2} < x < \frac{\pi}{2}$ includes 0 and numbers of small absolute value. When using the inverse tangent function to work with triangles, this will include angles from $-90°$ to $90°$. While a more desirable domain might be 0 to π, or $0°$ to $180°$, that is not possible due to the discontinuity of the tangent function at odd multiples of $\frac{\pi}{2}$, or $90°$.

7 **a.** $y = \tan^{-1} x$ has domain all real numbers and range $-\frac{\pi}{2} < y < \frac{\pi}{2}$.

INSTRUCTIONAL NOTE
Emphasize that the domain of the tangent is restricted to $-\frac{\pi}{2} < x < \frac{\pi}{2}$, while the sine is restricted to $-\frac{\pi}{2} \leq x \leq \frac{\pi}{2}$.

b.

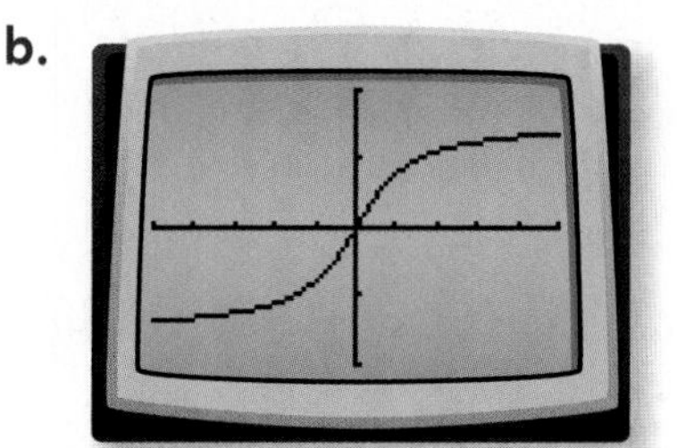

c. **i.** See the graph at the right.

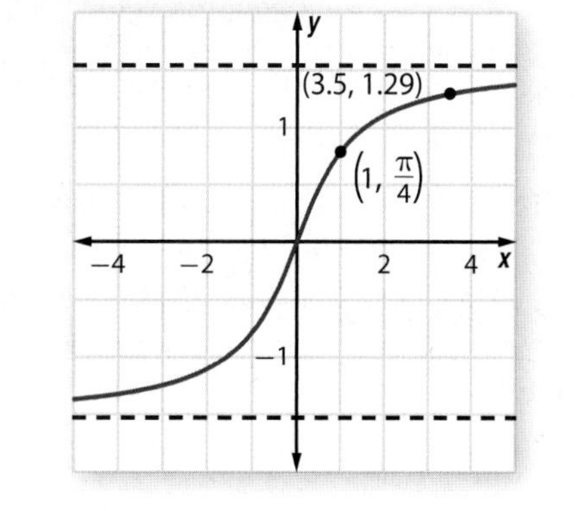

ii. The point on the graph that corresponds to a solution of $\tan x = 1$ is $\left(1, \frac{\pi}{4}\right)$.

iii. The point on the graph that corresponds to a solution of $\tan x = 3.5$ is $(3.5, 1.29)$.

iv. The x- and y-intercepts are both $(0, 0)$.

8 In the solutions below, n represents an integer.

a. $\frac{\pi}{4} + \pi n$, or $45° + 180°n$

b. $\frac{\pi}{6} + \pi n$, or $30° + 180°n$

c. $\tan^{-1}(-4) \approx -1.33 + \pi n$, or $-76° + 180°n$

d. $\tan^{-1}\left(-\frac{5}{\sqrt{3}}\right) \approx -1.24 + \pi n$, or $-71° + 180°n$

9 The angle of depression for a road with downgrade 9% would be $\tan^{-1} 0.09 \approx 0.0898$ radians, or $5.1428°$.

Unit 8

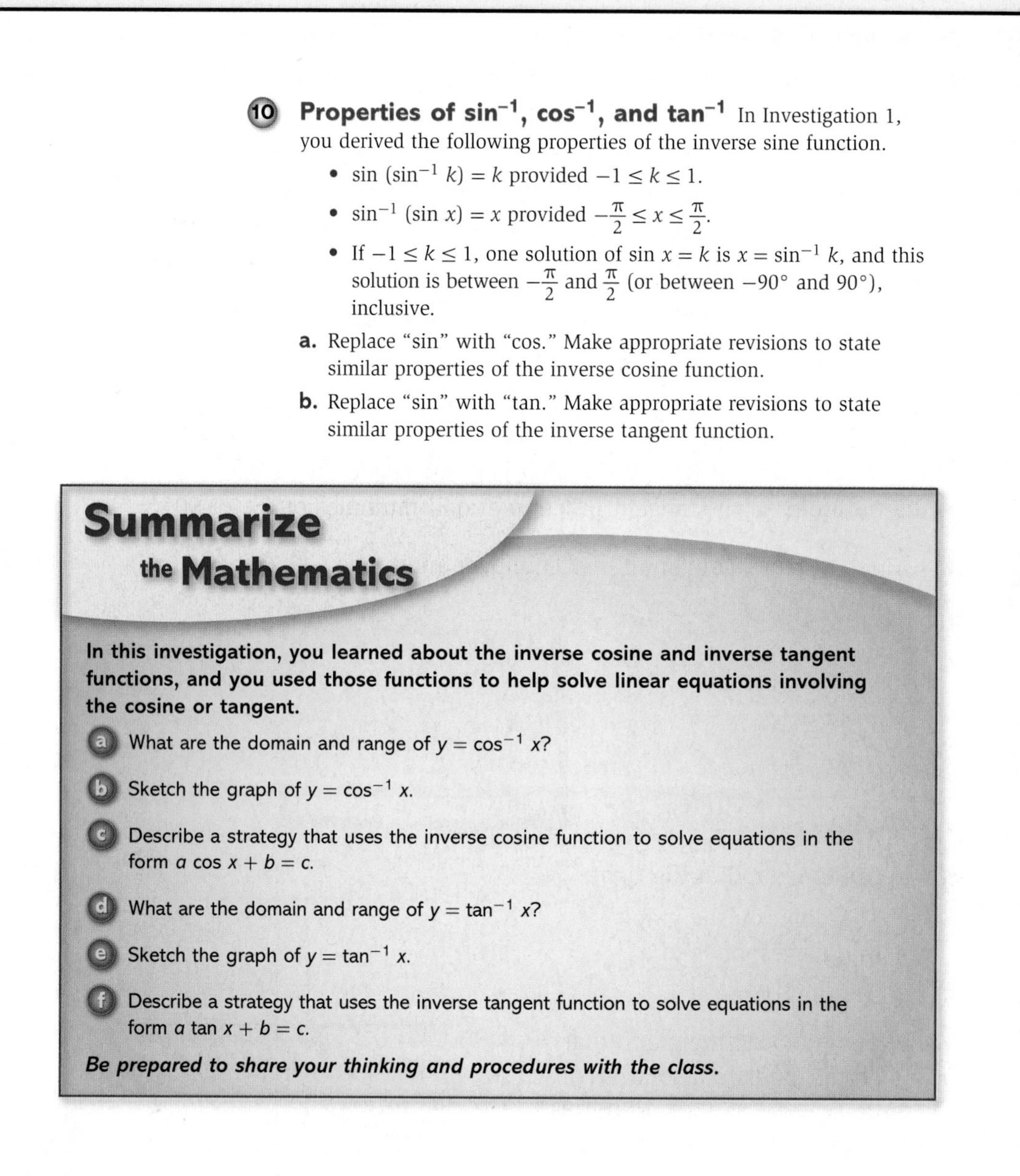

10 **Properties of $\sin^{-1}$, $\cos^{-1}$, and $\tan^{-1}$** In Investigation 1, you derived the following properties of the inverse sine function.

- $\sin(\sin^{-1} k) = k$ provided $-1 \leq k \leq 1$.
- $\sin^{-1}(\sin x) = x$ provided $-\frac{\pi}{2} \leq x \leq \frac{\pi}{2}$.
- If $-1 \leq k \leq 1$, one solution of $\sin x = k$ is $x = \sin^{-1} k$, and this solution is between $-\frac{\pi}{2}$ and $\frac{\pi}{2}$ (or between $-90°$ and $90°$), inclusive.

a. Replace "sin" with "cos." Make appropriate revisions to state similar properties of the inverse cosine function.

b. Replace "sin" with "tan." Make appropriate revisions to state similar properties of the inverse tangent function.

Summarize the Mathematics

In this investigation, you learned about the inverse cosine and inverse tangent functions, and you used those functions to help solve linear equations involving the cosine or tangent.

a What are the domain and range of $y = \cos^{-1} x$?

b Sketch the graph of $y = \cos^{-1} x$.

c Describe a strategy that uses the inverse cosine function to solve equations in the form $a \cos x + b = c$.

d What are the domain and range of $y = \tan^{-1} x$?

e Sketch the graph of $y = \tan^{-1} x$.

f Describe a strategy that uses the inverse tangent function to solve equations in the form $a \tan x + b = c$.

Be prepared to share your thinking and procedures with the class.

588 UNIT 8 • Inverse Functions

10 **a.** The following properties followed immediately from the definition of the inverse cosine function.

- $\cos(\cos^{-1} k) = k$ provided $-1 \leq k \leq 1$.
- $\cos^{-1}(\cos x) = x$ provided $0 \leq x \leq \pi$.
- If $-1 \leq k \leq 1$, one solution of $\cos x = k$ is $x = \cos^{-1} k$, and this solution is between 0 and π (or between 0° and 180°), inclusive.

b. The following properties followed immediately from the definition of the inverse tangent function.

- $\tan(\tan^{-1} k) = k$ for all real numbers k.
- $\tan^{-1}(\tan x) = x$ provided $-\frac{\pi}{2} < x < \frac{\pi}{2}$.
- For any real number k, one solution of $\tan x = k$ is $x = \tan^{-1} k$, and this solution is between $-\frac{\pi}{2}$ and $\frac{\pi}{2}$ (or between −90° and 90°), not including the endpoints of the interval.

Summarize the Mathematics

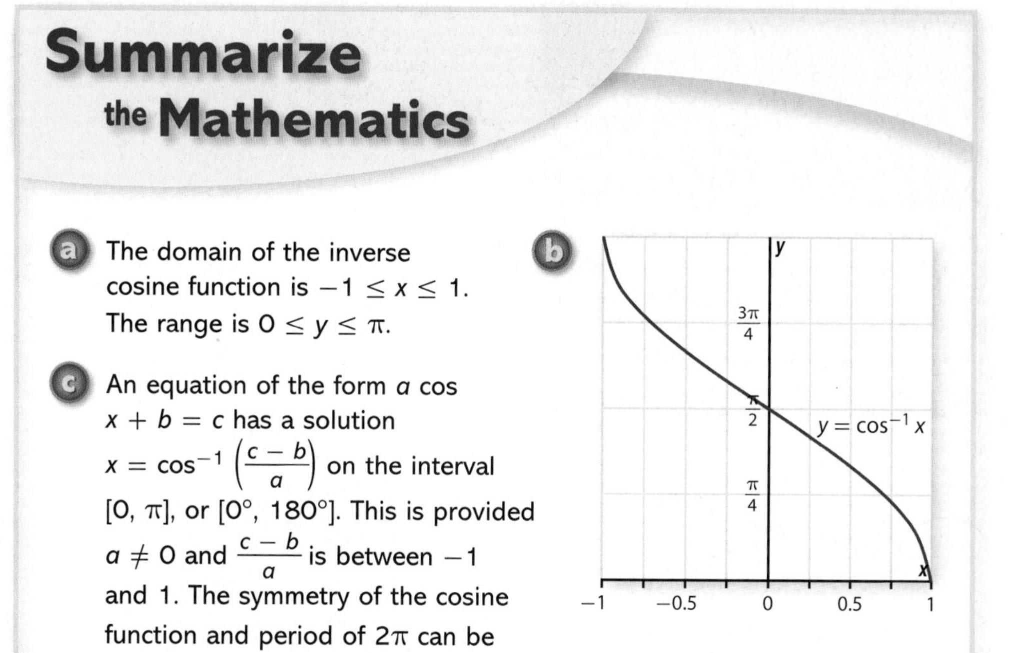

a The domain of the inverse cosine function is $-1 \leq x \leq 1$. The range is $0 \leq y \leq \pi$.

b (see graph)

c An equation of the form $a \cos x + b = c$ has a solution $x = \cos^{-1}\left(\frac{c-b}{a}\right)$ on the interval $[0, \pi]$, or [0°, 180°]. This is provided $a \neq 0$ and $\frac{c-b}{a}$ is between −1 and 1. The symmetry of the cosine function and period of 2π can be used to help find all solutions. These solutions are found by adding multiples of 2π to original solution x_1 on the interval $[0, \pi]$, $x_1 + 2\pi n$, where n is an integer.

d The domain of $y = \tan^{-1} x$ is all real numbers and the range is $-\frac{\pi}{2} < x < \frac{\pi}{2}$.

e

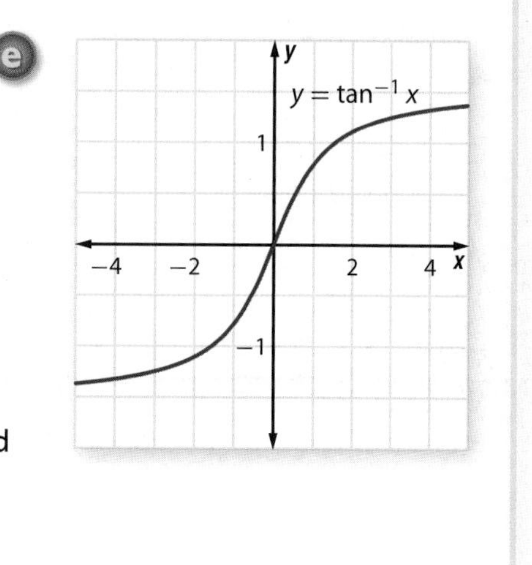

f Equations of the form $a \tan x + b = c$ have solution $x = \tan^{-1}\left(\frac{c-b}{a}\right)$ in the interval $\left[-\frac{\pi}{2}, \frac{\pi}{2}\right]$. This is provided that $a \neq 0$. All solutions can be found using the periodicity of the tangent function. $x = \tan^{-1}\left(\frac{c-b}{a}\right) + \pi n$, where n is an integer.

Teaching Resources

Transparency Master 30.

UNIT 8 *Inverse Functions*

Summarize the Mathematics

In this investigation, you learned about the inverse cosine and inverse tangent functions, and you used those functions to help solve linear equations involving the cosine or tangent.

a What are the domain and range of $y = \cos^{-1} x$?

b Sketch the graph of $y = \cos^{-1} x$.

c Describe a strategy that uses the inverse cosine function to solve equations in the form $a \cos x + b = c$.

d What are the domain and range of $y = \tan^{-1} x$?

e Sketch the graph of $y = \tan^{-1} x$.

f Describe a strategy that uses the inverse tangent function to solve equations in the form $a \tan x + b = c$.

Be prepared to share your thinking and procedures with the class.

MATH TOOLKIT Students should define the inverses of the sine, cosine, and tangent and explain how to use these functions to solve trigonometric equations.

Unit 8

Check Your Understanding

Use your understanding of the inverse cosine and tangent functions to help complete these tasks.

a. Find all solutions of each equation.

i. $3 - 4 \cos x = 6$

ii. $\tan x - 3 = 12$

b. The daily average temperature in a southern hemisphere city like Johannesburg, South Africa, varies throughout the year—warmest from November through February and coolest from May through September.

Suppose that the function $T(m) = 60 + 10 \cos 0.5m$ is a good formula for estimating the daily temperature in degrees Fahrenheit at a time m months into the year. Write and solve equations that answer these questions.

i. At what time of the year is the daily average temperature 65°F?

ii. At what time of the year is the daily average temperature 53°F?

Check Your Understanding

a. **i.** $3 - 4 \cos x = 6$

$-4 \cos x = 3$

$\cos x = -0.75$

$x = \cos^{-1}(-0.75)$

$x \approx 2.42 + 2\pi n$

or $x \approx -2.42 + 2\pi n$

for any integer n

ii. $\tan x - 3 = 12$

$\tan x = 15$

$x = \tan^{-1} 15$

$x \approx 1.50 + \pi n$

for any integer n

b. **i. Solve:** $60 + 10 \cos 0.5m = 65$

$\cos 0.5m = 0.5$

$m = \frac{\cos^{-1} 0.5}{0.5}$

$m \approx 2.09$

This is very early in March. Due to the symmetry of the cosine function, there is another time of the same average temperature: $m = 4\pi - 2.09$, or about 10.48, representing mid-November.

ii. Solve: $60 + 10 \cos 0.5m = 53$

$\cos 0.5m = -0.7$

$m = \frac{\cos^{-1}(-0.7)}{0.5}$

$m \approx 4.7$

This is about the third week of May. Due to the symmetry of the cosine function, there is another time of the same average temperature: $m = 4\pi - 4.7$, or about 7.87, representing a time in late August.

INSTRUCTIONAL NOTE

Students may not recognize that the period for the function in Part b is 4π rather than 2π. Encourage them to check their work by graphing the function associated with the equation or simply graphing $y = \cos 0.5x$.

On Your Own

Applications

1 Use the definitions of the sine and inverse sine functions to write the following equations in different equivalent forms.

a. $\sin\left(\frac{\pi}{3}\right) = \frac{\sqrt{3}}{2}$ **b.** $\sin^{-1}\left(\frac{\sqrt{2}}{2}\right) = \frac{\pi}{4}$ **c.** $\sin\left(-\frac{\pi}{6}\right) = -\frac{1}{2}$

2 Use information in the diagram to find the requested values. Be prepared to explain how you know that your answers are correct, without the use of technology.

a. $\sin^{-1} 0.259 =$ ____ **b.** $\sin^{-1} 0.966 =$ ____

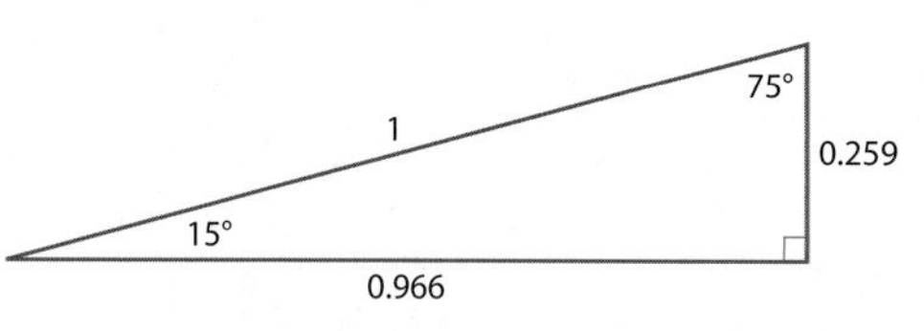

3 Use algebraic reasoning and the inverse sine function to find a solution for each of the following equations. Give exact solutions in both radians and degrees, if possible.

a. $\sin x = \frac{1}{2}$ **b.** $\sin 3x = \frac{1}{2}$ **c.** $8 \sin 0.4x - 1 = 3$

4 Use algebraic reasoning and the inverse sine function to find all solutions in radians for the following equations. Give exact solutions, if possible.

a. $2 \sin x + \sqrt{3} = 0$ **b.** $4 \sin x + 3 = 1$ **c.** $3 - \sin x = 2 \sin x$

5 Sarasota, Florida, like many cities in tropical climates, has a seasonal change in population each year. Suppose that the number of people living in Sarasota at any time of the year can be approximated by the function

$$p(t) = 50 + 25 \sin 0.5t,$$

where $p(t)$ is in thousands of people, t is in months after November 1, and $0 \leq t \leq 12$.

a. Graph the population function for a one-year period in an appropriate window. Start your graph using $t = 0$ to stand for November 1.

b. What is the maximum predicted number of people living in Sarasota? When does that maximum occur?

590 UNIT 8 • Inverse Functions

On Your Own

Applications

1. **a.** $\sin^{-1}\left(\frac{\sqrt{3}}{2}\right) = \frac{\pi}{3}$ **b.** $\sin\left(\frac{\pi}{4}\right) = \frac{\sqrt{2}}{2}$ **c.** $\sin^{-1}\left(-\frac{1}{2}\right) = -\frac{\pi}{6}$

2. **a.** 15°

   b. 75°

3. **a.** $\sin^{-1}\left(\frac{1}{2}\right) = x$

   $x = \frac{\pi}{6}$, or 30°

   b. $\sin^{-1}\left(\frac{1}{2}\right) = 3x$

   Since $3x = \frac{\pi}{6}$, or 30°, $x = \frac{\pi}{18}$, or 10°.

   c. Since $\sin 0.4x = \frac{1}{2}$, $0.4x = \frac{\pi}{6}$, or 30°.

   So, $x = \frac{5\pi}{12}$, or 75°.

4. **a.** $2 \sin x + \sqrt{3} = 0$

   $\sin x = -\frac{\sqrt{3}}{2}$

   $x = -\frac{\pi}{3}$ and by symmetry

   $x = -\frac{2\pi}{3}$; so, in general,

   $x = -\frac{\pi}{3} + 2\pi n$ or

   $x = -\frac{2\pi}{3} + 2\pi n$ for integer n.

   b. $4 \sin x + 3 = 1$

   $\sin x = -0.5$

   $x = -\frac{\pi}{6}$ and by symmetry,

   $x = -\frac{5\pi}{6}$; so, in general,

   $x = -\frac{\pi}{6} + 2\pi n$ or

   $x = -\frac{5\pi}{6} + 2\pi n$ for any integer n.

   c. $3 - \sin x = 2 \sin x$

   $\sin x = 1$

   $x = \frac{\pi}{2} + 2\pi n$ for any integer n.

5. **a.**

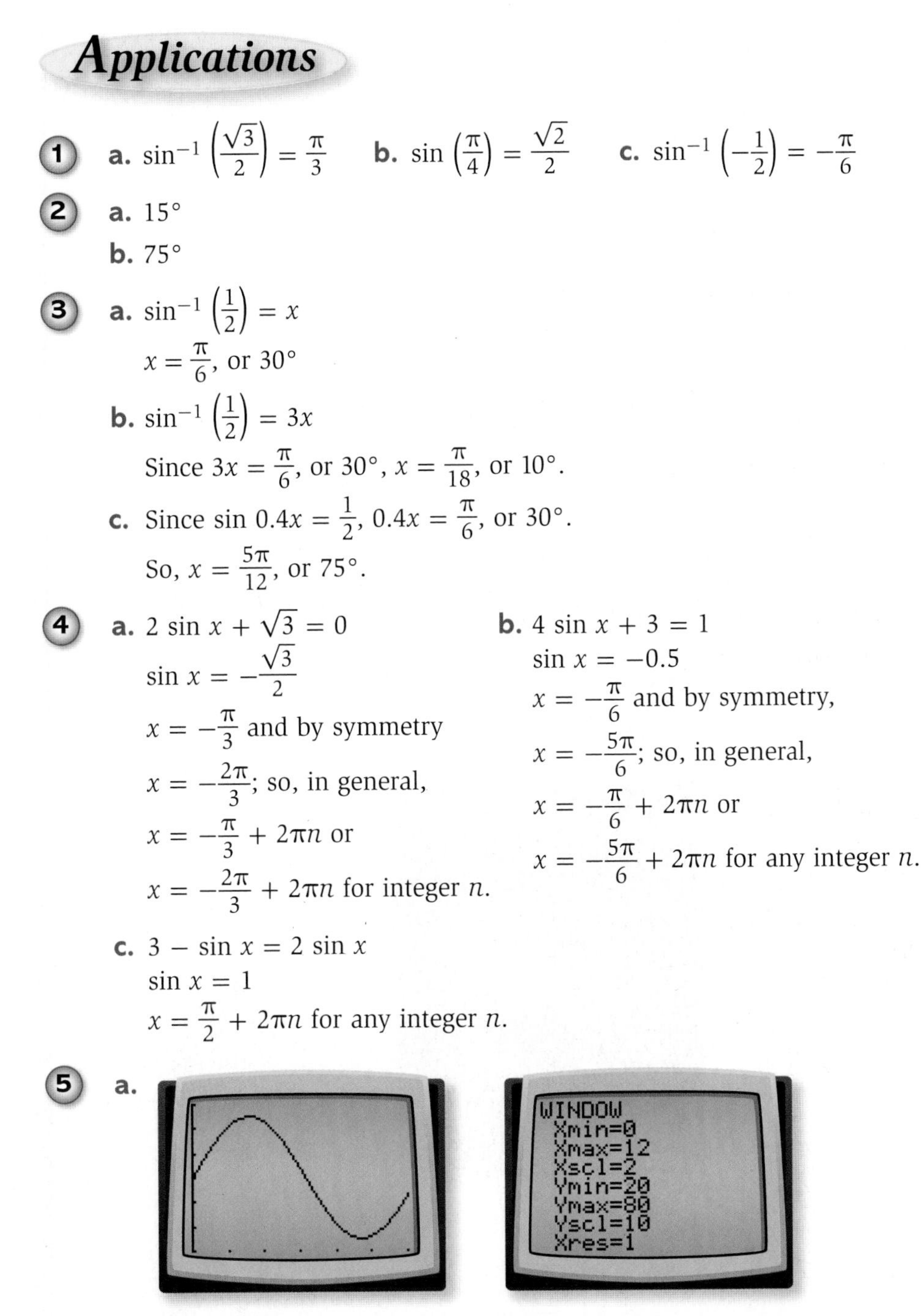

   b. The maximum predicted population is 75,000 people. The maximum occurs when $\sin 0.5t = 1$, or when $0.5t = \frac{\pi}{2}$, or when $t \approx 3.14$. So, the maximum number of people occurs on about February 4.

Unit 8

c. What is the minimum predicted number of people living in Sarasota? When does that minimum occur?

d. On what date(s) in the year is the number of people living in Sarasota about 60,000? Show how to find the answer to this question using algebraic reasoning and the inverse sine function.

6 Determine which of the following mathematical statements are true. Explain how you know without the use of technology.

a. $\cos\left(\frac{\pi}{3}\right) = \frac{1}{2}$ b. $\cos^{-1}\left(\frac{\sqrt{2}}{2}\right) = \frac{\pi}{4}$ c. $\cos^{-1}\left(\frac{\sqrt{3}}{2}\right) = \frac{\pi}{6}$

7 Use information in the diagram below to find requested values of the inverse cosine function. Be prepared to explain how you know that your answers are correct, without the use of technology.

a. $\cos^{-1} 0.259 =$ ____ b. $\cos^{-1} 0.966 =$ ____

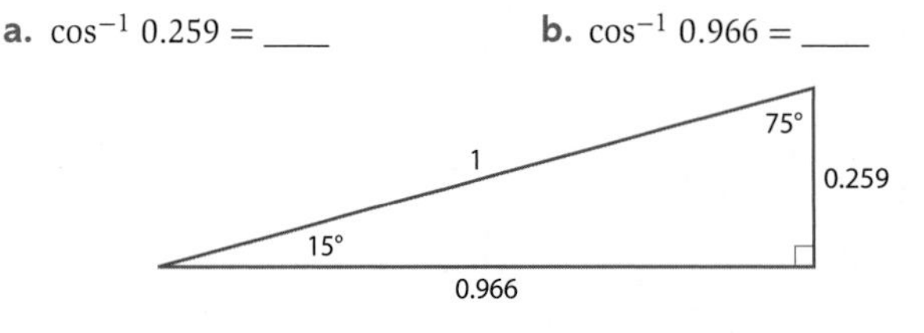

8 Use algebraic reasoning and the inverse cosine function to find a solution for each of the following equations. Give exact solutions in both radians and degrees, if possible.

a. $\cos x = \frac{1}{2}$ b. $\cos 5x = \frac{1}{2}$ c. $8 \cos 0.4x - 1 = 3$

9 Use algebraic reasoning and the inverse cosine function to find all solutions in radians for the following equations. Give exact solutions, if possible.

a. $2 \cos x - \sqrt{3} = 0$ b. $4 \cos x - 3 = 1$ c. $2 - \cos x = 3 \cos x$

10 The meandering path of a river often can be approximated by a sine or cosine curve. Suppose that two towns are located so that one is six miles directly east of the other and the path of the river between those towns is approximated by the graph of $y = 2 \cos x$ for $-2 \leq x \leq 4$.

The x-coordinate represents location from west to east in miles and y represents location north or south of the line connecting the two towns in miles.

a. Graph the path of the river over the six-mile interval between the two towns.

b. Answer parts i and ii relative to the origin of this graph.

i. What is the northernmost point of the river between the two towns?

ii. What is the river's southernmost point between the two towns?

c. The minimum predicted population is 25,000 people. The minimum occurs when $\sin 0.5t = -1$, or when $0.5t = -\frac{\pi}{2}$, or when $t = -\pi$. So, the minimum occurs approximately 3.14 months before November 1, or about July 26.

d. Solve $50 + 25 \sin 0.5t = 60$, or $\sin 0.5t = 0.4$. The first solution is $t \approx 0.82$. This solution corresponds to about November 25. By symmetry of the population graph, a second solution is $t \approx -4\pi + (2\pi - 0.82) \approx -7.10$. This solution corresponds to about March 28.

INSTRUCTIONAL NOTE
If students find the second value that solves the equations in Parts c and d using months after November 1, their answers will be about August 13 for Part c and April 14, respectively.

6 **a.** True, because $\frac{\pi}{3} = 60°$ and in a 30°-60° right triangle, the side adjacent to the 60° angle is one-half the length of the hypotenuse.

b. True, because $\frac{\pi}{4} = 45°$ and in a 45°-45° right triangle, the ratio of leg to hypotenuse is always $\frac{1}{\sqrt{2}} = \frac{\sqrt{2}}{2}$.

c. True, because $\frac{\pi}{6} = 30°$ and in a 30°-60° right triangle, the side adjacent to the 30° angle is always related to the hypotenuse by the ratio $\frac{\sqrt{3}}{2}$.

7 **a.** 75° because the cosine is the ratio of adjacent side to hypotenuse and in the given drawing, the ratio of the side adjacent to the 75° angle to the hypotenuse is 0.26.

b. 15° because the cosine is the ratio of adjacent side to hypotenuse and in the given drawing, the ratio of the side adjacent to the 15° angle to the hypotenuse is 0.96.

8 **a.** $x = \frac{\pi}{3}$, or 60°

b. Since $5x = \frac{\pi}{3}$, or 60°, $x = \frac{\pi}{15}$, or 12°.

c. Since $0.4x = \frac{\pi}{3}$, or 60°, $x = \frac{5\pi}{6}$, or 150°.

9 **a.** $x = \frac{\pi}{6} + 2\pi n$ or $-\frac{\pi}{6} + 2\pi n$ for any integer n.

b. $x = 2\pi n$ for any integer n.

c. $x = \frac{\pi}{3} + 2\pi n$ or $-\frac{\pi}{3} + 2\pi n$ for any integer n.

10 **a.** The graph of $y = 5 \cos x$ is with Part b.

b. **i.** The northernmost point is (0, 5); that is, 5 miles due north of the origin.

ii. The southernmost point is at $(\pi, -5)$; that is, π (about 3.14) miles east and 5 miles south of the origin.

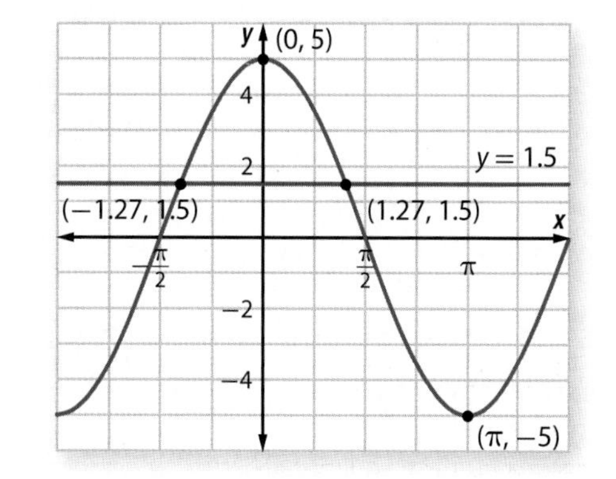

Unit 8

c. Suppose a west-east road lies on the line $y = 1.5$ and a north-south road on the line $x = 0$ on the graph.

i. How many bridges are needed for these straight roads?

ii. At what points on the map coordinate system are the bridges located?

d. If it was decided that the two towns build direct roads connecting the bridge on the north-south road to the bridges on the west-east road, how long will each of those roads be?

11 Determine which of the following mathematical statements are true. Explain how you know, without the use of technology.

a. $\tan 45° = \frac{1}{2}$ b. $\tan^{-1} 1 = 45°$ c. $\tan^{-1} \sqrt{3} = \frac{\pi}{3}$

12 Use information in the diagram below to find requested values of the inverse tangent function. Explain how you know that your answers are correct, without using the **tan** or **tan⁻¹** function of technology.

a. $\tan^{-1}$ (___) = 75° b. $\tan^{-1}$ (___) = 15°

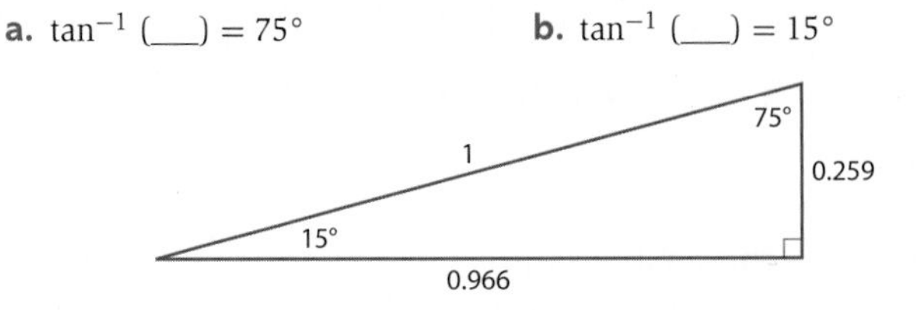

13 Use algebraic reasoning and the inverse tangent function to find all solutions for the following equations. Give exact solutions, if possible.

a. $\tan x = 1$ b. $5 \tan x = 1$ c. $5 \tan x - 1 = 19$

14 The center of the Ferris wheel at a county fair is 7 meters above the ground. The Ferris wheel itself is 12 meters in diameter. The angular velocity of the wheel is 18° per second.

a. Write an equation involving the sine function that gives the distance y in meters above the ground of a seat on the wheel t seconds from the time that it is at the 3:00 position on the wheel. (*Hint:* The seat will return to its starting point in 20 seconds.)

b. Using the equation that you wrote in Part a, write an equation in t whose solutions are the times at which the seat is 10 meters above the ground. Find all solutions between 0 and 30 seconds.

Unit 8

592 UNIT 8 • Inverse Functions

c. i. Three bridges are needed, one on the north-south road and two over the east-west road.

ii. The bridge over the north-south road is at (0, 5). To find the location of the other two bridges, solve $5 \cos x = 1.5$, or $\cos x = 0.3$. One solution is $x = \cos^{-1} 0.3 \approx 1.2661$, so one bridge is at about (1.27, 1.5). The second bridge is at the reflection of this point over the y-axis, that is, at about (−1.27, 1.5).

d. Using the distance formula, the length of one road is $\sqrt{(0 - 1.27)^2 + (5 - 1.5)^2} \approx 3.72$ miles. By symmetry about the y-axis, the second road is also approximately 3.72 miles long.

11 a. False, because in a 45°-45° right triangle, the two legs are congruent, so the tangent of 45° is 1.

b. True, because in a 45°-45° right triangle, the two legs are congruent, so the tangent of 45° is 1 and thus $\tan^{-1} 1 = 45°$.

c. True, because if a right triangle has one angle of $\frac{\pi}{3} = 60°$, the other acute angle is 30°. In a 30°-60° right triangle, the ratio of the leg opposite the 60° angle to the leg adjacent to that angle is always $\frac{\sqrt{3}}{1}$ or, in more familiar form $\frac{\frac{\sqrt{3}}{2}}{\frac{1}{2}} = \sqrt{3}$.

12 a. $\tan^{-1}\left(\frac{0.966}{0.259}\right) = 75°$, or $\tan^{-1} 3.73 = 75°$

b. $\tan^{-1}\left(\frac{0.259}{0.966}\right) = 15°$, or $\tan^{-1} 0.268 = 15°$

13 a. $x = \frac{\pi}{4} + \pi n$ for any integer n.

b. $x \approx 0.197 + \pi n$ for any integer n.

c. $x \approx 1.33 + \pi n$ for any integer n.

14 a. The amplitude is 6, the horizontal axis goes through the center of the wheel so it is $y = 7$, the period is 20 seconds, and the rotation begins at 0° or $t = 0$. Therefore, an equation for this motion is

$$y = 6 \sin 18t + 7.$$

Note that the units for $\sin 18t$ will be degrees, so a calculator needs to be set in that mode to graph the function.

b. **Solve:** $6 \sin 18t + 7 = 10$

$18t = \sin^{-1} 0.5 = 30°$, so $t = \frac{30}{18} = 1\frac{2}{3}$ or $t = \frac{30 + 360}{18} = 21\frac{2}{3}$.

$18t = 180° - \sin^{-1} 0.5 = 150°$, so $t = \frac{150}{18} = 8\frac{1}{3}$ or

$t = \frac{150 + 360}{18} = 28\frac{1}{3}$.

Solutions between 0 and 30 seconds are $t = 1\frac{2}{3}, 8\frac{1}{3}, 21\frac{2}{3}$, and $28\frac{1}{3}$ seconds.

Connections

15 One tool for determining missing parts of a triangle $\triangle ABC$ is the Law of Sines: $\frac{a}{\sin A} = \frac{b}{\sin B} = \frac{c}{\sin C}$.

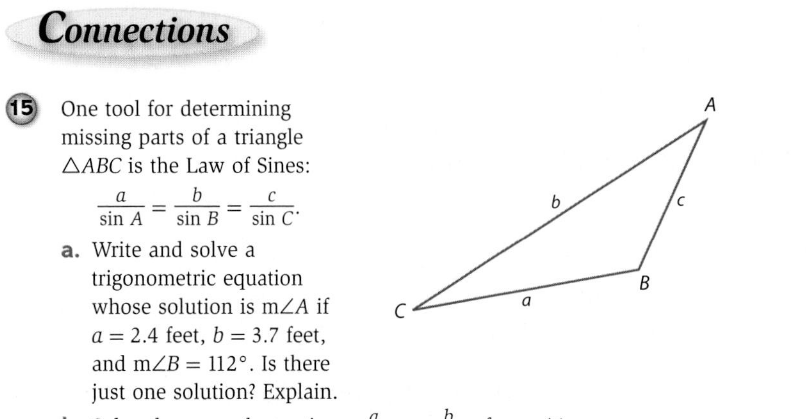

a. Write and solve a trigonometric equation whose solution is $m\angle A$ if $a = 2.4$ feet, $b = 3.7$ feet, and $m\angle B = 112°$. Is there just one solution? Explain.

b. Solve the general equation, $\frac{a}{\sin A} = \frac{b}{\sin B}$, for $m\angle A$.

16 Compare the use of inverse functions in solving exponential and trigonometric equations by solving each pair of equations using radians for the sine functions. Note similarities and differences in strategies used.

a. $20(10^x) = 5$ and $20 \sin x = 5$

b. $20(10^{3x}) = 5$ and $20 \sin 3x = 5$

c. $20(10^{3x}) - 3 = 5$ and $20 \sin 3x - 3 = 5$

17 An ice cream store in Indiana is a seasonal business. Stores that remain open all year have a fluctuation in daily income (in thousands of dollars) similar to that shown in the following table.

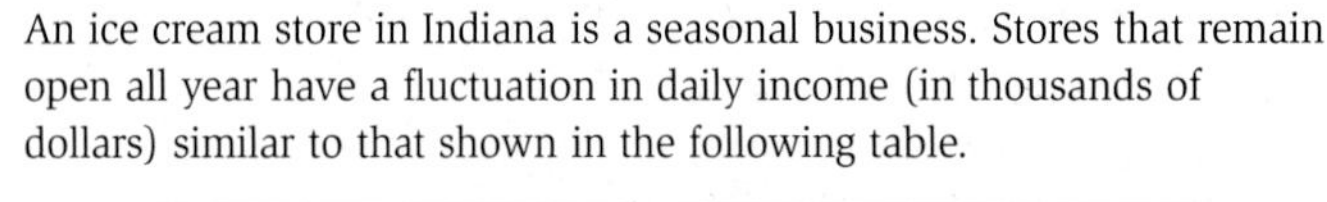

Date	Daily Income	Date	Daily Income
January 1	0.73	July 1	5.89
February 1	0.66	August 1	6.35
March 1	0.85	September 1	5.77
April 1	1.35	October 1	4.52
May 1	2.78	November 1	2.83
June 1	4.67	December 1	1.44

a. On which of the tabled dates does the store make maximum income? Minimum income?

b. Plot the income data y against x, time in months after January 1. Use January 1 as $x = 0$.

c. Given the shape of the plot in Part b, what kind of function might provide a good fit for these data?

d. Use your calculator or computer software to fit these data to a sine function. On some calculators, this is a statistics function called **sinreg**. What is the equation of the function that best fits the data?

e. Calculate the average daily income of the 12 values in the table. What average daily income is predicted by your equation in Part d?

Connections

15 **a.** $\frac{2.4}{\sin A} = \frac{3.7}{\sin 112°}$, or $\sin A = \frac{2.4(0.9272)}{3.7}$. Then the measure of $\angle A$ is approximately $\sin^{-1} 0.60 = 37°$. This is a unique solution because with one angle given as 112°, the other angles in the triangle must be less than 90°. There is only one angle between 0° and 90° that has sine equal to 0.60.

b. The general solution will take the form $m\angle A = \sin^{-1}\left(\frac{a \sin B}{b}\right)$.

16 **a.** $20(10^x) = 5$ has solution $x = \log 0.25$, or -0.6021.
$20 \sin x = 5$ has solution $x = \sin^{-1} 0.25$, or 0.2527.

b. $20(10^{3x}) = 5$ has solution $x = \frac{\log 0.25}{3}$, or -0.2007.

$20 \sin 3x = 5$ has solution $x = \frac{\sin^{-1} 0.25}{3}$, or 0.0842.

c. $20(10^{3x}) - 3 = 5$ has solution $x = \frac{\log 0.4}{3}$, or -0.1326.

$20 \sin 3x - 3 = 5$ has solution $x = \frac{\sin^{-1} 0.4}{3}$, or 0.1372.

In all three cases, the basic strategy was to get either the basic exponential expression or the basic sine expression isolated on one side of the equation. Then by applying the appropriate inverse function, you get an equation in the form $x = k$ or $mx = k$. These can be solved easily for x.

17 **a.** In the table, the store's maximum income is on August 1, and its minimum income is on February 1.

b.

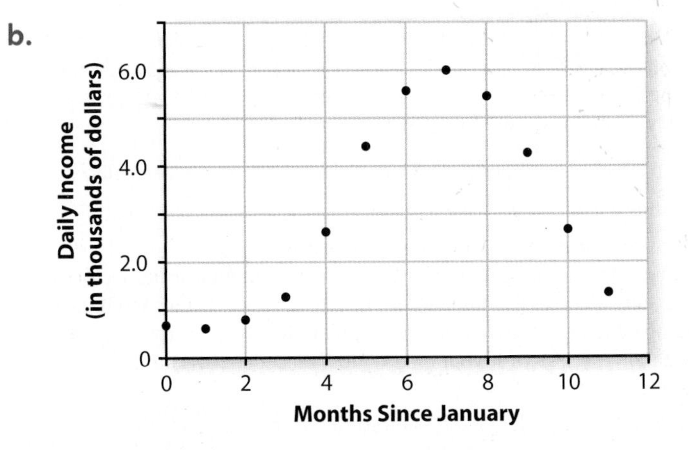

c. The shape seems to have roughly the shape of a sine or cosine graph.

d. $y = 2.96 \sin (0.55x - 2.28) + 3.27$

e. The mean daily income for the 12 days in the table is about 3.15 thousand dollars. The equation in Part d predicts a mean of 3.27 thousand dollars.

Unit 8

18 The Law of Cosines can be used to find unknown angle or side measurements in triangles. In $\triangle ABC$,

$$c^2 = a^2 + b^2 - 2ab \cos C.$$

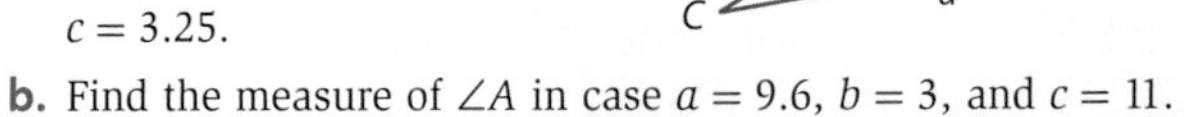

a. Find the measure of $\angle C$ in case $a = 5$, $b = 7$, and $c = 3.25$.

b. Find the measure of $\angle A$ in case $a = 9.6$, $b = 3$, and $c = 11$.

19 The daily attendance of California's scenic Yosemite National Park varies throughout the year with a maximum of about 20,000 visitors on August 1 and a minimum of about 2,000 visitors on February 1.

a. Show that if the function

$$A(m) = 9 \cos 0.5m + 11$$

is used to predict daily attendance in thousands at a time m months after August 1, the function has maximum and minimum values that agree with the given data.

b. About what daily attendance does your equation predict for January 1?

c. On what other day is the predicted daily attendance the same as that of January 1?

d. Members of the Stanford University Hiking Club dislike crowds, but they love to hike in Yosemite. They have decided to avoid the park on days when the predicted attendance is 16,000 or greater. On what days should they avoid Yosemite?

20 Use of the Law of Sines to find side lengths of triangles generally requires a computation like $a = (\sin A)\left(\frac{b}{\sin B}\right)$. Before electronic calculators were invented, that calculation was tedious. It involved multiplying and dividing by decimals accurate to four or more places. To avoid such messy computation, people used logarithms to change the operations to sums or differences that are easier to compute by hand. The logs of trigonometric functions could be found in published tables.

a. Write an equivalent expression for $\log\left((\sin A)\left(\frac{b}{\sin B}\right)\right)$ that requires only addition and subtraction of logarithms. Explain why the result is equal to $\log a$.

b. Suppose $b = 4.5$, $m\angle A = 42°$, and $m\angle B = 103°$.

i. Use the expression derived in Part a to find $\log a$.

ii. Use the value of $\log a$ to determine a.

594 UNIT 8 • Inverse Functions

18 **a.** $3.25^2 = 5^2 + 7^2 - 2(5)(7)\cos C$

$10.5625 = 74 - 70\cos C$

$m\angle C = \cos^{-1}\left(\frac{74 - 10.5625}{70}\right) \approx 25.01°$

b. Alternative form of Law of Cosines:

$a^2 = b^2 + c^2 - 2bc\cos A$

$9.6^2 = 3^2 + 11^2 - 2(3)(11)\cos A$

$m\angle A = \cos^{-1}\left(\frac{130 - 92.6}{66}\right) \approx 55.02°$

19 **a.** $A(0) = 9\cos(0.5 \cdot 0) + 11$ gives $A(0) = 20$ because $\cos 0 = 1$.
$A(6) = 9\cos(0.5 \cdot 6) + 11$ gives $A(6) = 2.1$ because $\cos 3 = -0.99$.

b. January 1 is 5 months after August 1. Predicted attendance on January 1 is $A(5) = 9\cos(0.5 \cdot 5) + 11 \approx 3.79$ thousand, or 3,790.

c. By the symmetry of the function about the local minimum, $x = 6.28$, predicted attendance will also be about 3,790 when $x = 7.56$, or March 15. Note that the model assumes a period of approximately 12.56 (4π), which does not match the 12-month year precisely.

d. Solve: $9{,}000\cos 0.5x + 11{,}000 = 16{,}000$, or $\cos 0.5x = 0.5556$.
$\cos^{-1} 0.5556 \approx 0.9818$; so, $0.5x \approx 0.9818$, or $x \approx 1.96$. The symmetric value for x is 10.61. The values $x \approx 1.96$ and $x \approx 10.61$ correspond to about September 29 and June 18. The Stanford Hiking Club should avoid Yosemite National Park between June 18 and September 29.

20 **a.** $\log a = \log(\sin A) + \log b - \log(\sin B)$ as a result of taking the logarithm of both sides of the original equation and applying two properties of logarithms—the log of a product is the sum of the logs of the factors and the log of a quotient is the difference of the logs of the dividend and the divisor.

b. **i.** $\log(\sin 42°) + \log 4.5 - \log(\sin 103°) \approx 0.4900$

ii. Since $\log a \approx 0.4900$, $a = 10^{0.4900} \approx 3.0903$.

Unit 8

21 The graph of each equation in the form $y = kx$, $x \geq 0$ meets the positive x-axis at the origin to form an angle with measure between $-90°$ and $90°$. The graph of the equation $y = -2x$, $x \geq 0$ meets the positive x-axis at an angle of approximately $-63°$.

a. Complete a copy of the following table to explore the relationship between angle and slope.

Slope	−4	−2	−1.5	−1	−0.5	0	0.5	1	1.5	2	4
Angle		−63									

b. Plot the (*slope, angle*) data.

c. Identify a function type that seems likely to model well the dependence of *angle measurement* on *slope*. Use a curve-fitting tool to find the best-fit model of that type.

d. Identify the intercepts, local maximum and minimum points, and asymptotes of the function model from Part c.

22 Use the coordinate definition of the trigonometric functions and properties of their inverses to determine the values of these expressions.

a. $\sin\left(\tan^{-1}\left(\frac{4}{3}\right)\right)$

b. $\tan\left(\arcsin\left(-\frac{3}{4}\right)\right)$

c. $\sin\left(\cos^{-1}\left(-\frac{1}{5}\right)\right)$

d. $\sin^{-1}(\sin(-300°))$

e. $\arccos\left(\sin\left(-\frac{\pi}{4}\right)\right)$

f. $\tan(\cos^{-1} x)$, $0 < x < 1$

23 Use your calculator to complete a copy of the following table. Explain interesting patterns you see in the table. Explain your results.

	Radian Measure (*x*)						
	1	2	3	4	5	6	7
$\sin^{-1}(\sin x)$	1						
$\cos^{-1}(\cos x)$				2.2832			
$\tan^{-1}(\tan x)$							0.7168

Reflections

24 Sketch the graph $y = \sin x$ for $-\frac{\pi}{2} \leq x \leq \frac{\pi}{2}$ and the line $y = x$ on the same coordinate system. Sketch the image of the graph of $y = \sin x$ reflected across the line $y = x$. What is the equation for this reflection image? Explain.

21 **a.** A table comparing slope and angle will look like this:

Slope	−4	−2	−1.5	−1	−0.5	0	0.5	1	1.5	2	4
Angle	−0.25	−63	−56	−45	−27	0	27	45	56	63	0.25

b. Answers will vary, but none of the basic function families that students have really studied carefully (linear, quadratic, exponential, sine, cosine, or tangent) match the pattern. However, this table is really the inverse tangent function.

c. A plot of the data will look like this:

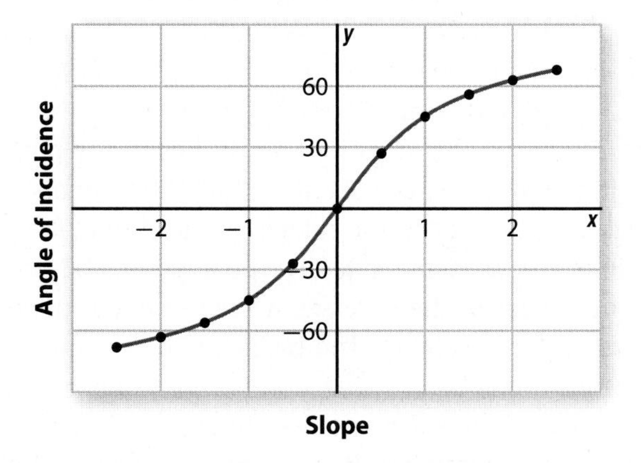

d. The x- and y-intercepts are both (0, 0). There are no local maximum or minimum points. The lines $y = 90$ and $y = -90$ are horizontal asymptotes. (Students might need to extend the table and consider more extreme slopes to find the asymptotes.)

22 **a.** $\tan^{-1}\left(\frac{4}{3}\right)$ is the angle θ in the first quadrant with tangent equal to $\frac{4}{3}$, so its terminal side contains the point (3, 4). For this point, $r = 5$ by the Pythagorean Theorem. Using the diagram at the right showing the angle θ, $\sin\left(\tan^{-1}\left(\frac{4}{3}\right)\right) = \sin\theta = \frac{4}{5}$.

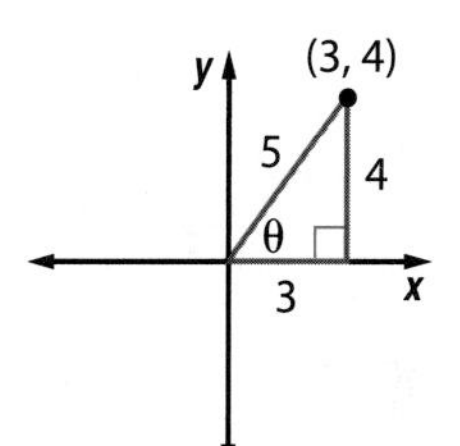

b. $\arcsin\left(-\frac{3}{4}\right) = \sin^{-1}\left(-\frac{3}{4}\right)$ is the angle in the fourth quadrant with sine equal to $-\frac{3}{4}$, so there is a point on its terminal side for which $y = -3$ and $r = 4$. For this point, $x = \sqrt{7}$, so $\tan\left(\arcsin\left(-\frac{3}{4}\right)\right) = -\frac{3}{\sqrt{7}}$.

c. $\cos^{-1}\left(-\frac{1}{5}\right)$ is the angle in the second quadrant with cosine equal to $-\frac{1}{5}$, so there is a point on its terminal side for which $x = -1$ and $r = 5$. For this point, $y = \sqrt{24} = 2\sqrt{6}$, so $\sin\left(\cos^{-1}\left(-\frac{1}{5}\right)\right) = \frac{2\sqrt{6}}{5}$.

d. $\sin^{-1}(\sin(-300°)) = \sin^{-1}(\sin 60°) = 60°$

e. $\arccos\left(\sin\left(-\frac{\pi}{4}\right)\right) = \cos^{-1}\left(\sin\left(-\frac{\pi}{4}\right)\right) = \cos^{-1}\left(-\frac{\sqrt{2}}{2}\right) = \frac{3\pi}{4}$

f. $\cos^{-1} x$ is the angle in the first quadrant with cosine equal to x, or $\frac{x}{1}$, so there is a point on its terminal side with x-coordinate of x and $r = 1$. For this point, $y = \sqrt{1 - x^2}$, so $\tan(\cos^{-1} x) = \frac{\sqrt{1 - x^2}}{x}$.

23

	Radian Measure (x)						
	1	2	3	4	5	6	7
$\sin^{-1}(\sin x)$	1	1.1416	0.1416	−0.8584	−1.2832	−0.2832	0.7168
$\cos^{-1}(\cos x)$	1	2	3	2.2832	1.2832	0.2832	0.7168
$\tan^{-1}(\tan x)$	1	−1.1416	−0.1416	0.8584	−1.2832	−0.2832	0.7168

The patterns in the table can be explained in terms of the quadrant in which the angle falls and the ranges of the inverse functions. The angle with measures 1 and 7 radians are in the first quadrant, those with measures 2 and 3 radians are in the second quadrant, 4 radians is in the third quadrant, and 5 and 6 radians are in the fourth quadrant.

Since 1 is in the first quadrant and it lies in the ranges of all three inverse functions, in each case the expression equals 1. Since 7 is in the first quadrant, but not in the ranges of these functions, the values of the expressions are the same, namely, the angle in the first quadrant and within the ranges of the inverses whose sine, cosine, or tangent is the same as that for 7 radians. The result, 0.7168 is approximately $7 - 2\pi$.

Angles in the second quadrant lie in the range of the inverse cosine, so for that function the expressions evaluated at 2 and 3 are, in fact, 2 and 3. In the second quadrant, sines of angles are positive but tangents are negative, and the reverse is true for angles in the third quadrant; hence, the difference in signs of the expressions for sine and tangent for 2, 3, and 4 radians. Notice that 1.1416 and 0.1416 are $\pi - 2$ and $\pi - 3$, respectively, and 0.8584 is $4 - \pi$. The expression for cosine evaluated at 4 seems entirely different from the values for the other two functions at 4. This is because the range of the inverse cosine includes the second quadrant; thus, the value 2.2832 is in the second quadrant and equals $\pi - (4 - \pi)$, or $2\pi - 4$.

Values of the expression for the cosine are positive for 5 and 6 radians and negative for the other two functions because the cosine is positive in the fourth quadrant, whereas the sine and tangent are negative.

Reflections

The reflection image is the graph of $y = \sin^{-1} x$, since the inverse reverses the coordinates of points and the range of the inverse sine is $-\frac{\pi}{2} \leq y \leq \frac{\pi}{2}$, the same interval as the restricted domain of the sine.

Teacher Notes

25 To remember the meaning of the inverse sine function, many students say to themselves:

The notation $\sin^{-1} x$ means to find the angle whose sine is x. For example, $\sin^{-1} 0.5 = 30°$, or $\frac{\pi}{6}$, because in a 30°-60° right triangle, the side opposite the 30° angle is one-half the hypotenuse.

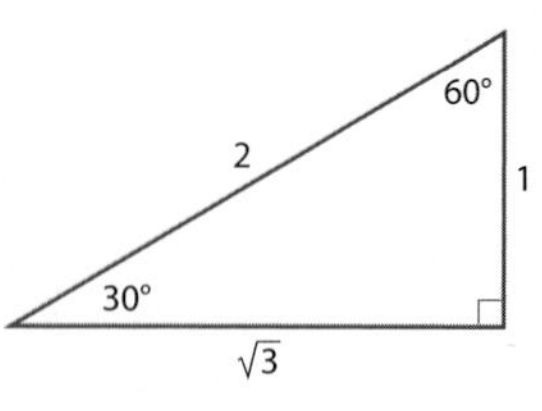

a. Do you agree that this is a helpful and correct way to think about the inverse sine function?

b. What does this way of thinking and the given drawing suggest is the value of $\sin^{-1} \frac{\sqrt{3}}{2}$?

c. What happens when you try to apply this way of thinking to find $\sin^{-1} (-0.5)$?

d. What somewhat similar way of thinking about inverse functions can be used when you are asked to find $\log x$, for example, to find $\log 1{,}000$ or $\log 0.01$?

26 Explain the meaning of each of the following expressions. Evaluate them for $t = 0.5$.

a. $\cos^{-1} t$

b. $\cos (t^{-1})$

c. $(\cos t)^{-1}$

d. $\arccos t$

27 Each of the following equations is true for some values of t and false for other values of t.

- For each equation, give one value of t for which the equation is true and one value for which it is false.
- Describe the set of all t for which each equation is true.

a. $\sin^{-1} (\sin t) = t$ (radians)

b. $\cos^{-1} (\cos t) = t$ (degrees)

c. $\tan^{-1} (\tan t) = t$ (radians)

Extensions

28 Simple sound waves can be represented by functions of the form $y = a \sin bx$. Certain sound waves, when played simultaneously, will produce a particularly pleasant sensation to the human ear. Such sound waves form the basis of music. For example, two sound waves are said to be separated by an *octave* if the ratio of their frequencies is 2:1.

a. The frequency of a middle C note is about 264 Hz, or 264 cycles per second. What is the period of this sound wave in fractions of a second?

Unit 8

596 UNIT 8 • Inverse Functions

25 **a.** The way of thinking (that involves triangles and finding the input value when you have the output value) works for positive numbers that correspond to angles between 0° and 90° readily and, with some more thought, to angles as large as 180°. That at least gives a start in the task of finding all solutions to an equation involving the sine.

b. $\sin^{-1}\left(\frac{\sqrt{3}}{2}\right) = 60°$

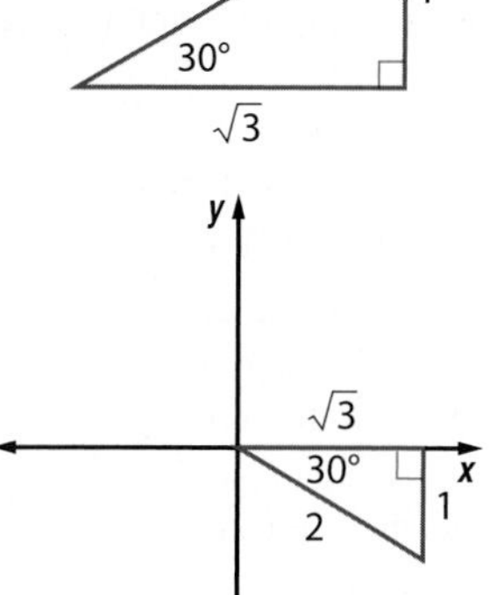

c. Dealing with negative sine values is not so natural in using the angles in a triangle. One approach is to ignore the negative sign temporarily to find the reference angle $\sin^{-1}(0.5) = 30°$ and then realize that the range for the inverse sine function would place the angle in Quadrant IV.

d. Many students think of logarithms as exponents and say things like "log of 1,000 is the exponent needed for base 10 to give 1,000." Thinking this way, $\log 1{,}000 = 3$ because $10^3 = 1{,}000$ and $\log 0.01 = -2$ because $10^{-2} = 0.01$.

26 **a.** $\cos^{-1} t$ is the inverse cosine function, so $\cos^{-1} 0.5 = 60°$, or $\frac{\pi}{3}$.

b. $\cos(t^{-1}) = \cos\left(\frac{1}{t}\right)$; so, $\cos(0.5^{-1}) = \cos 2 \approx -0.4161$.

c. $(\cos t)^{-1} = \frac{1}{\cos t}$; so, $(\cos 0.5)^{-1} \approx \frac{1}{0.8776} \approx 1.1395$.

d. $\arccos t$ is another way to write the inverse cosine function, so $\arccos 0.5 = 60°$, or $\frac{\pi}{3}$.

27 **a.** $\sin^{-1}(\sin t) = t$ is true for $-\frac{\pi}{2} \leq t \leq \frac{\pi}{2}$ and false otherwise. For example, $\sin^{-1}(\sin 1) = 1$, but $\sin^{-1}(\sin 2) = 1.1416 \neq 2$.

b. $\cos^{-1}(\cos t) = t$ is true for $0° \leq t \leq 180°$ and false otherwise. For example, $\cos^{-1}(\cos 110°) = 110°$, but $\cos^{-1}(\cos(-30°)) = 30° \neq -30°$.

c. $\tan^{-1}(\tan t) = t$ is true for $-\frac{\pi}{2} < t < \frac{\pi}{2}$ and false otherwise. For example, $\tan^{-1}(\tan 1) = 1$, but $\tan^{-1}(\tan 2) = -1.14$.

Extensions

28 **a.** Since there are 264 cycles in one second, each cycle must be $\frac{1}{264}$ seconds long.

Unit 8

b. If the note has amplitude 70, how can its fluctuating air pressure y be written as a function of time x in seconds?

c. Suppose that second note with equal amplitude and higher frequency is separated by an octave from middle C. Write a function for the sound wave associated with this note.

d. To begin to make music, these two notes can be played together. Write and graph a third function that is the sum of these two for $0 \leq x \leq 0.01$.

e. Suppose another note is separated from middle C by a third. That is, the frequencies of the two notes are in the ratio of 5:4. What are the two possible frequencies of this note?

29 Verify that each equation is true for all x where $0 \leq x \leq 1$. You will be showing that each equation is an *identity*, that is, a statement that is true for all replacements of the variable for which the statement is defined. (*Hint:* In Part a, the rotational symmetry of the sine function about the origin means that $\sin(-x) = -\sin x$ for all x.)

a. $\sin^{-1}(-x) = -\sin^{-1} x$

(*Hint:* In Parts b–d, make use of the fact that a point on the terminal side of $\sin^{-1} x$ at distance 1 from the origin has coordinates $\left(\sqrt{1 - x^2}, x\right)$ and a point on the terminal side of $\cos^{-1} x$ at distance 1 from the origin has coordinates $\left(x, \sqrt{1 - x^2}\right)$.)

b. $\sin^{-1} x + \cos^{-1} x = \frac{\pi}{2}$

c. $\cos(\sin^{-1} x) = \sqrt{1 - x^2}$

d. $\tan(\cos^{-1} x) = \frac{\sqrt{1 - x^2}}{x}$

30 More complicated trigonometric equations and other equations containing both trigonometric functions and other functions can be solved using symbolic reasoning. Use symbolic reasoning to solve the following equations in radians. *Hint:* It might help if you start by thinking about $\cos x$, $\sin x$, and $\tan x$ as unknown quantities u and solving first for u.

a. $\cos^2 x + 2 \cos x + 1 = 0$

b. $2 \sin x \cos x + \sin x = 0$

c. $\tan^2 3x = 4 \tan 3x$

d. $\sin^2 2x = 5 \sin 2x - 6$

e. $\log(\cos x) + 2.5 = 1.9$

f. $5(10^{\tan x}) + 15 = 64$

31 At one time in the history of scientific computer programming, some languages, like BASIC and FORTRAN, had only one inverse trigonometric function: the inverse tangent. The inverse sine and inverse cosine were both computed in these languages using expressions that involved the inverse tangent. Complete the following tasks to see how this can be done.

a. Let $y = \sin^{-1} x$. The goal is to write y in terms of the inverse tangent of a function of x. Start by writing x in terms of y.

b. Since $\frac{1}{264} = 2\pi$, $1 = 528\pi$.
So, $y = 70 \sin 528\pi x$.

c. $y = 70 \sin 1{,}056\pi x$

d. $y = 70 \sin 528\pi x + 70 \sin 1{,}056\pi x = 70 (\sin 528\pi x + \sin 1{,}056\pi x)$

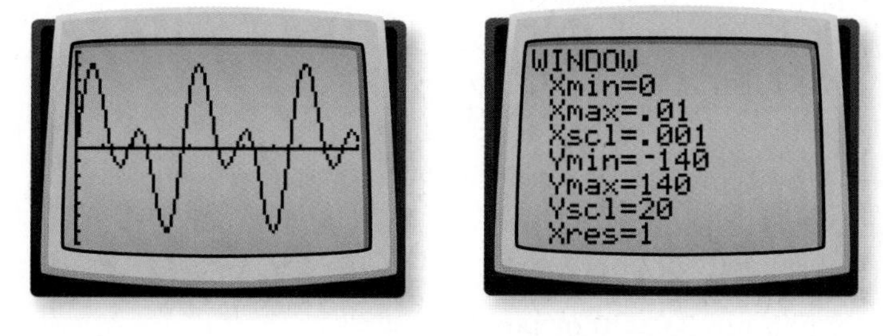

e. Solve $\frac{x}{256} = \frac{5}{4}$.
$x = 320$ Hz

Solve $\frac{256}{x} = \frac{5}{4}$.
$x = 204.8$ Hz

29 **a.** Proof that $\sin^{-1}(-x) = -\sin^{-1} x$ when $0 \leq x \leq 1$:

(1) $\sin(\sin^{-1}(-x)) = -x$ — Definition of inverse sine

(2) $\sin(-\sin^{-1} x) = -\sin(\sin^{-1} x)$ — $\sin(-x) = -\sin x$

In words, the sine of a value and the sine of the opposite of that value also are opposite signed values. In (2), you can think of $\pm\sin^{-1} x$ as two opposite signed input values for the sine function.

(3) $-\sin(\sin^{-1} x) = -x$ — Definition of inverse sine

(4) $\sin(-\sin^{-1} x) = -x$ — Substitution of (2) in (3)

(5) $\sin(\sin^{-1}(-x)) = \sin(-\sin^{-1} x)$ — Both equal $-x$ from (1) and (4)

(6) $\sin^{-1}(-x)) = -\sin^{-1} x$ — (See below.)

Since $0 \leq x \leq 1$, $-1 \leq x \leq 0$. The validity of (4) depends on the fact that the values of $\sin^{-1}(-x)$ and $-\sin^{-1} x$ are between $-\frac{\pi}{2}$ and $\frac{\pi}{2}$, and the sine function is one-to-one on that interval.

b. Using the coordinate definitions of cosine and sine, a point on the terminal side of $\sin^{-1} x$ at a distance of 1 from the origin has coordinates $(\sqrt{1 - x^2}, x)$.

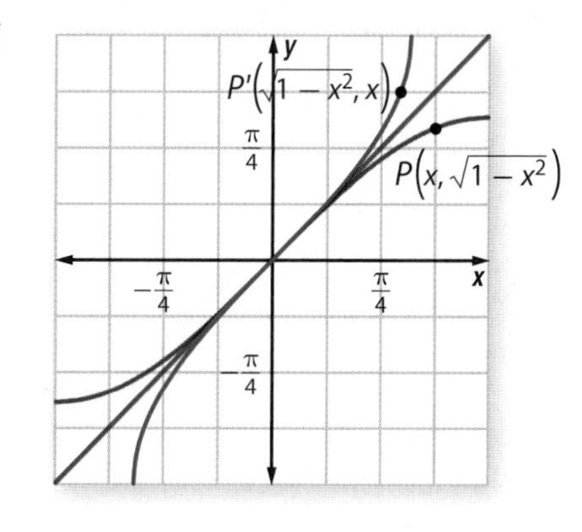

Similarly, $(x, \sqrt{1 - x^2})$ is on the terminal side of $\cos^{-1} x$ at a distance of 1 from the origin. These two points are reflections across the line $y = x$, which is the terminal side of an angle in standard position measuring $\frac{\pi}{4}$.

Then by symmetry about $\frac{\pi}{4}$, $\sin^{-1} x + \cos^{-1} x = 2\frac{\pi}{4} = \frac{\pi}{2}$.

c. The point $(\sqrt{1 - x^2}, x)$ is on the terminal side of $\sin^{-1} x$ at a distance of 1 from the origin. Thus, $\cos(\sin^{-1} x) = \sqrt{1 - x^2}$.

d. Using the coordinate definitions of cosine and tangent, a point on the terminal side of $\cos^{-1} x$ at a distance 1 from the origin has coordinates $(x, \sqrt{1 - x^2})$. Therefore, $\tan(\cos^{-1} x) = \frac{\sqrt{1 - x^2}}{x}$.

On Your Own

DIFFERENTIATION
Depending on the abilities of your students, you may wish to discuss the forms of these equations before students work on them. For example, the equation in Part a is quadratic in cos *x*.

30 **a.** $\cos^2 x + 2\cos x + 1 = 0$
$(\cos x + 1)^2 = 0$ or $\cos x = -1$
$\cos x = -1$
$x = \pi(2n + 1)$ for any integer n.

b. $2\sin x \cos x + \sin x = 0$
$\sin x\,(2\cos x + 1) = 0$
when $\sin x = 0$ or $\cos x = -0.5$
$x = \pi n, \frac{2\pi}{3} + 2\pi n$, or $\frac{4\pi}{3} + 2\pi n$
for any integer n.

c. $\tan^2 3x = 4\tan 3x$
$\tan 3x(\tan 3x - 4) = 0$
when $\tan 3x = 0$ or $\tan 3x = 4$
$3x = \pi n$ or $3x \approx 1.3258 + \pi n$
$x = \frac{\pi n}{3}$ or $x = 0.4419 + \frac{\pi n}{3}$
for any integer n.

d. $\sin^2 2x = 5\sin 2x - 6$
$(\sin 2x)^2 = 5\sin 2x - 6$
$(\sin 2x)^2 - 5\sin 2x + 6 = 0$
$(\sin 2x - 3)(\sin 2x - 2) = 0$ when
$\sin 2x = 3$ or $\sin 2x = 2$
No solution because $-1 \leq \sin 2x \leq 1$.

e. $\log(\cos x) + 2.5 = 1.9$
$\log(\cos x) = -0.6$
$\cos x = 10^{-0.6}$
$\cos x \approx 0.2512$ when
$x \approx 1.3169 + 2\pi n$ or $4.9663 + 2\pi n$
for any integer n.

f. $5(10^{\tan x}) + 15 = 64$
$10^{\tan x} = 9.8$
$\tan x = \log 9.8$
$\tan x \approx 0.9912$ when
$x \approx 0.7810 + \pi n$ for any integer n.

Unit 8

31 **a.** $x = \sin y$

b. If y is an angle in standard position and $x = \sin y$, then a point on the terminal side of y has y-coordinate of x and $r = 1$, that is, $(\sqrt{1 - x^2}, x)$ is on the terminal side of y. Therefore, $\tan y = \frac{x}{\sqrt{1 - x^2}}$.

c. $y = \tan^{-1}\left(\frac{x}{\sqrt{1 - x^2}}\right)$

d. $\tan^{-1}\left(\frac{0.5}{\sqrt{1 - 0.5^2}}\right) \approx 0.5236 \approx \frac{\pi}{6} = \sin^{-1} 0.5$

$\tan^{-1}\left(\frac{-0.8}{\sqrt{1 - (-0.8)^2}}\right) \approx -0.9273 \approx \sin^{-1}(-0.8)$

e. Let $y = \cos^{-1} x$, so $x = \cos y$. An argument like that in Part b shows that $\tan y = \frac{\sqrt{1 - x^2}}{x}$. Then $y = \cos^{-1} x = \tan^{-1}\left(\frac{\sqrt{1 - x^2}}{x}\right)$ if $0 < x < 1$.

If $-1 < x \leq 0$, $\cos^{-1} x$ is in the second quadrant and $\tan^{-1}\left(\frac{\sqrt{1 - x^2}}{x}\right)$ is in the fourth quadrant. In that case, $\cos^{-1} x = \pi + \tan^{-1}\left(\frac{\sqrt{1 - x^2}}{x}\right)$.

On Your Own

b. Consider the angle with measure y in standard position. Use your equation for x in Part a to write an expression for $\tan y$ in terms of x.

c. Transform this equation to one in which y is written in terms of the inverse tangent of a function of x.

d. Show that your equation gives correct values of $\sin^{-1} 0.5$ and $\sin^{-1} (-0.8)$.

e. Repeat the steps in Parts a–d to show how to write $\cos^{-1} x$ in terms of the inverse tangent of a function of x. You will need to take care that the equation you arrive at gives the correct value of $\cos^{-1} x$ if $x < 0$.

32 The graph of $x = \sin y$ is given at the right. This graph is clearly not the graph of a function of x. For that reason, your calculator in function mode will not draw this graph. Rather, you will need to set your calculator to parametric mode. With parametric equations, a third variable t is introduced, and the x- and y-coordinates are written as separate functions of t.

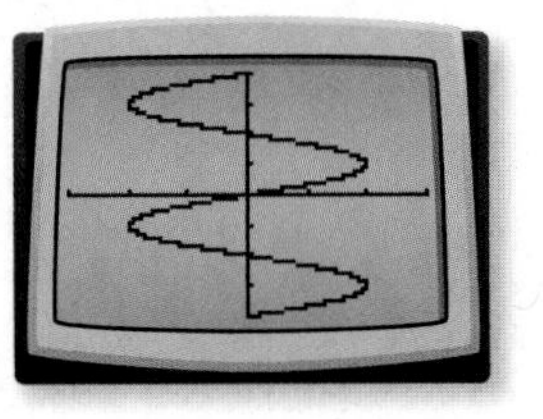

a. With your calculator set to parametric mode, press Y=. You will then enter a function of t for X_T (or X_{1T}). Enter **sin(T)**. If the resulting pair of equations, X_T and Y_T, is to be equivalent to $x = \sin y$, what should you enter for Y_T?

b. Experiment with window settings to get a graph that looks like this one. A good choice for Tstep is 0.1. What settings for x, y, and t worked for you?

c. Without changing the window settings for x and y, how could you change the settings for t so that the resulting graph is that of $y = \sin^{-1} x$? Explain.

d. Repeat Parts a–c with the graph of $x = \cos y$.

33 Earth travels around the Sun in an elliptical orbit. The distance d in kilometers between Earth and the Sun at time t in days since January 1 is approximated by the following equation.

$$d = \frac{1.5 \times 10^8}{1 - 0.0166 \cos\left(\frac{2\pi(t - 185)}{365}\right)}$$

a. What is the minimum distance from Earth to the Sun? On what date does the minimum distance occur?

b. What is the maximum distance from Earth to the Sun? On what date does the maximum distance occur?

c. Write an equation whose solutions are the two days during the year at which Earth is 1.48×10^8 km from the Sun. Use symbol manipulation methods to solve the equation. Check your solutions by substitution.

Unit 8

598 UNIT 8 • Inverse Functions

32 **a.** $Y_T = t$ or T

b. This graph at the right below is on the window $-1.5 \leq x \leq 1.5$, $-2\pi \leq y \leq 2\pi$, $-2\pi \leq t \leq 2\pi$, and t-step $= 0.1$.

c. $-\frac{\pi}{2} < t < \frac{\pi}{2}$

d. Graphs may vary depending on the window settings. A good choice is $-1.5 \leq x \leq 1.5$, $-\pi \leq y \leq 3\pi$, $-\pi \leq t \leq 3\pi$, and t-step $= 0.1$, but other windows that show at least two periods of $x = \cos y$ are fine. To graph $y = \cos^{-1} x$ without changing any window settings, except for t, restrict t so that $0 \leq t \leq \pi$.

NOTE Solutions to Task 31 Parts b–e are on page T597.

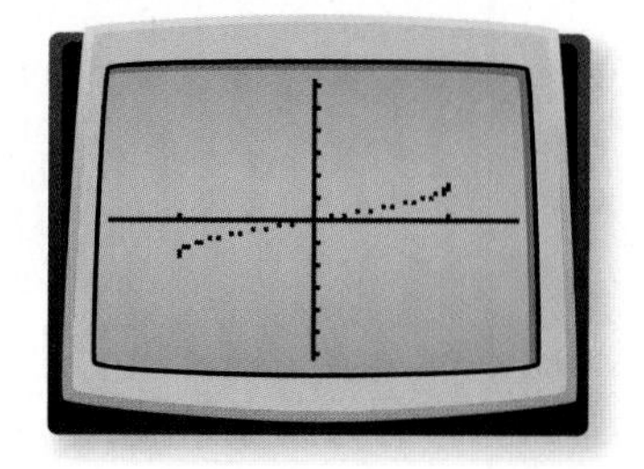

33 **a.** The minimum distance occurs when the denominator is at its maximum, that is, when $\cos\left(\frac{2\pi(t-185)}{365}\right) = -1$ (since it is subtracted from 1 in the denominator). In that case,

$$d = \frac{1.5 \times 10^8}{1 + 0.0166} \approx 1.475 \times 10^8 \text{ km.}$$

To find the date when the minimum occurs, solve $\cos\left(\frac{2\pi(t-185)}{365}\right) = -1$ as follows:

$$\frac{2\pi(t-185)}{365} = \cos^{-1}(-1) = \pi$$
$$2(t-185) = 365$$
$$t = 367.5$$

This value of t corresponds to about 2.5 days after January 1 or about January 3 or 4.

b. The maximum distance occurs when the denominator is at its minimum, that is, when $\cos\left(\frac{2\pi(t-185)}{365}\right) = 1$. In that case,

$$d = \frac{1.5 \times 10^8}{1 - 0.0166} \approx 1.525 \times 10^8 \text{ km.}$$

This minimum occurs when $\frac{2\pi(t-185)}{365} = \cos^{-1} 1 = 0$

$$t = 185.$$

This value of t corresponds to July 4 (July 3 if it is a leap year).

c. $\dfrac{1.5 \times 10^8}{1 - 0.0166\cos\left(\frac{2\pi(t-185)}{365}\right)} = 1.48 \times 10^8$

$$1.5 \times 10^8 = 1.48 \times 10^8\left(1 - 0.0166\cos\left(\frac{2\pi(t-185)}{365}\right)\right)$$
$$1.0135 \approx 1 - 0.0166\cos\left(\frac{2\pi(t-185)}{365}\right)$$
$$-0.8133 \approx \cos\left(\frac{2\pi(t-185)}{365}\right)$$

$\frac{2\pi(t-185)}{365} = \cos^{-1}(-0.8133) \approx 2.5205$

$t \approx 331$ days

This value of t corresponds to November 27 (November 26 if it is a leap year).

The second time when Earth is 1.48×10^8 km from the Sun can be found by solving $\frac{2\pi(t-185)}{365} = -2.5205$. $t \approx 39$ days, which corresponds to February 8.

34 The center of a water wheel with radius 4 meters is 2.5 meters above the surface of the water. A point P is located at (4, 0) on the circumference of the wheel when the wheel begins to rotate counterclockwise through an angle θ in radians.

a. Explain why point P is below the water's surface between consecutive solutions of $4 \sin \theta + 2.5 = 0$.

b. Find the interval of θ between 0 and 2π for which point P is below the water's surface by solving this equation.

35 Use symbolic reasoning and properties of the inverse trigonometric functions (in radian mode) to solve the following equations for x.

a. $2 \sin^{-1} x = 1$

b. $\cos^{-1} 2x = 0.3$

c. $3 \tan^{-1} \pi x = -3$

Review

36 Solve each equation or inequality. Graph the solution to each inequality on a number line.

a. $4 + 2x(x - 5) = (x + 3)(2x - 8)$

b. $2x^2 + 6x = 8$

c. $x + 3 = \frac{1}{x}$

d. $(x^2 + 4x)(x - 3) = 0$

e. $10x - 21 \leq x^2$

f. $12 - 8x \geq 4(x + 9)$

37 In the diagram at the right, $AC = AB$, $AD = AE$, and $DC = EF$.

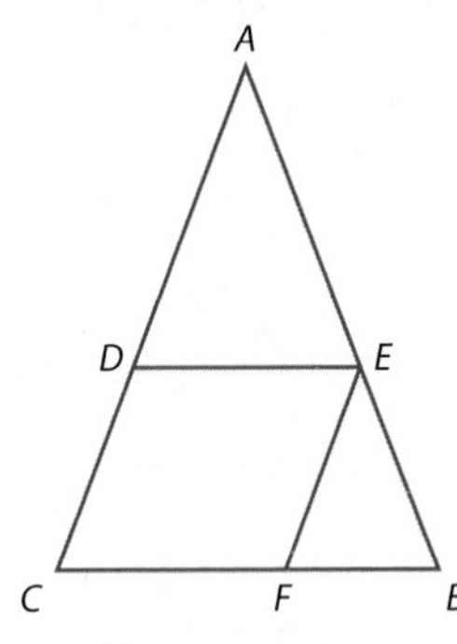

a. Prove that $\triangle EBF$ is isosceles.

b. Prove that quadrilateral $DEFC$ is a parallelogram.

c. Is $\triangle EBF \sim \triangle ABC$? Provide reasoning to support your answer.

d. If $m\angle C = 80°$, find the following angle measures.

i. $m\angle B$

ii. $m\angle ADE$

iii. $m\angle A$

iv. $m\angle EFC$

34 **a.** If the wheel is placed on a coordinate system with the origin at its center, then by definition of the sine function, the distance of point P from the horizontal axis is $y = 4 \sin x$ or $y = 4 \sin \theta$. If the axis is to be at ground level, the center of the wheel must be translated up by 2.5 meters. The rule is $y = 4 \sin \theta + 2.5$. Point P is at the water's surface when $y = 0$ or $4 \sin \theta + 2.5 = 0$ and is below the surface between consecutive third quadrant and fourth quadrant solutions of this equation on $[0, 2\pi]$.

b. $\sin \theta = -0.625$

One solution of this equation is $\sin^{-1}(-0.625) \approx -0.6751$. This solution is not between 0 and 2π, but $-0.6751 + 2\pi \approx 5.6080$ is in the target interval.

A second solution between 0 and 2π is symmetric to this one about the line $x = \frac{3\pi}{2}$ or $\frac{3\pi}{2} - \left(5.6080 - \frac{3\pi}{2}\right) \approx 3.8167$. Thus, point P is below the surface of the water when $3.8167 < \theta < 5.6080$.

35 **a.** $x = \sin \frac{1}{2} \approx 0.479$ **b.** $x = \frac{\cos 0.3}{2} \approx 0.478$ **c.** $\pi x = \tan(-1)$

$x = \frac{\tan(-1)}{\pi} \approx -0.496$

Review

36 **a.** $x = 3.5$

b. $x = -4$ or $x = 1$

c. $x = \frac{-3 \pm \sqrt{13}}{2}$

d. $x = 0$, $x = -4$, or $x = 3$

e.

f.

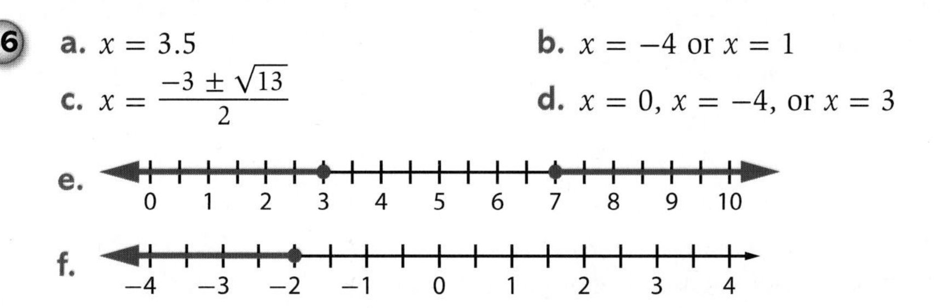

37 **a.** One possible proof is provided. Since we are told that $AD = AE$ and $AC = AB$, by the Subtraction Property of Equality $DC = AC - AD = AB - AE = EB$. Then, since $DC = EF$ and $DC = EB$, we can conclude that $EF = EB$. So by the definition of an isosceles triangle, $\triangle EBF$ is isosceles.

b. One possible proof is provided. We are given that $DC = EF$. From Part a, we know that $\triangle EFB$ is isosceles. Since base angles of an isosceles triangle are congruent, we know that $\angle C \cong \angle B$ ($\triangle ABC$ is isosceles) and $\angle EFB \cong \angle B$ ($\triangle EFB$ is isosceles). Thus, we can conclude that $\angle C \cong \angle EFB$. But $\angle C$ and $\angle EFB$ are corresponding angles formed by $\overline{EF}$ and $\overline{DC}$ and the transversal $\overline{CB}$. Since $\angle C \cong \angle EFB$ and they are corresponding angles, we can conclude that $\overline{DC} \parallel \overline{EF}$. Now, since $\overline{DC} \parallel \overline{EF}$ and $\overline{DC} \cong \overline{EF}$, quadrilateral $DEFC$ is a parallelogram.

c. Yes, $\triangle EBF \sim \triangle ABC$ by the AA Similarity Theorem. From Part b, we know that $\angle EFB \cong \angle C$. We also know that $\angle B$ is in both triangles.

d. **i.** $m\angle B = 80°$ **ii.** $m\angle ADE = 80°$

iii. $m\angle A = 20°$ **iv.** $m\angle EFC = 100°$

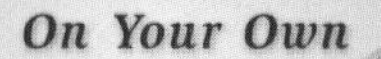

On Your Own

38 Antonio has an account balance of $1,500 on his credit card. His credit card company charges a monthly interest rate of 1.5%. He can afford to pay $50 a month to pay off his debt and has made a pledge to himself not to purchase anything more with his credit card.

a. How much will his credit card balance be after 1 month? After 2 months?

b. Write a recursive formula for the account balance from one month to the next.

c. How long will it take him to reach a zero balance?

d. How much interest will he have paid when his account reaches a zero balance?

39 Use relationships between angle measures and arc lengths to determine each indicated value.

a. In the circle with center O, $m\angle BOA = 5x + 16°$ and $m\angle BCA = 3x - 2°$.

i. $m\angle BCA$

ii. $m\widehat{BCA}$

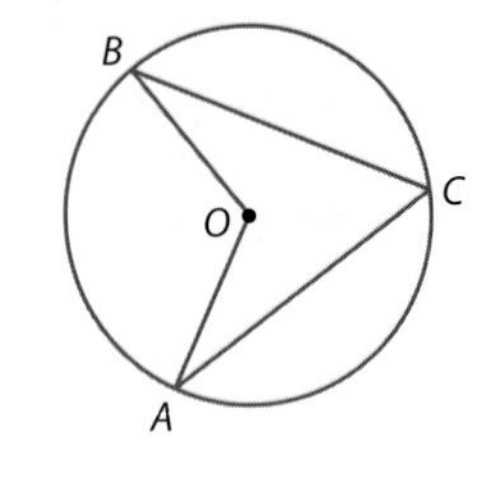

b. In the circle at the right, $AB = BC = CD$ and $m\angle C = 125°$.

i. $m\widehat{BAD}$

ii. $m\widehat{BCD}$

iii. $m\widehat{BC}$

iv. $m\angle BAD$

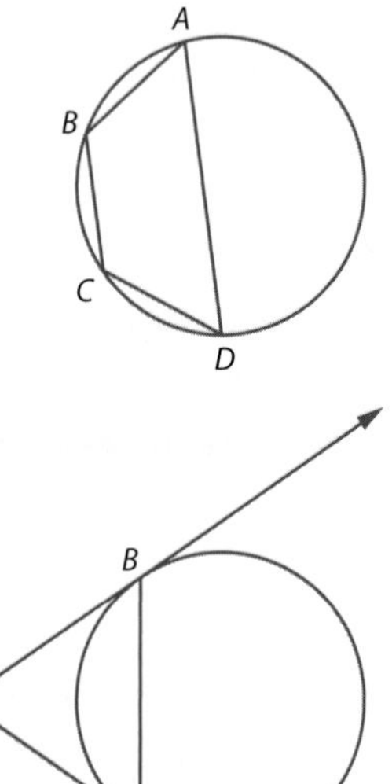

c. In the diagram at the right, $\overrightarrow{AB}$ and $\overrightarrow{AC}$ are tangent to the circle at points B and C, $m\angle A = 68°$, and $AC = 8$ in.

i. AB

ii. BC

iii. Radius of the circle

Unit 8

600 UNIT 8 • Inverse Functions

38 **a.** After 1 month, the balance will be 1.015(1,500) − 50 = \$1,472.50.
After 2 months the balance will be 1.015(1,472.50) − 50 = \$1,444.59.

b. $B_0 = 1{,}500$
$B_n = 1{,}015(B_{n-1}) - 50$

c. It will take him 41 months to pay off the credit card. His final payment will be \$7.63.

d. Since he will have paid \$50 for 40 months and then \$7.63 in the final month, he will have paid a total of 50 • 40 + 7.63 = \$2,007.63. So, the interest he will have paid will be \$2,007.63 − \$1,500 = \$507.63.

39 **a.** $5x + 16 = 2(3x - 2)$
$x = 20$

i. $m\angle BCA = 58°$ **ii.** $m\widehat{BCA} = 244°$

b. **i.** $m\widehat{BAD} = 250°$ **ii.** $m\widehat{BCD} = 110°$

iii. $m\widehat{BC} = 55°$ **iv.** $m\angle BAD = 55°$

c. **i.** $AB = 8$ in.

ii. $\sin 34° = \dfrac{\frac{1}{2}BC}{8}$
$16 \sin 34° = BC$
$BC \approx 8.95$ in.

iii. $\tan 34° = \dfrac{r}{8}$
$8 \tan 34° = r$
$r \approx 5.4$ in.

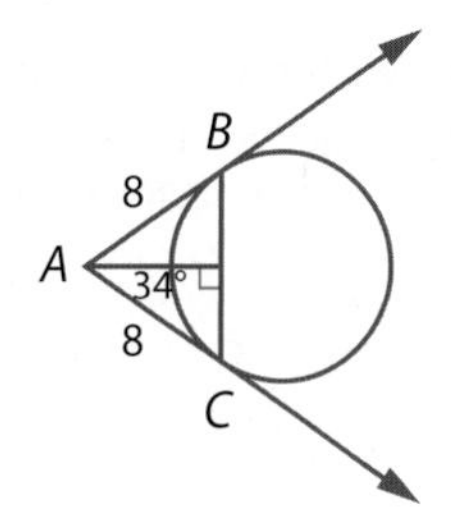

40 For each rational function below, use algebraic reasoning to:

- find coordinates of all x-intercepts and the y-intercept of the graph.
- describe the domain of the function.
- find equations of all vertical and horizontal asymptotes.
- sketch a graph on which you label intercepts and asymptotes.

a. $f(x) = \dfrac{5}{x - 2}$

b. $g(x) = \dfrac{3x - 4}{2x + 1}$

41 A national survey of 13–17-year-olds indicated that 43% of teens say they have experienced some form of cyberbullying. Suppose you randomly select 120 teens to survey about cyberbullying.

a. How many of them would you expect to say they have experienced some form of cyberbullying?

b. Is the binomial distribution of the number of teens who say they have experienced cyberbullying approximately normal?

c. What is the standard deviation of this binomial distribution?

d. Would you be surprised to find that only 42 teens in your sample reported having been cyberbullied? Explain.

42 Consider the graphs of $f(x)$ and $g(x)$ shown below. The two graphs intersect at the points $(-2, 0)$ and $(5, 7)$.

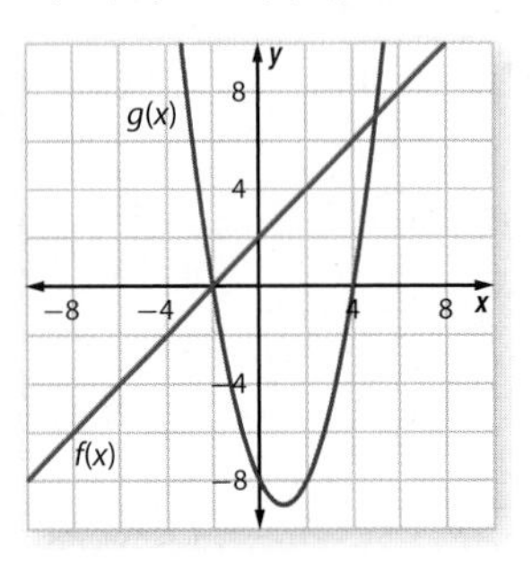

a. For what values of x is $f(x) - g(x) < 0$?

b. Find a formula for $f(x)$.

c. If $g(x)$ is a quadratic function with vertex $(1, -9)$, write the vertex and standard expressions for $g(x)$.

d. What is the degree of each of the following? Explain your reasoning.

- $f(x) \cdot g(x)$
- $f(x) + g(x)$

40 **a.**
- y-intercept: $\left(0, -\frac{5}{2}\right)$
  x-intercepts: none
- The domain of $f(x) = \frac{5}{x-2}$ is all real numbers except $x = 2$.
- Horizontal asymptote: $y = 0$
  Vertical asymptote: $x = 2$
- 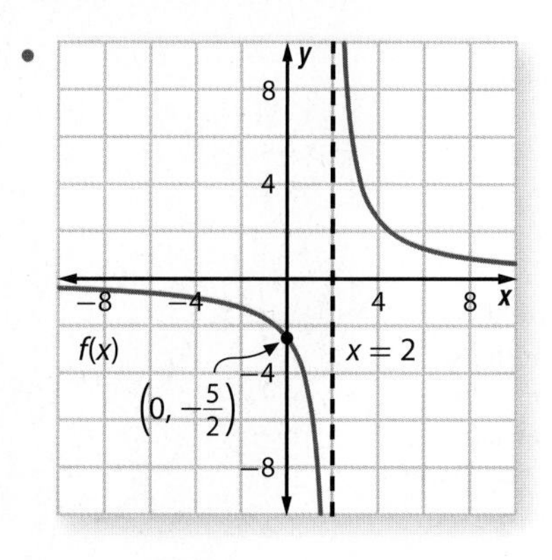

b.
- y-intercept: $(0, -4)$
  x-intercepts: $\left(\frac{4}{3}, 0\right)$
- The domain of $g(x) = \frac{3x-4}{2x+1}$ is all real numbers except $x = -\frac{1}{2}$.
- Horizontal asymptote: $y = \frac{3}{2}$
  Vertical asymptote: $x = -\frac{1}{2}$
- 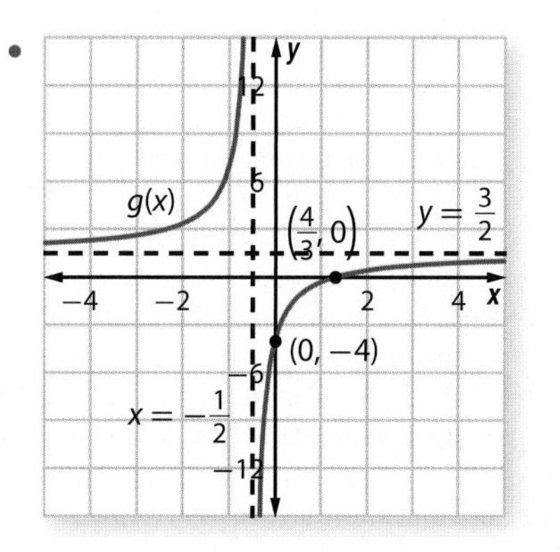

41 **a.** $(0.43)(120) = 51.6$ teens

b. The distribution will be approximately normal because both $np = 120(0.43) = 51.6$ and $n(1 - p) = 120(0.57) = 68.4$ are greater than 10.

c. The standard deviation of this binomial distribution is $\sigma = \sqrt{np(1-p)} = \sqrt{120(0.43)(0.57)} \approx 5.4$.

d. No, 42 is not more than two standard deviations from the mean of 51.6.

42 **a.** $f(x) - g(x) < 0$ when $f(x) < g(x)$. This occurs when $x < -2$ and $x > 5$.

b. $f(x) = x + 2$

c. $g(x) = (x - 1)^2 - 9$
$g(x) = x^2 - 2x - 8$

d.
- The degree of $f(x) \cdot g(x)$ is 3 because $(x + 2)(x^2 - 2x - 8)$ will be a cubic polynomial.
- The degree of $f(x) + g(x)$ is 2 because $(x + 2) + (x^2 - 2x - 8)$ will be a quadratic polynomial.

Teaching Resources

Assessment Masters 31–36.

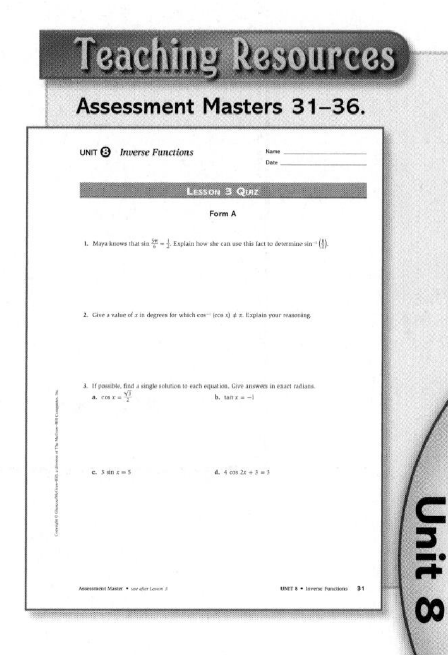

UNIT 8 *Inverse Functions* Name ____ Date ____

LESSON 3 QUIZ

Form A

1. Maya knows that $\sin \frac{5\pi}{6} = \frac{1}{2}$. Explain how she can use this fact to determine $\sin^{-1}\left(\frac{1}{2}\right)$.

2. Give a value of x in degrees for which $\cos^{-1}(\cos x) \neq x$. Explain your reasoning.

3. If possible, find a single solution to each equation. Give answers in exact radians.
   a. $\cos x = \frac{\sqrt{3}}{2}$
   b. $\tan x = -1$
   c. $3 \sin x = 5$
   d. $4 \cos 2x + 3 = 3$

Assessment Master • *use after Lesson 3* UNIT 8 • Inverse Functions 31

LESSON 4

Looking Back

The lessons of this unit extended your knowledge and skill in work with algebraic and trigonometric functions and expressions in three ways. First, you learned what it means for a function to have an inverse, how to find inverse functions when they exist, and how to use inverse functions to solve a variety of problems. Second, you learned the definition and key properties of an important inverse function that gives base-10 logarithms, and you developed strategies for using that function to solve exponential equations. Third, you extended your understanding of the basic sine, cosine, and tangent functions. Then you learned the definitions, properties, and applications of three inverse trigonometric functions.

The next several tasks give you an opportunity to review your knowledge of inverse functions and apply that knowledge to some new contexts.

1. In which of these situations will the indicated function have an inverse? For those functions that do have inverses, explain what information the inverse would provide.

   a. In most states, there is a rule that shows how to calculate sales tax as a function of the price of any purchase.

   b. The price for a package of cheese sold in a market is a function of the weight of the package.

   c. The time that it takes the sound of thunder to reach the ears of a person is a function of the distance from the lightning strike producing the thunder to the listener's ears.

   d. The depth of water at a particular location in an ocean harbor varies over time.

2. Sketch graphs of these functions. Tell which have inverses. Then find rules and sketch graphs for those that do.

   a. $f(x) = 0.5x$

   b. $g(x) = 1.5x + 4$

   c. $r(t) = \frac{500}{t}$

   d. $s(x) = \log x$

Unit 8

Looking Back

LESSON 4

The lessons of this unit extended student knowledge and skill in work with algebraic functions and expressions in three ways. First, they learned what it means for a function to have an inverse, how to find inverse functions when they exist, and how to use inverse functions to solve a variety of "decoding" problems. Second, they learned the definition and key properties of one important inverse function, the base 10 logarithm function, and ways to use that function to solve exponential equations. Third, they learned about the inverse trigonometric functions and how to use them to solve trigonometric equations.

The next several tasks give students an opportunity to put their new knowledge of inverse functions and logarithms to work in some new contexts.

1. **a.** No inverse. While every purchase price has an associated sales tax, several different prices might have the same sales tax. Thus, one cannot tell the purchase price from the sales tax.

   b. Typically, there is a one-to-one relationship between weight and price (within limits of accuracy of weight measurement). Thus, if one knows the price per pound and the total price of the purchase, one can make a very accurate estimate of the purchase weight.

   c. There is (within limits of special atmospheric conditions) a one-to-one correspondence between distance and time (usually based on 1,100 feet per second speed of sound). Thus, if one knows the time between lightning flash and sound of the thunder, one can accurately estimate the distance to the lightning strike in feet by multiplying 1,100 times the time in seconds. Inversely, if one knows the distance of a lightning strike, one can accurately estimate the time it takes for thunder sound to reach an observer by dividing the distance by 1,100.

   d. Although tide charts predict the depth of water as a function of time, it is not possible to infer the time from the depth of water because there will be several times in each 24 hour day when the tidal depth is the same.

2 **a.** 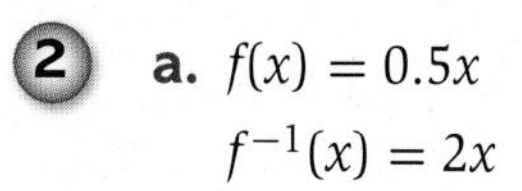
$f(x) = 0.5x$
$f^{-1}(x) = 2x$

b. 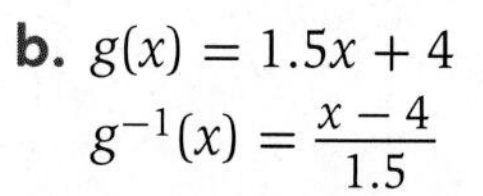
$g(x) = 1.5x + 4$
$g^{-1}(x) = \frac{x - 4}{1.5}$

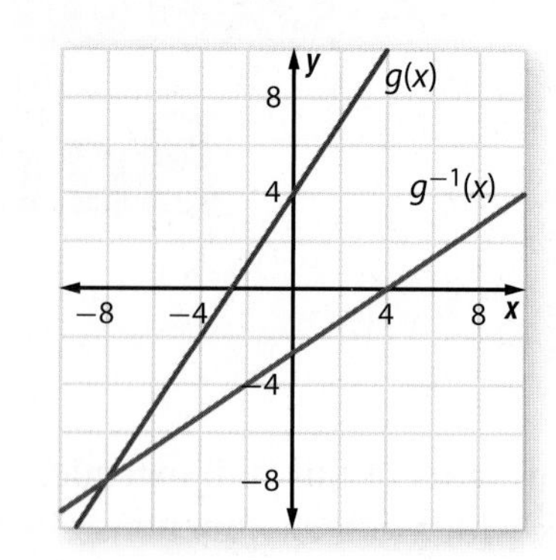

c. $r(t) = \frac{500}{t}$

$r^{-1}(t) = \frac{500}{t}$

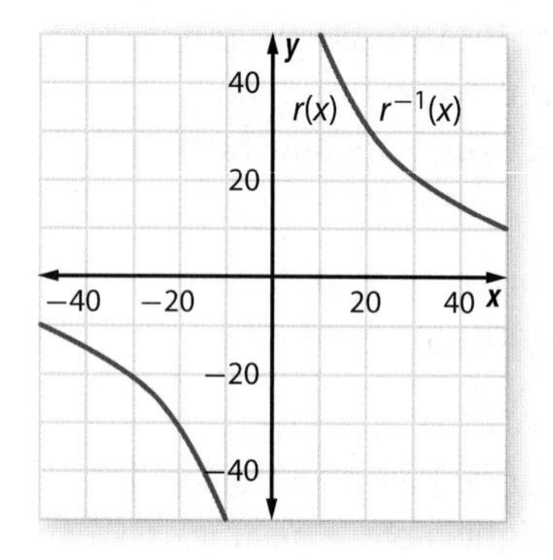

d. $s(x) = \log x$

$s^{-1}(x) = 10^x$

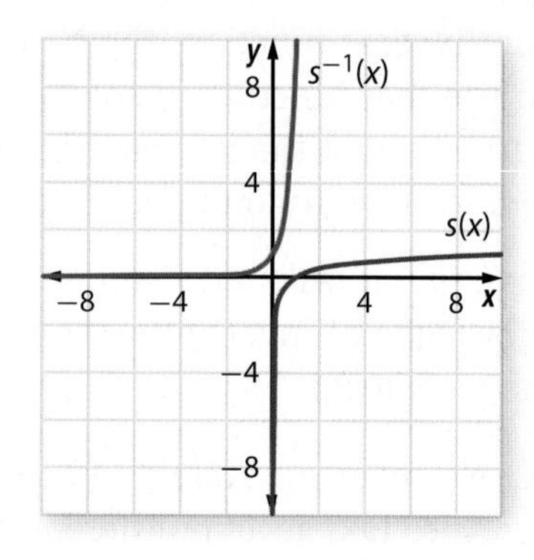

Unit 8

Teacher Notes

3. Light, radio and television signals, x-rays, and the waves produced by alternating electric current are forms of electromagnetic radiation. The next table gives frequencies for a sample of such electromagnetic waves.

   a. Write each frequency in scientific notation.

   b. Suppose that you had a table that gave logarithms only for numbers between 0 and 10. Show how you could use those table values, the results of your work in Part a, and properties of logarithms to estimate the logarithms of the given frequencies.

Type of Electromagnetic Wave	Frequency in Cycles per Second
Alternating electrical current	60
AM radio	from 540,000 to 1,600,000
Television and FM radio	from 54,000,000 to 216,000,000
Light	from infrared 390,000,000,000,000 to ultraviolet 770,000,000,000,000
x-rays	from 30,000,000,000,000,000 to 100,000,000,000,000,000,000

4. If you buy a new car for $25,000, its resale value decreases by about 20% each year. Write and solve equations representing these questions.

   a. When will the value of the car be only $10,000?

   b. How long will it take for the value of the car to be reduced to only $5,000?

   c. When is the car worth half the purchase price?

5. In wildlife preserves, like national parks, the populations of many animal species vary periodically in relationship to the populations of other species that are either predators or prey. For example, rabbits are prey for foxes, so when the fox population is high, it causes the rabbit population to fall, and vice versa.

   a. Suppose that the fox population in a study region is given by the function $f(t) = 20 \sin t + 100$, where t is the time in years after the first census in the region.

      i. What are the period and amplitude of cycles in the fox population?

      ii. At what time(s) was the fox population a maximum and when a minimum during the first cycle of change?

      iii. At what time(s) will the fox population be about 115? When about 90?

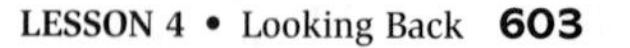

3 **a–b.** The following table shows frequencies expressed in scientific notation and then after log transformation.

Type of Wave	Frequency (in cycles/sec)	log Frequency
AC	6×10	1.78
AM radio	5.4×10^5	5.732
	1.6×10^6	6.204
TV/FM radio	5.4×10^7	7.732
	2.16×10^8	8.334
Infrared	3.9×10^{14}	14.591
Ultraviolet	7.7×10^{14}	14.886
X-rays	3.0×10^{16}	16.477
	1.0×10^{20}	20.000

To find the logarithm of a number in scientific notation, use logarithms of numbers between 0 and 10 and properties of logarithms as in the following example:

$$\log (3.2 \times 10^5) = \log 3.2 + \log 10^5 \approx 0.505 + 5 = 5.505$$

This is the value that you will get from technology by asking for the result of log 320,000.

4 **a.** $25{,}000(0.8^x) = 10{,}000$

$$x = \frac{\log 0.4}{\log 0.8} \approx 4.1 \text{ years}$$

b. $25{,}000(0.8^x) = 5{,}000$

$$x = \frac{\log 0.2}{\log 0.8} \approx 7.2 \text{ years}$$

c. $25{,}000(0.8^x) = 12{,}500$

$$x = \frac{\log 0.5}{\log 0.8} \approx 3.1 \text{ years}$$

5 **a.** **i.** *period* $= 2\pi$

ii. The maximum of 120 occurs when $t = \frac{\pi}{2}$, or about 1.57 years after start of the study. The minimum of 80 occurs when $t = \frac{3\pi}{2}$, or about 4.71 years after the start of the study.

iii. The population is approximately 115 at two points in each cycle—when $t \approx 0.85$ years and $\pi - 0.85 \approx 2.29$ years after the start of the study.

The population is approximately 90 at two points in each cycle—when $t \approx 3.66$ years and when $t \approx 5.76$ years after the start of the study.

Unit 8

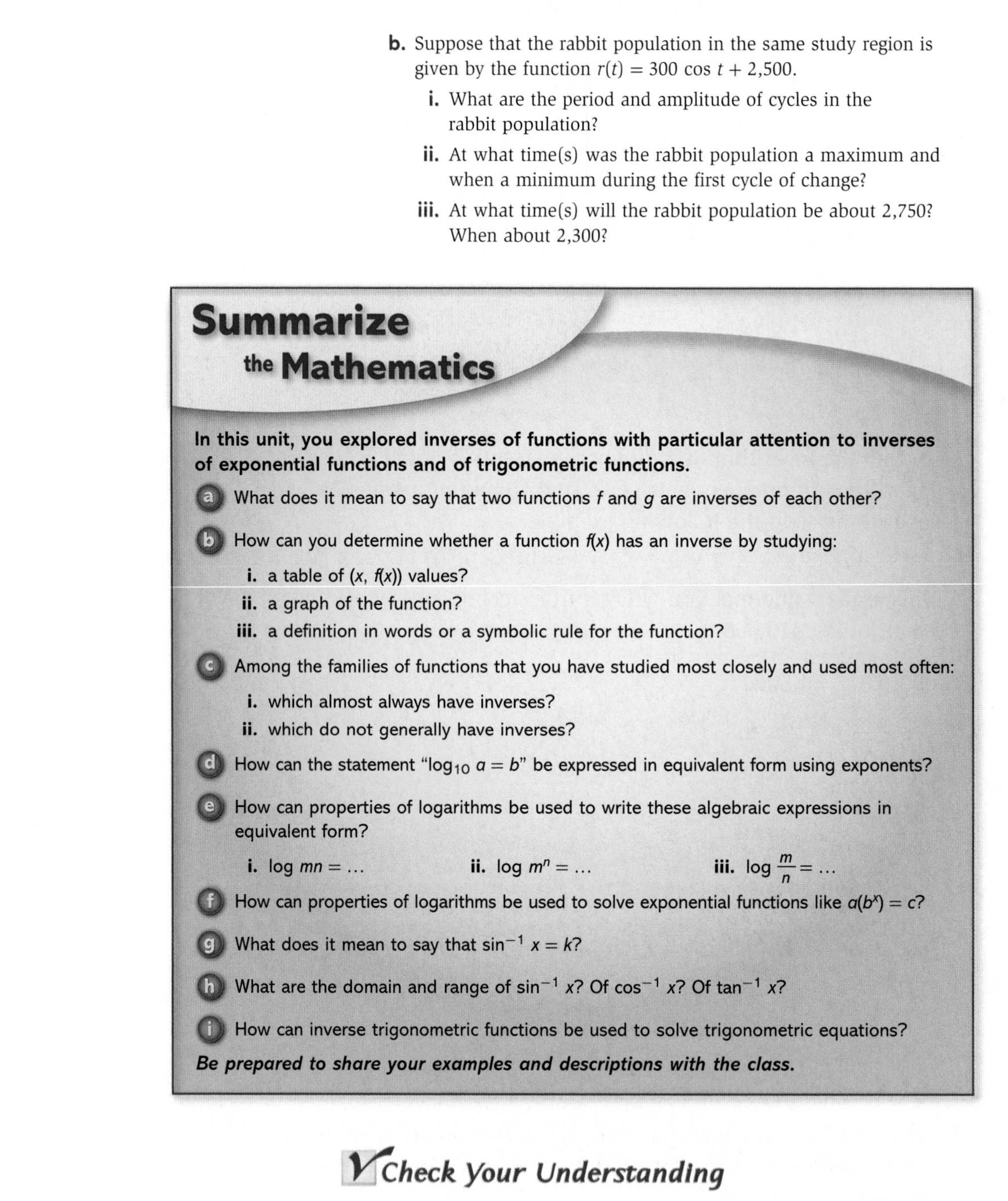

b. Suppose that the rabbit population in the same study region is given by the function $r(t) = 300 \cos t + 2{,}500$.

i. What are the period and amplitude of cycles in the rabbit population?

ii. At what time(s) was the rabbit population a maximum and when a minimum during the first cycle of change?

iii. At what time(s) will the rabbit population be about 2,750? When about 2,300?

Summarize the Mathematics

In this unit, you explored inverses of functions with particular attention to inverses of exponential functions and of trigonometric functions.

a What does it mean to say that two functions f and g are inverses of each other?

b How can you determine whether a function $f(x)$ has an inverse by studying:

i. a table of $(x, f(x))$ values?

ii. a graph of the function?

iii. a definition in words or a symbolic rule for the function?

c Among the families of functions that you have studied most closely and used most often:

i. which almost always have inverses?

ii. which do not generally have inverses?

d How can the statement "$\log_{10} a = b$" be expressed in equivalent form using exponents?

e How can properties of logarithms be used to write these algebraic expressions in equivalent form?

i. $\log mn = \ldots$ **ii.** $\log m^n = \ldots$ **iii.** $\log \frac{m}{n} = \ldots$

f How can properties of logarithms be used to solve exponential functions like $a(b^x) = c$?

g What does it mean to say that $\sin^{-1} x = k$?

h What are the domain and range of $\sin^{-1} x$? Of $\cos^{-1} x$? Of $\tan^{-1} x$?

i How can inverse trigonometric functions be used to solve trigonometric equations?

Be prepared to share your examples and descriptions with the class.

Check Your Understanding

Write, in outline form, a summary of the important mathematical concepts and methods developed in this unit. Organize your summary so that it can be used as a quick reference in future units and courses.

Unit 8

604 UNIT 8 • Inverse Functions

b. **i.** *period* $= 2\pi$

ii. The maximum of 2,800 occurs when $t = 0$, or at the start of the study. The minimum of 2,200 occurs when $t = \pi$, or about 3.14 years after the start of the study.

iii. The population is approximately 2,750 at two points in each cycle—when $t \approx 0.59$ years and $t \approx 5.69$ years after the start of the study.

The population is approximately 2,300 at two points in each cycle—when $t \approx 2.3$ years and when $t \approx 4.0$ years after the start of the study.

Summarize the Mathematics

a Two functions f and g are inverses of each other if and only if the range of f is the domain of g (and vice versa) and whenever $f(a) = b$, then $g(b) = a$.

b You can determine whether a function $f(x)$ has an inverse:

i. by studying a table of $(x, f(x))$ values to see that if $x_1 \neq x_2$ then $f(x_1) \neq f(x_2)$; that is, no number repeats in the $f(x)$ column.

ii. by studying a graph of the function to see that no horizontal line crosses the graph at more than one point (no repeated y values).

iii. by studying a definition in words for the function to assure yourself that each $f(x)$ value comes from a different x value, or by studying a symbolic rule and recognizing that the function is one of the types that you have shown earlier to always have an inverse, or by showing that you can always solve the equation $y = f(x)$ for x in terms of y to get the rule for the inverse.

c Among the families of functions that students have studied most closely and used most often:

i. linear, exponential, inverse variation, and logarithmic functions almost always have inverses.

ii. quadratic functions (higher degree polynomials) do not generally have inverses (unless one restricts the domain to focus on "one half" of the symmetric graph). Trigonometric functions do not generally have inverses (unless one restricts attention to a carefully chosen segment of the graph).

d The statement "$\log_{10} a = b$" can be expressed in equivalent form using exponents as $10^b = a$.

Teaching Resources

Transparency Masters 37–38.

UNIT 8 *Inverse Functions*

Summarize the Mathematics

In this unit, you explored inverses of functions with particular attention to inverses of exponential functions and of trigonometric functions.

a What does it mean to say that two functions f and g are inverses of each other?

b How can you determine whether a function $f(x)$ has an inverse by studying:

i. a table of $(x, f(x))$ values?

ii. a graph of the function?

iii. a definition in words or a symbolic rule for the function?

c Among the families of functions that you have studied most closely and used most often:

i. which almost always have inverses?

ii. which do not generally have inverses?

d How can the statement "$\log_{10} a = b$" be expressed in equivalent form using exponents?

e How can properties of logarithms be used to write these algebraic expressions in equivalent form?

i. $\log mn = \ldots$

ii. $\log m^n = \ldots$

iii. $\log \frac{m}{n} = \ldots$

Unit 8

e Properties of logarithms can be used to write algebraic expressions in equivalent form and solve exponential equations as follows:

i. $\log mn = \log m + \log n$

ii. $\log m^n = n \log m$

iii. $\log \frac{m}{n} = \log m - \log n$

f The solution of $a(b^x) = c$ is $x = \dfrac{\log \frac{c}{a}}{\log b}$.

g $\sin^{-1} x = k$ means that $\sin k = x$ and $-\frac{\pi}{2} \leq k \leq \frac{\pi}{2}$.

h The domain of $\sin^{-1} x$ is $[-1, 1]$ and the range is $\left[-\frac{\pi}{2}, \frac{\pi}{2}\right]$.
The domain of $\cos^{-1} x$ is $[-1, 1]$ and the range is $[0, \pi]$.
The domain of $\tan^{-1} x$ is all real numbers and the range is $\left(-\frac{\pi}{2}, \frac{\pi}{2}\right)$.

i To use inverse trigonometric functions to solve trigonometric equations, you manipulate the equation to the form $\sin x = k$ (or similar for cosine and tangent) and then the first solution is $x = \sin^{-1} k$. To see the other solutions (there are generally infinitely many if there is one), it helps to look at a graph of the sine, cosine, or tangent function and reason by symmetry and periodicity to where the other solutions occur.

Teaching Resources

Student Masters 39–40.

UNIT 8 *Inverse Functions*

UNIT SUMMARY

Check Your Understanding

You may wish to have students use the Teaching Master, *Inverse Functions* Unit Summary, to help them organize the information. Above all, this should be something that is useful to the individual student.

Unit 8

Practicing for Standardized Tests

Each Practicing for Standardized Tests master presents 10 questions in the multiple-choice format of test items similar to how they often appear in standardized tests. Answers are provided below.

Answers to Practice Set 8

1. (c)	**2.** (c)	**3.** (b)	**4.** (d)	**5.** (d)
6. (c)	**7.** (a)	**8.** (c)	**9.** (b)	**10.** (c)

Teaching Resources

Assessment Masters 41–60.

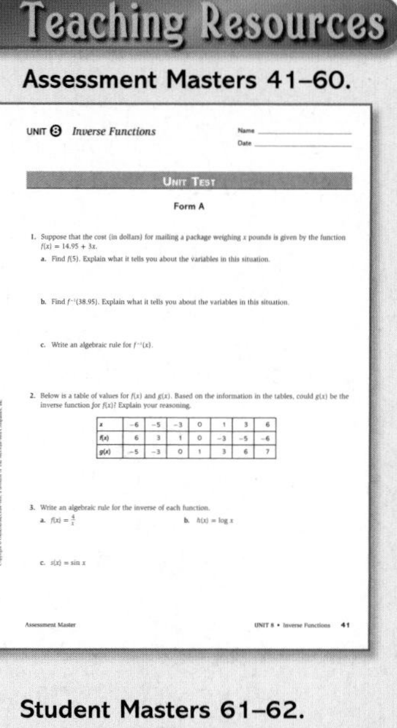
UNIT 8 *Inverse Functions* Name ______ Date ______

UNIT TEST

Form A

1. Suppose that the cost (in dollars) for mailing a package weighing x pounds is given by the function $f(x) = 14.95 + 3x$.
   a. Find $f(5)$. Explain what it tells you about the variables in this situation.
   b. Find $f^{-1}(38.95)$. Explain what it tells you about the variables in this situation.
   c. Write an algebraic rule for $f^{-1}(x)$.
2. Below is a table of values for $f(x)$ and $g(x)$. Based on the information in the tables, could $g(x)$ be the inverse function for $f(x)$? Explain your reasoning.

x	−6	−5	−3	0	1	3	6
$f(x)$	6	3	1	0	−3	−5	−6
$g(x)$	−5	−3	0	1	3	6	7

3. Write an algebraic rule for the inverse of each function.
   a. $f(x) = \frac{4}{x}$
   b. $h(x) = \log x$
   c. $s(x) = \sin x$

Copyright © Glencoe/McGraw-Hill, a division of The McGraw-Hill Companies, Inc.

Assessment Master UNIT 8 • Inverse Functions 41

Student Masters 61–62.

UNIT 8 *Inverse Functions* Name ______ Date ______

PRACTICING FOR STANDARDIZED TESTS

Practice Set

Solve each problem. Then record the letter that corresponds to the correct answer.

1. The endpoints of a diagonal of a square are (−2, 2) and (1, 5). What is the area of the square?
   (a) 3 (b) $3\sqrt{2}$ (c) 9 (d) 12 (e) 18
2. Frances can type 100 pages in h hours. At this rate, how many pages can she type in m minutes?
   (a) $\frac{mh}{60}$ (b) $\frac{60m}{h}$ (c) $\frac{100m}{60h}$ (d) $\frac{60h}{100m}$ (e) $\frac{100h}{60m}$
3. Find the measure to the nearest degree of the angle formed by the graph of $y = 1.5x$ $(x \geq 0)$ and the x-axis.
   (a) 51° (b) 56° (c) 59° (d) 60° (e) None of these
4. Which of the following is a solution to the equation $|3x - 6| = 3$?
   (a) −2 (b) −1 (c) 0 (d) 1 (e) 2
5. At a speed of 48 miles per hour, how many minutes will it take to drive 40 miles?
   (a) $\frac{5}{8}$ (b) $\frac{8}{5}$ (c) 32 (d) 50 (e) 1,920
6. If $a < 0$ and $b < 0$, which of the following must be less than 0?
   I. $a + b$ II. $a \cdot b$ III. $-\frac{a}{b}$
   (a) None of the above
   (b) I and II only
   (c) I and III only
   (d) II and III only
   (e) I, II, and III
7. If $\frac{n}{6} = 8$, what is the value of $\frac{n}{8}$?
   (a) 6 (b) $\frac{4}{3}$ (c) $\frac{3}{4}$ (d) $\frac{1}{6}$ (e) 2
8. For nonzero numbers x, y, and z, $3x = 4y$ and $12y = 5z$. What is $\frac{z}{x}$?
   (a) 4 (b) $\frac{16}{5}$ (c) $\frac{9}{5}$ (d) $\frac{6}{5}$ (e) $\frac{5}{16}$

Copyright © Glencoe/McGraw-Hill, a division of The McGraw-Hill Companies, Inc.

Student Master UNIT 8 • Inverse Functions 61

Assessment Masters 63–94.

END-OF-YEAR ASSESSMENTS

Polynomial and Rational Functions

1. One factor of $16x^3 - 4x$ is:
   A. $4x - 1$
   B. $2x + 1$
   C. $x + 4$
   D. $2x - 4$
   E. None of these
2. For which value of a will the equation $ax^2 + 8x = 4$ have no real number solutions?
   A. $a = -5$
   B. $a = -4$
   C. $a = 0$
   D. $a = 4$
   E. $a = 5$
3. Which of the following is a function rule for a quadratic function with a vertex at (a, b)?
   A. $y = (x - a)^2 + b$
   B. $y = (x + a)^2 + b$
   C. $y = (x - a)^2 - b$
   D. $y = (x - b)^2 + a$
   E. $y = (x + b)^2 - a$
4. The graph of $y = \frac{x^2 + ax}{x^2 - a^2}$ has a vertical asymptote at:
   A. $y = 0$
   B. $y = a$
   C. $x = 0$
   D. $x = a$
   E. $x = -a$

Copyright © Glencoe/McGraw-Hill, a division of The McGraw-Hill Companies, Inc.

Assessment Master UNITS 5-8 • Course 3 End-of-Year Assessments 63

Unit 8

Glossary/Glosario

Math Online A mathematics multilingual glossary is available at www.math.glencoe.com/multilingual_glossary. The Glossary includes the following languages:

Arabic	English	Korean	Tagalog
Bengali	Hatian Creole	Russian	Urdu
Cantonese	Hmong	Spanish	Vietnamese

English / **Español**

A

Alternate exterior angles (p. 36) In the diagram, transversal t cuts lines ℓ and m, forming angles 1 through 8. Pairs of alternate exterior angles are $\angle 1$ and $\angle 8$, and $\angle 2$ and $\angle 7$. The angles in each pair are not between the lines and are on opposite sides of the transversal.

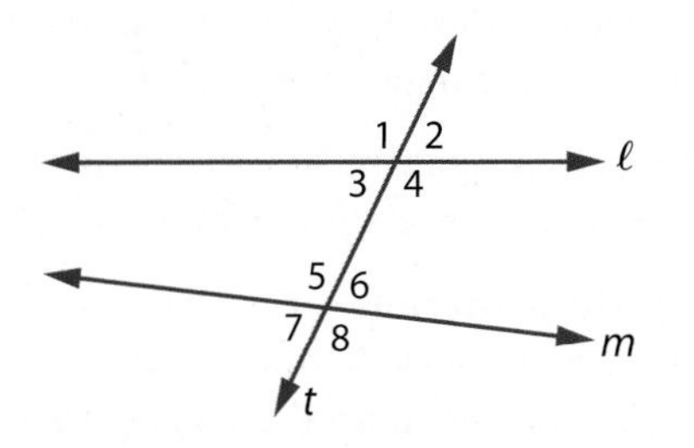

Ángulos alternos externos (pág. 36) En el diagrama, la transversal t corta las líneas ℓ y m. Los pares de ángulos alternos externos son $\angle 1$ y $\angle 8$, y $\angle 2$ y $\angle 7$. Los ángulos en cada par no están entre las líneas y están en lados opuestos de la transversal.

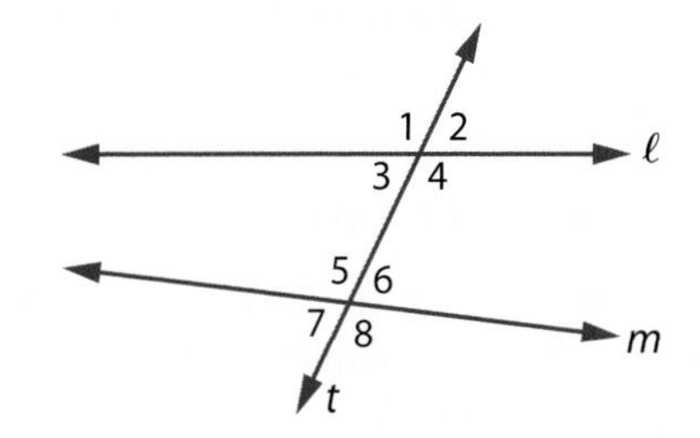

Alternate interior angles (p. 36) In the diagram, transversal t cuts lines ℓ and m, forming angles 1 through 8. Pairs of alternate interior angles are $\angle 3$ and $\angle 6$, and $\angle 4$ and $\angle 5$. The angles in each pair are between the two lines and on opposite sides of the transversal.

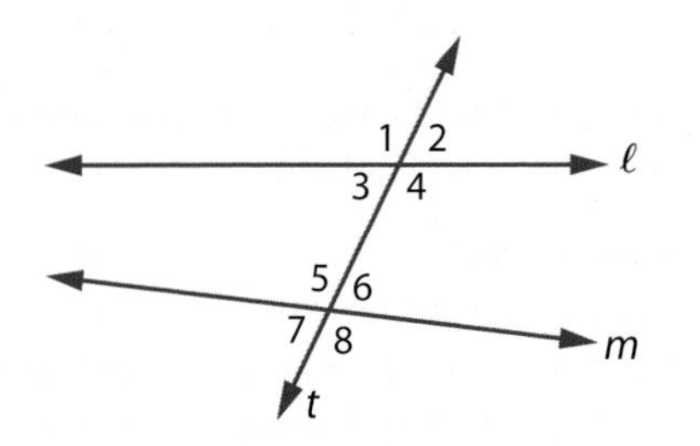

Ángulos alternos internos (pág. 36) En el diagrama, la transversal t corta las líneas ℓ y m, formando los ángulos 1 a 8. Los pares de ángulos alternos internos son $\angle 3$ y $\angle 6$, y $\angle 4$ y $\angle 5$. Los ángulos en cada par no están entre las rectas y están en lados opuestos de la transversal.

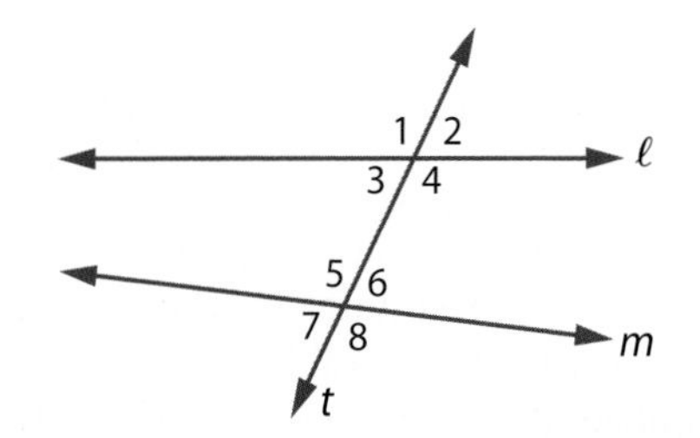

Amplitude (p. 434) Half the difference *maximum value – minimum value,* if they exist, in one cycle of a periodic graph.

Amplitud (pág. 434) Diferencia media entre *valor máximo – valor mínimo,* si existen, en un ciclo de una gráfica periódica.

Angular velocity (p. 421) The rate at which a rotating object such as a pulley, sprocket, or drive shaft turns.

Velocidad angular (pág. 421) La tasa a la que un objeto que rota, como una polea, rueda de engranaje o eje motor, gira.

Annual percentage rate or **APR** (p. 405) A standard way to state the effective annual interest rate on a loan.

Tasa anual porcentual o **TAP** (pág. 405) Forma estándar de enunciar la tasa de interés anual de un préstamo.

Annual percentage yield or **APY** (p. 473) The effective annual interest rate on an investment, taking into account the effect of *compounding interest.*

Renta anual porcentual o **RAP** (pág. 473) Tasa anual de interés de una inversión teniendo en cuenta el efecto del *interés compuesto.*

Glossary/Glosario

English

Arc intercepted by an angle (p. 404) For an angle whose sides cut a circle at points A and B, the portion of the circle that lies in the interior of the angle, together with points A and B (the *endpoints of the arc*).

Arithmetic growth (p. 483) Growth that is modeled by an *arithmetic sequence*.

Arithmetic sequence (p. 482) A sequence of numbers in which the difference between any two consecutive terms is a fixed nonzero constant. Symbolically, $a_n = a_{n-1} + d$.

Arithmetic series (p. 493) A *series* whose terms are those of an *arithmetic sequence*.

Attracting fixed point (p. 521) A *fixed point* such that function iteration sequences that start close to it converge to that point.

Average run length or **ARL** (p. 308) When using control charts, the expected number of items tested until a test gives a false alarm.

B

Balance (p. 406) In the case of a loan, the money still owed.

Binomial situation (p. 260) A probabilistic situation with a fixed number of independent trials, each with two possible outcomes, and the same probability of a success on each trial.

C

Central angle of a circle (p. 401) An angle of measure less than 180° whose vertex is at the center of the circle and whose sides contain radii of the circle.

Centroid of a Triangle (p. 203) The point of concurrency of the medians of a triangle.

Chord of a circle (p. 397) A segment that joins two distinct points on a circle.

Circle (p. 186) The set of all points in a plane that are equidistant from a given point O, called the *center* of the circle.

Español

Arco interceptado por un ángulo (pág. 404) Para un ángulo cuyos lados cortan un círculo en los puntos A y B, la porción del círculo que se encuentra en el interior del ángulo, junto con los puntos A y B (*los extremos del arco*).

Crecimiento aritmético (pág. 483) Crecimiento basado en una *sucesión aritmética*.

Sucesión aritmética (pág. 482) Secuencia de números en los que la diferencia entre dos números consecutivos cualesquiera es una constante fija diferente a cero. Simbólicamente, $a_n = a_{n-1} + d$.

Serie aritmética (pág. 493) *Serie* cuyos términos son los de una *sucesión aritmética*.

Punto fijo de atracción (pág. 521) Un *punto fijo* tal que las sucesiones de función de iteración que comienzan cercanas al mismo convergen en ese punto.

Longitud media de recorrido o **LMR** (pág. 308) En el uso de diagramas de control, el número esperado de artículos examinados hasta que la prueba da como resultado una falsa alarma.

B

Saldo (pág. 406) En el caso de un préstamo, el dinero que todavía se adeuda.

Situación binomial (pág. 260) Situación probabilística con un número fijo de pruebas independientes, cada una con dos resultados posibles y la misma probabilidad de éxito en cada prueba.

C

Ángulo central de un círculo (pág. 401) Ángulo que mide menos de 180° cuyo vértice está en el centro del círculo y cuyos lados son radios del círculo.

Centroide de un triángulo (pág. 203) Punto de concurrencia de las medianas de un triángulo.

Cuerda de un círculo (pág. 397) Segmento que une dos puntos de un círculo.

Círculo (pág. 186) Conjunto de todos los puntos de un plano que son equidistantes de un punto dado O, llamado *centro* del círculo.

Glossary/Glosario

English

Circumcenter (p. 201) The point of concurrency of the perpendicular bisectors of the sides of a triangle; this is the center of the *circumcircle* (*circumscribed circle*) of the triangle.

Closed-form formula for a sequence See *Function formula for a sequence.*

Combined recursive formula (p. 489) A *recursive formula* of the form $A_n = rA_{n-1} + b$. (Also called an *affine recurrence relation* or a *nonhomogeneous first-order linear difference equation.*)

Common difference (p. 485) The constant difference between any two consecutive terms in an *arithmetic sequence.*

Common logarithm (p. 560) If $10^x = y$, then x is called the base 10 logarithm of y; it is often denoted $x = \log y$.

Common ratio (p. 487) The constant ratio of any two consecutive terms in a *geometric sequence.*

Completing the square (p. 350) The process by which a quadratic expression is rewritten in the form $a(x - h)^2 + k$, called a *complete square* or *vertex form.*

Complex number (p. 355) Any complex number can be expressed in the form $a + bi$ where a and b are real numbers and $i = \sqrt{-1}$.

Components of a translation (p. 210) The horizontal and vertical directed distances that all points are moved in a plane (left or right, up or down) under a translation.

Composition of transformations (p. 208) The process of applying two transformations in succession. The transformation that maps the *original preimage* to the *final image* is called the *composite transformation.*

Compound interest (p. 465) Interest that is applied to previous interest as well as to the original amount of money borrowed or invested.

Concentric circles (p. 397) Two or more circles in the same plane that have the same center.

Español

Circuncentro (pág. 201) Punto de concurrencia de las bisectrices perpendiculares de los lados de un triángulo; este es el centro del *circuncírculo* (*círculo circunscrito*) del triángulo.

Fórmula cerrada de una sucesión Ver *Fórmula de la función de una sucesión.*

Fórmula recurrente combinada (pág. 489) *Fórmula recurrente* del tipo $A_n = rA_{n-1} + b$. (También llamada *relación recurrente afín* o *ecuación diferencial lineal de primer orden no homogénea*).

Diferencia común (pág. 485) Diferencia constante entre dos términos consecutivos cualesquiera de una *sucesión aritmética.*

Logaritmo común (pág. 560) Si $10^x = y$, entonces x se llama logaritmo en base 10 de y; con frecuencia se indica $x = \log y$.

Razón común (pág. 487) Razón constante de dos términos consecutivos cualesquiera de una *sucesión geométrica.*

Completar el cuadrado (pág. 350) El proceso por el cual una expresión cuadrática es reescrita en la forma $a(x - h)^2 + k$, llamada *cuadrado completo* o *forma del vértice.*

Número complejo (pág. 355) Todo número complejo puede expresarse con la forma $a + bi$ donde a y b son números reales e $i = \sqrt{-1}$.

Componentes de una traslación (pág. 210) Las distancias dirigidas horizontales y verticales en las que se mueven todos los puntos de un plano (derecha o izquierda, arriba o abajo) durante una traslación.

Composición de transformaciones (pág. 208) Proceso de aplicar dos transformaciones sucesivas. La transformación que relaciona la *preimagen original* con la *imagen final* se llama *transformación compuesta.*

Interés compuesto (pág. 465) Interés aplicado al interés anterior, así como también al monto inicial de dinero prestado o invertido.

Círculos concéntricos (pág. 397) Dos o más círculos en el mismo plano que tienen el mismo centro.

Glossary/Glosario

English	Español
Conclusion (p. 3) In an "if-then" statement, the condition that follows "then." Symbolically, in the statement $p \Rightarrow q$, the conclusion is q.	**Conclusión** (pág. 3) En una oración condicional, la condición que sigue al término "entonces". Simbólicamente, en una oración $p \Rightarrow q$, la conclusion es q.
Concurrent lines (p. 200) Three or more lines that intersect at a common point.	**Rectas concurrentes** (pág. 200) Tres o más rectas que se intersecan en un punto en común.
Conditional statement See *If-then statement.*	**Enunciado condicional** Ver *Oración condicional.*
Congruent figures (p. 162) Two figures are congruent if and only if they are similar with a scale factor of 1. Congruent figures have the same shape and size, regardless of position or orientation.	**Figuras congruentes** (pág. 162) Dos figuras son congruentes si y sólo si son semejantes con un factor de escala de 1. Las figuras congruentes tienen el mismo tamaño y la misma forma, sin importar su posición u orientación.
Consecutive integers (p. 15) Adjacent integers on a number line. These can be expressed symbolically as n and $n + 1$.	**Números enteros consecutivos** (pág. 15) Números enteros adyacentes en una recta numérica. Pueden expresarse simbólicamente como n y $n + 1$.
Constraint (p. 132) A limitation on values that variables may assume in a problem situation. For example, the linear constraint $3x + 5y < 21$ expresses a condition for acceptable combinations of values for the variables x and y.	**Restricción** (pág. 132) Una limitación en los valores que una variable puede asumir de una situación problemática. Por ejemplo, la restricción lineal $3x + 5y < 21$ expresa una condición sobre las combinaciones de valores aceptables para las variables x e y.
Contrapositive of an if-then statement (p. 22) Reverses the order and negates both parts of the if-then statement. In symbols, the contrapositive of $p \Rightarrow q$ is *not q* $\Rightarrow$ *not p*.	**Contrapositivo de una oración condicional** (pág. 22) Invierte el orden y niega ambas partes de una oración condicional. En símbolos, el contrapositivo de $p \Rightarrow q$ es *no q* $\Rightarrow$ *no p*.
Control chart (or, **run chart)** (p. 283) A type of plot over time where observations from an industrial process are plotted in order of occurrence and checked for patterns that indicate that the process has gone out of control.	**Diagrama de control** (pág. 283) Tipo de diagrama en el tiempo donde se registran las observaciones de un proceso industrial y se buscan patrones que indiquen que el proceso está fuera de control.
Control group (or, **comparison group)** (p. 77) In an experiment, a randomly selected group of subjects that gets no treatment, gets a placebo, or gets an established or standard treatment. Otherwise, the control group is treated the same as the group or groups that get the experimental treatment or treatments.	**Grupo de control (**o **grupo de comparación)** (pág. 77) En un experimento, un grupo de sujetos seleccionados al azar que no recibe tratamiento, recibe un placebo o recibe el tratamiento establecido o estándar. De otra manera, el grupo de control se trata de la misma manera que el grupo o los grupos que reciben el tratamiento experimental.
Converse of an if-then statement (p. 10) Reverses the order of the two parts of the if-then statement. In symbols, given the original statement $p \Rightarrow q$, its converse statement is $q \Rightarrow p$.	**Converso de un enunciado condicional** (pág. 10) Invierte el orden de las dos partes de una oración condicional. En símbolos, dado el enunciado original $p \Rightarrow q$, su enunciado converso es $q \Rightarrow p$.

Glossary/Glosario

Corresponding angles (p. 36) In the diagram, transversal t cuts lines ℓ and m, forming angles 1 through 8. Pairs of corresponding angles are $\angle 1$ and $\angle 5$, $\angle 2$ and $\angle 6$, $\angle 3$ and $\angle 7$, and $\angle 4$ and $\angle 8$. Angles in each pair are in the same relative position with respect to each line and the transversal.

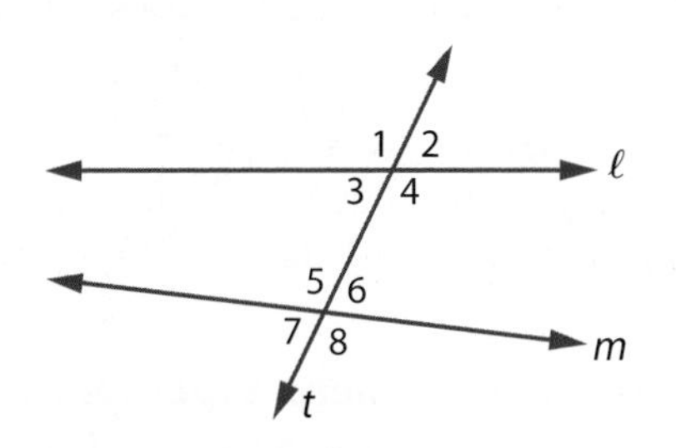

Ángulos correspondientes (pág. 36) En el diagrama, la transversal t corta las líneas ℓ y m, formando los ángulos 1 a 8. Los pares de ángulos correspondientes son $\angle 1$ y $\angle 5$, $\angle 2$ y $\angle 6$, $\angle 3$ y $\angle 7$, y $\angle 4$ y $\angle 8$. Los ángulos en cada par están en la misma posición relativa con respecto a cada recta y a la transversal.

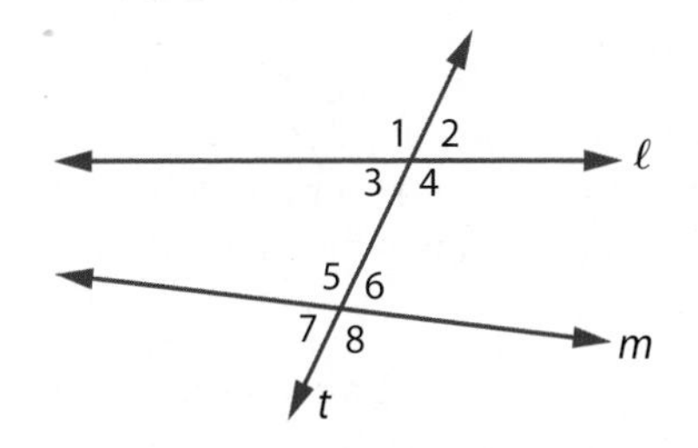

Cycle—function The graph of one period of a *periodic function*. In the case of circular motion, a cycle corresponds to one full revolution.

Ciclo—función La gráfica de un periodo de una *función periódica*. En el caso del movimiento circular, un ciclo corresponde a una revolución completa.

Cycle—iteration (p. 521) A sequence of numbers that repeats over and over when *iterating a function*.

Ciclo—iteración (pág. 521) Secuencia de números que se repite una y otra vez en la *iteración de una función*.

D

Deductive reasoning (p. 2) Reasoning strategy that involves reasoning *from* facts, definitions, and accepted properties *to* conclusions using principles of logic.

Razonamiento deductivo (pág. 2) Estrategia de razonamiento que involucra el razonamiento a partir de hechos, definiciones y propiedades aceptadas para obtener conclusiones que usan principios de lógica.

Degree measure of a circular arc (p. 401) The degree measure of a minor arc and the degree measure of its corresponding central angle are the same. The degree measure of a major arc is 360° minus the degree measure of its corresponding central angle.

Medida gradual de un arco circular (pág. 401) La medida gradual de un arco menor y la de su ángulo central correspondiente son iguales. La medida gradual de un arco mayor es 360° menos la medida gradual de su ángulo central correspondiente.

Degree of a polynomial (p. 324) The highest exponent of the variable that appears in the polynomial expression.

Grado de un polinomio (pág. 324) El mayor exponente de la variable que aparece en la expresión polinomial.

Difference equation See *Recursive formula*.

Ecuación de diferencia Ver *Fórmula recursiva*.

Discrete dynamical system (p. 462) A situation (system) involving change (dynamical) in which the nature of the change is step-by-step (discrete).

Sistema dinámico discreto (pág. 462) Situación (sistema) que involucra un cambio (dinámico) en la que la naturaleza del cambio se da paso a paso (discreto).

Distance from a point to a line (p. 202) The length of the perpendicular segment from the point to the line.

Distancia desde un punto a una recta (pág. 202) Longitud del segmento perpendicular desde el punto a la recta.

Double blind (p. 78) An experiment that is both subject blind and evaluator blind.

Doble ciego (pág. 78) Experimento en el que tanto el sujeto como el evaluador son "ciegos".

E

Equilic quadrilateral (p. 225) A quadrilateral with a pair of congruent opposite sides that, when extended, meet to form a 60° angle. The other two sides are called bases.

Cuadrilátero equílico (pág. 225) Cuadrilátero con un par de lados opuestos congruentes que, al extenderse, se encuentran para formar un ángulo de 60°. Los otros dos lados se llaman bases.

Evaluator blind (p. 78) An experiment in which the person who evaluates how well the treatment works does not know which treatment the subject received.

Evaluador ciego (pág. 78) Experimento en el cual la persona que evalúa qué tan bien funciona el tratamiento no sabe qué tratamiento recibe el sujeto.

Expected value (or, **expected number)** (p. 261) In probability, the long-run average or mean value of a probability distribution.

Valor esperado (o **número esperado)** (pág. 261) En probabilidad, el promedio a largo plazo o valor medio de una distribución de probabilidad.

Experiment (p. 77) A research study in which available subjects are randomly assigned to two or more different treatments in order to compare how responses to the treatments differ.

Experimento (pág. 77) Tipo de investigación en el que los sujetos son asignados en forma aleatoria a dos o más tratamientos distintos para comparar como difieren las respuestas a los tratamientos.

Explicit formula for a sequence See *Function formula for a sequence.*

Fórmula explícita de una sucesión Ver *Fórmula de la función de una sucesión.*

Exponential growth (p. 486) Growth that is modeled by a *geometric sequence* or an exponential function.

Crecimiento exponencial (pág. 486) Crecimiento basado en una *sucesión geométrica* o una función exponencial.

Exterior angle of a triangle (p. 46) The angle formed by the side of a triangle and the extension of an adjacent side.

Ángulo exterior de un triángulo (pág. 46) Ángulo que se forma por un lado del triángulo y la extensión de un lado adyacente.

Exterior angles on the same side of the transversal (p. 36) In the diagram, transversal t cuts lines ℓ and m, forming angles 1 through 8. Pairs of exterior angles on the same side of the transversal are $\angle 1$ and $\angle 7$, and $\angle 2$ and $\angle 8$.

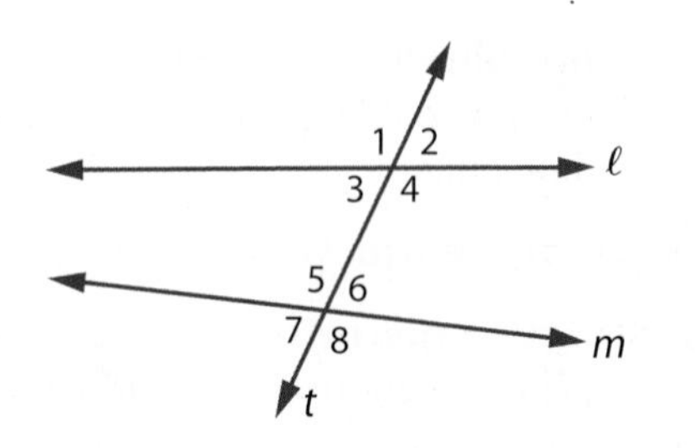

Ángulos exteriores en el mismo lado de la transversal (pág. 36) En el diagrama, la transversal t corta las rectas ℓ y m, formando los ángulos 1 a 8. Los pares de ángulos exteriores en el mismo lado de la transversal son $\angle 1$ y $\angle 7$, y $\angle 2$ y $\angle 8$.

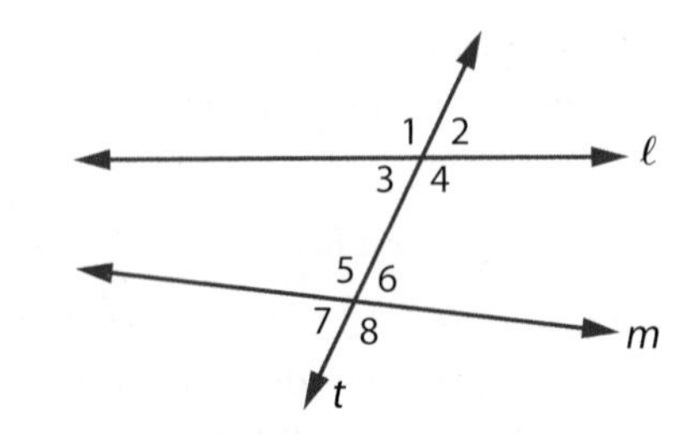

Exterior of a circle (p. 397) The set of all points in the plane of a circle whose distance from the center is greater than the circle's radius.

Exterior de un círculo (pág. 397) Conjunto de todos los puntos del plano de un círculo cuya distancia desde el centro es mayor que el radio del círculo.

Glossary/Glosario

English	Español

F

Factorial notation (p. 20) A compact way of writing the product of consecutive positive whole numbers. Symbolically, $n! = n \cdot (n-1) \cdot (n-2) \cdot \cdots \cdot 2 \cdot 1$.

Notación factorial (pág. 20) Forma compacta de escribir el producto de números enteros positivos consecutivos. En símbolos, $n! = n \cdot (n-1) \cdot (n-2) \cdot \cdots \cdot 2 \cdot 1$.

False alarm (p. 294) In statistical process control, this is when a test signals that a process may be out of control when it is in control.

Falsa alarma (pág. 294) En control de proceso estadístico, ésta ocurre cuando una prueba señala que el proceso puede estar fuera de control cuando está bajo control.

Feasible region (p. 136) In a linear programming problem, the feasible region is the set of all points whose coordinates satisfy all given constraints.

Zona factible (pág. 136) En problemas de programación lineal, la zona factible es el conjunto de todos los puntos cuyas coordenadas satisfacen todas las limitaciones dadas.

Finite differences table (p. 495) A table corresponding to a numerical sequence in which the first column of the table is a consecutive list of indices for the sequence, the second column is the corresponding terms of the sequence, the third column contains the differences of consecutive terms from the second column (called first differences), the fourth column contains the differences of consecutive terms in the third column (called second differences), and so on.

Tabla de diferencias finitas (pág. 495) Tabla correspondiente a una sucesión numérica en la que la primera columna de la tabla es una lista consecutiva de los índices de la sucesión, la segunda columna son los términos correspondientes de la secuencia, la tercera columna contiene las diferencias de los términos consecutivos de la segunda columna (llamada primera diferencia), la cuarta columna contiene las diferencias de los números consecutivos de la tercera columna (llamada segunda diferencia) y así sucesivamente.

Fixed point of a function (p. 520) For the function f, a value x such that $f(x) = x$. When *iterating a function* if you reach that value, you never leave it.

Punto fijo de una función (pág. 520) Para la función f, una valor x tal que $f(x) = x$. En el proceso de *iteración de una función*, cuando se alcanza ese valor, nunca se deja.

Function formula for a sequence (p. 489) A non-recursive formula that expresses the nth term in a sequence as a function of n. (Also called an *explicit formula* or a *closed-form formula.*)

Fórmula de la función de una sucesión (pág. 489) Fórmula no recurrente que expresa el término nth en una sucesión como una función de n. (También llamada *fórmula explícita* o *fórmula cerrada*).

G

Geometric growth (p. 486) Growth that is modeled by a *geometric sequence.*

Crecimiento geométrico (pág. 486) Crecimiento basado en una *sucesión geométrica.*

Geometric mean (p. 186) The geometric mean of two positive integers a and b is the positive number x such that $\frac{a}{x} = \frac{x}{b}$ or $x = \sqrt{ab}$.

Media geométrica (pág. 186) La media geométrica de dos enteros positivos a y b es el número positivo x tal que $\frac{a}{x} = \frac{x}{b}$ ó $x = \sqrt{ab}$.

Geometric sequence (p. 485) A sequence of numbers in which the ratio of any two consecutive terms is a fixed constant. Symbolically, $a_{n+1} = r \cdot a_n$.

Sucesión geométrica (pág. 485) Sucesión de números en la que la razón de cualquier par de números consecutivos es una constante fija. Simbólicamente, se presenta así: $a_{n+1} = r \cdot a_n$.

Glossary/Glosario

English	Español

Geometric series (p. 493) A *series* whose terms are those of a *geometric sequence*.

Serie geométrica (pág. 493) *Serie* cuyos términos son los de una *sucesión geométrica*.

Global maximum or minimum point (p. 343) A global maximum point for a function $f(x)$ is a pair $(a, f(a))$ with the property that $f(a) \geq f(x)$ for all x. The pair $(b, f(b))$ is a global minimum point if $f(b) \leq f(x)$ for all x.

Punto global máximo o mínimo (pág. 343) El punto global máximo de una función $f(x)$ es un par $(a, f(a))$ con la propiedad que $f(a) \geq f(x)$ para toda x. El par $(b, f(b))$ es el punto global mínimo si $f(b) \leq f(x)$ para toda x.

Graphical iteration (p. 519) A graphical representation of *iterating a function*, in which the graph of $y = x$ is drawn on the same set of coordinate axes as the graph of the function being iterated and the process of iteration is shown graphically by moving vertically to the graph of the function, then horizontally to the graph of $y = x$, then vertically to the graph of the function, then horizontally to the graph of $y = x$, and so on.

Iteración gráfica (pág. 519) Representación gráfica de la *iteración de una función*, en la que la gráfica de $y = x$ se dibuja en el mismo conjunto de ejes de coordenadas que la de la función que se quiere iterar, y el proceso de iteración se muestra gráficamente desplazándose verticalmente a la gráfica de la función, luego en forma horizontal a la gráfica de $y = x$, luego verticalmente a la gráfica de la función, luego horizontalmente a la gráfica de $y = x$ y así sucesivamente.

Great circle (p. 48) A circle on the surface of a sphere formed by a plane passing through the center of the sphere.

Gran círculo (pág. 48) Círculo en la superficie de una esfera formado por un plano que pasa por el centro de la esfera.

H

Horizontal asymptote (p. 367) A line with equation $y = k$ is a horizontal asymptote for the graph of a function $f(x)$ whenever the values of $f(x)$ approach k as a limit as $x \to +\infty$ or $x \to -\infty$.

Asíntota horizontal (pág. 367) Una recta con ecuación $y = k$ es una asíntota horizontal para la gráfica de una función $f(x)$ cuando los valores de $f(x)$ se aproximan a k como $x \to +\infty$ o $x \to -\infty$.

Hypothesis of an if-then statement (p. 10) The condition that follows "if." Symbolically, in an if-then statement $p \Rightarrow q$, p is the hypothesis.

Hipótesis de una oración condicional (pág. 10) La condición que sigue al "Si". Simbólicamente, en una oración condicional $p \Rightarrow q$, p es la hipótesis donde q es la conclusión.

I

If and only if statement (p. 21) A combination of an if-then statement and its converse. In symbols, "p if and only if q" is written as $p \Leftrightarrow q$, and is understood to mean $p \Rightarrow q$ and $q \Rightarrow p$.

Oración Si y sólo si (pág. 21) Combinación de oraciones condicionales y su inverso. En símbolos, "p si y solo si q" se escribe $p \Leftrightarrow q$, y se supone que significa $p \Rightarrow q$ y $q \Rightarrow p$.

If-then statement (p. 10) Frequently used in deductive arguments because if the hypothesis is satisfied then the conclusion follows. If-then statements can be represented symbolically as $p \Rightarrow q$ (read "if p, then q" or "p implies q"), where p represents the hypothesis and q represents the conclusion.

Oración condicional (pág. 10) Frecuentemente usada en los argumentos deductivos porque si se satisface la hipótesis, entonces sigue la conclusión. Las oraciones condicionales pueden representarse simbólicamente como $p \Rightarrow q$ (se lee "si p, entonces q" o "p implica q"), donde p representa la hipótesis y q representa la conclusión.

Incenter (p. 202) The point of concurrency of the bisectors of the angles of a triangle; this is the center of the *incircle* (*inscribed circle*) of the triangle.

Incentro (pág. 202) Punto donde se unen las bisectrices de los ángulos de un triángulo; éste es el centro del *incentro* (*círculo inscrito*) del triángulo.

Glossary/Glosario

English

Independent events (p. 308) In probability, two events A and B are said to be independent if the probability that B occurs does not change depending on whether or not A occurred.

Inductive reasoning (p. 2) Reasoning strategy used to discover general patterns or principles based on evidence from experiments or several cases.

Inequality (p. 108) A statement like $3x + 5y < 9$ or $t^2 + 2 \geq 4$ composed of numbers or algebraic expressions connected by an inequality symbol ($<, \leq, >, \geq$). The solution of an inequality is all values of the variable(s) for which the statement is true.

Inscribed angle in a circle (p. 455) An angle whose vertex is on the circle and whose sides contain chords of the circle.

Interior angles on the same side of the transversal (p. 36) In the diagram, transversal t cuts lines ℓ and m, forming angles 1 through 8. Pairs of interior angles on the same side of the transversal are $\angle 4$ and $\angle 6$, and $\angle 3$ and $\angle 5$.

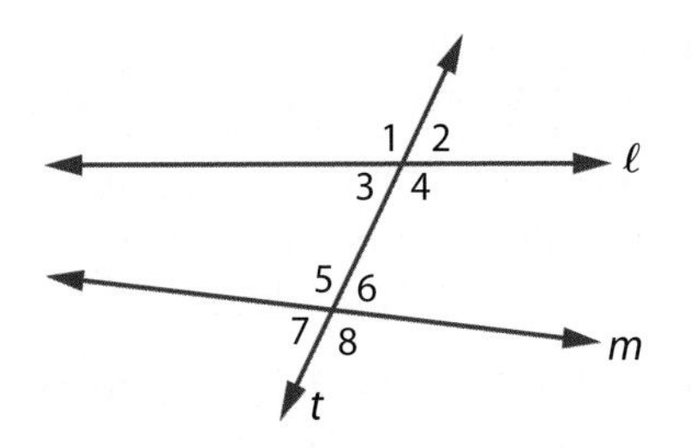

Interior of a circle (p. 397) The set of all points in the plane of a circle whose distance from the center is less than the circle's radius.

Interval (p. 116) All numbers on a coordinate line between two specified endpoints. The *closed* interval $[a, b]$ is all numbers x such that $a \leq x \leq b$. The *open* interval (a, b) is all numbers x such that $a < x < b$.

Inverse cosine function (p. 584) The inverse cosine or arccos function is defined as $\cos^{-1} k = x$ if $\cos x = k$ and $0 \leq x \leq \pi$.

Inverse function (p. 537) For a given function f, if the function g has domain equal to the range of f, range equal to the domain of f, and $g(f(x)) = x$ for all x, then g is called the inverse of f.

Español

Eventos independientes (pág. 308) En probabilidad, se dice que dos eventos A y B son independientes si la probabilidad de que B ocurra no cambia si A ocurre o no.

Razonamiento inductivo (pág. 2) Estrategia de razonamiento que se usa para descubrir patrones o principios generales, basándose en pruebas de experimentos o de otros casos.

Desigualdad (pág. 108) Oración como $3x + 5y < 9$ ó $t^2 + 2 \geq 4$ compuesta por números o expresiones algebraicas relacionadas por un símbolo de desigualdad ($<, \leq, >, \geq$). La solución de una desigualdad son todos los valores para la o las variables que hacen verdadera la oración.

Ángulo inscrito de un círculo (pág. 455) Ángulo cuyo vértice está en el círculo y cuyos lados contienen cuerdas del círculo.

Ángulos interiores en el mismo lado de la transversal (pág. 36) En el diagrama, la transversal t corta las rectas ℓ y m, formando los ángulos 1 a 8. Los pares de ángulos interiores en el mismo lado de la transversal son $\angle 4$ y $\angle 6$, y $\angle 3$ y $\angle 5$.

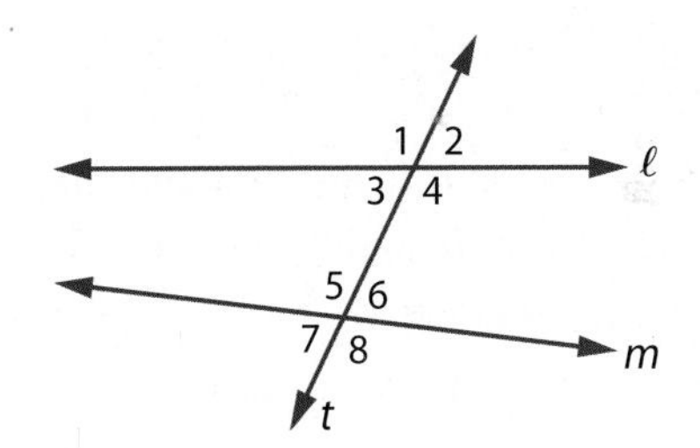

Interior de un círculo (pág. 397) Conjunto de todos los puntos del plano de un círculo cuya distancia desde el centro es menor que el radio del círculo.

Intervalo (pág. 116) Todos los números de una recta de coordenadas entre dos extremos especificados. El intervalo *cerrado* $[a, b]$ son todos los números x tal que $a \leq x \leq b$. El intervalo *abierto* (a, b) son todos los números x tal que $a < x < b$.

Función coseno inverso (pág. 584) La función coseno inverso o arcocoseno se define como $\cos^{-1} k = x$ si $\cos x = k$ y $0 \leq x \leq \pi$.

Función inversa (pág. 537) Para una función dada f, si la función g tiene un dominio igual al rango de f, rango igual al dominio de f y $g(f(x)) = x$ para toda x, entonces g se llama la inversa de f.

English	Español
Inverse sine function (p. 579) The inverse sine or arcsin function is defined as $\sin^{-1} k = x$ if $\sin x = k$ and $-\frac{\pi}{2} \leq x \leq \frac{\pi}{2}$.	**Función seno inverso** (pág. 579) La función seno inverso o arcoseno se define como $\text{sen}^{-1} k = x$ si $\text{sen } x = k$ y $-\frac{\pi}{2} \leq x \leq \frac{\pi}{2}$.
Inverse of an if-then statement (p. 21) The negation of the hypothesis and conclusion in an if-then statement. In symbols, the inverse of $p \Rightarrow q$ is not $p \Rightarrow$ not q.	**Elnverso de una oración Si y sólo si** (pág. 21) Negación de la hipótesis y la conclusión en una oración condicional. En símbolos, el inverso de $p \Rightarrow q$ es no $p \Rightarrow$ no q.
Inverse tangent function (p. 587) The inverse tangent or arctan function is defined as $\tan^{-1} k = x$ if $\tan x = k$ and $-\frac{\pi}{2} < x < \frac{\pi}{2}$.	**Función tangente inversa** (pág. 587) La función tangente inversa o arcotangente se define como $\tan^{-1} k = x$ si $\tan x = k$ y $-\frac{\pi}{2} < x < \frac{\pi}{2}$.
Isosceles trapezoid (p. 66) A quadrilateral with exactly one pair of parallel sides and the nonparallel sides congruent.	**Trapecio isósceles** (pág. 66) Cuadrilátero con exactamente un par de lados paralelos y lados no paralelos congruentes.
Iterating a function (p. 514) The process of sequentially feeding the outputs of a function back into itself as inputs.	**Iteración de una función** (pág. 514) Proceso de reingresar secuencialmente los resultados de una función en sí misma como valor de entrada.
Iteration (p. 462) The process of repeating the same procedure or computation over and over.	**Iteración** (pág. 462) Proceso de repetir el mismo procedimiento o cálculo una y otra vez.

L

English	Español
Law of Cosines (p. 168) In any triangle ABC with sides of lengths a, b, and c opposite $\angle A$, $\angle B$, and $\angle C$, respectively: $c^2 = a^2 + b^2 - 2ab \cos C$.	**Ley del coseno** (pág. 168) En todo triángulo ABC con lados de longitud a, b y c opuestos a $\angle A$, $\angle B$ y $\angle C$, respectivamente: $c^2 = a^2 + b^2 - 2ab \cos C$.
Law of Sines (p. 168) In any triangle ABC with sides of lengths a, b, and c opposite $\angle A$, $\angle B$, and $\angle C$, respectively: $\frac{\sin A}{a} = \frac{\sin B}{b} = \frac{\sin C}{c}$.	**Ley del seno** (pág. 168) En todo triángulo ABC con lados de longitud a, b y c opuestos a $\angle A$, $\angle B$ y $\angle C$, respectivamente: $\frac{\sin A}{a} = \frac{\sin B}{b} = \frac{\sin C}{c}$.
Line reflection (p. 209) A transformation that maps each point P of the plane onto an image point P' as follows: If point P is not on line ℓ, then ℓ is the perpendicular bisector of $\overline{PP'}$. If point P is on ℓ, then $P' = P''$. That is, P is its own image.	**Recta de reflexión** (pág. 209) Transformación que representa cada punto P del plano en un punto imagen P' de la siguiente manera: Si el punto P no está en la recta ℓ, entonces ℓ es la bisectriz perpendicular de $\overline{PP'}$. Si el punto P está en ℓ, entonces $P' = P''$. Es decir, P es su propia imagen.
Linear pair (p. 30) A pair of adjacent angles whose noncommon sides are opposite rays.	**Par lineal** (pág. 30) Par de ángulos adyacentes cuyos lados no comunes son rayos opuestos.
Linear programming (p. 128) A mathematical procedure to find values of variables that satisfy a set of linear *constraints* and optimize the value of a linear *objective function*.	**Programación lineal** (pág. 128) UProcedimiento matemático en el que la tarea es encontrar los valores de variables que satisfacen un grupo de *restricciones* lineales y optimizan el valor de una *función objetiva* lineal.
Linear velocity (p. 421) The distance that a point on a revolving circle moves in a unit of time.	**Velocidad lineal** (pág. 421) Distancia que un punto recorre en una unidad de tiempo en un círculo rotativo.

English	Español
Local maximum or minimum point (p. 324) A local maximum point for a function $f(x)$ is a pair $(a, f(a))$ with the property that $f(a) \geq f(x)$ for all x in an open interval containing a. The pair $(b, f(b))$ is a local minimum point if $f(b) \leq f(x)$ for all x in an open interval containing a.	**Punto local máximo o mínimo** (pág. 324) El punto local máximo para una función $f(x)$ es un par $(a, f(a))$ con la propiedad que $f(a) \geq f(x)$ para toda x en un intervalo abierto que contiene a. El par $(b, f(b))$ es el punto local mínimo si $f(b) \leq f(x)$ para toda x en un intervalo abierto que contiene a.
Logically equivalent statements (p. 22) Two statements p and q are logically equivalent if each implies the other. In symbols, $p \Rightarrow q$ and $q \Rightarrow p$.	**Enunciados lógicamente equivalentes** (pág. 22) Dos oraciones p y q son equivalentes desde el punto de vista lógico si cada una implica la otra. Simbólicamente, se representa así: $p \Rightarrow q$ y $q \Rightarrow p$.
Logistic equation (or logistic map) (p. 518) An equation of the form $f(x) = rx(1 - x)$.	**Ecuación logística** (pág. 518) Ecuación con la forma $f(x) = rx(1 - x)$.
Lurking variable (p. 79) A variable that helps to explain the association between the conditions or treatments and the response, but is not the explanation that the study was designed to test.	**Variable escondida** (pág. 79) Variable que ayuda a explicar la asociación entre las condiciones o tratamientos y la respuesta, pero que no es la explicación que el estudio debía probar.

M

English	Español
Major arc of a circle (p. 401) An arc with degree measure greater than 180°.	**Arco mayor de un círculo** (pág. 401) Arco con una medida mayor de 180°.
Minor arc of a circle (p. 401) An arc with degree measure less than 180°.	**Arco menor de un círculo** (pág. 401) Arco con una medida menor de 180°.
Modus ponens (Latin: mode that affirms) (p. 10) A fundamental principle of logic. If an if-then statement is true in general and the hypothesis is known to be true in a particular case, then the conclusion is also true in that case. In symbols, $p \Rightarrow q$, given p, conclude q. Also called Affirming the Hypothesis.	**Modus ponens (del Latín "modo que afirma")** (pág. 10) Principio fundamental de la lógica. Si una oración condicional es verdadera en general y la hipótesis es verdadera en un caso en particular, entonces la conclusión es verdadera en ese caso. En símbolos, $p \Rightarrow q$, dado p, se concluyes q. También se conoce como "afirmar la hipótesis".
Mutually exclusive events (or, **disjoint events)** (p. 305) Two events are said to be mutually exclusive if it is impossible for both of them to occur on the same trial.	**Eventos mutuamente excluyentes (**o **eventos desunidos)** (pág. 305) Se dice que dos eventos son mutuamente excluyentes si es imposible que ambos ocurran en el mismo experimento.

N

English	Español
Negation of a statement (p. 21) A statement that negates the given statement. In symbols, the negation of statement p is *not* p.	**Negación de una oración** (pág. 21) Oración que niega una oración dada. En símbolos, la negación de la oración p *no* es p.
Normal distribution (p. 237) A theoretical probability distribution that is bell-shaped, symmetric, continuous, and defined for all real numbers.	**Distribución normal** (pág. 237) Distribución de probabilidad teórica que es tiene la forma de una campana, y es simétrica, continua y definida para todos los números reales.

English	Español

O

Objective function (p. 137) In a linear programming problem, an algebraic expression like $7x - 3y$ whose value is to be optimized within the constraints of the problem.

Función objetiva (pág. 137) En un problema de programación lineal, es una expresión algebraica como $7x - 3y$ cuyo valor debe ser optimizado dentro de las restricciones del problema.

Observational study (p. 89) A statistical study in which the conditions to be compared are already present in the subjects that are observed.

Estudio observacional (pág. 89) Estudio estadístico en el que las condiciones que se comparan están presentes, en ese momento, en los sujetos que serán observados.

Odds (p. 278) An alternative way of expressing a probability. When outcomes are equally likely, the odds of an event are the number of favorable outcomes to the number of unfavorable outcomes. For example, if the odds that an event occurs are 3 to 5, then the probability the event occurs is $\frac{3}{(3+5)}$, or $\frac{3}{8}$.

Posibilidades (pág. 278) Forma alternativa de expresar una probabilidad. Cuando los resultados son igualmente posibles, las posibilidades de un evento son el número de resultados favorables al número de resultados desfavorables. Por ejemplo, si las posibilidades de que un evento ocurra son 3 a 5, entonces la probabilidad de que ocurra el evento es $\frac{3}{(3+5)}$, ó $\frac{3}{8}$.

Orientation of a figure (p. 214) Determined by the clockwise or counterclockwise cyclic labeling of at least three points on a figure.

Orientación de una figura (pág. 214) Está determinada por la clasificación del ciclo horario o antihorario de al menos tres puntos de una figura.

P

Parallelogram (p. 20) A quadrilateral that has two pairs of opposite sides the same length (congruent), or equivalently, a quadrilateral that has two pairs of parallel sides.

Paralelogramo (pág. 20) Cuadrilátero que tiene dos pares de lados opuestos de la misma longitud (congruentes), o de manera equivalente, cuadrilátero que tiene dos pares de lados paralelos.

Percentile (p. 241) A value x in a distribution lies at the pth percentile if $p\%$ of the values in the distribution are less than or equal to x.

Percentil (pág. 241) Un valor x de una distribución se encuentra en el percentil $p.^{o}$ si $p\%$ de los valores de la distribución son menores que o iguales a x.

Period (p. 434) The length of a smallest interval (in the domain) that contains a cycle of a periodic graph.

Período (pág. 434) Longitud del intervalo más corto (en el dominio) que contiene un ciclo en una gráfica periódica.

Periodic graph (p. 434) A graph of a pattern of change that repeats itself over and over again.

Gráfica periódica (pág. 434) Gráfica de un patrón de cambio que se repite una y otra vez.

Perpendicular bisector of a segment (p. 198) A line perpendicular to the segment at its midpoint.

Bisectriz perpendicular de un segmento (pág. 198) Recta perpendicular del segmento en su punto medio.

Placebo (p. 77) A sham or empty treatment that to subjects of an experiment appears to be the real treatment.

Placebo (pág. 77) Tratamiento simulado o falso para los sujetos de un experimento que parece ser el tratamiento real.

Placebo effect (p. 78) The phenomenon that people tend to do better when given a treatment, even if it is a placebo.

Efecto placebo (pág. 78) Fenómeno por el que las personas tienden a sentirse mejor con un tratamiento, incluso si es un placebo.

Glossary/Glosario

English	Español

Polynomial expression (p. 327) An algebraic expression in the general form $a_nx^n + a_{n-1}x^{n-1} + \cdots + a_1x + a_0$, where $a_n, a_{n-1}, \ldots, a_1, a_0$ are constants.

Expresión polinomial (pág. 327) Una expresión polinomial es cualquier expresión algebraica con la forma general $a_nx^n + a_{n-1}x^{n-1} + \cdots + a_1x + a_0$, donde $a_n, a_{n-1}, \ldots, a_1, a_0$ son constantes.

Polynomial function (p. 321) A function whose rule can be expressed in the form $f(x) = a_nx^n + a_{n-1}x^{n-1} + \cdots + a_1x + a_0$.

Función polinomial (pág. 321) Función cuya regla puede ser expresada en la forma $f(x) = a_nx^n + a_{n-1}x^{n-1} + \cdots + a_1x + a_0$.

Postulates (p. 31) Mathematical statements that are accepted as true without proof. Also called axioms.

Postulados (pág. 31) Enunciados matemáticos que son aceptados como verdaderos sin evidencia. También se les llama axiomas.

Present value (p. 476) The amount of money that, if invested today at a fixed *compound interest* rate, would give the same yield as a number of regular payments in the future such that at exactly the end of the payment period the *balance* is zero.

Valor actual (pág. 476) La cantidad de dinero que, si se invierte hoy a una tasa fija de *interés compuesto*, daría el mismo rendimiento en cuanto al número dado de pagos regulares en el futuro, de forma tal que al final del período de pago el *saldo* sería cero.

Prime number (p. 10) An integer greater than 1 that has exactly two factors, 1 and itself.

Número primo (pág. 10) Un entero mayor que 1 que tiene exactamente dos factores, 1 y sí mismo.

Principal (p. 465) In finance, the amount of money borrowed or invested.

Capital (pág. 465) En finanzas, la cantidad de dinero que se pide prestado o se invierte.

Proportion (p. 66) A statement of equality between ratios.

Proporción (pág. 66) Un enunciado de igualdad entre razones.

Q

Quadratic formula (p. 353) The formula $x = \frac{-b \pm \sqrt{b^2 - 4ac}}{2a}$ that gives the solutions of any quadratic equation in the form $ax^2 + bx + c = 0$, where a, b, and c are constants and $a \neq 0$.

Fórmula cuadrática (pág. 353) La fórmula $x = \frac{-b \pm \sqrt{b^2 - 4ac}}{2a}$ que da las soluciones de cualquier ecuación cuadrática en la forma $ax^2 + bx + c = 0$, donde a, b y c son constantes y $a \neq 0$.

R

Radian (p. 427) The measure of a central angle of a circle that intercepts an arc equal in length to the radius of the circle. One radian equals $\frac{180}{\pi}$ degrees, which is approximately 57.2958°.

Radian (pág. 427) Medida del ángulo central de un círculo que intercepta un arco de igual longitud que el radio del círculo. Un radian equivale a $\frac{180}{\pi}$ grados, lo cual es aproximadamente 57.2958°.

Random sample of size *n* (p. 89) A sample selected by a method equivalent to writing the name of every member of the population on a card, mixing the cards well, and drawing n cards.

Muestra aleatoria de tamaño *n* (pág. 89) Muestra que se obtiene por un método equivalente a escribir el nombre de cada miembro de la población en una tarjeta, mezclarlas bien y elegir n tarjetas.

Randomization distribution (p. 84) In an experiment, a distribution of possible differences between the mean responses from two treatments, generated by assuming that each response would have been the same had each subject been assigned to the other treatment.

Distribución aleatoria (pág. 84) En un experimento, la distribución de diferencias posibles entre las respuestas medias de dos tratamientos, generadas al suponer que cada respuesta hubiera sido la misma si a cada uno de los sujetos se le hubiera asignado el otro tratamiento.

Glossary/Glosario

English	Español
Randomization test (or, **permutation test)** (p. 85) A statistical test that can be used to determine whether the difference in the mean response from two treatments in an experiment is statistically significant.	**Prueba aleatoria** (pág. 85) Prueba estadística que se puede usar para determinar si la diferencia en la respuesta media de dos tratamientos de un experimento es estadísticamente significativa.
Rare event (p. 267) An event that lies in the outer 5% of a distribution. In a waiting-time distribution, rare events typically are in the upper 5% of the distribution. In a binomial distribution, rare events may be those in the upper 2.5% and lower 2.5%.	**Evento casual** (pág. 267) Evento que ocurre en el 5% externo de una distribución. En una distribución de tiempo de espera, los eventos casuales normalmente se hallan en el 5% superior de la distribución. En una distribución binomial, los eventos casuales pueden ser aquellos que se encuentran en el 2.5% superior y 2.5% inferior.
Rational expression (p. 369) A quotient of two polynomial expressions.	**Expresión racional** (pág. 369) El cociente de dos expresiones polinomiales.
Rational function (p. 364) A rational function is a function with rule that can be expressed as the quotient of two polynomials.	**Función racional** (pág. 364) Una función racional es una función con una regla que se puede expresar como el cociente de dos polinomios.
Recursion (p. 462) A sequential process in which a step is described in terms of previous steps.	**Recursión** (pág. 462) Proceso secuencial en el cual un paso es descrito en términos de los pasos previos.
Recursive formula (p. 467) A formula involving *recursion*. (Also called a recurrence relation or a difference equation.)	**Fórmula recurrente** (pág. 467) Fórmula que involucra *recursión*. (También llamada relación recurrente o ecuación de diferencia).
Recursive formula for a sequence (p. 483) A formula that expresses a given term in a sequence as a function of previous terms.	**Fórmula recurrente de una sucesión** (pág. 483) Fórmula que expresa un término dado en una sucesión como una función de los términos previos.
Regular polygon (p. 4) A polygon in which all sides are congruent and all angles are congruent.	**Polígono regular** (pág. 4) Polígono con todos los lados y los ángulos congruentes.
Remote interior angles of a triangle (p. 46) The two angles of a triangle that are not adjacent to a given exterior angle.	**Ángulos interiores remotos de un triángulo** (pág. 46) Los dos ángulos de un triángulo que no son adyacentes a un ángulo exterior dado.
Repelling fixed point (p. 521) A *fixed point* such that function iteration sequences move away from it (except for a sequence that begins at the fixed point).	**Punto fijo de repulsión** (pág. 521) *Punto fijo* tal que las sucesiones de iteración de la función se alejan de él (a excepción de la sucesión que comienza en el punto fijo).
Response variable (p. 76) In an experiment, the outcome to be measured.	**Variable de respuesta** (pág. 76) En un experimento, el resultado que se debe medir.
Rigid transformation (p. 208) A transformation of points in the plane that preserves all distances. Such a transformation repositions a figure in a plane without changing its shape or size.	**Transformación rígida** (pág. 208) Transformación de los puntos en un plano que conserva todas las distancias. Tal transformación reposiciona una figura en un plano sin cambiar el tamaño o la forma de la figura.

English	Español

Rotation (p. 208) A transformation that "turns" all points in a plane through a specified angle about a fixed point called the rotation center. That is, if points P' and Q' are the images of points P and Q under a counterclockwise rotation about point C, then $CP = CP'$, $CQ = CQ'$, y $m\angle PCP' = m\angle QCQ'$.

Rotación (pág. 208) Transformación que "gira" todos los puntos en un plano a través de un ángulo específico con relación a un punto fijo llamado centro de rotación. Es decir, si los puntos P' y Q' son las imágenes de los puntos P y Q en una rotación antihoraria alrededor del punto C, entonces $CP = CP'$, $CQ = CQ'$, y $m\angle PCP' = m\angle QCQ'$.

S

Sample survey (or, poll) (p. 89) Observation of a random sample in order to estimate a characteristic of the larger population from which the sample was taken.

Encuesta por muestreo (pág. 89) Observación de una muestra aleatoria para estimar una característica de la población total a partir de la muestra tomada.

Scale factor of a size transformation (p. 165) A positive constant that scales (multiplies) all lengths (or distances) in the plane. A scale factor greater than 1 produces enlarged figures, and a scale factor less than 1 produces reduced figures; in both cases, the figures transformed by the size transformation are similar to the original.

Factor de escala de una transformación de (pág. 165) Constante positiva que aumenta (multiplica) todas las longitudes (o distancias) en el plano. Una factor de escala mayor que 1 produce figuras ampliadas, y un factor de escala menor que 1 produce figuras reducidas; en ambos caso, las figuras transformadas son semejantes a la original.

Scientific notation (p. 571) Expression of a number in the form $a \cdot 10^k$, where a has absolute value between 1 and 10 and k is an integer. For example, 3.245×10^3 or 3.245×10^{-3} are expressed in scientific notation.

Notación científica (pág. 571) Expresión de un número en la forma $a \cdot 10^k$, donde a tiene un valor absoluto entre 1 y 10 y k es un número entero. Por ejemplo, 3.245×10^3 ó 3.245×10^{-3}, están expresados en notación científica.

Sequential change (p. 462) Change that occurs step-by-step.

Cambio secuencial (pág. 462) Cambio que ocurre paso a paso.

Series (p. 493) An expression in which the terms of a sequence are added together.

Serie (pág. 493) Expresión en la que los términos de una sucesión son sumados juntos.

Sierpinski Triangle (p. 188) A fractal that begins at the initial stage as an equilateral triangle. At each iterative step, in each remaining triangle, the middle triangle(s) formed by connecting the midpoints of each side are removed.

Triángulo de Sierpinski (pág. 188) Fractal que comienza en la etapa inicial como un triángulo equilátero. En cada paso de la iteración, en cada triángulo restante, se quitan el/los triángulo(s) del medio formado(s) al conectar los puntos medios de cada lado.

Similar figures (p. 164) Figures that are related by a size transformation or by a similarity transformation. Such figures have the same shape, regardless of position or orientation.

Figuras semejantes (pág. 164) Figuras relacionadas por una transformación de tamaño o por una transformación de semejanza. Tales figuras tienen la firma forma, sin importar la posición u orientación.

Similar polygons (p. 165) A special case of similar figures. Corresponding angles have the same measure and the ratios of lengths of corresponding sides is a constant.

Polígonos semejantes (pág. 165) Caso especial de figuras semejantes. Los ángulos correspondientes tiene la misma medida y la longitud de los radios de los lados correspondientes es una constante.

Similarity transformation (p. 208) Composite of a size transformation and a rigid transformation. Such a transformation resizes a figure in a plane without changing its shape.

Transformación de semejanza (pág. 208) Combinación de una transformación de tamaño y una transformación rígida. Tal transformación cambia las medidas de una figura en el plano sin cambiar su forma.

Glossary/Glosario

English	Español
Size transformation (p. 177) A transformation with center C and magnitude $k > 0$ that maps each point P of the plane onto an image point P' as follows: Point C is its own image. For $P \neq C$, the image point P' is on $\overrightarrow{CP}$ and $CP' = k \cdot CP$.	**Transformación de tamaño** (pág. 177) Una transformación con centro C y magnitud $k > 0$ que representa cada punto P en un plano sobre un punto de imagen P' de la siguiente forma: el punto C es su propia imagen. Para $P \neq C$, la imagen del punto P' está en $\overrightarrow{CP}$, y $CP' = k \cdot CP$.
Spherical geometry (p. 48) The geometry on a sphere in which all "lines" (shortest paths on the surface) are great circles.	**Geometría esférica** (pág. 48) Geometría en una esfera en la que todas las "rectas" (los caminos más cortos de la superficie) son grandes círculos.
Standardized value (or, ***z*-score**) (p. 243) The (positive or negative) number of standard deviations a given value lies from the mean in a distribution.	**Valor estandarizado** (o **valor *z***) (pág. 243) En una distribución, el número (positivo o negativo) de desviaciones estándar de un número dado a partir de la media.
Statistically significant (p. 85) In an experiment, the conclusion that it is unreasonable to attribute the difference in mean response from the treatments solely to the particular random assignment of treatments to subjects. The researcher may conclude that one treatment causes a larger mean response than the other.	**Estadísticamente significativo** (pág. 85) En un experimento, la conclusión de que no es razonable atribuir la diferencia de la respuesta media al tratamiento sólo a la asignación aleatoria particular de los tratamientos a los pacientes. El investigador puede concluir que el experimento establece que un tratamiento causa una respuesta media mayor que el otro.
Subject blind (p. 78) An experiment in which the subjects do not know which treatment they are getting.	**Sujeto ciego** (pág. 78) Experimento en el cual los sujetos no saben qué tratamiento reciben.
Subjects (p. 77) The available group of people (or animals, plants, or objects) to which treatments are applied in an experiment.	**Sujetos** (pág. 77) Grupo de personas disponibles (o animales, plantas u objetos) a los que se somete a un tratamiento en un experimento.
Supplementary angles (p. 35) A pair of angles whose measures add to 180°.	**Ángulos suplementarios** (pág. 35) Par de ángulos cuyas medidas suman 180°.

T

English	Español
Tangent line to a circle (p. 397) A line that intersects a circle in only one point.	**Rectas tangentes de un círculo** (pág. 397) Recta que interseca un círculo sólo en un punto.
Theorem (p. 32) In mathematics, a statement that has been proved true.	**Teorema** (pág. 32) En matemáticas, enunciado que se ha probado como verdadero.
Translation (p. 208) A transformation that "slides" all points in the plane the same distance (magnitude) and same direction. That is, if points P' and Q' are the images of points P and Q under a translation, then $PP' = QQ'$ and $\overline{PP'} \parallel \overline{QQ'}$.	**Traslación** (pág. 208) Transformación que "desliza" todos los puntos de un plano la misma distancia (magnitud) y en la misma dirección. Es decir, si los puntos P' y Q' son imágenes de los puntos P y Q en una traslación, entonces $PP' = QQ'$ y $\overline{PP'} \parallel \overline{QQ'}$.
Transmission factor (p. 443) The number by which the speed of the driver in a pulley system is multiplied to get the speed of the follower.	**Factor de transmisión** (pág. 443) Número por el que la velocidad del conductor en un sistema de poleas se multiplica para obtener la velocidad del seguidor.
Transversal (p. 35) A line that intersects two coplanar lines in two distinct points.	**Transversal** (pág. 35) Recta que interseca dos rectas coplanares en dos puntos distintos.

English	Español

Trapezoid (p. 10) A quadrilateral with two opposite sides parallel.

Trapecio (pág. 10) Cuadrilátero con dos lados opuestos paralelos.

Treatments (p. 76) The conditions to be compared in an experiment. Treatments should be randomly assigned to subjects.

Tratamientos (pág. 76) Condiciones que se deben comparar en un experimento. Los tratamientos deben aplicarse a los sujetos en forma aleatoria.

Trial (p. 260) In probability, one repetition of a random process.

Prueba (pág. 260) En probabilidad, una repetición de un proceso aleatorio.

V

Valid argument (p. xx) An argument that uses correct rules of logic. When the premises (hypotheses) are true, and the argument is valid, then the conclusion must be true.

Argumento válido (pág. xx) Argumento que utiliza reglas correctas de la lógica. Cuando las premisas (hipótesis) son verdaderas, y el argumento es válido, entonces la conclusión debe ser verdadera.

Venn diagram (p. 20) A diagram where mutually exclusive events are represented by non-overlapping circles and events that are not mutually exclusive are represented by overlapping circles.

Diagrama de Venn (pág. 20) Diagrama en el que los eventos mutuamente excluyentes se representan mediante círculos que no se superponen y los eventos que no son mutuamente excluyentes se representan mediante círculos superpuestos.

Vertex form of a quadratic See *Completing the square.*

Forma de vértice de una expresión cuadrática Ver *Completar el cuadrado.*

Vertical angles (p. 30) Two angles whose sides form two pairs of opposite rays. When two lines or two segments intersect, vertical angles are formed.

Ángulos opuestos por el vértice (pág. 30) Dos ángulos cuyos lados forman dos pares de rayos opuestos. Cuando dos líneas o dos segmentos se intersecan, se forman ángulos verticales.

Vertical asymptote (p. 367) A line with equation $x = k$ is a vertical asymptote for the graph of a function $f(x)$ whenever values of $f(x)$ approach $+\infty$ or $-\infty$ as $x \rightarrow k$ (from one side only, or from both sides).

Asíntota vertical (pág. 367) Una recta con ecuación $x = k$ es una asíntota vertical para el gráfico de una función $f(x)$ cuando los valores de $f(x)$ tiendan a $+\infty$ ó $-\infty$, en tanto $x \rightarrow k$ (de un lado solamente, o de ambos lados).

X

x-bar chart (p. 300) A control chart where the means of samples of measurements, rather than individual measurements, are plotted.

Gráfica de barras *x* (pág. 300) Tipo de diagrama de control en el que las medias de las muestras de mediciones, en vez de ser mediciones individuales, son combinadas.

Z

Zeroes of polynomials (p. 329) A number k is a zero of the polynomial $f(x) = a_nx^n + a_{n-1}x^{n-1} + \cdots + a_1x + a_0$ if $f(x) = 0$. The number k will be an x-intercept of the graph of f; k is also called a root of the polynomial.

Cero de un polinomio (pág. 329) Un número k es cero de un polinomio $a_nx^n + a_{n-1}x^{n-1} + \cdots + a_1x + a_0$ si $f(x) = 0$. El número k serán una intercepción en x de gráfica de f; k es también llamado raíz del polinomio.

Index of Mathematical Topics

A

Index of Mathematical Topics *(continued)*

Q

R

Index of Contexts

Photo Credits

COV (tl)Image State Royalty Free/Alamy Images, (tr)David Carriere/Jupiter Images, (br)Rim Light/PhotoLink/Getty Images, (bl)Corbis/Punchstock; **i** (tl)Image State Royalty Free/Alamy Images, (tr)David Carriere/Jupiter Images, (bl)Corbis/Punchstock, (br)Rim Light/PhotoLink/Getty Images; **xvi** (l)Jim Laser/CPMP, (r)Christian Charisius/Reuters/CORBIS; **1** Spectrum Colour Library/Heritage-Images/The Image Works; **2** Darren Matthews/Alamy Images; **3** CBS via Getty Images; **10** Courtesy of Audi of America; **11** (t)Jeremy Woodhouse/Getty Images, (b)Associated Press, AP Images; **12** Bettmann/CORBIS; **16** Royalty-Free/CORBIS; **18** Associated Press, AP Images; **29 30** CPMP; **35** (bkgd)Bryan Mullennix/Getty Images; Jim Laser/CPMP; **41** Mark Steinmetz/Amanita Pictures; **42** CORBIS; **43** Angela Reiter/CPMP; **47** Yannis Emmanuel Mavromatakis/Alamy Images; **52** Oote Boe Photography/Alamy Images; **57** David Crossland/Alamy Images; **71** AFP/Getty Images; **74** Digital Vision/Alamy Images; **75** CPMP; **76** Renee Morris/Alamy Images; **77** Bettmann/CORBIS; **79** David Young-Wolff/PhotoEdit; **80** (t)College Board/AP Program, (b)Photodisc/PunchStock; **81** Corbis Premium RF/Alamy Images; **82** Stockbyte/Alamy Images; **86** (l)Frank Blackburn/Alamy Images, (r)Getty Images; **87** (inset)Digital Vision, Photodisc/Getty Images; **89** David Young-Wolff/PhotoEdit; **91** Phototake/Alamy Images; **92** Stockbyte/Getty Images; **94** Blend Images/Alamy Images; **95** Kyle Robertson/Columbus Dispatch; **102** Spectrum Colour Library/Heritage-Images/The Image Works; **104** PictureQuest/CORBIS; **107** Associated Press, AP Images; **108** Photodisc/Alamy Images; **110** Image Plan/CORBIS; **111** CORBIS; **115** Comstock/PictureQuest; **118** Getty Images; **120** JJ/www.linestretch.net; **121** Thinkstock/CORBIS; **127** Michel Setboun/Sygma/CORBIS; **128** Eric Nathan/Alamy Images; **131** Image Source—Hola/Alamy Images; **132** Ryan McVay/Getty Images; **134** NASA; **136** Spencer Grant/PhotoEdit; **138** AFP/Getty Images; **140** NASA; **142** Associated Press, AP Images; **145** Dennis Gilbert; **146** (t)Royalty-Free/CORBIS, (b)Creatas Images/PictureQuest; **147** (inset)Photodisc/Getty Images, Brand X/CORBIS; **149** age fotostock/SuperStock; **152** BananaStock/PunchStock; **153** PhotoLink/Getty Images; **154** Geoff Manasse/Getty Images; **156** Purestock/Alamy Images; **158** Associated Press, AP Images; **159** (t)UpperCut Images/Alamy Images, (b)Design Pics/CORBIS; **161** Caro/Alamy Images; **162** (t)M.C. Escher Foundation, (b)M.C. Escher's "Regular Division of the Plane VI" © 2008 The M.C. Escher Company-Holland. All rights reserved. www.mcescher.com; **164** Sabrina Keller/CPMP; **170 171** Jim Laser/CPMP; **172** Trip/Alamy Images; **175** (t)Sandy Felsenthal/CORBIS, (b)Creatas/PunchStock; **179** Nicole Lanie/CPMP; **182** (t)Wesley Hitt/Getty Images, (b)David Tipling/Getty Images; **184** Villa Stein DesignWorkshop® model © Artifice, Inc.; **189** Steve Mason/Getty Images; **190** Corbis Super RF/Alamy Images; **195** Courtesy of Rock and Roll Hall of Fame, Cleveland; **197** Nicole Lanie/CPMP; **209** M.C. Escher Foundation; **216** FedEx service marks used by permission.; **218** JRC, Inc./Alamy Images; **227** Sally and Richard Greenhill/Alamy Images; **229** Flat Earth; **231** Construction Photography/CORBIS; **232** Corbis/Punchstock; **233** Dinodia Images/Alamy Images; **235** Darron R. Silva/Aurora Photos; **236** Gail Hanusa/AP Images; **239** Image Club; **240** Justin Sullivan/Getty Images News/Getty Images; **241** Michael Newman/PhotoEdit; **242** Daniel Acker/BLOOMBERG NEWS/Landov; **243** JupiterImages/Polka Dot/Alamy Images; **244** (l)Lisa O'Connor/ZUMA/CORBIS, (r)Dave M Benett/Getty Images Entertainment/Getty Images; **246** Getty Images; **247** LGI/CORBIS; **248** Tom Grill/CORBIS; **251** (l)Elsa/Getty Images, (r)James Poulson/CPMP; **252** (t)Getty Images, (b)Mango Productions/CORBIS; **255** (t)Paul A. Souders/CORBIS, (b)PhotoDisc/Getty Images; **257** Comstock/PictureQuest; **259** Gregory Shamus/Getty Images; **261** Hisham Ibrahim/Getty Images; **262** (t)SuperStock/SuperStock, (b)Jose Luis Pelaez Inc/Blend Images/CORBIS; **264** Digital Vision; **265** PhotoDisc/Getty Images; **266** Steve Sant/Alamy Images; **269** John Hicks/CORBIS; **270** Felicia Martinez/PhotoEdit; **271** Bettmann/CORBIS; **272** BananaStock/PictureQuest; **273** M. Thomsen/zefa/CORBIS; **279** Marcus Mok/CORBIS; **280** (t)Bettmann/CORBIS, (b)Kelly-Mooney Photography/CORBIS; **283** Digital Vision/PunchStock; **285** Lester Lefkowitz/CORBIS; **292** AT&T Archives & History Center; **295** DarleneBordwell.com; **299** REUTERS/Mario Anzuoni/Landov; **302** Burke/Triolo/Getty Images; **303** Tim Pannell/CORBIS; **304** Bill Pugliano/Stringer/Getty Images; **305** DarleneBordwell.com; **306** American Honda Motor Co., Inc.; **312** Jonathan Wiggs/Boston Globe/Landov; **313** Mark Steinmetz/Amanita Pictures; **316** Image by Harold (Hal) Pierce (SSAI/NASA Goddard Space Flight Center); **317** (t)BananaStock/Punchstock, (b)Jack Star/PhotoLink/Getty Images; **319** Cedar Point Amusement Park/Resort; **320** Purestock/Getty Images; **326** Richard Cummins/SuperStock; **327** Digital Vision/SuperStock; **334** Jim Laser/CPMP; **339** Andrew Resek/The McGraw-Hill Companies; **345** Nigel Cattlin/Alamy Images; **347** Lars A. Niki/The McGraw-Hill Companies; **349** Jim Laser/CPMP; **355** Mary Evans Picture Library; **357** David S. Holloway/Getty Images; **358** Photospin, Inc./Alamy Images; **360** 2007—Canadian National Exhibition; **364** Roberto Herrett/Alamy Images; **367** Jim Laser/CPMP; **368** Getty Images; **371** Jim Laser/CPMP; **372** Ken Karp/The McGraw-Hill Companies; **375** CORBIS; **377** SW Productions/Getty Images; **378** James Poulson/CPMP; **381** Ryan McVay/Getty Images; **384** (t)CORBIS, (b)David Papazian/CORBIS; **388** Digital Vision/Getty Images; **389** Getty Images; **390** Royalty-Free/CORBIS; **391** Image Source/PunchStock; **393** Celestial Panoramas Ltd/Alamy Images; **395** Doug Wilson/USDA; **396** Jason Reed/Getty Images; **398** StockTrek/Getty Images; **401** PhotoDisc/Getty Images; **403** Scenics of America/PhotoLink/Getty Images; **409** Thierry Ollivier/Muse Guimet/Getty Images; **413** Cadaco; **414** Michael Townsend/Getty Images; **420** (t)Itstock Free/PunchStock, (b)Transtock/Alamy Images; **422** Royalty-Free/CORBIS; **424** Thinkstock/Masterfile; **425** Larry Brownstein/Getty Images; **427** Ed Freeman/Getty Images; **430** Getty Images; **435** Jules Frazier/Getty Images; **436** CORBIS; **439** Dinodia Images/Alamy Images; **441** Blend Images/PunchStock; **442** Maria Ferrari/SuperStock; **445** Topix/Alamy Images; **446** CALVIN AND HOBBES © 1990 Watterson. Reprinted with permission of UNIVERSAL PRESS SYNDICATE. All rights reserved.; **449** Leonard Lessin/Peter Arnold Inc.; **453** David Buffington/Getty Images; **454** Digital Vision; **455** (t)Getty Images, (b)Ingram Publishing/AGE Fotostock; **460** Library of Congress Prints and Photographs Division [LC-USZ62-50927]; **457** M.C. Escher's "Drawing Hands" © 2008 The M.C. Escher Company-Holland. All rights reserved.; **458** Pedro Ramirez, Jr./U.S. Fish & Wildlife Service; **460** Greenshoots Communications/Alamy Images; **463** Wayne S. Davis, USEPA http://www.epa.gov/gioindicators; **465** Adam Gault/Getty Images; **467** Photodisc Collection/Getty Images; **468** Royalty-Free/CORBIS; **469** (t)Creatas/PictureQuest, (b)U.S. Census Bureau; **470** Travel Ink/Getty Images; **471** Brand X Pictures/PunchStock; **475** Roy Botterell/Getty Images; **476** Monkey Pod Games; **477** Keith Brofsky/Getty Images; **479** Agripicture Images/Alamy Images; **481** David Spurdens/CORBIS; **483** Tim Fuller; **485** Don Rubbelke/The McGraw-Hill Companies; **490** Getty Images/Digital Vision; **491** Phototake/Alamy Images; **493** Royalty-Free/CORBIS; **495** Marty Honig/Getty Images; **499** Photodisc Red/Getty Images; **502** (l)IT Stock Free/Alamy Images, (r)Mark Steinmetz/Amanita Pictures; **506** Photodisc/SuperStock; **507** Tohoku Color Agency/Getty Images; **509** Castlemedia Ent. Inc.; **510** Galen Rowell/CORBIS; **511** Sean Justice/CORBIS; **513** Photo courtesy of Great Wheel Corporation; **514** age fotostock/SuperStock; **515** Ingram Publishing/Alamy Images; **522** PhotoDisc/Getty Images; **524** Paul Nicklen/Getty Images; **525** D. Hurst/Alamy Images; **527** The McGraw Companies; **533** ThinkStock/SuperStock; **534** Photodisc Collection/Getty Images; **535** Miller Auditorium at Western Michigan University, Kalamazoo, Michigan; **537** CORBIS; **538** (t)Radius Images/Alamy Images, (b)Nick Koudis/Getty Images; **539 540** Jim Laser/CPMP; **542** Burke/Triolo/Brand X Pictures; **544** Royalty-Free/CORBIS; **545** Eric Meola/Getty Images; **549** Jim Laser/CPMP; **551** Dennis Whitehead/CORBIS; **553** Getty Images/SW Productions; **558** (t)Royalty-Free/CORBIS, (b)Digital Vision/Getty Images; **559** CORBIS; **561** Image Source/Getty Images; **562** Larry Aumiller/U.S. Fish & Wildlife Service; **563** Jim Laser/CPMP; **564** Associated Press, AP Images; **565** Purestock/Getty Images; **568** BananaStock/age fotostock; **569** worldthroughthelens-RF/Alamy Images; **570** Brand X Pictures; **571** Lyroky/Alamy Images; **574** CORBIS; **577** Peter Adams/Getty Images; **582** Jim Laser/CPMP; **584** Image State Royalty Free/Alamy Images; **585** Purestock/Getty Images; **586** L. Clarke/CORBIS; **589** AfriPics.com/Alamy Images; **590** Panoramic Images/Getty Images; **591** Creatas/Jupiter Images/Alamy Images; **592** Acclaim Images; **593** Photodisc/PunchStock; **594** Jim Laser/CPMP; **596** Brand X Pictures/PunchStock; **597** Time & Life Pictures/Getty Images; **598** CORBIS; **599** Hirohiko Minami/Getty Images; **602** Stockbyte/PunchStock; **603** CORBIS.